India and Pakistan

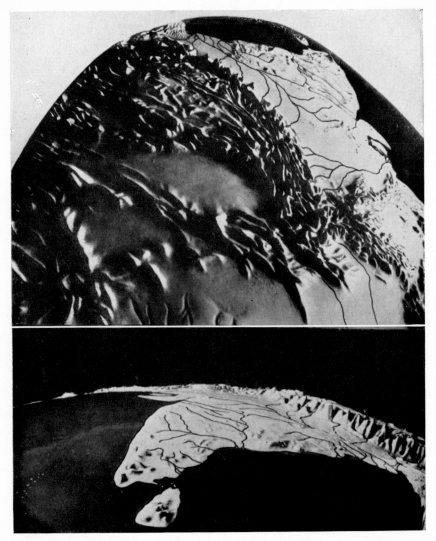

INDIA: APPROACHES BY LAND AND SEA

INDIA
AND PAKISTAN

A General and Regional Geography

O. H. K. SPATE & A. T. A. LEARMONTH
Australian National University

With the collaboration of A. M. LEARMONTH
and a chapter on Ceylon by
B. H. FARMER
St John's College, Cambridge

METHUEN & CO LTD

First published March 18th, 1954
Second edition, 1957
Reprinted 1960
Third edition revised and completely reset, 1967
© *O. H. K. Spate 1954 and O. H. K. Spate and A. T. A. Learmonth 1967*
Printed in Great Britain by
Richard Clay (The Chaucer Press), Ltd., Bungay, Suffolk

In Russian as
Indiya i Pakistan: obshchaya i regionalnaya geografiya
(Foreign Literature Publishing House, Moscow, 1957)

Distributed in the USA by Barnes & Noble Inc

To

ARTHUR GEDDES, P. C. MAHANALOBIS,

J. A. STEERS, L. S. SUGGATE

masters and friends

From the Preface to the First Edition

Among ruminant animals, writers on Indian affairs form a special class; some refreshing exceptions apart, they chew over and over again the cud of Royal Commissions, Tariff Enquiries, Gazetteers and the like. However rich the original material, nutritional returns soon diminish; hence the writer's vow, made in India, never to add to the mass of Indian literature; of which rash determination this volume is the natural nemesis.

Yet there is some justification, at least for the attempt, in the extraordinary fact that there has been no serious geography of India in English since Holdich's *India* of 1904. Like all Holdich's work, this has many merits: not least a vivid style and an admirable welding of history and geography. But there is surely something odd about a book which purports to be a geography of India and, in its regional sections, actually devotes 48 pages to Afghanistan and 28 to the Indo-Gangetic Plains and the Peninsula put together; a complete failure to subordinate local interest and special knowledge to the demands of a wider architecture. My own all too slight direct acquaintance with India at least shields me from this error. Apart from Krebs' admirable but not very accessible German work, for a really balanced geography of India on an adequate scale we must go back to Elisée Reclus' *Nouvelle Géographie Universelle*, of which the Indian volume was published in 1883. One does not – or at lest nowadays one should not – go to *L'Inde* for details other than historical; but for grasp of fundamental relationships, for really masterly presentation of broad essentials, I know of no geographer superior to Reclus. 'That Providence so often unacknowledged', as Febvre calls his book, shall not go unacknowledged here.

. . . . . .

I am aware that a good deal of this book is 'not geography'. One could of course defend this, without undue difficulty, by a discussion of the true content of geography, or could shelter behind the indubitable fact that in Asia, where so much of life is ruled by ancient concepts entirely novel to most Western students, no human geography could be intelligible without much presentation of purely social factors. I prefer a shorter answer: 'I am a man, and think nothing human indifferent to me.'

If anything in this book should give undesigned offence to Indian or Pakistani readers, may I say that I have written in good faith and with good will; and with the conviction that some things which should be said, but which before 1947 might have appeared arrogance or condescension from a member of a ruling caste, can now be said as friendly criticism between equals; and it is in this spirit that I have written. Similarly, it is no disparagement of the devotion of thousands of British 'servants of India' to point out that the results of their actions were at times socially ambivalent.

.   .   .   .   .   .

London, *April 1951*   O.H.K.S.

Preface to the Third Edition

The full-scale revision of *India and Pakistan*, rendered absolutely necessary by the changes of over ten years, would have been incomparably more difficult, if not absolutely impossible, but for the fortunate juxtaposition, within the same city, of Andrew and Nancy Learmonth with the original author; the last-mentioned is very firm on this. The result, naturally, is that though the older structure is preserved, this edition is in many aspects a new book. In particular, Part III – The Economy – has been so completely rewritten that little of the original remains; and the sections on climate and soils, on the whole the weakest parts of the original work, are entirely new, as is the chapter on population.

Generally speaking, the Learmonths are primarily, or indeed almost solely, responsible for Chapter 2 (Climate), the soils section of Chapter 3, Chapter 4 (Population), Chapter 9 (Power and Minerals), and the two 'planning chapters', 11 and 12. The remainder, except of course for Mr Farmer's chapter on Ceylon, can be considered as basically by Spate, but working with the advantage of a rigorous preliminary check by the Learmonths. Every page has been scrutinized, many of them more than twice or thrice, by all parties concerned. The collaboration was less gruelling, with far fewer strains and stresses, than might have been expected. Our thanks are also due to Mr Farmer for his good-natured acceptance of what must have seemed inordinate delays.

An endeavour has been made to get rid of the excessive use of abbreviation in the earlier editions, and to improve the documentation by giving publisher, as well as place of publication, for works likely to be still in print. In accordance with what we hope is a growing trend, metric equivalents of British units have been generally given.

It is most regrettable that Indian official policy imposes obstacles to the use of the 1957 National Atlas of India for purposes of *bona fide* scholarship. Despite early enquiries, it was only at a very late stage that we were made aware of the conditions attached to basing maps on the Atlas, and these were such as to necessitate the scrapping and replacement of several figures, with consequent delay in the appearance of this edition.

The original *India and Pakistan* has had a wonderfully generous reception in the sub-continent and other countries, including Russia; this seems the appropriate place to express gratitude for the award of the Prix Charles Garnier of the Société de Géographie of Paris and the Jawahar Lal Nehru Medal of the National Geographical Society of India, Varanasi. It can fairly be claimed as a work of general utility. It would be extravagant to hope that all imperfections

ix

have been removed; but it is reasonable to hope that this new edition, adjusted, to the best of our joint abilities, to the very much changed circumstances of the 1960s, will be received no less generously and prove no less useful.

Canberra, *July 1965*

O.H.K.S.
A.T.A.L.
A.M.L.

Acknowledgements

For information and for permission to reprint extracts or to reproduce maps
my thanks are due to many official agencies in India and Pakistan: the Surveys
of both countries; the Geological Survey of India; the Forest Research Institute
at Dehra Dun, the Central Board of Irrigation, the Damodar Valley Corporation.
Both in England and in Australia the Information Officers attached to the
Offices of the High Commissioners for India and Pakistan were most helpful.
Information on Goa was supplied by the Agencia Geral des Colonias, Lisbon.

Quotations of generous length were kindly allowed by: Chatto and Windus
(Aldous Huxley's *Jesting Pilate*); the Cambridge University Press (G. E.
Hutchinson's *The Clear Mirror*); Vora Bros., Bombay (Vakil's *Economic Consequences of Divided India*). Map credits are separately listed. Sections of the book
have appeared in *Eastern World*, *The Geographical Review*, *Geography* and *The
Indian Geographical Journal*, and thanks are due to their editors for permission to
reprint.

My large debt to such writers as Sir Malcolm Darling, Helmut de Terra,
Radhakamal Mukerjee and Jathar and Beri is evident, and is I trust amply
acknowledged in the appropriate contexts. Mr E. S. Lindley and Sir Robert
Bristow kindly gave me first-hand unpublished details on the Punjab canals and
the port of Cochin respectively.

From Indian academic colleagues, friends or strangers, I received the most
generous assistance. Prof. C. N. Vakil of Bombay and Prof. T. L. Sharma of
Agra gave me liberty to base myself solidly on their works. I received also useful
information from Prof. M. B. Pithawala of Karachi, Prof. S. P. Chatterjee of
Calcutta, and Dr Nafis Ahmad of Dacca. To Prof. George Kuriyan of Madras I
owe not only *carte blanche* for material from *The Indian Geographical Journal*,
but a detailed check on the Tamilnad and Kerala sections; and a special word is
due to the very friendly assistance of Mr C. D. Deshpande of Dharwar. My
Indian students at LSE were teachers as well as pupils: E. Ahmad, P. Dayal,
P. K. Dutt, M. Guha, S. A. Majid, Binapani Mukerjee. I trust that they will
accept this recognition as some apology for my too-frequent impatiences,
irascibilities and unpunctualities.

I doubt if this book could have been written had it not been for the facilities
of the London School of Economics; not least of which is its proximity to the
library of India House, where Miss W. Thorne's kindness and encyclopaedic
guidance have been main factors in the achievement of many Indian and other
students of the sub-continent. This book owes much also to discussion with

many colleagues at LSE, especially Prof. L. Dudley Stamp. Prof. R. Ogilvie Buchanan very kindly made the cartographical facilities of the LSE Geography Department available to me even after my departure. Most of the maps were redrawn or scripted by Miss Webb and Miss West, cartographers at LSE, and I also received much help from our technician Mr Judd. Mr W. T. W. Morgan compiled most of the crop distribution maps, and my friend Miss Marjory Fowler drew the vignettes of house types. But my chief debt is due to my colleague Mr D. J. Sinclair, who, on my departure for Australia, very generously offered to take over the supervision of the maps from my sketches – some very rough – to the blocks. It will be obvious that this was no light burden, and without his help the task would have been almost insuperable.

For discussions and criticism I should like to thank also Prof. Pierre Gourou of Paris, Prof. S. W. Wooldridge of London and Prof. Raymond Firth, a colleague both in London and in Canberra. My friend Mr B. H. Farmer of St John's College, Cambridge, stepped into the breach when it became clear to me that I could not hope to deal adequately with Ceylon in the time available.

A very special service was rendered me by Sir Douglas Copland, the Vice-Chancellor, Prof. Marcus Oliphant and Prof. W. R. Crocker, all of the ANU – the last in his other capacity of Australian High Commissioner at New Delhi. With them were associated Mr C. Rajagopalachariar, Mr K. P. S. Menon, Prof. S. Bhatnagar and Dr D. N. Wadia: to all of them my gratitude. And to Mr J. N. L. Baker for the inception of the book. I owe the conception of the frontispiece to a verbal hint from Dr Arthur Geddes.

Invaluable secretarial assistance was given by Miss Donne Shirwin at LSE, Miss Joan Binns in Canberra; the latter greatly lightened the labour of indexing.

It would be an impossible, though a most pleasant, task to thank all those who helped me on my later visits to India: but I cannot refrain from expressing my gratitude to Prof. P. C. Mahanalobis, through whom I was enabled to see much of the new India – Bhakra, Chandigarh, the Damodar, Hirakud – and also that jewel of the old, Konarak.

Lastly, I should like to place on record the inspiration I have received from Reclus' *L'Inde* and Preston James's *Latin America*; the latter is the best regional geography in English known to me. Their value has been immense, however far I have fallen short of such exemplars.

O. H. K. S.

Further Acknowledgements for Third Edition

Valuable assistance, in the form either of permission to use material or of direct comment, has been received from the following gentlemen in India and Pakistan: Professors Kazi S. Ahmad, O. P. Bharadwaj, Shyam S. Bhatia, S. P. Chatterjee, V. L. S. Prakasa Rao, M. Shafi; Col. N. Ahmed; Dr Mohammed Anas; Messrs R. D. Dixshit, C. Mukerjee and R. Sinha. Dr L. S. Bhat, Mr M. N. Pal, and

Mr C. Subramanian were especially helpful in gathering information, as was Mr A. A. Chowdury of the Office of the High Commissioner for Pakistan, Canberra. Elsewhere, thanks are due to Professors B. L. C. Johnson and G. T. Trewartha, Drs D. J. E. Schwartzberg and G. Whittington. To all, our gratitude.

A special word is due to our cartographers, Messrs H. Gunther and M. Pancino of the Research School of Pacific Studies and Mr P. Daniell of the School of General Studies, ANU.

By an inadvertence which is much regretted, earlier acknowledgements did not indicate that the source for the frontispiece was the 1:20,000,000 relief globe designed by Professor D. L. Linton, modelled by Mr C. d'O. Pilkington Jackson, and published (if that is the right word) by Messrs George Phillips, 1935.

Canberra, *July 1965*   O. H. K. S.

A. T. A . L.

Contents

page

PART II THE PEOPLE

4 Population and its Problems

5 The Peoples of the Sub-Continent

6 Historical Outlines

7 Village and Town in India

PART III THE ECONOMY

8 Agriculture and Agrarian Problems

CONTENTS

Maps and Diagrams

In the map captions certain abbreviations are used; these refer to the following authors, editors and publishers to whom grateful acknowledgement is made for permission to use various maps. Fuller references are to be found in the map captions or footnotes. Apologies are tendered for any inadvertent omissions.

AAG Association of American Geographers
AG Dr Arthur Geddes
Asia Asia Publishing House, Bombay
B & C Messrs M. R. Brearey and B. S. Connock
B & D Drs J. Coggin Brown and K. Dey
BM Dr Binapani Mukerjee
CDD Dr C. D. Deshpande
CE *Chamber's Encyclopaedia* (George Newnes Ltd., London)
COI Census of India
COP Census of Pakistan
EA Dr Enayat Ahmed
EG *Economic Geography*, Worcester, Mass.
Ek *Erdkunde*, Bonn

ES	Miss Ethel Simkins
FRI	Forest Research Institute, Dehra Dun
G, GA	*Geography*, The Geographical Association (UK)
GJ	*Geographical Journal*, London
GK	Professor George Kuriyan
GR	*Geographical Review*, New York
GSI	Geological Survey of India, Calcutta
GTT	Professor G. T. Trewartha
GW	Dr G. Whittington
ICAR	Indian Council of Agricultural Research
IGJ	*Indian Geographical Journal*, Madras
IJMG	*Indian Journal of Meteorology and Geophysics*
IMD	Indian Meteorological Department, Poona
ISI	Indian Statistical Institute (Regional Survey Unit, New Delhi)
JES	Dr Joseph E. Schwartzberg
K & J	Drs P. P. Karan and W. M. Jenkins
KSA	Dr Kazi S. Ahmad
KR	Dr K. Ramamurthy
LDS	Sir L. Dudley Stamp
LH	Mr L. Hoffmann
Longmans	Messrs Longmans, Green, London
LSB	Dr L. S. Bhat
MBP	Professor Maneck B. Pithawala
MR	Dr M. Rahmatullah
NISI	National Institute of Science of India, Calcutta
OUP	Oxford University Press
PS	Dr Paul Siple
RIIA	Royal Institute of International Affairs, London
RT	Dr R. Tirtha
SAM	Dr S. A. Majid
SOC	Survey of Ceylon, Colombo
SOI	Survey of India, Mussoorie
SOP	Survey of Pakistan, Karachi
SP	Shri S. Pandyan
SPC	Professor S. P. Chatterjee
SSB	Dr S. S. Bhatia
TESG	*Tïdschrift voor Economische en Sociale Geografie*, Rotterdam

Tables

(Excluding short tabular statements in the text. All the following Tables are grouped together at the end of Part 3, The Economy.)

Conventions and Preliminary Data

NOMENCLATURE

1. Now that India and Pakistan have existed as independent countries for twenty years, the distinctions used in earlier editions seem no longer necessary: the context should show when 'India' means the Republic and when it means the sub-continent. The cumbersome term 'Indo-Pakistanian sub-continent' is avoided solely on grounds of simplicity. 'Bharat' is apparently a legally correct style for India (cf. *The Statesman's Year Book*) but is not in fact used to any serious extent either popularly or officially, and is avoided here.

2. The internal territorial divisions of India and Pakistan now seem reasonably stable, and it is no longer necessary to distinguish the old Princely States from the units of the Republic of India, nor can one equate Madhya Pradesh with the (British) Central Provinces. In Pakistan, the merging of the former units in the one entity of West Pakistan leaves Baluchistan, the Punjab and Sind as regional names only.

3. There have been a number of changes in Indian place-names; the more important are listed in the Appendix, p. 828. The new names are normally used in this edition, with cross-reference from the old ones in the Index. It should be noted that the form 'Ganges' is retained in Pakistan for the Ganga, and the older form is used in Pakistani contexts.

ADMINISTRATIVE UNITS

4. Most of the States of India are divided into Divisions, and these into Districts, of which there are 326. The Districts may be taken as roughly equivalent to English Counties; in Uttar Pradesh, for example, they have an average area of 2,105 square miles (5569 km^2) and population of 1,365,674. Districts are sub-divided into *taluks (taluqs)* or *tahsils (tehsils)*, normally from 3 to 8 to a District. In Bengal, however, the next unit to the District is the *thana* or police-station area, which is much smaller than the average tahsil or taluk.

5. Some areas of India are 'Union Territories' under the direct control of New Delhi. Apart from the federal capital itself, they are all outlying, and some of strategic significance: Himachal Pradesh, the North-East Frontier Agency (NEFA), Nagaland (now being advanced to statehood), Tripura, the Andaman and Nicobar Islands, the Laccadive Islands and Minicoy. The former foreign holdings – French Pondicherry, Portuguese Goa, Diu, Damão (Dadra and Nagar Haveli) – are also under direct control. Sikkim is connected to India by special treaties.

6. The old Provinces of West Pakistan have now been merged in the one unit: the old West Punjab comprised the present Divisions of Rawalpindi, Lahore, Sargodha and Multan; Sind those of Khairpur and Hyderabad with Karachi District (now in Kalat Division); Baluchistan those of Quetta and Kalat; the North-West Frontier Province those of Peshawar and Dera Ismail Khan, in-

cluding various Tribal Agencies. The more local units of Pakistan are similar to those of India.

NUMERATION, ETC.

7. Indian statistics are increasingly given in metric units, and in this edition metric equivalents are normally given in parentheses after the British units, despite the typographical inconvenience. In one or two cases metric equivalents have been omitted where the typographical result of inserting them would have been too abominably messy; it seems needless to print '3 feet (1 m.)'; and where say a figure of 100 inches is followed closely by one of 25, it seems pedantically offensive to assume that the reader cannot divide by four.

8. There are a few exceptions to the general rule:

  (a) tons are usually given in long tons, except in the Tables where the Indian sources themselves use metric; the difference between long and metric tons is usually too slight to worry about;

  (b) water flow is given in cusecs: the conversion is 1 cusec = 101·9 cubic metres per hour;

  (c) population densities are given only per square mile, except in one or two special cases; the ratio is a simple one, 1 square mile = 2·59 km², so that the density per square kilometre is roughly two-fifths that per square mile.

9. The old Indian system of numeration, binary for smaller numbers and essentially decimal in the larger, is being increasingly decimalised: thus the Rupee is divided into 100 *naiye paise* (*pice* in Pakistan) replacing the old 16 annas. The Pakistani Rupee = 18*d*. stg, the Indian since devaluation = 11.4*d*.; 100,000 RI = £4,762, say £4,750 or $14,000; 100,000 RP = £7,471, say £7,500 or $21,000.

10. Notation of large figures differs from the European style. There are two useful words, *lakh* or *lac* = 100,000 of anything and *crore* = 100 lakhs or 10,000,000, and big numbers are often set out in lakhs and crores: thus 1,581,000 in European notation becomes in Indian 15,81,000 (15·8 lakhs) and the 1941 population of 388,997,955 may be written 38,89,97,955 (38·9 crores, or 38 crores 89·98 lakhs). The words lakh and crore are occasionally used in this book, but not the Indian notation.

OTHER CONVENTIONS

11. The standard form for periodical references is: Author, title in quotes, name of periodical (or abbreviation), volume in Arabic numerals, date, pages. However, since many Indian periodicals do not maintain continuous pagination through a volume, such references include the part number: *IGJ* 17/3 (1942), 23–36 refers to Volume 17 Part 3 of the *Indian Geographical Journal*.

12. Publisher as well as place of publication is given for all books published after 1945, though in a few cases the publisher has not been traced. In the case of such firms as the Oxford University Press, place of publication is London or Oxford unless otherwise stated. Most Indian Government publications are issued by the Manager of Publications, Civil Lines, Delhi.

13. Indian topographical or technical terms of frequent occurrence, such as 'doab', 'terai', 'sal', 'kharif', are italicized at the first mention only; those which occur more rarely are italicized wherever used. As such terms, if not explained

by their context, are fully explained at their first occurrence, the Index serves the purpose of a glossary.

14. Population figures are for 1961 unless otherwise stated; figures of density of population should be read as including the words 'per square mile'.

15. Capitalization presents problems. It still seems standard to use an initial capital for 'River' in specific river names; less standard to use 'Range' and 'Hills', but here lower case initials can cause ambiguity: the 'Purbeck Hills' are *not* the same as the 'Purbeck hills', which include all the hills of the Isle of Purbeck. On the other hand 'valley', 'delta', 'plateau' seem better with lower case initials except in what are virtually regional names, e.g. Damodar Valley, Bengal Delta, Shillong Plateau. Some inconsistencies doubtless remain in the text.

Abbreviations

Standard and self-explanatory abbreviations, such as ac. (acres), fn. (footnote), *Jnl* (Journal) are not given here.

BIBLIOGRAPHICAL:

CGR	*Calcutta Geographical Review*
Gaz.	*Gazetteer*
GJ	*Geographical Journal*
GR	*Geographical Review*
GRI	*Geographical Review of India*
HJ	*Himalayan Journal*
IGJ	*Indian Geographical Journal*
IR	*India Record*
JMGA	*Journal of the Madras Geographical Association*
NAI	*National Atlas of India* (Preliminary Hindi Edition, Calcutta 1957)
n.d.	no date, no data
ND	New Delhi
NGJI	*National Geographical Journal of India*
NY	New York
O(C)UP	Oxford (Cambridge) University Press
OPIA	Oxford Pamphlets on Indian Affairs
PGR	*Pakistan Geographical Review*
RCAI	(Report of) Royal Commission of Agriculture in India
Mem. (Rec.) GSI	*Memoirs (Records) of the Geological Survey of India*
SOI (P)	Survey of India (Pakistan)

OTHER:

BG	Broad Gauge
DT, ST	Double Track, Single Track
EIC	East India Company
NSA	Net Sown Area
TCA, TSA	Total Cropped (Sown) Area

PART I

The Land

FIG 0.1 INDIA AND PAKISTAN 1965. 1, international boundaries; 2, state boundaries; 3, cease-fire line in Kashmir; 4, national capitals; 5, other towns (those underlined are former French and Portuguese holdings); 6, state capitals; 7, Union Territories (also underlined islands). In November 1966 the Indian Punjab State was divided into a Punjabi-speaking largely Sikh Punjab States, some hill areas being transferred to Himachal Pradesh and the Hindi-speaking east becoming the new State of Hariana.

India as a Unit of Geographical Study

The lands which until August 15th, 1947, formed the Indian Empire, and are now divided into the Commonwealth Republics of India and Pakistan, were never one country until welded together by British power. At long intervals, indeed, a single dynasty secured loose but nearly universal sway; nor did the British themselves administer the sub-continent as a whole, large areas and populations remaining under vassal Indian rulers. But the British connection brought to most of India a common system of administration and law, railways, a common language for the intelligentsia, new forms of economic organization, new ideals of polity. To the extent that these transcended the fantastically interlocking internal divisions, India became one country; in that lay the British achievement.

Persians and Greeks extended the name Sindhu – 'the river' – from the Indus, to which it belonged, to cover such of the land as they knew; and hence the Muslim name Hindustan, properly applied to the area of most firmly based Islamic power in the north. Beyond the Narmada and the Chota Nagpur jungles, which lie across the root of the Peninsula, was the Deccan, the Sanskrit Dakshina-patha or 'Southland'; beyond the Krishna again Tamilnad lived its own life, inheriting the most ancient traditions of Hinduism, perhaps affiliated to the pre-Aryan Indus civilization, itself contemporary with the early empires of Meso-potamia and Egypt. In Hindu literature the sub-continent as a whole is styled Bharata-Varsha, the land of the legendary King Bharata; but it seems safe to say that there was little feeling of identity over the whole country.

Yet for twenty-five centuries at least the entire area, a few margins and enclaves apart, has received the impress of the complex, hardly definable but always easily recognizable culture of Hinduism, which indeed, with Buddhism, once stretched beyond the western borders to the Hindu Kush. Those regions where the cultural landscape displays few or none of the tokens of Hinduism are for the most part mountainous and arid, mountainous and cold, or mountainous and jungle-clad: the Islamic hill country of the western borderlands, the Buddhist high Himalaya in the north, in the east the hills of the Burma border inhabited by a congeries of spirit-worshipping Mongoloid tribes.

Historically, then, it seems pointless to stress the facts that 'India' was rarely (if ever) a single political entity and that its peoples, in common speech at least, had no one name for the whole. For at least two centuries there has been sufficient definiteness about the idea of 'India' to make the area so connoted a feasible unit of study; and despite its partition into two great states, 'India' remains valid as a

3

geographical expression for all the lands between Kanya Kumari (Cape Comorin) and the towering peak K2, respectively in 8° and 36° N.

Isolation and Contact by Land and Sea

Geographically also India is an intelligible isolate. The huge salient of the Peninsula, the keystone of the arch of the Indian Ocean shores, strikes the eye at once; and on the inland borders are the ramparts and fosses of the giant ranges which in large measure wall off the sub-continent from the rest of Asia. These are, however, by no means complete barriers: in that role they are most important as insulating India from the Polar air masses which rule so much of the climate of central Asia, and so ensuring to the sub-continent a practically self-contained monsoon system of its own. But from a human point of view the values of the mountain wall are often determined as much by what lies beyond as by its own topography.

Behind the stupendous bulwarks of the Himalayas lie the vast and all but empty plateaus of wind-swept Tibet, home of a twisted in-bred culture peculiar to itself. Clearly the contacts on this side have been few: a little trade creeping painfully through the high passes – many higher than the loftiest Alpine peaks – and, far more important, seekers of many faiths. To the east the ranges of Assam are much lower, but rain-swept for half the year, and guarded by thick jungle: contact with the Irrawaddy trough is far easier by sea, and it was by sea that the germs of civilization were brought from India to the ancestors of the Burmese, who had gradually filtered down from the marches of Tibet and China.[1] On the west the great arcs of Baluchistan, loop on loop of sharp arid ridges cleft by the narrowest and wildest of gorges, are backed by the burning deserts of Seistan; Makran in the south was once more fertile, and through it the Arabs passed to conquer Sind in the 8th century AD. But the great entry lies farther north, guarded on the Indian side by Peshawar and the Indus crossing at Attock.

Here the belt of mountains narrows to under 250 miles (400 km.) between Turkestan and the Punjab, and the core of the mountain zone, the Hindu Kush, is pierced by numerous passes, blocked by snow in winter but in other seasons practicable without great difficulty. Over this Oxus/Indus watershed lies the major passage through which people after people has pressed into the plains of Hindustan, whether impelled by desiccation in the steppe or by the political pressures of the constantly shifting fortunes of central Asian war. Of all these incursions, those of prime importance are the organized invasions of various Muslim leaders, culminating in the Mogul Babur's conquest of Hindustan in AD 1526; and the distant folk-wandering of the Aryan-speaking people of the steppes, who had entered certainly by 1000 BC and may have been in at the death of the Indus civilization a few centuries earlier. Horsemen, meat-eaters, mighty

---

[1] There was some cultural influence of Mahayana Buddhism through Manipur in Burmese proto-dynastic times (c. 9th–11th centuries AD), but it amounted to little; see G. E. Harvey, *History of Burma* (1924), Ch. I.

drinkers, they contrast strongly with the dark-skinned 'snub-nosed Dasyus', the Dravidian heirs of Indus culture. From the millennial interaction of these two great groups is woven much of the rich tapestry of Hindu myth, and probably also of the darker fabric of caste.

On the whole, then, India is clearly marked off from the rest of Asia by a broad no-man's-land of mountains, whether jungle-covered, ice-bound, or desert; though obviously among the mountain-dwellers themselves no hard and fast line can be drawn dividing those solely or mainly Indian in history and cultural affinity from those solely Burmese, Tibetan, Afghan, or Iranian. The critical area is in the northwestern hills, and here we find in the past great empires slung across the mountains like saddle-bags, with bases of power on the plateau at Kabul or Ghazni or Kandahar, and also in the Punjab plains.

The significance of the mountain barrier, and especially of this great gateway, is clear enough, and more than amply stressed in the British literature, since the Afghan disaster of 1842 almost obsessed with 'the Frontier'. The question of maritime relations is more difficult, and indeed they are often slurred over by easy generalizations about harbourless coasts. But for small craft the west coast is not lacking in harbourage, nor should the delta creeks of the Bay of Bengal be overlooked: Portuguese keels were far from the first to plough the Indian seas. It is true that, until the coming of European seamen, no considerable power was founded *in* India from the sea; but some were founded *from* India.

An active trade linked the Graeco-Roman world with Ceylon and southern India, and to Ceylon also came trading fleets from China. In the west – the significantly 'Arabian' Sea – the active agents were Arabs, who may indeed have been the intermediaries for the trade which indubitably existed between the Indus civilization and Sumeria. From the later Middle Ages onwards not only commercial but also political contacts with southwest Asia, and even northeast Africa, were important: an 'African' party played a prominent role in the politics of the Muslim Deccani Kingdoms, and until 1958 a tiny enclave of Oman territory, the Gwadar Peninsula, survived on the Baluchistan coast.

To the east the initiative came from India. Hindu traders and colonizers took their civilization by sea to the southeast Asian lands, and in the first centuries of the Christian era history in Burma, Indonesia and Indo-China begins with these pioneers. A few years before William the Conqueror impressed Europe with the organizing ability displayed in crossing the English Channel, the fleets of the Chola Kingdom in Madras and the equally Indian Kingdom of Sailendra or Sri Vijaya in Sumatra entered upon a century-long struggle across 1,000 miles of open ocean. So much for isolation by sea!

The actual node of shipping, however, was and is not in India itself but in Ceylon, and the full exploitation of the key position of India waited until the Indian Ocean was as it were subsumed into the World-Ocean by Vasco da Gama; a reminder of the importance of human and technological elements in locational relations. The reasons for the rapid supersession of Portuguese power by the less spectacular but more efficient Dutch and British are a matter of general European rather than Indian history. But it is worthy of note that the Portuguese, consciously pursuing a Crusade against the Moors, concentrated on the west coast, hemmed in by the Ghats and later by the Marathas, so that they had greater impediments to territorial acquisition than their rivals, even had the pattern of dominion laid down by their second and greatest Viceroy, Afonso de Albuquerque, called for landward expansion. Though Surat, seaward terminal of the great route to Hindustan, was bitterly contested by all three powers, the British were more active on the east coast: and when the Mogul Empire collapsed the land lay open before them.

Diversity and unity in the sub-continent

The isolation of India, then, is but relative; yet isolation there is, and within the girdle of mountains and seas has developed the almost incredibly complex culture of Hinduism: not unaffected by outside influences, certainly, but, in so far as we can dimly descry the origins of some of its yet existing cults in the earliest Indus civilization, native to this soil. Hinduism gives, or until very recently has given, a certain common tone to most of the sub-continent, but it contains within itself a vast range of diversities, not to mention the enclaves of primitive tribes and the fossils of ancient faiths, such as the Jains, the Parsees, the Jews of Cochin, the 'Syrian' Nestorian Christians whose traditions go back to St Thomas the Apostle. Confronting it, and ever drawing strength from its bases in arid Asia, is the great rival creed of Islam. For millennia the Peninsula has been virtually a cul-de-sac into which peoples and cultures have infiltrated or been driven, retaining much of their ancient rules of life and yet ceaselessly reacting upon one another, and, for the most part, if not welded together at least held together in the iron clasp of the caste system, a unique solution[2] to the problems of plural society, which are in essence resolved by recognizing, canalizing, and in fact sanctifying the plurality. It is no exaggeration to say that among the peoples of India are groups at all levels of economic development from that of jungle-folk barely out of the Stone Age to that of monopoly capitalism, with more than a tinge of state planning. The difficulties of building no more than two nations out of this heterogeneous human stuff are obvious.

This human heterogeneity is seconded by more purely geographical factors, which give some colour to the generally accepted description of India as a 'sub-continent'. The concept of a sub-continent is far from clear, but the term has its uses, especially now that 'India' as the name of a state is the name of but a part of the old India, and it will often recur in the following pages.[3] So far as it has a meaning distinct from the shorthand usage just mentioned, 'sub-continent'

[2] Unique at least in degree of development.

[3] The use of 'India' as a convenient geographical expression implies no disrespect towards Pakistan; the term 'Indo-Pakistani sub-continent' is rather cumbersome for general use.

conveys an idea of size and numbers, and these it certainly has: India and Pakistan together have an area of 1,628,194 sq. miles (about 4,215,000 km²) and a population, by the 1961 Censuses, of 532,955,695. As a demographic unit the sub-continent, and indeed India alone, ranks second only to China. This great population is of course unequally distributed: the sub-continent contains, in the deserts of Baluchistan and the Thar and in the high desolation of outer Kashmir, tens of thousands of square miles almost devoid of inhabitants, while in Bengal Dacca Division has 6,000,000 more people than Belgium on an area one-third greater, and this with only four towns of any size and with very little industry.

It is only to be expected that so vast an area, bordered by mountains incomparably the most massive of the world, intersected by rivers of the first rank, should contain very considerable physical diversity. In essence the sub-continent falls into only three macro-regions: the Extra-Peninsular Mountain Wall; the Indo-Gangetic Plains; the old Peninsular Block. But these contain a multitude of distinctive *pays* within themselves. Even in the broad alluvial monotony of the Indo-Gangetic Plains factors of climate, soil, aspect and hydrology give rise to clear, if not clearly-marked, regional divisions; and although the transitions, like those in a suite of fossil echinoderms, are almost imperceptibly gradual, the extremes are extreme indeed: from the desert environs of Karachi to the almost unbelievably dense stipple of homesteads between Calcutta and Dacca.

Yet there is a sort of massive architectural simplicity in the pattern of the three great divisions: the old Peninsular platform, wrapped round by the great trough from the Indus to the Ganga Delta, a trough filled with the debris of the mountains which again enfold it on three sides. This is not accidental, since it is the rigid resistance of the old block which has moulded the frozen waves of the mountains, though their onset has in turn warped the root of the Peninsula to form the scarps and ranges from Gujarat to Chota Nagpur. It is aesthetically fitting that the historic heart of India should lie on the divide between Indus and Ganga, which is also the passage between the Aravallis and the Himalayas, perhaps the oldest surviving and the youngest ranges on the globe. This is the great node of Delhi, for over two thousand years, since the far-off legendary battles of the *Mahabharata* epic, the key to power in Hindustan.

Underlying the life of India is one great common factor, expressed it is true in divers modalities and degrees: the rhythm of the monsoonal year. The peoples of India and Pakistan are predominantly agrarian, and even most of the industrialization of today, like the great dynastic achievements of the past, is after all built upon the ancient foundation, the toil of the dwellers in 650,000 villages. The tapestries of their lives are wrought in various colours – the lush green of the deltas, the drab khaki of the deserts – but nearly everywhere the fundamental lineaments of the pattern are similar, and are controlled by the seasonal cycle in which the great bulk of the rainfall comes in the warmer half of the year: this is so whether the annual fall is 450 in. (11,430 mm.) on the Assam Plateau, or under 15 in. (381 mm.) in the Punjab, the only really large exception being the

Tamilnad coast in the southeast. There is also – away from mountains – a certain sameness in the régimes of temperature, annual or diurnal; but here, though we commonly think of India as 'tropical', it must be remembered that half of the area and over half of the population are north of the Tropic of Cancer. To a large extent, however, this is offset by the mountain wall forming an insulated compartment; and although in the Punjab night frosts bring the mean January temperatures down to the level of an English May, clear skies and intense insolation raise day temperatures to a tropical level, so that all beneath the Himalayas is essentially tropical, despite latitudes of 25–30°. Outside the Himalayas agriculture is nearly everywhere tropical in type, and it is rain, not temperature, that essentially decides what crops shall be grown.

Problems of Economy

Rain, or at least water: for of all the physical problems of India those of soil and water are supreme, and in many areas life depends on canal, tank or well. Two-thirds of the people live directly from the soil, and the cultivated area is less than one acre to each dweller in the countryside. This simple ratio is the core-problem of India and Pakistan; the extension of agriculture (if that is possible to any large degree) and the security of much existing cultivation depend on a better use of the water which falls directly on to the face of the land and that which is locked in snowfields or sealed within the earth. The improvement of the pitifully low yields from a cultivated area barely adequate to present population depends in part on better water-control, in part on better treatment of the soil itself, in general inadequately manured and exploited for generations without ceasing, so that in many areas it seems to have reached the irreducible minimum of fertility. Here the 'peculiar institution' of cow-sanctity, with consequent bovine over-population, raises issues special to India.

Apart from food the resources of the sub-continent, and especially India, are extensive indeed: a wide range of minerals, of fibres, of vegetable raw materials, of timber products; wealth almost incalculable in iron and manganese. Yet it may be questioned whether, in relation to numbers, even India is really a rich country, and Pakistan on the whole is definitely a poor one, as well as being split into two very ill-balanced sections 1,000 miles apart. Power resources are as yet a weak link in the chain of industrialization: the really good coalfields are concentrated in one corner of the Peninsula, and while the hydro-electric resources are great, many potential sites are ill-placed for development, and exploitation is rendered costly by the great seasonal variation in the flow of the rivers. And in the last resort a prosperous industry must depend on a prosperous countryside: the agrarian problem is central to all the problems of development. On all fronts, progress depends on real co-operation between India and Pakistan, not just the present avoidance of war, and on a refashioning of social relationships, which still too often, in the long run, imperil social order. Some advance, at least, is being made in this respect.

A vast tropical land, mountain-ringed, the immeasurably old plateaus and warped eroded hills of the Peninsula girdled by rain-swept deltas, arid wastes and the long leagues of tillage in the Gangetic Plain; a landscape clad naturally by dense jungle or open thorny scrub, but profoundly changed by the toil of generations of peasants whose prosperity or dearth depends primarily on the secular rhythm of the monsoon; home of a diversity of cultures under the hegemony of Hinduism – one of the greatest, most individual, and most self-contained of human institutions; open on one side to wave after wave of peoples from the steppe, for a thousand years bringing with them a more rigid and more austere creed; subjugated by the alien strength, military and economic, of modern imperialism, and now newly free, though divided, to build if it can of its own strength and for its own purposes, to marry its ancient philosophies to new techniques: such is the skeleton of Indian geography which we shall endeavour to clothe with living flesh.

GENERAL BIBLIOGRAPHICAL NOTE

The amount of specifically geographical writing about India is relatively small, though Indian and Pakistani geographers are rapidly increasing it. But the amount of literature with a geographical bearing is vast. It is inevitable that any book on India will owe much of its background to works not cited nor even, perhaps, consciously remembered.

Specifically geographical works

There seems to be no modern geography in English, other than school texts, devoted solely to the sub-continent. Sir T. H. Holdich's *India* in the Regions of the World Series is very stimulating and admirably written, but its regional sections (apart from those on the northwest and the Himalayas) are rather slight, and it appeared in 1904. N. Krebs, *Vorder Indien und Ceylon* (Stuttgart, 1939) is a good text with interesting maps; but there is a certain lack of systematic treatment, and the Himalayas and Baluchistan are omitted. Recent general works which deal at some length with India and Pakistan include:

G. B. Cressey, *Asia's Lands and Peoples* (McGraw-Hill, NY, 3rd ed. 1963).
N. Ginsburg (ed.), *The Pattern of Asia* (Prentice Hall, Englewood Cliffs; Constable, London, 1958).
P. Gourou, *L'Asie* (Hachette, Paris, 1953).
J. E. Spencer, *Asia East by South* (Wiley, NY; Chapman & Hall, London, 1954).
L. D. Stamp, *Asia* (Methuen, London; Wiley, NY, 12th ed., 1966).

For Pakistan, there is a short but useful text: K. S. Ahmad, *A Geography of Pakistan* (OUP, Karachi, 1964).

9

Periodicals

The leading geographical periodicals in India and Pakistan, in alphabetical order, are:

Bombay Geographical Magazine (Ruparel College, Mahim, Bombay 16).

Deccan Geographer (Hyderabad).

Geographer (Aligarh).

Geographical Review of India (formerly *Calcutta Geographical Review*; Geog. Soc. of India, Senate House, Calcutta 12).

Indian Geographical Journal (formerly *Journal of the Madras Geographical Association*, Madras).

Indian Geographer (Association Indian Geographers, PO Box 644, New Delhi).

National Geographer (Allahabad).

National Geographical Journal of India (Banaras Hindu University).

Oriental Geographer (Dacca).

Pakistan [formerly *Panjab*] *Geographical Review* (Lahore).

Unless otherwise stated, these are obtainable from the respective University Departments of Geography. All contain articles of value, as the footnotes to this book will show; but there is some unevenness, partly due to the desire of each Department to run *the* national journal.

Non-geographical periodicals of value are too numerous to be noted here; exception may be made for *The Eastern Economist* (New Delhi). There are many official and quasi-official journals, mostly issued from Delhi or Karachi, such as *The Indian Forester, Indian Agriculture, Pakistan Development Review* and so on. The annual handbooks such as *Pakistan Economic Survey* (Ministry of Finance, Rawalpindi) and *India: A Reference Annual* (Ministry of Information and Broadcasting, Delhi 6) are indispensable.

Official Publications

The mass of official literature, especially in India, is intimidating. There are six fundamental sources which must be mentioned. These are:

(*a*) the Census Reports, both the general and the provincial volumes;

(*b*) the *Records* and *Memoirs* of the Geological Survey of India (Calcutta);

(*c*) the *Report of the Royal Commission on Agriculture in India* (1928);

(*d*) the *Gazetteers*;

(*e*) the *Settlement Reports*;

(*f*) the numerous drafts, outlines, and interim surveys of the progress of the Five Year Plans, issued for the Indian Planning Commission by the Ministry of Information or the Manager of Publications.

The *Gazetteers* are issued in three series: (i) the *Imperial Gazetteer of India* (Oxford, 1908) – four introductory volumes covering geography, history, ethnography, economics, etc. – containing much information of permanent value –

followed by 20 volumes with alphabetical entries, and an atlas volume; (ii) the *Provincial Gazetteers* (1908–9), one or two volumes to each major political unit (including states and Agencies); (iii) the *District Gazetteers* (various dates). Despite their age the *Gazetteers* are still of much use, though the District volumes, on which the others are based, are very unequal indeed, excellent or the reverse according to the conscience, enthusiasm, and ability of the local District Commissioners. They have been at once a blessing and a curse to Indian geographers; no comparable area of the world has anything like this survey of all aspects of life, county by county as it were, on a standard pattern which facilitates reference – a Domesday and much more; but they have to some extent fostered a gazetteer habit of mind – enumerating rather than selective – and the repetition of stereotyped statements long out of date; and since 'It's all in the *Gazetteer*' they have to some extent inhibited the essential geographical attitude of going to see for one's self. We have used the four general volumes and the Provincial series extensively, but not as a rule the District volumes, which are on a scale more appropriate to regional monograph work.

This remark applies also to the *Settlement Reports*, which are minute surveys of agricultural possibilities and development, made for the assessment of Land Revenue.

Maps

The most useful general series is the Survey of India, 'India and Adjacent Countries', 1/1,000,000, published in various styles at various dates. Larger-scale SOI maps are on 1/253,440, 1/126,720, and 1/63,360: the modern full-coloured sheets are beautiful and astonishingly accurate productions giving an immense amount of information on vegetation, land use, and the cultural landscape; most major regions of the sub-continent have at least fair coverage in this style, though for some areas there are only poor ¼-in. uncoloured maps with hachures and a generally archaic style. The SOI also publishes 'Guide Maps' to the major cities and hill stations on scale 1/21,120 or larger. Purchase of large-scale Indian maps, however, may be restricted.

The Geological Survey has a general map (rather out-of-date) on the 1/2,000,000 scale; ¼-in. maps will be found in the *Records* and *Memoirs* on selected areas.

Some special atlases and maps are referred to in the appropriate chapters. By far the most important is the *National Atlas of India* edited by Professor S. P. Chatterjee and published by the Ministry of Education. This is a splendid and most valuable production, though its usefulness is diminished by the fact that the legends and information are entirely in Hindi; an English version is given but, in the absence of an administrative overlay with English key, it is difficult to follow. A revised and entirely English edition of the *Atlas* is now in preparation. The following maps have already been published on the 1/1,000,000 scale: population maps of Delhi, Rajkot, Jaipur, Lucknow, Nagpur, Calcutta, Bombay,

Hyderabad, Madras, Trivandrum; physical maps of Bhopal, Nagpur, Calcutta, Bombay and Trivandrum; transport and tourism maps of Bhopal and Bombay. Also, on the 1/6,000,000 scale, India-Physiographic Regions and Parliamentary Constituencies. We do recommend to the reader to keep closely in touch with the publication programme. The best one-sheet map is Bartholomew's 'India and Pakistan' (1/4,000,000); there appear to be some inaccuracies in the contours, but on this scale they are not very serious. Many official maps are rather poor, but higher standards are now being set, for example in Census reports. The SOI issues several general maps on the scale 1/4,500,000 (71 miles to the inch), including a political map which is a very useful outline.

Background

Almost any book on India adds something to the general picture, though it may not be drawn on for any specific detail. Of travel books, Aldous Huxley's *Jesting Pilate* (1924) remains one of the most perceptive, and there is some good writing in R. Cameron, *Time of the Mango Flowers* (Heinemann, London, 1958); not perhaps a travel book in the ordinary sense, but invaluable as an overall picture of the rural scene, is Kusum Nair, *Blossoms in the Dust* (Praeger, NY, 1962) – the title, justified in the text, yet disguises a treatment both vivid and intensely serious.

Perhaps the most useful single volume on India before Partition and Independence was L. S. S. O'Malley (ed.), *Modern India and the West* (London, 1941). G. T. Garratt (ed.), *The Legacy of India* (Oxford, 1937) and H. G. Rawlinson, *India: A Short Cultural History* (London, 1943) remain perhaps the best introductions to the vast intellectual and aesthetic history of the undivided sub-continent. For those who wish to go further, there are such works as H. Zimmer, *Philosophies of India* (Meridian Books, NY, 1956) and his magnificent *The Art of Indian Asia* (Pantheon (Bollinger Series), NY, 1955). A. L. Basham, *The Wonder that was India* (Sidgwick & Jackson, London, 1962) may be mentioned here.

It is virtually impossible to select from the plethora of socio-political commentary, but the autobiographies of Gandhi and Nehru are essential for the Westerner wishing to understand the modern Indian scene; it is unfortunate that there is no Pakistani counterpart. Mention may be made of S. S. Harrison's thought-provoking book *India: The Most Dangerous Decades* (Princeton Univ. Press, 1960), H. Tinker, *India and Pakistan: A Short Political Guide* (Pall Mall Press, London, 1962), and I. Stephens' sympathetic study *Pakistan: Old Country, New Nation* (Pelicans, Harmondsworth, 1964).

The judicious student will not neglect more creative writers: *Kim* (despite its romantic view of the British Raj) and *A Passage to India* retain their classic value as interpretations. More recent novelists of insight are Philip Woodruff, Christine Weston, Rumer Godden; much of Mulk Raj Anand's writing suffers from being that of a political expatriate, but at his best he is very moving; Ahmed Ali's

Twilight in Delhi is an exceedingly subtle study of a society in decay; and for the Dravidian South, the incomparable novels and tales of R. K. Narayan give the very feel of small-town life with delicate and wistful artistry.

There is no good anthology of Indian verse, or indeed of Indian writing in general, either translated into or originally written in English; a wonderful volume could be compiled. It must suffice to mention two poets, one of them indubitably among the great: this is Mohammed Iqbal, whose *Secrets of the Self* is great philosophical verse with a biting edge; many of his poems have been translated by V. G. Kiernan in *Selections from Iqbal*, in Murray's Wisdom of the East series. Opposed to Iqbal's austerity is the Miltonic grandeur and all-embracing sweep of Sri Aurobindo's metaphysical epic *Savitri*. Finally, there is the other side of India – the rustic ethos, realist, salty, earthy, of the *Panchatantra* stories, still and deservedly a best-seller after a circulation of a millenium or two.

Postscript. To the list of general works on p. 9 should be added J. Durand-Dastes, *L'Inde* (Presses Universitaires Françaises, Paris, 1965); not seen but well reviewed; to the list of periodicals, *Indian Journal of Geography*, Jodhpur. Finally, Volume I of a new *Gazetteer of India* appeared in 1965, too late to be used in this work; it is an excellent volume, auguring well for the new post-Independence series. There is an admirable bibliographic survey by P. P. Karan, 'Recent Contributions to the Geography of South Asia', *Cahiers de Géographie de Quebec*, Sept. 1966, 317–32.

CHAPTER I

Structure and Relief

The Triple Tectonic Division

The familiar division of India into three major geomorphological components – the ancient block of Peninsular India, the Himalayas and their associated young fold-mountains east and west, and between these two the Indo-Gangetic Plains – is generally valid. The physiographic contrasts between these macro-regions are most striking; broadly speaking the Peninsula is dominated by an open senile topography, witness to vast periods of geological quiescence, while the Himalayas display the most youthful and highly differentiated relief on the face of the earth, and the Indo-Gangetic Plains present a monotonous aggradational surface of great extent.

Nevertheless the Peninsula has its youthful, or rather rejuvenated, landforms and the Himalayas their worn-down erosion surfaces, and structurally also the division is not absolutely clear-cut. The Peninsula has not been entirely immune from the impact of the great Tertiary orogeny, while conversely concealed extensions of the old block have exerted an important influence on the folding, on both local and regional scales, in the northwest and northeast Himalaya. Again, despite the sharpness (on the map) of the northern edge of the Indo-Gangetic Plains, the outermost Himalayan foothills – the Siwaliks – represent a late buckling of the erosion products of the mountains themselves, deposits not essentially different from some of those now forming. The three grand divisions are therefore related in a rather more intimate way than is implied by the bald statement that the Himalayan folding is the resultant of the relative moving together of the old blocks of Gondwanaland, of which Peninsular India is a part, and Angaraland or Laurasia.

I. THE PENINSULA

Geology (Figs. 1.1, 1.2)

The northern boundary of the Peninsular block may be taken as an irregular line running from Kutch along the western flank of the Aravalli Range to near Delhi, and thence roughly parallel to the Yamuna (Jumna) and the Ganga as far as the Rajmahal Hills and the Ganga Delta. Embayments of the Indo-Gangetic alluvium naturally penetrate south of this line, which in the west has a ragged contour in sharp contrast to the long smooth Himalayan front; and the ancient

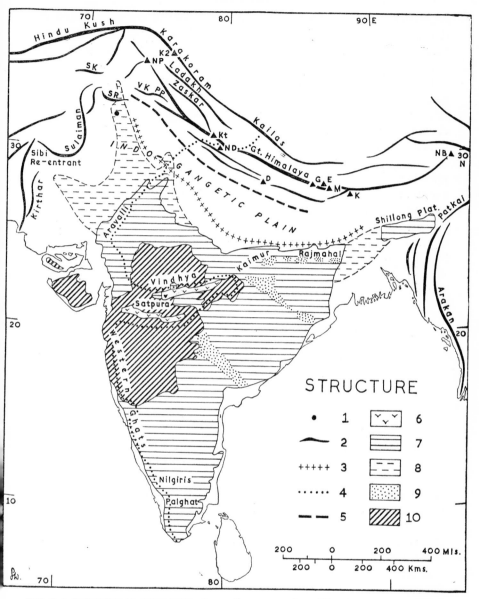

FIG 1.1 STRUCTURAL OUTLINES. 1, northernmost Aravalli outcrops; 2, trend of main Tertiary fold ranges; 3, boundary of Indo-Gangetic trough (Wadia); 4, Bay of Bengal/Arabian Sea watershed; 5, Siwalik Hills; 6, Narmada and Tapti troughs; 7, Peninsular Block; 8, concealed extensions of 7; 9, Gondwana troughs; 10, Deccan Lavas. SK, Safed Koh; SR, Salt Range; PP, Pir Panjal; VK, Vale of Kashmir. Peaks not on Fig. 1.5: G, Gaurisankar; Kt, Kamet; M. Makalu.

Peninsular rocks are relatively close to the surface in the gap between the Rajmahal Hills and the Shillong Plateau (which is indeed an outlier of the Peninsular block) and again in a northerly wedge indicated by the Kirana Hills of the Punjab (Figs. 1.1, 1.5).

The Peninsula is formed essentially by a great complex of very ancient gneisses and granites, which form the surface over more than half its area. The relations of this complex with the oldest metamorphosed sedimentaries are not clear; the old view that the gneisses formed a floor on which the younger rocks were deposited has been considerably modified, as it is now known that much of the gneiss is intrusive into the Dharwar rocks; there were at least three phases of granitic intrusion before the Cambrian. But at all events the Peninsula has been a great landmass from very early times and, except for the Deccan Lavas, rocks younger than pre-Cambrian have a restricted extension in synclinal and faulted troughs and basins.

The Peninsular formations, with their approximate ages, are:

Coastal Alluvium, with that of Narmada and Tapti basins
Coastal Tertiaries
Deccan Lavas (late Cretaceous to ? early Tertiary)
Coastal Cretaceous and Jurassic
Upper Gondwana (Jurassic)
Middle Gondwana (Triassic)
Lower Gondwana (Permian to Carboniferous)
Vindhyan (Cambrian, ? some Ordovician)
Cuddapah and Delhi (Algonkian)
Dharwar and Aravalli (Huronian)
Gneisses and Granites (at least in part Lewisian).

The Dharwar and Aravalli formations 'possess the most diverse lithologica characters, being a complex of all kinds of rocks – plastic sediments, chemically precipitated rocks, volcanic and plutonic rocks – all of which generally show an intense degree of metamorphism.'[1] The chief occurrences are in a series of narrow belts, the troughs of tight-packed synclines, in the Mysore–Dharwar–Bellary area; flanking the Chota Nagpur Plateau on the north and south, and in patches westwards as far as Nagpur city; and in the Aravallis. Those of the Bihar–Orissa area are of great economic importance as they contain the most valuable iron ores of India. The Aravalli Range was probably formed in the close of Dharwar times, and has since been peneplaned and again uplifted in the Cambrian, and possibly again before the Permo-Carboniferous glaciation; it may perhaps claim to be the oldest mountain system, still recognizable as such by its relief, on the earth's surface.

The earth-movements responsible for the folding of the Aravallis and other Dharwarian areas were succeeded by a prolonged period of erosion and sub-

---

[1] D. N. Wadia, *Geology of India* (Macmillan, London, 3rd ed. revised, 1961), 95.

sidence, though two diastrophic cycles may have intervened before the Delhi or
Cuddapah orogeny. A great unconformity separates the Dharwarian from the
20,000 ft. (6,100 m.) of slates, quartzites, and limestones which form the marine
Cuddapah system, deposited presumably in great synclinal basins. The Cuddapah

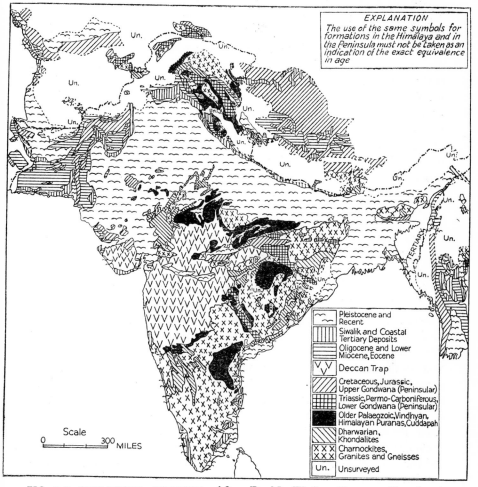

EXPLANATION
The use of the same symbols for
formations in the Himalaya and in
the Peninsula must not be taken as an
indication of the exact equivalence
in age

Pleistocene and Recent
Siwalik and Coastal Tertiary Deposits
Oligocene and Lower Miocene, Eocene
Deccan Trap
Cretaceous, Jurassic, Upper Gondwana (Peninsular)
Triassic, Permo-Carboniferous, Lower Gondwana (Peninsular)
Older Palaeozoic, Vindhyan, Himalayan Puranas, Cuddapah
Dharwarian, Khondalites
Charnockites, Granites and Gneisses
Un. Unsurveyed

Scale
0   300 MILES

FIG 1.2 GEOLOGICAL OUTLINES. After D. N. Wadia. *Courtesy* Chambers'
Encyclopaedia.

rocks are preserved mainly in a big belt on the east of the Deccan, between the
Krishna (Kistna) and Penner Rivers, and in the valley of the upper Mahanadi;
except in the long border-ridges of the Nallamalai and Velikonda Hills they are
little disturbed. The Delhi quartzites occur in narrow tightly-packed belts in
the centre of the great Aravalli synclinorium; they form the rocky echelonned
ridges, low but persistent, which terminate in the famous Ridge at Delhi.

Vindhyan rocks overlie the Cuddapahs in the lowest part of the Krishna–Penner trough, but their main occurrence is in a belt along the northern flank of the Peninsula from the Chambal to the Son, broken by the expanse of ancient Bundelkhand Gneiss around Jhansi; west of the Aravallis patches of lavas of Lower Vindhyan age are found around Jodhpur. In the lower part of the system marine shales, limestones and sandstones are found, but above these are great thicknesses of nearly horizontal fluviatile and estuarine sandstones, including the famous red sandstone used for many of the best Mogul buildings. In general the Vindhyans are little disturbed or metamorphosed, except in the patches west of the Aravallis. The most striking feature formed by the Vindhyan rocks is the scarp which marks the northern flank of the Narmada and Son valleys; in the west this is largely formed of Deccan Lavas, but Vindhyan rocks occur between Bhopal and Itarsi, and dominate farther east in the remarkably even and continuous Kaimur scarp overlooking the Son.[2] Much farther south, Vindhyan rocks are found in the Bhima valley between Sholapur and Raichur, and probably underlie much of the Deccan Lava country.

The *Gondwanas* consist of great thicknesses of sandstones with some shales and clays; they are of continental origin, fluviatile and lacustrine deposits laid down in geosynclinal troughs on the ancient plateau surface; these were formerly thought to be rifts produced by tensional faulting, but F. Ahmad has argued convincingly against this view. They show a striking parallelism to sequences of similar age in South Africa, Australia and South America, notably in the presence of glacial basal conglomerates and the famous *Glossopteris* flora; this parallelism is of fundamental importance in discussions of continental drift and cognate subjects. The isolated occurrence of marine limestone at Umaria (Madhya Pradesh) is now paralleled by a similar outcrop 100 miles to the southeast, and this 'solitary record of an evanescent transgression of the sea-waters into the heart of the Peninsula' is now less inexplicable.[3] More immediately important, perhaps, is the fact that nearly all India's coal comes from Gondwana formations, the bulk of it from the Damodar Valley on the flanks of the Chota Nagpur Plateau. More or less continuous belts of Gondwana rocks are found along the lower Penganga and Godavari Rivers, and between the Mahanadi and the Brahmani from Talchir on the latter river to the headstreams of the Narmada and the Son, while the Damodar is marked by a string of outcrops. This disposition suggests strongly that these rivers, in contrast to Narmada and Tapti, occupy *ancient* structural troughs.

---

[2] The geographical and geological usages of the word Vindhyan must be distinguished. The Vindhyan *Hills* are taken as extending roughly from 75 to 78° E and are mostly formed of Deccan Lavas; eastwards the same general line is continued by the Bhanrer and Kaimur Hills, which are formed of Vindhyan *rocks*.

[3] For Gondwana deposition, see Wadia, *op. cit.* 172–80, and F. Ahmad, 'Palaeo-geography of the Gondwana Period in Gondwanaland . . .', *Mem. GSI* 90 (1961), 64–68; for Umaria relationships, Wadia 231–2 and Ahmad 25–26, 71, 81–83. Ahmad's paper is a most important contribution to Peninsular problems.

The *Deccan Lavas* (styled Deccan Traps in the older literature) are generally from 2,000 to 5,000 ft. (610–1,525 m.) thick and reach a maximum of 10,000 ft.; they cover some 200,000 sq. miles (518,000 km²) with their mesa-like terrain. These practically horizontal and in the main remarkably homogeneous basalts were probably extruded from fissures towards the end of the Cretaceous, though a flora which seems to be of early Eocene age was found between some of the flows. The lavas were poured on to a land surface which had already attained an advanced stage of maturity, and form a most striking feature in the geomorphology of the Peninsula, with an obvious family likeness to the great basaltic flows of the Columbia Plateau and of southern Brazil.

Finally, in Kutch and Kathiawad and along the southeastern coast, patches of marine Jurassic, Cretaceous and Tertiary rocks bear witness to marginal transgressions of the sea; oil search may reveal seaward extensions.

Structural history

After the deposition of the older Peninsular sedimentaries the first clearly recognizable event seems to be the folding of the Aravallis in the earlier Vindhyan period. The Upper Vindhyan sandstones were probably formed of debris from these mountains, then at their highest elevation. It would seem also that the more disturbed portions of the Eastern Hills (Nallamalais and Velikondas) were elevated at the same time. The Aravallis then suffered planation, and presumably a later rejuvenation in early Gondwana times.

It does not seem necessary to posit a great 'Vindhyan Range' as the source of the Gondwana tillites, which were more probably deposited by ice-sheets than by valley glaciers. However, such orogeny as took place seems to have been Palaeozoic rather than pre-Cambrian, and the concept of the Peninsula as an almost completely stable block is dubious. The proto-Vindhyan ranges might be associated with the probably middle Palaeozoic Salt Range orogeny, and there was further uplift in post-Gondwana times, perhaps even in the initiatory phases of the Himalayan orogeny.[4] At all events, planation has more than once been followed by rejuvenation. Thus Wadia regards the highlands of Ceylon, and the Palani and Nilgiri Hills, not as merely 'the residual stumps of an eroded plateau' but as great horsts uplifted in post-Jurassic and early Tertiary times, and his conclusions are in general supported by Dupuis.[5] These periods are significantly close to those of intense mountain-building activity in the Himalayas, the extrusion of the Deccan Lavas, and possibly the subsidence of the Arabian Sea to form the Western Ghats.

These are the most striking events in the later history of the Peninsula. The date of origin of the Ghats is a major problem; there is palaeontological evidence

[4] Ahmad, *op. cit.* 69–71.
[5] D. N. Wadia, 'The three superposed peneplains of Ceylon', *Rec. Dept of Mineralogy, Ceylon*, Profl Paper No. 1 (1943), 25–32; J. Dupuis, *Les Ghat Orientaux et la Plaine du Coromandel*, *Travaux de la Section Scientifique* (Institut Français, Pondichéry, Tome II, 1959), *passim*.

for the existence until late Jurassic times of a Gondwana landmass separating the area north of the present Arabian Sea from a sea which connected South Africa and Madagascar with the east coast of India. The long straight edge of the Ghats, developed on practically horizontal Deccan Lavas and on ancient gneisses, itself strongly suggests faulting and subsidence on a very large scale; Krishnan speaks of downfaulting, probably Miocene, of the order of 6,000–7,000 ft. (1,830–2,135 m.). The view that the Ghats owe their origin to the subsidence of a landmass to the west seems supported by the absence of evidence for a simple eastwards tilting of the whole block: the main lines of the well-developed river-pattern are apparently of great age and carry no suggestion (such as gaps through an old more or less central watershed) of the reversal or diversion of an original west-flowing drainage. The Palghat Gap hardly throws any light on the problem; it has been regarded as the ancient valley of a river flowing either from the east or, before the assumed Arabian Sea subsidence, from the west. Questions of isostasy and continental drift are obviously involved; it is difficult to see how, on the generally accepted view of isostasy, foundering on this scale could take place in a relatively immobile sector of the earth's crust; and on the other hand an appeal to splitting and drift must face the youthfulness of the phenomena.

This youthfulness is indicated by the absence of river-capture on any significant scale, except in the valleys of the Kalinadi, Gangavati–Bedti and Sharavati; these are developed on the gneisses. The wide and almost senile valleys of the east-flowing rivers are on the whole graded almost to their heads, nearly in sight of the Arabian Sea, and contrast very strikingly with the youthful gorge-like courses of the west-flowing streams. These latter have only 50 miles (80 km.) in which to fall 2,000 ft. (610 m.) or more to base-level; the straight-line distance from the watershed to the Bay of Bengal is 300–600 miles (c. 480–965 km.); and the western slopes of the Ghats have a rainfall three or four times as great as that in their lee. Yet, on the Deccan Lavas at least, there has not apparently been time for large-scale capture, and the deep canyons suggest that the streams are still eroding vertically faster than they cut back the valley-sides. It seems likely, therefore, that the origin of the Arabian Sea coast must be very late, perhaps as late as the Pliocene.

On the east coast the lithology and stratigraphy of the marine deposits seem to indicate that since the latter part of the Palaeozoic the general run of the coastline has been sub-parallel to its present position, with alternating epeiro-genetic transgressions and retreats of the sea.[6]

The anomalous direction of the west-flowing Narmada and Tapti Rivers is another problem. The most favoured explanation is that they occupy two rifts formed by sag-faulting at the time of stress implied by the Himalayan folding: the long Vindhya/Kaimur and Satpura/Mahadeo scarps, and the trend of the south coast of Kathiawad, might be taken as supporting this view.

These troughs, however they originated, are now floored with considerable

[6] See the folding map in Dupuis, *op. cit.*

deposits of alluvium; in the Narmada trough, they are 500 ft. (150 m.) or more thick and occupy a definite rock-basin, another indication of faulting. The straightness and relative steepness of the Narmada from Handia to the sea indicates a recent origin for this section: below Handia the fall is 900 ft. in 300 miles (1 in 1,756 m.), the 300 miles upstream has just half as much. Possibly the Narmada once flowed out through the Burhanpur–Khandwa gap into the present Tapti; warping on a line Handia–Paithan (Fig. 1.3) would probably account for interruptions of profile producing this aggradation; this in turn might be con-

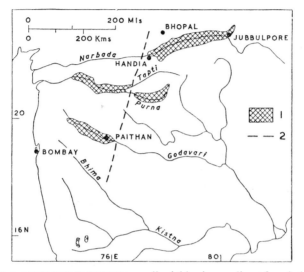

FIG I.3 DECCAN ALLUVIUM. I, alluvial basins; 2, line of probable warp. After E. Vredenburg. *Courtesy* GSI.

nected with the presumed faulting of the Western Ghats. The irregularities are slight, but in view of the degree of grading shown by the major Peninsular rivers they are significant, even though the warping is hardly strong enough to be readily detectable in the massive layers of the Deccan Lavas. 'All these changes agree in showing that a very extensive, though moderate, disturbance has affected the Peninsula at a late period previous to modern times.' The Marble Rocks Falls on the upper Narmada, near Jabalpur (Jubbulpore), may also be due to recent movement, or alternatively to superimposition.[7]

As has been mentioned, the major Peninsular rivers are as a rule remarkably graded; there are, however, marked interruptions to profile where they cut through the Eastern Hills in relatively constricted valleys. On the southern flanks of the Mysore plateaus there are numerous falls and gorges, and these again connect with the uplift of the southern horsts.

[7] See E. Vredenburg, 'Pleistocene movement as indicated by irregularities of gradient of the Narbada', *Rec. GSI* 33 (1906), 33–45.

Summing up, the main elements of Peninsular geomorphology are the great plateau of granite and gneiss (with higher bosses such as the Nilgiris) occupying nearly all the south and east; the mesa-like country of the Deccan Lavas in the west centre; the old shallow troughs of the Krishna, Godavari and Mahanadi systems; the much-worn Aravalli Range; and the Vindhyan scarplands of the north, with the Narmada–Son and Tapti troughs or rifts. Even this brief and incomplete generalization suggests that Peninsular India has much more geomorphological variety than is generally credited to it. The general aspect, however, is certainly one of old age, except along the escarpment of the Western Ghats and in a few hillier areas; but there are erosion surfaces of more than one cycle, and evidences of important and relatively recent changes of level, mostly negative.[8] On the whole, it may fairly be said that the general lineaments of the Peninsula seem to be much more in accord with Lester King's concepts of pediplanation than with classical Davisian peneplanation.

Present relief

The Peninsula thus consists of a great tabular block with a general slope to the east; its bold outlines are less simple on the north, owing to the very ancient but oft-rejuvenated Aravalli folding and the strain on the block of the tangential forces which produced the Himalayas; while in the south it is accidented by a number of relatively youthful horsts.

The Aravallis themselves are now no more than the stumps of a once lofty range; they reach their highest point at Mount Abu (5,650 ft., 1,722 m.) in the southwest, sink to low hills in the Jodhpur–Jaipur saddle, and rise again to the northeast before petering out in little echelonned ridges, half buried in the Indo–Gangetic alluvium, and reaching as far as the Delhi Ridge. Western Rajasthan is a debateable land, pene- or more likely pediplaned and largely smothered by the dunes of the Thar Desert, but with little hills of Vindhyan lavas and marine Jurassic and Tertiary beds. East of the Aravallis, the lower Chambal may be regarded as occupying a strike valley in the Vindhyan scarplands, but above Kota (Kotah) it is probably superimposed, cutting across the strike, and its upper reaches are more nearly consequent on the Deccan Lavas of Malwa. The Chambal and Betwa valleys are of great human and historical importance, providing a broad belt of relatively favourable country (Malwa) between the gnarled and arid Aravallis and scarp-rimmed Bundelkhand Gneiss terrain around Jhansi; the Malwa scarps face south and east at heights of 1,500–1,800 ft. (455–550 m.). The Vindhya (Deccan Lava) and Kaimur (Vindhyan sandstone) Hills form a great scarp overlooking the Narmada valley and that of the subsequent Son; their drainage is practically all northwards to Yamuna and Ganga, neither Narmada nor Son having any important north-bank tributaries. There is definite evidence in the Son valley of a drainage pattern superimposed from a

---

[8] Mostly, but not entirely, as is shown, e.g. by the presence of a submerged forest at Bombay, and of lignite 240 ft. (73 m.) below ground at Pondicherry.

higher plateau valley, the main outlines of which, however, were not dissimilar from those of the present.[9] This Vindhya–Kaimur scarp exceeds 2,000 ft. (610 m.) in only a few places, but is remarkably regular and free from gaps.

Beyond the Son, the gneissic plateaus of Chota Nagpur reach 3,500 ft. (1,070 m.) in the Hazaribagh Range, but the most extensive level, that of the Ranchi Plateau, is at rather more than 2,000 ft. with a few monadnocks. The Peninsula itself may be said to terminate in the Rajmahal Hills (largely basalts of Gondwana age), but a sill of old rock relatively near the surface of the Gangetic alluvium connects it with the outlying Shillong Plateau. South of the Rajmahals lie the economically very important coal-bearing Gondwana basins of the Damodar Valley, with sandstone ridges striking east–west in a synclinal trough; and south of the Ranchi Plateau a corridor at just over 1,000 ft. (305 m.) leads from the Ganga Delta to the Brahmani and Mahanadi basins, between the plateau and the broken forested hills of Orissa – the most northerly section of the Eastern Hills – at 3,000–3,800 ft. (915–1,160 m.).

Between Narmada and Tapti lie the Satpura/Mahadeo Hills; there are some suggestions of folding and upheaval, so that they may represent an ancient tectonic range, but their present aspect is of scarped blocks (on the whole steeper towards the Tapti) largely covered with Deccan Lavas but with some gneissic inliers. From their eastern continuation in the Amarkantak plateau (Maikal Hills), a mixed Deccan Lava and gneissic upland, radiate the headwaters of the Narmada, Son and Mahanadi, as well as those of the Wainganga, an important tributary of the Godavari. The Burhanpur–Khandwa gap, possibly once occupied by the Narmada, and the saddle used by the railway between Nagpur and Jabalpur should be noted.

All this northern sector of the Peninsula (except for the northeast/southwest trends of the Aravalli-lower Chambal area) is dominated by strong east–west lineaments, probably influenced by buckling and sagging of the northern flanks of the old block under the stress of the Himalayan orogeny; there are of course local deviations, such as northeast/southwest strikes in the Maikal and Hazaribagh Hills.

To the west, Kathiawad is mainly Deccan Lava, with a fringe of marine Jurassic and Tertiary rocks, which predominate in Kutch: a country of small folds, dissected plateaus, and scarplands, all on a minor scale, linked to the Peninsula by the great alluvial plain of Gujarat. The subsidence which has formed the salt-marshes and bare mud-flats of the Rann of Kutch is of recent date and perhaps still continuing; much of the flooding was produced by the earthquake of 1819.

South of the Tapti the Western Ghats begin; they are sometimes referred to as the Sahyadri Range, but this is an unhappy term as it attaches the idea of a mountain range to the crest of a scarp, and the name Sahyadriparvat is also

[9] R. D. Oldham, 'Notes on the geology of the Son Valley', *Mem. GSI* 31 (1901), 1–178; an amazingly 'modern' geomorphological study for its date.

applied to the Ajanta Hills. The Ghats almost at once reach a height of 3,000–4,000 ft. (915–1,220 m.) and maintain this, with many interruptions, but few of significance, for some 250–300 miles (400–480 km.), with some culminations up to 5,000 ft. (1,525 m.). There is a very steep and wildly dissected fall to the undulating and narrow coastal lowland of the Konkan, but once over the crest the broad practically senile valleys of the plateau begin almost immediately. The Deccan Lavas form the Ghats to a little north of Goa, and here the seaward face is like a great wall, but dissected by deep canyon-like valleys into spectacular mesas, buttes and pinnacles. South of Goa the old gneisses and granites come in, and here more rounded forms prevail; for about 200 miles (322 km.) the crest sinks below 3,000 ft. (and here are the only significant river-captures), but then rises again to the great gneissic boss of the Nilgiris, reaching in Dodabetta 8,760 ft. (2,670 m.). This culmination is essentially a much-worn massif, elevated and re-dissected, so that it forms bold, swelling hills and downlands, with very steep drops on all sides. Southwards, across the Palghat Gap, the wilder and more forested Anaimalais and the Cardamom and Palani Hills are similar in origin; Anaimudi in the Anaimalais is the highest point in the Peninsula, 8,840 ft. or 2,694 m. The falls on the rejuvenated rivers of these southern horsts are among the most important sources of hydro-electric power in India.

The Palghat Gap is apparently of tectonic origin; its summit is a broad table-land not much over 1,000 ft. Except for the little Shencottah gap right in the south (where the width of the Peninsula is too restricted for sea-to-sea communication to be of much importance) this is the only really easy passage across the Ghats from the Tapti to Kanya Kumari, a distance of some 880 miles (1,610 km.). The Kerala coastal lowland west of Palghat widens out and has more definitely the aspect of an emerged sea-floor than has the Konkan; it is fringed by a long series of lagoons and bars.

The 'Eastern Ghats' are something of a misnomer, and are much less strongly marked than the Western; indeed, between the Godavari and the Krishna they almost disappear. There is no structural continuity: dissected massifs of older Peninsular rocks in the north; relics of ancient mountains such as the Nallamalai, Velikonda and Palkonda in the centre, south of the Krishna; gneissic horsts, the Shevaroy, Pachamalai and so on in the south. In view of this heterogeneity the term 'Eastern Ghats' is avoided in this book, being replaced by 'Eastern Hills' for the northern, 'Cuddapah Ranges' for the central and 'Tamilnad Hills' for the southern groups; if less handy than the old name, this is also less misleading.[10] Except in the wild forested country of the Orissa hinterland

---

[10] The term 'Ghat . . . really implies a place of access. The Western Ghats were the places at which roads from the westward led up to the plateau . . . the "Eastern Ghats" are a figment of the imagination, the name . . . having been loosely applied to sundry groups of hills that have no connection' (W. T. Blanford in GJ 3 (1894), 193). The primary idea seems to be that of a step or terrace – as in burning ghats and other riverside platforms – and is thus appropriate to the mesa-like stepped topography of the Deccan Lavas of the Western Ghats. The comment by Dupuis (op. cit. 18) misses the point.

and Bastar, the most jungly part of India, these groups seldom exceed 3,000 ft. (915 m.), but are often very difficult dissected country.

In Andhra Desa and Coromandel the coastal plains, much wider than on the west coasts, have a complex origin. Here and there are small inland-facing cuestas of marine sediments, Tertiary or Jurassic; lines of gneissic inselbergen were once literally off-shore island-hills; inland, at the foot of the hills and plateaus, vast pediments formed by sheet-floods from the Pliocene onwards merge insensibly seawards into a Miocene marine abrasion surface. At the mouths of the greater rivers these features are masked by extensive deltaic deposits, and the coast is often fringed by lagoons.[11]

Within the frame formed by the Satpura/Maikal/Hazaribagh Hills, the Western Ghats, the Eastern Hills and the Cuddapah Ranges, lies the true Deccan. In Lester King's view, the plateau basically represents an early Cainozoic planation (his 'Indian' landscape cycle), with older Gondwana and post-Gondwana surfaces surviving in the southern horsts and Ceylon, and (as it were in fossil form) in the Lameta series beneath the Deccan Lavas: 'Quite clearly these basal formations represent the ancient calcreted Gondwana or post-Gondwana surface.'[12]

In the north the Bombay–Calcutta railway, once it has climbed over the Ghats into the Tapti basin, meets no serious obstacles; the watersheds between the Tapti, Godavari and Mahanadi drainages are often mere swells, with perhaps small serrated relict hills crowning the pediments which really completely dwarf the slopes from which they have been formed. In the northwest, the most typical Deccan Lava country, such 'ranges' as the Ajanta and Balaghat Hills are no more than maturely dissected flat-topped ridges, often enough, it is true, with steep flanks or even narrow hogsbacks caused by the juxtaposition of retreating scarps. But so geometrical are the lines of the lava flows that the landscape looks like nothing so much as an over-simplified block diagram. On much of the vast gneissic expanses in the east and south the aspect is even more monotonous: great, often sub-arid, plains separated by thin worn-down ridges, the disjointed vertebrae of watersheds. In places bosses or dykes of harder granite, gneiss or quartzite give a more rugged relief, low but very steep and fantastically cragged tors and serrated ridges; in Mysore and on its border with Maharashtra, the Dharwar quartzites, preserved in narrow synclines, crop out in belts of steep-sided little hills. But in comparison with the vast monotonous plains, these more accidented areas are but small.

The Peninsular rivers find their way from these broad uplands to the sea by relatively narrow corridors; the correspondence of the gap shared by the Brahmani and Mahanadi, and that of the lower Godavari, with belts of Gondwana rocks has been taken to suggest a tectonic trough origin; the Krishna and the

[11] For a full description, Dupuis, *op. cit.*, *passim*; there is an English summary.
[12] L. C. King, *The Morphology of the Earth* (Oliver & Boyd, Edinburgh and London, 1962), 325; the pages devoted to India are perceptive and stimulating.

Penner appear to be superimposed across the Cuddapah Ranges. The passage is generally marked by rapids. It is noteworthy that none of these rivers is directly followed by an important route to gain access to the plateau; thus the main Madras–Bombay railway crosses the Cuddapah Ranges diagonally, by a strike corridor between the Velikondas and the Palkondas, reaching the Penner above the point where it begins to break through the ranges.

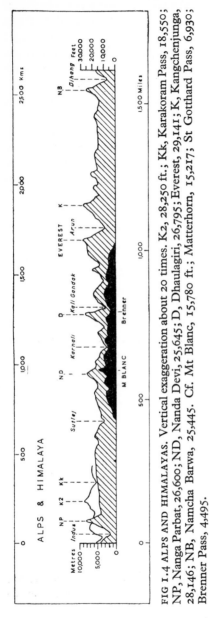

FIG 1.4 ALPS AND HIMALAYAS. Vertical exaggeration about 20 times. K2, 28,250 ft.; Kk, Karakoram Pass, 18,550; NP, Nanga Parbat, 26,600; ND, Nanda Devi, 25,645; D, Dhaulagiri, 26,795; Everest, 29,141; K, Kangchenjunga, 28,146; NB, Namcha Barwa, 25,445. Cf. Mt Blanc, 15,780 ft.; Matterhorn, 15,217; St Gotthard Pass, 6,930; Brenner Pass, 4,495.

II. THE HIMALAYAN OROGENY (Figs. 1.4–1.6)

Introductory

The vast scale of the ramparts which form the continental borders of India may be appreciated from Fig. 1.4, from which it will be seen that the main Himalaya alone, which stretches over 22° of longitude (some 1,500 miles, 2,415 km.) between the Indus and the Brahmaputra, could be wrapped round the Alps. Of the 94 Asian peaks which exceed 24,000 ft. (7,315 m.), all but two are in the Himalaya and the Karakoram; and no other continent has peaks of this height.

The unravelling of Himalayan structure is very far from complete, but already great nappes, perhaps less complicated than those of the Alps but much thicker and deeper-rooted, have been traced. Much of the area is still very imperfectly known geologically, and many phases of the history are still very controversial. There has of course been intense metamorphism and in many cases no reliable dating of the rocks is as yet possible: 'a large number of apparently independent rock groups has been established, each under a purely local name, thus giving rise to a confusing variety of sub-divisions, no two of which can be definitely correlated.' In some parts uplift has been considerable since the mid-Pleistocene, in others are great stretches of subdued topography at high altitudes, the relics of old planation; elsewhere the deepest gorges on earth alternate with the terraces of old lakes and the undulating hills of intermont basins. It is impossible in the space available to give a really comprehensive account of the geological and geomorphological complexities; but this may be the less serious in that the spectacular attractions of the Himalaya continue to draw expeditions and a consequent rich documentation.

During Mesozoic times the Himalayan area was occupied by the great geosynclinal Tethys Sea; there is a marked contrast in facies between the sediments of the Tibetan plateaus, laid down in this sea, and the rocks of the Himalayan area proper, which include both ancient and relatively recent crystalline intrusives and sedimentaries allied to those of the Peninsula. The orogenic activity which transformed the Tethys geosyncline appears to have taken place in three main phases:

(i) the elevation of the central axis of ancient crystallines and sedimentaries in Oligocene times; during this phase the important Nummulitic limestones were deposited in a series of basins, especially in Ladakh;

(ii) a Miocene movement, which folded the Murree sediments of the Potwar basin;

(iii) a post-Pliocene phase, which affected the Mio-Pliocene Siwalik sediments and which, apparently, has not yet entirely ceased.

Initial disturbances probably preceded the first of these, and the Karakoram, which has no marine Tertiary, may have been uplifted in the Cretaceous. There is naturally a great variety of structures and of tectonic relationships.

Geographically the Himalayas have been divided into five longitudinal zones:

(i) the outer zone of the Siwalik Hills and the *Duns* or longitudinal valleys behind them;

(ii) the Lesser Himalaya, including a great number of minor ranges at 6,000–10,000 ft. (1,830–3,050 m.);

(iii) the zone of spurs from the main ranges, presenting the general aspect of a very deeply dissected planation surface at about 15,000 ft. (4,570 m.);

(iv) the Great Himalaya itself, with many peaks over 20,000 ft. (6,095 m.);

(v) the Indus–Tsangpo furrow at about 12,000–14,000 ft. (3,660–4,270 m.); this is succeeded by the old worn-down mountains of the edge of the Tibetan Plateau, up to 19,000 ft. (5,790 m.) high.

To the north again are the Karakoram–Muztagh Ranges, which connect the Himalaya via the great Pamir knot with the Kun Lun and other ranges to the north of the Tibetan median mass.

The geological and tectonic zoning does not quite correspond to this purely topographical division. There are of course great local variations, but in general

27

the old Gondwana foreland (masked by the Tertiary Murree and Siwalik sediments) is succeeded by an autochthonous zone – 'recumbent folds of the Eocene with cores of Carboniferous–Trias rocks'; this again by a nappe zone which includes the pre-Cambrian slates of Hazara and the Kashmir basin; then the axial crystallines, 'a geanticline within a geosyncline', consisting of very ancient gneisses with many later gneiss and granite intrusions; and finally by fossiliferous Tethys or Tibetan sediments ranging from Cambrian to Tertiary in age. The axial crystallines, roughly along the Tsangpo furrow, really mark the tectonic boundary between India and High Asia; as King puts it, 'the fold-girdles of Gondwana and Laurasia here lie "back to back" '.[13]

The Himalayas: layout

The following account of the main components of the mountain system is intended not as a detailed regional description but simply as a framework for reference.

From the great Pamir complex the ranges splay out east and west in two vast virgations: the Tien Shan–Kun Lun–Karakoram and the Alai–Hindu Kush respectively. The Alai and Hindu Kush are succeeded on the south by the lower ranges of Afghanistan and Baluchistan, which in turn are looped around the Sibi re-entrant. North of this the Sulaiman presents a steep face to the Indus Plains, while to the south the hills fan out again, the Kalat country between the north–south Kirthar Range (on the Sind–Baluchistan border) and the east–west Chagai hills (in northwest Baluchistan) being a mass of echelonned ridges sinking to the Seistan depression and swinging round east–west, parallel to the coast, in Makran: 'each arc is in reality a series of concentric arcs connected at their extremities, leaving between them arid depressions.' These mountains are of simple anticlinal structure and developed for the most part in relatively soft Cretaceous and Tertiary sandstones, with a flysch facies in the north. The parallelism between the Sibi re-entrant and the greater re-entrant north of the Punjab is striking (Fig. 1.1); it is no accident that just as the northwestern syntaxial area culminates in the giant peaks of the Karakoram and Nanga Parbat, the highest points between the Safed Koh (34°N) and the sea are in the angle around Quetta. It seems likely that, as in the northwestern syntaxis, a concealed projection of the Gondwana block is responsible.

The structure of this northwestern syntaxis has been elegantly educed by Wadia: put briefly, the Tertiary folding has wrapped itself round a projection of Gondwanaland, indicated for example by the outcrop of old rock in the Kirana Hills (Fig. 1.5). Fronting the Punjab plains is the great (and much overthrust) monoclinal scarp of the Salt Range; behind this, between Indus and Jhelum, is the Potwar Plateau or basin, formed on folded Murree and Siwalik beds which are largely masked by a loess-like silt.

From Bunji to Hazara the Indus flows in a great gorge at about 3,000–4,500 ft.

[13] *Op. cit.* 470.

(915–1,370 m.) with sides up to 15,000 ft. (Fig. 14.1); west of it are the wild ⟨g⟩ ranges of Chitral and Kohistan. Northeast from the great bend at Bunji the country rises to the Karakoram, which in K2 (28,250 ft., 8,610 m.) has the second highest peak in the world; altogether there are 33 peaks over 24,000 ft. (7,315 m.) in an area comparable to that of the Swiss Alps (cf. Fig. 14.5). The ranges here are certainly older than those to the south, initially perhaps even Hercynian, but they have been much affected by rejuvenation and faulting. The Karakoram and Muztagh merge eastwards into the Kailas Range, which is simply the high edge of the Tibetan Plateau overlooking the Indus–Tsangpo furrow; the relationships and nomenclature of the ranges here are still a matter of some dispute.[14] Mention should be made of the Ladakh Range lying along and cut through by the Indus; in the east it separates that river from its important tributary the Shyok, which leads up to the Karakoram Pass (18,270 ft., 5,568 m.).

The Great Himalaya begins at the culmination of Nanga Parbat (26,629 ft., 8,127 m.) in the angle of the Indus. To the north it is flanked by the Zaskar Range, overlooking the Indus, and by the high dissected plains of Rupshu and Deosai; to the south by the series of more or less continuous or echelonned ranges known collectively as the Lesser Himalaya. The famous Vale of Kashmir lies between the Great Himalaya and the most westerly range of the Lesser Himalaya, the Pir Panjal; uplift here has been very considerable since the mid-Pleistocene. The Pir Panjal crest is merely a residual ridge on a broad plateau-like surface, and its accidented relief is due mainly to glaciation. The origin of the Vale itself is obscure: Wadia speaks of it as 'an exaggerated instance of a dun' or longitudinal valley, and his section shows it as occupying a synclinal on the back of the great Kashmir Nappe; while de Terra holds that it is a recently depressed intermont basin, pointing to marked evidence of faulting on the Himalayan flank. The floor of the Vale is formed mainly by the terraces of the Karewas beds, deposits of a Pleistocene lake. The longitudinal depression of the upper Jhelum in Kashmir is continued by the upper Chenab, and it seems likely that the upper Jhelum may have flowed out to the southeast before being captured by the present master-stream: the directions taken by its tributaries suggest this rather than the converse evolution, with the Chenab as captor, put forward by Pascoe. The longitudinal section of the upper Sutlej and its tributary the Spiti is not a continuation of this Jhelum–Chenab trough but lies north of the Great Himalaya, the Sutlej having a spectacular transverse course right across both Great and Lesser Himalaya.

On the southern flank of the mountains the Tertiaries of Potwar narrow out eastwards (Fig. 1.5) into the Siwalik Hills, which extend as far east as the Kosi River (87°E) and less continuously beyond that: the gaps in the Siwalik deposits

[14] It is almost as dangerous for the uninitiate to venture into Karakoram and Himalayan nomenclature as it would be to penetrate the mountains themselves. See the numerous papers in the *GJ* for 1936–38, ending with the report on 'Karakoram nomenclature', *GJ* 91 (1938), 125–52. For the relations of the Indus and the Ladakh Range see below, 443, and indeed all this section should be read in connection with Chapters 14 and 15.

around the Tista River have been attributed to the greater force of monsoon erosion opposite the passageway formed by the Ganga Delta, but the work of Heim and Gansser suggests that they may have been overridden by Himalayan nappes. The Siwaliks are formed of great thicknesses (15,000–20,000 ft., 4,570–6,100 m.) of Mio-Pleistocene sands, gravels and conglomerates, obviously erosion products of the Himalayas themselves, and although rarely exceeding 3,000 ft., they bear striking witness to the extreme youth of the mountain-building. The Siwaliks are backed by a discontinuous series of longitudinal vales – the *duns* – behind which are a number of southwards thrusts, the Boundary Faults once thought to represent successive boundaries between sedimentation and mountain-building but now recognized as the soles of great nappes. The Siwalik front to the plains is remarkably even and regular, and here again faulting may play a part – between Beas and Sutlej there is evidence for sub-recent thrusting of Upper Siwalik deposits over the older alluvium.

The Great Himalaya itself extends in a vast arc, convex to the south, from the Indus to the Brahmaputra; most of the peaks over 25,000 ft. (7,620 m.), though not Everest, are formed of granites and gneisses, but much of the area is made of old metamorphics which have some definite Peninsular affinities. After the great extent and height of the range, the most striking feature is the contrast between the relatively gentle and rounded forms of the slope to the Indus–Tsangpo furrow and the wildly fretted southern face. Apart from the great gorges of the Indus, Sutlej and Dihang (the transverse section of Tsangpo–Brahmaputra), the range is deeply cut into by the headwaters of the Ganga (Bhagirathi and Alaknanda Rivers), Sarda (Kali), Ghaghra (Seti, Karnali, and Bheri), Gandak and Arun; the last-named has a considerable plateau section behind Everest. On the whole the rivers tend to cut through the range in its culminating massifs; while the detailed work of Wager on the Arun strongly supports antecedence,[15] many features seem due to capture. Everywhere the descent is far steeper to the south than to the north, and some north-flowing streams seem to have lost much of their catchments and their valleys to be choked with their own debris. Thus in the Zoji La, north of Kashmir, the track up the south-flowing stream ends in a deep gorge and a 2,000-ft. (610 m.) ascent, beyond which is a well-graded valley opening to the north: very much the Maloja Pass type.[16] The assymmetrical development of the two slopes is, however, much more pronounced east of Sutlej, where the excess of precipitation on the southern face is much greater than in the west. Looking to the fact that elevation clearly took place in stages, a compromise view may be possible, that 'capture has created and antecedence maintained' the transverse gorges.

---

[15] L. R. Wager, 'The Arun river drainage pattern and the rise of the Himalayas', *GJ* 89 (1937), 139–50.

[16] R. D. Oldham, 'The making of Indian geography', *GJ* 3 (1894), at 187–90; despite its age this remains a most stimulating paper. Cf. L. M. Davies, 'Note on three Himalayan rivers', *Geological Mag.* 77 (1940), 410–12.

Corresponding to Nanga Parbat in the west, the eastern culmination of the Great Himalaya is the 25,000-ft. peak of Namcha Barwa, overlooking the Dihang gorges. The continuation of the axis farther east is very uncertain; Mason and Wadia incline to think that it swings round to a north–south alignment under the influence of the Shillong Plateau and the old Yunnan block; but Kingdon Ward adduces arguments (largely based on a floristic divide) to suggest that the real continuation is still eastwards and is cut across by the great antecedent trenches of the upper Salween, Mekong and Yangtse; the Himalaya may override the weaker folding of the Naga–Patkai arcs.[17]

This eastern area is much less known than the western and central Himalaya, but there seems to be at least a suggestive parallelism with the northwestern syntaxis; while the Shillong Plateau itself is relatively undisturbed, the Tertiaries to either side, in the Himalayan foothills and the Patkai–Naga ranges, show a good deal of thrusting and overturning, although further away from this peg or fulcrum the mountains of the Burma border are formed of simple open folds. On this view, the Brahmaputra valley in Assam is a ramp-valley forced down between the Shillong Plateau and the Himalayan thrusting. At any rate the Assam–Burma ranges seem to correspond in a general way with those of Baluchistan, and their north–south trends are doubtless associated with the northeastern wedge of the Peninsular Block and the resistance of the Yunnan Block. They are developed in relatively soft Cretaceous and Tertiary sandstones and shales, and have a markedly Jura-type structure of quite simple anticlines and synclines, with some shallow thrusting.

The northwestern syntaxis (Fig. 1.5)

The great syntaxis of the Himalayan arcs in the northwest, already briefly noted, is of much more than local significance: it forms a great knee-bend some 300 miles (480 km.) deep and affects the strike of the ranges probably as far as the foot of the Pamirs; a very striking expression of it is the wedge of Murree and Siwalik deposits at the sharp angle of the Jhelum near Domel.[18]

The extension of the old Gondwana block beneath the Punjab alluvium is evidenced by the Kirana outcrop, an outlier of the Aravallis only 60–70 miles (97–113 km.) from the Salt Range. The Salt Range itself, with its steep front to the plains, its long dip-slope northwards under the Potwar deposits, its thrusts showing a horizontal movement of some 20 miles, and its curiously twisted alignment, is very largely controlled by this concealed Peninsular salient. The stability and competence of the basement rocks of the old foreland, underlying the Tertiaries of Potwar, is shown by the fact that the mantle of Murrees and Siwaliks is merely wrinkled up on the basement, not metamorphosed or even much indurated; they are in fact only *plis de couverture* of no great depth. Again,

---

[17] F. K. Ward, 'The Himalaya east of the Tsangpo', *GJ* 84 (1934), 369–97.

[18] See Wadia's important paper, 'The syntaxis of the north-western Himalaya', *Rec. GSI* 65 (1931), 189–220.

the Murree sediments are strikingly different petrologically from those of the Siwalik Hills, being probably derived from iron-bearing Peninsular rocks rather than from the rising Himalaya.

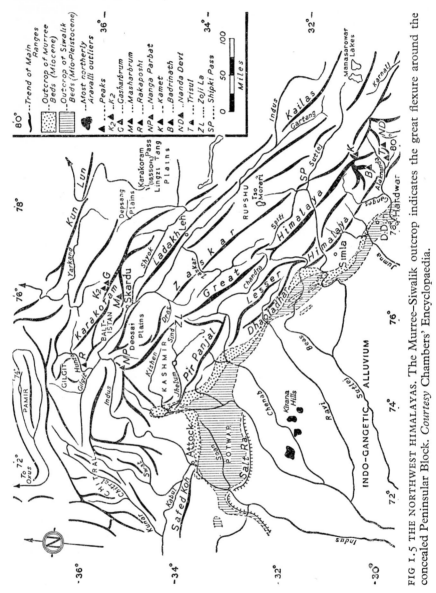

FIG I.5 THE NORTHWEST HIMALAYAS. The Murree–Siwalik outcrop indicates the great flexure around the concealed Peninsular Block. *Courtesy* Chambers' Encyclopaedia.

The influence of Gondwanaland on the alignment of the Himalayas has thus been profound: round the great salient the ranges are wrapped in loops, the strike of the rock systems paralleled by that of the planes of thrusting on to the foreland. The Great Himalaya represents the original axis of uplift of the Tethys geosyncline, bending sharply southwards at each end (into the Baluchistan and Assam ranges) where the northwards pressure of the Peninsular block ceases. The Himalayan compression, on this view, would not be merely the expression of an outward creep from central Asia, but largely due to underthrusting from the ocean floors and northwards drive of the old block, and this seems in reasonable accordance with modern views of isostasy and orogenesis.

Himalayan thrusts and uplifts (Fig. 1.6)
Current views on the rise of the Himalayas place great emphasis on tangentia processes analogous to nappe formation in the Alps; in fact it may be said that the detailed work of Auden in Garhwal, Heim and Gansser in Kumaon and Hagen and others in Nepal have established the Himalayas as essentially formed by the mightiest thrusting on the globe.

Heim and Gansser look on the border zone north of the Siwaliks as 'an old surface of erosion, over which the older Himalayan formations were thrust, and through the gaps of which they advanced in huge arch-shaped waves', as on the northern border of the Alps. The deposition of the great thicknesses of the Siwalik beds is regarded as made possible by tectonic downwarp; conditions were similar to those of the present-day Gangetic alluviation but the foredeep lay farther north, to be later pushed southwards by tectonic advances involving successive detrital accumulations.

The general concept is perhaps best shown by Heim and Gansser's scheme, which harmonizes very well with that of Auden in Garhwal:[19]

    (i) imbricated marginal thrusts, Simla–Kumaon;

    (ii) interior secondary thrust-sheets;

    (iii) the Main Central Thrust Mass, with deep-rooted injected crystallines, 10–20 km. thick covered with 10–15 km. of Algonkian–Mesozoic sediments; this is a *pli de fond*, produced by thrusting at depth succeeded by vertical uplift;

    (iv) Palaeozoic and Mesozoic sediments thrust and recumbently folded on to the back of the main root;

    (v) the 'exotic' Tibetan thrust (the Kiogar *Klippen*), one of the most baffling problems of Himalayan geology;

    (vi) Flysch zone south of the Trans-Himalaya, with a possible weak counter-thrust northwards.

The major thrust marks the contrast between the unfossiliferous undated rocks of the Lesser Himalaya, and the pre-Cambrian to Cretaceous fossiliferous sequence of the 'Tethys Himalaya'. Everest itself is formed of outliers of these sedimentaries perched on top of the truncated Khumbu nappe.

[19] A. Heim and A. Gansser, 'Central Himalaya: geological observations of the Swiss Expedition, 1936' (*Mem. Soc. Helvétique des Sciences Naturelles*, 73, Zurich, 1939); see also the magnificent illustrations in their more popular book, *The Throne of the Gods* (London, 1939). Gansser's important *Geology of the Himalayas* (Wiley, 1964), unfortunately arrived too late for use in this edition.

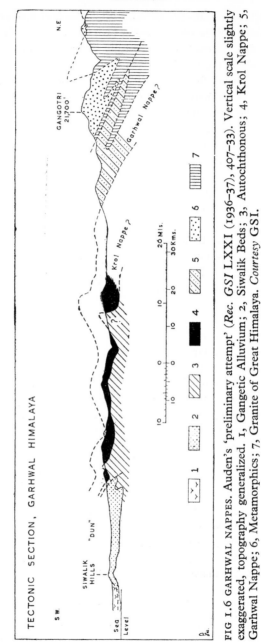

FIG 1.6 GARHWAL NAPPES. Auden's 'preliminary attempt' (*Rec. GSI LXXI* (1936–37), 407–33). Vertical scale slightly exaggerated, topography generalized. 1, Gangetic Alluvium; 2, Siwalik Beds; 3, Autochthonous; 4, Krol Nappe; 5, Garhwal Nappe; 6, Metamorphics; 7, Granite of Great Himalaya. *Courtesy* GSI.

The general nappe concept is reasonably straightforward, but the relations of the central crystalline core are very obscure, and thrusting is not the only mechanism involved; some allowance must be made for vertical movements, if

34

only because such vast transfers of load as are implied by the Siwalik and Gangetic deposition, and the thrust movements themselves, obviously must have isostatic implications. According to de Terra, there has been uplift of some 6,000 ft. (1,830 m.) in the Pir Panjal since the middle of the Pleistocene, and 'young uplifts must have affected the entire Himalayan and Karakoram ranges'. Garwood suggested that there was isostatic uplift consequent on the relief from load afforded by the shrinking of Himalayan glaciers; Wager, more plausibly, stresses that due to the removal of vast quantities of erosion products by the extremely active south-flowing rivers. He envisages horizontal compressive forces forming a Tibetan plateau in approximate isostatic equilibrium, but extending farther south than it does now; this phase was followed by a rise of the southern margins of the plateau to maintain this balance as the rivers carried away much of its substance, and this in turn would maintain or increase their erosive power.[20]

These conclusions may be to some extent supported by Heim and Gansser, who suggest that the position of the highest peaks opposite the greatest foredeep of the Gangetic Plain may be 'the expression of a balance movement' in areas of greatest exchange of load. But on the whole Wager's view seems to minimize unduly the role of persisting tangential movements – such as those mentioned by Heim and Gansser as overriding Siwalik features, which could only be possible at a late date. Hagen postulates Mesozoic compression of the Tethys between the Gondwana and Laurasian blocks, and later the formation of the 'old original Himalayas' by large-scale thrusts affecting the basal rocks from the northern edge of the Peninsular foreland, overturning them and producing southwards thrusting of the order of 100 km. To the north, the raised edge of the Tibetan plateau caused an 'unsymmetrical transformation' of the drainage pattern, the south-flowing streams having a greater gradient and more precipitation and cutting deep transverse valleys. Then 'once again . . . the nappe-roots were squeezed, like toothpaste out of a tube, at least 3,000 metres upwards'; this took place only about 600,000 years ago. There was then sinking in the main Himalayan area, presumably isostatic, and this forced up the Mahabharat mountains of Nepal, damming the southwards drainage and forming the longitudinal duns and lake basins.[21] On the whole a compromise seems called for, and is indeed implicit in recent work: thrusting may still be going on in the border regions and vertical uplift both there (e.g. in the Pir Panjal and the Kathmandu valley) and in the inner (Tethys) Himalaya.

[20] Wager, loc. cit.; cf. H. de Terra and T. T. Paterson, *Studies on the Ice Age in India* (Carnegie Inst. Pubtn No. 493, Washington, 1939).

[21] T. Hagen, *Nepal: The Kingdom in the Himalayas* (Kümmerley & Frey, Berne, 1961), 49–53. This is a popular (and most beautifully illustrated) account; the detailed evidence is in papers by Hagen (and also P. Bordet and A. Lombard) which have not been seen but are cited in the bibliography to P. P. Karan, *Nepal: A Cultural and Physical Geography* (Univ. of Kentucky, Lexington, 1960), 98.

The Tibetan Plateaus

There is a marked difference in facies between the deposits of the Tibetan Plateaus and those of the folded Himalaya. Marine Eocene sediments are found only south of the Ladakh and north of the Kun Lun, and during Upper Cretaceous times there seems to have been a major massif in the Karakoram–Kun Lun area, at a time when the ranges farther south either did not exist or were still in the early stages of uplift. Erosion was then more active in these areas, before the rising Himalaya shut off precipitation from the south, and de Terra has worked out several erosion-levels; his work tends to stress vertical uplift, at least in the later stages. An interesting approach is provided by the ecological work of G. E. Hutchinson: the fauna of Panggong and other west Tibetan lakes has an older appearance than that of Kashmir and Ladakh and points to central Asian rather than Indian associations.[22]

Relics of the old levels occur in the form of high rolling plains such as the Aksai Chin, Depsang and Lingzi Tang north of the Muztagh range, and these appear to be on the site of the oldest (late Cretaceous) uplift and to have extended southwards into the Karakoram region, where the spurs have high accordant levels and have been truncated by the former extension of the Karakoram glaciers. There are at least three old erosion surfaces in the Karakoram–Muztagh area: the high Muztagh peaks (24,000 ft., 7,315 m.) and planation surfaces at about 20,000 and 15,000–16,000 ft. (6,095 and 4,570–4,880 m.). Another level is represented by the Deosai plains east of Nanga Parbat and by the high spurs of the Kashmiri and Ladakhi mountains. According to Hayden the heights of the transverse ranges of the Lesser Himalaya are so uniform that it is impossible to resist the impression that they form parts of a dissected erosion surface, and this is confirmed by Heim and Gansser.

De Terra's general conclusion is that the wide extension of mature or old forms points to an uplift not earlier than the late Tertiary. The first level represents an early Tertiary very old relief, with a few monadnocks, which was uplifted and dissected to form a second series of mature or old forms. This phase was succeeded by the first Pleistocene glaciation and the formation of the third level during an interglacial. After the maximum glaciation the fourth level was established in the Riss–Würm interglacial, at which time much of the plateau was occupied by large freshwater lakes. The final retreat of the Würm ice was succeeded by 'recent uplift and post-Pleistocene rejuvenation, particularly effective along the Indus drainage', with local tilting of terrace and lake deposits in Rupshu, between the Indus and the Zaskar Range. The linking of such features in the west and in the heart of the orogeny with the more mobile

---

[22] 'Limnological studies at high altitudes in Ladakh', *Nature* (New Series), 77 (1933), 497–500; cf. his very curious and fascinating book, *The Clear Mirror: A Pattern of Life in Goa and Indian Tibet* (CUP, 1936).

phenomena of the southern border zones would be an interesting, if arduous, task.[23]

Himalayan glaciation, Recent and Pleistocene

The glaciers of the Himalayas and the Tibetan ranges, although much shrunken, nevertheless include in the Karakoram area the largest in the world outside sub-Polar regions: the Fedchenko (in the Pamir) and the Siachen are 48 and 45 miles (77 and 72 km.) long respectively, and the Biafo, Báltoro, Batura and Hispar all exceed 36 miles (58 km.). Elsewhere the glaciers are not so spectacular, but in Kumaon and Sikkim those of the Badrinath and Kangchenjunga massifs reach a length of 16 miles. The western glaciers are not only larger than those of the centre and east, but they descend to lower levels – in Kashmir as low as 7,000–8,000 ft. (2,135–2,440 m.) against 13,000 ft. (3,960 m.) on Kangchenjunga. This is attributable partly to higher latitudes (36° in the Karakoram to 28° for Kangchenjunga) and partly to the more direct exposure of the east to the monsoon: total precipitation is much greater in the east, but the air masses are warmer, while in the west a much higher proportion falls as snow. The snow-line on the southern face varies from about 14,000 ft. in the eastern to 19,000 in the western Himalayas (4,270–5,790 m.); on the drier Tibetan side it is some 3,000 ft. (910 m.) higher, except in the more northerly areas where precipitation conditions are more uniform; in Ladakh it is about 18,000 ft. (5,485 m.).

Mention may be made of the small glaciers of the Pir Panjal, which are exceptional (for the southern ranges) in being better developed on the north face: the Pir Panjal is a much less decisive climatic divide than the Himalaya proper, since we are here within the influence of the winter westerly depressions. The firns are largely fed by winter precipitation, so that aspect can have its usual value instead of being largely counterbalanced by greater precipitation on the southern slopes.

A distinction must be made between the longitudinal and the transverse glaciers of the Karakoram. The latter are naturally shorter and more fluctuant, variations depending largely on local topography, and have a much steeper grade. The Yengutsa glacier is believed to have advanced 3 miles in 8 days in 1903, 'coming out of its side valley and covering up the fields of Hispar village. . . . Such abnormally rapid movements may be due to earthquake shocks or to the sudden release of masses of ice that have accumulated to such a size and shape that they are no longer stable on the floor upon which they rest. Possibly accumulations of wind-swept snow would also cause instability.'[24]

The longitudinal movements are very complex; at times they are more rapid than those of the Alps – up to 5 ft. 10 in. (1.78 m.) on the Báltoro in 1909, while the Biafo snout has retreated by ablation as much as 400 yards (366 m.) in one

[23] De Terra and Paterson, *op. cit.*; de Terra, 'A scientific exploration of the eastern Karakoram and Zanskar-Himalaya', *Himalayan Jnl* 5 (1933), 33–45, and 'Physiographic results of a recent survey in Little Tibet', *GR* 24 (1934), 12–41.

[24] J. B. Auden, 'Glaciers', *CGR* 1/2 (1937), 46–52.

August. But in general they are 'either stationary or in very slight secular retreat owing to excess of ablation'. Thus the *net* movement of the Báltoro is practically nil as the contributions and deductions of its 50 transverse branches cancel out. The permutations due to aspect, shape, surrounding topography, gradient, climatic and seismic influences are endless, and variations in snout movement 'may be due to causes which are in distinct cases secular, periodic, seasonal, or accidental'. Even in the transverse glaciers there seems to be little evidence of any cyclical periodicity. Particular interest has been excited by the oscillations of the Chong Kumdan (Fig. 14.5) which intermittently advances across the upper Shyok, causing serious floods as far away as the Punjab when the ponded waters eventually break out. The great 1841 flood, which swept away a Sikh army on the dry bed of the Indus at Attock, was however probably caused by the release of water dammed by a landslide from the Hattu Pir cliff on the slopes of Nanga Parbat.[25]

An important general factor bearing on glacier movement is stressed by de Terra, who points out that 'the crustal mobility of the Kashmir basin locally determined the extension of glaciers' in the Pleistocene, and thinks that similar processes may be responsible for the rapid glacier movements of the Nubra/Shyok watershed. These western glaciers frequently appear almost smothered under morainic debris, especially in summer, when excessive ablation leads to a great development of fantastic ice-pinnacles.

Obviously the Pleistocene ice was far more extensive than that of today, but the amount of extension is a matter of dispute and the evidence is complicated by recent uplift. The maximalist view is that of Trinkler: 'it is highly probable that during the Ice Age the whole mountainous region, from the Kun Lun mountains in the north to the Himalaya in the south, was buried under ice.'[26] This view is not generally accepted. Dainelli worked out a sequence of four main glaciations corresponding to the Alpine Mindel, Riss, Würm, and post-Würm I; de Terra agrees with the sequence but would put it rather earlier.

Many of the Lesser Himalayan ranges which do not carry permanent snow have clear traces of glacial erosion and moraines; terminal moraines are found at about 8,000 ft. (2,440 m.) below Laching in Sikkim. Coulson, who thinks that in Kangra glaciers came down to 3,000 ft. (915 m.), emphasises the elevation of the Pir Panjal since the Pleistocene and argues that 'the general statement that there is no evidence of glaciation in the Himalaya and sub-Himalaya below 5,000 ft. (1,525 m.) must be discounted in view of the fact that elevation of these ranges has occurred after the main glaciation'.[27] This extreme view must be regarded

[25] K. Mason: 'Indus floods and Shyok glaciers', *Himalayan Jnl* 1 (1929), 10–29; 'Upper Shyok glaciers, 1939', *ibid.* 12 (1940), 52–65; 'The glaciers of the Karakoram and neighbourhood', *Rec. GSI* 63 (1930), 214–78; 'The study of threatening glaciers', *GJ* 85 (1935), 28–41.

[26] E. Trinkler, 'Notes on the westernmost plateaux of Tibet', *Himalayan Jnl* 3 (1931), 42–50.

[27] A. L. Coulson, 'Pleistocene glaciation in north-western India', *Rec. GSI* 72 (1938), 422–39.

as not proven, as is the case with the attribution of certain boulder beds in Siwalik rocks to the melting of ice-tongues from the Waziristan highlands. A minor problem is the existence on the Potwar Plateau, between Attock and Campbellpur, of erratic blocks, some of which apparently derive from the high central Himalaya; these may have been transported by floods consequent on the breaking of ice-dams, or by icebergs floating down a lake along the line of the present Indus.

Some Himalayan river problems

At an early stage in the exploration of the Himalayas the remarkable layout of its rivers attracted attention; in particular the longitudinal courses of the Indus, Sutlej and Tsangpo on the Tibetan Plateau, and the great gorges of these and other rivers cutting right across the Great Himalaya in the vicinity of its highest peaks, challenged explanation; on the southern flanks there is also a considerable development of longitudinal vales and such peculiar features as a series of sharp Vs pointing to the northwest in many of the rivers at or near their crossing of the Siwalik/alluvium boundary. The lithology of the Siwaliks, and especially their boulder and shingle beds, also calls for explanation, and there are such oddities as the similarity of Indus and Ganga dolphins to be accounted for.

In 1919 E. H. Pascoe and G. E. Pilgrim independently presented an elaborate and comprehensive hypothesis, the basis of which is essentially that Siwalik deposition took place along a great longitudinal river – Pascoe's 'Indobrahm', Pilgrim's 'Siwalik River' – which flowed to the northwest, the direction in which the Siwalik deposits coarsen and widen, between the still rising Himalayas and the northern flanks of a Peninsular block then continuous into Assam. This great master-stream was later disrupted in the west by headward erosion of left-bank tributaries of its own lower course (equivalent to the lower Indus of today), and in the west by similar action on the part of a proto-Ganga and a proto-Brahmaputra. Pascoe also envisaged a great 'Tibetan River' flowing northwestwards along the Tsangpo–Manasarowar Lakes–Sutlej–Gartang–Indus line, a trough which certainly seems to have some structural continuity; this river might have flowed out into the Oxus, or might have debouched on to the plains by one of a number of transverse gaps such as the Photu Pass, whose summit is only 250 ft. (75 m.) higher than the Tsangpo valley floor. This river also was disrupted by headward erosion on the part of the Irrawaddy–Chindwin, the Meghna–Brahmaputra, the Sutlej, and the Indus.[28]

The phenomena which these hypotheses sought to explain are extremely complicated: setting aside a mass of detail, some of the largest rivers in the world flowing in mature longitudinal courses, and then cutting across the loftiest mountains in the world, present a problem not paralleled in scale elsewhere. A

[28] E. H. Pascoe, 'Early history of the Indus, Brahmaputra, and Ganges', *Qtly Jnl Geol. Soc.* 75 (1919), 138–59; G. E. Pilgrim, ' . . . History of the drainage of Northern India . . .', *Jnl Royal Asiatic Soc. of Bengal*, New Series 15 (1919), 81–99. More detail was given in earlier editions of the present book, 28–33.

vast mass of evidence was adduced in support of these complicated orgies of river piracy and capture, and it is almost with regret that one admits that theories so ingenious and so elegantly worked out are now generally regarded as untenable. So far as concerns Pascoe's Tibetan River, de Terra in 1933–34 literally re-orientated the problem by drawing attention to the longitudinal valleys of the Karakoram–Panggong area, by contrast to 'the transverse drainage of the Central Himalaya. The ancient character of this pattern becomes clearer as we try to eliminate its secondary attributes such as transverse cutting or capture by the Indus.' He agrees that the longitudinal valleys antedate the transverse sections – as seems obvious – but holds that in pre-glacial times the drainage of the Karakoram–Ladakh area flowed southeast and east along the Tsangpo furrow and possibly into eastern Tibet and Szechwan; the southeasterly courses of the Shigar, Nubra and upper Shyok support this, whereas for his west-flowing river Pascoe had ignored these and relied on the westerly trend of a number of Tsangpo tributaries. The concept of two mighty longitudinal streams on either side of the rising Himalayas is indeed startling, but if the Indobrahm or Siwalik is accepted, the balance of evidence is in favour of its westwards course, and conversely for the 'Tibetan River'. The opposition is direct and unreconcilable.

On the main question of the Indobrahm, de Terra is decidedly hostile. He holds that the Siwalik deposits are 'local precipitates of an antecedent slope drainage', 'successive fan and basin sediments . . . their origin differs in no way from that of other foredeep fillings (Alps, Rocky Mountains)'. His arguments are not completely conclusive, but the hypothesis has also been cogently criticized, mainly on stratigraphic grounds, by Krishnan and Aiyengar. They stress (an old point) the maturity of the gap between the Rajmahal Hills and the Shillong Plateau, completely incompatible with the recency demanded by the Pascoe–Pilgrim hypothesis, and make a most telling criticism by bringing forward the width, thickness and lithology of the Tipam sandstones of Assam, corresponding to the Siwaliks and indicating (on Pascoe–Pilgrim principles) estuarine conditions near the *source* of the supposed river. The negative arguments seem strong enough to discredit the Indobrahm, even though the solution proposed – foredeep deposition on a littoral of almost continuous lagoons, with recently rejuvenated transverse streams forming the boulder beds – may not be final. But it seems probable that the solution will be somewhat along these lines, and this seems supported by Geddes's review of the problem. There remain a few doubts: those nasty little Vs at the Siwalik/alluvium boundary are ignored or glossed over by the critics; but on the whole it seems likely that the simpler answers are the more correct, and the Indobrahm is now a vanished river in more than one sense.[29]

[29] H. de Terra, *op. cit.*, 1934; cf. *Studies on the Ice Age in India*, 300–1; M. S. Krishnan and N. K. N. Aiyengar, 'Did the Indobrahm or Siwalik River exist?', *Rec. GSI* 75 (Profl Paper No. 6, 1940); A. Geddes, 'The alluvial morphology of the Indo-Gangetic Plain', *Trans Inst. British Geogrs.* 28 (1960), 253–76.

The Sutlej provides a problem of its own. Its source is apparently fed by underground water from the Manasarowar Lakes and in its longitudinal section it flows in a deep canyon cut in the soft fluviatile beds of Nari Khorsum; this upper course is distinctly arid and the river itself appears to be a misfit. This might be explicable if it were an old outlet for the 'Tibetan River', and Pascoe thinks that the Sutlej captured part of the Tibetan River and then lost again to the rejuvenated Tsangpo after the Dihang had cut back into the furrow; but this is not very clear. Burrard points out that the Sutlej has a much deeper trough than its neighbours the Giri (a headstream of the Yamuna) and the Beas, and has no large cis-Himalayan tributaries, which suggests that it is younger than the others: 'the question as to how the Giri and the Beas have confined their giant neighbour into a trough less than 20 miles wide remains worthy of consideration'; more worthy if it is put conversely, how the Sutlej has been inset between the two. On this, Davies thinks that the Sutlej is the youngest of the great Himalayan rivers and has developed owing to the collapse of the main Himalayan axis along the line of an old Gondwana fault-trough; in support he cites the deep Shipki gorge and a break in the Ladakh Range northwest of Gurla Mandhata.[30]

III. THE INDO-GANGETIC PLAINS

Structure and surface

The great crescent of alluvium from the delta of the Indus to that of the Ganga represents the infilling of a foredeep warped down between the Gondwana block and the advancing Himalayas. Its relations with the mountains are obscure and involve the interpretation of difficult geodetic data: the older view that the sediments are some 15,000 ft. (4,570 m.) deep, deposited in a great rift or trough sinking beneath the weight of alluvium, has been challenged by Glennie on the basis of gravity anomaly readings which indicate a maximum of around 6,500 ft. (1,980 m.).[31] The Himalayas themselves appear to be largely if not entirely compensated at some distance within the mountains, but on the plains deflections are to the south and suggest an upwarp of denser sub-crustal material from Orissa to Baluchistan.[32]

Be this as it may, it is clear that the filling is of very unequal depth and the Indo-Gangetic Trough does not correspond to the full extent of the Indo-Gangetic Plains; its approximate limits are shown on Fig. 1.1. Occasional outcrops of older rock indicate that the alluvial cover is thinner in the Indus than in the Ganga valley. There is evidence also for concealed ridges or swells of the

[30] L. M. Davies, 'Geographical changes in North-west India', *Proc. 6th Pacific Science Congress* (Univ. of California Press, Berkeley, 1940), 483–501.

[31] E. A. Glennie, 'Gravity anomalies and the earth's crust' (Survey of India Profl Paper No. 27, Dehra Dun, 1940); cf. C. A. Longwell, 'A challenge to isostasy', *GR* 23 (1933), 682–3.

[32] See King, *op. cit.* 16–17; M. S. Krishnan, 'The structural and tectonic history of India', *Mem. GSI* 81 (1953), at 80–84.

basement prolonging the Aravalli axis between Delhi and Hardwar, and also northwest from Delhi towards the Salt Range. There is also the very important and relatively shallow sill between the Rajmahal Hills and the Shillong Plateau; south of this the floor of the Ganga Delta seems to be still sinking.

The plains are remarkably homogeneous topographically: for hundreds of miles the only relief perceptible to the eye is formed by floodplain bluffs, the minor natural levées and hollows grouped by Geddes as 'spill patterns', and the belts of ravines and badlands formed by gully erosion along some of the larger streams, e.g. the lower Chambal (Fig. 18.5); the slopes of the broad interfluves or doabs (do=two, ab=water) are barely if at all perceptible. On this vast aggradational surface the only marked topographical changes are those associated with the numerous shifts and diversions of the rivers. These, however, are of the greatest importance: as Geddes points out, the plain on the Himalayan side is built up of great alluvial cones, with interlocking 'inter-cones'; and on the Peninsular flank, the Son likewise has built up a great cone or fan. On these cones the rivers swing from side to side; at present this is most notable on the Kosi (below, 565), but the past behaviour of the Yamuna, discharging now on the Indus and now on the Ganga side, has mixed their fauna and so meets one of the points raised in support of the Indobrahm.[33]

There are other important surface differences. Along the outer slopes of the Siwaliks there is commonly a fairly steep talus gravel slope, the bhabar, in which all but the larger streams lose themselves, seeping out lower down in the marshy, jungly and naturally intensely malarial terai strip. The older (Pleistocene) alluvium is known as bhangar and as a rule occupies higher ground than the Recent khadar, which occupies the floodplains and grades into the most recent deltaic silts. The bhangar in the Bengal Delta forms low and sometimes lateritic uplands such as the Barind and the Madhupur Jungle. Generally the alluvium is a fairly stiff clay, with more or less sand according as it is near to or far from the hills; in the bhangar there are irregular limey concretions (kankar) and in places there may be as much as 30% of calcareous matter in the alluvium. In the drier areas of Uttar Pradesh and West Pakistan there are stretches of barren saline efflorescence known as reh or kallar; this has spread with the spread of irrigation and, especially in West Pakistan, is a most serious and costly problem (below, 508 and Fig. 17.5).

Contrasts: Himalayan and Peninsular, Indus and Ganga

A factor of the greatest importance in the human geography of India is the strong contrast between the rivers of the Peninsula and those of the Himalayas. It is easy to overlook or underrate the very large proportions of the basins of the Indus, the Brahmaputra, and even the Sutlej, which are included within the mountain zone. The Himalayan section of the Indus drainage alone (excluding the Kabul River) is over 100,000 sq. miles (259,000 km²), larger than the entire

[33] B. Prashad, 'The Indobrahm or the Siwalik River', *Rec. GSI* 74 (1939), 555–61.

basins of most European rivers; its Sutlej tributary itself drains 20,000 sq. miles, 51,800 km². Even those rivers which do not penetrate behind the wall of the Great Himalaya have not inconsiderable mountain courses. Erosion is extremely active and vast quantities of detritus are brought down: the Ganga and the Indus have been estimated to carry some 900,000 and 1,000,000 tons of suspended matter daily, and the Brahmaputra more than either. Still more important, the rivers from the Himalayas are not solely dependent on the monsoon months for their water-supply, but have also a supply from the melting of the Himalayan snows. This is the more useful as it comes at the height of the hot weather – February to April – when the Peninsular rivers are lowest. Even in the north the régimes are indeed very variable; the Indus above the Panjnad confluence can vary from 10,000 to 1,000,000 cusecs. But there is usually some water available for irrigation, and the northern rivers are also locally useful for small craft, though except in the deltas inland water transport is of very little account in India.

By contrast, the Peninsular rivers flow in broad shallow valleys, graded almost to their heads and with only slight interruptions of profile, already noted, at the passages through the Eastern Hills. They are entirely dependent on a rainfall concentrated in five or six months of the year, flowing over or through a thin soil cover; they are therefore almost dry in the hot weather. A river like the Krishna, with a bed up to a mile wide and running a banker in the rains, may have a trickle of water only two or three yards wide in March. The Peninsular rivers are therefore less useful for irrigation than those of the north; and where irrigation is possible it needs a proportionately much greater expenditure on barrages and reservoirs; whereas in the north the best options were taken up long ago, under the British, India of the Plains has to face larger and economically less remunerative works in a time of rising costs.

Within the Indo-Gangetic Plains, Geddes draws attention to a significant difference between the Indus and the Ganga system. The Five Rivers of the Punjab combine to form one united stream which flows through a practical desert, receiving no other tributary; 'the Yamuna–Ganga system is enriched by one confluent river after another' and flows in the direction of increasing rainfall. Thus 'the Plain of the Ganga forms part of its water "catchment"; in contrast, the Plain of the Indus could truly be described as an area not of water catchment but of "losement" '. The Indus rivers, losing water, tend to drop their detritus early; those of the Ganga, continually reinforced by the many large tributaries, carry their load much further. Thus the Indus soils are generally coarser, there is a much larger area of fine silt in the Ganga basin, and the 100-fathom line is much farther out to sea off Ganga than off Indus.[34]

[34] Geddes, *op. cit.* in fn. 29; this is much the most authoritative recent study of the Plains.

IV. THE COASTS

The coasts of India are very little indented by large inlets, the only significant ones being the Gulf of Cambay and the Rann of Kutch, to which may be added the wide inlet of the Padma–Meghna mouth in East Pakistan; but the west coast has many small inlets, the east its delta creeks.

Beginning in the northwest, the Baluchistan coast west of Somniani Bay is markedly 'Pacific' in type, the Makran ranges trending parallel to the coast; Sewell's researches indicate that this is definitely a fault coast.[35] It is succeeded by the Indus Delta, off which a great trough reaches a depth of some 3,700 ft. (1,130 m.) at its mouth; this is thought to represent a former extension of the Indus during the glacial fall of sea-level. Kutch and Kathiawad have generally low alluvial coasts; the Rann embayment is, as we have seen, in part of extremely recent date, and the south coast of Kathiawad may be controlled by east–west faulting associated with the Vindhya–Narmada line. The alluvial east coast of the Gulf of Cambay is actively prograding, but from Damão down to Goa the coast is a succession of little inlets and rocky points with, however, a remarkably straight general alignment undoubtedly due to late (perhaps Plio-Pleistocene) faulting.[36] In detail the coast is complicated in both plan and elevation, and here, at Bombay and Goa and a few smaller inlets, are almost the only good natural harbours of India – maritime activity has always been relatively great here – associated with slight submergence.

From Karwar south to Kanya Kumari the coastal lowland widens out and in Kerala is faced by a great extension of long bars and lagoons; emergence is dominant, and the contrast with the northern part of the west coast suggests that there may have been a slight tilt, depression in the north under the weight of the Deccan Lavas and the pressure of the Himalayan folding, upheaval in the south: the pivot would be about Goa.

On the eastern side of the Peninsula the steepness of the submarine contours (sharper than on the west) is puzzling unless it indicates subsidence of the Bay of Bengal; but the most recent movements of any consequence have been elevatory. There are of course considerable stretches of prograding deltas, and off that of the Ganga is a submarine trough, the 'swatch of no ground' corresponding to that of the Indus. The east coast of the Bay of Bengal is again strongly longitudinal; changes of level have probably been complex, as raised beaches are found on some of the Burmese off-shore islands, while the general pattern suggests some subsidence complicated by the formation of deltas, mangrove swamps and large mud volcanoes.

[35] R. B. S. Sewell, 'Geographic and oceanographic researches in Indian waters', *Mem. Royal Asiatic Soc. of Bengal*, 9, summarized in *GJ* 73 (1934), 135–9, and 74 (1934), 154–6.
[36] See notes by S. K. Guha and M. S. Krishnan in *International Oceanographic Congress Preprints* (Amer. Asstn for Advancement of Science, Washington, 1959), 26, 34–36.

BIBLIOGRAPHICAL NOTE

D. N. Wadia's *Geology of India* (Macmillans, London, 3rd ed. revised, 1961) is the standard work; M. S. Krishnan's *The Geology of India and Burma* (Higginbothams, Madras, 4th ed., 1960) is rather lighter in weight than Wadia but deals with tectonic and geomorphological matters more consecutively. K. P. Rode, *Geo-Kinetic Evolution of Greater India* (Mem. Rajputana Univ. Dept of Geology, No. 4, Udaipur, 1954) has a very speculative approach somewhat akin to S. W. Carey's hypotheses; it is effectively criticized in F. Ahmad's 1961 paper cited in fn. 3 above.

On the Himalayas, the standard work of a sort is S. G. Burrard, H. H. Hayden, and A. M. Heron, *A Sketch of the Geology and Geography of the Himalaya Mountains and Tibet* (Govt of India, Delhi, 2nd ed., ?1933) – an indispensable mine of factual detail but exceedingly badly arranged and in places much less than scientific; such criticism might seem presumptuous from a critic who has never penetrated beyond Simla, but the curious reader is referred to K. Mason's review in *The Himalayan Journal*, 7 (1935), 113–24, a critique equally authoritative and amusing. This journal contains a wealth of papers on Himalayan topics; other Himalayan papers not directly cited in the text include:

K. Mason, 'The Himalayas as a Barrier to Modern Communications', *GJ* 84 (1934), 1–16.

J. B. Auden, 'The Structure of the Himalayas in Garhwal', *Rec. GSI* 71 (1936–37), 407–33.

A. Heim, 'The Himalayan Border Compared with the Alps', *Rec. GSI* 72 (1938), 413–21.

A thoughtful paper on the Plains is W. A. Wood, 'Rivers and Man in the Indus–Ganges Alluvial Plains', *Scottish Geog. Mag.* 40 (1924), 1–15. There is a comprehensive review of the Peninsula in E. Ahmad, 'Geomorphic Regions of Peninsular India', *Jnl of Ranchi University*, 1/1 (1962), 1–29; in his conclusion Ahmad, without committing himself, seems to lean towards King's pediplains rather than the classic peneplain concept.

CHAPTER 2

Climate

INTRODUCTION

Almost every aspect of life in the Indian sub-continent is affected or even dominated by the monsoon. This is a truism, but how far is it true? In this popular sense the monsoon climate implies a climate with a cool dry season of northerly winds – the 'Northeast Monsoon' in December to February giving way to a hot dry season from March to early June, a hot wet season of south-westerly winds, the 'Southwest Monsoon' – *the* monsoon of the opening sentence – and a retreat to the dry cool season around the winter solstice. The picture is useful, but the sub-continent has several climates rather than a single climate. The popular image of the monsoon climate best fits the tract lying north and west of a line joining Goa to Patna, and even within this area is upset by the presence of the small but significant depression rains of the cooler months in Punjab and the northwest. With this qualification the popular usage will be accepted for the moment, without any implication as to the causation of the seasonal reversals of wind and weather.[1] Discussion of the causes of the monsoon has long been dominated by the classic hypotheses of workers of the late 19th century, notably Blanford and Eliot, based on interpretation of the data then available concerning pressures and winds, temperatures and rainfall, at that time based on surface recording stations only.[2] Knowledge of the influence of upper air conditions upon the climate of India has greatly increased in the last forty years, and though much more knowledge is still required it is now possible to weave together a description of the seasons and their variations from year to year with something of modern theory on the causal factors at work.

The following account of the seasons takes count especially of modern views

---

[1] For a most interesting discussion of the different meanings attached to the word monsoon, see P. Pédélaborde, *Les Moussons* (Paris, 1958), trans. M. J. Clegg (Methuen, London, 1963), Chapter 1. Future references to this work will give page references from the English translation.

[2] For a modern appreciation and critique, M. J. Webb, 'Some aspects of the early work of H. F. Blanford and Sir John Eliot on pressure disturbances over the Indian land areas 1867–1893', *IGJ* 35/1 (1960), 1–9. The original works include: H. F. Blanford, *The Climates and Weather of India, Ceylon and Burmah* (1889); Sir J. Eliot (ed.), *Climatological Atlas of India* (1906); [Sir J. Eliot], 'Meteorology' (Chapter III, 104–56 in *Imperial Gazetteer of India*, Vol. I, Oxford, 1909. W. G. Kendrew, *Climates of the Continents* (OUP 5th ed., 1961), 155–92, gives a splendid account blending modern and classic views.

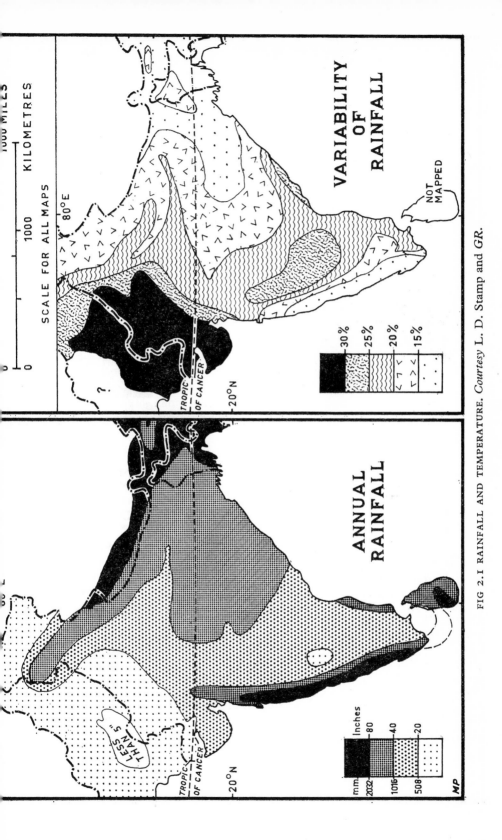

FIG 2.1 RAINFALL AND TEMPERATURE. *Courtesy* L. D. Stamp and *GR.*

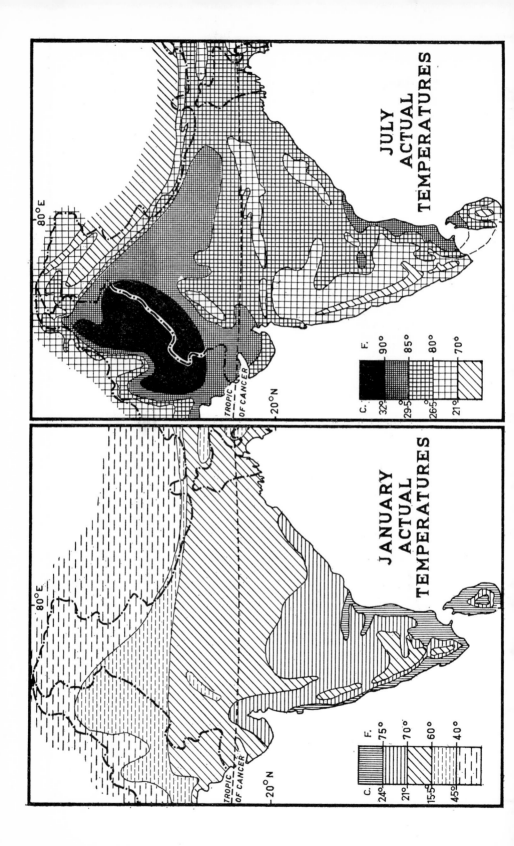

JULY
ACTUAL
TEMPERATURES

80° E

TROPIC
OF CANCER

20° N

	F.	C.
■	90°	32°
	85°	29.5°
	80°	26.5°
	70°	21°

JANUARY
ACTUAL
TEMPERATURES

80° E

TROPIC
OF CANCER

20° N

	F.	C.
	75°	24°
	70°	21°
	60°	15.5°
	40°	4.5°

that storms yielding precipitation are commonly associated with surface convergence of air containing some moisture, and also with upper troposphere
divergence of air currents which permits the upward movement of the moist air
to altitudes sufficient for condensation and precipitation to take place; and that

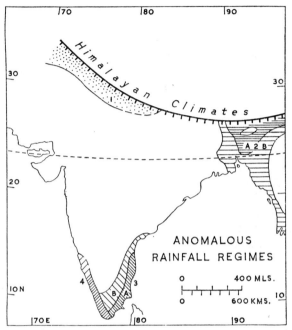

FIG 2.2 ANOMALOUS RAINFALL REGIMES. I, 1–5 in. in cold weather (January–
February); 2A, over 20 in., 2B, 10–20 in., in hot weather (March–May) from
Nor'-Westers; 3A, over 10 in., 3B, 5–10 in., in retreating monsoon (November–
December); 4, dry season only 3 or 4 months. (10 in.=254 mm.)

jet-streams in the lower stratosphere – narrow corridors of high winds in a cloud-
less sky and a means of equilibrium in the global circulation whose importance
has only been realized in the last twenty years or so – also have a marked bearing
on rainfall at the surface, for precipitation tends to occur especially around its
right entrance and left exit sectors.[3] A synthesis concerning this modern viewpoint will follow the seasonal accounts, on pp. 56–63.

The cool season

In January the cool and mainly dry season is at its height. The northern two-
thirds of the sub-continent have mean temperatures below 70°F. (21°C.),

[3] The reader new to the jet-stream might start with G. T. Trewartha, 'Climate as
related to the Jet Stream in the Orient', *Erdkunde*, 12 (1958), 205–14, an authoritative
account up to that date and relevant to the Indian sub-continent. The *Proceedings* of the
Delhi Symposium on the Monsoons of the World in February 1958 (New Delhi, 1960)
takes many of our points much further, with stimulating discussion by meteorologists
well versed in modern data and theory.

commonly with afternoon temperatures of 80° F. (27° C.), with night temperatures quite often at or below freezing point and sometimes a morning fog. This is a pleasant season for the well-clad, well-fed and well-housed, but also a season of ill-health from bronchitis and pneumonia, for many and especially poorer people. The nights are broken by the sound of coughing resounding through flimsy buildings. The rainy western disturbances bring rainfall, important for the growing of wheat and barley though small in total (Peshawar 8 in. (203 mm.) in November to April, Lahore 4 in. (102 mm.), Delhi 3·1 in. (79 mm.), Benares 2·3 in. (58 mm.)), and in the rear of a depression there is often a wave of cold weather extremely cold by local standards. Meantime the northern mountains and especially the Himalayas receive considerable amounts of precipitation, largely in the form of snow.

The southern third of the sub-continent has rather warmer, fine conditions in the west, with frosts occasionally in plateau areas and commonly in valley sites in the highest tracts (Nanjanad in the Nilgiris has an average of 12 nights of frost in January).[4] The southeast by this time has had its main rainy season, but there are appreciable amounts in a few hill-stations (Kodaikanal) and in Ceylon, especially the northeast (Trincomalee). Here rice is still green, when in the north wheat is almost ready for harvest.

The cool season weather and climate are dominated by locally subsident air: the Himalayan barrier protects the sub-continent from the true winter monsoon current blowing from Siberia across China, and it may be considered as part of the seasonally quasi-permanent or recurrent sub-tropical high pressure cell (centred over Turkestan not Siberia), giving the light, cool, dry winds from north to northeast – a land trade-wind if you will. At about 40,000 ft. (12 km.) and just south of the Himalaya is the quasi-permanent winter position of a westerly jet-stream. (See Fig. 2.5.)[5] In contrast, the Himalayan region is within the westerlies; this westerly stream reaches the surface, or almost so, in the extreme north of the Indo-Gangetic plains and southwards from there it continues as an upper westerly stream over the north to northeast subsident air, above an inclined plane of discontinuity in the atmosphere, higher to the south and reaching heights of 10 km. (32,800 ft.) or more over Ceylon (see Fig. 2.6). Also this westerly air-stream bears the westerly disturbances already noted, bringing small but agriculturally significant cool season rains to the north of the

[4] C. Balasubramanian and C. M. Bakthavathsalu, 'A preliminary study of frost formation at Nanjanad (Nilgiris District)', *Indian Jnl Met. & Geophys.* 7 (1956), 404–5.

[5] K. M. Ramamurthi, 'A jet stream over northern India revealed by a Comet de-briefing report', *Indian Jnl Met. & Geophys.* 6 (1955), 277–8 is interesting for its source – an early case of the captain of a jet airliner in the lower stratosphere asking for permission to depart from his agreed route because of encountering an adverse jet-stream. Various observations have been put together to give the generalized picture shown in Fig. 2.5, and there has been much controversy in the meteorological literature as to whether this quasi-stationary cool-weather position of the jet-stream is orographically controlled by the Himalaya, as a sort of standing wave, just as a submerged boulder may cause a curved standing wave reaching downstream in a fast-flowing river.

sub-continent, and important even beyond that for their influence on other weather phenomena such as the nor'westers of Bengal (see p. 575). These western disturbances have long been regarded as continuations of Mediterranean depressions, and recent work confirms that many are of this origin. Some, on the other hand, arise as secondary depressions over Iran, connected with primary depressions farther north, over southeastern Europe and southern Russia – occasionally the secondary being much more significant than the primary

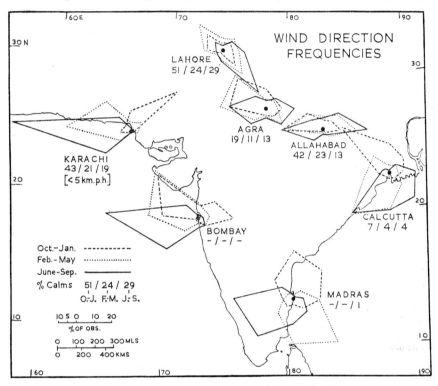

FIG 2.3 WIND DIRECTION FREQUENCIES, 1939. Angles of polygons at distances from station proportionate to number of observations of winds from each quarter. It should be noted that: (i) the southeast winds at Madras come mainly in January–April; (ii) the Arabian Sea current was relatively weak in 1939. *Source:* Indian Meteorological Dept., *Scientific Notes*, VII, No. 80.

depression. Some of the western disturbances of the northern part of the sub-continent, in contrast, arise locally, possibly from waves in westerlies in the upper troposphere or much lower and reaching or almost reaching the surface in the north of the Indo-Gangetic plains. The disturbances from the Mediterranean reach the Punjab more or less occluded, with little frontal structure at the surface. Their frequent deepening and activity is related to upper air divergence, either ahead of a trough in the upper troposphere westerlies, or in relation to the jet-stream, which, it must be remembered, fluctuates and moves from its mean position like a streamer in the wind.[6]

The hot weather

By March the days and nights are getting hot in many northern and inland areas, and heat continues to increase through April and May, causing tension in families and communities, until the 'bursting of the monsoon' (i.e. the southwest monsoon) in early or mid-June. The heat equator has migrated to the northwest of the sub-continent, in latitudes of 25–30°N. In the middle Ganga plains, day shade temperatures are commonly 100–110°F. (38–43°C.) and night temperatures reach 60–65°F. (16–18·5°C.), but as yet with relatively low humidities (c. 40–50% and 20–30% respectively at 8 a.m. and 4 p.m.). Hard work and concentration, even in sedentary occupations, become more difficult, and rest more evasive. Bed-clothes are hot to the touch and rooms stifling, so that many people carry their beds out of doors to flat roofs, gardens, waste ground or road-side spaces. In the afternoon there is often a hot dusty wind, and turbulence carries dust into the air to give the peculiar brassy sky of mid-summer. Vultures and kite-hawks soar on upward wind-flurries, and there may be a whirling dust-storm, when a little rain may reach the ground. Diseases of dust increase. In areas of heavy soils, deep cracks give a place of aestivation for insects and for a whole ecological complex including small snakes and rodents, only revealed in the search for the mode of transmission of relapsing fever. After the wheat harvest and early ploughing there is little work in the fields until the rains come. In May temperatures are higher and humid air may add to the discomforts and stresses (morning relative humidity 30–40% at 80–85°F. (28–30°C.) and 20–30% at 105–110°F. (41–43·5°C.) in mid-afternoon). In the south and east early though variable rains may come with the violent squalls of the nor'westers or the even greater violence of a tropical cyclone. Rainy days are interspersed with trying humid days; wherever monthly rainfall is over an inch or so ploughing and the sowing of paddy in nursery beds begins. The southwest of Ceylon has one of its main peaks of rainfall.

During the hot dry weather, conditions are at first mainly anticyclonic both at the surface and aloft. Westerly disturbances continue, yielding less rainfall in the hot dry conditions at first, though later involved in the formation of the nor'-westers of Bengal. Towards midsummer the heat low develops over the north-west of the sub-continent and the unpleasantly humid equatorial air is drawn in, but the north and west do not enjoy widespread rains. In the upper troposphere the air-stream remains westerly, but now dry and relatively warm, so that the

---

[6] P. R. Pisharoty and B. N. Desai, '"Western disturbances" and Indian weather', *Indian Jnl Met. & Geophys.* 7 (1956), 333–8; M. S. Singh, 'Upper circulation associated with a western disturbance', *ibid.* 14 (1963), 156–72; N. C. Rai Sircar *et al.*, 'A preliminary study of 5-day mean flow patterns in relation to 5-day precipitation in North India during winter season', *ibid.* 11 (1960), 238–57.

temperature inversion along with the lack of upper air divergence prevent widespread precipitation. The jet-stream remains, or better fluctuates in force and position, around its winter station. Meantime the upper troposphere easterlies occur over only Ceylon and Kanya Kumari. Local indraught of sea-breeze type, perhaps along with some upper air divergence over Kerala, permits the development of considerable precipitation, giving high yields over the central highlands of Ceylon and the Cardamoms and the Western Ghats, but also widespread falls over the interior plateaus of South India.

The early rains of northeast India and East Pakistan, mainly due to the nor'westers, are much better studied at present. They are line squalls bringing thunder and lightning and intense precipitation often in the form of hail, the line sometimes regenerating several times, the downdraught from the first line promoting enough turbulence, especially downwind, to provoke the second and so on. They are commonly associated with divergence related to the westerly jet-streams, or to westerly disturbances in the upper troposphere, sometimes intensified by 'inphase superposition' of a wave in the upper troposphere easterlies,[7] and develop, given an association of favourable conditions: (1) low level convergence, (2) upper air divergence, (3) sufficient inflow of moist air at low levels, and (4) unstable lapse rates – often provided through cold air advection aloft. The almost tornado-like dust-storms of Punjab, *andhis* of Uttar Pradesh, and the *kal baisakhis* of Bengal are closely related phenomena, involving very strong convectional movements, in which the tops of the cumulonimbus clouds quite commonly reach 50,000 ft (15·25 km.). There is a very rich literature on these storms, on account of their danger for aircraft and their occurrence within range of a well-equipped weather radar station at Calcutta.[8] Other thunder-storms are associated with random convection within the same air mass, or with cold fronts, often with advection of cold air aloft.

In the early hot weather, too, there is the season of cyclonic storms and tropical cyclones (the hurricanes or typhoons of other sub-tropical regions) in the Bay of Bengal and less frequently in the Arabian Sea. These bring consider-able amounts of rainfall, though very variable from place to place and time to time, and often cause terrible havoc in the densely peopled Bay of Bengal deltas, particularly if gravity, normal tide and wind action conspire to cause a storm

[7] 'In-phase superposition' involves, in this case, the merging of an upper (upper tropo-sphere) wave with a lower wave nearer the ground, with which it has come to be 'in phase' or coincident.

[8] Examples from the *Indian Jnl/Met. & Geophys.* include: S. Mull, H. Mitra, S. M. Kulshreshtra, 14 (1963), 23–36 ('Tropical thunderstorms and radar echoes'); A. C. De, *ibid.* 37–45 ('Movement of pre-monsoon squall lines over Gangetic West Bengal as observed by radar at Dum Dum airport'); A. C. De, *et al.*, 8 (1957), 72–80 ('Regenerative drift of a thunderstorm squall of the S.W. Monsoon season'); N. S. Rai Sircar, *ibid.* 21–32 ('On the forecasting of Nor'westers in Gangetic West Bengal'); P. Koteswaram and V. Srinivasan, 9 (1958), 301–12 ('Thunderstorms over Gangetic West Bengal in the pre-monsoon season and the synoptic factors favourable for their formation'); see also C. Ramaswamy, 'On the sub-tropical Jet Stream and its role in the development of large-scale convection', *Tellus*, 8 (Stockholm, 1956), 26–60.

surge (cf. p. 575 below). Tropical cyclones will be discussed more fully in dealing with the months of the retreating monsoon when they are most active.

The rains

In the weeks before the bursting of the southwest monsoon over much of the continent, the ebb and flow of the various participating forces in the lower troposphere, the upper troposphere and the lower stratosphere (i.e. the jet-stream) impart great variability to these early, locally vital rains – a topic which will be discussed later in relation to the year as a whole.

Over all the north and west of the sub-continent the 'bursting' of the monsoon, commonly in a great thunderstorm, is something of an emotional experience, a relief after the mounting tensions of the last humid weeks of hot weather. Roughly south and east of a line from Goa to Patna the rains have already started, though in many parts there also the coming of the monsoon proper is eagerly awaited. Yet after the initial relief the season is trying enough. Mean temperatures for July of 80–90°F. (27–32°C.) over much of the sub-continent, and over 90°F. (32°C.) in the northwest, imply high afternoon temperatures uncomfortable in the humid air, and nights are often hot and sticky (relative humidity 60–70% at 4 p.m. and 70–80% at 8 a.m.). Work in the fields includes bursts of really strenuous activity, ploughing, transplanting rice, and so on, and even since the widespread control of malaria an older man may have a malarial rigor, or anybody an attack of dengue; the return of conditions more congenial for houseflies spreads dysentery from carrier to fresh host, and periodically cholera also from its endemic homes in the deltas fronting the Bay of Bengal. After the burst of the monsoon the sub-continent mostly settles down – or so everyone hopes – to an alternation of sudden, intense, and quite local thunderstorms with more widespread, long but less intensive rainfall of depression type. But the onset of the monsoon may be late, or it may withdraw for considerable periods – 'breaks in the monsoon' over nearly the whole sub-continent, though often accompanied by very heavy downpours over the Himalayas with consequent flooding in riverine parts of the Indo-Gangetic or Brahmaputra plains. Or the monsoon may withdraw early. It is vital to complement maps of averages with maps of variability, or of probability of receiving some figure of rainfall crucial in some particular context (Figs. 2.4 and 2.8). Even beyond that one should bear in the mind's eye a yet more kaleidoscopic picture of local variations which may be literally a matter of life and death for this or that group of rural communities.[9]

The warm humid air of the monsoonal indraught towards the heat 'low' of the northwest of the sub-continent, invoked in the classical interpretation of the Indian monsoons, is clearly a factor of significance today as in 1686 when Halley

[9] The *Indian Jnl Met. & Geophys.* contains topical reports on the seasons, and also from time to time articles on local rainfall for Community Development Blocks; the States also issue Season and Crop Reports, and while these can not be used for quantitative assessment of out-turn of crops, they do broadly reflect the vagaries of the weather.

wrote, or as in the late 19th and early 20th centuries when Eliot and Blanford made their fine syntheses.[10] So too the air-mass school have made their contri-

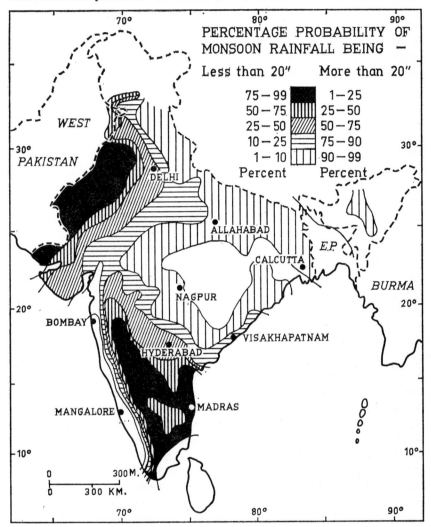

FIG 2.4 PERCENTAGE PROBABILITY OF MONSOON RAINFALL: comparison with the variability map in Fig 2.1 suggests the more precise tools now available. After B. N. Sreenivasaiah and S. Yegnarayan in *Proc. Symposium on . . . Floods and Droughts in India, 1958* (Indian Met. Dept, Poona, 1959). The strip near the Western Ghats should be shaded as for 1–10% probability of less than 20 in.

[10] M. J. Webb, *op. cit.*; E. Halley, 'An historical account of trade-winds and monsoons with an attempt to assign the physical cause of the said winds', *Phil. Trans. Roy. Soc.* (London, 1686); P. R. Crowe, 'The trade wind circulation of the world', *Trans. Inst. British Geog.* 15 (1959), 39–56; Y. P. Rao, 'Some characteristics of the S.W. monsoon circulation', *Indian Jnl Met. & Geophys.* 12 (1961), 413–18.

bution to thought about this most discussed of monsoon climates: contrasts between tropical continental air and equatorial maritime air, for instance, are significant, causing some storms, though contrasts within Em air, for instance between the Bay of Bengal and the Arabian Sea branches of the Indian monsoon, do not seem to be sufficient by themselves to generate the easterly depressions which bring widespread monsoon rains to the Ganga plains and the north of the sub-continent generally.[11] The recently prevailing school of thought in tropical meteorology, which may be called the 'upper air and perturbation school', began by making some positive contributions at points where the previous theories were weakest – notably in offering a fresh approach, if not as yet a complete explanation, concerning the later and sudden 'burst' of the monsoon over the north and west of the sub-continent as compared with the south and east and Burma. More recently still, papers mainly from the Indian Meteorological Department promise that we may soon have an explanation for the 'burst' of the monsoon, its 'breaks' or lulls, and its regional vagaries from year to year, integrating for the first time the dynamics of air moving in the lower troposphere, the upper troposphere and the lower stratosphere.

The 'burst' of the southwest monsoon, according to most modern authorities, is connected with a sudden change of the upper troposphere air-stream over the sub-continent from westerlies to easterlies, and in particular with the sudden withdrawal of the quasi-permanent winter and hot-weather station of the westerly jet-stream from south of – and rather higher than – the Himalayas, to a position north of the Tien Shan (Figs. 2.5 and 2.6). An east to west jet-stream does appear in the lower stratosphere above the upper troposphere easterlies; this jet is not as yet well studied, but is commonly at about $15°N$, and believed to be related to a modification in the 'normal' global heat exchange mechanism necessitated by 'over-heating' of air above the Tibetan plateau, an enormously hot area in summer for its latitude and altitude.[12] A quasi-permanent upper-air trough moves from a position over the Bay of Bengal between Ceylon and the Kra Isthmus to a summer station over the northwest of the sub-continent, and with this change there is now upper-air divergence over the lower troposphere convergence of the long-studied heat low at and near the surface. Cumulus formation in unstable equatorial maritime air is now able to tower up to heights of 30,000–50,000 ft. (9·1–15·25 km.) or even more, and in a normal year widespread storms, often thundery, sweep across the hitherto parched north and west of the sub-continent over the course of a week or ten days.

In many years the extreme northwest, the Thar desert and the lower Indus

[11] M. A. Garbell, *Tropical and Equatorial Meteorology* (Pitman, London, 1947), for an immediately post-war synthesis; but cf. H. Riehl, *Tropical Meteorology* (McGraw-Hill, New York, 1954).

[12] P. Koteswaram and C. A. George, 'On the formation of monsoon depressions in the Bay of Bengal', *Indian Jnl Met. & Geophys.* 9 (1958), 9–22; V. Srinivasan, 'Southwest monsoon rainfall in Gangetic West Bengal and its association with upper air flow patterns', *Indian Jnl Met. & Geophys.* 11 (1960), 5–18.

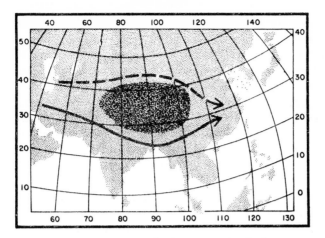

FIG 2.5 SHIFT IN THE JET STREAM: the jet stream in the lower stratosphere is thought to occupy a quasi-stationary winter position south of the Himalaya, moving about early June to a position north of the Tien Shan; this move, with the consequent adjustment of upper air flows, is believed to be an important factor in the 'burst' of the monsoon over India. From G. T. Trewartha in *Erdkunde*, 12 (1958), 205–14, after M. T. Yin in *Jnl Meteorology* (1949).

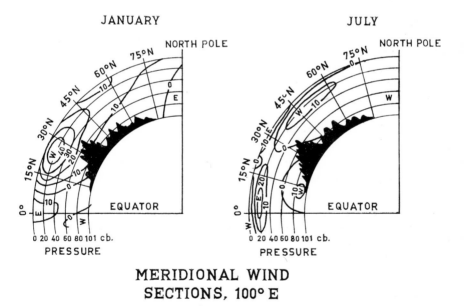

MERIDIONAL WIND
SECTIONS, 100° E

FIG 2.6 MERIDIONAL WIND SECTIONS, illustrating the shift in the upper troposphere westerlies ('W'); cf. Fig 2.5. After Y. Mintz, cited by K. R. Ramanathan in *Symposium on Monsoons of the World*, 1958 (Indian Met. Dept, Poona, 1960).

area, remain rainless or almost rainless. The relatively thin lower troposphere layer of equatorial maritime air is prevented from rising by a marked temperature inversion, the upper air having been influenced by a trajectory above the plateaus of southern Iran and West Pakistan, and the warm upper air has been portrayed as projecting above the lower Indus in a kind of snout, which may extend to spread drought, or contract to permit the occasional rainy year in the desert lands.[13] The semi-arid and famine tract inland from the Western Ghats is often regarded as a rain-shadow area, dry because of adiabatic tendencies in descending air. Poona does receive katabatic winds[14]; but modern workers query whether the descent is of sufficient order to account for the phenomenon and suggest an anticyclonic curve in the trajectory of the air.[15] The 'dry zone' of Ceylon is regarded as receiving föhn-like winds during the southwest monsoon.[16] Thunderstorms have a predilection for some particular sites, as along the Western Ghats where orographic rising occurs along the scarp facing the southwest monsoon or somewhat to its leeward in a standing wave, notably during the spectacular burst of the monsoon behind Bombay. Or, as already noted, it may be associated with random convection, or with cold air advection aloft, often connected with some form of trough or wave or depression.[17] West of the Western Ghats much rainfall is generated by small-scale vortices, about 50–100 miles (80–160 km.) in diameter, larger than those with a cumulo-nimbus cell but smaller than a tropical cyclone; the whirling movement is probably started by the deflection of the monsoon current by the Ghats, and their discovery helps to explain the very heavy rainfalls experienced away from the Ghats edge (Mangalore 117 in. (2,971 mm.)).[18] Tropical cyclones may form; fewer storms start in the Arabian Sea than in the Bay of Bengal, but at this season the Bay storms are generally milder, cyclonic storms or even depressions rather than the severe type classed as tropical cyclones.[19] The broad easterly depressions of great

[13] J. S. Sawyer, 'The structure of the inter-tropical front over N.W. India during the S.W. Monsoon', *Quart. Jnl Roy. Met. Soc.* 67 (1947), 346–69; later authorities have had doubts about the hypothesis put forward – e.g. P. Koteswaram, "The easterly Jet Stream in the tropics', *Tellus,* 10 (1958), 46.

[14] S. Atmanathan, 'The katabatic winds of Poona', *Indian Met. Dept. Sci. Notes,* 4 (1931), 101–15.

[15] G. T. Trewartha, *The Earth's Problem Climates* (Univ. of Wisconsin, Madison; Methuen, London, 1961), 168.

[16] G. Thambyahpillay, 'The kachchan-föhn wind in Ceylon', *Weather* (London, 1958), 107–14.

[17] E.g. K. L. Sinha, 'Influence of distant monsoon lows on weather around Jodhpur', *Indian Jnl Met. & Geophys.* 9 (1958), 251–4; on the other hand local influences may at least complement an upper-air/lower-air relationship, see B. N. Desai and C. Ramaswamy in correspondence discussing a paper by the latter on the jet-stream, *Tellus,* 9 (1957), 135–6.

[18] P. A. George, 'Effects of off-shore vortices on rainfall along the west coast of India', *Indian Jnl Met. & Geophys.* 7 (1956), 225–40; K. Raghavan, 'On the strong monsoon winds at Nagercoil', *ibid.* 6 (1955), 274–6.

[19] S. N. Raychoudhuri, Y. N. Subramanyan and R. Chellappa, 'A climatological study of storms and depressions in the Arabian Sea', *Indian Jnl Met. & Geophys.* 10 (1959), 283–90.

climatological significance moving up the Ganga from Bengal, and also depressions, cyclonic storms and tropical cyclones in the northern part of the Bay of Bengal, are now known to be related to waves or troughs in the upper troposphere easterlies, passing westwards at the rate of about 10 per month at this season, and occasionally to the passages of troughs in the easterly jet stream or in jet-fingers related to it.[20] As already noted, the recurrent station of this jet-stream seems to be farther south, at about 15°N, and further advances in understanding the main synoptic types yielding regional rains and lulls may be expected when further upper-air soundings become available from radiosonde and rawin balloon ascents (recording pressure, temperature, etc., and wind respectively).

Even now, however, some explanation is available for several of the five main synoptic types classified by Rahmatullah (1952) – for which no clear link with the upper air perturbations was clear even to a leading authority like Riehl writing in 1954 (see Fig. 2.7).[21] Waves in the upper troposphere easterlies are noted above as explaining weather activity over the classic position of the intertropical convergence of earlier workers (here between the Bay of Bengal and Arabian Sea branches of the south-west monsoon) over the Ganga plains. (The modern view might be that occasionally the Arabian Sea and Bay of Bengal branches of the monsoon may be sufficiently different in temperature to generate frontal activity on Bjerknes lines, but that this is seldom the primary cause of 'weather'.) Similarly, periods of heavy rain over South India may well become more intense and widespread when a synoptic situation similar to Rahmatullah's type e is reinforced by acceleration in the jet-stream at about 15°N up to its trajectory over South India (thereafter it decelerates), with upper vorticity advection, therefore vertical ascent, expected around its right entrance and left exit sectors.[22] And the 'break' in the monsoon over all the plains and peninsula of the sub-continent is related to the passages of several *westerly* disturbances in close succession over the Himalaya (where westerlies still hold sway even during the southwest monsoon); these are believed to pull the monsoon trough north into the Himalaya, causing heavy rains which may flood riverine tracts in the plains but cause the cessation of actual rains over the whole area south of the sub-montane tract.[23]

---

[20] V. Srinivasan, 1960, *op. cit.*; D. N. Moghe, 'Periodicity of the Indian S.W. monsoon current', *Proceedings* of the Delhi symposium on the Monsoons of the World in February 1958, Delhi, 1960, 229–34; but cf. S. Jayaram, 'Test of the randomness of the series of occurrences of depressions/cyclones in the Bay of Bengal', *Indian Jnl Met. & Geophys.* 12 (1961), 529–30.

[21] V. Rahmatullah, 'Synoptic aspects of the monsoon circulation and rainfall over Indo-Pakistan', *Jnl of Meteorology* 9 (1952), 176–9, cited in Riehl, *op. cit.*

[22] P. Koteswaram and C. A. George, 'On the formation of Monsoon depressions in the Bay of Bengal', *Indian Jnl Met. & Geophys.* 9 (1958), 9–22.

[23] D. A. Mooley, 'The role of western disturbances in the production of weather over N.E. India during different seasons', *Indian Jnl Met. & Geophys.* 8 (1957), 253–72; P. R. Pisharoty and B. N. Desai (1956), *op. cit.*

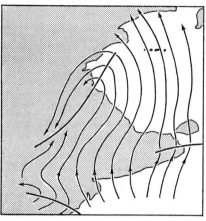

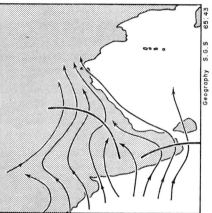

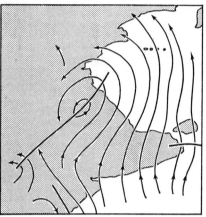

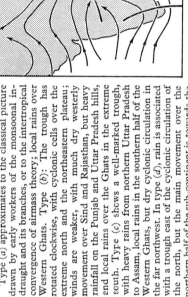

Type (a) approximates to the classical picture drawn by early workers of the monsoonal indraught and its branches, or to the intertropical convergence of airmass theory; local rains over Western Ghats. Type (b): The trough has rotated clockwise, with cyclonic cells over the extreme north and the northeastern plateau; winds are weaker, with much dry westerly movement over Sind and Rajasthan, but heavy rainfall on the Punjab and Uttar Pradesh hills, and local rains over the Ghats in the extreme south. Type (c) shows a well-marked trough, with heavy rains from northern Uttar Pradesh to Assam, local rains in the southern half of the Western Ghats, but dry cyclonic circulation in the far northwest. In type (d), rain is associated with a trough east of the cyclonic circulation of the north, but the main movement over the northern half of the sub-continent is towards the

Geography S.G.S 65.43

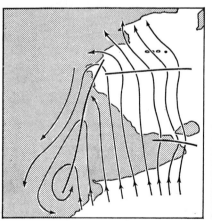

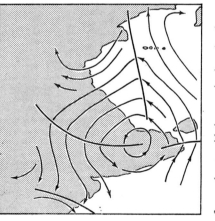

far northeast, with heavy rain there but lower air divergence and anticyclonic conditions from eastern Uttar Pradesh to southern Maharasthra and south to the Gulf of Manaar. Type (e) shows a great cyclonic circulation centred on the Mysore Plateau; in the north, a trough in the easterlies has moved to the extreme west, leaving a great swathe of anticyclonic conditions behind it so that all the north is dry; local rains over the Western Ghats in the south and possibly some widespread rain over Mysore. Read (a)–(e) clockwise from top left.

FIG 2.7 SYNOPTIC WEATHER CHARTS: representative types at 5,000 ft. (1·5 km., i.e. lower air) windfield, August 1949.

These lines of thought are beginning – if only beginning – to throw some light on possible causes of fluctuation in date of onset of the southwest monsoon. High temperatures in March over north India seem to relate to good monsoon rains in the south (and high March temperatures over the south itself with poor monsoon rains),[24] while late heating over the Himalayas and the Tibet plateau is related to late retreat of the westerlies from over the sub-continent and therefore late onset of the monsoon (and *vice versa*).[25] Variability of this, the main source of rain for most of the sub-continent, is clearly of vital moment to the people, farmers and townsfolk alike; and it is not just a problem of variability of total amount but also of variability within the rainy period in relation to crop needs. This is discussed elsewhere, but meantime the complex strands involved should be noted.[26]

The retreating monsoon

The southwest monsoon retreats gradually across the north and west of the sub-continent, in contrast with its sudden burst, sometimes with recrudescences. Over much of the north September is a fairly dry month, but sticky and hot – there is a distinct rise in temperatures in many stations. Then there is a gradual cooling, and at last a day when the first cool northerly breeze arrives, welcome and stimulating or foreboding of chilly nights to come, according to circumstances. The main rice harvest is gathered and the threshing is done in pleasant conditions; fields to be sown with wheat or barley are ploughed. The Hindu festival of light (Dewali) often takes place on a beautiful, still, starlit autumn night. Meantime the retreating monsoon brings the second and main peak for the ragi and rice lands of the Mysore plateau and the main rains of the year to eastern Madras and northeast Ceylon, and paddy fields are ploughed and planted, millet and groundnuts sown. The general pattern is towards the re-establishment in the north of the cool season pattern already seen for the early weeks of the year, towards the return of the westerlies and the westerly jet south of the Himalayas, interacting with subsident air at the surface. By October storms may be related to troughs in the upper troposphere westerlies or in the westerly jet stream – sometimes interacting violently with a trough in the retreating upper troposphere easterlies as in a violent storm over the lower Yamuna plains.[27] Farther south the rains of southeastern India may also occur in violent thunderstorms, but are commonly in wider disturbances in which an

[24] P. Jaganathan, 'Predisposition of the upper air structure in March and May to the subsequent rainfall of the Peninsula', *Indian Jnl Met. & Geophys.* 13 (1962), 305–16.
[25] N. C. Rai Sircar and C. D. Patil, 'Horizontal distribution of temperature over India in May in years of early, normal and late S.W. monsoons', *Indian Jnl Met. & Geophys.* 12 (1961), 377–80, and also their 'Study of high level wind tendency during pre-monsoon months in relation to time of onset of S.W. monsoon in India', *ibid.* 13 (1962), 468–71.
[26] B. N. Sreenivasaiah *et al.*, 'Reliability of rainfall during the monsoons in India and a study of the rainfall excesses and deficiencies', *Proceedings* of the 1958 New Delhi Symposium on the Meteorology and Hydrology of Floods in India (Delhi, 1959), 39–48.
[27] D. R. Swaminathan, 'On a destructive hailstorm in the Gormi area of Bhind district on 30 Oct., 1961', *Indian Jnl Met. & Geophys.* 13 (1962), 481–4.

easterly depression from the Bay of Bengal moves across the peninsula – sometimes resulting in very hot weather in the western coastal plains, in the lee of the Western Ghats where katabatic effects are accentuated in a zone of subsident air.[28]

The late summer and autumn months have the most frequent occurrence of tropical cyclones, in the Arabian Sea and especially and more disastrously in the Bay of Bengal, where the recurved maritime course commonly causes terrible havoc in densely peopled deltaic lands, both by winds and often also by flooding following the building up of a storm surge in the Bay. Recent work has again shown that heavy rains from these easterly disturbances are associated with upper air divergence, and that this may come from upper air *westerly* waves, and it has been shown how varying positions of the renascent sub-tropical high pressure area (or zone of recurring cells of high pressure), and varying altitude of southerly and northerly winds contribute to a drought year like 1949 and a wet year like 1946 or 1960.[29]

The violent tropical cyclones seem to arise in a basically similar fashion, but have very marked pressure gradients, destructive surface winds almost parallel to the isobars around the calm of the 'eye of the storm'. Very strong convergence vorticity is associated with very heavy rainfall, and the whole mechanism is sustained by strong upper air divergence while moving for two or three days – rarely for five or six even on recurved tracks – along a path often starting as easterly then curving round to become westerly, and probably reflecting the influence of both a lower air easterly and an upper air westerly trough.[30] These cyclones are similar to the hurricanes and typhoons of other sub-tropical areas. They are nowhere of greater human significance, because of the vast populations affected by this phenomenon primarily of maritime weather in the semi-aquatic rice-growing environment of the low-lying deltas. Fortunately, means of forecasting are improving, partly through greater understanding as knowledge grows concerning the dynamics of the upper atmosphere, and also through new means such as microseismic recording instruments, permitting early detection of storms at sea where weather records are scarce or by the chance of passing ships.

In opening the discussion of the Indian monsoons, we elected to use at that stage a mainly popular usage – though one deep rooted in the people of the sub-continent – for the concept of the climate of alternating monsoons and for *the* monsoon, the rains, the southwest monsoon. More technically, the most widespread usage, at least as yet, probably involves a marked reversal of winds as between cool dry land-winds in winter and warm rain-bearing sea winds in

---

[28] I. V. Doraiswamy, 'High maximum temperatures on the North Konkan coast', *Indian Jnl Met. & Geophys.* 9 (1958), 259–66.

[29] K. V. Rao, 'A study of the Indian north-east monsoon', *Indian Jnl Met. & Geophys.* 14 (1963), 143–55; P. R. Pisharoty and B. N. Desai, 1956, *op. cit.*

[30] P. Koteswaram and S. Gaspar, 'The surface structure of tropical cyclones in the Indian area', *Indian Jnl Met. & Geophys.* 7 (1956), 339–52; N. C. Rai Sircar, 'Note on vertical structure of a few disturbances over the Bay of Bengal', *ibid.* 7 (1956), 37–42.

summer, preferably through 180°, on the lines of a gigantic land and sea breeze mechanism, annual instead of diurnal in pulsation. So far as monsoon Asia as a whole is concerned, this concept remains useful, granting that dynamic as well as purely thermal factors, pulsations, waves and perturbations have to be taken into account rather than simple monsoonal indraught and outblowing – 'In fact, Asia breathes out during the winter and in during the summer, as the first authors thought'.[31] The Indian sub-continent shares in this, 'probably the largest local perturbation on the general circulation of the atmosphere'.[32] Yet in the Indian monsoon there are many singularities, due largely to relief so far as can be seen at present. The shape of the Peninsular block, the Indo-Gangetic plains and the great Himalayan arcs together with the lesser mountain arcs of the northeast and northwest, interact to place the sub-continent under the influence in winter of a poleward displacement of recurrent cells of sub-tropical high pressure, over Turkestan and over the Bay of Bengal, the northern plains and the peninsula being protected by the Himalayas from the intense cold of the Siberian high pressure system. In the summer monsoon, again, the junction zone between the Bay of Bengal and the Arabian Sea branches of the southwest monsoon recurrently becomes the site of a marked poleward displacement of the inter-tropical convergence zone. We have seen how upper air conditions interact, including poleward movement of these in turn; these compare with a more complete reversal in an 'upper air monsoon' over the rest of Monsoon Asia,[33] so that the Indian sub-continent has an end-product milder, less violent in contrast – if also less widespread in the diffusion of ample rains – compared with the rest of Monsoon Asia. Much of the detailed mechanism has long been known to be in common with other tropical climates, and as knowledge of tropical perturbations grows, and of their relations with waves in the easterlies – over the Pacific as over the Gangetic plain – and with troughs in the upper troposphere and the jet-streams, more is seen to be in common. At present, however, the easterly jet at about 15°N, continuing over the Sahara, seems to be distinctive, and perhaps related in an area to the summer heating noted over Tibet. Analogues from other tropical climates, too, can be described, and with considerable profit in comparative regional geography. There remain the many singularities in assemblage, in interplay of local topography and climate with the currents and waves at various atmospheric levels up to the stratosphere – in fact a rich and by no means fully studied regional climatology – and if the distinctiveness in meteorological and climatological principle is perhaps less than might have been claimed a few years ago, it is sufficiently stimulating in itself and especially so now that we can view it more clearly and more in a global perspective.

Climate and human activities

In the account of the march of the seasons, the briefest remarks have been made

---

[31] P. Pédélaborde, *op. cit.* 173.　　[32] Y. P. Rao, 1961, *op. cit.*
[33] P. Pédélaborde, *op. cit.* 172–3.

concerning the feel of the Indian monsoons to people living there, and also about selected climatic relations with particular diseases. Looking back over the whole field, no aspect of climate is of greater human import than the incidence of flood and drought. These have been mapped in a general way for India only (Figs. 2.4 and 2.8); this kind of mapping is useful in general appreciation of the problem, particularly when complemented by knowledge of the local patterns of

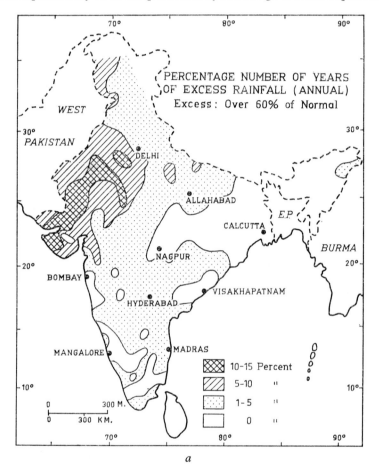

a

settlement, cropping, etc. Beyond this, a great deal of meteorological work goes on in the hope of being able to make better forecasts of these climatic accidents, at short, medium and long range, and on various areal scales also. An important geographical contribution, a generation ago, was in the mapping of variability of rainfall for the sub-continent, for the year as a whole.[34] This pioneer map may now be complemented by a more recent map using a more refined formula than

[34] A. V. Williamson and K. G. T. Clark, 'The variability of the annual rainfall of India', *Quart. Jnl Roy. Met. Soc.* 57 (1931), 43–56.

64

was available to the pioneer workers (see Fig. 2.8).[35] Such work is of great value in making our regional thinking more quantitative. In specific fields it is less valuable than probability maps dealing with the chances of a certain severity

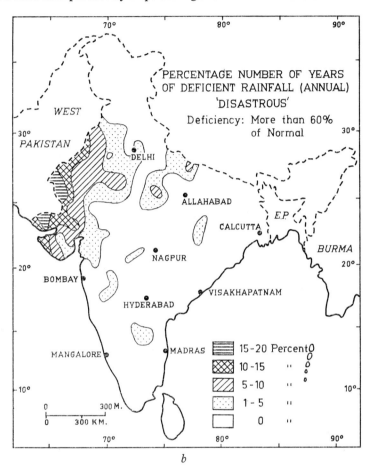

b

FIG 2.8 EXCESSIVE AND DEFICIENT RAINFALL. Like Fig 2.4, and from the same source, these maps illustrate the probability approach to climatology.

[35] B. N. Sreenivasan and S. Yegnarayan, 'Reliability of rainfall during the monsoon in India and a study of the rainfall excesses and deficiencies', *Proceedings* of the 1958 New Delhi Symposium on Meteorological and Hydrological Aspects of Floods and Droughts in India (Delhi, 1958), 39–48. Other mapping of interest includes: M. N. Pal's combined mean monthly rainfall and variability maps in A. T. A. Learmonth and L. S. Bhat (eds) *Mysore State Vol. I An Atlas of Resources* (Asia Publishing House, Bombay, 1960); H. A. Mathews, 'A new view of some familiar Indian rainfalls', *Scottish Geog. Mag.* 52 (1936), 84–97 (using quartile diagrams in the way suggested by P. R. Crowe), along with similar work included in the long series of articles by S. B. Chatterjee, included in his *Indian Climatology* (Commercial Printers, 63a Hari Ghose St., Calcutta, 1955); see also *GRI* 12–15, 1950–53).

of flooding or drought, or a certain degree of crop failure. Climatic relations with crop yields are clearly important in a society still largely peasant and partly though decreasingly dependent on subsistence cropping and local self-sufficiency. At a teaching or exploratory level, simple cartographic correlations like Stamp's maps of particular crops and selected isohyets are useful, though not always able to stand up to statistical testing because of exceptions on both sides of a climatic line. There is a major technical difficulty in going farther. The moisture requirements of a particular crop may be generalized – though in work designed for practical use it is better to deal with an individual variety – but there remains the complex task of relating the detailed seasonal incidence and intensity of precipitation to the changing needs of the growing crop. Progress is being made, notably at the Agricultural Meteorology Division of the Indian Meteorological Department, situated at Poona, with which is associated since 1945 the standardized recording of crop-weather data (with reference to locally important varieties of particular crops) at 40 stations throughout India. When sufficient data have accumulated it may be possible to correlate crop moisture requirements with regional climates, but the time for geographical synthesis is scarcely ripe.[36]

Classification of the climates

The classification of the climates discussed earlier in this chapter should serve to pull together the preceding discussion and give a basis for cross-reference with other chapters in the book, both regional and systematic. It is an extremely interesting exercise to compare different classifications, whether designed specifically for the study of the regional climatology of the sub-continent or as world classifications. In this edition of the present work the author of this chapter has sought rather to select only one or two classifications likely to be most useful to the reader of this book as such.

The Kendrew–Stamp classification of the climates of the sub-continent is given, along with some comment and additional information, in Fig. 2.9. This classification is empirical, arbitrary and subjective, but uses quantitative limits to the regions in easily understood units like temperature and rainfall. It does reflect some of the main climatic regions as they appeal to the people or the traveller, and it is simple enough to carry in the mind's eye. Stamp's addition of a line dividing continental from tropical India – roughly across the root of the peninsula – is useful at least as a reminder of a significant division. It is based on the 70° F. (21° C.) isotherm for mean monthly temperature for January, reduced to sea-level; it might have been better, though more complex cartographically, to use actual temperatures. It indicates something of the areas where temperate crops like wheat and barley are important as cool season crops, a feature of profound significance to diet and health and many aspects of the human

---

[36] Editorial: 'Agricultural meteorology in the Indian Meteorological Department 1932–57 – a review', *Indian Jnl Met. & Geophys.* 8 (1957), 1–28, and indeed the whole of this Agricultural Meteorology Silver Jubilee Number.

geography. (Actually wheat growing as an important food crop extends a good deal farther south in the uplands of the western Deccan.)

Of the world classifications, Thornthwaite's second (1948) classification is, like most others, oriented largely to plant requirements.[37] But it does manage to

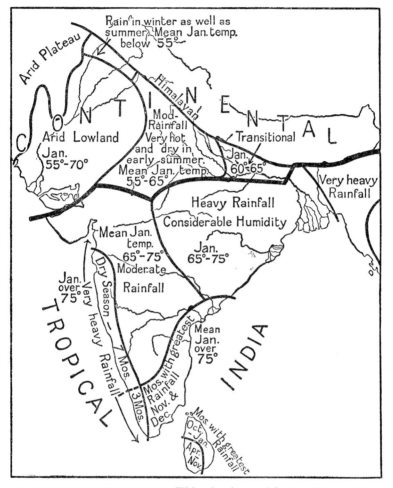

FIG 2.9 THE CLIMATES OF INDIA. This simple empirical and descriptive map may be compared with Köppen's (Fig 2.10); it brings out forcibly the distinction between the more 'continental' North and the Peninsula.

[37] C. W. Thornthwaite, 'An approach towards a rational classification of climate', *GR* 38 (1948), 55–94. See also, however, a major critique from an experienced Indian worker, and an alternative proposal of criteria for the sub-continent, in G. Y. Shanbag, 'The climates of India and its vicinity according to a new method of classification', *IGJ* 31 (1956), 1–25. Shanbag holds that Thornthwaite's concept is too little rooted in observations in growing plants, and proposes a formula related to actual plant growth at different temperatures, related in turn – by purely empirical formula it appears – to mean monthly

break away from the nexus to particular plant associations as means of defining climatic limits, and depends on limits which, though arbitrary, are objective. Thornthwaite seeks to classify the climates in degrees of aridity or humidity according to regularly spaced values of an index, a ratio, based on (1) annual water need or potential evapotranspiration, (2) annual water surplus, when actual precipitation received exceeds potential evapotranspiration, and (3) annual water deficit, when potential evapotranspiration exceeds actual precipitation received. Seasonal variations in aridity or humidity are to be similarly classified.

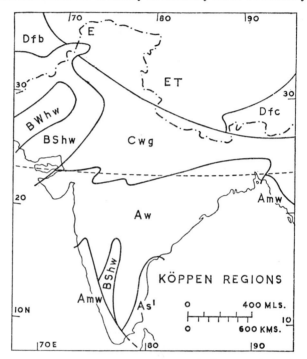

FIG 2.10 KOPPEN CLIMATIC REGIONS. Aw, tropical savannah (at least 1 month under 2·4 in.); Amw, monsoon with short dry season (rain-forest); As¹, dry season in high sun period. BShw, semi-arid steppe, hot, winter drought (wettest month 10 times rainfall of driest); BWhw, hot desert. CWg, dry winter (wettest month 10 times rainfall of driest, 'Gangetic' temperature régime (hottest month before solstice and rains). Dfb, cold humid winters, cool summers; Dfc, as Dfb with shorter summer (over 4 months below 50° F.). E, 'Polar' – warmest month under 50° F.; ET, 'Tundra', warmest month between 32 and 50°F. (0 to 10° C.).

---

precipitation for each month of the year. An approximation is used to minimize computation. The maps resulting are extremely attractive, on the whole, to the geographer with a good knowledge of Indian plant and crop distributions. One great difficulty, admitted by Shanbag, is that his basic formula relating temperature to plant growth is founded on one rather old set of experiments dealing with maize. Pending further work, it seems best to prefer Thornthwaite's, with disadvantages widely known to workers all over the world, for the main discussion.

Similarly temperature classes – microthermal, mesothermal and megathermal – are to be classified according to regularly chosen intervals in potential evapotranspiration, as a measure of temperature efficiency, the classification again to be subdivided according to seasonal variations in temperature efficiency. A fourfold basis of classification results (humidity or precipitation effectiveness and its seasonal variations, temperature efficiency and its seasonal variations). When more measurements of potential evapotranspiration become available, some such method as Thornthwaite's will certainly offer a considerable advance in climatic classifications oriented towards vegetation. Meantime, he has offered a method of estimating potential evapotranspiration based on two variables only, recorded temperatures and latitude, testing it from a large number of irrigated areas in North America. The formula has yielded reasonable results from other parts of the world, and a map of moisture régime drawn by V. P. Subrahmanyan for the Indian sub-continent is reproduced in Fig. 2.11.

The map of moisture régime is particularly sensitive and useful, and though empirical – and the connection with local experimental data remote – its objectivity alone makes it worthy of serious study. Granting the need for much more observational work, a correlation of a crop or vegetation pattern with this map can be taken seriously, and not as evidence of circular reasoning in which apparent cartographic correlation 'proves' a relationship, which is in fact an assumption on which a certain map was based!

Thornthwaite's version of the temperature régime is disappointing, in that almost all the sub-continent is classed as megathermal – for simplicity in mapping the author disregarded subclasses in temperature efficiency and in seasonal incidence therein.[38] Unfortunately the table of values published with his paper is for 30 representative stations only, not for the 250 stations for which estimates were made, and so interpolations cannot be made to see whether one of the boundaries corresponds to Stamp's divide between continental and tropical India. It would be worthwhile to investigate this, and also to apply the new Thornthwaite formula to a succession of years, so that the core area of a particular climate might be distinguished from the area of fluctuating climates.[39]

Finally, the classification of climates from the point of view of human comfort and efficiency has still many formidable obstacles to overcome. Meantime Fig. 2.12 is offered as a very tentative and interim solution to this problem.[40]

[38] For this reason the map is not reproduced. Instead the Köppen map, Fig. 2.10, is used to represent a map based on a widely used and understood formula which does distinguish North from South India in respect of temperature régime.

[39] R. J. Russell, 'Climatic years', GR 24 (1934), 92–103. An Indian worker, not traced at present, has applied this concept to the Thornthwaite 1933 formula, since superseded.

[40] D. H. K. Lee, 'Clothing for global man', GR 39 (1949), 181–213, and personal communication from P. Siple, American Embassy, Canberra, November, 1964.

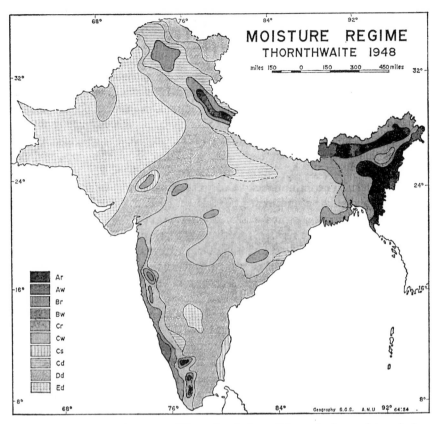

FIG 2.11 MOISTURE RÉGIME, on Thornthwaite's 1948 formula, i.e. moisture index $(Im) = \dfrac{100s - 60d}{n}$, where s = annual water surplus, d = annual water deficiency, and n = annual water need (or potential evapotranspiration), all expressed in the same units. From V. P. Subramanyam in *Indian Jnl Met. and Geophysics*, 7/3 (1956), 253–64.

KEY

Moisture index	Climatic type	Sub-types
100 and above	A Perhumid	r = little or no water deficit
		s = moderate summer water deficit
20 to 100	B Humid	w = moderate winter water deficit
		s_2 = large summer water deficit
0 to 20	C$_2$ Subhumid	w_2 = large winter water deficit
0 to −20	C$_1$ Dry subhumid	d = little or no water surplus
−20 to −40	D Semiarid	s = moderate winter water surplus
		w = moderate summer water surplus
−40 to −60	E Arid	s_2 = large winter water surplus
		w_2 = large summer water surplus

On this map, types C$_1$ and C$_2$ have been merged, types s and s_2, and **types** w and w_2.

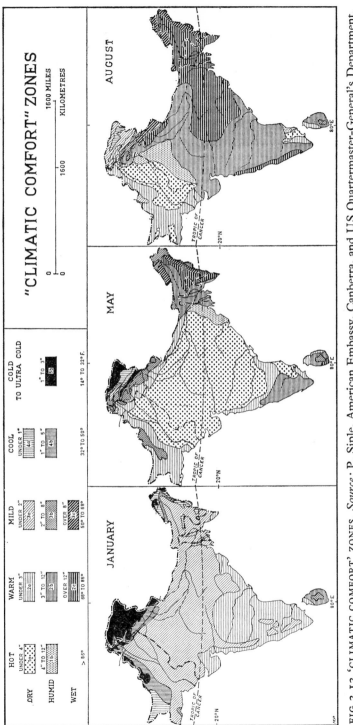

FIG 2.12 'CLIMATIC COMFORT' ZONES. *Source:* P. Siple, American Embassy, Canberra, and US Quartermaster-General's Department.

BIBLIOGRAPHICAL NOTE

In this edition the main sources, including classics in the field, are indicated in the text and footnotes. For up-to-date work, the reader is referred to the oft-cited *Indian Journal of Meteorology and Geophysics*, the various geographical journals published in the sub-continent – for instance the valuable series of articles on climate in the *Pakistan Geog. Rev.*, and S. S. Bhatia, 'Bibliography of Indian Climatology', *Indian Geographer*, 1, 1956, 55–64.

CHAPTER 3

Vegetation and Soils

I. VEGETATION

Original forest dominance

The natural vegetation of the Indian sub-continent, except on the higher mountains and in the more arid parts of Baluchistan and the Thar, is essentially arboreal. It has, however, been cleared, exploited and degraded to such an extent that this statement has little practical significance today. Something like a fifth of India is officially regarded as forest, against a notional optimum of a third; but of this area of 277,000 sq. miles (717,000 km²), nearly 100,000 sq. miles are 'unclassed' and most of this is forest only by courtesy, and this also applies to a good deal of the nominally 'Protected' forest. 'Reserved' forests are under half of the total forest area, and many of these, especially in the drier areas, are more subject than they should be to grazing and even illicit exploitation under cover of vague rights to minor forest produce. In any case, many of the best and least degenerated forests are in largely inaccessible Himalayan areas, there is very little forest of any sort in the Indo-Gangetic Plains, and much of the forest area of the Peninsula is really only scrub-jungle, very open or stunted. Pakistan is in even worse case, with only 13,500 sq. miles (35,000 km², 3·7% of area) under forest. Yet there is good historical evidence for large forests even in the central Punjab in Alexander the Great's day, on the Yamuna in the time of Mahmud of Ghazni (11th century); and the Gangetic Plain was probably originally covered with vast forests, mainly of sal. Today, as Legris points out, it is only very rarely that one can travel as much as 186 miles (300 km.) through even secondary forest that looks like forest, and then only by avoiding main routes, even on the Madhya Pradesh/Orissa borderland.[1]

Three millenia of clearing for cultivation and of unregulated grazing, both often promoted by burning the jungle, have thus stripped the forest from nearly all of the plains and much of the lower hills and plateaus, or turned it into scrub (Figs. 3.1, 3.2). In the Indo-Gangetic Plains as a whole woodland is practically confined to the terai, riverine strips, and village groves of mangoes and tamarinds, while over vast areas of the Deccan men and animals have produced the *aspect* of a short-grass savannah with scattered trees. 'Thin grass cover and scattered acacias . . . rough pasture, scattered acacias . . . thin cover of acacias, euphorbias'

[1] P. Legris, *La Végétation de l'Inde* (full reference in Bibliographical Note), 336–8, 343–8.

– such phrases occur time and again in field-notes of Peninsular journeys. But 'it is doubtful if there are any examples of tropical climax grassland [except in a few small scattered instances], though grassland is common enough as a secondary seral stage and it may be a very stable preclimax under the influence of fire and grazing. The typical savannah type of other countries is also apparently absent as a true climatic climax, closed deciduous forest grading into thorn forest without any open grassy park-like stage, in the absence of biotic influences.'[2] Legris goes further: 'Savannah results essentially from the regular passage of fire, but it presupposes a feeble density of human and cattle population. . . . It has practically disappeared in all the highly populated regions of the Deccan, where it remains theoretically possible but has been replaced by a bio-edaphic pseudosteppe.'[3] In effect, the biotic factor in the production of the 'savannah' areas of India is even more predominant than in other countries, and hence it is not possible to equate them in India with particular climate–soil complexes with any degree of confidence.[4] The forest classification must be taken as the basis of any vegetation study; but recent work has made it possible to indicate, at least provisionally, the ecological niche of the main grassland types.

The lack of gregariousness in tropical forests is well known; on the whole the floral landscape is rarely marked by an absolute preponderance of one species or even an assemblage of species. The nearest approaches to this condition are the Himalayan rhododendron belts, the semi-desert vegetation of the northwest, and bamboos locally in the south and the northwest, usually on old clearing. Palms, and especially acacia and sal, 'give a mark to the vegetation over considerable areas, but they are far from taking the place of assemblages. They are at best conspicuous features of the landscape.' The floristic affinities of India are in the main with the Malaysian realm, but, in the northwest, Mediterranean and southwest Asian elements have entered on a broad front, and Legris indicates some penetration from tropical Africa down the east of the Western Ghats. In the Himalayan temperate belt, Chinese forms are not few, with some European ones in the north and west; and other European, and even American, elements are represented, presumably by unrecorded importations of the last four centuries. An example is the cashew nut, so important in Goa and Kerala, brought from Brazil by the Portuguese.[5]

Climate is the major determinant of forest types, and on a broad view rainfall is more important than temperature, except in the Himalayas, since its range of

[2] H. G. Champion, *Forest Types* (full reference in Bibliographical Note), 14. Much of the terai is a tall-grass savannah. Important grasses are *sabai*, used for paper-making, and *khaskhas*, for the mats which, kept constantly wet, are a useful hot-weather cooling device.

[3] Legris, *op. cit.* 361.

[4] As is done for example by C. A. Cotton, 'The theory of savanna planation', *Geography*, 46 (1961), 89–101, and M. M. Cole, 'Vegetation and geomorphology in Northern Rhodesia', *GJ* 129 (1963), 290–310.

[5] C. G. Calder, 'An outline of the vegetation of India', in S. L. Hora (ed.), *An Outline of the Field Sciences of India* (India Sci. Congress, Calcutta, 1937), 71–90; Legris, *op. cit.*, Carte 20.

variation is so much the greater. Soil factors are generally of secondary significance, though of course they play a decisive role in controlling the distribution of species and associations within the major types, mainly through variations in

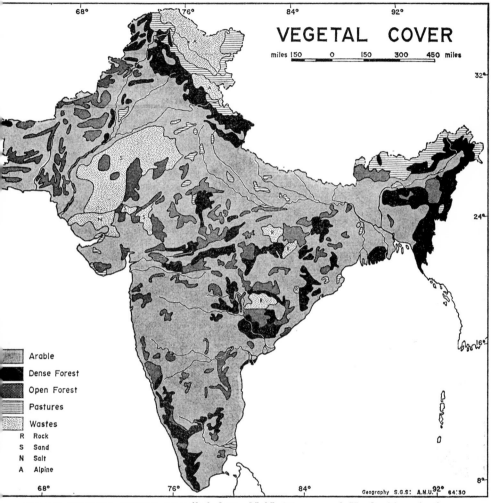

FIG 3.1 VEGETAL COVER: compiled from *NAI*, Pl. 11 and K. S. Ahmad, *A Geography of Pakistan* (1946).

ground moisture leading to the occurrence of wet types well outside their normal rainfall limits, and *vice versa*. Topography in the narrow sense is responsible for certain minor types, e.g. alpine flora, tidal forest, some savannahs on sub-Himalayan terraces; these are limited in extent but of interest as specialized adaptations to environment or as being of special economic importance. Excluding these, four grand vegetation divisions may be recognized on a rainfall basis:

over 80 in. (2,032 mm.): evergreen (rain) forest;

40–80 in.:   deciduous (monsoon) forest;

20–40 in.:   drier deciduous forest grading into open thorny scrub;

under 20 in.:   thorny scrub and low open bush merging into semi-desert.

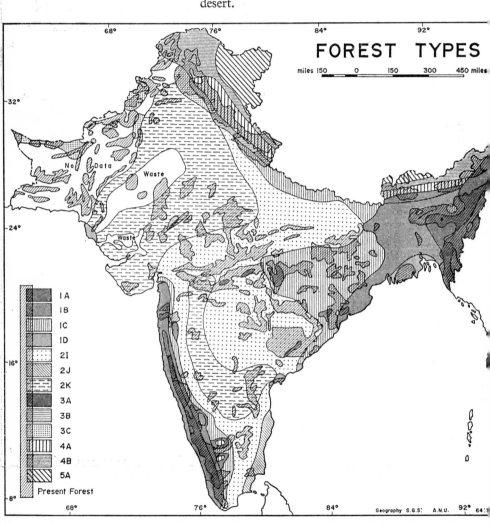

FIG 3.2 FOREST TYPES. *Sources:* As for Fig 3.1, with addition of H. G. Champion, *op. cit.* (1936) in text. Key to symbols is given on pp. 77–79.

Legris takes a rather more physiognomic approach, distinguishing humid, dense dry, thorny, and Himalayan formations.

It must be emphasized that these limits are approximations only, that tran-

76

sitions are usually gradual, and that there are numerous anomalies of detail: 'the familiar 80 inches rainfall limit for rain forest . . . is open to the exceptions of the occurrence of the type with only 50 inches [1,270 mm.] under very favourable conditions, and its absence with even 200 inches unsuitably distributed when it is associated with either a very porous or an impervious soil.' Again, while the broad lines are clear enough, there is considerable confusion of nomenclature; Legris cites one Himalayan type which has been given 17 names by various authors, and classified as high-altitude tropical, temperate, montane temperate, cool temperate, and subalpine.[6]

Vegetation classification

The classic forest classification is that of H. G. Champion, who distinguished altogether 116 types, some of them subdivided. But many of these are local, and they fall into 15 main types, or 13 if we group Alpine forests and scrubs together. Legris considers that, even after Schweinfurth's elaborate work, Champion's classification is still the most useful for the Himalayas. However, since Champion's book was published in 1936, a good deal of critical work has been devoted to the problem, largely on lines he himself anticipated, and in particular his work has been complemented, though not as yet superseded, by that of G. S. Puri. The biotic modification of the forest cover is emphasized by Puri, who is reasonably confident that three of Champion's main types – dry deciduous, thorn, and dry evergreen forest – are biotic seral stages to moist deciduous forest; or, to put it conversely (as does Legris) are essentially degraded from more humid formations.[7] Puri also considers that the Nilgiri grasslands are biotically controlled, and in this he is at one with Legris, who cites peat borings showing little if any sign of climatic change but definite carbonaceous layers indicating extensive burning.[8]

The following tabular statement therefore follows Champion in general, with some modification and rearrangement along Puri's lines. Prefixed numbers (1A, 1B . . .) refer to the keys of Figs. 3.2 and 3.3; grassland types are enclosed in square brackets; asterisks indicate types thought by Puri to be definitely biotically induced.[9]

1. *Moist Tropical Types*
   1A. Tropical wet evergreen
   1B. Tropical moist semi-evergreen

[6] Legris, *op. cit.* 285.
[7] *Ibid.* 204–8, 236, 248–9.
[8] *Ibid.* 219–23; Puri, *Indian Forest Ecology* (Oxford Book Co., New Delhi, 1960), 249.
[9] A more detailed treatment may be found in A. T. A. Learmonth, *The Vegetation of the Indian Sub-Continent* (Dept of Geography, School of General Studies, Australian National University, Canberra; Occasional Paper No. 1, 1964); this includes floristic data, especially on the grasslands, difficult to fit into the scale of this book, and types not mappable on the scale of the map used for figs. 3.2 and 3.3 (hence the gaps in the system of code-letters used below).

IC. Tropical moist deciduous

ID. Tidal (edaphic)

[IP. Savannah grassland of moist plains*]

[IR. *Dichanthium-Cenchrus* grasslands on sandy soils*]

2. *Dry Tropical Types*

2I. Tropical dry deciduous*

2J. Tropical dry evergreen*

2K. Tropical thorn

[2L. *Dichanthium-Cenchrus*]

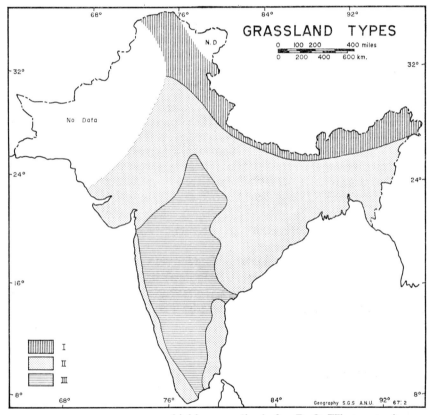

FIG 3.3 GRASSLAND TYPES, highly generalized after R. O. Whyte, *op. cit.* (1957) in Bibliographical Note. For symbols 3E, 4L, etc., see pp. 77–79. I, Northern mountain and hill grasslands (3E, 4L, 5F); II, Grasslands on sandy soils, alluvial deserts and crystalline plateaus (mainly IR and 2L, with IP along the northern hillfoot and 3E on Aravallis and Assamese hills); III, Deccan Grasslands (typically 2M, with 2N in rare paddy tracts, some 2L and 3D and some 3E on ridges, dissected hills and scarps).

2. *Dry Tropical Types*
   [2M. *Sehima-Dichanthium**]
   [2N. *Bothriochloa* in paddy tracts*]

3. *Montane Subtropical Types*
   3A. Wet hill
   3B. Subtropical pine
   3C. Subtropical dry evergreen
   [3D. Hill savannah, *Cymbopogon**]
   [3E. Hill savannah, *Arundinella**]

4. *Montane Temperate Types*
   4A. Wet temperate and Himalayan moist temperate
   4B. Himalayan dry temperate
   [4L. Temperate grassland*]

5. *Alpine Types*
   5A. Alpine
   [5F. Alpine and Subalpine grasslands*].

Moist Tropical types

1A *and* 1B. *Tropical wet evergreen and semi-evergreen.* These are typical rain-forests. The true evergreen is found in a strip along the Western Ghats at 1,500–4,500 ft. (455–1,370 m.), south of Bombay, and up to 3,500 ft. (1,070 m.) in Assam; much of Bengal and the Orissa littoral may once have been covered by semi-evergreen forest. The best evergreen forest is naturally found in the areas with really high rainfall, over 120 in. (3,048 mm.), and a relatively short dry season; on the drier side it is bordered by the semi-evergreen, which in turn merges with 1C, tropical moist deciduous. The rain-forest is very dense and lofty, the upper storey reaching 120–150 ft. (37–46 m.) with individuals of 200 ft.; some of the largest are dipterocarps. Owing to the deep shade the floor is relatively bare, but along the edges of breaks in the cover (such as stream-margins) undergrowth of palms and bamboos may be extremely dense. Buttressed trunks are common and epiphytes highly developed. The number of species is very large indeed, especially on the Ghats; the Assam forests and still more the semi-evergreen tend to be rather more gregarious, representing a transition to moist deciduous.

The forests are exploited under State forestry departments to favour the more economic species. So far elephant rather than tractor power is used, and seasonal saw-pits are common; but more advanced methods for pulp and paper mills, such as those of Bhadravati in Mysore and Karnaphuli in East Pakistan, are increasing. Veneer and plywoods are produced; rattan-canes have been over-exploited.

IC *and* 21. *Tropical deciduous.* These may conveniently be treated together; 21, tropical dry deciduous, is regarded as a biotically-induced variant of the moister IC, theoretically seral to it but more practically regarded as degenerative from it: it is most unlikely that the process of degradation is reversible, under Indian conditions, on more than a very limited scale.

These, the monsoon forests *par excellence*, form the natural cover over nearly all of India between the Himalayas, the Thar and the Western Ghats; areas with a moderate (40–80 in., 1,016–2,032 mm.) rainfall. But they are, of course, less resistant to fire and other man-induced interference; vast areas have been completely destroyed, and the biotically controlled drier facies has replaced the moister over very much of its original area. The moist forest forms a long strip on the east of the Western Ghats, and the economically very important sal type covers the northeast of the Peninsula – Chota Nagpur, Orissa, eastern Madhya Pradesh; and there is a long strip along the Siwaliks, the bhabar, and the terai from 77 to 88° E. The rest of the area is of the drier type, shading off into thorn forest.

Although most trees lose their leaves for some 6 to 8 weeks in the hot weather, the actual leaf-fall periods vary from species to species, so that the forest is rarely absolutely leafless, and undergrowth in moister areas is often evergreen. Nevertheless the general aspect is decidedly burnt-up and bare in April–May. The moist forest is higher (80–120 ft. against 50–75) than the dry, which indeed breaks down into thorn or scrub in climatically or edaphically arid areas. Undergrowth is usually denser than in the rain-forest; climbers and bamboos are very common, especially perhaps in the moister types.

Economically these are the most important forests of India; the number of commercially important species is greater than in the evergreen, and they are also on the whole more gregarious. This is so more particularly of sal (*Shorea robusta*), which 'is very generally more aggressive than any of its associates and competitors in natural gregarious habit, coppicing power, resistance to burning, regeneration under burning and grazing, adaptability to soil and site conditions; though it suffers from frost, it survives where few other species could'.[10] These traits have been fostered by selective forest management. Sal often forms pure stands (perhaps biotically induced rather than the climatic climax) of close and high forest (80–120 ft., 24–36 m.), with a shrubby undergrowth replaced by grass in areas liable to burning. Edaphically it avoids purer sands and clays, too dry or too wet. The hard durable timber is in great demand, especially for railway sleepers and constructional work; 50 miles of railway construction is said to have demanded 20,000 tons of sal or teak. Teak (*Tectona grandis*) is characteristic of the monsoon forest in the west; its distribution is to some extent complementary to that of sal in the Peninsula, sal dominating the northeastern quadrant. While teak is a calcicole, sal is probably a calcifuge. Like sal, it is reasonably resistant to burning, which indeed may assist regeneration, by splitting the pericarps, if it

[10] Champion, *op. cit.* 76.

takes place before the seedling stage; but it is a poorer colonizer, and except where artificially aided not nearly so gregarious as sal.[11] Indian teak production, mostly from Mysore, is much less than that of Burma (in normal times), and despite its greater fame the timber is on the whole less important in India than is sal, though valuable for its termite-resistant qualities.

The evergreen sandalwood (*Santalum album*) is a valuable resource in Mysore; a very hard and close-grained yellow wood with a fragrant scent, it is used for carved boxes and ornaments and for incense, and more or less sandalwood may be included in more or less expensive funeral pyres. Other important trees are sissoo or shisham (*Dalbergia sissoo*), very common along the eastern sub-Himalayan zone, producing a hard timber used for building, furniture, cart-frames and wheels; hurra (*Terminalia chebula*), less significant for its timber (which is nevertheless hard and suitable for furniture, carts and turnery) than for its fruits, the myrobalans which provide a valuable tan-stuff and are also used for dyes and mordants; mahua (*Bassia latifolia*), the flowers of which are eaten as a sweetmeat and are a potential source of alcohol; and khair (*Acacia catechu*), common on the more arid margins of the dry deciduous type. Minor forest products range from honey to bats' dung for manure.[12]

1D. *Tidal forests*.[13] The tidal forests are the most widely known of the specialized tropical types, but confusion has been caused by the indiscriminate use of the word 'mangrove' and by even more indiscriminate descriptions by travellers of the most luxuriant parts of mangrove forests as if they were the standard. While the *Rhizophora* mangroves which border tidal channels do form dark high forests, much mangrove is low and light olive in colour, most disappointing to those who have been led to expect giant knee-roots and crocodiles behind every tree.[14] The common feature of the numerous species of mangroves, and of other trees of the tidal marshes, is the existence of pneumatophores or breathing-roots, sticking out of the mud like a field of tent-pegs driven in upside-down. In the early stages of colonization of the mud-banks the plants are scattered, and in conditions of poor silt-supply (e.g. on parts of the west coast) the mangrove 'forest' remains very open and the trees low, at high tide looking like olives growing out of the water. Just as the reputation of rain-forest as impenetrable is based largely on its luxuriance along the streams, where the

[11] These statements may need some qualification. Sal is more dependent on soil moisture than is teak, which is more sensitive to chemical properties of the soil, and the former is thus more affected by lowering of the water-table owing to biotic interference; this encourages fungal attacks on the shallow root system. In places sal seems to be degenerating and even retreating before teak. See K. N. Chaudhuri, 'Regenerating of the dry peninsular sal forests of West Bengal', *Indian Forester* 84/1 (1958), 4–18; D. H. Kulkarni, 'Geography of sal and teak', *Proc. IX Silviculture Conference 1956* (Dehra Dun, 1960), 108–16; and cf. Puri, *op. cit.* 183.

[12] M. N. Ramaswamy, *Minor Forest Products in Mysore: A Survey* (Govt Press, Bangalore, 1945).

[13] There is a good discussion in Legris, *op. cit.* 320–5; for the economic side, see 'Symposium on mangrove vegetation', *Science and Culture* (Calcutta), 23/7 (1958), 329–36.

[14] Personal experience!

whole side of the orest is accessible to light, so the popuiar conception of mangrove swamp is based on the gallery of high dense growth along the tidal channels, trapping the silt at every tide. Behind this rapidly accreting zone is usually an infilling of smaller species; both the ground surface and that of the vegetation canopy are saucer-like in section.

Mangroves fringe the seafaces of most of the Indian deltas. In the Bengal Delta they are backed by the great tidal Sundarbans, named from the sundri tree (*Heritiera fomes*). This pneumatophore forms a closed forest which is over 100 ft. high in the higher areas where the water is fresh or brackish in the rains. At still higher levels, in Bengal and elsewhere, are tangled brakes of screwpines (*Pandanus* spp.), canes, and palms such as *Phoenix paludosa*. The creeks are often lined by *Nipa fruticans*, a palm with dense masses of fronds springing directly from a low stump. These forests have a considerable economic value. The mangroves themselves are an important source of fuel, sometimes under management as such; sundri is a hard durable timber much used for construction and boat-building; gewa (*Exeocaria agallocha*) is used for newsprint; the fronds of *Nipa* are a common thatching material, its sap can be made into gur or toddy, the leaf-stalks are used as fishing-floats and to give buoyancy to sundri logs.

[1P. *Savannah grassland of moist plains.*] This is found in a long strip eastwards from about 77°E; it is a hygrophilous to mesophilous vegetation of coarse grasses including *Phragmites karka*, *Saccharum* spp., and *Imperata cylindrica*. Itself biotic in origin, it is even more sensitive than the forests to heavy grazing and burning, and the drier soil climate which ensues leads to the formation of a distinctly xerophytic vegetation or even to bare ground not even invaded by prostrate forms such as *Eleusine* and *Paspalum*. Nevertheless there are still very considerable stretches of tall grassland along the terai.

[1R. *Dichanthium-Cenchrus grassland.*] This very wide-spread grassland is also a dry formation (1R is grouped with 2L on Fig. 3.3); it is seral to very varied forest types. The distinction between 1R and 2L is that the former is found on sandier soils in climatically more humid areas. As in all the Indian grasslands, burning and overgrazing have led to very severe deterioration, and there are very many degraded sub-types. These include poor grasslands dominated by non-palatable annuals such as *Aristida* spp. and a low scrub of *Cassia auriculata* over bare eroded soil, and in extreme cases great swathes of badland erosion as along the Chambal.

Other Edaphic Types. These include beach vegetation (not of course confined to the moist tropical habitat), tropical freshwater swamps, riverain forests, khair-sissoo on sandy floodplains, bamboo brakes, various scrubs on lateritic soils, and alluvial savannahs. Owing to limitations of data and still more of scale, they have not been included on Figs. 3.2 and 3.3.

On beaches and dunes fringes of casuarina are common; along the eastern littoral it is often planted on sandy soils as a quick-growing source of firewood, and it also helps to stabilize coastal dunes.

Freshwater swamp forests are found in badly drained and aerated clayey depressions in areas with over 50 in. (1,270 mm.) of rain: they form pure stands of medium-sized trees, largely evergreens, which may or may not have an evergreen undergrowth according to the amount of biotic interference. The riverain and freshwater swamp forests vary greatly with local climatic and edaphic factors, and with interference by men and animals; they range from dense jungle and cane-brakes through thin strips of more or less open woodland into swampy savannah. A notable riverain type is the khair-sissoo association on new sandy alluvium in northern India. In areas where the progression would be towards semi-evergreen forest, as in alluvial tracts of Assam, canes trailing horizontally as much as 200 ft. (61 m.) form dense brakes, an impenetrable thorny thicket with a few tall trees, including palms. Some of these subsidiary edaphic types, for example bamboo brakes and secondary dipterocarp forest, are of course also strongly influenced by biotic factors, and one of Puri's types – moist alluvial savannah – is firmly biotic: grazing and burning on useful floodplains and terraces keep the vegetation, naturally seral to a riverain woodland and eventually to tropical moist deciduous forest, at the savannah stage.

Dry Tropical types

21. *Tropical dry deciduous.* This has been discussed with the moist deciduous type, from which it is by and large a biotically controlled regression. Occupying a vast area in central and Peninsular India and also along the Siwaliks and terai from central Nepal to Himachal Pradesh it is, as Legris points out, in contact with practically all types, and transitional facies are important. The common climatic characteristic of its domain is a long and intense dry season, with a moderate rainfall concentrated into a few months. On the drier side, it degenerates into thorn forest, 2K.

2J. *Tropical dry evergreen.* This is a very peculiar formation with a very limited range, almost confined to the Madras littoral between Point Calimere and Madras itself. Legris, who thinks its general significance has been exaggerated, casts doubts on its affinities to the dry forest of northern Ceylon. It is found with a rainfall of about 40 in. (1,016 mm.), received mostly in October through December, and with generally high humidity. The forest, where it still exists, has a closed but low (30–40 ft.) canopy with shrubby, often spiny, undergrowth. Bamboos are rare, but lower grasses may be present. The existence of an evergreen forest with such low rainfall is botanically interesting, but most of it has been cleared for agriculture or casuarina plantations. The residuals are now regarded as a biotically controlled forest, degraded from evergreen high forest.[15]

2K. *Tropical thorn forest.* In areas with under 30 in. (762 mm.) annual rainfall, such as the northwest and the Peninsular interior to the lee of the Western Ghats, the dominant vegetation is open stunted forest breaking down into

[15] Only small patches are shown on the Cape Comorin sheet of the Pondicherry 1/1,000,000 vegetation map (see Bibliographical Note). See also Puri, *op. cit.* 246, and Legris, *op. cit.* 227–33. He prefers the term semi-deciduous.

xerophytic bush, and in the northwest grading into practically complete desert. Biotic factors over the centuries are regarded as more important than climate and soil in producing and maintaining these forests, degraded from the tropical dry deciduous type, itself largely biotic. As Legris puts it:

'This vegetation taken as a whole continues to degrade, or at most seems stabilized in a peneclimactic stage in equilibrium with the biotic factors. Can one in such a case speak of a progressive vegetational series? . . . One finds in each region a whole series of stages of floristic and physiognomic degradation deriving from each other. One can, then, consider each of these ensembles as constituting a phylum, a progressive vegetation series ending at the most evolved type existing in present ecological conditions, which is the plesioclimax. This plesioclimax is definitely not the most evolved physiognomic type possible, and *a fortiori* it differs from the floristic climax. It is only an evolved stage of the series, useful for determining the direction of the progression.'[16]

In this type, trees are low (20–30 ft., 6–9 m. maximum) and may be widely scattered; acacias are very prominent, widely and pretty evenly spaced in consequence of the wide radius of the roots, which ensures each tree its own little territory. Euphorbias are also conspicuous, sometimes locally dominant and attaining the size of small trees. The Indian wild date, *Phoenix sylvestris*, is common, especially in damper depressions; its fruit is far inferior to that of the true date-palm (*P. dactylifera*) and is rarely used directly as food, though a thick molasses-like gur can be got by tapping the tree from an incision into a pot (still used to ferment for *todi* in some states).

There are patches of taller and fairly close woodland in locally favoured areas, but the general effect is depressing, and well depicted by Aldous Huxley:

'Once in every ten or twenty yards, some grey-green plant, deep-rooted, and too thorny for even camels to eat, tenaciously and with a kind of desperate vegetable ferocity struggles for life. And at longer intervals, draining the moisture of a rood of land, there rise, here and there, the little stunted trees of the desert. From close at hand the sparseness of their distantly scattered growth is manifest. But seen in depth down the long perspective of receding distance, they seem – like the in fact remotely scattered stars of the Milky Way – numerous and densely packed. Close at hand the desert is only rarely flecked by shade; but the further distances seem closed with a dense dark growth of trees. The foreground is always desert, but on every horizon there is the semblance of shadowy forests. The train rolls on, and the forests remain for ever on the horizon; around one is always and only the desert.'[17]

This admirable passage was written of Rajasthan, but it applies to much of the Indus Plains (and of Australia), and, with larger trees and a less dead foreground, to vast areas of those of the Ganga and the Peninsula.

[16] Legris, *op. cit.* 258–84, gives a most interesting account of some of the detailed variants; the quotation is at 258–9.
[17] *Jesting Pilate* (1927 ed.) 71–72; quoted by courtesy of Messrs Chatto & Windus.

In many areas deterioration continues through grazing by cattle and browsing by goats, and this type is more important as a source of fuel and fodder than of timber. Khair (*Acacia catechu*), however, which sometimes forms fairly dense closed stands over considerable areas, is used for carts, tool handles and so on, and also, more importantly, for tan-stuffs and *cutch*, a brown or yellow-orange dye for sails, cordage and nets, canvas bags, and in Burma for the robes of the Buddhist monks. Another product of this tree is *kath*, mixed with lime, betel-vine leaves, and areca nuts to form the red *pan* chewed all over India. Babul (*A. arabica*) is perhaps more common than khair in the northwestern lowlands, and has similar uses.

[2L. *Dichanthium-Cenchrus grassland*.] As noted above, this grassland is found also over large areas with more humid climate and has not been distinguished from IR on Fig. 3.3. Most of the species are erect grasses 3–5 ft. high; it covers a very wide range of climates and soils.

[2M. *Sehima-Dichanthium grassland*.] This is the most typical grassland of the Deccan, at its best on well-drained *regur* or black soil sites. It is seral to the tropical dry deciduous forest; many of its grasses are excellent as fodder, but it is easily degraded into poorer associations with *Aristida* and *Cymbopogon* spp.

[2N. *Bothriochloa grassland*.] This is a very localized type, found in irrigated paddy lands east of Poona, on immature black soils. The dominant grass is the sweet-scented purple-headed kanker (*Bothriochloa odorata*), which is unpalatable to cattle but used for thatching.

Other Edaphic Types. As in the moist tropical zone, there is a great variety of minor types, both strictly edaphic and what Puri terms subsidiary edaphic, that is edaphic variations within a climax type. These include riverain woodlands or gallery forest, a great variety of more or less open and often thorny scrub forests, dune and saline vegetation.

In the north, the khair-sissoo riverain association extends into these drier areas and may be seral to the tamarisk–poplar association which occupies similar soils. Inundation babul (*Acacia arabica*) occupies floodplains in central India and the northern Deccan; where flooding lasts for six weeks or so, babul may form pure stands up to 40–50 ft. (12–15 m.) high, with some *Populus euphratica*. The dry stiff alluvial clays of the Gonda–Bahraich area in Uttar Pradesh are dominated by *Aegle marmelos*, a tree used as it were mainly for by-products rather than timber – the pulpy rind-fruit for beverages and drugs, the seeds for pill-boxes and necklaces.[18] In the upper Gangetic plains, recent clayey alluvium with high salinity is occupied by scrub of coarse halophytic grasses and scattered acacias and wild dates. Dry bamboo brake, dominated by *Dendrocalamus strictus*, occurs on the dry hillsides and sandy or gravelly alluvium of the Siwaliks.

Puri's somewhat arid floristic lists may be supplemented from Legris, who traces the very interesting transition from fairly dense but low *Anogeissus*

[18] There is a wealth of such detail, impossible to give consistently here, in *The Wealth of India* (Council of Scientific and Industrial Research, New Delhi, 1948—).

pendula forest on the Aravallis, through the very open *Prosopis spicigera* belt east of the Aravallis from Kutch to the Punjab, to the desert of the Thar. The area of the Thar and middle Indus was certainly more wooded in protohistoric and early historic times (this may have a bearing on the Indus Civilization), but it has been and still is ravaged both by overgrazing, especially of goats, and a desperate search for fuel. Now shrubs and trees are absent; plants have a bushy or tussocky habit, scattered tussocks ensuring a more complete distribution of the scanty soil moisture, and are marked by such xerophytic adaptations as pilosity and the disappearance of leaves; in some places edible herbs and grasses can only survive under the protection of spiny bushes. There are tracts of pseudosteppe where grasses may reach 6 ft. high and serve to stabilize the sand; but in some cases even the tussocks of *Calligonum* are uprooted for fuel by the village women, and here fixed dunes may become mobile once more. In the *Prosopis* belt there is an interesting type of 'forest farming': individual trees are carefully conserved and pruned and may reach 50 ft. (15 m.); millets, mustard, and where possible irrigated wheat are grown in their shade. *Prosopis juliflora*, however, introduced to reclaim the dunes, invades such cultivable land as there is.[19]

Montane subtropical and temperate types: (a) Southern

The tropical formations cover almost all extra-Himalayan India where forests exist; the subtropical and temperate types, however, occur in two widely separated areas: the Nilgiris and Anaimalai–Palani Hills in the extreme south, and the Himalayan and Assamese mountains in the north. Although the Nilgiri flora shows marked affinities, as yet unexplained, with that of Assam and Manipur,[20] it seems simpler to depart from the Champion–Puri sequence and to treat the two areas separately.

3A. *Wet hill forest (southern)*. Owing to the restricted area of the southern hills, the subtropical zone is difficult to distinguish from the clearly differentiated tropical rain-forest below and the temperate forest above. It occurs at 3,500–5,000 ft. (1,070–1,525 m.) on the Nilgiris and Palanis, and is described as essentially a 'stunted rain-forest', not so luxuriant as the true tropical evergreen. Sub-types occur on the higher parts of the Western Ghats and the summits of the Satpura and Maikal Hills, and perhaps as far away as Mount Abu in the Aravallis; but in these localities the forests have been so much reduced and changed that it is difficult to trace connections.

[3D. *Subtropical hill savannah, Cymbopogon type.*] This type has a very wide range, from the Aravallis to the Nilgiris, with local variations both seral to wet hill forest in regressional sub-types. The dominant is usually *Cymbopogon martini*, which is of poor grazing value, but there are scattered stands of the more useful *Themeda* spp. In some places very degraded grasslands are dominated by

[19] Legris, *op. cit.* 270–9.
[20] Calder, *op. cit.* 87; *Imperial Gaz.*, I, 188.

xerophytic *Aristida* spp., and this is especially marked in the more northerly extensions on the hills of central India.

4A. *Wet temperate forest (southern)*. This occurs above 5,000 ft. on the Nilgiris, Anaimalais and Palanis, with rainfall of 60–250 in. (1,524–6,350 mm.) or more and monthly mean minima of about 45–55° F., maxima of 60–75° (7–13 and 16–24° C.). The forests (*sholas*) are found as a rule in the lower or sheltered aspects of bold open downland, often on the steep sides of V-shaped valleys incised into the hillsides and plateaus; the effect is often that of a rich rolling savannah or parkland with occasional peat-bogs. The forest is climatic but its boundary with grassland is biotic; once the smoother areas have been cleared wind, with fire, is a powerful inhibiting factor. It is dense but rather low (50–60 ft., 15–18 m.) with much undergrowth and many epiphytes, mosses, and ferns; both tropical and temperate elements are found: magnolias, laurels, rhododendrons, planes, elms and *Prunus*. Exotics include cinchona, wattle and eucalypts.

Montane types: (b) Himalayan

In the north the great altitude range of the Himalayas and the higher latitudes (up to 36° N) introduce new climatic and topographic features; the topography is far more fragmented; temperature and aspect, and hence insolation, become of great importance. There is a general distinction between the wetter east and the drier west, the change occurring at about 86–88° E; an outline of the zoning is shown in the tabular statement on page 88.

3A. *Wet hill forest (Himalayan)*. This is a fairly high (70–100 ft., 21–30 m.) and dense forest at 3,000–6,000 ft. on the Himalayan ranges east of 88° E, reaching rather higher levels in Assam. Evergreen oaks and chestnuts predominate, with some ash and beech. Sal may be found in suitable sites at lower levels, probably owing to biotic interference; climbers and epiphytes are common.

3B. *Subtropical pine forest*. This occupies a long belt from 73 to 88° E on the Himalayan slopes, mostly at 3,000–6,000 ft.: patches occur on the higher Khasi and Assam–Burma Hills. The dominant tree is chir or chil (*Pinus roxburghii* = *longifolia*), forming large pure stands; there is often a grassy floor with bulbous plants and little undergrowth, except for stunted evergreen oaks in wetter areas. Chir is a useful timber for furniture, boxes, building and railway sleepers; resin tapping is important, and there is a potential paper industry from offcuts. In the Khasi Hills and the Assam–Burma border area, the dominant species is *Pinus khasya*, at 4,000–5,000 ft.

3C. *Subtropical dry evergreen forest*. Like the tropical dry evergreen, this occurs in a restricted area, but at the opposite corner of the sub-continent. It is found at 1,500–5,000 ft. on the Himalayan foothills and the Salt Range in Kashmir and West Pakistan, with patches in Baluchistan: rainfall is 20–40 in. (508–1,016 mm.) and about a quarter of this falls in December through March; summers are very hot, and winters cold enough for frosts to be fairly common.

Wild olives (*Olea cuspidata*) are thought to represent climax forests; *Acacia modesta* is also common and seems to be a pioneer species establishing itself on

TABULAR STATEMENT OF HIMALAYAN FOREST ZONATION

W 40–80 in. ←——————————— 86–88° E———————————→ 80–100 in. + E
(1,016–2,032 mm.)   (2,032–2,540 mm.)

	Western vegetation	Altitude	Eastern vegetation	
		16,000 ft. (4,880 m.)		
			Rhododendrons plentiful	
		15,000 (4,570)	Junipers	
	Birch			
		14,000 (4,270)		ALPINE
	Junipers			
ALPINE		13,000 (3,960)		
	Silver Fir			
	Shrubby rhododendrons	12,000 (3,660)		
		11,000 (3,355)	CHIEFLY CONIFERS	
	CONIFERS *Abies pindrowi* 7,500–11,000		Junipers	UPPER TEMPERATE
		10,000 (3,050)	Rhododendrons, willows	
	Pinus excelsa 6,000–10,000	9,000 (2,745)	Bamboo (*Arundinaria racemosa*)	
	Cedrus deodara 6,000–8,500	8,000 (2,440)	BROAD-LEAVED Oaks, chestnuts,	
TEMPERATE	*Pinus longifolia* 3,000–7,000		maples, magnolias,	
	Yew, cypress BROAD-LEAVED Oaks spp. 4,000–12,000	7,000 (2,135)	laurels, alders, birches	
		6,000 (1,830)		LOWER TEMPERATE
	Walnuts, elms,			
	poplars, maples,	5,000 (1,525)		
	. . . . horse-chestnut			
		4,000 (1,220)	Mixed forests, often evergreen,	
	Rhodo. arboreum	3,000 (915)	with moist bamboo	SUB-TROPICAL AND TROPICAL
SUB-TROPICAL AND TROPICAL	Mixed deciduous, sal, dry bamboo (Siwaliks)	2,000 (610)		
	Riverain, savannah (terai)		Sal, mixed deciduous, tropical evergreen,	
	Dry thorn and scrub (extreme W)	1,000 (305)	riverain, moist savannah (terai)	

Adapted from Troup's Figs. 46 and 47 in Tansley and Chipp,
'Aims and Methods in the Study of Vegetation'.

open, exposed and skeletal soils. The forest is low and scrubby and has a general resemblance to Mediterranean maquis; though it is a climatic type, grazing and fire are certainly biotic controls over its limits and variations. Considerable tracts are covered by the dwarf creeping palm *Nannorhops*.

[3E. *Subtropical hill savannah, Arundinella type.*] Above 4,500 ft., from the western Himalaya to the Burmese border, grasslands are dominated by various species *Arundinella* and *Themeda*. The Shillong Plateau has considerable stretches of almost treeless grassland, biotically induced, with various species of *Saccharum, Themeda* and wild sorghum, as well as the tall *Imperata cylindrica*. Most of the grasses flower at the end of the rains or in the cold weather, and are subject to great fires in the hot weather.

4A. *Moist temperate forest.* This is the most widespread Himalayan type, extending over the whole length of the range in the 40–100-in. rainfall zone. There is a *wet temperate forest* at 6,000–9,500 ft. east of 88° E, a closed forest mainly of evergreen oaks, laurels and chestnuts, with undergrowth often dwarf bamboo, confined to the wetter areas. The moist temperate type ranges from 5,000 to 11,000 ft.; in the more humid east it occupies the outer ranges, and here broad-leaved evergreens are mixed with the dominant conifers, becoming fewer to the west. Aspect is of great importance: 'the conifers tend to avoid hot southern exposures, being there replaced by oak forests.'[21] Pines, cedars, silver firs, spruce are the most important trees, forming high but fairly open forest with shrubby undergrowth including oaks, rhododendrons, laurels and some bamboos. The forests have suffered greatly from fires and from lopping to clear land for grazing. West of 80° E deodar (*Cedrus deodara*) forms large pure stands in the intermediate ranges of moderate rainfall (45–70 in., 1,143–1,778 mm.); its fine, durable wood is much used for construction timber and railway sleepers.

4B. *Dry temperate forest.* In the inner Himalayan ranges, as in Kashmir and northern Sikkim, areas with under 40 in. precipitation (much of it as snow) carry a somewhat open and xerophytic forest. Conifers, including deodars and junipers, predominate, with scattered oak and ash; in places there is a *Quercus-Ilex* community with a shrub layer of plants such as *Daphne*, and a ground layer of various grasses and oak seedlings.

[4L. *Montane temperate grassland.*] At about 6,500 ft. decreasing temperatures bring in a grassland association in which representatives of subtropical genera such as *Arundinella, Pennisetum, Chryosopogon* and *Dichanthium* are mixed with more temperate forms such as species of *Deyeuxia, Stipa, Agrostis, Danthonia* and *Poa*. Like the alpine grassland higher up, these are used for transhumant herds and flocks; they may owe their preservation from overgrazing and erosion to the simple fact that weather conditions make all the year round grazing impossible; such uninterrupted grazing takes place in all other grasslands, though the proper period would be only three or four months.

Edaphic and Biotic Types. Cypress occurs on dry sites overlying limestone and on steep slopes protected from fire; the undergrowth is xerophytic. Deep moist recent soils may carry a temperate deciduous forest with mixed plane, birch,

---

[21] Champion, *op. cit.* 225.

elm and so on; riverain types include alder forest on new shingle deposits, and *Hippophae* scrub on stream gravels at 7,000–10,000 ft., forming thickets with some poplars and willows. Biotic types include various pine forests and oak scrubs, and *Thach* parkland which is formed by grazing, lopping and burning in oak forests until the undergrowth is replaced by a close sward with scattered trees. Most of these types are widely distributed in suitable sites, and the vegetation mosaic in the topographical conditions of the Himalayas is naturally often very complex; it is impossible in a general review to do justice to its permutations.

5A. *Alpine forest.* The vegetation of the Himalayas from about 9,500 to 11,500–12,000 ft. is largely a dense shrubby forest of silver firs, junipers, pines, birches and rhododendrons, the last growing to over 30 ft. high. Most of the trees are crooked and tend to branch low down on the bole.

[5F. *Alpine grasslands.*] Above 7,000–8,000 ft., the temperate grassland (4L) gradually gives way to pastures dominated by temperate forms such as those mentioned above and species of *Poa*, *Glyceria* and *Festuca*, among other genera. Drier areas, such as parts of Kulu and Kangra, have xerophytic variants which include genera (such as *Themeda*, *Dichanthium*, *Cenchrus*) and even species common in the subtropical and even the dry tropical grasslands. All the alpine grasslands are used for extensive transhumant grazing.

Alpine Edaphic and Biotic Types. Deodar forests seem to be peculiarly and quite permanently adapted to Himalayan floodplains at any altitude between 4,000 and 11,000 ft., while blue pines seem equally at home on the lacustrine Karewas terraces of the Vale of Kashmir. High level blue pine forests occur on moraine and similar loose detrital material, especially where the progression has been set back by new snow or earth slides; they are rather ephemeral forests quickly dispersed by fire. The Alpine forest grades into a low evergreen scrub, and this again, on the drier Tibetan side with under 15 in. (264 mm.) precipitation, into very open xerophytic bush, with willows along the streams. Edaphic factors, including soil moisture from glaciers and periglacial phenomena, may be responsible for tracts of birch–rhododendron and *Pinus excelsa* seral to silver fir–birch, especially on moraines; the climax may be dominated by oaks. Where the forests give way to transhumant pastures, their limits are biotic, and biotic factors are also important in the scrubs.

Bamboos and palms

Two groups of plants are of such peculiar importance in the life of India as to deserve a special note; these are the bamboos and the palms.

The bamboos are of course really grasses; they are found throughout India except in the extra-Peninsular mountains west of the Sutlej. The commonest and most gregarious of the hundred and more species is *Dendrocalamus strictus*, with stems 30–50 ft. high and 1–3 in. diameter. This is an 'all purpose' bamboo: huts and scaffolding, basketry and mats, sticks, furniture, household and agricultural implements; the leaves are used for fodder and the stems and rhizomes are burnt. In wetter Bengal and Assam it is replaced by *D. hamiltonii*, a larger plant used among other things for timber-rafting. Also in Assam is *Melocanna bambusoides*, forming immense thickets like giant hay-fields on abandoned areas of shifting cultivation: this secondary growth is practically impenetrable and vast areas of good forest on the hills of Chittagong and Arakan have been replaced by *Melocanna*. In accessible areas, however, it is exploited as a raw material for paper-making, and is the basis of the East Pakistan paper industry at Karnaphuli. In southern India the thorny *Bambusa arundinacea* is common, often cultivated in magnificent clumps up to 100 ft. (30 m.) high.

In the Shan States and many other parts of southeast Asia, including southern China, bamboo enters into almost everything in daily life, including the soup, and one might almost speak of an essentially bamboo-based culture. Probably no part of India, except the Assamese hills, has such a well-developed 'pure' bamboo culture, but the wide usefulness of the plant is attested by the ubiquity with which it is cultivated in village groves. Its quick regrowth provides an immense resource for the expanding Indian paper industry; a resource, however, which is not inexhaustible and needs proper conservation. A possible future use is as a source of industrial cellulose. The output of bamboos from Indian groves and forests must be reckoned in hundreds of millions of stems yearly.[22]

Of the palms, there are eight wild species of the date (*Phoenix*), as well as the cultivated date which is grown especially in the Punjab and Sind but has nothing like the importance it possesses in southwest Asia. The common wild date (*P. sylvestris*) 'is one of the most conspicuous trees in India. . . . In some regions it is almost the only tree visible . . . on salt lands and about springs in the Deccan, forming a gregarious forest growth.'[23] The stems of the wild date are often tapped for the juice, which is turned into gur or a kind of toddy (cf. above 84).

The coconut (*Cocos nucifera*) is found all round the coasts, but is especially important in Kerala, its greatest concentration, the Cauvery and Godavari deltas, and East Pakistan; and inland, it is widely grown in central Mysore. Its scores of uses are far too many to enumerate, but we may note here that the densest rural populations are found where paddy and coconut are the leading crops, so that not even the village site is unproductive (cf. below, 679). The toddy or Palmyra palm (*Borassus flabellifer*) occurs both wild and planted in most plains regions, especially perhaps in the drier southeastern coastlands, though it is also important in Bihar. On the sandy *teri* tracts of Tirunelveli in the extreme south it forms forests which, while primarily important for tapping, can be managed for timber. Palmyra sap is the chief source of toddy, the only spirituous drink of the rural masses, and with tens of millions of trees scattered over the countryside, liquor control is likely to be difficult. Probably, however,

[22] There is a comprehensive view of bamboo and its uses in J. Oliver, 'Bamboo as an economic resource in southern Asia', *Geography*, 41 (1956), 49–56.
[23] J. S. Gamble, *A Manual of Indian Timbers* (2nd ed., 1902), 731.

more is used in the making of gur. An important cultivated palm is the areca (*Areca catechu*), grown in such hot and humid regions as Kerala, Bengal and Assam. The nuts, which hang down in long strings and bunches, are used for necklaces and other ornaments; cut and polished their reticulate convolutions are very handsome. But its most important use is for chewing with lime wrapped in the leaves of the betal vine; this is the *pan* responsible for the great gouts of red saliva which disfigure so many streets and buildings.[24] *Nannor-hops*, branched and with a half-creeping habit, covers large areas in the Salt Range, the Kurram valley, and Baluchistan with its matted thickets; the leaf-buds and fruits are edible, the seeds used for rosaries which used to be exported (through the one-time Omani port of Gwadar) to Mecca. In the jungles are many climbing palms (*Calamus* spp.), often thorny, supplying canes and rattans. The estuarine *Nipa fruticans* has already been mentioned.

Nearly all the palms are valuable sources of matting and thatch; many can be used for light constructions, house-posts, water-troughs, and so on; and while coir, from the coconut, is the best-known palm fibre, it is far from being the only one. The sheaths of the leaves, like those of bamboo stems, are used as a wrapping material. In earlier cultures palm leaves were used as a writing surface, especially those of areca and palmyra. Most important for this purpose was the Talipot (*Corypha umbraculifera*), the largest of Indian palms, sometimes over 100 ft. high. It is common in Kerala and Kanara, planted in Bengal. The leaves, often 10 ft. in diameter, are used as mats, fans and umbrellas. This is indeed one of the most magnificent of tropical trees.

Importance of the forest cover; climate and erosion

Much has been written in India of the direct climatic influence of forests, and they are of vital importance in increasing the effectiveness of precipitation by checking run-off, maintaining the water-table, and increasing humidity by transpiration. The problem of rehabilitating India's forests, which in most of the more accessible areas have been virtually ruined, is extremely serious.[25] In the early 19th century the increasing demands of the towns, and later of the railways and of the growing population for arable land, led to a very rapid deforestation: the Company's governments seemed simply unaware that a problem existed – there was obviously a great deal of jungle. . . . The first (ineffectual) step towards conservation was made in 1855, and in 1878 a Forest Act set out the general policy of reservation and protection. This was to assure the timber supply

---

[24] 'Betel-nut' is a misnomer. *Pan* has astringent qualities and its chewing, in moderation, is probably mildly beneficial. It is not unpalatable, tasting rather like tooth-paste, but very salivatory, and thus may be a source of acute embarrassment to the polite Westerner, whether the disposal problem be his own or another's. Only when chewed with tobacco, as in some areas, is it clearly a carcinogen.

[25] Sir H. Glover, *Erosion in the Punjab* (Govt of Punjab, Lahore, 1946); R. M. Gorrie, 'Countering desiccation in the Punjab', *GR* 38 (1948), 30–40; A. P. F. Hamilton, 'Siwalik erosion', *Himalayan Jnl* 7 (1935), 87–102.

– still very low per capita – as well as for catchment protection. Despite the efforts of the Indian Forest Service, however, deterioration can scarcely be said to have been kept within bounds, in face of the continuous population increase.

Erosion is severe in almost all States, and it has been conservatively estimated that some 150,000,000 acres (60,700,000 ha.) are affected more or less seriously. In the Punjab Siwaliks, indiscriminate lumbering and charcoal burning, over-grazing (especially by goats), and annual fires produced conditions in which often torrential rains gouged out ravines hundreds of feet deep, and large areas in the plains were ruined by sandy outwash, changes in stream-courses, and a falling water-table as seepage from the hills diminished (Fig. 18.1). Progress has now been made both in checking erosion and in reclamation; farther east the Siwalik forests in Uttar Pradesh are less damaged, and, despite recent inroads, the forests of Nepal are likely to remain a protection for some considerable time.

In the wetter and less-populated eastern Himalaya and the Assam–Burma Hills erosion is not so spectacular, but a new factor is introduced by *jhuming*, the shifting agriculture of the hillmen, also widespread in the hillier parts of central and Peninsular India. The more valuable deciduous monsoon forests are more affected than the rain-forests, and as it is generally easier to clear new forest (which is more fertile and produces more ash) than to return to old ground, large areas become covered with secondary growth, usually dense and useless even for grazing: bracken, the tangled bush *Eupatorium odoratum*, dense thorny thickets of *Lantana*, bamboo brakes. While it is now recognized that *jhuming* is not so black as it was once painted, it does require careful regulation, difficult to enforce, if it is not to lead to serious erosion and forest deterioration. With increasing population and official encouragement, the tribes may change to settled agriculture, but for this they must have land and this means a demand for opening forest reserves.

Throughout central and southern India forest control is rendered extremely difficult by shifting cultivation, the complex intermingling of forest, often poor and open, with village lands, and immemorial rights of grazing, lopping and collecting all sorts of minor products. Hence much land once decently wooded has now become a mere scrubby waste, water-tables have been lowered, sheet-erosion is very prevalent. Spectacular gully-erosion has formed badland belts along the Yamuna, the Chambal and the edges of the Punjab doabs. Contour-bunding, afforestation, excluding of grazing (leading to dense grass cover which can be *cut* for fodder), the introduction of the *kudzu* bush as a soil-binder and for fodder, have produced some effect; but much remains to be done.

The importance of the close linkage of grazing, fuel and manure problems cannot be overemphasized. There is a vicious circle: lack of firewood in the all but treeless plains enforces the use of cattle-dung as fuel instead of manure; grazing areas are extremely limited and the pressure of the cattle population on scraps of village waste inhibits forest growth. To replace cow-dung by wood fuel would call for nearly 25,000,000 acres (10,000,000 ha.) of quick-growing plantations on a 10-year rotation: a theoretical solution virtually impossible to realize.[26] The use of cow-dung to produce domestic gas, retaining the sludge as manure, may in time provide a way out (cf. below, 265, 291).

Ecology of the plains

As a coda to this discussion we may take the plains of Uttar Pradesh as a sample of the present ecology of a densely-settled area.[27] It was originally densely forested: in the 16th–17th centuries, wild elephants, buffaloes, bison, rhinoceros, lions and tigers were hunted in the Ganga–Yamuna doab. Some of these animals have disappeared, such as the bison, the rhinoceros (surviving under protection, in Assam), and the lion, whose last Indian home is the Gir sanctuary in Kathiawad. The rest have been enormously reduced in numbers, but with fewer predators and food-competitors wild pigs, small deer, rodents, and monkeys (these with a certain religious sanction) have improved at least their relative position; and all are highly destructive to crops.

Away from the terai and the riverain strips of khair, sissoo, and tamarind, very little woodland survives. There are patches, partly planted, of useful trees, dhak (*Butea frondosa*), mahua, and nim (*Melia indica*); the first is more durable in water than out of it, and is used for well-piling, water-coops, and so on; nim is a sacred tree, used for images as well as ordinary furniture and tools, with a variety of pharmacological uses. But the commonest tree, at least in the west, is babul. This acacia is not palatable to cattle, but its seeds are spread by sheep and goats, and it is more likely to expand than to contract as a result of grazing. Another plant highly resistant to cattle is *Zizyphus* spp., which forms dense masses of thorn-bush. Along with deforestation there go lessened soil-humidity and, owing to loss of transpiration, micro-climatological desiccation. Such secondary wild or waste vegetation as can exist is thus markedly xerophytic, such as the 'dry meadow' of western Uttar Pradesh, which with overgrazing breaks down to coarse tussocks, useless annual grasses, and a few rosette-plants.

A different type of ecological change is the provision of a free field for indigenous or introduced pest plants. The coarse *kans* grass, particularly prolific on the borders of Uttar and Madhya Pradesh, seizes upon fallow and may be so densely matted as to inhibit ploughing, though after a cycle of 10 to 15 years it dies away and the land can be reclaimed. In Bengal the water-hyacinth, introduced as an ornamental pond-plant, has completely blocked scores or even hundreds of miles of minor streams, dislocating the drainage, and it may even overrun flooded paddy fields; and its possible economic uses are a poor return for the difficulty of holding it within bounds.

Mukerjee sums up:

---

[26] For the interesting calculation, see Legris, *op. cit.* 337.
[27] Based on R. K. Mukerjee, *The Regional Balance of Man* (Madras, 1938), Chs VI and VII. There are many thumb-nail sketches in the Gazetteers.

'. . . the vegetation is now rather delicately balanced against man at about the dry grass-land or the thorn-scrub stage. The soil over most of the Indo-Gangetic plain seems to be supporting about all the human and bovine life that is possible under existing methods of exploitation. . . . Relaxation of pressure immediately results in a movement of vegetation towards the climax. But no relaxation is possible under present conditions. Dry grass-land and thorn-scrub formations remain practically stationary.'

And if, as he thought, the plains were demographically saturated when he wrote, they are super-saturated now. The picture is depressing.

II. SOILS

Introduction

In a general view of the soils geography of a large region such as the Indian sub-continent, it is wholly proper to consider first and even mainly the broad pattern of soil orders and sub-orders largely related by pedologists to macro-regional and regional complexes of climate and vegetation, slope and regolith. Some more detailed pedological surveys will be discussed in this chapter, for their value in critical appraisal of the broader classifications discussed, but as in the earlier editions of this book the regional chapters will be the main recipients for some of the myriad local names for soils and the shrewd empirical accounts of their differential productivity described in the District Gazetteers and in the Settlement Reports assessing the land revenue for a certain period for each District. In many places there is nothing to replace these fascinating accounts for intimate local detail, based in close observation through centuries of intensive farming.[28]

Up to the 1930s – and not uncommonly since – the traditional classification of the soils was in four main categories: alluvium, regur (black cotton soils), red soils and laterite. Alluvium was distinguished according to the main rivers depositing it, along with coastal alluvium, while there was a useful recognition of calcareous soils, soils including a concretionary layer a few inches deep and saline soils.

In 1932 came Z. J. Schokalskaya's gallant but premature effort to synthesize existing knowledge in the framework of Russian pedological principles. The key to Fig. 3.4 is sufficient indication of her lines of thought. While there were inevitably grave flaws in her interpretation, such as the wide area of 'tropical and sub-tropical dry steppe on older alluvium and on hard rocks' from the Bastar highlands to the Maikal hills, it was a remarkable achievement for a

[28] V. L. S. P. Rao, 'A note on soil classification', *Bombay Geog. Mag.* 4/1 (1956), 21–25 contains an interesting table comparing Revenue classification ('local classification') with laboratory classifications based on mechanical analysis of top-soils.

E

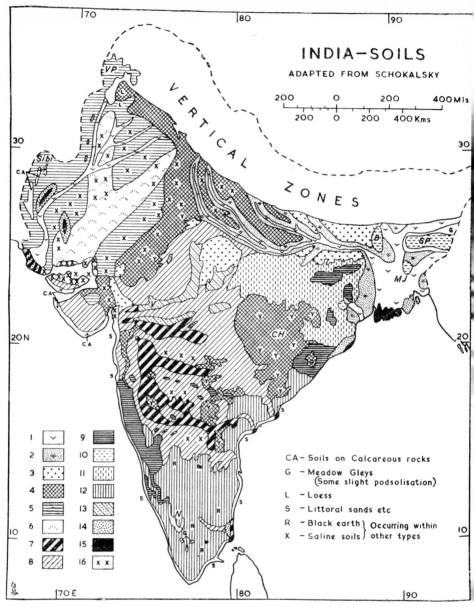

FIG 3.4 SOIL TYPES. Adapted from Schokalskaya. 1, alluvial, traces of bog process, on newer alluvium; 2, meadow type on older alluvium; 3, prairie type; 4, tropical and sub-trop. dry steppe on older alluvium and hard rocks (Y = yellow soils); 5, serozems, often saline, some loess; 6, sandy semi-desert serozems; 7, deep regur; 8, medium-light black soils (incl. re-deposited regur in valleys); 9, laterite (high and low) and some higher lateritics; 10, lateritic; 11, sub-trop. red, less leached; 12, trop. red; 13, brown under deciduous forest, slightly or not leached; 14, swamp, peat-bog, and muck; 15, solonchaks; 16, solonetz. B, Barind; CH, Chhattisgarh; MJ, Madhupur Jungle; N, Nilgiris; SP, Shillong Plateau; V. Vindhyan Hills; VP, Vale of Peshawar.

scholar working abroad, and still stimulating today, despite the changes in pedological science in the generation since she wrote.

The Soil Survey of India was set up in 1956, and it has done a great deal of useful work. The large contiguous tracts for which soil surveys have been completed are some of the main river valley project areas such as the Damodar basin and the Hirakud command area. Other areas have been surveyed, but they tend to be in small scattered plots, apparently selected haphazard – but not at random in the statistical sense – or for convenience in access. Many of the studies also suffer from the drawback that they are excessively purist in approach, selecting mainly, or even exclusively, soil borings for profile study which are 'natural' or as little as possible affected by human activity, and avoiding say borings from paddy fields. In recent years, however, there are moves towards a less selective and purist approach, in which the mapping of soil erosion, for instance, is regarded as an integral part of general soil survey, and not something that belongs to a separate department, though soil conservation is in fact handled by a separate government organization.

It is significant that the soil map in the 1957 Preliminary Hindi Edition of the National Atlas of India is simpler and less ambitious than is Schokalskaya's map, though if the time had been ripe for an advance on her techniques this would surely have been attempted; however, it adds indications of soil texture (in overprinted colour screens) and maps the wide areas subject to accelerated soil erosion of varying severity, notably in problem areas now subject to soil conservation measures such as the Chambal valley and the Siwalik Hills. Here we have generalized from these and other sources on a rough working map, Fig. 3.5, to assist the following discussion; soil texture is treated in an expanded caption opposite, and in the text. While it would have been simpler and far safer to accompany these maps with an empirical description of the soil distribution patterns, an attempt will be made in the following pages to interpret the areal patterns of the National Atlas soils map in the light of modern soil classifications, notably the United States Department of Agriculture (USDA) 7th Approximation of 1960, and the attempt in 1962 to establish an internationally acceptable classification of the soils of southeast Asia by Moormann and Dudal of FAO. The writer has found that, working from all available material, Indian soils agree broadly with these.

The sources just cited are studies in pedological taxonomy, whereas soils geography is properly a correlative study of the areal distribution patterns of soils. While it would be as premature to attempt a soils geography of the subcontinent today as was Schokalskaya's pioneer pedological study in 1932, some skeletal geographical analysis will be offered. In particular an attempt will be made to complement the National Atlas soils map – interpreted thus at hazard in the light of modern sources – by some local studies illustrating the gain in understanding if one can gain detailed knowledge of repetitive soil patterns within soil macro-regions (corresponding to soil orders and sub-orders). These

97

studies will be approached from the point of view of Milne's catenary concept.[29] By implication, the catenary concept offers an opportunity for reassessment of major soil regions by building up inductively from numerous catenary cross-sections. This is at least an alternative or complementary method pending the detailed soil mapping of the whole land surface.

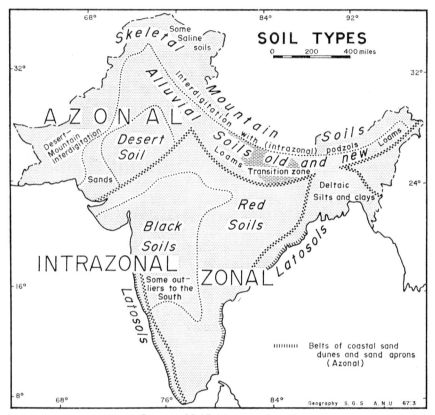

FIG 3.5 *Sources: NAI*, Pl. 10 and earlier maps.

[29] A. G. Milne, *A Provisional Soil Map of East Africa with Explanatory Memoir*, Amani Memoirs, East Africa Agricultural Research Station, 1936. See *GR 26* (1936), 522–3. Milne pointed out from East Africa repetitive patterns which may be studied for instance by following the sequence of soils from the break of slope between say a plateau of red tropical soil (to use a neutral and empirical term meantime) and the steep slope of a valley, often crowned by a laterite cornice, which then becomes less steep after the fashion of a hanging chain or rope. The only example found in the literature for India and Pakistan so far has been a comparative study of a long forested tract with a cultivated alluvial tract west of Kanpur: A. N. Pathak, Harishanker and P. K. Mukherjee, *Jnl of Soil & Water Conservation in India*, Hazaribagh, 10/1–2 (1962), 7–65 (hereafter cited as *Jnl Soil & Water Cons.*).

FIG 3.5 SOIL TYPES AND TEXTURE. These Soil Type zones of course include intricate inter-digitation of soil type and also of soil texture. Some examples are given on pp. 108–13. Meantime some regional generalizations about soil texture may be useful, bearing in mind, however, that in detail complex inter-digitation must again be expected.

Mountain (Skeletal) Soils naturally vary greatly with the local rocks, and from the stony sandy hillfoot fans and slope colluvium of the Northwestern Hills or the Aravallis to a more clayey product of mass-movement in the humid south and east of the Himalayas and in Assam.

The Alluvium-based Soils of the Indus–Ganga–Brahmaputra plains, the East Coast deltas and the smaller stretches of floodplain, terrace and deltaic and lagoon alluvium of the rest of Peninsular India vary greatly, in depth and on the present surface, with the alternation of deposition conditions between coarser and finer alluvium and as between older and very recent alluvium. But there is much sandy soil, coarser or finer, in the Lower Indus plains, and rather more loams and clay loams in Punjab and the western Ganga plains; the loams increase and the sands decrease in the central Ganga plains. West of the Transition Zone shown, there is much calcareous *kankar* pan, while irrigation in recent generations has brought waterlogging and saline encrustation to many of the heavier soils in relatively low-lying areas, subject to seepage from canals and lacking in adequate drainage ditches and canals. Farther east in the Ganga–Brahmaputra plains, in more humid atmospheric and soil climates, textural sequences are finer throughout, from loams to very fine silty clays, with some lateritization; and throughout the vast alluvial plains, 'coarse' alluvium has quite a local connotation, much coarser where a major river emerges from the mountain arcs or from the Deccan plateau, finer out into the plain, and more so in the Bengal (and East Coast) deltas. Old alluvium in the Bengal delta and in humid coastal tracts has much lateritic clay.

The Black Soils have the predominantly clay character associated with the soil cracking and 'self-ploughing' of the hot dry weather and the viscous to glutinous stickiness of the west monsoon period. They are less viscous in hillfoot areas with an admixture of slope collumium, and in the redeposited alluvial black soils of river terraces and floodplains.

The Red Soils have mainly a sandy to loamy texture, with rather gravelly sands on upper slopes, then sandy soils, then deeper loamy soils on lower slopes, and loams or sometimes rather clayey soils on the valley bottoms. River terraces and floodplains, and deltas large and small, bring inter-digitation with the alluvium-based soils noted above, and sensitively mapped by Simkins (*op. cit.* p. 693). Within the great Red Soil zone of mainly Peninsular India, there are also the clays of the true laterites – the high laterites of the summit planes of the Western Ghats and of some plateau areas like that near Bidar in northeastern Mysore, and low laterites like those originally described by Buchanan in Kerala or on the low lava ridges running parallel to the coast south of Bombay. There are also a number of indeterminate red, yellowish and whitish clay soils, particularly in the perhumid region of Southwest India discussed in the text in relation to possible identification of the soil type as a latosol.

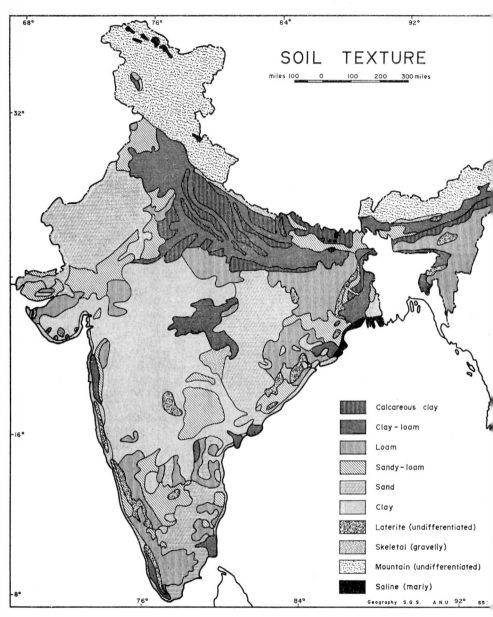

FIG 3.6 HIMALAYAN SOIL AND FOREST ZONES

SOIL TEXTURE

miles 100   0   100   200   300 miles

Calcareous clay
Clay - loam
Loam
Sandy - loam
Sand
Clay
Laterite (undifferentiated)
Skeletal (gravelly)
Mountain (undifferentiated)
Saline (marly)

Geography S.G.S.   A.N.U   65:

The soils map in the National Atlas, a critique and synthesis

Here we shall review the National Atlas map of soils in the light of the older pedological work of Schokalskaya as well as the more recent work of Moormann and Dudal and the United States Department of Agriculture.

The National Atlas has two zonal soils I, laterite soil and II, red soil. The laterite soil appears to be Buchanan's laterite[30] rather than a true soil profile – i.e. an often rather porous clay, dominantly hydroxides of iron and aluminium, hardening to brick-like consistency on exposure to the weather. The distribution is mainly in the Western Ghats and Cardamoms; apparently high-lying in the northern half of the Eastern Ghats and on the eastern margins of the Chota Nagpur plateau, which also has a patch of laterite farther west in the Hazaribagh Range; in Assam; in a few patches round Kathiawad; and in two areas in the centre of the Peninsula, north of Bangalore and west of Hyderabad. These occurrences differ widely in their present climate–vegetation complexes; many lack a complete soil profile, the laterite being found (often quarried) near the surface. The Schokalskaya–Spate map specifically includes high and low laterites, and the areal distribution is somewhat different, but similar arguments seem to apply. It seems almost inevitable that the 'laterite soils' as mapped should be regarded as the laterite horizons of truncated soil profiles, partly denuded by erosion on uplift, and fossils or relics of a past climate–vegetation-soil complex including deep soil profiles with a laterite horizon. In places, however, they appear to be alluvial or redeposited. If protected from erosion these soils are far from worthless, but the humus content is confined to a shallow top layer, as the forest trees are shallow rooted: their removal endangers the humus content and regeneration is difficult.[31]

The Red Soils of the National Atlas map are as much of an omnibus category as ever, comparable with the hedging bet of the 'lateritic soils' classification of some years ago. The Schokalskaya–Spate map does attempt to break up this very large area into tropical red soils, sub-tropical red – less leached – soils, sub-tropical and tropical dry steppe soils on hard rocks, with much yellow soil, and once again, 'lateritic soil'. In the earlier editions of this book attention was drawn to the improbability of the large tract of sub-tropical steppe soils in the northeast of the Peninsula, and it is significant that the editor of the National Atlas has judged that there was insufficient detailed knowledge to justify any subdivision. Do the more modern classifications, approaching through soil profile analysis, offer any help? It seems likely that between the Western Ghats and the sea there may lie a coastal belt of humid climates, natural vegetation

[30] F. Buchanan, *A Journey from Madras through the Countries of Mysore Canara and Malabar*, 1807; cf. C. G. Stephens, 'Laterite at the type locality, Angadipuram, Kerala, India', *Jnl Soil Sci.* 12 (1963), 214–17.

[31] G. Aubert, 'Soil with ferruginous or ferralitic crusts of tropical regions', *Soil Science*, 95 (1963), 235–42; M. N. Ramasawamy and D. R. Gouda, 'The humus content of lateritic soils in the tropical evergreen forests of Mysore', *Indian Forester*, Dehra Dun, 82/8 (1956) 395–8.

approaching rain-forest, and of dark red and reddish brown latosols or locally of red-yellow latosols in the classification of Moormann and Dudal. This was of course evolved for southeast Asia, and one can only argue from climatic and biogeographic analogues. Many of the soil profiles one sees in the field, in recent roadside cuttings and the like, seem to correspond well with their description of deeply weathered and leached soils, with a low content of primary minerals and the clay fraction dominated by kaolinite and sesquioxides, the profile generally deep and uniform with little horizon differentiation. The surface layers are of low organic content and the soils are fairly acid (about 4·5–6·5). It is notable, and confusing, that Buchanan's laterite is not regarded as a marked feature of these soils. It is true that in the hot humid zones of south and southeast Asia, occurrences of Buchanan's laterite, indeed of any well-marked C horizon, are surprisingly rare in the field if one approaches field exposures without any preconceived ideas on pedogenesis. But the attachment of the name latosol to soils in which laterite proper seldom occurs is unfortunate; the only justification seems to be that within the same general area there do occur many of the known occurrences of laterite proper, including that originally observed by Buchanan. But presumably their origin lies either with a different climate–vegetation complex or with a different parent material in solid rock or regolith (maybe with a different *soil* climate).

In the USDA 7th Approximation these soils would be classed as oxisols (soils dominated by oxides), of the sub-order udox (an oxide soil in a humid climate); bizarre as the vocabulary is at first, one can see by comparison with Moormann and Dudal the advantages of a fresh approach, empirical and descriptive rather than prematurely genetic in concept.[32] If Buchanan's laterite does not occur in the latosols or oxisols, where does it belong? In the scheme of Moormann and Dudal laterite proper, and the deep white or whitish-grey B horizon often streaked horizontally or reticulated horizontally and vertically by red iron-rich bands, belong to the red-yellow podsolic soils or the grey podsolic soils. In the USDA classification, these correspond to the ultisol order (ultimate soils), mainly in the sub-order ochrult (pale or light-coloured ultisols), but some with some characteristics of oxisols (see above) and some of alfisols (soils dominated by iron and aluminium derivatives). These soils have a humiferous A_1 horizon, a somewhat paler and more leached A_2 horizon, and normally 1–2 m. of pale, blocky Bt horizon with clay coatings on the peds, and low SiO_2/R_2O_3 or SiO_2/Al_2O_3 ratios (i.e. a very heavily leached horizon under conditions of very effective chemical weathering resulting in the leaching out of silicates and rutiles). There are often one or more C horizons of red Buchanan's laterite, rich in iron and aluminium oxides (Fe_2O_3 or Al_2O_3).

[32] Soil Conservation Service, U.S. Department of Agriculture, *Soil Classification: a Comprehensive System*, 7th Approximation, Washington, 1960. See Addendum for a note of the derivations of the mainly classically-based technical vocabulary suggested: this is an interesting nomenclature even if some of the names come strangely to the eye and tongue.

These soils occur over a very wide range of climate from about 40 in. (1,016 mm.) mean annual rainfall (about 60 in. (1,524 mm.) in equatorial and sub-equatorial latitudes) upwards to very wet climates indeed. They seem to form especially on acid to medium-basic parent material, whether bedrock or regolith, and this may account for their inter-digitation with the latosols or oxisols, and they may in fact paradoxically contribute the true laterite to the latosol zone. In wetter climates they are deeper and more acid than in the less humid areas. Schokalskaya found only limited evidence of podzolization, in meadow gleys, mainly round the Assam hills, and in the Nilgiris and other high areas in the south. It is possible that considerable parts of peninsular India, mapped as in the Red soil zone, have or originally had what Moormann and Dudal class as Non-calcic Brown Soils – rather shallow kaolin-rich clays under open forest in climates with a severe dry season and under 60 in. mean annual rainfall (perhaps a little less in northern India?). This soil-type is described as usually uncultivated in southeast Asia; in peninsular India it may have been cultivated for millennia and over-cultivated for centuries, and so difficult to identify – but degenerate profiles may be important. Erosion is widespread and remedial measures, while understood, are difficult to put into practice; they may involve treatment of entire catchment areas, closing of grazing lands or expensive works.[33]

The National Atlas map distinguishes two intra-Zonal Soil types – III, Black Soil and IIIA, Podzol Soil. The latter appears to be confined to the lower parts of the Himalayas, neither alluvial like the Vale of Kashmir, saline like some of the intermont basins of northern Kashmir, nor mountain soils like most of the mountain chains. Podzolization is not here regarded as an important pedogenetic process in the plains or in peninsular India, in contrast to the views of Moormann and Dudal.

The Black Soils are mapped as intra-zonal within the Red Soil zone, and noted in the text of the Atlas as mainly on the Deccan traps but also found on gneisses and schists in the Krishna–Tungabhadra basin and south of the Vaigai basin in Madras. By far the largest part of the Black Soils are mapped as clays, but relatively small areas are distinguished as clay loams, loams and sandy loams. The clay loams are mainly in an area marginal to the Black Soils around the upper Narmada and the upper Tapti, while the loams and sandy loams are apparently related to alluvial tracts, though not all actual occurrences of these are mapped. The Schokalskaya–Spate map distinguishes deep *regur* (the indigenous name for black cotton soil) in the western Deccan and in a series of belts about WNW–ESE across the west-central part of the Peninsula. The rest is classed as medium-

[33] For illustration of the complexity of the problem see (1) C. S. Pichamathu, *Soil Erosion and its Prevention* (Mysore Govt Dept Bangalore, 1951), a first rate analysis of types, causes and remedies; (2) B. C. Acharya, 'Nature and extent of soil erosion in parts of Kalahandi Dt, Orissa', *GRI* 20 (1958), 93–96, a specific case of soil erosion linked with shifting cultivation; (3) K. Venkoba Rao, 'Need for pasture development in Bellary Dt', *Jnl Soil & Water Cons.* 7/4–5 (1959), 91–98 indicates the effects of closing an area on the regeneration and soil patterns.

light black soils (including re-deposited *regur* in valleys); the occurrences in the southern part of the Peninsula are not mapped. Much of the Vindhya and nearby hills and of the Mahadeo Ranges are mapped as 'brown soils, under deciduous forest, slightly or not leached'; this differentiation seems of value, and might be linked with Moormann and Dudal's (Acid) Brown Forest Soils (in the USDA classification in the order of Inceptisols, i.e. soils in the stage of inception, sub-order ochrept, i.e. pale inceptisols, with some in the order of mollisols, i.e. soft soils).[34] The soils are normally up to 31·5 in. (800 mm.) deep, with a lighter and brighter brown B horizon under a darker A or A_p horizon, and pH values usually over 5 and often over 6 on parent material intermediate between acid and basic rocks. They occur in rainfalls of wide range, from some 24 to 120 in. (610–2,748 mm.), and it may well be that it is soil of this type that one has seen on forested slopes in western Mysore; in fact there may be important occurrences of these forest soils within the Red Soil zone wherever the forest cover is considerable.

Moormann and Dudal term the black soils grumosol (viscous soil); in the USDA classification they fall within the order vertisols (soils which are inverted, in the well-known 'self-ploughing' process of exchange of top-soil and sub-soil through cracking in the dry season, with soil fragments falling from near the surface down the cracks to a depth of one or two metres); the sub-order is normally aquert (vertisols associated with wetting) on flat land, with ustert or dry vertisols on undulating terrain. These soils are the widely known clays, dark brown to black (darker on flat or relatively low-lying areas), usually rather poor in organic matter, often strongly granular, and with an A horizon usually 2–4 in. (5–10 mm.) deep giving way to an AC then a C horizon, the sub-surface horizons often with prismatic pod-like blocks. Clays are generally of the montmorillonite group, strongly swelling and shrinking with changes in moisture content; hence the very marked cracking and fissuring of the dry season already noted. There seems to be a general correlation with rainfall conditions ranging around semi-aridity; grumosol pedogenesis may occur more readily on basic parent rock like the Tertiary basalts of the Deccan, which underlie much the greater part of these soils; considerable tracts are on acid igneous rocks like gneisses, and there the clay minerals differ in detail, while the soils are on the more acid side of the range encountered in general – about 6·0–7·5 on the surface, 7·8–8·5 in depth, but under 7·0 over acid rocks. Naturally a very wide range of conditions is seen in the field, from the special type of alluvium of redeposited *regur* noted in Schokalskaya (and earlier by Simkins, for instance), to the stony *regurs* near the foot of a basalt scarp which are presumably a special case of entisol (recent soil) or inceptisols (soils near the stage of inception) – or mixed soils (category VI in terms of the National Atlas map).

[34] Within these the next smaller category, the great (soil) groups include the eutrochrepts ('fertile' pale inceptisols, i.e. with high base exchange capacity), dystrochrepts ('infertile' pale inceptisols, i.e. with low base exchange capacity) and some ustochrepts ('burnt' pale inceptisols, i.e. in climates with dry hot summers).

The azonal soil types of the National Atlas map are: IV, alluvial soil (new); V, alluvial soil (old); VI, colluvial and skeletal (mixed) soil; VII, coastal soil; VII, saline soil; IX, desert soil and X, mountain soil. As noted earlier, the Atlas maps broad patterns of textural differences; these are very important, here as elsewhere, to the man on the land, and some are noted in our Fig. 3.5 and its caption, and to some extent in the ensuing discussion of inter-digitation of soil types (p. 108). Meantime types IV to X are treated in a different order.

Category VI, the colluvial and skeletal (mixed) soils are clearly very important. Their origin implies a close relation to parent material, in which sense they are azonal, though there may be an intra-zonal element by admixture with the prevailing zonal soil type. The main area of this soil type shown in the National Atlas is in the Wainganga basin in central India, quite conformably with its irregular and undulating topography (see p. 707); but these colluvial soils are of much wider significance, even though they can not be mapped as yet for the whole country. To appreciate their importance one should compare the broad areas of the zonal and intra-zonal types with a relief map say of part of peninsular India, on as large a scale as possible, not smaller than 1:1,000,000, and consider that a belt of colluvial and mixed soil lies along each scarp-foot. Some of these belts may have or have had profiles similar to Moormann and Dudal's (Acid) Brown Forest Soils, discussed earlier. Most of these soils, however, would lie within the Regosols of Moormann and Dudal, in their sub-category of variously textured slope colluvium, mostly sandy loams, clay loams or sandy clay loams, but extending to sandy and gravelly soils, and even stony 'lithosolic regosols'. All these would be entisols (recent soils) in the USDA classification. The discussion of these soils will be taken up again later in the chapter, in relation to the inter-digitation of the several soil types, and the catenary concept.

Category V alluvial (old) soil of the National Atlas is also an important type. It is shown mainly along the northern and southern hillfoot zones of the Ganga and Brahmaputra plains, and along the western margin of the Bengal delta (the eastern margin is in East Pakistan). Comparison with climatic and vegetation maps suggests that there must be major differences in present pedogenetic processes over such a large and diverse area – apart from differences in the parent material provided by the alluvium, like the lime-rich deposits of the Gandak in Uttar Pradesh.[35] In the west, these soils are not shown farther west than the middle of the Ganga–Yamuna doab and the lower Chambal basin, whereas there must be, indeed there are, comparable types even though gradually changing under drier climates, in the Punjab. There are also small but locally important

[35] An area of heavy incidence of goitre is associated with lime-rich alluvium and drinking water, unusually severe for the plains and comparable with isolated populations in limestone mountains. See a series of papers beginning with H. Stott, 'Distribution and causes of endemic goitre in the U.P., Part I', *Indian Jnl Med. Res.* 18 (1930–31), 1059–85. For a study of the effects of irrigation on these soils see R. D. Baksi *et al.*, 'Investigation of the soils of North Bihar and their role in irrigation projects', *Jnl of Soil & Water Cons.* 4/4 (1956), 152–8.

areas of old alluvium on the margins of the east coast deltas, and probably in a few other areas. The Schokalskaya–Spate map is interesting here, for easterly tracts in the Ganga–Brahmaputra plains are shown as meadow type on older alluvium; in Bihar the map shows prairie type soils on these areas though without specific reference to old alluvium, while in Uttar Pradesh and Punjab it shows sub-tropical steppe on older alluvium with saline patches, while the comparable tracts in lower Punjab and Sind are mapped as serozems, often saline with some loess.

Moormann and Dudal note the varying development of horizons, on alluvium from little even of the A_1 or A_p horizons in very well-drained soils, to well-marked A_1 or A_p or even peaty surface horizons where the water table is high. Some old alluvium would come within their category of wind-blown sands, within the regosols, the A horizon being weakly developed or absent (e.g. in shifting dunes) and little or no B horizon, yet there may have been a long period of weathering with the development of strong colouring, marked leaching of carbonates, and even the disappearance of weatherable minerals. This process would presumably vary, being related to the red-yellow podzol soils process in the humid areas, to semi-desert processes, with calcareous concretions (kankar) at some inches' depth, in the drier north and west. It seems likely that some of the older river terraces have developed some Low Humic Gley Soils of Moormann and Dudal (by analogy with their territory). A little-disturbed soil of this type is a grey or greyish-brown hydromorphic soil, the A_1 or A_p horizon not very thick and giving way to a much lighter and distinctly leached A_2 horizon and then to a textural B horizon, alluvial and with a much higher clay content. The B horizon is conspicuously mottled, with a light brownish-grey to light olive grey matrix and weak to moderate subangular blocky structure not necessarily with conspicuous clay coatings round the peds. Some of the mottling may tend towards concretionary laterite on drying, and there may be a C horizon of groundwater laterite, commonly at 3–6 ft. (1–2 m.). It seems likely that much paddy land on river terraces is of this type, altered by cultivation over the centuries. In the USDA classification these are of the order of ultisols (ultimate soils), of the aquult sub-order (hydromorphic ultisols) and great group ochraquult (pale or leached aquults).

Type IV of the National Atlas, alluvial soil (new), corresponds with two types in the Schokalskaya–Spate map – alluvial soils, with traces of bog processes on newer alluvium, and in places swamp, peat-bog and muck soils. Moormann and Dudal note the variation from little or no horizon development to well-marked, even peaty, A horizons, as already noted in relation to older alluvia; they note the well-marked variations in soil texture from sandy to loamy to clayey, which Geddes has shown so evocatively to relate to present and former water-channels wandering across alluvial fan or cone, flood-plain or delta and not only at the surface but also in depth. He notes the variations according to the catchment of the river – dark, relatively heavy clay from calcareous or basaltic hinterlands, whereas if red-yellow or grey podsolic soils predominate in the catchments there may be a much poorer alluvium, often lighter in colour, and with a dominance of 1 : 1 lattice clay.[36] The east coast deltas have often been cited as examples of poorer alluvial soils derived from mainly red-soil hinterlands, though this applies to the Mahanadi and the Cauvery rather than the Godavari and Krishna.

Some of these new alluvial soils are very acid, with pH values sometimes under 2 and commonly 3–4·5 and sometimes with free aluminium and sometimes iron also. Acid soils, at about 4·5–6 are typical, but in contrast some give very basic reactions, as in the areas already noted. In the USDA classification these are all entisols, and they probably cover the gamut of sub-orders, aquents (wet recent soils), psamment (sandy recent soils), ustent (burnt, i.e. dry-climate and especially hot–dry summer recent soils), and udents (humid-climate recent soils).

The Coastal Soils, type VII of the National Atlas, are the littoral sands, etc., of the Schokalskaya–Spate map, Moormann and Dudal's regosols of the wind-blown sand variety, and in the USDA classification are of the order of entisols, mainly of the psamment sub-order. Horizon development may be entirely lacking, or there may be a slight organic-rich A horizon development, possibly at several depths, especially in drier areas; correspondingly in wetter areas older and especially relatively fixed dunes may show some progress towards podzolization, and there is probably similar development, less easily observed, on coastal sand-aprons.

The Saline Soils (National Atlas type VIII) correspond well with the solonchaks of the Schokalskaya–Spate map, except that the latter does not show the saline tracts of northern Kashmir; Schokalskaya's solonetz, however, interestingly if fairly diagrammatically portray the high and growing incidence of saline-crust on heavy-soiled interfluvial hollows associated largely with seepage from irrigation canals and consequent water-logging. The National Atlas category IX, Desert Soils, corresponds in a general way with two types in the Schokalskaya–Spate map, serozems, often saline, with some loess, and sandy semi-desert serozems. The sandy semi-desert serozems envelop the Aravalli ranges, extending to the Rann of Kutch, towards Delhi and north almost to the Salt Range, whereas the National Atlas treats the Aravallis as in the Red Soil zone, southern Punjab as simply alluvium differentiated by texture, and the rest as desert. Here we have lost the analogic guidance of Moormann and Dudal, for there are no deserts in southeast Asia and therefore none in their classification. All these soils, and probably Schokalskaya's solonchaks and solonetz as well, are in the USDA order of aridosols, which name does explain itself; it is too early to try to discuss even generally the sub-orders of orthid (true arid) and argid (arid, with illuvial argillic white clay) and their interesting sub-divisions into great groups according to exchange of horizons, hardness, saltness, etc.

[36] A. Geddes, 'The alluvial morphology of the Indo-Gangetic plain, its mapping and geographical significance', *Trans. Inst. British Geog.* 28 (1960), 253–76; H. Stott, *op. cit.*

Category X of the National Atlas is confined to the Himalaya, where it is broken by small areas of podzols, of alluvium (only in the Vale of Kashmir) and of saline soils in patches in the north of Kashmir. The Schokalskaya–Spate map notes the presence of strong vertical zoning; Moormann and Dudal would treat these as regosols of their second category, variously textured slope colluvium, and some of their skilful generalization about a very varied group has already been noted. Here the vertical zoning from tropical to Alpine and glacial climates would add to the variety. Again these recent soils would be entisols in the USDA classification; one can see the relevance of the sub-order (already noted) and of the great groups distinguished according to relations with cold climate, sand, water, minimal horizon development, agriculture, sod development and the like, but so much work would be needed to apply them to this enormous and complex region that it seems unlikely that we shall ever see this except by example or type study.

The inter-digitation of zonal, intra-zonal and azonal soil types;
human interference and soils geography

Even in the preceding discussion it has been explicit or implicit at several points that there is inter-digitation of soil types; obviously some of this is on such an intimate scale that it can best be discussed in a regional context; sometimes, however, it is on such a large scale that it could be shown on a map of India, even on the small scale used in this book, but for the lack of data of comparable nature from all over the sub-continent. Some examples may make the point, and at the same time illustrate some of the biotic influences on soils geography.

The southwest of India, with its long wet season, is perhaps in the latosol zone, but if so acid parent material seems to encourage also deep red-yellow podzols, as on the low plateaus of Kerala and western Mysore. From the high laterite of the Cardamom Hills and the southern part of the Western Ghats west-wards down the steep face, lie acid brown forest soils, still partly under rain-forest, partly under plantations for tea at high levels, coffee a little lower, and rubber on the lower slopes. Shade trees are left in the coffee and tea gardens, and though clear-felling precedes rubber planting, precautions against soil erosion are taken – terracing fits in with easy tapping – and cover crops under the rubber trees are now common.[37] The low plateaus of Kerala have a good deal of laterite, exposed on the cornices above the valleys, elsewhere with a relatively thin and vulnerable cover of residual podzolic clay, with scrub or grassland, locally forest, and some clearing for tapioca gardens. A valley section or catena in this area shows an increasing depth of slope colluvium below the laterite cornice, with

[37] Farther north, the forests east of the Ghats edge in Satara District have so far proved to protect soils against excessive erosion even in the presence of *kumri* or shifting cultivation; but in the interests of the longevity of the reservoir for the Koyna project (see p. 656), mixed farming with grazing of cattle may be encouraged. M. M. Kibe and N. B. Puranik, 'Note on soil conservation survey for land use planning in Koyna project, Satara, Bombay State', *Jnl Soil & Water Cons.* 6/4 (1958), 176–83.

scrubby grazing and perhaps some tapioca patches – rather liable to soil erosion – and some paddy terraces on the lower, gentler slopes. The river terraces and flood plains have sandy to silty alluvium, and rice terracing and bunding have led to widespread, mainly biotic development of grey paddy soils, with some signs of wetness and mottling. Rather similar development has taken place in the intrinsically rather infertile lagoon alluvia in belts parallel to the coast and the multiple sandbars. The sandbars and sand-dunes show early development of dark A horizons, probably partly biotic, under the coconuts and other orchard trees, and in older dunes some progress towards podzolization, with hard-pan formation. Sand-aprons show very pure sand, perhaps in a field of pineapples, but there may be some groundwater laterite at a foot or two down.

The Red Soil zone as a whole has important but narrow belts of slope colluvium on the lower slopes and on the pediment at the foot of many hundreds of miles of steep scarps in the Western and Eastern Ghats, the Hazaribagh ranges and the scarps bordering the Chota Nagpur plateau and the Damodar rift valley, the Aravallis, and many others. These soils may bear recent additions through accelerated soil erosion higher up, notably associated with overgrazing, though the National Atlas map classifies most of this as moderate rather than severe. There are of course ribbons of alluvium following most major rivers for most of their courses – gorges are the most notable exceptions – and in places with older alluvium on terraces.[38] In places these alluvia include redeposited *regurs*, as in parts at least of the black soils reaching far east near the Godavari and Krishna rivers. The major rivers have considerable alluvial deltas – note the Cauvery, Godavari–Krishna, and Mahanadi, but the last is mapped as dominated by coastal alluvia in the south and by saline swamps in the north; all these deltaic soils have been much altered by paddy cultivation, tending to equate them in a sort of biotic gley soil. Between the major deltas, coastal alluvia including dunes and sand-aprons are important, some altered by casuarina plantations, irrigated for the first few years by shallow *kuchcha* (unlined) wells tapping the water-table in the dunes. The largest single area of moderately severe erosion on these soils is in the Chota Nagpur plateau, partly through the activities of tribal people practising shifting agriculture, partly through overgrazing from settled Hindu villages with rice and millet fields; part of this area has had considerable experience of both problems and successes in soil conservation measures under the Damodar Valley project, including terracing and exclusion of grazing from vulnerable slopes, usually measures involving land consolidation or close co-operation between farmers.

The Black Soils area similarly includes important areas of slope colluvium, bordering the Vindhya–Bhanrer ranges, the Satpura–Mahadeo hills, the

[38] These are well-mapped for Peninsular India in E. Simkins, 'The agricultural geography of the Deccan plateau of India', Supplement to *The Geography Teacher*, n.d., ?1926. See also B. N. Murthy and N. S. Iyengar, 'Estimate of life of reservoirs in first phase of development of Damodar Valley Corporation', *Jnl Soil & Water Cons.* 5/1 (1956), 17–20, and other papers in this journal.

Chandor–Ajanta or Sahyadriparvat ranges (and much of the gently sloping plains fringing the structural valleys of the Narmada and Tapti), as well as the fingers of high plateau extending east along the interfluves from the laterite-capped platforms crowning the northern part of the Western Ghats. These belts are important, for their mixed and immature nature makes them more versatile and in particular more easily irrigable than are the mature grumosols of great flat stretches across the Deccan plateaus. In some places man imitates nature by bringing newly weathered black sand from basalt crags to mix with the silts of small flood-plains, and small dams are also made to trap more silt. The alluvial ribbons of river terraces and flood-plains, again, of redeposited *regur*, are important in varying the picture. Again they are better aquifers than the grumosols proper over solid basalt, they are more irrigable and wells can be dug or bored. The region as a whole has a very high proportion under cultivation, particularly on the black cotton soils proper; accelerated soil erosion is heavy, despite the generally flat character of the land, for the viscous soils of the wet season almost flow, and field runnels are heavily overloaded with eroding soils and roadside ditches contain new miniature deltas after a storm. The table

Sholapur Dt (total rainfall) 23·9 in. (607 mm.) – ground condition	Mean annual runoff as % total rainfall	Mean annual storm rain of 13·7 in. (348 mm.) in 10·6 storm runoffs causing erosion	
		Soil loss	No. of years to erode 7 in. (178 mm.) topsoil
Natural vegetation	4·77	0·53	1,852
Natural vegetation removed	19·75	17·69	57
Shallow cultivation	22·50	24·82	
Rabi cultivation	18·67	34·54	27
Kharif plot with scoop irrigation	9·92	14·75	68
Bajri-tur (kharif)	16·5	23·8	42
Ploughed and harrowed (fallow)	17·12	32·7	40
Ploughed and harrowed (double-length fallow)	17·5	27·4	

Source: M. M. Kibe, 'The role of vegetal cover in Soil Conservation', *Jnl Soil & Water Cons.*, 6/4, July 1958, 160–6.

shows the influence of different vegetation covers. The grumosols have poor engineering qualities, so that soil erosion bunds must have a masonry base, and it is difficult to give them an effective and useful plant cover though some progress has been made; bushes like *Cassia auriculata* (yielding tanning bark) seem to succeed rather than grasses;[39] and even the closing of an area to grazing may bring a cover of scrub, no doubt seral to higher forms.[40]

[39] C. P. Raju et al., 'Bunding in deep black soils of Andhra State', *Jnl Soil & Water Cons.* 4/6 (1956), 143–8, and N. K. Ghumare, 'Studies in the behaviour of contour bunds', *ibid.*, 10/1–2, (1962), 44–64.

[40] G. S. Puri, 'The study of dry scrub vegetation under forest management at Dhond, Poona', *Proc. Nat. Inst. Sci. India*, New Delhi, 24, Part B/3 (1958), 145–9.

The desert and semi-desert soils have their own problems. Much land fringing the heart of the Thar Desert is in fact cultivated for wheat, barley, linseed, etc., at an extensive scale; there seems to be some tendency to over-cultivation and for dunes long fixed to start moving. Severe gullying is developing, extending outward from the steep sides of desert and semi-desert wadis, and associated no doubt with overgrazing. Work in the area has shown how effective even the exclusion of grazing stock can be in rehabilitating the vegetation of a developing badland tract, restoring its water-table and gradually building up its soil status again. Check-dams in major gullies, brush-wood cover to help planted trees to begin growing, and a whole range of conservation measures can be deployed in the worst or most urgent cases.[41] Following treatment, rotational grazing may be possible.

The well-known belt of badlands lying several miles deep on both banks of the lower Chambal, in slightly more humid conditions, can in time be controlled by similar measures, planting fuel wood and grass; but the economics are such that the more urgent task is to protect soils still agriculturally viable on the Malwa plateau.

Even the great alluvial plain of the Indus–Ganga–Brahmaputra contains a surprising element of inter-digitation within it. The old alluvium a few feet higher than the fringes of the Bengal Delta, and in 'islands' within it, is relatively lightly populated and relatively well-wooded, with a relatively infertile residual red-yellow podsolic clay over laterite, which is exposed on the margins as a cornice.[42] The delta contains slight variations in texture, from sandy soils to sandy loams, to loams, to silty clays, and with them variations in soil acidity to some very saline soils – those fringing the seaward edge of the delta uncultivable as yet.[43] Everywhere along the hillfoot, from Assam to the exit of the Ganga from the mountains, hillfoot slope colluvium gives way to coarse hillfoot gravels and major alluvial fans or cones. Farther west, accelerated soil erosion following late 19th-century deforestation of the ill-consolidated sediments of the Siwalik ranges has added a veneer of sandy and gravelly fans spreading even across valuable well-irrigated hillfoot fields. (See also p. 535.) In the great alluvial plains are the alternations of texture according to their recent patterns of

[41] The large literature includes: O. N. Kaul, 'Management of the Chambal ravines in Rajasthan', *Indian Forester*, 88/10 (1962), 725–30; V. Srinivasan, W. C. Bonde and K. G. Tejwani, 'Studies on grasses and their suitability to stabilize and maintain bunds in ravine lands of Gujarat', *Jnl Soil & Water Cons.* 10/1–2 (1962), 72–77, and many other papers in these useful journals.

[42] See S. J. Bhunan, M. Zacharia and F. Rahman, 'Soils of the Khiyar Tract, East Pakistan', *Soil Sci.* 91/5 (1961), 369–74: A. Karim and A. Qasem, 'Study of the soils of Barind Tract, East Pakistan', *Soil Sci.* 91/6 (1961), 406–12; S. Bhattacharya, 'Soil erosion in Santhal Parganas', *GRI* 18/2 (1956), 1–4; Forest Directorate Govt of Bengal: *An Afforestation Scheme for the Laterite Zone of West Bengal* (Calcutta, 1956).

[43] For West Bengal we owe a long series of detailed papers to Professor S. P. Chatterjee and his colleagues; an early example is: S. P. Chatterjee, R. Lahiri, S. Venkatraman and S. Mukherjee, 'Pedogenesis in West Bengal', *GRI* 18/3 (1956), 1–10; the series may be followed in successive volumes of the *Review*.

alluviation,[44] sometimes varying markedly according to the parent material in the river catchment in the Himalaya or the Plateau – e.g. the easily shifted mica-rich deposits of the Kosi, the lime-rich alluvia of the Gandak, and the sandy spread of the Son. The lower Chambal deposits are subject to the five to ten-mile wide belt of notorious badland erosion, now being controlled in a multi-purpose project mainly aimed at soil conservation. In the western half of the Ganga plains and in the Indus plains old alluvium tends first to contain *kankar* (a calcareous concretionary deposit) a few inches down, and farther west to be saline. Seepage from irrigation canals has greatly increased the incidence of waterlogged soils and of saline-encrusted soils, especially in heavy-soiled hollows in the alluvium, and major campaigns to combat the salt are in progress, particularly in West Pakistan, including the use of tube-wells to lower the water-table, to irrigate and to drain and flush saline tracts.[45]

The difficulties of generalizing about the Himalayas have already been noted. Acid brown forest soils must be important locally, and slope colluvium very widely, deeper on lower slopes; while the National Atlas map shows belts of podzols on the highest slopes there can be only the most skeletal Alpine soils, developing on glacial and peri-glacial material, even on rock wastes in the north of Kashmir and the far northwest of West Pakistan. In places the forest has been stripped, sometimes succeeded by gullying, sometimes by terraces for paddy, as in parts of Nepal, sometimes by terracing for tea plantations as in the Darjeeling area. Naturally there is particular concern over grossly accelerated soil erosion and landslides in the Kosi catchment (mainly in Nepal), where a multi-purpose project partly to control floods from violently fluctuating river is under way.[46] Farther west the deforestation and consequent soil erosion in the Siwaliks has been noted; parts of this area have now been subject to soil conservation measures for well over 20 years, and it has been shown how vegetal cover, soil and the water-table may be restored, so that the way may be open for limited and rotational use of the slopes for pasturing or cutting fodder.[47] Many of the hill arcs of West Pakistan are almost devoid of vegetation or soil on the many steep slopes. If there ever was a thin desert scrub, it has yielded to the attack of over-grazing. The process of accelerated soil erosion may have added to the slope colluvium of the lower slopes and the hillfoot fans giving the basis for a little

[44] A. Geddes, *op. cit.*

[45] An example is given from each of the main journals, many articles from which are here subsumed: *Jnl Soil & Water Cons.* 6/4 (1958), 169–76 (B. V. Mehta and R. S. Desai); *Indian Jnl Agric. Science* 33 (1963), 28–33 (S. P. Raychaudhuri et al.); *IGJ* 35/1–2 (1960), 10–18 (M. M. Menon); *Proceedings* 8th Silvicultural Confce, 1951, Pt. 2 (Dehra Dun, 1956), 78–82 (K. C. Malhotra); *Indian Forester* 82/4 (1956), 206; *Pak. Jnl Forestry* 11/4 (1961), editorial note.

[46] As in fn. 45, examples are: *Jnl Soil & Water Cons.* 3/3 (1955), 106–15 (P. R. Ahuja); *Indian Forester* 87/4 (1962), 210–19 (O. N. Kaul).

[47] As in fn. 45, examples are: *Pak. Jnl Forestry* 11/4 (1961), 367–74 (N. A. Ali); *Indian Forester* 82/8 (1956), 411 (A. P. Bhattacharya); *Jnl Soil & Water Cons.* 7/4–5 (1959), 3–7 (P. D. Stracey).

irrigation including the use of *karez* (see p. 486). After a scrutiny of the Himalaya and the other northern mountain ranges from this point of view, it is easy to appreciate the great, almost emotional significance attached to the exception – the broad alluvial terraces and plains of the Vale of Kashmir.

Soil conservation

Soil conservation has been mentioned in its context in relation to the main soil regions in the preceding pages. Many problems of research and application surely remain, but for the main regional environments sufficient basic methods have been worked out for one to generalize, as in relation to many other developmental matters, that the remaining and most intransigent problems are social rather than technical. In particular it seems clear from the soil conservation literature, admittedly biased in favour of the measures recommended but weighing the evidence quantitatively, that soil conservation is a good investment even in the short to medium term.[48] Within a few years the increased crop yields pay for the capital costs, and the results are even more impressive if one looks to the saving as against the often irreparable loss of the soil for posterity. For instance the costs of terracing the steep and difficult slopes of the Nilgiris for potato cultivation, which at present causes such devastating soil erosion, are repaid within a few years.[49] The problem of persuading farmers to adopt the measures appropriate to their region and soils is particularly severe; for soil conservation, though it can be done piecemeal on a village by village scale, does need co-operation within the village if it is to succeed, and this may be difficult to secure in an atmosphere of extreme land hunger and where the land is held in scattered plots and strips. Consolidation may have to precede conservation. Perhaps the most significant and hopeful pointer from a small but inspiring experiment in the Upper Damodar is that there followed requests from many other villages for help in framing similar programmes once the news of the increased yields became disseminated.

Soil types, soil fertility, soil productivity

The map of the main climatic-vegetation soil types has been qualified by a discussion of the inter-digitation of differing soils because of geological factors like differential mineral composition of decomposed rock, geomorphological factors like slope or alluviation old and new, and biotic influence both destructive and conservative. There are numerous studies relating to inherent fertility in relation to ecologically suited crops or varieties, but these are often not comparable, based on the experimental farm, plot, or even pot, rather than on peasant

---

[48] General references include: C. A. R. Bhadran, 'Conservation measures in catchment areas and flood control', *Indian Forester*, 84/12 (1958), 710–17; A. D. Khan, 'Measurement of increase in productivity by adopting soil conservation practices, I & II', *Jnl Soil & Water Cons.* 7/4–5 (1959), 45–50; 50–55; and other papers in these journals.

[49] B. M. Lakshmipathy and S. Narayanswamy, 'Bench terracing in the Nilgiris', *Jnl Soil & Water Cons.* 4/4 (1956), 161–8, and several other papers in these journals.

farmers' fields, and in any case not sufficiently numerous or evenly spaced to allow of mapping on the sub-continental scale treated in this chapter. Some examples may, however, illustrate their potentialities:

An experiment in cultivators' fields in Bihar showed that optimal levels of nitrogenous fertilizers were:

	Fertilizer	Previous Yield	Additional Yield
Clays	40	18	6
Loams	10	17	4
Sandy Loams	15	22	4

The clays, initially more fertile, need more fertilizer for a given response than the medium or low fertility soils.[50]

Such studies multiplied form at once a spectrum and a kaleidoscope, un-mappable at present though this may be possible some day. Meantime one admittedly gross and indirectly derived measure is a soil rating index, made up by awarding points to the particular soil for certain characteristics including the predominant crops grown. Mukerjee illustrates the technique in relation to part of the Bengal delta in Howrah district[51]; most of the area rates as of moderate fertility, grade 2, needing more manure than the small area of grade 1 soils yielding some 1,600–2,400 lb. of paddy per acre; even parts of the grade 2 soils are slightly saline, while the grade 3 soils are heavy clays tending to salinity in the swamp of a deltaic hollow. Fig. 3.7 is based on such an index unfortunately calculated by administrative Districts rather than for soil tracts or even for 'spot heights' from which an isopleth map might have been drawn;[52] meantime it may serve *faute de mieux* as a synthesis of this section, at least for India, on the side of application and utilization, as against the bio-ecological aspects with which we began.

[50] P. Sinha and K. P. D. Gupta, 'Crop responses to added fertilizers in cultivators' fields', *Jnl Soil & Water Cons.* 4/3 (1956), 24–30; and many other papers in the soil science journals.
[51] S. N. Mukerjee, 'Productivity rating of the paddy soils of Howrah, Bengal', *GRI* 25/3 (1963), 35–43.
[52] K. B. Shome, 'Rating of soils in India', *Proc. of National Institute of Sciences India,* Silver Jubilee No., (1960), Part A Vol. 26, Physical Sciences Supplement, 260–89.

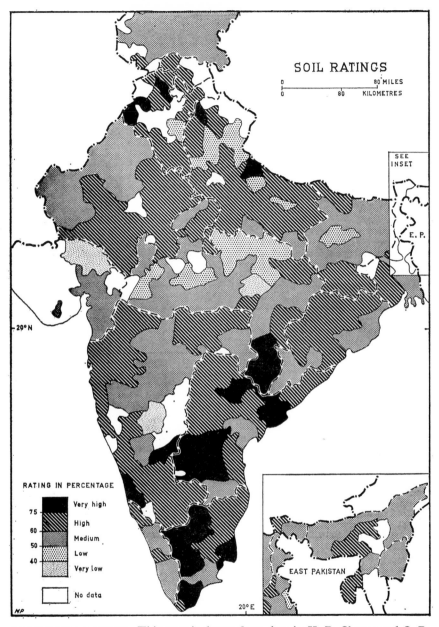

SOIL RATINGS

RATING IN PERCENTAGE

- Very high
- 75
- High
- 60
- Medium
- 50
- Low
- 40
- Very low
- No data

EAST PAKISTAN

FIG 3.7 SOIL RATINGS. This map is drawn from data in K. B. Shome and S. P. Raychauhuri in *Proc. Natl Inst. of Science of India*, 126/A (1960), 260–9. Ratings, unfortunately given on a District basis, were arrived at by multiplying factors of profile, permeability, degree of weathering, texture, structure, stoniness, salinity, natural fertility, and others; pending more refined work interesting regional groupings emerge: the very high ratings of the middle and upper Gangetic Plains and the south and east of the Peninsular plateau, and the low values in a belt flanking the North of the Peninsula.

ADDENDUM TO CHAPTER 3

FORMATIVE ELEMENTS IN NAMES OF SOIL ORDERS *

Name of order	Formative element in name of order	Derivation of formative element	Mnemonicon and pronunciation of formative elements
Entisol	ent	Nonsense syllable	recent
Vertisol	ert	L. *verto*, turn	invert
Inceptisol	ept	L. *inceptum*, beginning	inception
Aridisol	id	L. *aridus*, dry	arid
Mollisol	oll	L. *mollis*, soft	mollify
Spodosol	od	Gk. *spodos*, wood ash	Podzol; odd
Alfisol	alf	Nonsense syllable	Pedalfer
Ultisol	ult	L. *ultimus*, last	ultimate
Oxisol	ox	F. *oxide*, oxide	oxide
Histosol	ist	G. histos, tissue	histology

* From *Soil Classification: A Comprehensive System* (USA Dept of Agriculture, Washington, 7th Approximation, 1960).

FORMATIVE ELEMENTS IN NAMES OF SUBORDERS

Formative element	Derivation of formative element	Mnemonicon	Connotation of formative element
acr	Gk. *akros*, highest	acrobat	Most strongly weathered
alb	L. *albus*, white	albino	Presence of albic horizon (a bleached eluvial horizon)
alt	L. *altus*, high	altitude	Cool, high altitudes or latitudes
and	Modified from *Ando*	Ando	Ando-like
aqu	L. *aqua*, water	aquarium	Characteristics associated with wetness
arg	Modified from argillic horizon; L. *argilla*, white clay	argillite	Presence of argillic horizon (a horizon with illuvial clay)
ferr	L. *ferrum*, iron	ferruginous	Presence of iron
hum	L. *humus*, earth	humus	Presence of organic matter
ochr	Gk. base of *ochros*, pale	ocher	Presence of ochric epipedon (a light-coloured surface)
orth	Gk. *orthos*, true	orthophonic	The common ones
psamm	Gk. *psammos*, sand	psammite	Sand textures
rend	Modified from Rendzina	Rendzina	Rendzina-like
ud	L. *udus*, humid	udometer	Of humid climates
umbr	L. *umbra*, shade	umbrella	Presence of umbric epipedon (a dark-coloured surface)
ust	L. *ustus*, burnt	combustion	Of dry climates, usually hot in summer

BIBLIOGRAPHICAL NOTE

Vegetation

The classic work is H. G. Champion, *A Preliminary Survey of Forest Types of India and Burma* (Indian Forest Records, New Series, Silviculture, Vol. I, Delhi, 1936); a good deal of this chapter is based on it by courtesy of the Director,

Forest Research Institute, Dehra Dun. It is now supplemented by G. S. Puri, *Indian Forest Ecology* (Oxford Book Company, New Delhi, 2 vols 1960), which goes into great floristic detail. Earlier works which are still useful are E. P. Stebbing, *The Forests of India* (London, 1922), for forest administration; R. S. Troup, *The Silviculture of Indian Trees* (London, 1921), which is helpful for the reader outside India who wishes to attach a definite image to a Latin name; and, for its general views, Sir J. D. Hooker, 'Botany' in *Imperial Gazetteer*, Vol. I (1909), the last contribution of a worker whose career began with *Himalayan Journals* in 1847–51!

Recent ecological studies in India owe much to the Section Scientifique et Technique of the Institut Français at Pondicherry. Especially useful is P. Legris, *La Végétation de l'Inde: Ecologie et Flore*, Tome VI of the *Travaux* of the section (Pondichéry, 1963); Tome VII is V. M. Meher-Homji, *Les Bioclimats du Sub-Continent Indien* (1963). The Institute has also begun an extremely detailed vegetation map on the scale of 1/1,000,000, with handbooks; the following sheets have appeared: Cape Comorin, Madras, Godavari, Jagannath, covering the entire littoral from Cannanore round to Lake Chilka and a good deal of the interior. At the other end of the sub-continent, there is a detailed study by U. Schweinfurth, *Die horizontale und vertikale Verbreitung der Vegetation im Himalaya* (F. Dümmler, Bonn, 1957). An important contribution is R. O. Whyte, *The Grassland and Fodder Resources of India* (Indian Council of Agric. Research, Scientific Monograph No. 22, Delhi, 1957).

Soils

Many readers would still wish to progress historically, in relation to thinking about soils at various relatively recent dates. For the traditional classification see *Royal Commission on Agriculture*, 1928, 70–79. An essential and stimulating complement is Z. J. Schokalskaya, 'The natural conditions of soil formation in India', in B. Polynov (ed.), *Contributions to the Knowledge of the Soils of Asia*, No. 2 (Leningrad, Dokuchaiev Institute, 1932), 53–155 – available from the library of the Rothamsted Experimental Station.

A broad and authoritative survey is available, dating from about the beginning of the work of the Soil Survey of India and by its former head, in S. P. Raychaudhuri, Presidential Address on Survey and Classification of Indian Soils, 43rd Indian Science Congress, Agra, 1956, Section of Agricultural Sciences (Indian Science Congress Association, Calcutta – 1), 1–16. The various journals cited in the chapter contain many valuable articles on soil profiles and fertility, erosion and conservation. Much more material of high quality remains meantime in the files of the Indian Soil Survey and analogous bodies in Pakistan and Ceylon. For India, it may be that the time is approaching when we may expect a provisional synthesis of the valuable soil survey documents now available for widespread if patchily distributed parts of the country.

Meantime the foregoing chapter is based very largely on the approach and classification of F. R. Moormann and R. Dudal, 'Major Soils of South-east Asia', Regional Congress of the International Geographical Union (Kuala Lumpur, 1962, mimeographed, 1–52+iv). The author of this section acknowledges deep indebtedness to Moormann and Dudal; error or over-extension of their classification to a part of South Asia almost entirely outside the area they studied, however, must be ascribed solely to the present author. The author, then, found the work of Moormann and Dudal invaluable: the reader may wish to follow, at least until there is available a first-hand modern soil map, pedological study or soils geography of the Indian sub-continent.

PART II

The People

CHAPTER 4

Population and its Problems

INTRODUCTION

The population of the Indian sub-continent in 1961 was about 533,000,000. The recorded rate of increase (1951–61) was about 2·2% per annum in both countries.[1] These rates have often been approached by Western countries during phases of rapid population increase; the absolute numbers involved, however, are very large; at least two-thirds of these very large populations are dependent on agriculture; and while industrialization has made a start and is now being expanded, the position is very different from that of say Britain during the phase of rapid population increase accompanying the Industrial Revolution, the period when the country was becoming 'the workshop of the world'. This is by common consent a sub-continent of over-population, but the degree of over-population in relation to the population capacity at some widely acceptable standard of living is extremely difficult to gauge. Clearly knowledge of population dynamics is as important as five year plans for economic development to employ the extra hands, feed the extra mouths, and in time attain standards of living which we may expect to be associated with lower rates of population increase.

POPULATION DISTRIBUTION

'The density of population is as it were the synthesis of all the geographical phenomena: it expresses eloquently the manner in which man has taken

---

[1] Demographic critiques of the censuses of the two countries suggest that in India the 1951 Census included under-enumeration of perhaps 6–7% (largely of children under 5 and perhaps females also), while the 1961 Census may also include some under-enumeration; the 1951 Census in Pakistan included substantial under-reporting of children, and also of women so that the male predominance at all ages is probably overstated, and the 1961 Census may include under-reporting of over 5%. For Pakistan, the under-reporting in 1951 may have been sufficient to make the calculated population increase of 2·2% per annum 1951–61 also an over-statement. See respectively, for instance, A. J. Coale and E. M. Hoover, *Population Growth and Economic Development in Low-Income Countries: A Case Study of India's Prospects* (OUP, 1959), 354, and K. J. Krotki's valuable series of articles in Vol. I of the *Pakistan Development Review*. India's Registrar-General points out that in the 1961 Census there were almost 1,000,000 enumerators (A. Mitra, 'Population on the land in the 1961 Census', *Indian Jnl Agric. Statistics* 15 (1963), 13–82). Since there were almost 200,000 in the 1961 Census of Pakistan, one can appreciate the problems of training and supervision, and the chances of error.

advantage of the land he occupies.' (J. Robert, 'La densité de population des Alpes françaises d'après le dénombrement de 1911', *Rev. de Géographie Alpine* 8 (1920), 124.)

The analysis of a population distribution map which seemed so satisfying in the early 1920s, at least within an area of a relatively homogeneous culture and standards of living, remains a useful exercise for students, though one raising more questions than it solves and inviting further analysis, often impossible for lack of data. The population density map now appears as a beginning rather than an end-product, to be complemented by mapping and analysis of *per capita* income or consumer expenditure, nutritional standards and (in advanced societies) measures of consumer goods and the like to produce estimates of the standard of material living. We shall start with discussion of rural population density and urban population distribution, even if few of the desirable complementary analyses can be more than hinted at for the present. Since Robert wrote, moreover, visual cartographic correlation of the population density map can now be complemented by statistical correlation, even where the base of recording the distribution differs, e.g. as between population and rainfall distributions over areas. Probing attacks using this type of approach for Indian data show that simple statistical analysis breaks down because the relationships involved are too complex and intertwined. Meantime, therefore, we shall use broad generalizations based on visual and subjective analysis.[2]

The excellent map of rural population density in the National Atlas of India (Preliminary Hindi Edition, 1957), on an isopleth basis and in fifteen colours, is based on the 1951 Census and hence is seriously out of date; it is also too complex for easy comprehension. It can, however, provide the starting-point for the compilation of a new and more generalized map of the rural population of the sub-continent, allowing for an over-all intercensal increase of 20% in 1951–61, ignoring as a matter of expediency regional variations: the general pattern is not likely to be significantly altered. For Pakistan the 1961 Census can be directly used; this involves chloropleths based on the smallest administrative units, *tehsils* for West and the smaller *thanas* for East Pakistan. There is therefore an unconformity within the map at the national boundary: in Pakistan the densest shadings are understated, and patches of low populations cutting across administrative boundaries are not well mapped. To avoid irksome repetition of figures in the following discussion, we have given the term 'medium' to densities at around the average for the sub-continent, i.e. about 345 per sq. mile (134 per km^2), and as the key to the map indicates we have given similar descriptive terms to densities ranging from 'extremely high' with over 1,800 per sq. mile (720 per km^2) to 'very low' for densities of under 12 per sq. mile (5 per km^2).

[2] Valuable analyses in the literature include: S. P. Chatterjee, 'Regional patterns of the density and distribution of population in India', *GRI* 24/2 (1962), 1–28; M. K. Elahi, 'Food supply and population growth in Pakistan', *PGR* 21/1 (1957), 1–38.

Densities from medium to extremely high, about or above the average density for the sub-continent, cover nearly all the mainly humid coastal lowlands fringing the Peninsular Block; in the Indo-Gangetic Plains they extend westward into semi-arid country and south into the northern edge of the Peninsular Block, while in the northeast of the sub-continent they cover nearly all of East Pakistan and extend into the Assam valley and west into the Damodar valley and parts of the Chota Nagpur plateau. Clearly these areas include much of the most productive land, especially in respect of food crops, and notably much of the rice land of the sub-continent. Within this great stretch of country, variations, reflecting many and diverse factors, include:

1. A belt of high density stretches north from the rice and market gardening lands north of Bombay, through the Baroda area, and after a gap includes a tract of the cotton-growing country tributary to Ahmedabad.

2. High medium densities south of Bombay, in the terrain of low dissected laterite plateaus and drowned valleys, between the Ghats edge and the sea and reaching south beyond Goa.

3. After a narrowing where the forested high plateaus almost meet the sea near Karwar, this belt broadens and includes considerable belts of very high and extremely high densities almost to Kanya Kumari; the coastal rice lands of Kerala comprise one of the largest stretches of extremely high rural populations in the sub-continent, declining inland in the low coastal plateaus and the spice garden and plantation country of Kerala and Mysore and then falling very rapidly as the country rises in the almost precipitous Ghats edge, to very low densities.

4. Near Kanya Kumari the narrow coastal lowlands show a sharp change to medium and high medium densities associated with the contrast between perhumid Kerala and semi-arid Tamilnad (and between dispersed-linear settlement pattern in Kerala and nucleated settlements based on tank irrigation); there are patches of high density in the main river plains, rising to very high in the lower Cauvery flood-plain and in the rice lands of the delta and in the peri-urban tract round Madras; it is remarkable that the millet and groundnut unirrigated country includes so much medium to high medium density, but one must allow for the effects not only of tank irrigation of part of the land, but also for narrow belts of well-irrigation along the hillfoot zone flanking the low medium to low density hill tracts of the Pachamalais and Shevaroys, and the southeastern raised rim of the Mysore plateau; the high densities of the lower Cauvery extend towards the cotton-millet country round Coimbatore and almost link up with those of coastal Kerala.

5. The coastal belt of above-medium densities narrows north of Pulicat lake, then broadens in the Godavari–Krishna delta which is mostly high with very high densities in the Godavari delta; a salient of high densities reaches northwest along the railway line to the coal-mining area of Singareni and Warangal.

6. The inselberg-studded coastal plains of Northern Circars, with rice and sugar-cane alternating with millet and groundnuts, have high densities, almost linking with those of the Orissa (Mahanadi) deltaic rice lands, which in turn links up with the next feature.

7. The great stretch of populations of high to extremely high densities (over 600 per sq. mile or 240 per km^2) in the rice lands of the Bengal delta: West Bengal is generally high, rising to very high and locally to extremely high in a belt following the Hooghly and especially around the Hooghlyside conurbation, and falling to medium in the lateritic Barind tract near the Ganga's turn southeastwards (and extending into East Pakistan); East Pakistan on the other hand is mainly very high, with considerable areas of extremely high densities in the rice and jute tract flanking the lower Padma and Meghna. Islands of lateritic old alluvium, like the Barind or the Madhupur jungle, are mainly of high medium density but might be lower with more sensitive mapping (see introductory paragraph).

8. Most of the Assam valley has high densities, rising to very high in the Nowgong–Tezpur area.

9. The rice lands of the lower Ganga flood-plain tract, including the lower Gandak and Ghaghra, and north to the *terai* on the Nepal border, form a stretch of some 80,000 sq. miles (200,000 km^2) of very high densities, the biggest continuous belt in the sub-continent though the densities are a little lower than those of East Pakistan; densities fall to high medium and locally medium on the cone of the still wandering Kosi.

10. Leaving the main rice lands for the wheat-growing northwest, the upper Ganga and Yamuna plains contain a further very large tract, as much again, of high densities with a tract of very high following the East Yamuna canal tract between Delhi and Meerut; and an aureole of high medium to medium densities surrounds these high densities of the Ganga plains, extending into the northern slopes of the Peninsular block in places, or extending in salients like that of the lower Son valley, and also stretching across the Indo-Gangetic divide.

11. In East Punjab (India) and West Punjab (West Pakistan) and through to the Vale of Peshawar, the long densely settled and intensively cultivated hillfoot tracts of well-irrigation have high densities, but most of the canal tracts high medium – though more sensitive mapping of West Pakistan data might raise this a little.

12. Nearly all of this continuous stretch of above-medium density covering over half the sub-continent has been in the coastal plains or the Indo-Gangetic plain, and much the greater part has been in rice lands: there remain the more densely peopled parts of the Peninsula, mainly of medium density – the Mysore plateau, rising to high rural densities between Bangalore and Mysore, the long transitional and contact zone east of the forests of the crest zone of the Western Ghats, in Mysore and Maharashtra, rising to high densities in the

tobacco growing tract southeast of Kolhapur, much of the tank-irrigation country of Andhra, the upper Godavari valley, the middle Tapti basin and after an interruption a belt stretching east through Nagpur and the Wardha and Wainganga basins to the middle Mahanadi rice-bowl, and the interruption to harsh semi-arid conditions where the Aravallis give a little more rainfall and opportunities for tank building.

The tracts with rural population densities *below* medium (below 240 per sq. mile, 96 per km²), may be considered more briefly:

1. There are considerable tracts of low and very low densities in the forested hills of the northeast, the forested to glaciated and harsh arid plateaus of the far north, and the great tract of semi-arid to arid conditions from the Thar desert to Baluchistan – this last interrupted by low medium to medium densities of the lower Indus plains (locally probably somewhat higher on more sensitive mapping).

2. Low medium densities stretch from the far north of West Pakistan, and after the higher densities of the Punjab along the wetter eastern part of Rajasthan to inland Gujarat and much of Kathiawad and southern Kutch; thence stretching across about half of the Peninsular Block including much semi-arid country of variable rainfall and harvests, but also some humid country of rather poor and easily eroded soils in the northeast of the Plateau; within this great swathe of country are several large tracts of very low densities, largely tribal country – parts of the Satpuras, Vindhyas and Bundelkhand, the Kaimur Range, the Maikal Hills and across the higher parts of Chota Nagpur, the Cuddapah ranges of Andhra, the Bastar highlands north of the Godavari delta, linked to the northeast with the 'Eastern Ghats' of Orissa.

We cannot at the moment complement analysis of rural population density with a geography of standards of living in the countryside, though some hints are available. The falling cultivated area per head has often been pointed out, implying an additional strain on efforts to improve rural living standards;[3] rural unemployment in India is about 7% in young adult groups, and some 15% of those with employment regard themselves as underemployed, and while unemployment in Pakistan is reported as much lower, 3·5% in East Pakistan and 2·8% in West Pakistan, underemployment is high in East Pakistan (some 17%) though under 5% in West Pakistan.[4] The National Sample Survey has revealed the broad picture of consumer expenditure in India (i.e. a rupee value for all items consumed whether bought or home produced): values grade downward

---

[3] Kingsley Davis, *The Population of India and Pakistan* (Princeton Univ. Press, 1951); P. Dayal, 'Population growth and migration in India', *NGJI* 5/4 (1959), 179–85.

[4] 'Unemployment and Underemployment in India, Indonesia, Pakistan and the Philippines', *International Labour Rev.* 86 (1962), 369–87, drawing largely on the National Sample Survey for Indian data.

from Punjab to Kerala and Madras, and from Punjab to Bengal and the north-east, though here values do not fall as low as in the far south.[5] South India certainly appears as the most underprivileged area, even despite the awful problems of West Bengal including the absorption of refugees, and this picture is

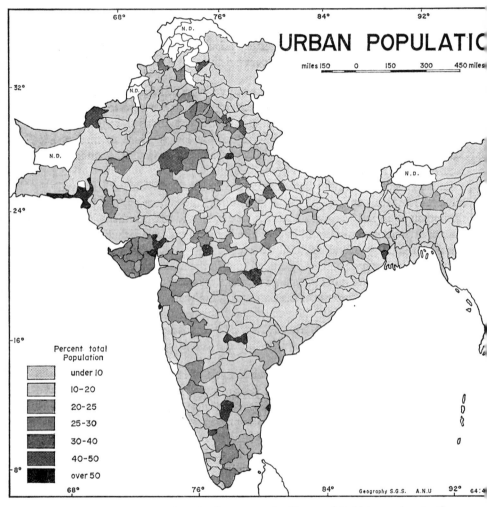

FIG 4.2 URBAN POPULATION. *Sources: 1961 Census of Pakistan* and *1961 Census of India*, Map 9 in Paper No. 1 of 1962 – actually a map of rural population, of which urban is the complementary percentage.

consistent with higher proportions of agricultural labourers in the east and south, and also with the long history of the south as a source of emigrants whether to

[5] For an indication of some stimulating potentialities of material from the 1961 Census, from the Registrar-General himself, see A. Mitra, *op. cit.*

Ceylon or Malaya, Madras city or Bangalore.[6] But there is one slight ameliorating factor, difficult to quantify – in the north, including the northeast, better housing and more clothing and food are needed to cope with the cool weather than generally in the south.

Urban population

The urban geography is discussed as such in Chapter 7, to which frequent cross-reference will be necessary, but both the extent of existing urbanism and of rates of growth in urbanization are essential to understanding of the population distribution map. In India the proportion of population classed as urban was 17·4% in 1951, 17·8% in 1961 (61,800,000 and 79,200,000 respectively);[7] in Pakistan the proportions were 10·4% in 1951 and 13·1% in 1961 (7,900,000 and 12,300,000).

Fig. 4.2 is a map of urban population distribution. There are relatively few under-urbanized areas (i.e. at or under the national averages quoted above): (1) all the northern mountain tracts except the Vale of Kashmir, the Kulu valley and the Darjeeling area; all Assam and the northeastern extremity of India except for the upper part of the Assam plain round Dibrugarh, the Shillong part of the Khasi plateau and the Tripura–Silchar area, in all of which the mapping may be swayed by relatively slender urban resources in relation to quite sparse population; (2) on the Gangetic plains the eastern terai, still partly in marshy forest, is the only large under-urbanized tract, along with the eastern part of the Yamuna–Ganga doab, two small areas southwest of Agra, and the northern fringe of the Ganga delta. In the Peninsula, apart from two small areas north of Bombay, there are two large and significant under-urbanized areas – along the Eastern Ghats from the Godavari gorge northeast to the Orissa hills, and the fringes of the Mahanadi delta.

Large tracts which are relatively highly urbanized include Hooghlyside, parts of the plains of Punjab and western Uttar Pradesh, Rajasthan especially along the fringes of the Aravalli, the Ahmedabad cotton area and Kathiawad with its array of former princely capitals, southern Malwa for similar reasons. The tract from Bombay to Baroda is well urbanized and several parts of the black cotton soil tracts – from Nasik and East Khandesh to Nagpur, from Poona to Sholapur, and away south to Dharwar and Hubli and even past the spice towns of the Ghats crest to the seaport towns from Karwar to Bhatkal.

The core of the former princely state of Mysore is well urbanized between

[6] J. E. Schwartzberg, 'Agricultural labour in India: a regional analysis with particular reference to population growth', *Econ. Devpt & Cultl Change*, 11 (1963), 337–52.

[7] In 1951 a town normally had a population of 5,000 or more, but larger places without urban characteristics might be excluded, smaller places with them included; State Government or Census Superintendents had some discretion. In 1961 there was a more rigorous definition, without discretion to States; all places with municipal or other recognized administration were classed as urban, plus other places meeting three tests: (a) population not less than 5,000, (b) population density not less than 1,000 per square mile, and (c) at least three-fourths of adult male population engaged in pursuits other than agriculture.

Bangalore and Mysore, and so are the core of the Krishna delta area, the Coimbatore and Madurai areas and the relatively sparsely peopled tract north of Kanya Kumari, as well as the much more densely peopled tract of southern Kerala. Several other areas have considerable urban networks, but are not classed as highly urbanized in relation to the dense populations – the Madras area, the Cauvery and Godavari deltas, and much of the lower Ganga riverine belt. The vast majority of the 2,448 towns classed as such in the 1961 census are small market, service and handicraft centres, with a few other urban functions or amenities. Most are growing at about the national rate of increase. The total urban population increased from 62,603,291 in 1951 to 78,835,939 in 1961, an increase of about 21% comparable with the national growth rate of 22%. A typical rate of increase for a small market town over the decade is again about 20%. Some towns are stagnant or even actually declining. These are usually in very poor or backward areas (Sholapur in Gulbarga District, Mysore – not the large textile centre – population 18,352 in 1951 and 17,689 in 1961; Freelandganj in Panchmahals District, Gujarat, 16,696 in 1951 and 14,951 in 1961). A typical older commercial, administrative or industrial centre has increased at about 25% during the decade, and one with new and rapidly expanding industrial elements at about 30% – even a very large unit like Bangalore (1951, 786,343; 1961, 1,206,961).

The data for Pakistan have been mapped using the same class-boundaries for the shadings, and interestingly enough there is relatively little reflection of a pattern of urbanization. The line of hillfoot towns in East Punjab continues into West Punjab in Pakistan, but with this exception West Pakistan shows only individual Districts of high urbanization dominated by particular towns or cities – Karachi, Quetta, Hyderabad, Khairpur and the like. And East Pakistan shows low urbanization: in relation to the very dense population even Dacca, with over half a million people, does not bring its District into the denser shadings. At the same time Pakistan like India has its considerable autochthonous urban tradition, more than many underdeveloped countries, as well as its outward-looking seaports like Karachi and administrative centres like Dacca.

Apart from the great flow of studies in urban geography, especially in classification and land use, referred to in Chapter 7, a great deal of study has been applied to urbanization in relation to population growth as a whole, and in relation to industrialization and programmes to improve standards of living. Much of the literature was written under the influence of the great increases in urban populations in the decade 1941–51, culminating perhaps in the remarkable international seminar on urbanization in India at Berkeley, California, in 1960.[8] The estimates in the table seemed not only reasonable, but also to many inevitable, assuming that they would be attained through industrialization and accompanied by improvements in living standards (cf. p. 130).

[8] R. Turner (ed.), *India's Urban Future* (Univ. of California Press, Berkeley, 1962), especially Kingsley Davis, 'Urbanization in India: past and future', 3–26.

An attempt to programme rapid industrial-urban expansion in consonance with quite conceivable perspective planning was made by one of India's leading workers in this field within the Planning Commission.[9] There were some supporters of at least moderate decentralization, but perhaps the main current of thought was to accept the likelihood of massive centralized development, and

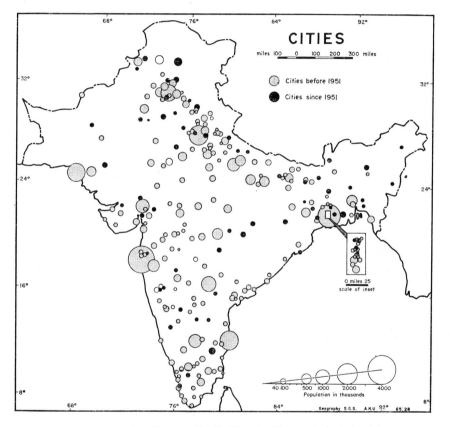

FIG 4.3 CITIES 1951–61. *Sources:* L. S. Bhat in *Geography*, 48 (1963), 315–17; *1961 Census of Pakistan*, Vol. 2.

to work towards improved efficiency in the process of urbanization, to avoid the horrible slums and shanty-town developments described elsewhere in this book.

The period 1941–51 included Partition and the massive population movements of some 7,000,000 moving from India to Pakistan and about as many

[9] P. Pant, 'Urbanization and the long-range strategy of economic development', *ibid.*, 182–91.

ESTIMATED SIZE OF THE TEN MAJOR CITIES IN INDIA
IN 1970 AND 2000
(*In millions of inhabitants*)

| Metropolis* | Estimated proportion in cities: | | | |
| | low | | high† | |
	1970	2000	1970	2000
Calcutta	12·0	35·6	16·0	66·0
Delhi	6·0	17·8	8·0	33·0
Bombay	4·0	11·9	5·3	22·0
Madras	3·0	8·9	4·0	16·5
Bangalore	2·4	7·1	3·2	13·2
Ahmedabad	2·0	5·9	2·7	11·0
Hyderabad	1·7	5·1	2·3	9·4
Kanpur	1·5	4·5	2·0	8·3
Poona	1·3	4·0	1·8	7·3
Nagpur	1·2	3·6	1·6	6·6

* Ranked according to their relative position in the year 2000.
† These estimates were based on a *medium* projection of the population as a whole, from which estimates were worked out, as tabulated, for low and high projections of the proportion of urban to total population. In the cited source a different answer was obtained using (a) 20,000 and (b) 100,000 as the lower limit of city size, but the difference was slight enough to warrant averaging the two to yield the figures as presented in this table.

Source: *India's Urban Future*, p. 25.

from Pakistan to India;[10] it now appears that this great upheaval was associated with particularly rapid urbanization, and there was some falling off in 1951–61 in rate of increase, though with absolute numbers not very different from the previous decade (urban population in India in 1941, 43,810,000); in 1951 61,870,000 (increase 41·2%); in 1961 79,240,000 (increase 28·1%).[11] On

[10] M. L. Qureshi (ed.), *Population Growth and Economic Development with Special Reference to Pakistan*, Institute of Development Economics, Karachi, 1960; especially W. P. Mauldin and S. S. Hashmi, 'Illustrative projections of the population of Pakistan, 1951 to 1991', 61–84. The total movements amounted to some 7,400,000 from Pakistan to India, 7,200,000 from India to Pakistan; there was a net outflow from East Pakistan mainly to West Bengal of 1,900,000, and of 1,800,000 from northern India to West Pakistan according to this source. There are useful maps in K. S. Ahmad, 'Urban population in Pakistan', *PGR* 10/1 (1955), 1–16. It may be added that casualties during communal riots and massacres were severe, perhaps amounting to 750,000 deaths, mainly in the Punjab.

[11] A. Bose, 'Population growth and the industrialization–urbanization process in India', *Man in India*, 41/4 (1961), 255–75; for a stimulating critique in this field, combining elements from the thinking of Gandhi and Patrick Geddes, see N. K. Bose, 'Some problems of urbanization', *ibid.*, 42/4 (1962), 255–62. In Pakistan for the period 1901–51 there was a fall in the proportion employed in industry, and even in absolute numbers of industrial workers, though changes in classification may be involved. See K. U. Kureishy, 'An analysis of civilian labour force in its bearing on growth of urban population in West Pakistan 1901–51', *PGR* 13/2 (1958), 89–99.

the whole there has been some disappointment that the rate of really successful urbanization and industrialization has not been higher, so as to relieve population pressure in the rural areas. Rapid urban-industrial increase is probably inevitable, at least if the five year plans are to succeed in their objectives. Meantime this slackening in rates of increase still represents very large urban increments in absolute numbers – some 17,000,000 of additional urban dwellers in India alone from 1951 to 1961 – and conditions are by no means good, nor even rapidly improving, for poorer urban groups. Urban unemployment and underemployment remain high – in India 17% unemployed and 16% underemployed, in large towns in East Pakistan over 10% unemployed but only 6% in West Pakistan.[12] There is crowding into the towns from pushing out of poor rural tracts and social groups, rather than urban pull to vacant jobs. The male preponderance in sex-ratio, general throughout the sub-continent, is accentuated in towns, particularly in north India and Pakistan, less so in south India where rural-urban migrants tend more to move in family groups and even to maintain some social cohesion in urban slums.[13] The underprivileged urban groups are above all the casual day-labourers, the coolies or *mazdoor*; there is a strong and positive urban pull when jobs in factories are known to be available, opening the door to what is much more a sort of middle-class life with good regular wages and supervised labour conditions.[14]

To sum up, there is an existing urban tradition and framework sufficient to cope with increasing urbanization and industrialization either in a few large centres or by considerable dispersion and evolution throughout hundreds or even thousands of towns. The prestige and efficiency of municipal authorities is seldom strong in large or small towns, though there are honourable exceptions. Many of the influx into large cities are housed in poor shanty-town slums and many small towns have as yet few urban amenities and services (see Fig. 4.11). But there is little doubt that India is a more fruitful and hopeful field for urban and industrial expansions than are many underdeveloped countries. Census data show that manufacturing industry at larger than household scale employs more than 10% of the population chiefly in a handful of places – Hooghlyside, Bombay, the Ahmedabad area, the Poona area and round Delhi, Agra, Kanpur, Madras, Coimbatore (just under 10%) and in one or two local and isolated areas. Of course, the detailed picture also shows individual small towns with over 10% of the population depending on household industry including weaving, and the 1951 Census (or the National Atlas) shows that several large areas have over

[12] ILO., *op. cit.*
[13] J. C. Sen, 'The sex composition of India's towns from 20,000 to 50,000, according to the 1961 census', *IGJ* 37/3 (1963), 90–100; note also the references to G. M. Woodruff's doctoral thesis to Radcliffe College in R. Turner, *op. cit.* and A. Lall, 'Age and sex structures of cities of India', *GRI* 24/1 (1962), 7–29. See also K. S. Ahmad, 'Urban population in Pakistan', *PGR* 10/1 (1955), 1–16, and H. Hussain, 'Some aspects of the rural-urban composition of population in East Pakistan', *ibid.*, 13/1 (1958), 24–28.
[14] Something of this emerges in various social surveys, e.g. R. D. Lambert, 'Factory workers and non-factory population in Poona', *Jnl of Asian Studies*, 18 (1958), 21–42.

10% of the population in village and small scale industries while about half the country has over 5%.[15] Since industrial population is commonly only about one-third of the population engaged in commerce, transport and services, it is clear that India's urbanization and industrialization have not so far progressed fast enough in relation to her problems of population growth and low standards of living, but that there is a very substantial foundation compared with many underdeveloped countries.

Internal migration

Gosal, who has carried out much of the recent geographical analysis of this important topic, has remarked that though the absolute numbers of migrants are large, they are relatively very small in relation to total population, and this remains true following later analysis based on the 1961 Census.[16] Refugee movements apart, migrants move from densely peopled or drought-ridden agricultural tracts to areas newly won for agriculture or where irrigation offers fresh possibilities, or of course to the towns and cities; movements are generally over relatively short distances, and economic motivations predominate.

Notoriously, this is a field where findings vary according to the administrative units for which data are available, but Gosal's work using district data has the advantage of relatively uniform criteria in relation to the size and population convenient for centralized administration. He accounts for the relatively low migration rates by lack of opportunity, ignorance, linguistic problems, and caste and joint family ties. He recognizes regions of low mobility, with under 8% not born in the district: (a) 'saturated' areas in the lower Gangetic plain and delta, and the coastal plains, and (b) sparsely peopled hill areas, lacking in opportunities. Urbanization and industry are little developed, but there is local migration to market, administrative and craft industry centres, which swells to considerable proportions in Andhra and Madras where quite rapid urban-industrial growth has been fed from quite local catchment areas of intense population pressure. High mobility areas (with over 16% not born in the district) include: (a) Assam, a unique case, with almost 20% of immigrants, many long-range, and up to 25% in the upper valley; most came before Partition including many Muslims, about a third since, and while the Bengalis have come mainly as farmers to new rice lands, many migrants from Bihar, Orissa and Madhya Pradesh were wage-labourers on tea plantations, though some have since settled as cultivators: (b) the Hooghlyside conurbation and the Damodar coalfield, with 33%, about equally from local

[15] There is good evidence that at least locally the figures for industrial employment in local areas are distorted because census enumerators have counted traditional caste occupation, not actual employment, while these are in fact often at variance (conversation with Dr J. Schwartzberg, July 1964, and see Bibliographical Note at the end of the chapter).

[16] G. S. Gosal, 'Internal migration in India – a regional analysis', *IGJ* 36/3 (1961), 106-21 and later papers; see also A. Lall, 'Patterns of in-migration in India's cities', *GRI*, 23/3 (1961), 16-23, and detailed studies such as U? Singh on Allahabad (*NGJI*, 4/4 (1958), 163-88, and E. Ahmad on Bihar (*Bombay Geog. Mag.*, 8-9 (1961), 61-68.

districts and from Uttar Pradesh, Orissa and parts of Bihar: (c) northwestern India, where 60% of urban immigrants were refugees, largely for whom a number of 'model towns' (usually in fact suburbs of existing towns) were built, with industrial estates, while Ganganagar is the focus of a new irrigation area attracting a steady stream of immigrants from Punjab: (d) south and southwest Mysore, with 20–40%, attracts coffee plantation labourers, while Bangalore is a rapidly expanding State capital and industrial town, and Kolar Gold Fields have a constant turnover of labour (but a decline in total population 1951–61); (e) in western India Greater Bombay has 73% of migrants, half from the coastal Districts of Ratnagiri and Kolaba, Ahmedabad (32%) draws in people from Saurashtra and Kutch, and Poona (18%) from nearby districts; (f) isolated urban foci of immigration – Madras, Hyderabad, Gwalior, Nagpur, Jabalpur, Indore, Ujjain, Kanpur, Lucknow and Dehra Dun.

The regions of medium mobility include for instance the Upper Gangetic plain, with short- to medium-range movement to new agricultural lands, notably in the terai, movements to areas of expanding well-irrigation in Rajasthan and local movements to towns in Madhya Pradesh.

Linguistic and cultural differences remain sufficiently great to present a real problem to individuals and particularly to families migrating over long distances. It is quite common, for example, to find clusters of south Indian middle-class families in Calcutta or Delhi, exercised to provide schooling for their children in south Indian languages, particularly if their stay is likely to be for a few years only. The progress of Hindi as a national language is of some help, but since long-range migration may be essential in the coming decades, these problems essentially of social geography probably deserve further study.

Demographic structure and trends

Rates of population increase already referred to are quite high but by no means unprecedented, and are exceeded by several countries, notably by much of Latin America today. Rates of increase have, however, been accelerating for the last 60 years, and the demographic situation is clearly a very dynamic one. The expectation of life of a baby born in 1901 was 24 years, in 1921 20 years, in 1941 32 years, and in 1960 45 years. It has been a cliché that in India and else-where death control has been achieved before birth control. While this was also true of Britain during the past phases of demographic expansion already referred to, there is an additional factor – one of India's main causes of death, now largely removed, was malaria. Malaria control or eradication has actually caused an increase in births, previously heavily reduced not only by missed conceptions but notably by increased abortions associated with disease.

Within this broad picture there have been marked regional variations mapped for the period 1881–1941 in Fig. 4.4.[17] Geddes believes that the regionally

[17] A. Geddes, 'The population of India: variability of change as a regional demographic index', GR 32 (1942), 562–73.

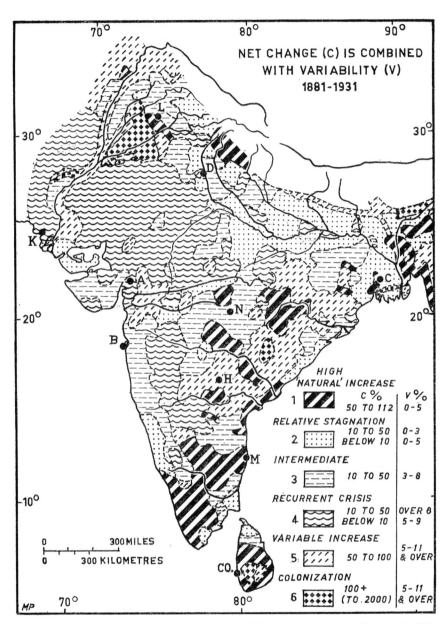

FIG 4.4 DEMOGRAPHIC REGIONS, from A. Geddes' pioneering contribution in *GR* 32 (1942), 562–73. Of the four most distinctive demographic types, stagnation was closely related to endemic malaria, recurrent crisis to periodic famine and epidemics, high natural increase to agricultural opportunities, usually in fertile soils or prolific climates; while colonization is self-explanatory.

differentiated demographic experience portrayed has had significant socio-psychological effects which may remain of importance for some time.[18] There is some confirmation from a psychiatric worker.[19] It may be that Geddes has put his

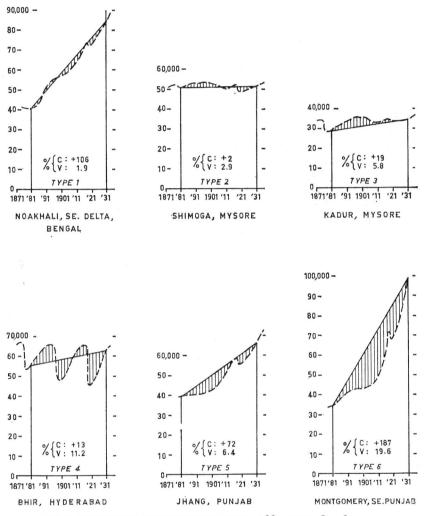

FIG 4.5 REGIONAL DEMOGRAPHIC TYPES, 1881–1931. See fig. 4.4.

finger on one of those socio-psychological blocks to full local participation in community development projects which have been qualitatively described by several

[18] A. Geddes, 'The social and psychological significance of variability in population change with examples from India 1871–1941', *Human Relations*, I (1947), 181–205.

[19] A. Hyatt Williams, 'A psychiatric study of Indian soldiers in the Arakan', *British Jnl Med. Psychology*, 23 (1950), 130–81.

observers. Since he wrote and compiled his map, however, the picture has become much less clear-cut – largely through the complete or partial control of famines, epidemics and not least malaria. Even a study of the period between the

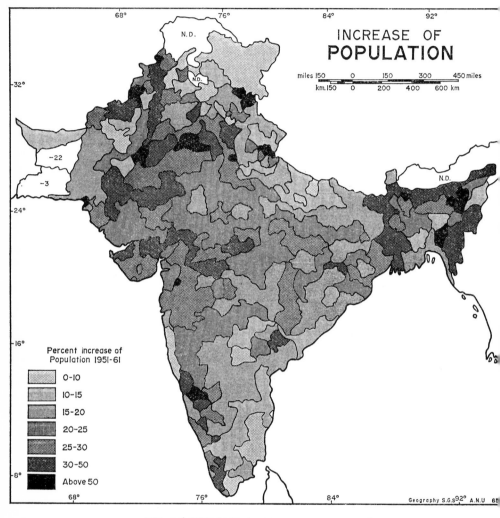

FIG 4.6 INCREASE OF POPULATION, 1951–61.

wars showed some blurring of these demographic regions,[20] and a map of population increase 1951–61 shows that regions of demographic stagnation have been wiped out (Fig. 4.6). There may be a residual in the Cauvery delta, with

[20] A. Geddes and A. T. A. Learmonth, 'Variability in population change and regional variations therein 1921–40', *IGJ* 28/1 (1953), 69–73.

relatively low rates of increase of 5–10%, but all the other regions of stagnation have given way to increases of 15–20% or even 25–30% or more in the Bengal delta (where urban-industrial immigration and refugee influx have contributed). In the forested hilly Malnad of western Mysore, again, formerly very malarious, and from which Geddes's type graph of stagnation was chosen, there are now similar rates of increase. The highest rates of increase of 30–50% or even more over the decade are due to immigration, including refugee movement, and development of fresh resources in areas of population densities relatively sparse in relation to resources – note the contrasting densities within the area of high increase in the Assam valley and in Rajasthan and Kutch. Looking back over a span similar to that studied by Geddes, but later (1891–1951), Trewartha and Gosal point out the significance of a turning point in population trends generally about 1921, with much lower rates of increase (actual decrease in about half the sub-continent) in 1891–1921, and higher rates 1921–51.[21] The first thirty-year period was one of frequent floods, droughts, epidemics and famines, including the last great famine to go comparatively unrelieved in 1899–1900,[22] several plague years and India's heavy share in the world influenza pandemic of 1919–20. The second thirty years was relatively free from these catastrophes, despite the Bengal famine of 1943 and the slaughter accompanying Partition in 1947.

Some population projections indicate that the current, or even a slightly increased, rate of population increase is likely to continue for at least two generations or so. There are indications that the economic level at which family size diminishes, over whole populations, is not beyond the possibilities, for very large masses of the population, within the period of two or three further five year plans – assuming these are successful.[23] Of course, the populations already attaining this modest level of 'middle-class prosperity' may have somewhat different backgrounds and social attitudes as compared with the much larger groups who may reach this level of income over the next ten or fifteen years. So a falling-off in population increase may take rather longer than is needed simply for these income figures to be attained. It is often assumed that urban families tend to be smaller than rural ones, and that this may afford at least to neo-Malthusian thinkers an additional reason for favouring rapid urbanization. Except for limited urban groups, there is little evidence as yet of lower fertility

---

[21] G. T. Trewartha and G. Gosal, 'The regionalism of population change in India', *Cold Harbor Symposia on Quantitative Biology*, 22 (1957), 71–81.

[22] One cannot maintain, of course, that relief measures were effective in the terrible Bengal famine, markedly concentrated in very densely peopled deltaic country and with many complicating factors, see p. 581. See also C. B. Memoria, 'Growth of population in India', *GRI* 19/4 (1957), 13–26 for an interesting review of the historical geography of population including famines, etc.

[23] P. C. Mahalanobis and A. Das Gupta, 'The use of sample surveys in demographic studies in India', *Proc. World Population Conf. 1954 Rome* (Papers, Vol. VI, UN, New York, 1955), 363–84.

in towns.[24] On the other hand in towns there is some evidence of more rapid adoption of family planning measures, like other innovations, but this is a topic so important that we shall return to it in the conclusion to the chapter.

Medical geography[25]

Regional differences in the incidence of disease have already been discussed, along with important sequelae when disease control became established. No single topic in this field is of greater importance than malaria control.

Large-scale malaria control campaigns in India began in 1947, yet by 1956 serious academic workers new to the country found it difficult to believe that malaria had been an important factor in the lives of the people, and the anonymous writer of the first report in the 1961 Census found it necessary to recall something of the pre-1947 situation for the benefit of the generation who had grown up unaware of the revolution in health and demographic trends so recently and so dramatically effected. Figs. 4.7–4.10 may suffice here to record the changes, and the demographic results have already been outlined. (See also Bibliographical Note, p. 149.)

The great epidemic diseases of India, cholera, plague and small-pox, received a great deal of attention, partly because India is something of a world endemic home of cholera and small-pox, from which the diseases burst forth in occasional epidemic years to bring death and terror in a random harvest of epidemics in all areas and places where the infections find conditions favouring their spread. Yet over the inter-war period they accounted on the average for only about 3% of the total mortality of India, although the figure was higher, up to some 20% or so, in an epidemic year. Plague has been associated for millennia with urban centres of the hillfoot zone of the Indo-Gangetic plains, as an enzootic in rats, epizootic in a cycle of about six years, and with a corresponding tendency towards endemicity in urban human populations, and to epidemic spread from the towns along routes of trade or pilgrimage in epidemic years. These towns are part of a ring of endemic foci including market centres strung around central Asia which contain the reservoir of infection in the 'silent zone' of the disease, the region of enzootic conditions among wild rodents like the marmot. The last great plague cycle came by sea to Bombay in 1896, spreading thence along routes followed by the cotton trade to the cotton collecting and market centres in particular. As well as the short term cycle of six years plague seems also to run in long term cycles.

[24] W. C. Robinson, 'Urban–rural differences in Indian fertility', *Population Studies*, 14 (1960–61), 218–34: for lack of good registration data, the fertility ratio is used, i.e. the ratio of children of 0–4 to 1,000 females, or to 1,000 married females, or 15–39; this ratio was formerly much lower in cities (especially large cities), but the urban–rural differentiation seems to be diminishing, perhaps because of more rapid decreases in infant and child mortality in cities as compared with the country, and perhaps because of a change in the nature of urban populations in the last few decades, from long-term city dwellers of lower fertility to recent immigrants of higher fertility.

[25] A. T. A. Learmonth, 'Medical geography in Indo-Pakistan: a study of twenty years' data for the former British India', *IGJ* 33/1 (1958), 1–59.

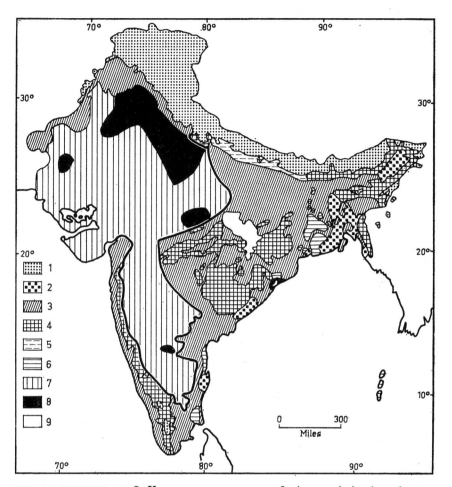

FIG 4.7 MALARIA, 1938. Key: 1, areas over 5,000 ft. (non-malarious); 2, known healthy plains (spleen rate under 10%); 3, more or less static moderate to high endemicity, intensity depending on local factors – seasonal variations moderate, fulminant epidemics unknown; 4, hyperendemic jungly hilly tracts and *terai*; 5, probably hyperendemic hill areas; 6, hyperendemic other than hills; 7, variable endemicity of drier areas, usually with autumnal rise in fever incidence (potential epidemic areas), spleen rate low except in years following epidemics or in special local circumstances, much affected by irrigation conditions; 8, known areas liable to fulminant epidemicity (diluvial) malaria, spleen rate high during and immediately after epidemics, slowly falling to low rates in *c.* 5 years; 9, unsurveyed. The heavy line marks the broad division between endemic and epidemic areas. From *IGJ* 33/1–2 (1958), 12; but ultimately from *Annual Report of the Public Health Commissioner . . . for 1940* (Delhi, 1941), based on work by S. R. Christophers and J. A. Sinton.

This major cycle seems to have been on the decline when the malaria campaign using residual insecticides like DDT seems to have discouraged the plague-bearing rat flea sufficiently to speed the departure of the waning plague cycles. There are up to a few hundred cases a year, but plague has not been an important health problem for a decade or more.

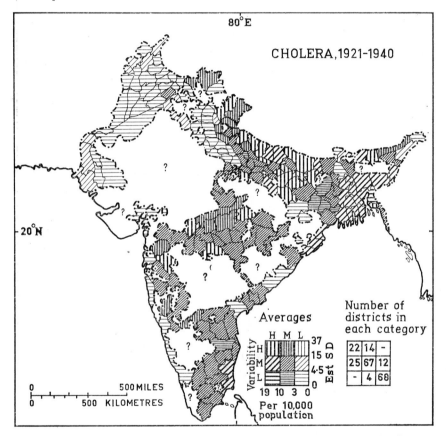

FIG 4.8 CHOLERA 1921–40. The east coast deltas are endemic homes of the disease, showing medium to high average mortality with medium variability; the other areas of high death rates show high variability – these are epidemic areas, to which the infection spreads from the endemic foci in 'favourable' years. There is a rather sharp drop in mortality in the relatively little-affected semi-arid areas, though local outbreaks (perhaps started by a pilgrim carrier) can be unpleasant enough.

Cholera is mapped for British India for the inter-war period as Fig. 4.8. The endemic homes of cholera, a mainly water-borne infection by *Vibrio cholerae*, are particularly low-lying deltas with organic-rich water and a high water table. Even there, cholera vanishes as a human disease causing illness and death in the later years of a cycle of about five or six years. The disease may be present in immune carriers or there may be a cyclic, perhaps genetic change in the virulence of the cholera organism. Illnesses and deaths tend to increase in the endemic homes following this cycle, about every fifth year, and thence to fan out along lines of communications. On many past occasions pilgrimage to the Jagganath (Juggernaut) festival at Puri has caused explosive outbreaks to spread widely, and similarly if a cholera outbreak and widespread rainfall and humid conditions have coincided with one of the particularly large gatherings of pilgrims at Allahabad at the Yamuna–Ganga confluence every twelfth year, or every fourteenth year at Hardwar where the Ganga leaves the mountains. In other years cholera spreads more gradually, more widely, less explosively, from the Ganga–Brahmaputra delta, moving slowly *up*stream on a wide front, and with scattered widespread occurrences rather than highly localized explosive outbreaks round a particular well or other source of drinking water. It has been argued that under these conditions the disease must be fly-borne.[26] Inoculation against cholera is now possible, though not very long-lasting, but over the last thirty years or so the health authorities have attained considerable success in the control of explosive outbreaks dispersing from pilgrim centres through the mass inoculation of pilgrims.[27]

Small-pox, a mainly droplet-borne virus infection, is a disease of squalor and overcrowding, though no respecter of persons, especially the un-vaccinated, in a virulent epidemic outbreak. It is again largely concentrated in the densely populated Bengal delta, including the dreadful urban slums. Again, there is something of a cyclic tendency due to changes in acquired immunity in the population – if only through births and therefore largely in growth of the non-immune and often un-vaccinated – or to changes in virulence of virus, of which many sub-types of different characteristics have been identified. Again it fans out in epidemic years, and the incubation period is such that in these days of rapid travel a single incubating or carrier individual may cause an outbreak in a foreign population low in immunity acquired through previous infection or from vaccination. Many years of mass vaccination campaigns in the Indian sub-continent have met with some failures and with some obstacles set by apathy or by religious objections to vaccination. But these efforts are being intensified, for the sake of internal health as well as external relations.

The great causes of mortality, the major public health problems are much less dramatic than these three epidemic diseases. Among the infections, tuberculosis has been important up to now. A major campaign is being planned using BCG inoculations, and pilot projects under different epidemiological, social and living conditions are being carried out. Bronchitis and associated pneumonia are important causes of mortality, especially in the northern half of the sub-continent, in the cool weather, and among poor, ignorant, ill-clad, ill-fed and

[26] W. C. Ross, 'The epidemiology of cholera', *Indian Jnl Med. Research*, 15 (1928), 951–64.
[27] A. L. Banks, 'Religious fairs and festivals in India', *Lancet*, Jan. 1961, 162–3.

ill-housed groups, in the country and especially in urban slums. Various forms of intestinal infection classed as dysentery, less dramatic than cholera, nevertheless cause much chronic ill-health and inefficiency, and also many deaths. There is an association with fly-breeding and with intimate contacts between flies and family life, especially if the generally poor sanitation is associated with moderate crowding of buildings – wide dispersion permits some poor disposal of faecal

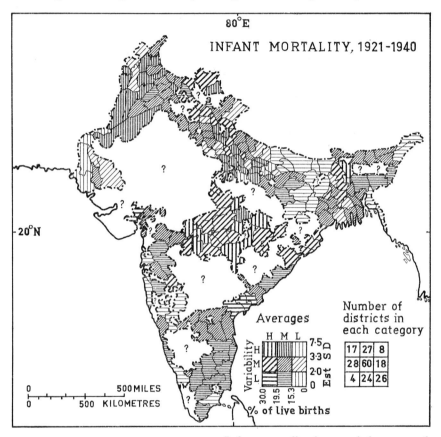

FIG 4.9 INFANT MORTALITY, 1921–40. Infant mortality is regarded as a good index of general conditions of health and hygiene. Rates were generally high by modern standards, but particularly so in central India (liable to variable harvests and epidemics), in the east coast deltas (with lower variability), and in the hills and hillfoot areas, long densely settled, of the north; as also in the overcrowded towns and cities.

matter, while real crowding enforces some systematic disposal of night soil. And there may be a relationship with shallow wells as in much of the Peninsular Block, subject to pollution from run-off rather than fed by water which has undergone thorough filtration through alluvium.

Dysentery will long remain an important public health problem unless a *deus ex machina* is forthcoming as happened with malaria control where only minimal public co-operation with spraying teams is needed. The ultimate remedy lies in improved diet, housing, sanitation and personal hygiene. Indeed, these factors, the very stuff of the improved standards of living sought in the five year plans, will do as much as specific campaigns, it seems, to reduce these remaining major problems of public health. All of these contribute to the still high infant and child mortality rates (Fig. 4.9; Learmonth *op. cit.* in chapter bibliography). As these diseases become less important – and there are hopeful signs from some areas and socio-economic classes – with better general nutrition and infant and child feeding as well as maternal care and welfare, these rates are also gradually improving.

Pakistan – some demographic considerations
The foregoing discussion has been conducted mainly for the sub-continent as a whole – mainly because some of the major sources were written before Partition or maintain this viewpoint in order to follow up the census records of the British period which are good, by comparison with most underdeveloped regions, since about 1881. Pakistan has, however, some particularities from the demographic viewpoint.

The 1961 census revealed a total population of 93,810,000, but a leading demographer working in this area estimates that allowing for under-enumeration, the figure would be 100,000,000 by mid-1961.[28] The official totals of 50,800,000 for East Pakistan and 40,800,000 for West Pakistan plus 2,200,000 in Karachi represent densities of 1,200 per sq. mile (460 per sq. km²) and 130 per sq. mile (50 per km²) respectively. East Pakistan would rank with Java, of the predominantly rural areas, and is as densely peopled as many industrialized countries (Belgium, 785 p.s.m., 302 per km²), though of course with much lower standards of living. West Pakistan, on the other hand, would compare say with Malaya, though it must be remembered that much hot desert is more uncompromisingly uninhabitable than a humid wilderness like interior Malaya; densities of the order of 750 per sq. mile (290 per km²), as in Sialkot and Lyallpur may represent population saturation given existing agricultural techniques and proportions of industrially employed, though granted at rather higher standards of living (and lower population pressure) than are common in East Pakistan.

The recorded rate of population increase 1951–61 was 2·2% per annum, though this may be a little overstated, as some demographers suspect, owing to under-registration (or greater under-registration) in the 1951 as compared with the 1961 census. Even if there is slight overstatement, the increase is considerable, especially since Pakistan's anti-malaria campaigns are only now getting fully into their stride. Rates of increase are higher in West than in East Pakistan;

[28] K. J. Krotki, 'First release from the second population census of Pakistan, 1961', *Pak. Dev. Rev.* 1/2 (1961), 66–71; this article is extensively used in this section.

though the East may have more under-registration, it is the more likely area to have rates of increase damped down by malaria until the disease is eradicated, and the West to be affected by malaria epidemics (cf. p. 139), so that the contrast is probably justified. Also the West has had considerable irrigation projects and inward migration. It is likely that one cause of the upward trend in rates of increase is later marriage (say from early to late teens) which reduces excessively early child-bearing causing maternal mortality, or sterility in later years. The upward trend is likely to be maintained, at least for some time, and the implications for economic planning are serious. As Krotki points out, investment of 12% of the national income – a high figure outside totalitarian states – would only keep pace with the population increase, allowing existing and unsatisfactory standards of living to be maintained – and that on the assumption of even distribution of benefits from the investment among socio-economic groups; an investment of 16% would, on such population trends, only permit of the doubling of the present standard of living by the end of the century.[29]

Conclusion – demographic prospects and policies

There are surely regional demographic differences of academic and practical importance. The rural population density map today invites not merely an academic exercise in synthesis, but a systematic study in population capacity – by no means impossible with modern techniques though it would be expensive in skill, time and money. A map of urban population invites study both of broad urban patterns and characteristics and amenities, and of individual city spheres of influence preferably built up systematically until one can appreciate the complex and dynamic web of urban influence over the sub-continent. Both of these studies have been the subject of probing attacks and are certainly practicable. Regional differences in demographic history are apparently becoming blurred at present as all parts of the country enter the phase of population increase differentiated only by degree of rapidity: if there are in fact associated regional differences in social psychology, as Geddes believes, these may be of academic and practical importance. But this is a topic difficult to investigate conclusively because of the extraordinarily complex and multi-dimensional matrix of factors involved, and equally because of political sensitivity about contemplating some of them, almost amounting to aversion. Regional forecasts of population using projections can be done, and may be increasingly necessary should regional planning be used in the future as a complement to national planning. (Such regional forecasts might in fact permit greater accuracy in a macro-demographic projection, or at least a useful check on these.) But naturally enough most concern among educated Indians and Pakistanis and abroad is focused on the

[29] K. J. Krotki, 'Population control – a review article', *Pak. Dev. Rev.* 1/3 (1961), 89–98; the paper bears a significant sub-title, a quotation from R. L. Meier: 'We cannot be optimistic and honest at the same time.' See also S. M. Haider, 'Study of population pressure in relation to agricultural development in Pakistan', *Indian Jnl Econ.* Vol. 38, No. 153, Pt. 3 (1958), 239–48.

national situation, on macro-demographic problems and policies, specifically on population projections and on family planning programmes, especially in India.

Authoritative projections, made in the 1950s, ranged from 408,000,000 to 424,000,000.[30] India's 1961 population, over 439,000,000, exceeded the highest estimate based on projections, as the preliminary census report points out. More than any other single factor, this discrepancy is due to the demographic revolution effected at a stroke and without much need for widespread public co-operation by malaria control. This underestimate of the upsurge of population was a serious matter particularly in relation to the Second Five Year Plan, many of the benefits of which were eaten up, as it were, by the extra mouths. (While it may be argued that the effort in the Second Plan was maximal and would not be effected by better population forecasts, there is on the other hand the possibility that more foreign aid might have been forthcoming if the full seriousness of the demographic prospect had been realized.) Neither demographers nor planners realized the significance of the effects of malaria control upon both death rates and birth rates, although in a country as near and in some ways as similar as Ceylon, population increase had gone up to 3% per annum within a year or two of the establishment of malaria control, and a very carefully worked out paper on the effects of malaria on mortality had been proved quite wrong.[31] There can be no better example of the need for co-ordinating disciplines in both academic and practical affairs.

Even before the rate of population increase swung up in this way, the government of India had however been greatly concerned about the population problem. After all even an increase of 1·2% per annum as it was in 1951 represented an annual increase of 4,500,000 people – a sufficiently daunting prospect for a nation trying to combat poverty.

There are many strands of thinking, sometimes conflicting, about family planning in India – neo-Malthusian, from the 1920s or even before; Gandhian, with much emphasis on abstinence; anti-colonialist and Marxist, perhaps changing a little as the problems have increased even following Independence.[32] But

[30] R. P. Sinha, *Food in India* (OUP, Bombay, 1961), Ch. IV.

[31] C. A. Gill, 'The influence of malaria on natality with special reference to Ceylon', 1940, *Jnl Malaria Inst. of India*, 3, 201–52; for a recent critical review see H. Fredericksen, 'Economic and demographic consequences of malaria control in Ceylon', *Ind. Jnl Malariology* 16/4 (1962), 379–91.

[32] S. Thapar, 'Family Planning in India', *Population Studies*, 17 (1963), 4–19, gives a very useful history; R. C. Cook, 'India: high cost of high fertility', *Population Bulletin*, 14/8 (1958), for a recent, by no means entirely negative neo-Malthusian view; G. Chand, *Some aspects of the population problem of India* (Patna, 1954), is an extremely well-written socialist view, stressing the need for a positive approach to family size and spacing, and showing resentment of foreign neo-Malthusian views including earlier work by R. C. Cook; S. Chandrasekhar's many works include *Demographic Disarmament for India* (Bombay, 1951), a very clear brief statement, and 'The population factor in economic development', *Population Rev.* (1964), 54–7; see also W. S. Thompson, *Population and Progress in the Far East* (Chicago, 1959).

there is now widespread agreement on the need for population control in order
that the very tiny improvements in standards of living of the great bulk of the

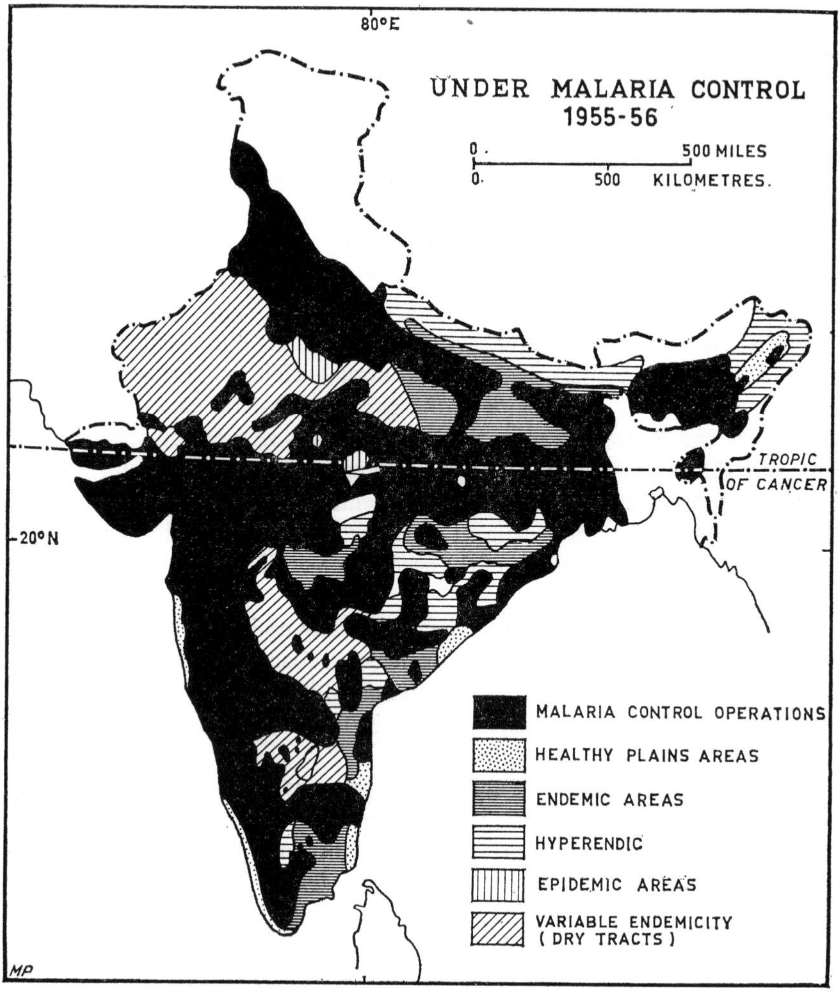

FIG 4.10 AREA UNDER MALARIA CONTROL, INDIA, 1955–56. During the four or
five years up to 1956, malaria control had spread very rapidly over the most
malarious areas; by now almost the whole country has been controlled and the
emphasis has shifted to eradication. Figs 4.8 to 4.10 from A. T. A. Learmonth in
IGJ 33/1–2 (1958); Fig 4.10 is ultimately from the Malaria Institute of India's
1956 conference.

people since Independence should be much increased in future. So far it has
been a matter of running hard to do little better than keep standing still. Family
planning has been officially promoted, especially research and experimental work,

ever since the First Five Year Plan. Naturally enough there is, on the whole, readier acceptance of the ideas of family planning in the cities where even the poorer groups rapidly become more sophisticated in some respects than their rural cousins. There is not unexpectedly a great desire for family limitation among the women, and fairly widespread acceptance of the idea even among the men. The main difficulty in towns is the cost of any form of mechanical or chemical contraceptives, especially in the poorer groups where the need is greatest. The same groups also suffer from ignorance, illiteracy and notably 'innumeracy' when attempting to apply the rhythm method – a fickle one at best. There is also a widespread demand for treatment for sterility among childless couples, and it is one of the stronger cards of the family planning clinics in establishing *rapport* with their communities that they are frequently able to help with this problem.

In the villages all the problems are large, there is much more conservatism, ignorance, illiteracy even among fairly prosperous groups, much less acceptance from the men of the very concept of the need for family planning; and the crushing burden of ignorance even among actively interested women is illustrated by the now well known example of misunderstanding: beads representing the menstrual cycle differentiating the most likely period for conception – the 'danger period' for the couple with a large enough family or desiring to space the family more widely – were in fact placed around the neck of a goat, in a village near the experimental clinic in Ramanagaram in Mysore, in order to *induce* a caprine pregnancy! Constant effort is applied to improving the methods both of contraception and of communication, and to increasing the coverage of the enormous population by family planning clinics. If as yet there has been no effort comparable to that in China at times when population control is desired by the Communist government, there are some additional problems, such as the linguistic ones, and of course there is no channel of communication comparable in power to the Communist Party caucus and Party member down to village level. At present, success with contraception and the rhythm method has been so limited that the government department concerned has turned, as a desperate remedy, to sterilization, especially of men once they have say three children including at least one son; there is even some tendency to regard the planned increase of medical practitioners as an additional force of potential vasectomists, a sterile objective! From the beginning of the campaign to encourage vasectomy in 1956 to April 1962 the total number of operations performed was only some 98,000 mostly in Madras and Maharashtra. This form of campaign seems doomed to failure, probably implying undesirable social, psychological and international consequences.[33] On the other hand, the time-lag is considerable before improved

[33] S. Chandrasekhar, 'The population factor in economic development', *Population Rev.* 8/2 (1964), 54–7; for a view, not against sterilization, but on the dangers of bad communications concerning it, see E. Wood, 'Science in family planning', *Thought*, 24 (1961), 9.

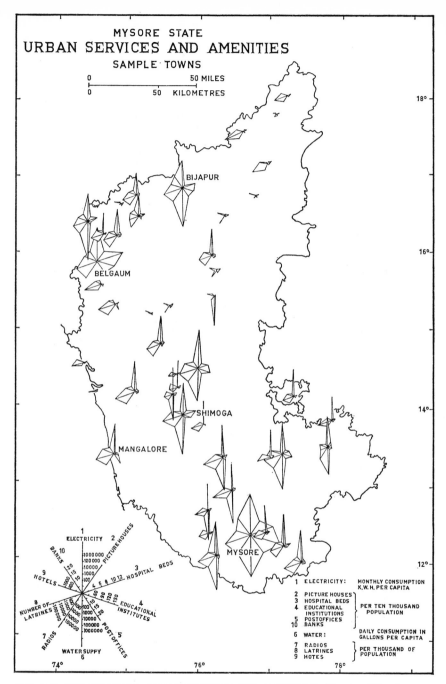

FIG 4.11 MYSORE STATE: URBAN SERVICES AND AMENITIES. Mysore City shows a good balance, whereas Belgaum at the time of survey (1956–58) was reasonably served except for water, while Bijapur's most notable lack was less serious – entertainment. From V. L. S. Prakasa Rao in A. T. A. Learmonth and L. S. Bhat (eds), *Mysore State: I. An Atlas of Resources* (1961).

standards of education and of material living can be expected to cause a moderation in population increase to rates compatible with the provision of food and a good standard of living (see pp. 137, 281). Assuming continuance of India's five year plans, one can think ultimate success possible, and look forward to a prosperous and relatively stable population in this great sub-continent, but the next generation or two can hardly fail to be very difficult, strained, painful and dangerous. Is there any possibility that a *deus ex machina* may come to solve the problem created by that other *deus ex machina*, the residual insecticide? A really cheap oral contraceptive without side effects on health may be just around the corner. If so, or if the high hopes placed on the 'loop' are realised, the Malthusian spectre may be laid once more.

BIBLIOGRAPHICAL NOTE

Perhaps the best advice we can give to a reader wishing to explore this topic in depth is to start with Kingsley Davis and then follow up the footnotes in this chapter. Davis' book *The Population of India and Pakistan* (Princeton, 1950), is a sort of bench-mark survey very useful on the demographic side though insufficiently critical about the nature of the statistics in places – e.g. in his view of 'culturable waste'. R. P. Sinha's *Food in India* (OUP, Bombay, 1961), is an admirably clear account. The Censuses of India and Pakistan continue to be fundamental sources, of high quality, and the publications of the Indian Census in 1961 include some particularly stimulating items, including an atlas volume, village surveys and a monographs series, e.g. Vol. V – Gujarat, Part VII – A(1), R. K. Trivedi, 'Selected Crafts of Gujarat: Agate industry of Cambay', 1964; Vol. IX – Madras: Part VII, A(1), P. K. Nambiar, 'Handicrafts and Artisans of Madras State – Silk Weaving of Kanchipuram'; Vol. IX – Madras, Part VI, P. K. Nambiar, 'Village Survey Monographs 3, Arkasanhalli'. At the same time one should take account of the growing body of critical material on both demographic and economic data like occupational structure, e.g. Krotki's papers cited earlier, or J. E. Schwartzberg, *Occupational structure and level of economic development in India: a regional analysis*, 1960 (University Microfilms, Ann Arbor). The Indian view of the problem of population is reflected in *Population Review*, published from The Indian Institute for Demographic Studies and edited by Dr S. Chandrasekhar; the best articles are at a high level. The Institute of Applied Manpower Research, New Delhi, has published an interesting *Fact Book of Manpower* (1963), used at various points in the chapter.

A. T. A. Learmonth, *Health in the Indian Sub-Continent 1955–65* (Australian National University, Dept. of Geography School of General Studies Occasional Paper No. 2, Canberra, 1965), provides a comprehensive review of the medical literature bearing on the problems treated in this chapter. Older but fundamental work on the ecology of malaria is reviewed in his paper in *Trans. Inst. British Geogrs.* 23, 1957, 37–59.

CHAPTER 5

The Peoples of the Sub-continent

GENERALITIES

That the diversity of the peoples of India baffles description is a commonplace. Only less frequent is the observation that there is an underlying – or overlaying – cultural unity. This is undoubtedly true of India proper: everywhere, except in some Himalayan and jungle areas, the structure of society and the architectural landscape bear the strong impress of Hinduism. If we think of caste rather than religion, the ambit of common cultural features is yet wider, since even groups whose origin was an avowed or implied rejection of caste still retain traces (sometimes more) of caste attitudes, or are influenced, in greater or less degree by caste spirit: Indian Christians, Sikhs, some fractions at least of the Tribes and even the Muslims. In fact it is hardly an exaggeration to say that the only considerable groups with a culture not at least strongly influenced by Hinduism are the hillmen of West Pakistan, some of the Assam border tribes, and the Buddhists of Ladakh or 'Little Tibet'.

Despite the Pakistani 'Two Nations' theory, the main mass of Muslims have a culture which, if dominantly Islamic, is yet shot through with strands of 'Indianism' (to avoid the word Hinduism). Only Islam has had sufficient strength to exert a reciprocal influence and that has been rather limited, perhaps most clearly seen in the extension of *purdah* (the seclusion of women); and here other sociological factors clearly have their part. In more recent times Christianity has compelled some reassessment of Hindu ideals; like Islam, it had most to offer to those towards the bottom of the caste ladder. But the role of Christianity is difficult to disentangle from that of Westernization in general; Western secular humanism does at least provide some neutral ground on which the adherents of various faiths can meet.[1] Finally it must always be remembered that the religion of the masses – Hindu, Muslim, and Christian – is pervaded by more primitive beliefs.

Ethnic and linguistic divisions do not, in general, correspond to any marked extent; and both are cut across by religion. The division of most practical

---

[1] It has been pointed out, for example, that some Indian leaders, whose final attitude is known to be essentially agnostic, would by that fact be almost certainly precluded from high political office in the United States. It is 'community' rather than actual belief which counts.

significance is that of 'community': this is for the most part a religious differentiation, but it has some ethnic, linguistic and cultural connotations in the 'Tribes', and in the 'Scheduled Castes' it recognizes a cleavage within the main religious community. The minor religious communities – Sikhs, Parsees, Jains – may

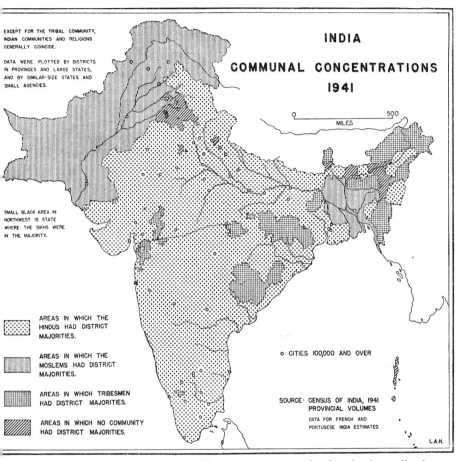

EXCEPT FOR THE TRIBAL COMMUNITY, INDIAN COMMUNITIES AND RELIGIONS GENERALLY COINCIDE.

DATA WERE PLOTTED BY DISTRICTS IN PROVINCES AND LARGE STATES, AND BY SIMILAR-SIZE STATES AND SMALL AGENCIES.

SMALL BLACK AREA IN NORTHWEST IS STATE WHERE THE SIKHS WERE IN THE MAJORITY.

INDIA

COMMUNAL CONCENTRATIONS

1941

0   500
        MILES

AREAS IN WHICH THE HINDUS HAD DISTRICT MAJORITIES.

AREAS IN WHICH THE MOSLEMS HAD DISTRICT MAJORITIES.

AREAS IN WHICH TRIBESMEN HAD DISTRICT MAJORITIES.

AREAS IN WHICH NO COMMUNITY HAD DISTRICT MAJORITIES.

o CITIES 100,000 AND OVER

SOURCE: CENSUS OF INDIA, 1941 PROVINCIAL VOLUMES

DATA FOR FRENCH AND PORTUGESE INDIA ESTIMATED.

L.A.H.

FIG 5.1 MAJOR COMMUNITIES, 1941. This map represents the situation immediately before, and essentially responsible for, the Partition of 1947. *Source:* L. Hoffmann in *GJ* 91 (1948).

perhaps best be thought of as kiths as defined by Huntington: 'A group of people relatively homogeneous in language and culture, and freely intermarrying with one another.'[2]

Ethnic stocks

Only the baldest summary, following B. S. Guha, can be given here; it would be the vainest of labours to attempt a description of the salient physical and cultural

[2] *Mainsprings of Civilization* (Wiley, NY, 1945), 102 fn.

characteristics of even the main groups in the few available pages. There has been some criticism of Guha's scheme, notably by D. N. Majumdar; but, although the latter has taken blood-group surveys into account, it cannot be said that anything very clear emerges, except that Guha may have overstressed the Negrito element. The populations of the sub-continent exhibit in varying degree characteristics from the four major stocks of mankind: Negroid, Australoid, Mongoloid and Caucasoid.

Of earlier peoples, almost the only known skeletal remains of much significance are those of the Indus Valley civilization: these show very close affinities with those of pre-Sargonic Mesopotamia (Al-Ubaid and Kish). The numerous Megalithic remains of the Peninsula undoubtedly hold vital evidence on the peopling of India; their scientific exploration is but beginning.

The earliest of existing groups are the *Negritos* (Negroids of small stature), of whom the Andaman Islanders are good examples. The Kadars of Cochin, like the Andamanese still hunters and gatherers (except where contaminated by outside influence), also show some Negrito characteristics; and traces at least of Negrito physical types have been reported from the Rajmahal Hills.

Far more significant are the evidences of *Australoid* stock which appear in the tribal populations of the south and centre (e.g. Mundas, Santals). In varying mixtures, this is the underlying strain in very much of the Hindu population, especially of lower or 'exterior' castes, south of the Narmada–Chota Nagpur line. The Veddas of Ceylon seem to represent a more specialized development from this group, which is also often styled pre-Dravidian; but Dravidian, like Aryan, is better kept as a linguistic term.

The tribal peoples of the north are essentially dissimilar, and, as might be expected, show marked *Mongoloid* characters. They occupy a broad band of Himalayan and sub-Himalayan country from Kashmir to Bhután; in the hills on either side of the Assam valley a long-headed Mongoloid type is dominant; the Burmese are more brachycephalic. The Assam Valley itself has an interesting fusion of Mongoloids (the Shan Ahoms, who were the mediaeval rulers) with Palaeo-Mediterraneans, the bearers of Hindu culture.

The populations which show the most marked evidences of these three major stocks (Negroid, Australoid and Mongoloid) are mainly tribal, though of course these elements are not confined to the tribes, nor are they represented in all tribes. The 'higher' populations are more complex still.

The largest *Caucasoid* element is *Mediterranean*; 'moderate stature, long head, slightly built body, dark complexion'. The Palaeo-Mediterraneans appear to have introduced a Megalithic culture, perhaps originally Neolithic; they form the main component of the Dravidian speakers. Another Mediterranean group, Guha's 'Large-brained Chalcolithic Type', represented by the numerous skeletons of the Indus valley civilization, is dominant in northern India and form a large proportion of the upper classes elsewhere. There is also an 'Oriental' type, mainly in the northwestern hills and the Punjab; it is intrusive elsewhere with upper-class Muslims, descendants of Pathan invaders, and has strong affinities with Anatolian and Arabian groups.

Somewhat later, apparently, than the 'Chalcolithic' type, there was a considerable penetration of Western Brachycephalic types – Alpines, Dinarics and Armenoids. They entered probably via Makran, mingling with the Mediterraneans (they are represented among the Indus valley skeletons), and thence moved as far as Ceylon, while another branch followed the Ganga to Bengal.

Finally, and in many respects more important, there were the great folk-wanderings which brought the *Proto-Nordic* Indo-Aryans. These steppe pastoralists, tall, fair, meat-eating, entered northern India in the latter part of the 2nd millennium BC; together with Mediterraneans they are dominant in the country between the Indus and Bundelkhand, and in Maharashtra form an important element in fusion with Palaeo-Mediterraneans, Alpo-Dinarics, and Proto-Australoids. In the extreme northwest almost blond types are found, and even in Maharashtra almost 10% of the Chitpavan Brahmins have light eyes.

The ethnic history of India is thus complicated, in keeping with the general diversity of the sub-continent. The various stocks have brought diverse gifts, material and cultural, to the common store. The Vedic hymns and the treasury of Sanskrit literature are the obvious contributions of the Indo-Aryans; but the basic concepts of Hinduism seem rather Dravidian, stemming from the Mediterraneans of the Indus valley and the Proto-Australoids.[3]

Language and literacy

There is only a very rough correlation between ethnic stock and language. The Himalayan and Assam tribes speak mainly Tibeto–Burman languages, those of the central hills Dravidian or yet older Austric languages; the south is almost solidly Dravidian, the north mainly Indo–Aryan. That is about as far as one can go; both Indo–Aryan and Dravidian tongues are spoken by representatives of almost all the main racial groups. And even so there are many outliers, of which perhaps the most interesting is the Dravidian Brahui of Baluchistan (cf. p. 184).

The 'racial' element has indeed its importance – a very great importance – in the cultural history of India; it is of little practical significance today. Few Indians (and for that matter few Englishmen) could speak with any degree of scientific accuracy as to their racial origins; everyone knows what language he speaks. Next to religion language is the greatest divisive force in India (and Pakistan) today.

The diversity of tongues was one of the standard imperialistic arguments against nationalist claims. Actually there is not a great deal in it as it was presented. It is true that the 1931 Census showed 225 Indian and Burmese languages; but the great majority of these were mere tribal splinters spoken by a few hundred

---

[3] See B. S. Guha, *Racial Elements in the Population* (OPIA No. 22, 1944), 27–29, for a brilliant summary; and cf. D. N. Majumdar, *Races and Cultures of India* (Asia, Bombay, 1958).

or at most a few thousand people: very interesting to philologists, but not insuperable obstacles to the unity of over 300,000,000 people. The communist writer Palme Dutt criticized the *Imperial Gazetteer* for citing Andro, spoken by one person only; however, the 1951 Census of India lists 720 languages or dialects with less than 100,000 speakers each, and of these no less than 73 were returned as spoken by one speaker: lonely souls.[4] On the other hand, ten languages accounted for 319,000,000 out of a total population of 357,000,000 – 89%.

There are indeed only some 12 or 15 really major languages, and some of these are closely akin: hardly an alarming total for an area and population comparable to Europe. The most important distinction is that between the Dravidian tongues of the south and the Indo–Aryan of the north and centre. The chief Dravidian languages are Telugu and Tamil (Figs. 5.2, 23.4) with over 33,000,000 and 26,500,000 speakers respectively in 1961, Kanarese or Kannada (14·5 million), and Malayalam, the speech of Kerala (13·4 million). The Indo–Aryan languages account for about three-quarters of the population of the sub-continent, and one of them, Hindi, with its branches ranks numerically as one of the greater languages of the world: in 1935 Western Hindi was spoken by over 105,000,000 people, and it has been gaining rapidly by nationalist and (since 1947) official favour. Other important languages are Bengali with 25,000,000,[5] leader in the literary renaissance in India, Marathi with 27,000,000, and Gujarati, less important numerically (16,000,000) but the main language of indigenous commerce in western India.

Bi- and even tri-lingualism are widespread among all classes except the peasantry of linguistically homogeneous areas. It is probable that there are not many market towns in which the traveller equipped with Hindustani, Tamil and English could not be readily understood.[6]

Yet the problem of a common language remains serious: the world has seen too much use of the linguistic weapon by forces making for disunity. So far English has been the language of most serious scholarship (outside theology) and has been a *lingua franca* for the intelligentsia; but only about 1–2% of the population is literate in English, though English of sorts is understood by many illiterates. Bazaar or camp English is a wasting asset (as well as an insult to Shakespeare's tongue), but the disappearance of academic English would be an intellectual catastrophe of the first order, gravely limiting contacts with the outside world, and especially with the main currents of scientific and social thought. In the past the too-exclusive use of English as a medium of instruction may have impeded learning in other subjects, without always imparting noticeable mastery

[4] There was also, surprisingly, one speaker of Newzealandian.
[5] Figures for India only; Bengali is of course the dominant language of the 51,000,000 people (1961) of East Pakistan.
[6] Cf. G. Slater's remark (*Southern India* (1936), 33): 'Ability to read and write . . . are the Indian census tests of literacy, and by these India makes a very bad showing. If ability to speak and understand a second language were also tested, Madras would show far better results than London. . . .'

in its own use; but there seems to be already some decline in the standard of English in the universities.

Yet it is only to be expected that really creative work will tend more and more to be written in the great mother-tongues of India and, despite expedient delays, the policy of replacing English in provincial and eventually in central

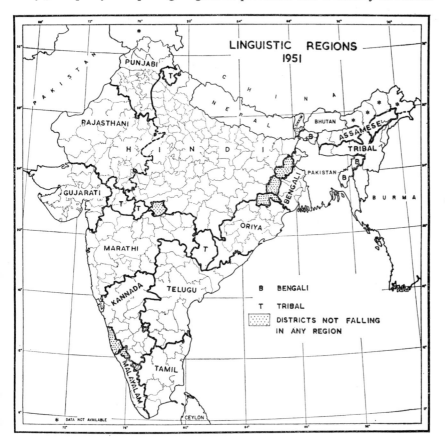

FIG 5.2 LINGUISTIC REGIONS, 1951. The dominance of Hindi in no less than 86 Districts will be noticed. *Courtesy* R. Tirtha.

administration will doubtless prevail in the end. Nevertheless, there are reasonable and serious doubts as to how far the supersession of English should go.[7] Despite its scores of millions of speakers, it will be a long time before Hindi can rank as a world language in the sense in which English is a world language. Its advance to such status is of course retarded by indiscreet Sanskritization instead

[7] Pandit Nehru himself expressed such doubts. For balanced comment, see S. A. Husain, *The National Culture of India* (Asia, Bombay, 2nd ed. 1961), 209–11; Irawati Karve, *Hindu Society – an Interpretation* (Deccan College, Poona, 1961), 131–42.

of transliterating quasi-international technical terms, and by its special script which is, however, one of the factors in its bid to become not only the dominant internal but even the 'national' language.

Nationalist opinion on the whole favours the spread of Hindi as a common language, though it meets with considerable opposition especially in Tamilnad, conscious of its high literary tradition. With its Hindustani form it is undoubtedly the most widely known language; but Hindustani is often a debased *patois*: it has been said, with picturesque exaggeration, that the vocabulary of 'bazaar Hindustani' could be written on a postcard and its grammar under the stamp. High Hindi has a heavily Sanskritized vocabulary and uses the Sanskritic Nagari script. The attachment of the various linguistic groups to their scripts is a serious bar to intercourse, the more irrational in that languages orally more or less mutually intelligible become much more differentiated when written. Yet practically all the Indo–Aryan languages (with the major exception of Urdu) use scripts which stem from Sanskrit characters, and all the Dravidian from those of Pali. They all have the same ancient and very scientific syllabary, but the number of types necessary for printing is excessive (some 450 for Nagari) owing to special forms for joined characters; and they are difficult to write quickly, though aesthetically far superior to any *modern* European scripts. Romanization would seem a feasible and an impartial solution, but for obvious reasons is not likely to be adopted.

The real danger to unity arises not from the existence of hundreds of little languages, but from the rivalries of a few great ones. The agitation for linguistic states was a handy stick for beating the British Raj, but it has been admitted by a Congress committee that its implications were not properly considered. Andhra Pradesh – the Telegu-speaking area – was early accepted as a special case; it was formed from the northern districts of Madras in 1953 and in 1956 absorbed the Telangana region of the former princely state of Hyderabad. Naturally this success spurred on other claimants, and the entire political map of India has now been reorganized.

There are of course reasonable arguments for linguistic states, especially that the mass of the population and its immediate governors should have a common tongue. Nevertheless it is clear enough that the principle carries with it the risk of separatism, and this was recognized by the able *Report of the States Reorganization Committee* (1955) which accepted the risk in face of the high degree of popular expectation which had been aroused. Some changes were carried out smoothly enough: the formation of *Kerala* from Cochin, Travancore and a small Malayalam-speaking area of Madras; of *Mysore* from Mysore, Coorg, the Bombay Karnatak, the Kanaras and the Kannada-speaking Districts of Raichur and Gulbarga in Hyderabad and Bellary in Madras; of *Madhya Pradesh*, essentially the old British Central Provinces minus a Marathi-speaking area and plus many old princely states, of which the most important were Gwalior and Bhopal. But the attempt at combining the Marathi areas of the Deccan with Gujarat broke down completely, and the latter became a separate state in 1960; and there are still tensions arising from the Gujarati commercial dominance in Bombay city, which remains in Maharashtra.

Other states were left as they were, apart from minor mergers and boundary changes; but some of these led to serious disturbances, especially some territorially minor but economically significant changes on the borders of Bihar, West Bengal and Orissa, while there is still some difficulty in the Punjab where the Sikh-dominated west speaks Punjabi rather than Hindi (cf. p. 172).

The linguistic solution cannot of course be complete; there are anomalies such as the queer protrusion of Jhansi from Uttar Pradesh into Madhya Pradesh. More seriously, the principle lends itself to undue local patriotisms, which are likely to be reflected for example in school histories. Allegations of cultural neglect of minority languages provide yet another factional element in already factionalized state politics; but such cross-currents may be some offset to the potentially most dangerous latent separatism, that of the non-Aryan south expressed in terms of 'Dravidastan'.

Apparently as a more formal offset to the inherently fissiparous tendency of linguistic states, the government in 1955 put forward, in a curiously casual way, the idea of forming five (later six) great Zones. Zonal councils group states for planning purposes, for example in relation to the use of common rivers for irrigation or power, and may act as a liaison between New Delhi and the states. It is not clear that this insertion into the bureaucratic structure of another tier of councils and committees has had a great deal of practical effect.[8]

The official language of Pakistan is, or is designed to be, Urdu; similar to Hindi in grammatical construction and basic vocabulary, it developed as the Court or camp language of the Moguls, uses Persian script and largely draws on Persian for its higher vocabulary. The script is also ill-adapted for printing, lithography being still important. It is being introduced into university teaching in West Pakistan, but in East Bengal the hold of Bengali is too strong for its supersession by Urdu to be lightly undertaken.

Literacy has shown a marked increase since Independence:[9] of those over five years of age, in 1951 one in six in India could write a simple letter, in 1961 one in four; for Pakistan the 1961 figure is one in six. Female literacy, though increasing more rapidly than male, still lags: 12·9% and 34·4% respectively in India in 1961, 8·0% and 25·8% in Pakistan. Literacy of course is very unequally distributed both regionally and communally: almost universal among such a small and select group as the Parsees, it is still almost nil in large tribal and peasant groups; in Kerala the literacy rate in 1961 was 46·8%, in Kashmir only 11%. The advance, though irregular, is gratifying; but a good deal of it is by way of adult education and mass literacy campaigns, and at a low level.

[8] For these matters, see J. V. Bondurant, *Regionalism versus Provincialism: A Study in Problems of Indian National Unity* (Univ. of California, Berkeley, 1958).

[9] There is a good review in G. S. Gosal, 'Literacy in India: an interpretative study', *Rural Sociology*, 29 (1964), 261–77.

Education remains badly balanced: the imposing concrete buildings of the universities rest on the timber and brick of the Government High Schools, they in turn on the mud or thatch huts of the primaries. The proportion of literates who have been to a university is higher than in the West (or at least was until the recent mass-literacy drive); but standards are very unequal and wastage appalling. The preference for arts and legal subjects led to the creation of a vast clerical and professional proletariat, too many for available openings and not infrequently driven to miserable shifts for existence; but good technicians are too few for the country's needs. This ill-balance is perhaps due pretty equally to Indian traditions and the British demand for clerks, but its redress is essential, and happily there are some signs of change. Healthy progress will depend also on more serious attention than has generally been given to the elementary schools; the foundations of a building are after all its most vital part. And on a broader view the liquidation or mitigation of many social ills calls for education, particularly in the villages, in the widest and most liberal sense. There is no room for shallow enthusiasm about moral uplift and more literacy drives: their gains have all too frequently been dissipated by lack of *sustained* effort.

Religions and communities

The 'communities' recognized by the Indian Census, in Indian politics, and in daily life[10] are primarily religious divisions, although race, language, caste, geographical localization, and broad cultural distinctions also shape them in part. Thus the 'Aboriginal Tribes' include Hindus, Christians and even Muslims, though the majority follow particularist religions in which emphasis is given to the worship of spirits. The great bulk of the population is of course either Hindu or Muslim; it is important to note that the Partition was not a 'solution' of the communal problem, and (except by a few extremists on both sides) was not intended to be so. Of the 92,000,000 Muslims in All-India in 1941, only 22,000,000 were in West and 29,000,000 in East Pakistan; some 5,000,000 of the remainder were in Kashmir and Hyderabad. This still left some 36,000,000 in India; but although the enforced migrations of the immediate post-Partition period (and after later outbreaks of communal violence) reduced the 'unredeemed' Muslims, and conversely rendered West Pakistan over 97% Muslim, there were in 1961 about 46,939,000 Muslims in India. This is, however, a bare 9·5% or less against the 24% of undivided India, and there is now not a single Muslim majority District in India – excluding Kashmir.

The extent and nature of Muslim invasions and cultural influence are discussed in Chapter 6 (Historical Outlines) and the relevant regional sections.

Hindus in 1961 numbered some 366,500,000 or 83%, including *Scheduled Castes*; but this cleavage will be discussed as part of the general question of caste. We may note, however, that most Muslims in the sub-continent are the des-

[10] Their significance will be diminished, but in practical affairs far from ended, by the abolition of separate communal electorates.

cendants of converts from Hinduism, generally from lower castes, and though some caste attitudes were retained it is probable that the egalitarian elements in Islam formed a great part of its appeal. This is also the case with Christianity, though here too some compromise with caste has at times and places been considered expedient: perhaps more frequently by Roman Catholics, though Protestants have by no means been immune. Moreover, three Indian religions arose largely as reactions against the caste domination of the Brahmins. These are the faiths of *Buddhists, Sikhs* and *Jains.*

Incomparably the greatest of these is *Buddhism,* but until the last few years it hardly survived in the land of its birth: only a few monks, mostly Nepalese and Sinhalese, were to be found in the holy places, Buddh Gaya where Gautama received Enlightenment, Sarnath where he began his mission. Early Buddhism had a simple and rational humanistic code, independent of theism and as far from the more pathological forms of asceticism as from hedonism, and with an emphasis on the fellowship, irrespective of caste or station, of men (and women) of good will. When Asoka, desolated by the horrors of his Kalinga war, devoted himself to 'the chiefest conquest' – of the hearts of men – he initiated the great missionary period which has resulted in the survival of the earlier and purer form (though shot through with Animism) in Ceylon, Burma and Thailand. The Graeco-Buddhist sculptures of Gandhara, the ruins of the great University at Taxila, and the colossal cliff-figures at Bamian in Afghanistan, attest the long vitality of Buddhism in the northwest, whence it penetrated High Asia. Deterioration of the creed itself, Brahmin opposition and some persecution, gradually weakened it; by the time of the Muslim invasions it was strong only in its original home, Magadha. But the discontent of the Scheduled Castes or 'Untouchables' with the progress of promised reforms has led to a dramatic change; under the impulsion of a dynamic leader, the late Dr B. R. Ambedkar, many thousands of this community now return themselves as Buddhists, though their degree of informed belief may be doubtful. Whereas in 1951 the Census showed under 200,000 Buddhists, mostly in Sikkim and Baltistan or 'Little Tibet', the 1961 Census showed over 3,250,000, and of these just on 2,800,000 were in Maharashtra. There has also, of course, been a considerable influx of Tibetan refugees into the traditional Buddhist areas of Baltistan and Sikkim.

Jainism antedated Buddhism, and may even represent a continuation of pre-Vedic opposition to Brahminism. It developed an exaggerated asceticism (particularly in the renunciation of clothing) and carried *ahimsa* – reverence for organic or rather animal life – to almost incredible extremes: the practice of wearing a cloth over the mouth to avoid accidentally swallowing insects probably gave rise to the report by the Greek Megasthenes (*c.* 302 BC) of a race which had no mouth and lived on delicate savours. Jainism hardly exists outside India, but its adherents number over 2,025,000. They are strongest in Rajasthan (especially Marwar), Gujarat and Maharashtra, which have about 85% of the Jains; their chief sanctuary is Mount Abu in the Aravallis. Many Jains are traders and financiers, Marwari Chambers of Commerce being powers in the land as far afield as Calcutta; nor, if common repute may be relied on, is their tenderness for physical life reflected in their business ethics: there are few more hardheaded forestallers and usurers than some Marwaris.

The *Sikhs* are much younger; their founder, Guru Nanak (1469–1538) was an eclectic drawing from Islam and Hinduism. Ironically, in view of their later reputation, the Sikhs were originally politically quietist, even pacifist; their military virtues were a response to Muslim persecution after the death (1605) of Akbar, himself the greatest of eclectics. Ideologically they are nearer Hinduism than Islam, but they reject caste; and, though diverse in origin, they have developed by inbreeding and strict discipline into a distinct people, recognizable as such even to the newcomer: their badges are the 'five K's' – *Kesh* (uncut hair and beard), *Kanga* (wooden comb), *Kachh* (shorts), *Kara* (an iron ring in the hair) and the short sword or *Kirpan* which they are (or were) legally entitled to carry – sometimes to the detriment of public order. Rulers of the Punjab under the great Ranjit Singh (1780–1839), they were the last country power of note to be subjugated by the British; and there is little doubt that their feeling of being a chosen people played a major part in the disastrous violence which accompanied Partition. The great majority of the Sikhs (7,845,000) are now in the Punjab, where they form local majorities as a result of the expulsion of Muslims.[11] This concentration, and their rather assertive sense of mission, may present some problems to the state and central governments.

The largest community neither specifically Hindu nor Muslim is that comprehensively labelled 'Tribes'; but it is very heterogeneous and very scattered, with two major zones of concentration: the Assam–Burma Hills and the jungles of central India (cf. Fig. 5.1). It is difficult to say how many people should be regarded as tribal, since recent census policy seems to have led to a great deal of nominal assimilation to Hinduism, and indeed it is impossible to draw any definite line between animism and some forms of rural Hinduism. In general they are shifting cultivators and spirit-worshippers, but Christianity as well as Hinduism has made progress among them, and the passage to a (*soi-disant*) higher civilization has not infrequently been attended by the usual disastrous effects on social culture and individual well-being. It is shallow and imperceptive to write off these often balanced and integrated societies as totally 'savage' because they lack the tricks of technologically more advanced cultures; in the true decencies of life some at least (e.g. among the Nagas) yield to few peoples. We have already mentioned their general racial and linguistic affinities; to attempt to particularize would be hopeless, but special mention may be made of the Bhils, Gonds and Santals. The Bhils are found mainly in the marches of Rajasthan, Maharashtra and Madhya Pradesh; very jungly and great shifting cultivators.

[11] Most of the rulers of these states were Sikhs, but in 1941 they had an absolute majority in only one District (Ludhiana) and a relative one in only one small state (Faridkot). Cf. Postcript, p. 172.

More important are the Gonds (the largest group, most of whom are in Madhya Pradesh); once the rulers of much of central India, forced back into their jungles by stronger powers, they have left the name Gondwanaland as a symbol of their ancient domain. The Santals live on the Bengal–Bihar borderland, and are best known for the rebellion of 1855, provoked by plainsmen taking unscrupulous advantage of legalistic land regulation.

Individuals among the tribal peoples have been able to make the best of both worlds: 'the Gond Raja of Savangar lives in a palace which is equipped with every modern comfort; his well-stocked library includes the works of Aldous Huxley, Bernard Shaw and [significantly] Malinowski; he is a brilliant cricketer and tennis-player. Yet he insists that he is a true Gond; his house is decorated with representations of his totem animal, the tortoise, and in the heart of the palace is a small thatched hut where the cult of the old tribal gods is maintained.'[12] At the other extreme are such groups as the Kadar of Cochin, hardly out of the Stone Age. In between, most tribesmen have often been economically exploited and increasingly morally degraded, admitted to become the lowest stratum of Hindu society, or rescued from that by a Christianity which too often consists largely in destroying all that remains of a once-integrated material and moral culture.[13]

The problem of ensuring reasonable conditions of life is sometimes complicated by wider economic issues: the legitimate interests of the forester and of the shifting cultivator may be hard to reconcile. The British policy of excluding tribal areas from the control of elected provincial legislators was naturally resented by nationalist opinion as another trick to divide and rule; even research was regarded with suspicion since, as Elwin remarks, the official ethnographic surveys were sometimes 'too dependent on facts collected by [untrained] subordinates . . . collections of sensationally interesting but often somewhat discreditable superstitions and customs'.[14]

It is of course true that the hills cannot be artificially fenced from the economic life of the country, to form scientific game-sanctuaries with a human fauna; but there is grave danger, if the barriers to exploitation go down too rapidly in the supposed interests of national unity and development, that the tragic histories of the Santals and the Mundas may be repeated.

Christians numbered about 10,725,000 in 1961, plus 750,000 in Pakistan; about three-quarters are Roman Catholics. It is not, perhaps, a very impressive total after four and a half centuries of missionary effort, it is true discontinuous.[15]

[12] V. Elwin, *The Aboriginals* (OPIA No. 14, 1943), 11.
[13] For instance, by banning animal sacrifices among the Kachins of Burma; as the diviners proportioned the sacrifice to the known wealth of the individual, from a buffalo to a chicken, and as the victim was communally consumed, suppression of this custom cuts down the meat-ration and accentuates economic class-cleavage.
[14] *Loc. cit.* 28.
[15] The EIC took so strict a view of the necessity of non-interference with established religions that in the early 19th century Baptist missionaries (American and British) had to work from Danish Serampore.

Most success has been obtained among the lower Hindu castes and the Tribes – especially, perhaps, those half-Hinduized and beginning to be aware of the disadvantages of coming in at the bottom. Christianity is strongest in the south, where in Kerala it is professed by 3,587,400 or 21% of the population; Madras and Andhra Pradesh have over 3,200,000 Christians. Here they are largely the result of Portuguese mass-conversions and the assimilation to Rome of the Nestorian churches, which claimed continuity from St Thomas the Apostle and are certainly at least fifteen centuries old. Mylapore (San Thomé), just south of Madras, contains the Apostle's reputed tomb, and is still a centre of some Portuguese cultural influence, while some Nestorian or 'Syrian' Christians retain their ancient liturgies and usages.

There are of course innumerable other sects, pure survivals of ancient faiths such as the mysterious 'White Jews' of Cochin, or eclectic crossings of all known beliefs: one person in 1931 'described himself as "spiritually universal", but manifestly could not be distributed to the various heads'.[16] Three numerically minor groups must be discussed: *Parsees, Anglo-Indians, Europeans*.

The *Parsees* numbered only about 112,000, over 80% of them in Greater Bombay. Zoroastrian fire-worshippers, they came, as their name implies, from Fars (Persia) about the 8th century AD, to avoid conversion to Islam. Socially they were regarded as hardly Indian and yet definitely not European; but they escaped the usual disabilities of an intermediate position by virtue of wealth and education, and were indeed a valuable lubricant, contributing greatly to the relative harmony of Indo-British relations in Bombay as compared with Calcutta. Like the Quakers, they have an altogether disproportionate share of economic activity and public spirit; the name of Tata bears witness to their energetic and diverse achievement. But their numbers appear to be kept low by inbreeding and a low birth-rate; proselytism is unknown, perhaps to avoid strain on their very complete internal social welfare arrangements and, again like the Quakers, they are essentially a professional and upper-middle class group.

The *Anglo-Indians* are unfortunately named; the effort to avoid the stigma of 'Eurasian' has deprived us of the useful original meaning of Anglo-Indian – an Englishman who had spent his working life in India. In any case many 'Anglo-Indian' families, including some not the least in standing and social usefulness, are really Luso-Indian. Both Portuguese and British initially adopted deliberate miscegenation policies, to surround themselves as it were by a penumbra of subordinates bound by ties of feeling to the invaders. The history of British attitudes to Anglo-India is distressing; as Cox points out, the existence of caste enabled the British to be virtually a dominant caste, and so 'able to make almost unlimited demands upon the mixed-bloods without necessarily making any concessions to them'.[17] This has not always been so; in earlier days families such as the Skinners and Hearseys were among the most valued servants and soldiers of the EIC.

[16] 1931 Census, Vol. I, Pt. I, 391.
[17] O. C. Cox, *Caste, Class and Race* (Monthly Review Press, NY, 1948), 385.

The change is perhaps to be associated with the opening of the Suez Canal: home leaves became more frequent, and, more important, many more European wives (actual or potential – the cold weather saw the arrival of the 'fishing fleet') came out.

In the circumstances the Anglo-Indians naturally became mere clients of the British rulers; and the community was always liable to erosion at the top as its most successful members managed to 'pass' as Domiciled Europeans, while there was some – though decreasing – accretion at the bottom. Physically, of course, the Anglo-Indians include all shades from 'pure white' to almost black; judging by names and physique, the Portuguese element is more important than is usually allowed.[18]

That mixed ancestry in itself means 'the vices of both sides' it should not be necessary to refute; what matters is the social environment, often more secure where the husband was Indian, the wife European but assimilating. It may be mentioned, as one example of many, that Amrita Sher-Gil, after Jamini Roy perhaps the outstanding modern Indian painter, was the daughter of a Magyar mother and a Punjabi father. But the social scales have been weighted heavily against the Eurasians, and their political fortunes were hitched only too obviously to the British star; as that set, their pleas that they were as Indian as anybody were not unnaturally discounted as death-bed repentances.

Hinduism and Caste

Hinduism and its symbiote, Caste, are entities so complex as to defy definition; as a counsel of despair Hinduism has been defined as 'those beliefs held by Hindus', but this takes us too far and not far enough, as these include all possible metaphysical attitudes (not perhaps excluding solipsism, if that be a possible attitude) and on the theological side everything from virtual atheism in some of the Sankhya school (6th century BC) to pantheism and the spirit-worship of those tribes who have accepted a position in the Hindu scheme of things. Until recently it was roughly true to say that Hindus were those who accepted caste society and Brahminical hegemony; but there are now many who would consider themselves good Hindus but yet would condemn caste, even if they cannot always in practice repudiate it.

Into this maze of jarring sects (far more than Omar's two-and-seventy) and conflicting theogonies we cannot go, even were the author technically competent to do so. But Hinduism as a way of life impinges directly on the relations between men and the Indian environment in two important aspects: the special position accorded to the cow, and caste. The first is more appropriately considered in Chapter 8 (Agriculture); the second must be discussed, with much

[18] Cox is, I think, misled on this point by reliance on the more articulate *Anglo*-Indian writers, for whom 'the call of (British) blood' was an article of faith. The Goanese cross is of course a different issue (below, 669). As for colour, I have seen a man with unimpeachably Saxon names who was better known to his Burmese neighbours as *Kala byu* – 'the *black* black man'.

diffidence, here. But many fundamental questions cannot even be touched upon, such as the movement of castes up and down the scale, *ahimsa*, and the linked concepts of rebirth and *dharma* with its peculiar connotation of both destiny and duty.

There are probably some 3,000 castes in India, and the literature on them is enormous; nor is there any general agreement on the origins and rationale of the system. Any definition can be effectively queried, unless it is so hedged about with qualifications as to fill a book. It would be folly for a novice to attempt even a rough working definition; but from a résumé of some admitted facts and of what appear to be the more tenable hypotheses it is hoped that some idea of the nature and workings of caste may emerge.

The salient features are clear enough. The caste system is the most intensely hierarchical organization of society in existence; the accident of birth is the absolute determinant of a man's caste, and hence of his standing in society. Exclusivism is carried to an extreme; not only is marriage (with rare exceptions) strictly confined within the caste, but normally eating and drinking with members of other castes are banned. The idea of purity is indeed fundamental in the practice of caste. In some cases the cult of ceremonial purity was carried to pathological lengths – in Kerala Nayadis (quasi-aboriginals) could not approach within 72 feet of a Brahmin without occasioning defilement, and as late as 1932 the existence in the same region of an 'unseeable' group, emerging only at night, was reported: these unfortunates washed the clothes of untouchables.[19] On the other hand, ceremonial purity has given rise to some undesignedly hygienic practices, such as the provision in Post Offices of stamp-moisteners to avoid licking, or the use as dishes of leaves or of cheap pottery subsequently discarded.

There are, or at least were, four great caste groupings: Brahmins (priests), Kshatriyas (warriors or, better, rulers), Vaisyas (traders), Sudras (cultivators); together with the lower groups known variously as Untouchables, Depressed Classes, Scheduled or Exterior Castes.[20] The 'Laws of Manu' (1st–5th centuries AD) represent the four as sprung from different parts of the body of Brahma; they have also been equated with *varna* or colour (from light Indo–Aryan to black Dravidian). These seem to be rationalizations; and as *varna* has wider connotations it does not seem that the racial theory of caste origins, so far as built on this equation, has very secure foundations.

Rigid as the system is, in course of time castes may improve their ranking, often by restricting intermarriage to a narrower group within a caste; or they may lose ground. In times of war and revolution energy and ability have carried

[19] J. H. Hutton, *Caste in India.* CUP (1946), 70–71.

[20] *Not* 'outcastes': this means no more than those outside the pale (e.g. Englishmen), but carries with it the suggestion of 'outcast' or expulsion – a sanction which may be used on castemen, but these castes, unless by their own volition, are an integral part of the system, with essential ritual duties. Some groups have developed their own *pujaris* (functioning as priests though without benefit of Sanskrit)—a slight qualification of the Brahmin monopoly mentioned below.

men of lower castes to place and power, and the situation may then be legitimated by faking the pedigree, this adjustment being made by complaisant Brahmins. Today individuals have obviously much greater facilities for breaking away, owing to the increased mobility and the increasingly economic values of modern society. Hence the *broad* occupational correlations suggested above have long been practically meaningless, except that only Brahmins can be priests. (As Brahmins are essential to many necessary rituals they have an obvious key position, and as the educated class, the clergy, they tended (as the clergy of mediaeval Europe) to monopolize or at least dominate administration. Hindu rulers usually were Kshatriyas, or got Brahmins to say they were;[21] trading castes are still largely Vaisya. But all groups include large numbers of cultivators. It is in individual castes, and still more in the innumerable sub-castes, that the usual Western concept of caste as occupational most nearly holds good. Many caste distinctions based on occupation appear very trifling: between those who yoke to the plough one bullock or two, who make white or black pots, and so on. But in towns at any rate occupational significance, while not unimportant, is of less and less account, except for definitely impure tasks such as those of Dhobis (washermen), Chamars (tanners), Doms (scavengers). In any case the cross-divisions are almost incredibly complex: 'it suggests a division of the inhabitants of England into families of Norman descent, Clerks in Holy Orders, positivists, ironmongers, vegetarians, communists, and Scotchmen';[22] except that the groups are mutually exclusive, and there are no classifications such as vegetarian iron-mongers.

As to origins, it would appear obvious that no simple explanation can possibly suffice. Hutton lists 15 contributing factors, and does not regard this as exhaustive; he inclines to regard the geographical juxtaposition of many differing ethnic groups in India – the end of so many migrations – and beliefs in *mana* and taboo, especially associated with food, as among the most important. This can be supported by a wide range of anthropological evidence, from India and outside. Ethnic and occupational factors clearly play an important part, and the element of deliberate exploitation by Brahmins cannot well be evaded.

What is the objective function of caste? At first sight it appears to be (and indeed it is) a negation of democracy as known in the West: and after all, the values associated with the word 'democracy', while not the peculiar property of the west, are at least so much interwined with Occidental views of the world as to give validity to western judgments on the meaning of the word.[23] To us, then, caste is alien and repellent. Yet it would be superficial to condemn out of hand a system which has met the social needs of so large a fraction of mankind for so many centuries. Loyalty to caste has inhibited the development of national

[21] For a good example – no less a person than Sivaji – see Karve, *op. cit.* 43–44.
[22] J. C. Molony, *A Book of South India* (1926), 106.
[23] On the other hand, of course, social stratification, with only less rigid rules of inter-dining and intermarriage than those of the caste system, is by no means lacking outside India.

patriotisms: but in the conditions of ancient and mediaeval India this was no unmixed evil, since it made adjustments to the constantly changing political pattern so much the easier. There was a place for everybody, for the intrusive conqueror and the aboriginal conquered; the structure was so integrated, so self-regarding, that few groups could long resist the temptation to find their assured niche, humble as it might be. At the same time Cox undoubtedly overstates his case when he claims that 'its practice and theory are in complete synchronization; it does not rationalize its position . . . it has no shortcomings; it does not excuse itself; it is totally excellent. . . . Before the impingement of Western culture upon the system there was no "caste question" in India.' This is to forget Buddhists and Jains and Sikhs, the wide gains of Islam from the lower castes, and not a few Hindu thinkers, poets, and saints who taught that not birth but conduct was the ultimate determinant of a man's right rank in society. But the other phrases from the passage quoted sum up the situation as it was until recently: 'The caste system does not represent a social order in unstable equilibrium; rather a powerful norm towards which social variations tend to gravitate. . . . Resting securely upon universal consensus, the system is taken for granted, and it cannot be legislated out of existence. . . .'[24]

This gift of stability to a highly plural society, always in peril of being shaken to pieces by constant war, is perhaps the most positive argument in favour of caste. On a somewhat lower plane it fulfilled – and to some extent still fulfils – many of the functions of friendly societies and trade unions; its conservatism has acted as a check on despotisms more capricious even than itself. But these are things of historical rather than contemporary significance; the price of stability is too high if it means ossification in a rapidly changing environment; resistance to new forces may indeed be more prolonged, but the ultimate wreck is more disastrous.

It is very difficult indeed to see how any really democratic society can co-exist with such an avowed, not to say violent, assertion of human inequality – not the natural inequality of individuals, but the automatic inferiority of whole classes of men, utterly irrespective of any individual talent or virtue; and rationalizations by such apologists as Radhakrishnan, though eloquent and sincere, are not altogether convincing, even to many Hindus, when they suggest that the role of the lower castes is in fact honoured as being essential. Not all men are philosophers, and much of caste teaching and practice seems to have a demoralizing and certainly has a divisive social effect. Stripped of metaphysic and translated into the terms of day-to-day life, caste retains uncomfortable overtones of *Herrenvolk* and *apartheid*. This can scarcely be afforded in a country committed to modernization on democratic and quasi-socialist lines.

Today, therefore, caste faces what is probably the greatest crisis in its history.

[24] *Op. cit.* 22. Buddhism and Sikhism are relegated to a four-line footnote (110); but even if they 'did not seriously change the course of Hindu society', they certainly questioned it sufficiently to induce re-assessments.

The new urbanism has greatly weakened it: without spending a prohibitive fraction of one's time and income on purificatory ceremonies, as a commuter it is simply not possible to escape contamination; and, with all the cultural loss implied in the rootlessness of modern city life, the gift of anonymity does enable the individual to break bonds which are unbearable but unbreakable in a village where all are known to all. Nor can an expansionist industrial economy submit to the occupational shackles of caste, shackles like those of mediaeval guilds, but more rigorous, as Batanagar (p. 596) has shown.

On a different plane the influence of Western ideology and the ideals of secular humanism (probably more than those of Christianity), compel a revaluation of the old attitudes, on the part of the intelligentsia at least. Much of value may be lost in this process of adjustment, and the risk of disintegration and social schizophrenia is profound; but, short of some great and unforeseeable historic catastrophe, it has gone too far to be checked. These factors are clearly seen by most of those in whom leadership is now vested. Some of the earliest legislation of independent India was to enforce the right of untouchables to free access to temples and wells. Articulate opinion has welcomed this overwhelmingly. Yet it is a long way from the Council Chamber at New Delhi to the thousands of villages in the deep South: 'In the city of Bombay, any barber or hotel owner or temple priest who refused admission to a Harijan would soon find himself in the dock. In a Tanjore village the Harijan himself would probably not try to get himself shaved by a caste barber or enter a caste shrine; and if he did, the caste villagers would probably soon bring him to heel, law or no law.'[25]

There is evidence of a distinct decline, especially of course in urban life, of the taboos connected with pollution; but in other ways caste may actually be stronger than it was. The political manipulation of caste groupings in a system of universal suffrage obviously provides a magnificent field for the most complex manoeuvre and chicane; but also for wider caste alliances and a relaxation of the lines between *sub*-castes, since in any one locality the sub-caste will normally be too small to form a politically effective unit.[26] In the village, again, the introduction of producers' co-operatives, the runnings of Community Development Projects, the revival of the old *panchayat* or inter-caste council of (nominally or originally) five representatives, all mean that whereas 'In the past, caste conflict and feud could lie beneath the surface of daily affairs', and those not immediately concerned in a dispute could be neutral, 'Now that overt choices must be made, there is more apparent fragmentation. . . .' To some extent this is offset by wider groupings – inter- rather than intra-village – permitting of more varied and less personal contacts; but it is a main factor in the apparent lack of effectiveness in the panchayat revival.[27]

[25] Taya Zinkin, *Caste Today* (OUP, 1962), 60. This brilliant little essay is perhaps the best introduction for the Western student.
[26] Zinkin, *op. cit.* 62–66; M. N. Srinivas, *Caste in Modern India* (Asia, Bombay, 1962).
[27] H. Orenstein, 'Village, Caste, and the Welfare State', *Human Organization*, 22 (1963), 83–89.

'Perhaps a sceptic whispers, "Such revolutions are not brought about in the lethargic types of Indian climes." Him we only remind . . . that the phenomenon of the conquering Indo-Aryans, who were passionate eaters of flesh and drinkers of intoxicating beverages, settling down as the upper castes of Hindu society and abjuring their food and drink for centuries, is a moral triumph of the people of India, for which there is hardly any parallel in human history. The same people, now called upon to throw off caste, would rise to the occasion and achieve a still greater triumph.'[28]

These are brave and sincere words; but the phenomenon was not a sudden one, and it is a long way back; nor are those conditioned by three millennia of caste 'the same people'.

Caste, then, dies hard; but in anything like its fully developed form it cannot persist indefinitely in the sort of India which most Indians seem to want. The necessary changes are vast, but they are fostered by a great variety of forces, both material and spiritual. The monster may still be lively, but his sharpest teeth have been drawn.

Some social tendencies

A description of the manners and customs of the Indian peoples, or even only those associated with caste, would itself fill an encyclopaedia. Such is their diversity that it has been justly remarked that the only valid generalization about them is that any generalization is both true and false according to *milieu*. The differences are extreme: from primitive tribesmen not far above a Stone Age level to the highly sophisticated urban intelligentsia, from rulers claiming descent from the sun to industrial families such as the Tatas and the Birlas forming economic dynasties in two or three generations. Yet, underlying this diversity, is an unmistakable cultural unity provided by the polymorphic complex of ideas and social and individual observances which is Hinduism, a culture which baffles definition but is everywhere recognizable.

A few leading tendencies may be briefly indicated. India is today the theatre of an indescribably complex interaction between the forces of modern technology (with its own metamorphosing mental outlook) and of an age-old metaphysical tradition. Two examples, admittedly extreme, may illustrate the fantastic interdigitation – it cannot be called a synthesis – of east and west. The attainment of independence was accompanied by a campaign to prohibit cow-slaughter, even if need be under penalty of death; in Kerala an unexpected result of Communist activity was the emergence of an embryonic sub-caste of Communist bridegrooms, more progressive and so better endowed economically than their fellows, and hence more eligible, and commanding higher dowries.

The love of metaphysic, so often noted, was ascribed by Buckle and other geographical determinists to the influence of the natural environment. It is

[28] G. S. Ghurye, *Caste and Race in India* (1932), 188; cf. his second thoughts in the revised version, *Caste and Class in India* (Popular Book Depot, Bombay, 1957), 238.

perhaps more reasonable to regard it as the natural reaction to centuries, if not millennia, of political absolutism: in one sphere at least, that of cloudy imaginings, man was free. Since the suppression of Buddhism, Hinduism, however rigid in matters of ritual observance, has been extraordinarily tolerant doctrinally – hence its astonishing congeries of beliefs, practically from Animism to atheism. The result has been a metaphysical hangover, shown in the constant tendency among intellectuals to accept an analogy as a demonstration. Moreover, even the most intellectual arguments are not infrequently betrayed into unregulated emotionalism; perhaps not more often than those of Western Europeans, but certainly in a more obvious way.

The hackneyed antithesis of Western materialism and Eastern spirituality, however, is as a rule grossly exaggerated, especially by Western neophytes. The trading castes have a religious sanction to gain almost for its own sake, resembling (but with greater intensity) the attitude of the Puritan bourgeosie in the West. The observer in India certainly does not see any widespread neglect of material advancement in the interests of salvation, and if 'by their fruits ye shall know them' be true, the ethical advantage is not always conspicuously on the side of the East. In the long run it is not likely that the standard patterns of economic and political power-conflicts will differ fundamentally from those of the rest of the world, however exotic their forms of overt expression.

These remarks, of course, apply mainly to the educated and vocal classes of the towns. It must never be forgotten that the vast majority of Indians live in over half a million villages, most of them small and isolated. Here Custom is a king not yet and not easily dethroned (though increasingly tottering), and his laws are enshrined in a multitude of pithy proverbs which, with the religious songs, form a true and remarkable folk-culture. The ancient panchayat or village council, which through all the mutability of dynasties made the villages so many unfederated little republics, became atrophied under British rule, in which administration was legal rather than customary and was far more all-embracing, impinging far more directly on all classes, than under any previous régime. It is doubtful whether, as some nationalists hope, the panchayat can be sufficiently resuscitated to play a very useful function in the epoch of change which has begun to penetrate the Indian countryside (see p. 275 for references to the role hoped for of the panchayat in the Five Year Plans).

In this excessively complex situation it is of course impossible to forecast what changes in the norms of society will take place under a government modelled, in principle, on Western parliamentary democracy and relying for its administration on the inheritance of an immense bureaucratic machine. That there will be both loss and gain appears certain; there may be a loss of formal efficiency mitigated by more ready accessibility to public opinion. But for the latter to be constructive a new revolution of thought is needed, a break from the old traditions of community and caste to new groupings based primarily on economic function and with intelligible and coherent political and economic programmes. And somehow

– this may well be the most difficult task of all – the programmes for the future must be brought to the rural masses and their participation, not just their acquiescence, be assured. In the last resort it is on this more than on anything else that the future, in both India and Pakistan, depends, for without it neither the material struggle for food nor the ideological struggle to create free, active and united nations can be won.

The Pakistani evolution

In contrast to the India of Nehru, avowedly dedicated to the formation of a secular state, the Pakistan of Jinnah was rooted in the belief that there was in the sub-continent a separate religious nation. Rationalistically, many of the points adduced in support of the 'Two Nations' theory may be open to question; but if a sufficient number of people are determined to be a nation, then practically they are one. The history of Pakistan is thus the history of a struggle to transform this feeling of Islamic identity and of the all-pervading social dictates of the faith into a well-knit state; a struggle made peculiarly difficult by the unique division of the country into two unequal parts, separated by 1,000 miles of India, and with very marked differences in language, in cultural tradition, and (though both were agrarian) in economy. There is also the difficulty of reconciling the traditional Islamic element in the polity with the demands of modern administration and economic development. Apart from caste, many of the more social problems of Pakistan are not dissimilar from those of India; but the problem in Pakistan is perhaps more directly political as expressed in the state structure.

Sectionalism in Pakistan is not confined to the obvious division between the West, with the Punjab making the running against more local loyalities and that of the centre at Karachi (or now Islamabad), and the East, more homogeneous in itself (but for the sizeable Hindu minority, some 12%) but on the whole playing a less dynamic and less dedicated role in the making of Pakistan. However, the sectionalisms of West Pakistan seem to have been largely exorcized by its recasting into one unit, and with the greatly enhanced power of the central government under the régime of Ayub Khan, the country seems to have got into as nearly a unitary condition as can be expected when its two major components are geographically so distant and environmentally so different from each other.

The problem of parity remains difficult. East Pakistan has the larger population (51,000,000 against 43,000,000) but is economically not so diversified as the west; yet its jute accounts for up to two-thirds of total exports. The attachment to Bengali sets East Pakistan apart from the main currents of Islamic literary culture as expressed in Urdu; its pre-Partition élite was largely Hindu, and the drive for Pakistan came from the west. During the intense factionalism of the period of constitution making and breaking, East Pakistani politicians had some plausible grounds for expressing, and exaggerating, fears that the East would become merely a colony of the west, while to Karachi they appeared just as plausibly to be irresponsibly trifling with national unity. The present régime seems to have gone a long way in concession to the east; for example, longer tax-free period for new industries in Dacca than in Karachi, and the seating of the legislature (limited as its powers will be) in Dacca. Reservation of official posts in East Pakistan to local personnel, however, though doubtless tactically expedient, may not conduce to real integration.

President Ayub Khan's 1962 constitution, based on indirect election through some 80,000 local units known as 'Basic Democracies', may not fulfil the formal requirements of parliamentary democracy, but may well be more efficient in Pakistani conditions and may enlist wider participation of the people, however indirectly, than the ineffective representative régime. It seems also to have muted the old conflict between Islamic traditionalists and the proponents of a modern state. The extreme position of the traditionalists – back to the golden days of the 8th-century Caliphate – is obviously incompatible with the complexity of modern life, and there is still a wide area for dispute on such matters as the status of women, the rule of secular law, the degree to which minorities (including dissident Muslims such as the Ahmadiyya) may partake of high administrative responsibility, how far traditional Islamic inhibitions against usury may be waived in the interests of capital formation, relations with other Muslim states and the attitude to those Muslims who have remained in India, and so on; while Islamic law on inheritance imposes some difficulties in efforts to prevent excessive fragmentation of landholdings.

Moreover, all Pakistani affairs are overshadowed by the Kashmir dispute with India, and the recent rapprochement with Communist China introduces a certain ambiguity into Pakistan's international position; yet she is very dependent on the west, notably the USA, for economic aid. The setting up of a state in the appalling confusion of Partition was a tremendous achievement in itself, but the gains of Jinnah and Liaquat Ali Khan seemed in danger of dissipation during ten years of political factionalism; a new stability seems to have been attained, but there remain critical difficulties, internal and external.

BIBLIOGRAPHICAL NOTE

Most of the works referred to in earlier editions of this book retain much value; the older standard authors such as J. H. Hutton, Verrier Elwin, W. C. Smith, O. C. Cox, L. S. S. O'Malley, G. S. Ghurye, R. K. Mukerjee, are by no means entirely superseded; still less such essential primary sources as the auto-biographies of Gandhi and Nehru or the writings of Muhammad Iqbal and Rabindranath Tagore. Iqbal's 'conversation between Ganges and Himalaya' (in *Secrets of the Self*, Ashraf, Lahore, 1943), for instance, apart from its poetic greatness, seizes unerringly on the cardinal contrasts between the Muslim and the Hindu genius, the Sheikh and the Brahmin.

However, this literature, vast as it is, is increasing with terrifying acceleration, and any sampling must depend largely on the accidents of local availability and personal taste. Much of the recent literature is far more firmly founded in general sociological concepts than the highly idiosyncratic and subjectivist (but often so much more readable!) works of older writers. Much is owing to the active interest of American students, whose detailed studies show promise of breaking away from older stereotypes about caste and tribal influences. A good bridge between old and new is afforded by N. K. Bose, *Cultural Anthropology* (Indian Asstd Publishers, Calcutta, 1943); of newer books already cited, those of Taya Zinkin and Irawati Karve are perhaps most stimulating.

So much, in the current phase, depends on detailed case-studies rather than 'literary' sources that perhaps the best way to gain some insight into the complex fascinations of Indian society is through co-operative works such as M. Singer (ed.), *Traditional India: Structure and Change* (American Folklore Soc., Philadelphia, 1959); the special number of *Human Organization* (Ithaca, New York, Vol. 22, No. 1, 1963) devoted to 'Contours of culture change in South Asia'; A. R. Desai (ed.), *Rural Sociology in India* (Indian Soc. Agric. Economics, Bombay, 3rd ed., 1961); S. Maron (ed.), *Pakistan: Society and Culture* (Human Relations Area Files, New Haven, 1957); A. F. A. Husain, *Human and Social Impact of Technological Change in Pakistan* (OUP Dacca, 1956). At the opposite pole from the village is the brilliant essay by E. Shils, *The Intellectual between Tradition and Modernity: The Indian Situation* (Mouton, The Hague, 1961). But the list would be well-nigh endless.

On Islam and Pakistan, some good studies have been overtaken by events: I. Jennings, *Constitutional Problems in Pakistan* (CUP, 1957); K. Callard, *Pakistan: A Political Study* (Allen & Unwin, London, 1957); even perhaps L. Binder, *Religion and Politics in Pakistan* (Univ. of California, Berkeley, 1961). R. D. Campbell, *Pakistan: Emerging Democracy* (Van Nostrand, Princeton, 1963) is more up-to-date as to facts (except that he dodges the Chinese issue) but excessively naïve in interpretation. More general works of interest include M. T. Titus, *Islam in India and Pakistan* (YMCA, Calcutta, 2nd ed. 1959); I. Lichtenstadter, *Islam and the Modern Age* (Bookman Assoctes, NY, 1958); I. H. Qureshi, *The Muslim Community of the Indo-Pakistan Sub-Continent* (Mouton, The Hague, 1962).

Postscript. Early in 1966 the Government of India decided in principle on the formation of a new Punjabi-speaking State of Punjab, separated from the Hindi-speaking parts of the existing Punjab which would form a new State of Hariana. Some hill areas were likely to be joined to Himachal Pradesh. The new Punjab, formed in response to Sikh agitation (cf. pp. 157, 160), might have a population of about 12,000,000 (probably around 55% Sikh), Hariana about 7,000,000, some 1,500,000 going to Himachal Pradesh. (*Keesings' Contemporary Archives*, 22/4–7/5/66, p. 21378). The formation of the new States was announced in November 1966.

CHAPTER 6

Historical Out¹ ̣es

Indian archaeology has made great strides in the past two decades, and there is now a good deal of evidence on the extension of various palaeolithic and meso-lithic cultures, although unfortunately interpretation has as yet to rely more on extensive typology than on intensive stratigraphical analyses. This phase of horizontal reconnaissance is already yielding to more detailed vertical soundings, and the next few years may see discoveries almost as revolutionary as those of Harappa and Mohenjo-Daro.

The Indus civilization

Surface finds of pictographic seals at Harappa in the Punjab had long hinted the existence of an unknown civilization; in 1922 excavations at Mohenjo-Daro ('Mound of the Dead') in Sind disclosed the existence of an urban and basically Bronze Age culture, not dissimilar to that of Sumeria in technical accomplishment. The earliest definitely Harappan remains can be fairly confidently dated to around 2500 BC, and there is evidence of trading contacts with Sumeria about 2350–2100 BC; but by this time the civilization was fully developed. Its origins seem thus sudden and obscure, and no less difficult to account for is the fact that, having early reached a high pitch of organization, it then seems to have stagnated for centuries.[1]

It seems to have been a trading 'empire', polarized around the great cities of Mohenjo-Daro and Harappa; and it is now known that, in its later phases, its offshoots spread as far as Rupar on the Sutlej, and southwards into Kutch and around the Gulf of Cambay; these later protrusions may represent a dispersal before barbarian inroads. The cities were impressively, if unimaginatively, planned; what seems to strike most observers, perhaps by reaction to the Indian present, is the high standard of the drains.

Aesthetically, however, the impression is drab, though this may be due to gaps in the record – nothing like the superb monarchic tombs of Sumeria and Egypt has been found. There was a businesslike efficiency, shown for example in

[1] Unless indeed we accept the ingenious but not altogether convincing view, based on geomorphological arguments, of R. L. Raikes ('The End of the Ancient Cities of the Indus', *American Anthropologist*, 66 (1964), 284–99), that the main civilization may have endured for only a century or two at Mohenjo-Daro, ending *c.* 2300 BC as a result of earthquake and flooding, Harappa being a subsequent and not a contemporaneous centre.

the standardized layout of workers' quarters with the great grain-mortars massed between them and the granaries. Artistically, the best things are a handful of (rather anomalous) sculptures and especially the splendid stylized animals of the seals. These include tigers, rhinoceroses, elephants and buffaloes, which together with an architecture of kiln-burnt bricks (implying large fuel supplies) suggest a distinctly more humid climate than now prevails. The seals carry an undeciphered script, and their symbolism suggests that some elements in Hinduism, notably Siva-worship, may stem from Harappan culture.

The end of the Indus Civilization is as obscure as its origin. It seems likely that, in the great cities at least, it was a violent one, though too much may have been built on the dramatic evidence of massacre and burning in the last stage at Mohenjo-Daro. Elsewhere, especially in Kathiawad, there may have been some carry-over into the chalcolithic cultures of those dark ages before the lineaments of Vedic India can be clearly discerned. The gap of about a millennium – more rather than less – between the end of the Indus Civilization and the crystallization of the north Indian kingdoms in Buddha's day may soon be closed. Indeed, if the suggestion of a revised date of 1200 BC for the end of Harappan culture is confirmed, it would seem that the civilization must have met its fate at the hands of the Aryan invaders; and decadent successor-states may have lingered on in Kathiawad as late as 500 BC.[2]

The coming of the Aryans

The Aryan invasions, from their date in the middle of the 1st millennium BC, may well have been a part of the great folk-wanderings represented farther west by the Hyksos in Egypt and the overthrow of the Babylonian Dynasty by the Kassites. Be that as it may, the newcomers when settled in their original Indian territory – *Sapta Sindhu* or the Seven Rivers from the Kabul to the Jumna – retained many elements of a pastoral culture: a diet based largely on milk and meat, chariot-racing, the sacrifice of horses. Their religion, expressed in the often obscure but often noble hymns of the *Rig-Veda*, was essentially worship of personified natural phenomena – Sun, Moon, Fire and so on – and at its height tended to monotheism. The Vedic hymns are the only sources of information: the impression is of an initially simple society based on the family and the village, with at least distinct classes of warriors, priests and artisans; divided into monarchical or republican clans, gradually becoming more complex with the growth of towns, trade and crafts.[3] Archaeology is beginning to shed a new, if dim, light on this difficult period, although it suggests that – as in that other Heroic Age which Homer sang – life was ruder than the poets fable.

Larger kingdoms coalesced, and the frontiers of Aryandom were pushed outwards in struggles with the dark-skinned snub-nosed *Dasyus* or *Dasas* – struggles

[2] B. Subbarao, *The Personality of India* (University of Baroda, 2nd ed. 1958), 96, 129–32.
[3] Stuart Piggott, *Prehistoric India* (Pelican, Harmondsworth, 1950), Ch. VII, gives a brilliant interpretation.

in which some have seen the prime origin of caste, though that is probably far more complex. By about the 1st millennium BC the Aryans had passed the Ghaghra, and later pushed through the Vindhyan barrier into the northern Deccan. In Buddha's day (6th century BC) there were four major kingdoms in Madhyadesa, the 'middle country': Kosala (roughly Oudh), Avanti (Malwa), Vatsa (around Allahabad), Magadha (southern Bihar). The last was the most powerful and exerted a certain ascendancy over much of northern India; its later capital Pataliputra is represented by modern Patna, which may thus claim to be the oldest Indian city with a more or less continuous history; but excavations at Hastinapura and Achichchatra, near the Ganga in eastern Uttar Pradesh, 'proclaim the emergence of a comfortable and organized city-life' some centuries earlier.

So far the story has to be pieced out from religious texts and the great epics, *Ramayana* and *Mahabharata*: but the former do not profess to be history or even (until the Jain and Buddhist scriptures) biography, while the epics (especially the *Mahabharata*) are very composite collections of ballads and didactic verse (including the famous *Bhagavad Gita*) containing some material probably not added until the earliest Christian centuries. Socially their content is rich: this is the Heroic Age, an age of myths giving a vivid, if confused, picture of a culture in which cities and arts are increasingly important. The original clan society has developed the complex structure of caste, the austere beauty of the Vedic hymns gives way to elaborate metaphysics; and, by reaction to caste and excessive religiosity, Buddhism has arisen, in its origins simple and emotional, though in turn developing a refined and intellectual psychology and philosophy. But the patterns are shifting, splendid and vague.

The major geographical lineaments of Indian history

Already, however, we can see one of the major structure-lines of Indian historical geography: the Narmada–Chota Nagpur line which has been easily the most persistent internal boundary in India, rivalled only by the terai frontier zone between the mountains and the Indo-Gangetic Plain and by the Bengal march between 'Hindustan' and alien Assam (Fig. 6.1). The Aryans infiltrated beyond the Narmada, but except on the Lavas of Maharashtra the 'Southland', *Dakshina-patha* or the Deccan, is still mainly Dravidian: in the east, Dravidian (and other non-Aryan) languages extend farther north, and the Chota Nagpur–Orissa hill country is very mixed linguistically, while in the west the Marathi (Aryan) and Telugu (Dravidian) boundary shows a remarkable correlation with that of the Deccan Lava (below, Fig. 23.4). North of the Narmada–Chota Nagpur line, then, we have Hindustan, essentially the Gangetic Plain and its outworks in central India; south of it lies the Deccan, essentially Dravidian except on the lavas.

The other major structure-line is more clear-cut in the Muslim phase, but it is, perhaps, dimly foreshadowed in the limitation to the Indus basin of the earliest civilization and of Persian and Greek penetration. This line runs slantwise from

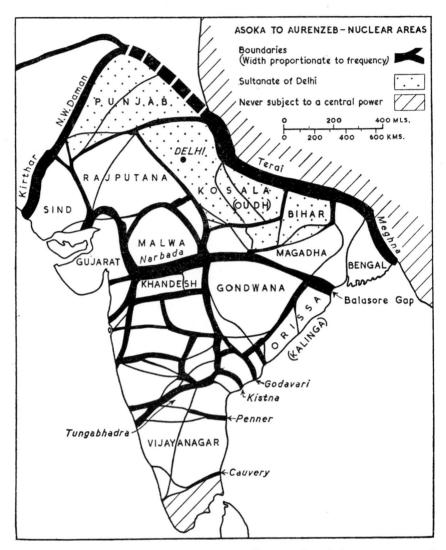

FIG 6.1 ASOKA TO AURENZEB: an attempt to illustrate the relative permanence of
boundaries and the persistence of nuclear areas such as Malwa and Gujarat. The
evidence permits of rough approximations only, but it is believed that a fair representation is attained. Based largely on maps in C. C. Davies, *An Historical Atlas of the
Indian Peninsula* (1949) and E. W. Green, *An Atlas of Indian History* (Bombay,
1937), and on standard histories. Cf. map in W. M. Day, 'Relative permanence of
former boundaries in India', *Scottish Geog. Mag* XLV (1949), 113–22.

about Mathura, on the Yamuna above Agra, along the Aravallis to the Gulf of Cambay. North and west of this the generally arid physical environment and the Islamic heritage combine to produce a cultural landscape strongly reminiscent of southwest Asia: it has been said that the true India does not begin before the temples of Mathura, birthplace of Krishna.[4] In the northwest, the mountain girdle of India narrows significantly between Turkestan and the Punjab, and is pierced by numerous passes, of which the Khyber and the Bolan are only the most famous. The importance of this entry is a commonplace and needs no stressing.

We have thus three great divisions: the Indus Valley, open to cultural and political influences from central and southwest Asia; Hindustan, accessible only when the Delhi gateway has been forced, and more receptive than the south, to which it has acted as a shock absorber; the Peninsula south of the Narmada, which, except in Maharashtra, has been far more resistant to influences from Asia: largely, no doubt, owing to mere distance, but to some extent owing to the barriers of hill and jungle, especially in the northeast. It is noteworthy that Deccan Lavas extend far north of the Narmada in Malwa: this is the great passageway from Hindustan into the Deccan, and on its glacis in Maharashtra alike the Aryans, the earlier Muslims and the Moguls established their first serious lodgements in the Southland. The pattern of the sub-continent as a whole – diminishing ripples of alien influence radiating from an entry in the northwest – is thus repeated in the Deccan.

The perennial nuclear regions

Thus early we can also discern the emergence of some nuclear regions or bases of power which are perennially significant in Indian historical geography: Gandhara in the Vale of Peshawar and Potwar; Sapta Sindhu narrowed down to the Punjab, seven rivers to five; Kurukshetra (Sirhind), the Delhi or Sutlej/Yamuna Doab; Panchala in the Yamuna/Ganga Doab and Rohilkhand; Saurashtra (Kathiawad) and Gujarat; the four great kingdoms already apparent in Magadhan times. In the Dravidian south the pattern is more confused, but not without some relatively permanent pieces in the dynastic kaleidoscope: the Kalinga country or Orissa; Andhra, the Telugu country; the Chola (whence Coromandel) and Pandya kingdoms in the Tamil country; Kerala or Malabar, the isolated southwest littoral. There are of course many smaller areas which have preserved an historic individuality, e.g. Bundelkhand, Chhattisgarh, Konkan, Kanara. Some areas again have been debatable marches: such are Khandesh, between Narmada and Tapti, or the Raichur Doab between Tungabhadra and Krishna. It is noteworthy that many of the ancient names survived in the regional

[4] Cf. S. Piggott, *Some Ancient Cities of India* (OUP, 1945), 1, 42. Against this is the Hindu as well as Muslim past of Delhi; less seriously, a remark made to the author in Lahore: 'Ah, this is the real India.' As the speaker was a Muslim striving to get as much as possible into Pakistan, the remark has a delightful irony – dare I say characteristically Indian?

consciousness of the people, although not corresponding to any existing political unit, e.g. Kerala, Matsya, Maharashtra, and some are now used as the names of new states of the Indian Union. Research, geographical rather than linguistic, on *pays* names is needed.

These nuclear regions clearly represent the major agricultural areas, for the most part alluvial; intersecting them are arid, broken or jungly refuge areas such as Rajputana and the wild country of the Bhils between it and Maharashtra; the jungly Gondwana country between Son and Mahanadi; Bastar; the Rajmahal Hills in the angle of the Ganga between Bihar and Bengal. These are still the homes of most of the aboriginal tribes, and until the mergers of 1948 the great belt of country between Rajputana and Orissa was a major shatter-zone, a congeries of scores of semi-feudal states.

This pattern is perhaps more clearly grasped if we look at the Indo-Chinese peninsula, where its homologue persisted into our own century. Here we have the great rice-growing basins, deltas or (as around Mandalay, the heart of ancient Burma) irrigated dry zones: these are the bases of organized kingdoms. Around these, on the more or less open plateaus of the Shan country (Burma), Korat (Thailand) and the Laos country (Indo-China), was a penumbra of semi-feudal statelets, subject to Burma, the Thai Kingdom, or Annam, but with an allegiance the quality of which depended on distance from the centre and on the personality, vigorous or effete, of the reigning monarch. And in the wilder mountains, dissected and densely forest-clad, the hillmen lived their ancient and primitive tribal life. In India the Vale of Kashmir and Manipur corresponded to the larger plateau-states of the Shans, formed round an unusually large agricultural base in an old lake-floor silted into a rice-growing lowland.

Three regions have not been mentioned in this survey: the arid northwestern hills; Bengal; Assam. The first were generally dependencies of the dominant power in Iran – Medes, Persians, Macedonians, Parthians, Sassanids and their Muslim successors. Often, indeed, the western Punjab and the Afghan basins were part of the same 'saddle-state', loosely straddling the hills and incapsulating rather than assimilating their tribesmen; power was sometimes based on the Kandahar–Ghazni–Kabul line, sometimes on the Punjab. This Afghan–Punjab relationship, foreshadowed by the Greek Bactrian Kingdoms and the Kushan Empire, naturally bulks larger in the Muslim period: but preoccupation with Hindustan inhibited effective power to the northwest, and vice versa. Often the boundary has been the *daman-i-koh* – 'the skirts of the hills' – the sharp break of slope at the detrital pediment. This, the boundary of the Punjab under the Sikhs, under the British was still that between Administered and Tribal territory in the North-West Frontier Province. The India/Nepal boundary in the terai, the East Pakistan boundary with the Shillong Plateau and Tripura, and many internal boundaries (e.g. that of the Santal Parganas in the Rajmahal Hills) are essentially similar.

As for Bengal, until it became the base for British territorial aggrandizement in the northeast, it was always something of a marchland: beyond lay the Ahom kings of Assam or the Arakanese. Assam itself in early days had something of the Kashmir or Manipur pattern: an agricultural lowland surrounded by hills and jungles, and though the Shan Ahoms were soon Hinduized, Assam remained *mlechcha* – foreign, 'beyond the pale', unsubjugated even by the Moguls.

The Delhi–Agra axis and the Cambay node

One area stands out with peculiar importance: '*The* Doab', a long fillet between Yamuna and Ganga, with Delhi and Agra as its poles. The reasons are clear: at the northwestern end is the gateway between the Aravallis and the Thar Desert on one hand, the Himalayas on the other; to the southeast are the approaches to the great Malwa passageway.

The strategic significance of the Delhi gate is shown not only by the cities – more than the traditional seven – which have intervened between Aryan Indraprastha and British New Delhi, but by its role as the cockpit of northern India. It is the theatre of the great warfare of the *Mahabharata* between the Kurus to the west and the Panchalas to the east of the Yamuna; but at least seven less legendary and more decisive battles have taken place a few marches north of Delhi, where the great highway from the northwestern entry, along the well-watered sub-montane Punjab strip, approaches the Yamuna.[5] The heart of Muslim rule in northern India lay between Delhi and Agra, alike in the great days of the Tughluks and the Moguls and in the decadence under the Lodis (15th century) and the later Moguls. Agra shared with Delhi the prestige of being the Mogul capital, and near it, at Khanua, Babur consolidated his conquest by defeating a powerful Rajput attempt to take over from the discredited Lodis.

Only second in importance to the great highway through the Punjab was the ancient trade route from Agra to the Gulf of Cambay through Ujjain, which by 500 BC was a centre of a Gangetic-type culture. If the views of D. H. Gordon have any validity, the Cambay entry may already have been important in the late or immediately post-Harappan phase in Kathiawad, and may indeed have some bearing on the vexed question of Dravidian origins. In classical times its significance is well attested by Ptolemy's Barygaza (Broach), and the importance of this great commercial entry persisted at least until the 17th century, when the trade of Surat, the most flourishing port of the Mogul Empire, was fought for by Portuguese, Dutch and English: until 1961 the Portuguese enclaves of Diu and Damão, useless as they were in this age, still attested their preoccupation with this entry to the Mogul realms. It will be noted that the two great structure-lines converge here.

[5] Muhammad Ghori's two battles with the Rajputs at Thanesar (1191 and 1192); Babur's victory at Panipat in 1526 and Akbar's 30 years later, the first putting the Moguls on the throne of Delhi and the second securing them there after a usurpation; the Persian Nadir Shah's defeat of the Moguls at Karnaul in 1739; the Afghan victories over the Marathas at Thanesar again in 1759 and at Panipat in 1761, which checked the Maratha flood at its highest tide. Outside Delhi itself Lord Lake defeated the Maratha Sindhia in 1803; and the significance of Delhi in 1857 needs no stress.

Pre-Muslim invasions and empires

After the rich confusion of the Heroic Age, it is a relief to be able to resume the historical narrative with a definite date at last. In 326 BC Alexander the Great, after defeating various Punjab princes, reached his farthest east on the Beas.

The immediate results of Alexander's Indian campaigns were practically nil; not so the long-term effects. The Satrapies formed along the Indus soon reverted to Indian control; even Gandhara, which had been one of the richest provinces of the Achaemenid Persian Empire, was ceded by Alexander's successor Seleucus Nikator to Chandragupta Maurya. But it seems very probable that it was a reaction against the Yavana (=Ionian) invaders that enabled Chandragupta, the Sandrocottos of Greek historians, to seize the throne of Magadha from a decadent dynasty and so to found the first of the great empires which have endeavoured to bring all India under one sway. At its height, under Chandragupta's grandson Asoka (*fl. c.* 250 BC), the Mauryan dominion stretched from the Hindu Kush to the Brahmaputra, and well beyond the Krishna to the Penner. Not all of this area, of course, was directly under Asoka or his viceroys, but frontier kingdoms such as those of the Rashtrakutas (in the Konkan) and the Andhras were subordinate to him. From archaeological evidence it seems plausible that the remarkable south Indian megalithic culture was stimulated by the introduction of iron into a chalcolithic culture, through the medium of Mauryan border kingdoms.

The fragments of the account of India written by Megasthenes, the Seleucid ambassador to Chandragupta, and perhaps some of the traditions embedded in the manual of polity known as Kautilya's *Arthasastra*,[6] attest the high degree of fiscal and administrative organization of the Empire, in which most of the familiar features of Hinduism were firmly established. From Asoka's time onwards brick and stone replace the earlier timber of Pataliputra and other towns. The moral crisis which Asoka experienced as a result of the horrors of his Kalinga war brought him very close to Buddhism, probably actually within its fold; and the later years of his reign were devoted to a pacifist policy (even the royal hunt was abolished) and the fostering of Buddhist missionary activity: the inscriptions of the 'Asoka pillars'[7] and rock edicts scattered over India record missions to Tamilnad, Ceylon and the Hellenistic World. The unique spectacle of a great Emperor publishing (in stone, for all time) his repentance for the sins of his imperialism, and doing all in his power in expiation, makes Asoka perhaps the

[6] The *Arthasastra* is ascribed to Kautilya, adviser to Chandragupta, but in great part at least it is probably of post-Christian date, since the elaborate rules for foreign policy (including alliance with the next state but one, and avoidance of alliance with a stronger state) point to a chaotic 'time of troubles'. Nevertheless it is a most remarkable work whether it is a guide to existing administration or (more probably) a blueprint of what ought to be; it strongly resembles Machiavelli's *The Prince* in temper, though not in conciseness. It is indeed a sort of Gauleiter's Guide, with references, *inter alia*, to the inner ring of spies within and on the secret service, and to the authoritarian control (through gilds) of trade and industry down to the duties, rights and fees of courtesans.

[7] The fine lions from the capital of the Sarnath pillar (near Varanasi) have become the badge of the Indian Republic.

most sympathetic monarch in all history: but, though the mission to Ceylon had results still important today, 'the Greeks apparently were not much impressed by lessons in non-violence', and the wilful decay of the central military power led to provincial disintegration, not checked by Asoka's institution of touring officials analogous to Charlemagne's *Missi Dominici*. After his death disruption set in; the Dravidian south exerted its independence (or rather independences), and in the north the Greeks of Bactria (northern Afghanistan) subjugated Gandhara once more. This Hellenistic domination lasted only a century or so, but to it belongs a fine coinage (a most important contribution to chronology) and the wealth of Gandharan or Graeco-Buddhist sculpture – much of which, it must be admitted, bears the mark of mass production.[8]

Renewed incursions from the northwest – Sakas, Parthians, the Yueh-Chi or Kushans – make the centuries around the beginning of the Christian era a time of troubles. The most important of these 'Scythian' peoples were the Kushans, probably displaced from their homes by Chinese expansion under the imperialist Han dynasty. The Kushan Empire, centred on Purushapura (Peshawar), reached its height under Kanishka (1st or 2nd century AD), whose domains extended from Sinkiang to Varanasi; he carried on the Gandharan Buddhist traditions. During this generally chaotic period a strong Andhra power included most of the Deccan north of the Penner and disputed possession of Malwa – and the Ujjain trade route – with the northern kingdoms.

In the middle of the 4th century AD the Gupta dynasty revived some at least of the Mauryan glories. Under Chandragupta II Vikramaditya (*c.* 385–413), the empire extended, more or less loosely, from the Kirthar Range and the Chenab to Bengal, and south to the Narmada–Chota Nagpur line, with occasional penetrations along the western and eastern littorals. Vikramaditya's court was at Ujjain, centre of a cultural revival which marked the end of Hellenistic influence (except in coinage and astronomy), and the home of Kalidasa, whose delightful lyrical drama *Sakuntala* is perhaps the secular writing in Sanskrit best known to the West. Around 500 the Gupta Empire was shattered by the invasion of the White Huns, who destroyed the ancient Buddhist university at Taxila in Potwar. A long period of anarchy was only briefly mitigated by Harsha (mid-7th century), who seems to have ruled (with considerable local variation in his real power) from the Sutlej to Bengal and the Narmada–Chota Nagpur line. The centre of his power, at all events, was in the Delhi–Agra region, where lay his capital Kanauj on the Ganga.

During these centuries the south was the seat of a bewildering array of dynasties. Between 800 and 1000 India was more than usually disunited, three major and a host of minor kingdoms locked in an indecisive struggle for power. The three were the Gurjara–Pratihara kingdom, within the old Aravalli–Himalaya–Narmada triangle; the Palas of Bengal, Kalinga and the northeast Deccan;

[8] See R. E. Mortimer Wheeler, 'Romano-Buddhist Art: an old problem re-stated', *Antiquity*, 23 (1949), 4–19.

the Rashtrakutas in Maharashtra. The country south of the Penner was, as usual, under its own ever-shifting dynasties, of whom the most generally successful were the Cholas, who in the 11th century held Kalinga and sent armies as far as the Ganga; on the northwest they were held, by the Chalukyas of Maharashtra, roughly on the Deccan Lava boundary in Hyderabad. The Cholas also took much of Ceylon from its native Buddhist rulers – whence a still existing minority problem – and at sea reached out as far as Sumatra.

But, as in Italy, wealth and disunity combined to attract invaders from beyond the mountains; and the newcomers were armed with ideological as well as material weapons. Already in the 8th century the Arabs had conquered Sind, later extending their power as far as Multan and raiding into Rajputana and Gujarat. The stage was set for the great Muslim invasions which

> Cast the Kingdoms old
> Into another mould.

But the changes were political and social rather than geographical: the nuclear regions of power, the great lines of advance, the refuges for the dispossessed, remain the same.

India between East and West

As we have seen, the earliest civilization of India had commercial relations with Sumeria; and it is probable that Solomon's Tarshish and Ophir were southern India and Ceylon. Herodotus knew of northwestern India as part of the Achaemenid Empire, and relates the exploration of the Indus and the Makran coast by Skylax on the orders of Darius (521–485 BC). But Alexander's campaigns, the scientifically organized exploration of the sea route to the Persian Gulf by his admiral Nearchus, and the reports of Megasthenes put classical knowledge of India on a firmer footing. Egypt under the Ptolemies had an active trade with India, which expanded greatly with the luxury demand of Rome. The Greek names for rice, ginger and pepper are Indian, the Sanskrit for tin probably Greek;[9] the Byzantines had an official stationed at Clysma near Suez who visited India yearly to report on trade and political conditions; 'Roman' guards, 'the dumb *mlechchas*', were in demand by south Indian kings owing to their isolation from local faction. All-land routes were subject to interference by Parthia, often at war with Rome and always anxious to inflate transit profits; most trade was by sea, either via Palmyra or Petra and the Persian Gulf, or by Berenice and other Red Sea ports. The chief Indian ports concerned were Barbarikon on the Indus Delta, Barygaza (Broach), Kalyan near Bombay, and Musiris (Cranganore). The drain of precious metal in exchange for luxuries, including spices and sandalwood, is lamented by Roman publicists such as Pliny; evidence of Mediterranean

[9] K. de B. Codrington, 'A geographical introduction to the history of Central Asia', *GJ* 104 (1944), 27–40 and 73–91.

exports has been found in the form of warehouses of Roman pottery at Arika-medu near Pondicherry.[10] Ceylon and the extreme south of India were the meeting-places of Graeco-Roman and Chinese traders.

Cultural exchanges, though often indirect, were also important:

> 'Embassies were exchanged with the Hellenic powers by the sovereigns of Magadha and Malwa. Indian philosophers, traders and adventurers were to be found in the intellectual circles of Athens and the markets of Alexandria. The first of the Mauryas had entered into a marriage contract with a Greek potentate (Seleucus Nikator). His son was eager to secure the services of a Greek sophist. The third and greatest of the Mauryas (Asoka) entrusted the government of a wealthy province and the execution of important irrigation works to a Yavana chief. The services of Greek engineers seem to have been requisitioned by the greatest of the Kushans. Greek influence on Indian coinage and iconography is unmistakable.'[11]

Converse influences were those of Buddhism on the Graeco-Bactrians (their king Menander is the eponymous protagonist of the Buddhist *Milindapanha*); Indian thought may also have had some influence on Manicheism and hence on the early Christian Gnostic heresies. The early legend of St Thomas the Apostle (whose traditional tomb is to be seen in the Portuguese church at San Thomé, Madras) contains an indubitable reference to a Parthian king in the Indus borderland, and the Syrian Christian church of Malabar was possibly in existence in AD 200. Religion apart, the greatest gift of India to the West – and to the whole world – is the 'Arabic' numbers, without which it is difficult to conceive of modern scientific method.

The Western trade was largely in the hands of Asiatics, especially before the 'discovery' of the monsoon (long known to the Yemen Arabs) by Hippalus about AD 50. It is, naturally, much better known in Europe than the Indian expansion into southeast Asia, which began in the 1st and 2nd Christian centuries. Yet this had in a sense a more positive effect, since the beginnings of high civilization in Burma, Malaya, Indonesia and parts of Indo-China were due directly to Hindu and Buddhist traders, colonists and missionaries. Indian dynasties ruled for over a millennium (2nd–15th centuries) in Champa (Annam); Kambuja (Cambodia) at times dominated the whole peninsula beyond Burma, then truly Further India; Sivaism has left its memorial in Angkor Vat, and the culture of Cambodia remains Indo-Buddhist to this day. In Indonesia the Sailendra or Sri Vijaya Empire, centred at Palembang in Sumatra, dominated the archipelago from the 8th to the 11th centuries. Sailendra was Buddhist, deriving its inspiration from Bengal and leaving in the 400-ft.-square terraces of Borobudur (Java) perhaps the grandest material monument of any religion, alike in the superbly massive planning of the whole and in the richness and beauty of the innumerable

---

[10] R. E. M. Wheeler *et al.*, 'Arikamedu: an Indo-Roman trading station on the east coast of India', *Ancient India*, No. 2 (ND, July 1946), 17–124.

[11] H. C. Raychaudhuri in *An Advanced History of India* (1946), 142.

sculptures. In the 9th century Java (a Hindu kingdom conquered by Sailendra) broke away; in the 13th and 14th the Javanese Majapahit dynasty gradually supplanted Sailendra and in turn controlled the archipelago, only to fall before the Islamic tide in the 15th century. Hinduism survived in Bali, the arts and customs of which reflect, if on a diminished scale, the golden days of classical Hinduism. The *Ramayana* and the *Mahabharata* are still the basis of much popular art – puppet- and stage-plays, poems and folk-tales – in Indonesia and even the Indo-Chinese peninsula.

Naturally the major part in the foundation of these distant sea-states was played by the kingdoms of the eastern littoral, especially Kalinga and the Chola Empire. How false is Lyde's still current concept of an almost solely inward-looking India, with its sea-contacts those of alien traders, may be seen from the fact that the decline of Sailendra was due in large part to an attack by Rajendra Chola II (1012–44); the Cholas were driven out after a century of intermittent war, but in the 13th century a disastrous expedition against Ceylon fatally weakened the power of Sri Vijaya. These armadas presuppose high standards not only in navigation and seamanship, but in naval organization, on both sides of the 1,200-mile-wide waters between Coromandel and Sumatra. Certainly no European power of the day could have dreamt of such oceanic adventure: only the Viking voyages are as impressive, while the Crusading fleets were in comparison mere coastal forays. On the terraces of Borobudur the carved ships of Sri Vijaya still sail, immobile and endlessly, over their seas of stone.

Hindu expansion remained vigorous until about AD 1000–1100; but the declining fortunes of Hinduism in the homeland sapped its strength, and indigenous elements, seconded by Islam, reasserted themselves. Long before then an even greater work had been accomplished from India: by devious ways through mountain and jungle Buddhism had spread over the Far East and High Asia; the Chinese Buddhist pilgrims Fa Hien and Hiuen-Tsang (5th and 7th centuries) give us the first comprehensive accounts of India by outside observers. Buddhism hardly recovered from the devastation of the Huns in its northwestern strongholds, and in succeeding centuries it declined before a Brahmanic revival. By the time it was dead in its birthplace its heirs had developed the strength to stand alone and to evolve the complex cosmogony and psychology of later Buddhism in China, Tibet and Japan, the lands of the Mahayana or 'Greater Vehicle' as opposed to the 'Lesser', the simpler Hinayana form which survives in Ceylon, Burma and Thailand.

The Muslim advance

Apart from the early occupation of Sind, never really followed up, the first Muslim incursions of significance were the almost annual raids of Mahmud of Ghazni, between 1000 and 1030. Mahmud, a first-class soldier and a patron of the arts, was in India no more than a ruthless plunderer; he penetrated as far as Mathura and Somnath (Kathiawad), but only the Punjab – as far as Thanesar –

was held, and that only as the frontier march of a domain covering most of Persia and at times much of Turkestan. But the ferocity of his devastations weakened the economy and morale of the Hindu states, and though there was a respite of 160 years before the arrival of the next great Muslim leader, Muhammad of Ghor in southwest Afghanistan, northern India remained politically fragmented. Muhammad's victory over the Rajput princes near Thanesar in 1192 was decisive; the Delhi gateway was finally forced, the Rajputs split into the petty Pahari (=hill) chiefs of the sub-Himalaya and the better-known princes of the Aravalli fortresses – Rajputana or Rajasthan. Within 10 years the entire Gangetic Plain, as far as Nadia in Bengal, had been overrun; and henceforth Islam was politically dominant in Hindustan.

The Ghaznavid realm, and the new Empire in its first few years, had straddled the northwestern hills. By dynastic accident this Afghan–Punjab relationship was broken in 1206, and the famous Sultanate of Delhi took form, to survive in some sense until 1857, though in evil days the 'Ruler of the World' sometimes ruled effectively 'from Delhi to Palam', nine or ten miles. The Delhi Kingdom now formed a separate entity in the Muslim world, a state at once Indian and Islamic. Under Iltutmish (1211–35), the greatest ruler of the first 'Slave' or Turco-Afghan dynasty, it corresponded roughly with the perennial northern triangle we have already seen as held by the Guptas, by Harsha, and by the Gurjaras; with the difference of a firm hold on the Indus Plains. The heart of Rajputana, and outlying regions such as Kathiawad and Bengal, generally retained a quasi-independence under their own princes or subordinate governors; and internal faction, wars of succession, and at times Mongol raids were constant impediments to consolidation. Under the second dynasty, the Khaljis (1294–1320), forays into the Deccan were frequent, and in 1311 reached Madurai in the far south. The rulers of these dynasties included some able if ruthless leaders, such as the astonishing megalomaniac Ala-ud-Din Khalji, a *soi-disant* 'Second Alexander', who ruled in the most totalitarian manner. Nevertheless the general standards of society and government were probably not very different in degree from those of contemporary Europe, and at Delhi architecture around the Qutb Minar shows an extremely successful fusion of Hindu and Islamic tradition. The Qutb is the highest free-standing stone tower in the world (234 ft., 71·3 m.); it is characteristic of Ala-ud-Din that he began a minar designed to be twice as high.

The Tughluks (1320–1412) represent a sterner and more austere Islam, well shown by the stark cyclopean grandeur of Tughlukabad, only three miles from the Qutb complex but worlds away in spirit. The greatest of them, Muhammad bin Tughluk, was an energetic despot who would have been enlightened in the European 18th-century manner had any enlightenment been to hand. Like the Khaljis, he had a bad press, since he based his politics on the world as he saw it rather than on Quranic commentaries (again a parallel with mediaeval Europe, i.e. the Emperor Frederick II). Muhammad extended his power almost to the southern extremity of India; it was in pursuance of a policy of definite conquest, rather than the mere depredations of preceding rulers, that he transferred the population of Delhi (or a large part of it) to Deogir in the Deccan, renamed Daulatabad and provided with spectacular fortifications. But although his domains were equalled in extent only by Asoka's before him and Aurenzeb's after, 'it was impossible to control the Deccan from an external centre in Hindustan, just as it was equally impossible to rule Hindustan from Deogir'[12] – the same problem as faced the Hohenstaufen in Germany and Italy, or Ghaznavids and Moguls in their relations with their Iranian holdings; realization of this probably accounts for so many invaders reaching Delhi and turning back, e.g. Timur, Nadir Shah, Ahmad Shah Durrani. Despite these and other aberrations Muhammad was a man of large ideas in many directions, not least in his conciliatory policy towards the Hindus. His successor Firoz Shah was more orthodox in this respect, taking piety indeed so far that he endeavoured to spare the blood of believers; an ineffective policy. He has at least the merit of initiating large-scale irrigation canals in the Punjab. Disintegration had set in before Muhammad's death – especially (as usual) in the south and Bengal, and after the death of Firoz (1388) the prestige of the Tughluks was irretrievably ruined in 1398 by the ferocious sack of Delhi by Timur (Tamburlaine). Centrifugal tendencies were scarcely checked by the weak successors of the Tughluks, the 15th-century Sayyids and Lodis.

In the south a strong new Hindu power, Vijayanagar, arose on the ruins of the older Dravidian dynasties, shattered by the Tughluk incursions, and made head against the Muslim princes, whose revolt had set into motion the disintegration of Muhammad bin Tughluk's Empire. In the Deccan, between Tapti and Tungabhadra, the Bahmani kingdom split off from the Tughluk dominions, and in turn split into five Deccani Sultanates: Ahmadnagar, Berar, Bidar, Golconda and Bijapur; the broken country of the northeastern Peninsula was left to Gond tribal chieftains. Gujarat, at the height of its commercial importance, was an independent Muslim kingdom, as were Khandesh south and Malwa north of the Narmada, Sind and Multan in the west, Bengal in the east and for a few years even Jaunpur in the heart of Hindustan. All these were under Muslim rulers, but the Rajputs formed a confederacy under the leadership of Mewar, threatening the diminished Lodi realms, which at best formed a belt from the Punjab to Bihar, but were often not much more than the Delhi–Agra region.

Thus, after 300 years of Muslim conquest and attempted consolidation, all the old patterns of pre- and post-Mauryan India have once more emerged. Nothing better illustrates the perennial significance of the geographical factor in Indian history than this continual re-assertion of the nuclear regions as the power-bases of political entities. But two mighty forces were looming on the horizon of Indian politics: in 1526 Babur, who began his career as a boy of 12 dispossessed of his petty principality of Ferghana, utterly overthrew the Lodis at Panipat; and already in 1498 Vasco da Gama had reached Calicut, precursor of yet stronger

[12] C. C. Davies, *An Historical Atlas of the Indian Peninsula* (1949), 34.

and more alien powers who were to rule as much by economic chains as by the sword.[13]

The Mogul synthesis

The key significance of the Delhi–Agra region is strikingly illustrated by the incidents of early Mogul rule. By 1529 Babur was in possession of Bengal; he died in the next year and his son Humayun, after an expedition as far as Cambay, was defeated at Kanauj in 1539 and expelled from Hindustan. His supplanter, Sher Shah, was a very capable ruler, who laid out the Grand Trunk Road from Bengal to the Indus, and whose principles of land revenue administration influenced, through the Moguls, British practice. Disputed successions enabled Humayun to return in 1555 after a victory at Sirhind; but in 1556 his son Akbar, on any reckoning one of the world's great men, succeeded at the age of 14 to a military situation in which Delhi and Agra had been lost. Once more the field of Panipat saw a Mogul triumph. The old significance of these sites – Kanauj, Sirhind, Panipat – will be remembered.

Before his death in 1605 Akbar had secured not only Hindustan and the north-west, but had crossed the Narmada as far as the Godavari, and in the east held Orissa; between these salients the wild Gondwana country remained under independent or tributary chiefs. Territorial expansion, however, was the least of Akbar's achievements, nor, splendid as were his capitals at Agra and Fatehpur Sikri and his patronage of artists and scholars, were these his greatest. His administration was one of the best India had known, at least in its principles: but in all these vast empires, even-handed and accessible as might be the sovereign, he could not be accessible and effective everywhere, and there was much local tyranny. Nor were communications adequate to avert such natural disasters as the Gujarat famine of 1632; and the Empire was hardly so strong as it looked: in the later 17th century Tavernier estimated that 30,000 good European troops could march through it. Nevertheless it is impossible to visit Delhi, Agra and above all Fatehpur Sikri without an involuntary comparison with the Versailles of Louis XIV – a comparison unfavourable to the latter. Man for man Akbar was immeasurably the greater of the two, and he was as well served by men as able and loyal as Colbert or Vauban. But with all this, social organization was essentially semi-feudal, and India lacked the Enlightenment: when it came it was through the distorting prisms of an alien rule.

The grasp of Akbar's mind is the more astonishing when it is recalled that an excellent memory had to serve him in the place of formal literacy. He advanced from the tactical alliances of expediency with Rajput chiefs to a real tolerance and some degree of synthesis of the two great cultures, Hindu and Islamic: in

---

[13] See A. J. Toynbee, 'The Unification of the world' (*Civilization on Trial*, OUP, 1948, esp. 65–71). This is a very penetrating analysis of the situation; as always with Toynbee brilliantly written, and getting to the heart of the relations of geography, history and technology much more effectively than usual.

his last years indeed he went so far as to foster an eclectic creed drawing from these and even from Christianity; but this artificial construct had only a temporary following of courtiers. Under his successors Jahangir and Shah Jahan the policy of toleration was still followed, with less conviction, and advances were made in the Deccan, as far as Bijapur and Golconda, though effective action here was hampered by preoccupations in Afghanistan.

With Aurenzeb (1658-1707) the Empire reached its greatest extent: from Kabul to the Cauvery. But the seeds of disruption, always latent, were fertilized by Aurenzeb's intolerance, which completely alienated the Rajputs, by this time probably the most valuable military elements in the Empire. More serious was the situation in the Deccan. Here, after long wars centring round the Raichur Doab, the allied Sultanates had in 1565 finally crushed Vijayanagar at Talikota, southeast of Bijapur; only to fall in turn to the ceaseless Mogul attrition, advancing by the historic Malwa–Khandesh–Maharashtra route on the Deccan Lavas. But long before the definitive Mogul conquests of Bijapur and Golconda (1686–87) the Western Ghats were overhung by a cloud, at first no bigger than a man's hand, but destined in the next century to sweep over nearly all India. And behind the Marathas another cloud was setting in from the sea.

The founder of Maratha power, Sivaji, son of a minor noble of the Ahmadnagar Kingdom, from his little fief of Poona had won fortress after fortress in the wild Ghats country; when he died in 1680 he held the Konkan less Bombay, the Portuguese towns and Janjira – the last a holding of the Abyssinian Sidis, nominally the Bijapur and later the Mogul admirals. The core of Maratha power was a belt of country along the Ghats and as far east as the Bhima; and they had also various outliers in the south – Bellary, Bangalore, Tanjore. Sivaji's rise was of course aided by the extraordinary perfidy of Deccani politics, a tangle of ever-shifting alliances: war was generally triangular and might be polygonal. And the Moguls were long past their best: their Hindu subjects were sullen or in revolt; their armies were vast, cumbered with camp-followers, in a war of movement no match for the tough and mobile Maratha light horse; their leaders, no longer dominated by an Akbar or a Babur, but by a politician at once shifty and bigoted, more and more played their own hands. The stage is set for the chaos and anarchy of the 18th century; and by now the coasts from Diu to Chittagong were dotted with the trading stations and forts of Portuguese, Dutch, French, Danes and English.

The Mogul collapse

European expansion in India can be understood only against the background of 'country powers'. The successors of Aurenzeb were all ineffective, and the throne of Delhi became the plaything of internal and alien factions. Such morale as the Empire retained was shattered by the almost unopposed invasion of the Persian Nadir Shah and his savage sack of Delhi in 1739.

The Marathas represented the effervescence of a long-fermenting Hindu revival. Initially they kept tight discipline and were conscious of a mission as the liberators of Hinduism; but this element of idealism faded as they found their account in manoeuvres among the distracted factions of Muslim India. As their power expanded it became looser, a confederacy headed by the Poona Peshwas, ministers and supplanters of Sivaji's heirs; but the centre had influence rather than power. That was in the hands of the great warlords: the Gaekwar in Baroda, Bhonslas in Nagpur and Berar, Holkar in Indore (Malwa), most powerful of all Sindhia in Gwalior. Even Calcutta had its 'Maratha Ditch'. At the same time Mogul and other Muslim warlords set up for themselves.

Thus by the 1750s Haidar Ali subverted the Hindu dynasty in Mysore; the Viceroy of the Deccan had become the Nizam of Hyderabad; Bengal and Oudh were but very nominally subject to the ghost of empire at Delhi. Sind and the trans-Sutlej Punjab were under Afghan domination, and there was a separate Afghan state so near Delhi as Rohilkhand. So low had the Empire fallen that the Hindu Jats – little more than an armed peasantry – could dominate the Agra–Mathura region, plundering the Taj Mahal and Akbar's tomb near Agra.

Already in 1719 the Marathas had marched to Delhi as allies of one of the king-making Mogul factions. Before the repeated invasions of Ahmad Shah Abdali, founder of the Durrani dynasty which still rules Afghanistan, the Muslim rulers of the Punjab, unsupported by their 'government' in Delhi, called in the Marathas, who as a mere incident took possession of capital and Emperor. But they alienated the Rajputs and the rising Sikh chieftains, while Ahmad Shah rallied the Rohillas and Oudh. In 1761 Panipat once more saw the climax of the drama, when the Marathas were utterly overthrown, losing thousands of their best men and nearly all their best leaders: 'Two pearls have been dissolved, twenty-two gold Mohurs have been lost, and of the silver and copper the total cannot be cast up.' This was a decisive check to Maratha expansion; although Afghan affairs prevented Ahmad Shah from consolidating his power, the Sikhs filled the gap. Originally a quietist, even pacifist, reforming Hindu sect, Mogul persecution forged them into a nation, and under the extraordinarily tough one-eyed Ranjit Singh (1780–1839) they rose to dominate the Punjab. The Marathas remained dominant at Delhi, the Emperor being merely Sindhia's puppet. But Muslims and Marathas virtually cancelled each other out; four years before Panipat, Plassey had been fought, and the future, for nearly two centuries, lay with its alien victors.

Europe in India: Portugal

The British Empire in India was only the latest phase of four and a half centuries of European intrusion. This long history falls into distinct periods: Portuguese monopoly (1500–1600); the age of conflict between the European powers (1600–1763); the rise to power of the East India Company and its Indian Summer before the Mutiny (1757–1857); the unchallenged hey-day of the British Raj (1858–c. 1900); and the struggle for independence.

It is important to remember that Vasco da Gama's voyage was not only the climax of decades of patient African discovery; it was also a part of the Iberian crusade against Islam. Once the road was known experience soon taught the value of the monsoons to Portuguese fleets, which developed regular sailing habits, leaving Lisbon in time to reach Moçambique (where Lourenço Marques founded his colony in 1554) for the southwest monsoon to take them across to Goa. But it was certainly not timidity which led da Gama to work up the east African coast as far as Malindi (north of Mombasa) before striking into the open ocean: the journey (c. 1486–90) of Pero da Covilhan by the Red Sea to Calicut and down the African coast to Sofala (20°S) had taught the Portuguese of the Arab hold on the Indian Ocean trade and something of navigation conditions; da Gama knew that on this coast he could find a pilot to bring him through.

The Portuguese fixation on western India was thus influenced by sailing conditions; but in large part also by their preoccupation with the 'Moors' as well as with the monsoon. This bias is suggested by the title adopted by the King of Portugal: Lord of the Conquest, Navigation and Commerce of Ethiopia, Arabia, Persia and India. The 'Moors' fought tenaciously for their monopoly, with the support of the Muslim rulers of Bijapur and Gujarat, of Egypt and of the Turks after their capture (1518) of Alexandria, hitherto the great emporium of eastern trade. Afonso de Albuquerque, greatest of the Viceroys (1509–15), saw the key points for domination of the Indian Ocean: Goa, Malacca, Aden.[14] Goa was an island site, defensible behind its tidal creeks yet large enough to give a local agricultural base; it controlled the valuable trade in Arab horses for the armies of the Deccani kingdoms: it was taken in 1510. In the next year Albuquerque took Malacca, guarding the approach to the Spice Islands and the Far East. At Aden he failed, though the moral effect of his expedition beyond Bab-el-Mandeb was great; but he secured Socotra and Ormuz, the latter guarding the alternative seaway to the Levantine portages. With the fortification of Ormuz, Albuquerque's last act before he died in Goa harbour, Portuguese domination in the Indian Ocean was complete: it was only seventeen years since da Gama's arrival at Calicut. The Portuguese achievement was secured against very heavy numerical odds, and with a much lesser margin of technical superiority than that enjoyed by later Europeans: by the time of the great sieges of Diu in 1538 and 1545 there was little that Europe could teach the 'Rumi' (Turkish) gunners in Indian service. But there have been few better geopoliticians than Albuquerque.

Besides Goa and a number of minor stations on the Konkan, Malabar and Coromandel coasts, the Portuguese held by 1540 the flourishing ports of Chaul, Bassein, Damão and Diu; in the east they were established – more precariously – at San Thomé (Madras), Hooghly and Chittagong; they had forts in Ceylon

---

[14] Four and a half centuries later these were the only important points on the Asian mainland shores of the Indian Ocean to remain in European hands.

and were beginning to dominate its politics; they were in official contact with China and freelance adventurers reached Japan in 1542 –

> *E se mais mundo houvera, lá chegára.*[15]

But the royal trading monopoly was always cumbrous and usually corrupt; ill-paid officials made their fortunes where they could find them; the bigotry of the ecclesiastics often wrecked promising political combinations; the administration, in theory tightly organized, was as a rule ramshackle in practice – to find money for the rebuilding of Diu after the second siege the Viceroy D. João de Castro had to pawn his beard as security for a loan from the citizens of Goa. On the other hand, the archaic theocratic outlook of the Portuguese fitted into the Asian scene better than the secular temper of their supplanters, and, together with their tolerance of miscegenation, accounts for the deep cultural impress of Portugal in Ceylon and parts of the Konkan.

Decay had set in before the catastrophe of 1580, when the crown passed to Philip II of Spain and Portuguese holdings were open to Dutch attacks, without any compensating aid from Spain. The Portuguese effective was locked up in too many scattered small garrisons; at Tuticorin 'the Captain-Major of the Fishery Coast' points to 'what is little more than a hut: "The fortress is that house in which I live. All the Portuguese consist of myself."'[16] Yet the old Lusian spirit flared up in gallant last-ditch defences, as when Bassein fell to the Marathas in 1739; and indeed the *Novas Conquistas* of Goa were won in the 18th century.

Europe in India: the age of conflict

In 1600 the English East India Company was founded, in 1602 the Dutch: more efficient commercial mechanisms than the Portuguese monopoly, backed by the more modern ideology of energetic and youthful bourgeoisies rather than the inept control of a half-feudal state. In the struggle which ensued the English played a minor part, though they helped the Persians to capture Ormuz in 1622. But after this they and the Portuguese were as a rule on fairly friendly terms: after all, the Dutch might be Protestants but were obviously more dangerous trade rivals. As for the Dutch, they were greatly interested in the Spice Islands and not at all interested in warring with the enemies of Christendom: they based themselves well to the east, at Batavia, founded in 1619 to guard the Sunda Straits breach in the island barrier between the Indian Ocean and the Far East.[17] Malacca they took in 1641, Colombo in 1656, and Goa itself was blockaded in the open season for several years from 1639. Cochin was taken in 1653 and other

[15] 'And had there been more of the world, they would have reached it' – Camões, *Os Lusiadas*, VII. 14.

[16] João Ribeiro, *The Historic Tragedy of Ceilão* (1685; trans. P. E. Pieris, Colombo, n.d.), 238. This simple, stout-hearted captain speaks much more sense on the decline than is found in either the modern Portuguese rhetorical historians, or in the traditional Popery-and-immorality English view of Portugal in the East.

[17] The Dutch normally sailed with the Westerlies to about 100° E before turning north, which led them to the discovery of western Australia – for two centuries 'New Holland'.

Malabar forts in 1661–64. By this time Portugal was finished, and Bombay after it became English (1661–66) soon outstripped all other European bases on the western littoral.

Nevertheless the Portuguese had pre-empted this coast, and except at Surat, terminal of the Malwa trade-route, and the pepper coast of Malabar, it was hardly worth while turning them out. Dutch and English factories at Surat date from 1616 and 1612, and both fought the Portuguese in Swally Roads off the port. But the main interest turned to the east coast, where the 'country powers' were weak and disunited. The Dutch had stations at Pulicat (1610), Chinsura on the Hooghly (1653) and Negapatam (1659); the English at Masulipatam (1611), Armagaon (1626), and above all Madras (Fort St George, 1639) and Calcutta (Fort William, 1691–98). In the 18th century the Dutch, weakened by the long struggle with Louis XIV and now definitely a junior partner to their British allies, gradually lost ground in India and concentrated on Indonesia, though Chinsura was not ceded to the EIC until 1825.

In the meantime a far more serious competitor had appeared. In 1668 the first French factory was established at Surat – then nearing its decline – followed in 1669 by one at Masulipatam; and while they were dispossessed of San Thomé by the Dutch in 1673, the same year saw their establishment at Pondicherry, and 1690–92 at Chandernagore. This initial development, largely due to Colbert, was not followed up, and the years of Marlborough's wars saw a general decline in French activity. In the 1720s, however, Mauritius, Mahé and Karikal were occupied.

At this stage the French, like the Dutch and English, were content with 'factories': small extra-territorial holdings granted by the local ruler, and if possible further secured by a *firman* from the Mogul Emperor. Here, within a fortified *enceinte*, were offices, warehouses, official residences; and sometimes there were jurisdictional rights over native settlement attracted by the trade (and the security) afforded by the factory. All were managed by monopolistic chartered companies, an organization adopted by other countries which took a hand: Sweden, Austria (the Ostend and Imperial Companies, 1722–44 and 1781–84), Prussia (the Emden Company) and Denmark. Only the last had any significance: Danish Serampore and Tranquebar were not sold to the EIC until 1845, and were important missionary centres when the EIC took its policy of non-interference in religion to the point of discouraging Christian zeal; Tranquebar has still a Lutheran Bishopric, with an Indian Bishop.

The Franco-British struggle for power was in appearance no more than a side-show to the War of the Austrian Succession (1744–48) and the Seven Years' War (1756–63). But it laid the foundations of an Empire which at its height included some 1,750,000 sq. miles and 410,000,000 people (including Ceylon and Burma).

Ever since 1505, when the Captain of Colombo reported to the King of Kandy of the Portuguese strangers that 'their guns were very good', European military aptitudes had been held in respect; but they had been mainly confined to the defence of fortifications. A chance clash in the open field between a small French and a large local force opened the eyes of all parties.[18] The Europeans were now courted for military assistance; and in the whirlpool of Indian politics the possible gains were immense. Always liable to be cut off from France by superior British sea-power, the French under Dupleix and Bussy tended to fall back on this game, played with vigour and skill. There was a ding-dong struggle in which both Pondicherry and Madras changed hands, and at times it seemed that French influence would dominate the Deccan. But lack of steady metropolitan support ruined their chances. After 1763 there was never a serious French menace, though the British were long nervous of possible French-inspired coalitions, such as those suggested by Napoleon's intrigues with Tipu Sultan of Mysore.

Territorial rise of 'John Company'

The serious beginnings of British territorial power were the acquisition of the Northern Circars (Madras–Orissa coast) and the 24 Parganas around Calcutta in 1757–59. There is truth in the traditional view that the subsequent advance was to some extent involuntary, since the anarchic turmoil of war and intrigue beyond the Company's borders made advance essential for security. Yet the appetite grew by what it fed on, and within 20 years of Plassey (1757) the Gangetic Plain as far as Kanpur was either directly under Company rule, or under clients such as the Nawab of Oudh. In the west the Marathas were a more solid obstacle than the effete Mogul succession states of the northeast; here even Salsette Island, immediately adjacent to Bombay, was not occupied until 1775–76. The great years, in which it became clear that no likely combination of 'country powers' could withstand British arms, were those of the Napoleonic Wars. Mysore, a serious menace under the vigorous and able soldiers Haidar Ali and Tipu Sultan, ceased to be so on the defeat and death of the latter in 1799; the Nizam of Hyderabad (one or two lapses apart) had been Our Most Faithful Ally almost from the beginning; the Marathas, rarely able to co-ordinate their powers, were finally defeated in 1818. By 1849 the last serious opponents (and perhaps the toughest of all), the Sikhs, had been subjugated, but the early disasters of the First Afghan War (1839–42) were a clear warning of the limits on this side. Apart from Baluchistan, annexed in part as a reaction to the Anglo–Russian crisis over the Balkans in 1878, Lower Burma (1852), and Upper Burma, annexed in 1885–86 to forestall French penetration from Indo-China, India was substantially as it stood in 1947, except for the separation of Burma in 1937.

> 'The actual distribution of British territory is too significant, in the broad, to be a mere absent-minded accident, although no other explanation will account for some of its fantastic local fragmentations and aberrations. The bases lay in the great Presidency provinces of Bengal, Madras, and Bombay,

[18] See Sir J. Fortescue, *A History of the British Army*, II (1910), 184–5.

securing all the coasts with the unimportant exceptions of those of Travancore
and Cochin in the southwest, one or two tiny states south of Bombay, and
arid Kutch, Kathiawad, and Baluchistan (and the Oman outlier at Gwadar)
in the northwest; apart of course from the Portuguese enclaves of Goa, Damão,
Diu, the French of Mahé, Karikal, Pondicherry, Yanaon, and Chandernagore,
the total area of these amounting to under 1,750 square miles. The entire
alluvial crescent between the Ganges and the Indus deltas, a few enclaves
apart, was British, and the three bases were linked by practically continuous
bridges, with a wedge of the United Provinces reaching down to contact the
Bombay–Calcutta corridor of the Central Provinces. The two great states of
Mysore and Hyderabad were neatly cut off from the sea and from each other.
From Kathiawad through Gujarat, Rajputana, and Central India, as far as the
Orissa hinterland, stretched great but broken blocks of states' territory; but
no single state in these groups exceeded 36,210 square miles or 3,050,000
inhabitants in 1941, and the political fragmentation (now largely swept away
by the Union) was indescribable verbally and well-nigh unmappable: it was
as if the feudal map of England in the anarchy of Stephen's reign had been
frozen. In the northwest money, diplomacy, and arms, in adroit and ever-
varying combinations, held a disjointed buffer-strip firmly under British
control; and the key points, Peshawar and Quetta, were in British hands.'[19]

The Indian Empire

'There have been in Asia, generally, from time immemorial, but three departments of Government: Finance, or the plunder of the interior; War, or the
plunder of the exterior; and the department of public works . . . the British have
neglected entirely that of public works.' This indictment by Marx was ceasing
to be true when he wrote it in 1853, as indeed he himself points out; but it is no
unfair description of the India of Warren Hastings. In the next century came the
economic catastrophe of the free entry of Manchester goods, ruining the old
craft industries. Against this must be set an administration which at least set its
face against corruption, and, in most times and places, a general peace which
must have been unspeakably comforting after the atrocious warfare of the post-
Mogul anarchy.

Yet revolutionary changes were afoot in 1853. Railway development had but
begun – a few miles at Bombay. At least, according to Marx, the British were
'laying down the material premises' for emancipation and social improvement:
'They intend now drawing a net of railroads over India. And they will do it. The
results are incalculable.' This laying of the foundations of a modern state in India
was the historic task of the British Raj, however blindly, and sometimes
reluctantly, carried out.[20]

[19] W. G. East and O. H. K. Spate (eds.), *The Changing Map of Asia* (Methuen, London,
4th ed. 1961), 131.

[20] See pp. 180–94 of *A Handbook of Marxism* (Gollancz, London, 1935); a vigorous and
astonishingly acute analysis. Lest Marx's attack should seem overdrawn, cf. the even
more severe contemporary judgements of Sleeman and Lawrence (both British officials)
cited in L. S. S. O'Malley (ed.), *Modern India and the West* (OUP, 1941), 76–77.

Nevertheless, after the EIC lost its trading function in 1833, it stagnated in a *laissez-faire* world, improving its administration, but doing little else: the Heroic Age was over with the defeat of the Sikhs. Into this Indian Summer crashed the tremendous thunderstorm of the 1857 Mutiny – or War of Independence.

Uniting, if imperfectly, the most diverse factions, it was complex in its proximate origins: resentment at Dalhousie's high-handed 'doctrine of lapse', whereby several states had passed to the Company in default of male heirs, but in disregard of Hindu adoption law; the grievances of the landowners of Oudh, which had recently been annexed on account of the chronic misgovernment of its rulers; the famous scandal of the greased cartridges. Yet perhaps at bottom it was simply the last rally of the old indigenous India, a gigantic protest against a revolution from above and to the profit of an alien race. Delhi – significantly on historic and geographical grounds – was the major storm-centre. It ended in the death of one Empire and the birth of another. The last Mogul, Bahadur Shah, a blind old poet hardly understanding his proclamation by the mutineers, was taken to Rangoon to die; the discredited Company was superseded by the direct rule of the Crown, and twenty years later Queen Victoria was proclaimed Empress of India.

Nationalism

The first fifty years of the Empire saw much material change – the spread of railways and telegraphs, the initiation of great irrigation works; the cotton boom of the American Civil War years (1861–65) gave an impetus to commercial speculation; the Suez Canal (1869) brought England and India nearer;[21] large sectors of the peasantry were now tied to the world market. Yet it was possible to maintain that the fundamentals of Indian life and society had changed little, beneath the surface layer of public works, though in two directions forces of great significance were stirring. The necessity of staffing an enormous administrative machine led to the production of a vast clerical army trained (however inadequately) in Western techniques, and far too large to be profitably employed: hence the frustration of the unemployed intellectual, and the schizophrenia of those no longer believing in the old gods, yet with no secure place in the new world.[22] And by the turn of the century a vigorous capitalist class was growing, as yet industrially weak, almost confined to the cotton mills of Bombay and Ahmedabad, but conscious of potentialities and girding at fiscal restraint in the interests of Lancashire. These provided the sinews of war, the intellectuals the ideology, the young men of the urban middle-class (and increasingly the town workers) the rank and file; and at times sections of the peasantry gave massive

---

[21] And, by facilitating the coming of English wives and the development of more exclusively English social life, contributed to detach the English in India yet farther from their subjects. The old officials were not infrequently kept in good touch with Indian feeling by alliances, temporary or permanent, with Indian mistresses.

[22] On this, see G. Wint, *The British in India* (Faber, London, 1947), (a most acute analysis); L. S. S. O'Malley, *op. cit.* 763–97; East and Spate, *op. cit.* 25–29.

weight to the attack. The Indian National Congress travelled fast from its innocuous beginnings in 1885; and in 1905 the Japanese victory over Russia ended the automatic acceptance of European invincibility.

This nationalism began in the 1890s with Tilak's appeal to Maratha traditions and gained strength from the agitation against Curzon's partition of Bengal in 1905. It was thus largely Hindu in tone, and after the collapse of the Hindu-Muslim united front in defence of the Caliphate in 1921 this bias was on the whole strengthened by the ideology of Mahatma Gandhi. The distress and disturbances of the years after 1914–18, culminating in the appalling bloodshed at Amritsar in 1919, and the great mass Civil Disobedience movement of 1931, showed that the temper of articulate India was far ahead of the reforms, which seemed doled out in niggardly instalments. In 1937, however, Congress decided to work, at least temporarily, within the 1935 Constitution, and Congress governments in nine major provinces gained valuable experience and showed both the potentialities and the limitations of constitutionalism. The automatic entry of India into the war in 1939 without consultation with Congress led to a decisive breach; and the Japanese successes of 1941–42, bringing them to the very borders of India, gave point to the dictum (whether or not Gandhi uttered it) that the Cripps promise of Dominion status (with right of secession) was 'a post-dated cheque on a failing bank'. At the same time Congress blunders, the communal struggle for patronage, resentment of the fact that the numerical majority controlled an even greater share of the economic life of the country, fed Muslim separatism.[23] At the end of the war two things were inescapably clear: British rule could by no possibility be said to retain or to be able to regain the consent of the governed, and could be maintained only at the cost, unthinkable morally and materially, of a 'super-Palestine'; and no settlement within a single state could meet the demands of the Muslim League, which now represented the political mass of Muslims. The Gordian knot was cut by the British government, and on August 15th, 1947, the Dominions of India and Pakistan came into their inheritance. On January 26th, 1950, the Indian Union declared itself a Republic and five years later Pakistan became an 'Islamic Republic'; both within the British Commonwealth. By a strange irony the fragments of Portuguese and French dominion survived, for a little while, their mighty supplanter the British Raj.

BIBLIOGRAPHICAL NOTE

The standard large work, superseding The Cambridge History of India, is the multi-volume History and Culture of the Indian People, edited by R. C. Majumdar and published by Bharatiya Vidya Bhavan, Bombay; a co-operative work of massive scholarship. There are numerous shorter histories, of which R. C. Majumdar, H. C. Raychauduri and K. Datta, An Advanced History of India

[23] For fuller discussion see O. H. K. Spate, 'Geographical aspects of the Pakistan scheme', GJ 102 (1943), 125–35; and 'The partition of India and the prospects of Pakistan', GR 38 (1948), 5–29.

(Macmillan, London, 1946) is perhaps the best, full and balanced, if rather text-booky in style. J. Nehru, *The Discovery of India* (Doubleday, Anchor Paper-backs, 1946) is a highly stimulating nationalist treatment. On the cultural side, H. Zimmer, *The Art of Indian Asia* (Pantheon, NY, 1955) is authoritative and lavishly illustrated. C. C. Davies, *An Historical Atlas of the Indian Peninsula* (OUP, Madras, 2nd ed. 1954) has useful maps and brief but acute notes.

On pre- and proto-historic India, the best introduction is R. Mortimer Wheeler's *Early India and Pakistan* (Thames & Hudson, London, 1959); more specialized are D. H. Gordon, *The Prehistoric Background of Indian Culture* (Desai, Bombay, 1958), A. H. Dani, *Prehistory and Protohistory of Eastern India* (Mukhopadhaya, Calcutta, 1960), and H. D. Sankala, *Prehistory and Proto-history in India and Pakistan* (Univ. of Bombay, 1962). B. Subbarao's *The Personality of India* has a strong geographical framework, and another stimulating survey published by the Maharaja Sayajirao University, Baroda, is Y. A. Raikar, *Indian History: A Study in Dynamics* (1960).

Turning to later times, for the Mogul period (which administratively formed the mould for the British Raj and even, in some respects, for the present Republics), the 17th-century travels of Bernier, Tavernier and especially Nicolo Manucci (*Storia do Mogor*) are available in good libraries and throw much light on social conditions, as well as being exceedingly good reading. W. H. Moreland's economic histories, *India at the Death of Akbar* and *From Akbar to Aurengzeb* (London, 1920, 1923) are classic pioneer works in a field which Indian scholars are now tilling. It was time, however, that the Eurocentric bias of Indian (and Asian) historiography was redressed, though it may be questioned whether K. M. Pannikkar's *Asia and the European Dominance* (Allen & Unwin, London, 3rd ed. 1961) does not tilt too far on the other side.

Works on the British period are often, and naturally enough, tendentious on one side or the other. Perhaps the most candid from the British side is G. T. Garratt and E. Thompson, *The Rise and Fulfilment of British Power in India* (London, 1934). Philip Woodruff's *The Men Who Ruled India* (Cape, London, 1953, 1954) gives a vivid picture of the British Raj at work, occasionally too nostalgic but at least not sinking into hagiography.

For the origins of Pakistan, ideological and political, see W. C. Smith, *Modern Islam in India* (Gollancz, London, 2nd ed. 1947), R. Symonds, *The Making of Pakistan* (Faber, London, 1950), and the works cited in the preceding Biblio-graphical Note. The Partition and its immediate effects are well presented in E. W. R. Lumby, *The Transfer of Power in India and Pakistan* (Allen & Unwin, London, 1954) and in the first-hand narratives of an actor in these affairs, V. P. Menon, *The Story of the Integration of the Indian States* (Longmans, Green, London, 1956) and *The Transfer of Power in India* (Princeton Univ. Press, 1957). Two excellent books are H. Tinker, *India and Pakistan: A Short Political Guide* (Pall Mall Press, London, 1962) and I. Stephens, *Pakistan: Old Country, New Nation* (Pelicans, Harmondsworth, 1964).

CHAPTER 7

Village and Town in India

I. THE INDIAN VILLAGE

Of the 1961 population of India, about 360,000,000 – 82% – lived in villages. Altogether there were 564,258 villages, of which about 4,200 had over 5,000 people, and no fewer than 349,195 had under 500. Pakistan is even more dominantly rural. Some general remarks on the villages and their life seem desirable, although settlement patterns, house-types, and so on are treated in some detail in the regional chapters.

The village in general

The great majority of the country folk live in small or large nucleated settlements, and areas of dispersed habitations are few: the Himalayan zone is perhaps the only extensive area of true dispersal, of the type found in European highlands; elsewhere, even in the hills, the normal unit is the small hamlet rather than the homestead. In the arid west this is enforced partly by the paucity of water-points, partly by the needs of defence – still visibly attested by the watch-towers of Pathan villages. In the Assam–Burma Ranges defence is also an important factor: villages are on hilltops or spurs, often stockaded; it must be remembered that in these jungly hills the valleys are extremely malarial, and the communication is easiest along relatively open ridgeways. The Bengal Delta – especially the East – is *sui generis*: there is indeed much settlement that is not nucleated, but 'dispersal' appears an exceedingly inappropriate term for the dense stipple of separate homesteads, hardly isolated except in the most literal sense of the word when, during the rains, each is an island on its little earthen plinth.[1] Other more or less dispersed zones are found in the Konkan, in areas of recent or temporary reclamation by squatters in the Assam jungles, or in the great floodplains by farmers using the rich khadar for high-value crops after the rains. But in both groups the very small hamlet – say 6 to 12 huts – is the rule, rather than true dispersal; and in the latter case the huts are often only temporary, inhabited during the dry weather by people normally resident in big villages on the bluffs above.

[1] See J. C. Jack, *The Economic Life of a Bengal District* (1916), 16–38; and below. Figs. 19.6 and 19.7.

These are anomalies: in the great homogeneous plains nucleation is almost invariable. In the past defence played its part, and in areas open to constant disturbance (e.g. the Sutlej/Yamuna and Yamuna/Ganga Doabs, Rohilkhand, the fringes of central India, Khandesh, the Raichur Doab) villages are often grouped around a petty fort; and even today the close-packed houses, with blank outer walls and low doorways, massed into a ring with few entrances, present a defensive aspect. Often there is not much in the way of site selection; one place is as good as another, and the village rises are as often as not their own creation, the rubbish of generations. But any discontinuity, any break in the almost imperceptible slope, produces linear settlement patterns: especially notable are the bluffs above floodplains and the margins of abandoned river courses. The bluff villages tend to be larger than those on the drier interfluves; they have the advantage of two types of terrain, the upland doab and the valley-bottom with its tamarisk brakes and the excellent soil of its *chars* or *diaras* – the floodplain islands – submerged in the rains and liable to disappear completely in floods, but cropping up again sooner or later. These alluviated areas are often given over to cash crops of high value; near large towns they are often used for market gardens, easily irrigated by wells taking advantage of the high water-table.

Settlement lines tend to occur also at the marked break of slope where steep residual hills grade into a fan, which has usually a fairly high water-table. Lateritic shelves along deltaic margins are also important building sites, poor in themselves but offering rough grazing, scrubby woodland (the source of a great range of minor necessities from timber to illicit alcohol), and providing space for dry crops, the flats below being entirely given over to paddy. They form as it were neutral ground between the jungly hills and the waterlogged paddy-plain. Here not only the general arrangement of settlements but also the village itself is often linear; islands of lateritic and older alluvium in the deltas are often completely ringed with houses. Linear settlement is also, of course, prominent in the deltas and wider floodplains themselves, strung out along levees or artificial embankments, and in places (e.g. Kerala and the Contai area of southwest Bengal) along old beach ridges. Very often such sites are the only dry points in the rains and the only water-points in the hot weather.[2]

There is in general very little that looks like a 'plan', other than that dictated by such site factors as alignment along bluffs or levees, grouping round a fort or a tank; but within the seemingly chaotic agglomeration there is, as a rule, a strong internal differentiation, that of the separate quarters for various castes.

A village in detail: Aminbhavi (Figs. 7.1 and 7.2)

These points are best brought out by a close view of a specific village, not indeed 'typical' (no single village could be that) but certainly the most random

---

[2] For analogues cf. G. T. Trewartha, *Japan* (Univ. of Wisconsin, Madison, 1945), Figs. 64 and 68; E. H. G. Dobby, 'Settlement patterns in Malaya', *GR* 32 (1942); O. H. K. Spate, 'The Burmese village', *GR* 35 (1945).

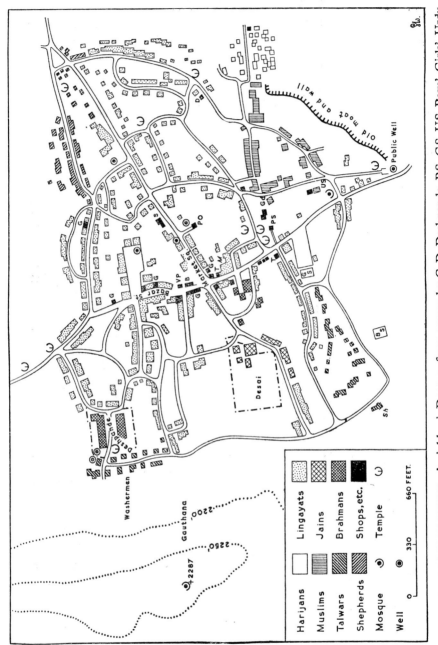

FIG 7.1 A VILLAGE IN DETAIL. Aminbhavi, Deccan, from survey by C. D. Deshpande. BS, GS, US, Boys', Girls', Urdu Schools; G, B, T, Grocers', Bania's and Tea-Bidi Shops; PO, PS, Post Office, Police Station; D, Dispensary; Gd,

of samples.[3] Our example is in the Deccan, more precisely in north-western Mysore.

Aminbhavi lies 7 miles NNE of Dharwar; an old settlement, going back at least thirteen centuries, originally walled and moated. Essentially its site is governed by the junction of the Dharwar rocks, forming poor red soils around the mosque-crowned hill to the west, with the crystallines which have weathered into deep black cotton soils in the east. It is a typical black soil agricultural village, with a rainfall of about 24 in. (610 mm.), devoted mainly to dry crops (cotton, jowar, wheat, pulses, safflower, in that order), tending to become a satellite of Dharwar, the market of its dairy and agricultural produce. On the poorer land to the west is rough grazing, supporting a few shepherds, and immediately west of the village the common or *gauthana*, an essential part of its economy, the centre of all harvesting.

Caste and community largely govern the layout. Of its 4,106 inhabitants, Lingayats, the sturdy agricultural caste of the Karnatak, number some 2,650. Next come 550 Muslims, an unusually high proportion, but the place was of some importance in the days of the Bijapur Kingdom. But the culturally dominant groups are the Jains (250) and the Brahmins (75); an *Inam* (landlord) village, most of it belonging to the Desai (Jain) and Deshpande (Brahmin) families, whose *wadas* (more or less equivalent to manor houses) stand on the best sites, within large compounds. The Desais provide the village *patel* or headman. For the rest, each caste tends to occupy a solid block of contiguous houses in a lane named from the caste; where, as with the Lingayats, several lanes are occupied, each is named from the leading family residing in it. Besides those mentioned, there are 300 Talwars (domestic servants and agricultural labourers), 200 Harijans ('untouchables'), and smaller groups of other low castes: Wadars (quarrymen), Shikalgars (backward semi-nomadic casual labourers), washermen, and so on. These groups live on the circumference of the village, or even beyond the old moat. (Fig. 7.1.)

Occupations likewise are still mainly on a caste basis: the Lingayats provide the bulk of the tenant-farmers, Talwars and Harijans landless agricultural labour; carpenters, smiths, cobblers, washermen, barbers are all separate castes. Apart from these crafts and agriculture, there is some handloom cotton weaving, a subsidiary occupation of the Lingayats.

Houses are generally built on to each other, or at least the mud walls of the compounds are continuous. The house layout (Fig. 7.2) is as standard as in any English working-class street. In front is a porch (*katte*), used for drying agricultural produce, as a formal reception room, as 'a place of female gossip when the

[3] The coincidence of the writing of this chapter and a correspondence with Dr C. D Deshpande then of Dharwar led me to appeal to him for a sample survey; the choice was left entirely to him. Nothing could be more random and free from preconceived choice. I am deeply indebted to Dr Deshpande and his students for the very full and admirable maps, photographs and notes on which this section is entirely based. For the general setting, see 703–5 below. Cf. also the Addendum to this chapter.

master of the house is out', and above all as a sleeping-room in the stifling summer nights. Behind this is the main room, some 25 ft. (7·6 m.) square, part

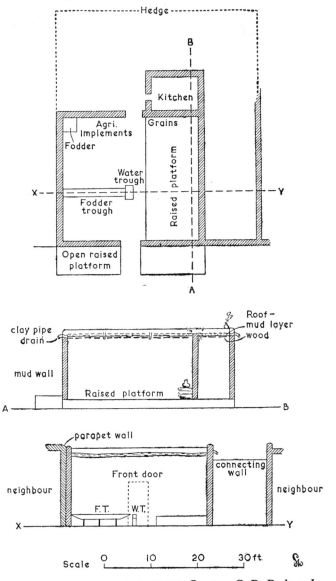

FIG 7.2 AMINBHAVI HOUSE PLAN. *Courtesy C. D. Deshpande.*

of which is a cattle pen, at threshold level; the remainder, raised some 2 or 3 ft., is the general living-room, for sleeping, eating, more intimate entertainment of guests, and perhaps handicrafts. The most prominent object is the pile of grain stored in gunny bags and sadly depleted towards the end of the agricultural year. Behind is a separate kitchen (with a corner for the bath) and the backyard with manure-pits and haystacks. This is the standard pattern; construction is similar in all groups (except the lowest), differences in economic status being reflected merely in size, except that the well-to-do have more separate single-purpose rooms. Jains and Brahmins do not live so tightly packed as the rest, either in the spacing of the houses or within them.

The poorest castes live in wretched one-room wattle huts with thatched roofs. Apart from these all houses have walls 1 or 2 ft. thick of mudbrick, with few (and high) or more likely no windows: Indians in general have a doubtless well-founded burglar-phobia. The flat roof is supported by wooden posts and made of mud on a framework of crude beams and babul (acacia) branches; they have rounded mud parapets and clay rain-water pipes.

As for services, these are mostly grouped around the main village lane: market-place for the weekly bazaar, eight shops (four grocery, two cloth, one tailor, one miscellaneous) and a number of booths selling tea and *bidis*, the cheap crude cigarettes of the Indian masses. Near the market-place is the room of the village *panchayat* or caste council, an ancient institution generally fallen into desuetude but now being fostered as the first step in local government. Associated with this tiny 'urban core' are the government establishments – Police Station, Post Office, grain warehouse. There are three mosques, one giving its name to the Idgah hill in the west, and eight temples, including that of the Deshpandes, as well as the Lingayat *math*, a centre of religious and charitable fellowship. The professions are represented by an Ayurvedic (indigenous) dispensary, an Urdu school for the Muslims, and separate schools for boys and girls. The boys' school is the most modern building in Aminbhavi, its stone walls and red-tiled roof standing in sharp contrast to the monotony of mud walls.

Finally we may note the large masonry-lined public well, sunk in what was once the moat; it is no mean excavation, an apt reminder of the all-importance of water-supply in Indian life.

Once more, no one village can be typical of the whole sub-continent; but many of the features detailed above can be paralleled over and over again in most parts of India. Our random sample is at least very representative.

The village : its aspect and life

The aspect of the village varies not only with the general regional setting, with building materials and house-types, but with social factors. The generally greater emphasis on caste in the south takes social fragmentation allied with spatial separation to the extreme, segregating the untouchables in outlying *cheris* or sub-villages, sometimes located several hundred yards from the main villages of which they are service-components. This is indeed the climax of geographical differentiation; *apartheid*. A typical *cheri* may consist of two rows of huts with a narrow central 'street'; in the middle this widens to make room for a tiny temple. The huts have thick mud walls, roofed with palmyra thatch, and low mud porches scrupulously swept. To enter one must bend double; the only light comes from the door and from under the eaves, and the furniture consists of a few pots and pans, a couple of wooden chests, and the essential paddy-bin, 4 to 6 ft. high and 3 to 4 in diameter, raised from the ground to escape the rats, and built up of hoops of mud. Poor as they are, these dwellings are yet homes, and obviously loved as such: their cleanliness, the surrounding mangoes, coconut and palmyra palms, redeem them from utter squalor. The nadir is reached in the bustees of Calcutta and the revolting camps of casual tribal labour found on the outskirts of the larger towns: shelters (they cannot be called even huts) of matting, of rags, of petrol tins beaten flat, on waste spaces open to the sun and reeking with filth.

A geographical study of Indian house-types (Fig. 7.3) would be a work vast in scope and rich in instruction; a few of the more striking instances are mentioned in the regional chapters.[4] Social factors are no less important than environmental, at least once we go beyond the fundamental antithesis of the northwestern (or southwest Asia) type and the thatched gable of the more humid areas. Not only the site and layout of the village, but the 'geography of the house' often reflects age-old religious and magical traditions: the round huts of some lower castes in Telangana, with bold vertical stripes of white and rusty red, are clearly culturally rather than geographically influenced. At the other extreme from the rude massive huts of Bundelkhand we have the elaborate courtyard house of the richer Uttar Pradesh farmer, with some pretensions to elegance – the survival of decayed traditions – in doorways and arcading. Some Indian domestic building indeed reaches a high standard of artistry: the carved timber of Kumaon or of the small towns of the Konkan, the restrained but excellent brick details and the very pleasant white bungalow-style houses, with low gables of semi-cylindrical tiles, found in small Maharashtra towns. Environmental influence is well seen in the flat-roofed blank-walled box standard in the Punjab and western Uttar Pradesh – so strongly reminiscent of arid southwest Asia, and fitting so well into the four-square planned villages of the Canal Colonies. Against these may be set the Bengal house, matting-walled, with thatched gables pitched high to shed the rain and ingeniously designed to take the strain of cyclonic gales. In Madras

'we see flat-roofed stone houses in the Ceded Districts (Deccan), so constructed as to protect the dwellers from the severe heat of the sun, the rocks and slabs locally available being used. In contrast we find in Malabar timber entering into the construction. Here the buildings are on high ground and have sloping roofs, both necessitated by the high rainfall. . . . In the Tamilnad we have tiled brick houses with open courtyards, reflecting an equable climate and moderate rainfall'.[5]

[4] The most comprehensive survey for a large area I have seen is Enayat Ahmad's unpublished London Ph.D. thesis, 'Settlement in the United Provinces' (1948).
[5] K. M. Subrahmanyam, 'Four main house types in south India', *JMGA* 13/2 (1938), 168–75.

As for what life in the Indian village is really like, who knows save the Indian villager? The insight of officials like M. L. Darling and of some devoted social workers, Indian and European, Christian and otherwise, has now been supplemented by much sociological research, some of it excellent; and from this the lineaments of village life (and especially the role of caste groupings) may be drawn, and now and then something of the psychological reality. The alien may perhaps glean something from that rich harvest of salty rural proverbs (a comparative anthology of them would be fascinating) which are as vital a part of India's cultural heritage as the lyrical and metaphysical visions of her sages. Not that this latter strain of culture is absent from the village: the great epics *Ramayana* and *Mahabharata* pass from lip to lip in folk-versions, to some extent at least every man is his own poet, and not a few of the noblest figures in India's predominantly devotional literature sprang from the village rather than the schools: Kabir the Weaver, Tukaram. The things that strike the outsider, then, are not perhaps ultimately the most important: the flies and the sores, the shrill clamour of gaunt pi-dogs, the primitive implements, the utter lack of sanitation.

At its worst the Indian village is infinitely depressing: in the plains where so much ground is cultivated that the scanty village site cannot grow with its growing population, or where a few miserable huts cling to shadeless stony rises in the drier parts of central India or the Archaean Deccan. Yet cheerfulness keeps breaking in, in the most unfavourable circumstances; fatalist as he is and must be, the peasant often displays an astonishing resilience and refuses to be broken by his often bitterly hard geographical and social environment. And over much of the land the villages have their amenities, even their beauties: in the plains and deltas they rise out of the sea of cultivation, emerald or gold or drab grey in the stubble season, like dark green islands, shaded in mango or orange trees, tamarinds, bamboos, palms. The tank or the well, the shade of the great banyan or the porch of the headman's hut, are essentially free clubs for the women and the menfolk respectively. Though the substratum of life – the gruelling round of the seasons – remains and will ever remain the same, though a miserable livelihood exacts an exorbitant price in endless toil, there have been great changes, material and psychological, since Edwin Montagu, Secretary of State for India, spoke in 1918 of the 'pathetic contentment' of the Indian village. Pathetic it still too often is; contented, less and less; which is as it should be. As Marx put it, 'These idyllic village communities confined the human mind within the narrowest possible compass.' This is overstated: there *were* the epics and the proverbs; but the horizons were far too narrow for a full life. Now new motifs are changing the tempo of life in the large villages: perhaps a radio, perhaps a mobile film unit, more and more frequently a school. Despite the weaknesses in Community Development projects, all are helping to break down the isolation and lack of information which rendered the villager so helpless a prey to the moneylender, the retailer and the grain-broker – often all three being one and the same person. Perhaps the most powerful agent of change is the battered, ramshackle motor-bus, packed to the running-board and coughing its way through clouds of dust along the unmetalled roads to the nearest town. There may be loss as well as gain in all this; but it is idle to bewail the break-up of integrated codes of life – too often integrated by religious, social and economic sanctions which were a complete denial of human dignity. In any case the

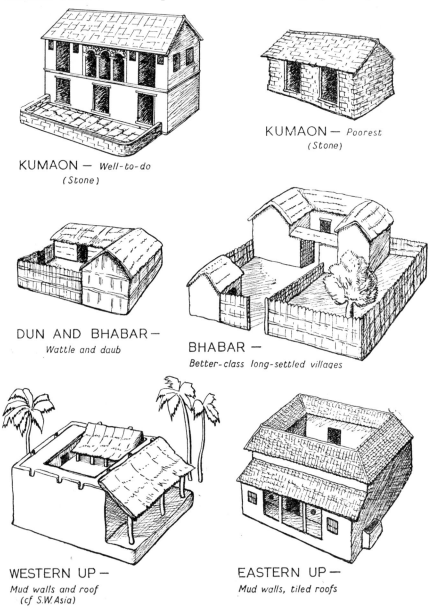

KUMAON — *Well-to-do*
(*Stone*)

KUMAON — *Poorest*
(*Stone*)

DUN AND BHABAR—
Wattle and daub

BHABAR —
Better-class long-settled villages

WESTERN UP —
Mud walls and roof
(*cf S.W. Asia*)

EASTERN UP —
Mud walls, tiled roofs

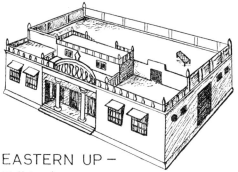

EASTERN UP –
Well-to-do, masonry

EASTERN UP –
Poorest, mud walls, tiles

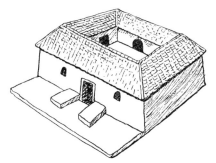

BUNDELKHAND –
Mud walls, tiled

BUNDELKHAND –
Stone, stone slab roofs

BENGAL (CONTAI) –
Well-to-do, bamboo and thatch
on mud plinth. Double roof

BENGAL – *Poorest.*
Bamboo . thatch

FIG 7.3 SOME NORTH INDIAN HOUSE TYPES. Redrawn by Marjory Fowler from illustrations in theses by E. Ahmad and B. Mukerjee.

disintegration set in long ago, with the impact of the world market; and it is high time that new horizons should be opened, that the villager should see whence the forces that have subverted his old life have their origins, and what of good they may bring.

II. THE INDIAN TOWN

Some general characteristics

Urbanization is considered demographically in Chapter 4; the greater cities receive separate treatment in the regional chapters. There would be little point in classifying the towns of India and finding that after all they occupy similar positions and perform similar functions as do their compeers in the rest of the world. The fossil stronghold and the place of pilgrimage are perhaps commoner than in most countries: Carcassonne and Lourdes occur over and over again. The purely railway town is common, as in North America. The most distinctive Indian contributions to modern urbanism are the hill station and the cantonment: but even these have their analogues elsewhere.

It would also be possible to describe the aspect, function and morphology of a hypothetical generalized town: but its characterization would certainly be inadequate to convey the real richness of the Indian urban scene. It seems more profitable and interesting to examine in some detail four scattered and very diverse towns which the author knows at first hand. Before doing so, however, it may be as well to make some points of general application which are in fact largely specific to the towns of India.

1. *The agrarian setting.* It hardly needs stressing that the great majority of 'census towns' have still very strong agricultural elements within them; this holds, at the very least, for the 1,926 Indian towns (out of a total of 2,689 in 1961) which had under 20,000 inhabitants; the proportion of such towns in Pakistan would be higher. The smaller ones are indeed little more than large market villages, with some very local administrative functions added; perhaps two or three central streets inadequately paved and lighted give the semblance of an urban *cachet*. Even in so large a city as Agra herds of dairy buffaloes are driven out in the morning, back in the evening 'hour of cow-dust'.

2. *Administrative uniformity.* A large number of the towns are primarily administrative; they may have been local commercial centres and market villages picked as headquarters of Districts or their subdivisions mainly on account of centrality. Many of these go back at least to Mogul times as District headquarters; the somewhat bureaucratic motif of the territorial structure is shown by the fact that 242 of the 304 Districts of India are named from the chief town, and nearly all those of Pakistan. They have a strikingly uniform cast. The same official buildings occur; the architecture of the Public Works Department is standard practically everywhere, and Economy has obviously been the watchword.

3. *Building types.* These, of course, vary with local materials and traditions;

but there are certain very widespread features, ancient and modern. Of the former the bazaar streets with open booths raised 2 or 3 ft. above the pavement are typical. Middle-class Hindu town residences tend to have a verandah-plinth on the street, perhaps pillared, perhaps a mere recess between the party walls; there is usually room for a rope bedstead or two, used for daytime lounging and at night by the *durwan* or watchman. By the door is a little recess for a light; sometimes this is virtually a tiny shrine, but often it has degenerated into a vestigial niche, too shallow to perform its original function. On the modern side, new shopping areas are strikingly similar: box-like concrete shops-cum-houses, with cast concrete balustrades and so on. The glaring whiteness is often offset by pastel colours, very sensibly in view of the noonday dazzle. The monotonous architecture of the Public Works Department has been touched on; the railways are sometimes more imaginative, but with results often even more disastrous, until really ambitious efforts like Bombay's Victoria Terminus can hardly be described as other than Indo-Saracenic-Byzantine-Italo-Gothic-Baroque.

4. *Incomplete internal differentiation.* Most Indian cities (and large sections of even the greatest of them) have not separated residential and other functions to the same extent as Occidental towns. Well-to-do merchants still live over their shops and offices; and a large proportion of day-to-day consumer needs is still met by artisans living or working in tiny shops at street corners or in the bazaar area. Very often, as in mediaeval Europe, all of one trade will live in one or two adjoining streets: this, of course, links up with caste segregation. But differentiation by class and wealth is also not so advanced – on the whole – as in the West: of course in the Civil Lines and similar areas there will be very few poor people other than domestic servants, and at the other extreme there are homogeneous slums; but in the older and more indigenous parts of the towns opulence and indigence often live cheek by jowl.

5. *Community quarters.* Yet if the separation of work from residence often hardly exists, there is a very strong tendency (at all levels from village to metropolis) for members of each religious community, caste or race to live together. This is only to be expected in the general social context of India. Notable examples are the *pols* of Ahmedabad (see below, p. 653) and the Parsee housing estates of Bombay; and where there are very large numbers of Chinese, as in Calcutta, there is a Chinatown – as indeed happens universally.

6. *Western elements: cantonments, civil lines, railway colonies.* The British in India as it were fused this communal separatism with their own emphasis on class. Large Indian cities generally consist of two entirely distinct areas: the old Indian city, a squalid but picturesque confusion, and the monotonously planned open-developed town of European-style bungalows in large gardens along straight, broad roads, aloof and boring in a high degree, and absolutely dead in the heat of the day. These two are very often separated by the railway which – in some cases apparently by design – forms a broad barrier with few crossings: the motivation of 'internal security' is obvious. The 'Civil Lines' contain the

official residences of the local bureaucracy and such hangers-on as the more flourishing lawyers; architecture is European, with an interesting climatically induced variation: absence of chimneys (except in the northwest) and presence of a carriage-porch, essential in the rains. The European population is now generally very small indeed. The Railway Colony is generally planned on a far less generous scale, but on mathematically rectilinear lines. The Cantonments explain themselves; but they generally had a little Indian enclave, the bazaar to serve the needs, material and sometimes other, of the troops: this was necessary as for the most obvious reasons the Indian city was strictly Out of Bounds.

Generally the cultural divide made by the railway lines is sharp; but sometimes there is a transitional zone, as in the Mall and Anarkali Bazaar at Lahore: here are European and European-style shops, banks, offices, cinemas, some official buildings and a variety of places of resort, from the first-class (in price at least) hotel to the seedy eating-house.[6]

Four representative towns

We may now consider our four towns: in order of antiquity (which is approximately the order from south to north) Kanchipuram, Poona, Qadian and Simla. They form a good sample from several points of view: the geographical scatter is wide, Tamilnad, Deccan, Punjab, sub-Himalaya; two are well-known and typically Indo-British, two of much less note and representing almost solid Hindu and Muslim communities. They include a minor commercial and religious town, Kanchipuram; a great military, administrative and educational centre, Poona; the queen of hill stations, Simla; and in Qadian the headquarters of a religious sect. Qadian is at once unique but typical, since the particular ruling group is unique, but the phenomenon itself is not uncommon: one interesting example is Chettinad in Madras, seat of the remarkable Chettiar banking caste whose children lisp in numbers and accounts, inheriting a tradition of business acumen which enabled them to dominate indigenous finance and actually secure control of about one-third of the rice lands in Lower Burma.

Kanchipuram (Fig. 7.4)

Kanchipuram, 40 miles (64 km.) southwest of Madras on the Palar River, lies in a gently undulating countryside, paddy-floored bottoms and lateritic rises largely under poor grass and scrub. Agriculture is largely dependent on tanks; Kanchipuram lies in the heart of the Pallava kingdom (4th–9th centuries AD) and many of the larger masonry-bunded tanks were built by the Pallava kings, whose engineers had an uncanny flair for detecting the slightest usable drainage-line.

It is a fairly widespread town of 82,714 people; a market for the agricultural produce of its *umland*, with some hand industry, notably the weaving of silk

[6] Many of the points in this section are illustrated in O. H. K. Spate and Enayat Ahmad 'Five cities of the Gangetic Plain', *GR* 40 (1950), 260–78; cf. O. H. K. Spate, 'Aspects of the City in South Asia', *Confluence* (Chicago) 7 (1958), 116–28.

saris; pottery, basketry and bamboo crafts are also carried on. But it is far more famous as a religious centre, the shining or golden city; popular tradition assigns

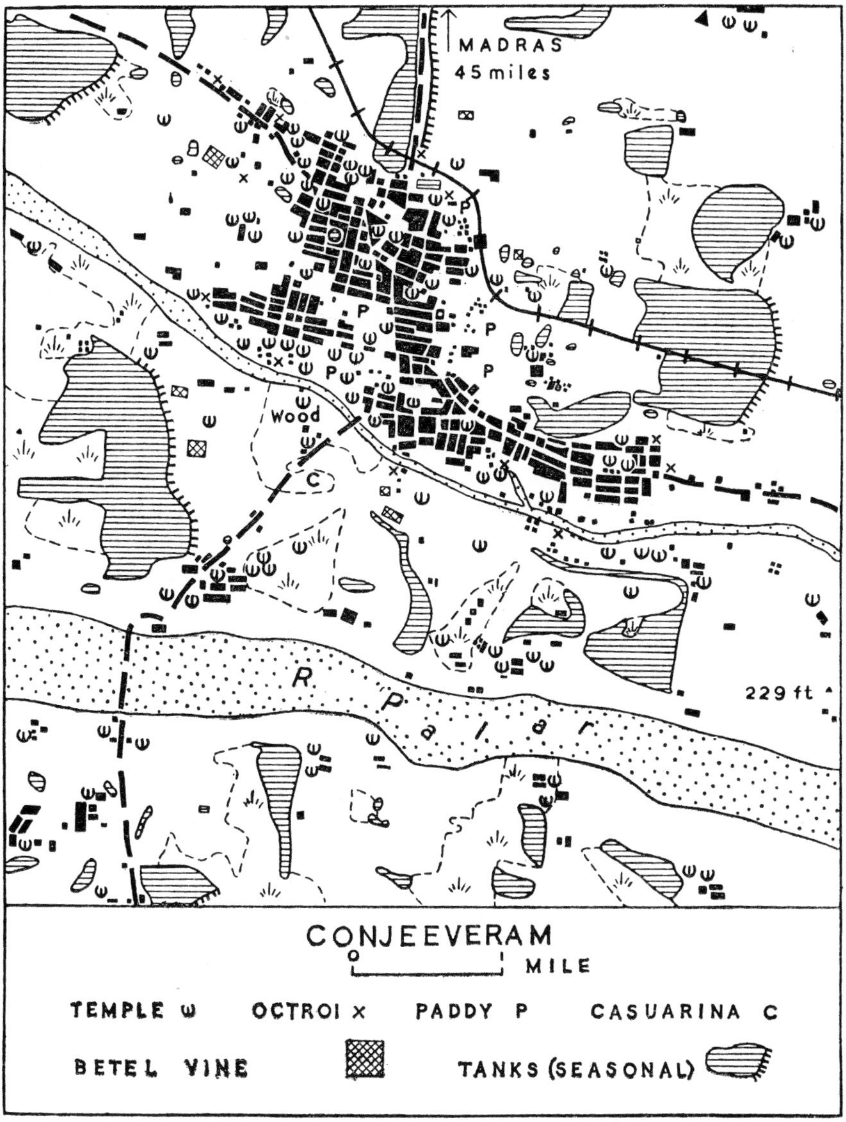

FIG 7.4 KANCHIPURAM (CONJEEVERAM). Heavy broken lines are main roads. Surrounding country mainly paddy; streams seasonal. *Courtesy* SOI.

it a thousand temples, not without exaggeration; indeed the thousand pillars of the great hall in the Sivaite Ekambaranath temple are really only 540. But the great temples – largely dating from Vijayanagar times – are very impressive indeed, culminating in the lofty many-storeyed *gopurams* or gate-pyramids, covered with innumerable sculptured figures. There are also ancient Jain and Buddhist associations.

Not unnaturally, the population is almost solidly Hindu: there were only 3,452 Muslims in 1941, and 600 Indian Christians, with more in the *cheris* of surrounding villages; Europeans were represented by one or two missionary families.

The most notable thing about the plan of Kanchipuram is that it has obviously got one: the town is intersected by great streets some 60 ft. wide. This is, however, due not so much to *a priori* town planning ideas as to the practical necessity of accommodating the crowds, numbering several thousands, which on festival days haul the huge temple cars. The largest of these is some 50–60 ft. (12–15 m.) high, with solid wooden wheels 10 or 12 ft. high and proportionately thick. These great streets are found in other towns with similar observances, but are not very common; the general aspect and life of Kanchipuram's streets are, however, thoroughly typical. Houses are low, with whitewashed walls, roofs of several layers of semi-cylindrical tiles, the usual thin-pillared porches, and the lamp-niches by the doors: when well-maintained they have a very pleasing appearance. There are the usual municipal and *taluk* offices and schools, built of brick in the invariable Public Works Department style. Passenger transport is mainly by light carts with a semi-cylindrical matting roof, drawn by ponies or trotting bullocks; goods travel largely by pack-donkeys. The importance of the motor-bus is recognized by a large, well-built bus station; during the war, with its petrol shortage, the poverty of India was brought home by the sight of women scrabbling for the cinders dropped from the gas-charcoal plants of the buses. Hardly a golden city now.

Poona (Fig. 7.5)

Poona is in itself by far the most important of our four towns. As such its general significance is more appropriately treated in Chapter 23; the treatment here concentrates on history, morphology and aspect.

The primary reason for the rise of Poona is historical. The Bhor Ghat, 48 miles (77 km.) to the northwest, gives easy access to the lowlands around Bombay, and the town is now an important road centre. But almost any site between Poona and the Bhor Ghat would have done as well. It was not until the 17th century that Poona became of any note, though as early as the 13th the sanctity of the Mutha-Mula confluence had led to the construction of two fairly important temples. Sivaji, founder of Maratha power, was brought up in this poor *jagir* (fief) of his grandfather, an obscure Hindu noble in the service of the Ahmadnagar sultan; but his own capital was at Rajgarh, 30 miles (48 km.) to the south, a typical site on the saddle between the bases of Maratha power in the Konkan and the Deccan. Poona did not become the capital until 1735.[7] Thereafter for

---

[7] A vivid sketch of Sivaji's career will be found in Denis Kincaid's delightful book, *The Grand Rebel*.

nearly a century it was the seat of whatever central authority the Maratha confederacy possessed; their decisive overthrow by the British took place across the river at Kirkee in 1817. The core of the city is the old Maratha capital; to it

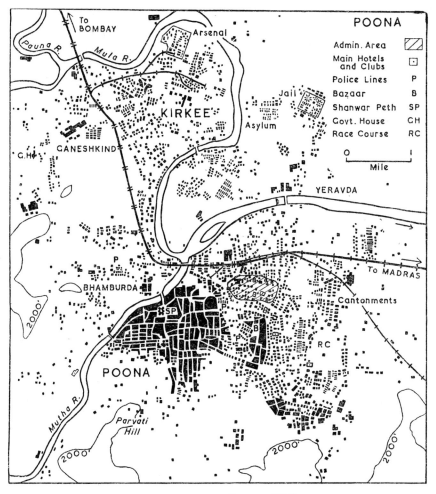

FIG 7.5 POONA. *Courtesy* SOI.

have been added the great Cantonments and the even more military suburb of Kirkee; these form three distinct units. The population was 737,426 in 1961, and expansion, including industrial estates, has gone beyond the limits of Fig. 7.5.

The general level is about 1,800 ft. (550 m.); to the north extends a great plain broken by a few remarkably symmetrical buttes 200–300 ft. high; the entire terrain is of course Deccan Lava. To the south the hills are closer and several mesas at about 2,000 ft. abut directly on to the town, such as the temple-crowned

Parvati Hill. These dissected table-lands extend southwards until the horizon is closed by the steep scarps of the Singarh Hills (*c.* 3,200 ft., 975 m.), carrying the great fortress of Singarh (='Lion Fort'), famous in Maratha history, clearly visible from Poona despite the distance of 15 miles.

The City proper lies along the Mutha, built fairly high along the east bank, which suggests indeed an old river-wall. The most striking monument of Maratha days is the citadel, Shanwar Peth, of which, however, only the simple but impressively solid *enceinte* remains, its gate studded with 9-inch iron spikes to discourage the use of elephants as battering rams. Around it lie the twisting streets of the old town, less irregular than those of many Indian cities. Here 18th-century timbered houses, with richly carved balconies, produce a Jacobean effect, while others are of thin bricks set in herring-bone patterns or with a shallow false arcading of little 'Norman' arches; roofs are low gables of semi-cylindrical tiles. Altogether these represent two of the most pleasing domestic styles in India. The functions of the old town are mainly those of a commercial centre for the surrounding agricultural area; here industry is mostly of artisan type, the modern factories (including cotton mills) lying away from the town near the railway station, and the important Deccan Paper Mills 5 miles to the east, while there is an important grouping of ordnance and allied industries at Kirkee, and new industries are locating to the northwest along the Bombay road.

The Cantonments are not, as is so often the case, sealed off from the old City by the railway; but the cultural divide is sharp enough, the whole aspect changing in the width of one street. There is indeed some trace of a marginal or transitional fringe, largely Anglo-Indian; Eurasian would be a better adjective, since the most prominent outward and visible sign is the Portuguese Church.

The Cantonments lie to the south of the Mutha-Mula, here bunded to form an elongated lake even in the dry weather. They are of course much more spaciously laid out than the City, with broad, clean, tree-lined avenues; but there does not appear to be any very intelligible general plan. Most of the official buildings, banks, clubs, hotels and cinemas lie on the City side of the Cantonments, south of and close to the railway station; and southwards again lie the two main shopping streets. Farther out the cultural landscape becomes more and more military; even the Anglican Church seems standing to attention, and the very trees are numbered. This was the Poona of popular legend, of Colonel Sahibs and exclusive clubs; and (as again at Simla) the legend was nearly true. Across the river in Kirkee militarism reigns supreme, but here it is the more workaday side of army life – sappers, gunners, ordnance, the great arsenal and munitions factories.

The more important suburbs lie to the west; Yeravda in the east is notable only for the Aga Khan's remarkably hideous palace, honoured by the involuntary residence there of Mahatma Gandhi. Bhamburda, across the Mutha from the City, is more interesting: here are the engineering and agricultural colleges, the District Courts, and the headquarters of the Indian Meteorological Department.

Northwards in Ganeshkind is Government House – Poona was the hot-weather capital of Bombay Province. The European buildings are not striking – the best is perhaps the Meteorological Office and Observatory – but they have at least the advantage of being built of Deccan Lava, a sombre material but one in which it is difficult to be undignified.[8]

To sum up, there were really three Poonas: the old regional capital of Maharashtra; the vast sprawl of military installations, individually tidily laid out but as a whole dumped down anyhow; and the educational and administrative suburbs in the west. Poona is thus in many respects a typical, if better than average, expression of the juxtaposition of Indian and British civilizations: for on the whole it is probably true to say that the two lived side by side, to some extent symbiotically, in a state of unconsummated matrimony. There were inter-digitation, reciprocal reactions, but no fusion into a common culture; though materially, perhaps, there was an Indo-British civilization. Now, however, the city is coming into its own as the central seat of Maharashtrian regional culture.

Qadian (Fig. 7.6)

Qadian, like Poona, originated in a local *jagir*; there the resemblance ends. It was[9] the headquarters of a heretical and reformist Muslim sect, the Ahmadiyya, founded about 1908 by one Mirza Ahmad, the 'Promised Messiah'. This group numbers perhaps a million adherents and has missions not only in the more usual Muslim fields of Africa and Indonesia, but as far as Glasgow and Buenos Aires; it represents a remarkable combination of fundamentalism with a keen appreciation of modern technique. This is not the place to discuss its sociology, fascinating as it is to observe at first hand the growth of a new religious movement; but some points will emerge in the following pages.

According to the Ahmadis, the original land-grant was made by the first Mogul, Babur (1526–30). The Ahmadi family lived the usual life of local lords through all the vicissitudes of Mogul rule, Persian and Afghan incursions, Sikh

[8] There is a detailed study: D. R. Gadgil, *Poona: A Socio-Economic Survey* (Gokhale Inst., Poona, 1945). Geography is limited to a page of gazetteer-stuff, but the description of trades and crafts is thorough and interesting. More recently as Dr C. D. Deshpande showed Learmonth in the field in 1965, a particular catastrophe has moulded the dynamics of Poona's urban geography – a flood caused by the collapse of a still unconsolidated earth dam during exceptionally heavy monsoon rain in July 1961, devastated the riverside central belt, necessitating emergency erection by the army of temporary hutments, the more leisured but still urgent construction of middle-class and working-class suburbs (the latter unfortunately too far from work for low-income groups), and plans for riverside redevelopment including gardens tending to be defeated by a slow drift back to the devastated area. Government House is now the headquarters of the University.

[9] This section must unfortunately be written in the past tense; the material geography is doubtless still there, the spirit has fled. My visit was in August 1947; as a result of the Partition which left it in India, all but 3 or 400 of the Ahmadis have been forced to migrate to Pakistan. For the Ahmadi movement, see W. C. Smith, *Modern Islam in India* (Gollancz, London, 2nd ed. 1947), 298–302.

and finally British power, until the great revelation to Mirza Ahmad.[10] For nearly forty years (1908–47) Qadian was as it were a miniature Vatican; not sovereign, but something of a state within a state. Crime in Qadian, for instance, was invariably reported first to the Ahmadi office and then to the police.

Qadian lies in the Bari Doab, on the Indian side of the border 35 miles (56 km.) northeast of Amritsar. The old town, still called 'the Fort', and retaining traces of a town ditch, is like hundreds of others in southwest Asia: some

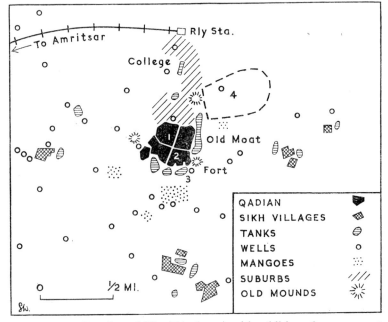

FIG 7.6 QADIAN. Based on SOI44M/5 (1913) with additions from personal observation. 1, Bazaar; 2, Ahmadi admin. and religious centre; 3, Ahmadi cemetery (guest-house, etc., between 2 and 3); 4, modern planned area (villas, offices). The nearer suburbs are closer-built and more industrial than the northern protrusion to the railway. Mounds (15–25 ft. high) mark old settlements. The area lies midway between the Kasur and Sobraon branches of the Bari Doab Canal.

12–15,000 people (the great majority were Ahmadis) living on the area of an English village of 2,000; narrow twisting alleys, encroached on by stalls and swarming with children and donkeys; two bazaar streets, covered with rough awnings of sacking (poor relations of the Damascus *suqs*), and significantly a Hindu enclave; mud-walled houses, windowless, built round courts where spinning, milking of buffaloes and all women's work is carried on; flat roofs

[10] 'I tell the tale that I heard told,' and have no means of checking it; it is inherently not improbable, though some of the embellishments perhaps are so, e.g. that at one time during the Mogul decadence the Ahmadis were thought of for the throne of Delhi. But then, anything is credible of a family which speaks of an ancient quarrel with the House of Timur for all the world as if Tamburlaine the Great were a rather unfriendly uncle.

littered with rope bedsteads, where the men smoke and gossip in the cool of the evening. A few large brick houses rise like monadnocks out of a peneplain. These include the Ahmadi offices, in a house once belonging to a wealthy Hindu, as is architecturally obvious from the details of the extremely beautiful brick façade and doorways, perhaps 18th century and certainly built when the now-decayed traditions of Hindu architecture were still vigorous; exterior windows are few and small – significantly – but within is a galleried court. Here was the vault containing the treasury, and the offices of a bureaucracy under seven 'Secretaries of State', including one for Entertainment of Guests, whose department was wonderfully efficient. An important feature was the guest-house, a caravanserai of courts and cubicles and cookhouses (more hygienic than many in the British Army), where disciples from all the Islamic lands endlessly commented on the Quran and the writings of Promised Messiah.

From the 120-ft. minar of the mosque all this warren lay at one's feet: to the north stretched the open modern development; to the south, on the rich fields of the Bari Doab, half a dozen large villages, darkly shrouded in mango-groves, seemed to enclose Qadian in a ring: all were Sikh.

In the new town, as in the old, women were in the strictest *purdah*; there were few other common features. Apart from an industrial fringe on the edge of the old town, this area was laid out in wide streets, with strict zoning and regulated densities. Architecture on the whole was poor, but sanitation superior to that in Lahore's best hotel. The most grandiose building was the big college, PWD Mogul in style, and well equipped especially in physics and chemistry labs. Between the town and the railway lay the industrial area, largely powered by Mandi hydro-electricity. On the fringe of the old town factories were largely private enterprises, but in the more open areas the community was building more modern workshops for vegetable oil, paint and varnish, and plastic industries – linked with research in the college labs. The most important activities actually existing were hosiery and knitwear, and all sorts of light electrical goods, all on a small scale (e.g. plastic presses electrically heated but hand-operated) and with apparently rather happy-go-lucky management; in which Qadian very faithfully reflected conditions in a large sector of Indian industry.

In a sense Qadian was a sociological freak, a combination of modern enterprise with fundamentalist theology; one might compare it with Salt Lake City. But the material expression of this duality was by no means un-typical. The day-to-day life of the old town stood on the ancient ways, life as it has been lived in many Asian lands for centuries or millennia. The new, in its slapdash planning, in its architectural tawdriness or rawness (whether the 'style' was traditional or modernistic), in its mixture of considerable drive and adroit improvisation with a certain lack of poise and stamina, can be paralleled over and over again on India's expanding industrial frontiers. But rarely are the contrasts of ancient and modern so sharply pointed within such narrow room; and yet in this too Qadian could stand for an epitome of India, if not of Asia.

Simla (Figs. 7.7 and 7.8)

The most famous of Indian hill stations lies at over 7,000 ft., (2,133 m.), 175 miles or 282 km. north of Delhi, approached by motor road and mountain railway from Kalka on the edge of the plains. Nearly half of the railway has a gradient of 1 in 33, and it has 103 tunnels; Fig. 7.7 shows its necessarily roundabout entry into Simla.

The building and maintenance of a town of some size – approaching 20,000 in the hot weather – on such a site was something of a *tour de force*. Every piece of metal had originally to come up the cart-road from Kalka; even today the internal transport services are mostly human, rickshawmen or porters bent double under tremendous packs. Both the Indian and the Punjab Governments used to migrate annually to Simla, and until 1912 this involved, for the Central Government, the 1,115-mile journey (1,794 km.) from Calcutta. Army Headquarters was permanently located there. The clerks in some offices had to climb 800 ft. (244 m.) in a quarter of a mile to reach their work: this in a climate with nearly 35 in. (889 mm.) of rain in July and August together. Other services had a yet inferior situation: laundry-men had a pull of 1,000 ft. from their dhobi-ghats to their customers. There can be few places in the world where the upper ten was so literally upper; the Viceroy and the Commander-in-Chief had naturally the best peaks. But all these inconveniences were subordinated to mean summer maximum temperatures of 67–82° F. (19–28° C.) compared with 110–120 (43–49°) in the plains below.[11] And, if Englishmen (and women) set the fashion, beginning in 1819, well-to-do Indians soon found Simla essential to physical and still more to social health.[12] Yet in a sense the whole place was a parasite.

The plan (Fig. 7.8), very typical of Indian hill stations, resembles nothing so much as a dissection of some invertebrate, an elongated tangle of guts and nerves with two or three ganglia. Roads tend to run sub-parallel to contours, and of course nearly all junctions are acute forks. Traffic would be a problem were it not nearly all banned (even bicycles, which could be used along the Mall) in the interests of rickshaw-men and porters – or their masters. The main axis lies along a saddle between Jakko (8,040 ft., 2,457 m.) in the east and Observatory Hill (7,050 ft., 2,150 m.) in the west; on the latter is what was the Viceregal Lodge. The hub of Simla lies under Jakko, on the broad Ridge between the Town Hall and Christ Church; here are the chief cinemas, libraries, and so on. The main road, the Mall, runs from end to end of Simla; the part of the Mall immediately below the Ridge is the only real shopping street, for all the world like the shopping street of some very minor English inland resort, say Crowborough. And indeed the whole atmosphere is like that of a watering-place without any waters.

[11] In winter, indeed, it is inconveniently cold, with mean minima below freezing in December–February. Absolute maxima and minima are about 95 and 17° F., 35 and 8° C. Communication with the plains is sometimes blocked for 3 or 4 days by snow.

[12] Some hill-stations like Dalhousie have declined, others, like Naini Tal and Ootacamund, continue to flourish. In 1965 in West Pakistan a new hill-station called Ayubia, after the President, was developed to add to the facilities of nearby Murree.

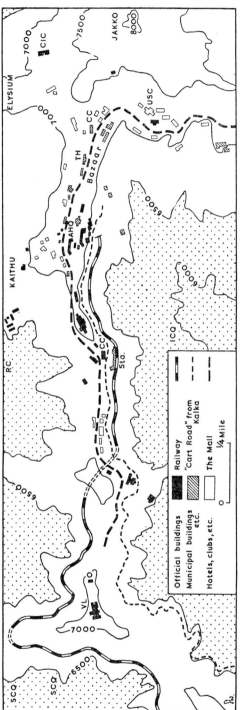

FIG 7.7 SIMLA: GENERAL PLAN. AHQ, Army HQ; CC, Christ Church; CC¹, Council Chambers; CIC, Commander-in-Chief's residence; I (S) CQ, inferior (superior) clerks' quarters; O, Observatory; RC, Racecourse; TH, Town Hall; VL, Viceroy's Lodge; USC, United Services Club. Based (as in Fig 41) on SOI plan on scale 1/7920. *Courtesy* SOI. Under 6,500 ft., stippled.

Below the eastern Mall is the Bazaar, the only close-built area, approached by roads at each end but transversely by steps in narrow winding alleys, a good deal steeper than those of Clovelly. The Bazaar area is a mass of tin-roofed houses clinging to what seems an impossibly steep hillside. Southwest, towards the railway station, is the office quarter. Here the hill is so steep that many buildings can be entered by a short bridge on to the top-floor back, while the ground-floor front entrance is half a mile or so away by road. Around this central belt is a great penumbra of villas and bungalows, for the most part on south-facing slopes but with two protrusions northwards along the Kaithu and Elysium spurs. Underneath Kaithu is the racecourse, sunk in a shadowed and gloomy combe.

Apart from its setting of forests and ravines, which is splendid, and its suitability as a centre for anthropological study of Indo-British tribal customs, there was not much of interest in Simla. Architecturally, besides the nondescript or Swiss-chalet bungalows, there were three main styles: baronial chateaux with corrugated-iron roofs (one or two, seen against the sunset, not so awful as it sounds); dull but relatively dignified Tudor-Gothic; and concrete and cast-iron boxes which did not even pretend to be 'modernistic'. The Bazaar was dull, apart from some good silversmiths and the Sikh woodworkers of Lakkar Bazaar north of the Ridge; itinerant Tibetans and Ladakhis sell various barbaric but effective ornaments, especially necklaces and bracelets of rough turquoise.

Simla has still some official functions under the new régime; the physical atmosphere is perhaps conducive to the efficient conduct of conferences. But the glory, such as it was, is departed.

ADDENDUM TO CHAPTER 7

Recent changes at Aminbhavi

A note received from Dr L. S. Bhat gives some interesting details of recent changes at Aminbhavi; these came to hand too late for incorporation in the body of the text, and in any case it seems better to maintain the original account so that the contrast should stand out more clearly.

The village is now a real satellite of Dharwar, separated by only four miles from the nearest suburb, and marginal village lands are cultivated by Dharwar residents. About 150 travel daily to markets, courts, schools and entertainments in Dharwar, and this figure rises to 5–600 for the Tuesday market. Bus traffic on a good asphalt road is increasing; vegetables, flowers and dairy products go to the Dharwar bazaar.

The population is now 5,538 and the village council has become a Town Panchayat. Community proportions remain much the same: 2,950 Lingayats, 650 Muslims, 350 Jains, 100 Brahmins, 300 Talwars, 300 Harijans. The last group has now a separate planned colony, and the Shikalgar housing has also improved, with tiled roofs. Services now include another Ayurvedic and a Homaeopathic medical practitioner, a Government Rural Medical Practitioner and trained midwife, as well as telegraph and telephone facilities.

There have been changes in land use: groundnuts have partly replaced cotton

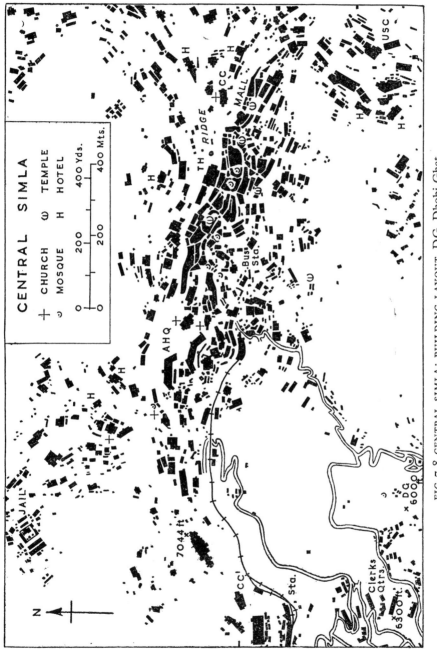

FIG 7.8 CENTRAL SIMLA: BUILDING LAYOUT. DG, Dhobi Ghat.

as a cash crop, partly owing to quick returns in the middle of the year just before the Diwali festival; increasing quantities of vegetables and flowers are grown under the influence of the Dharwar market. Pump irrigation, chemical fertilizers, better seeds, insecticides, composting, are being used by a few of the better-off and more progressive farmers, but poverty and debt still inhibit their spread among the mass of the peasantry. Those who can apply these improvements estimate an all-round increase in yields of about 10%.

On the whole, the changes seem to show Aminbhavi as still a microcosm of rural India: increasing mobility, increasing urban influence (this not so typical), better diffusion of information about the world through mobile libraries and so on, a definite, but very uneven, increase in productivity so far largely confined to the already well-found and progressive farmers. Two Community Development officers sum up – and in view of Aminbhavi's locational advantage, this may well stand as a comment of very wide application: 'It is too early to say anything about the impact in terms of cash or buildings and things like that, but there is a change in the outlook of the villagers. Nothing more can be said at this stage.'

BIBLIOGRAPHICAL NOTE

The settlement geography of the sub-continent has attracted a good deal of attention in the last few years; in addition to Enayat Ahmad's excellent study already mentioned (summarized in his 'Rural settlement types in Uttar Pradesh', *Annals Asstn American Geogrs* 42 (1952), 223–46), articles too numerous to mention, and on regional scales as well as of specific cases, are scattered through the Indian and Pakistani journals. The increasing sociological interest has also produced many studies, and several of the references to Chapter 5 apply here also. Special reference may be made to M. Marriot (ed.), *Village India* (Univ. of Chicago, 1955). An important critical paper is H. Tinker, 'Authority and community in village India', *Pacific Affairs*, 32 (1959), 354–75.

A fascinating illustrated survey of the 'material culture' of the countryside, from village types to shoes and carts, will be found in *Peasant Life in India*, (Anthropological Survey of India, Memoir 8, Calcutta, 1961).

There are also a very large number of studies of towns; some of the more important are referred to in the appropriate regional chapters. Perhaps the best study of a single town in modern geographical terms is R. L. Singh, *Banaras* (Nand Kishore, Banaras, 1955), and a most important general work is R. Turner (ed.), *India's Urban Future* (Univ. of California Press, Berkeley, 1962); this contains a very full review of recent literature by B. F. Hoselitz. For the 'feel' of town and village life, more creative writers are invaluable, e.g. novels such as Ahmed Ali's *Twilight in Delhi* or R. K. Narayan's many books set in 'Malgudi', which is Somewhere in Tamilnad. On the village side, there are M. L. Darling's unmatched 'Rural Rides' in the *Punjab*, or Kusum Nair's *Blossoms in the Dust* (Praeger, NY, 1962).

Where available, the Survey of India's 'Guide Maps' (1/21,120 or larger scales) are invaluable for the chief towns.

PART III

The Economy

CHAPTER 8

Agriculture and Agrarian Problems

Comments on the data

India, and even more Pakistan, will remain predominantly agrarian countries for many years or decades; and over the millennia they have evolved an indescribably complex mosaic of tenures and techniques which defies generalization. Moreover, the various aspects of rural life and its problems are inextricably interwoven, so that the organization of even the most generalized account is a matter of great difficulty. The volume of the literature is enormous, even though some important topics such as farm management and marketing are neglected; but the single Report of the Royal Commission on Agriculture in India (RCAI) of 1928 runs to 755 closely printed pages, and even so contains hardly any detail on crop distributions, no statistical tables, and no discussion at all of the extremely intricate matter of land tenure – a subject strangely barred by its terms of reference. And it is extremely difficult to separate the grain from the chaff in this literature, while some fields have been ploughed over and over again, and one suspects that diminishing returns long ago set in: some studies are tendentious and many more unbearably repetitious.

In recent years the churning of the ocean of facts contained in official reports has been more assiduous than ever, while since Independence vast surveys of such topics as rural indebtedness and agricultural labour have been issued. There are now many more, and more competent, first-hand village and regional surveys than were available fifteen years ago; qualitative material on everything from lac to leather is to be found in a vast mass of official papers, and in a plethora of private reappraisals of all aspects of the agrarian situation. All that can be done in a limited space is to set out some of the basic facts, to sketch rather than to discuss some agrarian maladies, and to indicate some recent developments. The fundamental factors of climate and soil should need no recapitulation.

Crude statistical data are superabundant, but subject to serious limitations. Despite the spread of sampling, too many official figures still depend on the conscience and efficiency of half a million or more badly paid and not very literate village officials; there are of course some checks, and the pious hope that errors cancel out. But too often real accuracy is sacrificed to 'a formal kind of precision'; 'roughly two-thirds' may be much more accurate, and much less misleading, than '68·2%'.[1] In some cases the anomalies are glaring on the face of it: when one finds that the acreage irrigated by wells in the single District of Bhagalpur (Bihar) is given for nine years running as 9,752, to spurt to 100,000 in the tenth and collapse to 500 in the eleventh year, one is tempted to scrap the lot.[2]

It is simply not possible for the most perfect bureaucracy to know the actual output; the surplus after deducting grain for family use (and a large wastage from attack by rodents, insects and moulds) is largely dissipated in millions of petty sales. Probably something between a quarter and a third enters the commercial market. Here again the village official is at the bottom of a shaky pyramid; his estimates are in their nature impressionistic and subject to bias. Yield figures in particular are open to grave doubt; the discrepancies between those obtained by actual crop-cutting samples and those obtained by dividing area into recorded output have amounted to over 36%; two official estimates of the gross value of crop output, those of the National Income Committee and the Rural Credit Survey, were Rs 4,887 crores and Rs 2,921 crores respectively, a difference of 67%.[3] Sampling will give better results in the future, but of course any comparative study over a long term is rendered hazardous by the non-comparability and varying reliability of the earlier data. All yield figures, and arguments based on them, must be used with circumspection, as *relative* approximations and indicators of trends and intensities, and not taken as absolutes.

The National Sample Surveys, conducted by the Indian Statistical Institute under the leadership of Professor P. C. Mahanalobis, have now been running for some 15 years; they cover an enormous range of information on many aspects of economic life, though many findings are of sociological rather than geographical significance. The NSS apart, however, not all surveys under official auspices can be taken at face value: apart from what seem questionable sampling techniques, as for instance in the All-India Rural Credit Survey, the capacity and training of some of the host of enumerators are very probably inadequate, and it seems certain that many farmers – and this would apply in countries much more literate than India – cannot really understand all the questions or recall all of the large assemblage of facts demanded from them.[4]

With all their limitations, these statistical assemblages do represent a big achievement. Bearing in mind always that they are indices rather than absolute statements, they are useful enough in regional or crop comparisons and as evidences of trends. The wonder is not that there should be large errors, but that so large a mass of data should exist. But in view of the vital importance of forward planning for food, this does not absolve the governments from making every effort to improve their statistical machinery.

[1] Cf. D. J. M. Hooson, *A New Soviet Heartland* (Van Nostrand, Princeton, 1964), 15.
[2] P. Dayal, *The Agricultural Geography of Bihar* (London Ph.D. thesis, 1947), xii–xiii.
[3] D. and A. Thorner, *Land and Labour in India* (Asia, Bombay, 1962), 208–9.
[4] For a severe but apparently justified critique of some recent enquiries, see D. and A. Thorner, *op. cit., passim.*

I. GENERALITIES

Classification of area

The primary division of the land is shown in Table II (p. 391); it will be seen that the *oikoumene*, represented by the area 'from Village Papers', amounts to about 90% of the geographical area of India, and of this about 45% is sown, or allowing for multiple cropping over 51%. For Pakistan the position is different: some 36% of the total geographical area is 'not reported', and there is a very striking difference between the two wings: a mere 631,000 ac. (255,000 ha.) of East Pakistan is not reported, only 1·8% of total area against 42·5% in the west. The net sown areas (NSA) in East and West Pakistan are 58·5 and 27·4% of the reporting area, but the west has only 15·8% of its total area under crop. Multiple cropping brings the total cultivated area (TCA) of East Pakistan up to almost three-quarters of the total area, but to only 31·4% of the reporting or 18% of the total area in the west.

The breakdown of the Indian figures has been improved since the old days when about one-fifth of British India – some 90,000,000 ac. (36,400,000 ha.) – was returned as 'Culturable Waste'; a figure patently absurd and, as the RCAI remarked, 'calculated to give rise to misconceptions'. With no undue haste, the government met the Commission's demand for a more reasonable classification by simply re-naming the 'Culturable Waste', which became 'Other Uncultivated Land excluding Current Fallows'. More recently the old term has been used again, but applied to a much more limited area – 51,000,000 ac. (20,600,000 ha.), though it is doubtful whether many even of these diminished acres exist at all, and still more whether most of those which do exist could be cultivated without an inordinate capital outlay. Perhaps about half might be reclaimed in a not impossibly distant future. 'Other Uncultivated Land' also includes permanent pasture and grazing and land under miscellaneous tree crops, though apart from village fruit groves and so on it is not very clear what these are.

In 1950–51 a uniform distinction between current and other fallow was adopted: 'Current Fallows' are those lying fallow for less than one year, 'Fallow, other than current' has been unploughed for between one and five years, and anything above that is distributed into Culturable Waste or miscellaneous tree crops and groves. It would seem that there is room for a good deal of subjectivism about such classifications.

Perhaps the most striking aspect of the Indian figures is the very small proportion – 4·5% of Village Papers area – under permanent pasture or grazing; and this in the country with the largest bovine population in the world. Of course much of the Culturable Waste – and probably not a little of the 'Not Available' – is grazing of a sort: roadside verges, rough rocky patches of scrub, and so on. Much of West Pakistan's 'Other uncultivated land' is rough (very rough) grazing. The Pakistani poverty in forests, as against India, will be noted, though a good deal of the 'not reported' area is more or less forested.

The most essential fact in Table II, however, is that even allowing for multiple cropping, only a little over half of the more settled area of India is cultivated. By 1961–62 the TCA had reached 347,300,000 ac. (140,650,000 ha.), and this amounts to under three-quarters of an acre (0·303 ha.) for each person in a population in which 73% of the work force is *directly* dependent on the land for livelihood.

For Pakistan the man/land ratio is of the same order: overall, 0·66 cultivated acres per person, with a distinct disparity once more between east and west, with 0·53 and 0·8 ac. respectively (in hectares, 0·27, 0·21, 0·32). Yet the dependence on the land is as strong as in India; 70% of the civilian labour force is engaged in agricultural pursuits, and in East Pakistan, with about half an acre per head (allowing for multiple cropping!) and scarcely any scope for expansion of the cropped area, this figure rises to 85·25%.

When we add the further fact that in both countries unit yields for virtually every crop are below, and often very much below, world averages, the keynote of the whole agrarian problem is at once struck by these simple but terrifying figures.

Types of farming: Kharif and Rabi

Farming practices are considered in some detail in the regional chapters; broadly speaking the types of cultivation in India may be grouped as follows:

1. Shifting hill cultivation.
2. Sedentary peasant agriculture:
    (*a*) food crops, dry or irrigated;
    (*b*) cash crops, dry or irrigated;
    (*c*) arboriculture and gardening.
3. Capitalist farming:
    (*a*) estates;
    (*b*) plantations.

The first and last may be briefly dismissed; the second is the norm of Indian farming, and forms the staple of this chapter.

Shifting agriculture – the *jhum* of Assam, the *kumri* or *podu* of the Peninsula – conforms to the standard pattern so widespread in tropical regions.[5] Dry rice, buckwheat, maize, poor millets, sometimes poor tobacco or sugar-cane, are grown on burnt-over clearings; in, say, two to five years, when the ash-given fertility dwindles, new clearings are made, preferably in new forest as the dense twisted scrub of abandoned jhums is often less tractable than untouched high forest. Obviously this can usually support only a sparse population, but on all

[5] E.g. *taungya* in Burma, *chena* in Ceylon, and so on; agreement on one name (or two, to cover the distinction between the 'nomadic' and the 'long fallow' types) is most desirable. For a general discussion, see P. Gourou, *Les Pays tropicaux* (Presses Universitaires de France, Paris, 1948), and H. G. Conkling, 'The study of shifting cultivation', *Current Anthropology* 2 (1961), 27–61.

the borders of Assam and in the wilder parts of central India it is dominant, while on the Western Ghats and the sub-Himalayan slopes both shifting and sedentary cultivation are carried on, as well as intermediate forms recalling 'run-rig' or the long fallowing (15–20 years) of south-central Africa.

Dry deciduous forest is obviously especially suited to jhuming, and as it is also the most generally valuable commercially, this devastating practice is frowned on by authority; moreover it may initiate severe soil erosion. But in some areas it is the only cultivation topographically possible, and in many there is at present no alternative to a considerable amount of controlled jhuming, sometimes turned to account by making the planting of commercial timber on abandoned fields a condition of licensing.

As for *capitalist farming*, there are or were a few large estates run on modern lines, though often cultivated by tenants; these include military dairy and vegetable farms, and some factory estates for sugar, cotton and oilseeds. Interesting as these estates are, they are alien to the whole structure of Indian farming, and can hardly play a decisive role in agricultural advance. *Plantations* are almost entirely for tea, rubber and coffee, and are therefore dealt with in Section II.E of this chapter; it may be added that in the prevailing climate of Indian opinion, there is little scope for extending plantations, which may indeed have some difficulty in holding their own.

Our second type is by far the most important. The overwhelming majority of Indians living by the land are smallholders, usually very small indeed, or landless. It is clear from Table III that their major activity is the growing of cereals (2a), though in some areas oilseeds, sugar and fibres (2b) are nearly as important to the economy as are foodgrains, and locally minor branches (2c) are significant: market gardening, spices, sericulture, perhaps even lac-collecting come under this head.

Two vitally important cross-divisions are those between (i) wet and dry crops and (ii) the autumn (*kharif*) and spring (*rabi*) harvests.

(i) Irrigation demands a separate place, but we may note here that 'wet' crops are not necessarily irrigated. While in much of West Pakistan crops of any sort are virtually impossible without irrigation, at the other extreme East Pakistan cultivation is wet enough but practically independent of irrigation.

(ii) Kharif is the monsoon crop, sown soon after the onset of the rains (June–July) and harvested in autumn: rice, jowar, bajra, sesamum, cotton (though this is long on the ground), jute. Rabi crops are sown after the rains and harvested in spring: wheat, barley, gram, linseed, rape and mustard. Kharif and rabi may be, but as a rule are not, sown on the same ground; rabi is essentially the crop of doabs and uplands, kharif of flood-plains and the areas under tanks. A given crop need not fall exclusively into one category, and in the southern half of the Peninsula, and particularly in Tamilnad with its October–December rain, the distinction is blurred; and sugar, which may be 10–18 months in the ground, clearly does not fit in. Locally, of course, there are minor harvests, especially in

Bengal and Bihar, where the relations of the two (or even three) crops are exceedingly complicated.

Irrigation (Fig. 8.1 and Table V)

Altogether about 9% of the total area of the sub-continent is irrigated – over 130,000 sq. miles (336,700 km²), an area nearly half as large again as the entirety of Great Britain. Irrigation of some sort has been practised since time immemorial – the Grand Anicut on the Cauvery, a million cubic feet of masonry, was built in the 11th century; but most canal development is the work of the last hundred years. With a net irrigated area of around 60,000,000 ac. (25,000,000 ha.), India uses about a quarter of her estimated usable flow, and this may increase to about a third by the end of the Third Plan. Canals account for about 42% of the irrigated area, tanks 20%, wells 29%, the balance being accounted for by minor weirs and so on. About two-thirds of the TCA of West Pakistan is irrigated, and only a small fraction of the total 24,000,000 ac. (9,700,000 ha.) under irrigation is in the East. Canal irrigation is dominant in West Pakistan, though there is an important area of well-irrigation in the sub-montane strip of the Punjab, and in Baluchistan *karez*, irrigation tunnels, are common (below, p. 485).

(i) *Canals* fall into two groups: inundation canals, mere cuts parallel to the rivers in the flood-plains, and perennial canals fed by elaborate headworks, with regulated flow, generally aligned along the doabs so as to command a wider area. Many of the former date from Mogul times, a few even earlier, but the perennial systems, a creation of the British period, now cover a much wider area (cf. Fig. 17.6). Details of the layout and working of a modern canal system are given in Chapter 17.

Inundation canals merely fill with the rising river, and if it does not rise enough they remain empty. They are thus liable to fail precisely when most needed. Their offtakes silt readily. Perennial canals also have disadvantages, of which the most important is that their headworks may trap much of the silt so valuable to the ill-manured fields. Again 'it is just as important to get the water off the land as to get it on, and few ryots still seem to know it. The water comes to the cultivator without much labour on his part, and the high esteem in which he holds it leads to over-irrigation without adequate drainage'.[6] Hence waterlogging and the formation of alkali pans – menaces which have reached alarming proportions in parts of West Pakistan and northern India leading to very serious losses of cultivated land. By the late 1950s the situation in West Pakistan was extremely serious, by official figures something like 15,000,000 ac. (6,000,000 ha.) being water-logged or saline and another 11,000,000 (4,450,000 ha.) having saline patches; altogether about 70% of the cropland was more or less affected, and in

[6] G. Kuriyan, 'Irrigation in India' (*Journal of the Madras University*, 15, No. 1, Sec. A, 1943), 167; payment by volume has been suggested, instead of by area irrigated as at present; for objections to this, see RCAI, 336.

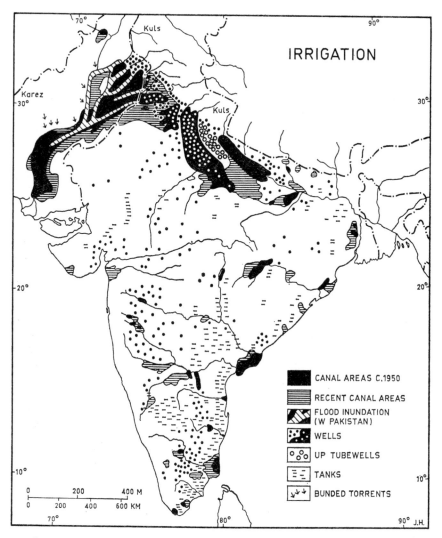

FIG 8.1. IRRIGATION. Apart from the classic areas of canal irrigation in the Indo-Gangetic Plains, the areas of close well-irrigation (especially by tube-wells in Uttar Pradesh) and the tank-fed areas of Telangana, Mysore and Tamilnad stand out. Compiled from various sources.

the Rechna Doab (between the Ravi and Chenab Rivers) 15% of the area had gone out of production. A vigorous effort in pumping and drainage has been started, but to deal effectively with the problem may well cost Rs 500–600 crores. A detailed analysis of the complex difficulties met with in the long-cultivated Cauvery Delta in consequence of changing from direct (inundation) to perennial irrigation will be found on pp. 764–67. When all is said, however, such great achievements as the Punjab Triple Project form a most impressive memorial of the British Raj.

(ii) *Tanks* are illustrated in some detail in Figs. 25.11 and 25.12. Their siting speaks to a wonderful flair for detecting the minutest variations in the terrain. A reliable tank needs a considerable catchment, which is usually waste; rice is the usual tank-fed crop, on gently falling terraces designed to secure an even flow of water over the fields. Often a whole stream is reduced to a string of tanks, the lower ones trapping the surplus water from those above. The high water-table below the tanks supplies good wells, used either for security in bad years or a second crop in good ones.

Nevertheless tanks are on the whole unsatisfactory. The water-surface is large in relation to volume, so that loss by evaporation is high, as is that by seepage; relatively few tanks hold water throughout the year (cf. Fig. 25.12). Sooner or later they silt up; the bed will retain some ground-water, held up by the bund, and for a while at least be very fertile; but the problem of a new supply remains.

Irrigation tanks must be distinguished from the small rectangular tanks for domestic water-supply. These are often built-up as much as excavated, rain- and not stream-fed, and except in wet areas like East Bengal (where they occur in tens of thousands, as a by-product of excavating mud for house-plinths) are obviously very likely to fail in the hot weather.

(iii) *Wells* of course command individually small areas; even in the Punjab, where they are large and permanent, the average area is only 12 acres (4·9 ha.). But in aggregate they are exceedingly important, and not only quantitatively.

A *pukka* – masonry or brick-lined – well is costly to construct, and the use of any well makes great demands on human and animal labour; well-irrigation is thus six or seven times as expensive as canal, and so tends to be reserved for high-value specialized crops – vegetables for urban markets, sugar, or, where soil is good, really first-class cereals. This is in fact garden cultivation; over-watering is obviously unlikely, and the well can be used exactly when needed, which is by no means always so with other methods. The small areas lend themselves to fencing and individual care, and are usually well weeded and manured.

Several types of lift are used. The simplest, for shallow wells, is the *picottah* (=Egyptian *shaduf*), merely a weighted pole pivoted on an upright; for lifts of over 15 ft. bullocks are used. In the north, and especially in West Punjab, the 'Persian wheel' is common: an endless chain of pots on a vertical wheel geared to a horizontal and worked by bullocks endlessly circling the well. Also common is the *mhote*, a steep ramp up which the bullocks are backed to depress the bucket, raising it on the forward downhill movement. In Tamilnad the *kabalai* is an ingenious variant (below, p. 753).

Oil-driven pumps have been used, but unless they can be worked for four hours a day – which would probably exhaust most wells rapidly – they are no more efficient than the *kabalai*, and to be economic they would demand large holdings of 10–15 ac. (4–6 ha.).[7] This last argument, however, loses much of its force when put against the general high cost of well-irrigation, which means that only large holders could contemplate such methods anyhow. The introduction of cheap electricity is already causing major changes, and there is an increasing demand for electric pumps in the areas served by Pykara and other south Indian hydro-electric plants. Another development of great significance is the introduction of tube-wells tapping the huge resources of water at depth beneath the Indo-Gangetic Plains; here Uttar Pradesh has led the way (below, p. 554).

(iv) *Other Sources* consist for the most part of small temporary dams and channels (e.g. the *ahars* and *pynes* of south Bihar), the 'spring channels' of Tamilnad river-beds, mere water-holes in flood-plains, direct lift from rivers, and so on. The most interesting type – Iranian rather than Indian – is the *karez* of Baluchistan (Fig. 16.2), tunnels constructed by connecting lines of shafts sunk in the detrital fans of the piedmont, which has a relatively high water-table. *Karez* may be a mile long, but most are much smaller, and the best probably do not discharge more than 9–10 cusec. In this semi-desert zone much of what little cultivation exists is by means of bunds across the drainage-lines of the hill-slopes (Fig. 17.3). This holds up the ground-water and is water-conservation if not irrigation.

The area under wells and other sources is capable of rapid, if temporary, expansion and fluctuates widely, being especially important in years of deficient rain.

II. MAJOR CROPS AND THEIR DISTRIBUTION[8]

A. FOOD AND FODDER

1. *Cereals and Pulses*

(i) *Rice.* About a quarter of the net cultivated area of India, and over 45% of that of Pakistan, are under rice; East Pakistan indeed would be almost monocultural were it not for the competition of jute. The Indian acreage has risen fairly steadily of recent years and now runs at about 85,000,000 (34,500,000 ha.); that of Pakistan is around 25,000,000 (10,000,000 ha.), some 92% of which is in the eastern wing; however, the wheat-eating West has a surplus of 100,000–200,000

[7] Kuriyan, *loc. cit.* 56. Ch. VI of *Imperial Gaz.* Vol. III (1908) is still valuable for a discussion of the indigenous types of irrigation.

[8] Reference may be made to the distribution maps in the *National Atlas of India* (Ministry of Education, 1957, unfortunately in Hindi) and the *Indian Agricultural Atlas* (Ministry of Food & Agriculture, 1958, in English).

tons a year available for East Pakistan. Indian output of cleaned rice from 1955–56 to 1960–61 averaged about 29,500,000 tons, that of Pakistan about 10,000,000. There is, of course, much wastage, and the deduction for seed alone must be of the order of 5,000,000 tons of paddy (rice before any treatment).[9]

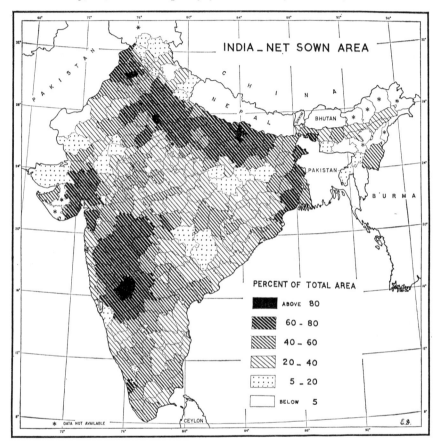

FIG 8.2 INDIA: NET SOWN AREA. Figs 8.2, 8.3, 8.6 to 8.8, 8.10, 8.12 to 8.14, are by courtesy of S. S. Bhatia and are based on statistics for 1950–52; see *Economic Geography*, 41 (1965), 39–56.

The high temperature and water requirements of paddy – except the practically negligible dry hill rice – make it dominantly a crop of the deltas and flood-plains, and the dominant crop there. It is at its best when the growing season has a mean temperature of 75°F. (24°C.) or more and, in non-irrigated areas, 60–80 in. (1,524–2,032 mm.) of rain. The fact that rice is so pre-eminently a 'wet crop' is responsible for the not uncommon fallacy that it is grown almost entirely by

[9] The remainder of this section is largely based on G. Kuriyan, 'Rice in India', *IGJ* 20/1 (1945), 28–36, 76–84, 110–26 – a very comprehensive account.

irrigation. The plant certainly can mature satisfactorily only if it grows in a few inches of water; a five-month crop will need about 70 ac.–in. But in the great domains of paddy this is supplied by the rain on the fields themselves or by natural flood, and is simply retained by the low mud field-walls (bunds); whereas

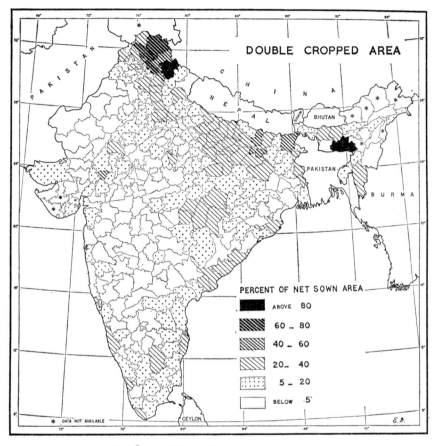

DOUBLE CROPPED AREA

PERCENT OF NET SOWN AREA

ABOVE 80

60 – 80

40 – 60

20 – 40

5 – 20

BELOW .5

✳ DATA NOT AVAILABLE

FIG 8.3 INDIA: DOUBLE CROPPED AREA.

'irrigation' surely implies an artificial supply. This is necessary wherever the rainfall is below 40–45 in. (1,016–1,143 mm.), and at least very desirable at 50–55 in. (1,270–1,397 mm.). Paddy favours rather heavy soils – clays, clayey loams, the clay-with-silt of the deltas and is fairly tolerant of salinity (hence its tendency to expand in waterlogged areas—for instance in the Punjab).

As a rule it is sown soon after the beginning of the rains and harvested in November–January, but in Bengal there are three crops: *aus* (harvested June–September), *aman* (November–January; *c.* 75% of acreage), and *boro* (February–May). This last is grown on the shrinking margins of lakes and swamps and has a very small acreage. Broadcasting is used, in Bengal for about half the crop, but more generally seedlings are raised in heavily manured beds and transplanted; this is back-breaking work, often done by the women. The soil is puddled and tends to become very heavy; organic and especially green manures are useful, but probably most paddy-fields get little fertilizing except the burning of the stubble and sometimes of branches and twigs.

Of the complexities of paddy cultivation and the rice trade there is no end; in India alone some 4,000 varieties are known, each with special requirements and qualities. An increasing area is under improved strains produced by the agricultural research institutes.

The grading of paddy for sale and milling is a fine art. Rice is not in itself a very good food, with only fair though easily assimilated protein content. Unfortunately the taste for polished rice – purely a matter of prestige – seems to be spreading, though of course village consumption is mostly home-ground or pounded in mortars and retains much of the valuable husk. Coolies often eat cheap parboiled rice, which is steamed before milling; this is valued as it keeps well when cooked, and the vitamins and minerals of the husk are not lost to such an extent as in ordinary milling. A diet based on milled rice, deprived of vitamin B, definitely predisposes to beri-beri, one of the most serious deficiency diseases of India, and not confined to the quantitatively under-fed. The famous experiment on rats fed on diets typical of provinces from the Punjab to Madras also shows the low dietetic value of poor rice diets.[10] But these qualitative failings are offset by heavy yields per acre – nearly twice those of jowar and bajra – and rice retains its place as the staple food of the wetter areas, and of the better-off classes nearly everywhere.

Paddy has developed a strikingly individual landscape, broadly similar from the Ganga to the Yangtse: myriads of tiny mud-walled fields, in the rains with only the bunds and the villages rising above the grey water through which the young paddy shows like thin flames of a most wonderful glowing emerald; in the hot weather a grey expanse of baked mud and thin stubble, dotted by the threshing-floors with their bamboo tripods whence swing open-meshed baskets into which the threshed grain is thrown to be winnowed by the wind. Here and there are the gaunt corrugated-iron roofs and spindly chimneys of small rice mills. More significant are the social correlates of this landscape so intensively moulded by man. If intensive rice farming draws much energy from the soil, much energy must also be put in, and 'the investment of effort required to develop paddy land immobilizes the population itself. . . . Industrial development may enable a people to levy on the produce of other lands and develop a denser population than any agriculture will support', but no other way of life (except the not dissimilar economy of Egypt) has led to the evolution of a cultural system

---

[10] The average body-weights of the rats of each diet group (in grams) at the end of the experiment were: Sikh 235, Pathan 230, Maratha 225, Kanarese 185, Bengali 180, Madrassi 155. The Maratha/Kanarese drop is most significant, as these areas adjoin, the Marathas being practically confined to the wheat and jowar-bajra Deccan Lavas. See R. K. Mukerjee, *Food Planning for 400 Million* (London, 1938), 167–8.

so stable and so permanent as that associated with the great paddy-plains of Monsoon Asia.[11]

(ii) *Wheat.* The distribution of wheat shows an even more marked climatic correlation than that of rice, but inverse to it. Of the total acreage (*c.* 37,000,000 ac., 15,000,000 ha.) two-fifths are in arid West Pakistan, and about half of the rest in East Punjab and western Uttar Pradesh. Wheat extends down the Ganga as far as west Bihar, and across Malwa into the drier northwestern quadrant of the Deccan; beyond these limits it is negligible. In the Peninsula, wheat is usually a dry crop on black soils; in the Indo-Gangetic Plains, irrigated on alluvial loams. The few inches of winter rain in the sub-montane strip of the Punjab enable good rabi crops to be grown. Most Indian wheats are hard.

The export of wheat through Karachi always fluctuated, falling off sharply in years succeeding a bad monsoon and has now dwindled to almost nil. The reason is obvious, and it is not likely that there will ever again be much significant export from the sub-continent.

(iii) *The Millets.* The total millet acreage perhaps equals that of rice, jowar and bajra alone having a combined area of 70,000,000–75,000,000 ac. (28,000,000–30,000,000 ha.). Yields, however, are on the whole low, the output of these two being only 10,000,000–12,000,000 tons. In location millets are intermediate between rice and wheat, jowar and bajra, for example, being usually rain-fed, in areas with *c.* 25–40 in. (635–1,016 mm.). Nothing displays more strikingly the contrast between the two Pakistans, wet in the east and dry in the west, than the fact that their acreage of these 'intermediate' crops is almost negligible. The concentration of jowar and bajra in the Deccan is also striking; ragi, the third of the more important millets, has a rather wider spread.

The idea, often held in Europe, that the millets are spindly plants little better than grasses, and of inferior nutritive value, will hardly bear analysis. Jowar and bajra grow 6–8 ft. high, or even more, and jowar indeed looks like a field of bulrushes. Table VII shows clearly that in many respects lesser millets are better-balanced as food than is rice, and bajra ranks high indeed – level with wheat and oats in calcium content, between them in phosphorus, and with five and two times as much respectively of these minerals as even home-pounded rice. Yet there is a strong prejudice against them and as they are generally grown on poorer soils and in the precarious 25–40 in. (635–1,016 mm.) rainfall zone, yields are insecure.

(a) *Jowar (Sorghum vulgare)*,[12] known as cholam in the south, is both kharif and rabi. As kharif it needs 30–40 in. (762–1,016 mm.) of rain and is grown mainly on black soils, often rotated with cotton and usually mixed with pulses or sesamum. Rabi jowar is less often mixed with other crops; it needs moisture-retaining soils which have received good rain in September–October, and is

[11] G. Kuriyan, *loc. cit. ad fin.*

[12] The 'bread sorghum' of American writers, who apparently do not count it among the millets. American and British usages of the terms 'millet' and 'sorghum' are difficult to disentangle; here standard Indian usage is followed.

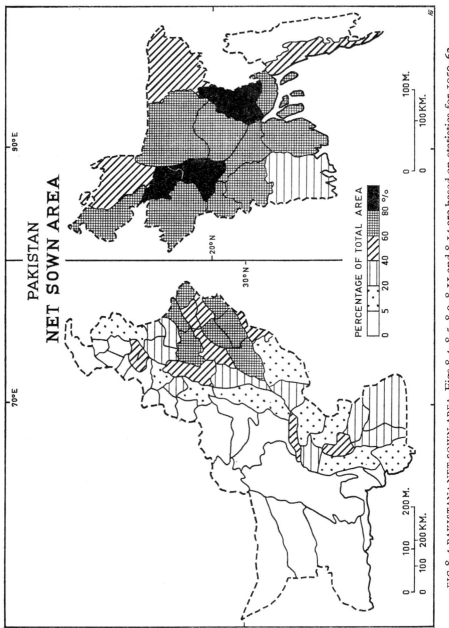

FIG 8.4 PAKISTAN: NET SOWN AREA. Figs 8.4, 8.5, 8.9, 8.11 and 8.14 are based on statistics for 1959–63.

perhaps most notable in Tamilnad – where, of course, the 'rabi' is the monsoon crop. Jowar stalks form valuable fodder; the yield per acre may be 500 or more pounds of grain plus 100–200 lb. of inter-grown pulse and anything from 1,000–3,000 lb. of fodder (100 lb./ac.=112 kg./ha.). When grown specifically for fodder, as in Gujarat, parts of the Deccan and Coimbatore, jowar is sown very closely to make it run to stalk; in the Deccan a rude pit silage is practised.

(b) *Bajra* (or bajri, in the south cumbu or cambu, *Pennisetum typhoideum*) tolerates lighter soils than jowar, and is therefore grown extensively on the poorer Deccan Lava uplands, and on sandy or stony soils generally. It is nearly all kharif, but too much rain is harmful, and it is usually sown after the first force of the rains is spent. As a rule it is mixed, usually with pulses,[13] so that rotation is less necessary; but it may be 'rotated' with jowar in years of weak monsoon. Its nutritional value has been noted.

(c) *Ragi* (marua or madua, *Eleusine coracana*) ranges from the Himalayan slopes almost to the extreme south. Again it is a kharif crop, which may be transplanted; sometimes irrigated, in the Archaean Deccan it is often grown under tanks. Dry ragi is usually intercropped but not irrigated ragi. The highest yielder of the millets, with improved strains and careful culture it can give as much as 1,500 lb. per ac. (1,681 kg./ha.) or more; but as a rule only the nurseries receive much manure.

Ragi is perhaps the most important, though far from the most esteemed, food in such poor regions as Telangana. Although it is in some respects a better food than rice, with a remarkably high calcium content (0·33%), 'it is often regarded as food suitable for poor and ignorant villagers – also as the food of prisoners in the jails'.[14] He who rises in the world exposes himself to beri-beri, while the diet and physique of the convict are generally better than those of his less enterprising fellows. It is often eaten as balls of the hard small seeds, dipped in a sauce of pulse or spices to impart flavour.

(iv) *Other Cereals: Pulses.* Apart from wheat, the only temperate cereals grown on a really large scale are barley (8,000,000–10,000,000 ac., 3,250,000–4,000,000 ha.) and maize (up to 13,000,000 ac., 5,250,000 ha., plus probably a good deal unrecorded). Half to two-thirds of the barley and a quarter of the recorded maize are in Uttar Pradesh, largely in the sub-Himalaya; in the higher Himalaya ordinary barley and the naked Tibetan variety (*grim*) are staples. The Ford Foundation Agricultural Team which visited India, briefly, in 1958 attached great importance to hybrid maize (at least seven of these thirteen advisers came from the Corn Belt), but little seems to have come of this. The pulses, served in innumerable attractive forms, are of great importance in protein intakes, and are probably of greater importance than the statistics suggest; they are often, perhaps usually, sown mixed, and the only ones for which separate figures are available are gram (25,000,000–30,000,000 ac., 10,000,000–12,000,000 ha.) and

[13] Thus further, and indeed insolubly, complicating the statistics.
[14] National Nutrition Research Laboratories, *Rice* (Bull. No. 28, Coonoor, 1940), 16.

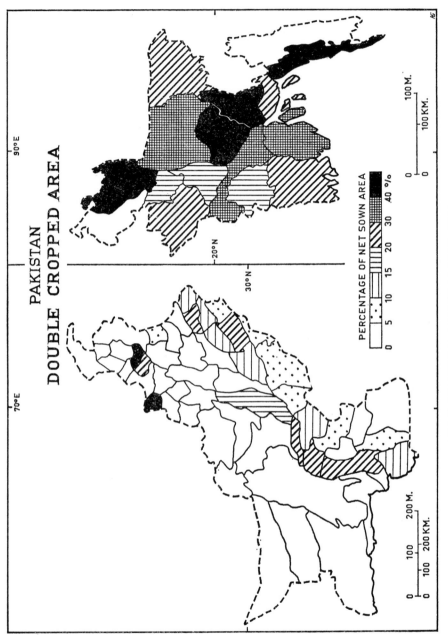

FIG 8.5 PAKISTAN : DOUBLE CROPPED AREA.

tur, rather over a quarter of the gram area. The main areas for gram are Uttar Pradesh and East Punjab, each with around 6,000,000 ac. (2,500,000 ha.) and in Pakistan the Punjab with about half this area. The pulses are useful as catch crops on poor soils or in bad years, and they are of course extremely valuable as

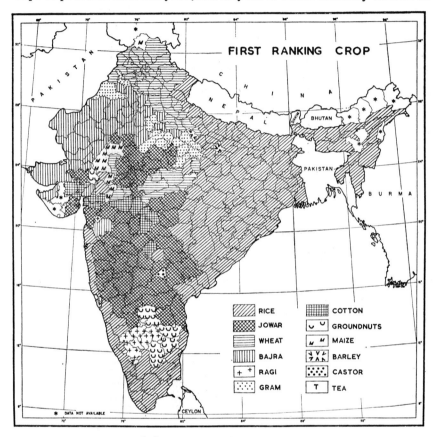

FIG 8.6 INDIA: FIRST RANKING CROP.

'nitrogenizers'; the extension of their use as green manure is desirable. As *dal*, a sort of lentil purée, pulses form an essential adjunct to most Indian curries.

2. *Other Food Crops*

Sugar and edible oilseeds demand separate treatment; no other crops cover a large area individually, the area returned under fruits, vegetables, spices and miscellaneous tree crops being divided among plants far too numerous to be listed, except perhaps for coconuts, which account for 1,700,000 ac. (700,000 ha.) in India alone. Except on some specially favoured areas such as floodplains near large cities, or around hill stations, horticulture is generally neglected: lack of storage and transport facilities, and of purchasing power in potential markets, account for this dietetically deplorable situation. Mangoes, however, are all but universal, oranges – small and loose-skinned – and plantains (bananas) widespread; the Himalayan regions and the western border hills grow most temperate fruits, including grapes, and in the northwest Himalaya apricots are an essential food. The fruit industry is best developed in Kashmir and around Peshawar, and there are possibilities of extension in Baluchistan. A dried- and canned-fruit industry may develop in West Pakistan.

Condiments such as chillies, essential to give a specious appearance of variety to a poor rice diet, are grown almost everywhere; spices mainly along the Western Ghats and the coast south of Goa; pepper is probably still the most important. In the better rice diets of the predominantly vegetarian south, plain boiled rice is served on a banana leaf (or a silver or, nowadays, stainless-steel plate) with a number of small dishes containing a variety of 'hot' or spicy soups and vegetable sauces; a ball of rice is mixed with a chosen sauce and eaten with the right hand. Curds, slightly sour like yoghourt, are often taken as a chaser after a hot-spicy mouthful; south Indian languages have a special term for 'hot-spicy'. Coconuts are officially oilseeds, but have too many uses to be easily categorized; other palms of value include dates in West Pakistan (the ubiquitous wild date has a practically useless fruit, but is tapped for toddy); palmyra, widespread but especially important in the extreme southeast, used for toddy, sugar and thatching; and the areca palm with its associate the betel vine, sources of the red *pan* chewed by high and low, Hindu and Muslim. There is some export of cardamoms pepper and areca nuts.

3. Fodder Crops

Little, unfortunately, need be said about these: some 10,000,000–12,000,000 ac. (4,000,000–5,000,000 ha.) only, nearly half in the Punjab and nearly a quarter in Maharashtra. Even allowing for the larger areas of rough, and usually very poor, grazing, this is exceedingly low for a country which contains nearly a third of the world's cattle, but the reason is distressingly simple: few peasants will devote land which might grow food for men to grow food for beasts, and indeed such are the demands on the scanty holdings that the ryot often cannot do so even if he would. The results, however, are directly deplorable for the bovine population, and ultimately for the human. To this problem we shall return.

B. FOOD/CASH CROPS: OILSEEDS AND SUGAR

These occupy an economic position intermediate between the cereals and the fibres; some oilseeds, such as castor and linseed, are exclusively for industrial use, while rape, mustard and sesamum are mainly foods, and the internal consumption of groundnuts is rapidly increasing. Sugar is distinguished from the purely food crops by the strong industrial element in its development.

1. *Oilseeds*

Pakistan's share of oilseeds is slight – neglecting cottonseed, some 2,000,000 ac. (809,000 ha.), almost all rape and mustard. In India oilseeds acreage for the decade before 1945 was fairly steady at 20,000,000–23,000,000 (8,000,000– 9,000,000 ha.), about 9% NSA, of which four-fifths were edible – sesamum,

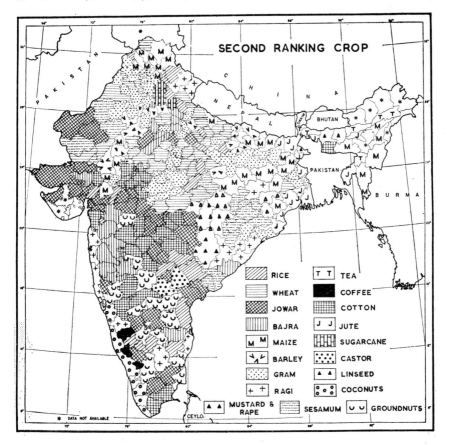

FIG 8.7 INDIA: SECOND RANKING CROP.

groundnut, rape – and the rest mainly linseed and castor. Within the group the most striking development was that of groundnuts, insignificant before 1913. The Indian oilseeds area is now about 32,000,000 ac. (13,000,000 ha.), of which nearly half is devoted to groundnuts, which have a considerably larger area than sesamum and rape combined.

Groundnut is a crop of the Peninsula, about half being grown in the Deccan with a strong concentration behind Pondicherry) and about a quarter in Gujarat. Its export value has led to its receiving marked attention from the

Agricultural Department, and a main factor in its spread has been its suitability to light sandy soils, of little use for cereals or cotton; it is a kharif crop. *Sesamum* (til or gingelly, *Sesamum indicum*) has rather more than a third of the area of groundnut, but is far more widely distributed, being significant everywhere except in the wetter Peninsular margins and Pakistan. It is the source of the most widely used cooking oil; in Bengal and Assam mustard is the staple. It can be grown as kharif (usually mixed) on light soils and as rabi, rotated with jowar and cotton, on heavy. Of the coconut area, the bulk is in south Madras and Kerala, with a subsidiary concentration in East Bengal.[15]

2. Sugar-cane

Sugar is probably indigenous to India, the word itself apparently coming from Sanskrit through Hellenistic Greece. In terms of raw cane, India is the largest producer in the world, but the low saccharine content of the cane and perhaps poor techniques bring its output in terms of sugar (including the semi-refined fudge-like *gur*) to third place, after Cuba and Brazil. The annual output of 3,000,000 tons or so comes from about 5,500,000 ac. (2,200,000 ha.) of which some 60% is in Uttar Pradesh, followed by Bihar and East Punjab. Pakistan has about 2,000,000 ac. (809,000 ha.), three-quarters of it in the West, where the factory at Mardan in the Vale of Peshawar is one of the largest in the sub-continent, if not in Asia.

The distribution shows some peculiarities. Northern India is the largest producer of cane-sugar in the world *outside* the tropics; and although in the south temperature régimes are closer to those of other cane-producing countries, and southern canes produce 2·5 to 3 tons of sugar per acre[16] against 0·6 (Punjab) to 1·5 (Bengal) in the north, yet 80–90% of total output comes from Indo-Gangetic regions, with thin, probably indigenous, canes in contrast to the thick varieties, perhaps Pacific in origin, of the south. One point in this low standing of the south is lack of humidity: the really heavy producers – Java, Cuba, Hawaii, Mauritius – all have insular climates to which the nearest Indian homologue would probably be coastal Kerala, already entirely devoted to paddy and with no room for a cash crop. But for several physical reasons costs of production are much higher in the south than in the north. Outside the middle Ganga Plains (Bihar and eastern Uttar Pradesh) sugar-cane must usually be irrigated, and irrigation is as a rule much easier and cheaper in the Indo-Gangetic Plains than in the Peninsula; moreover, the loamy alluvium, with sufficient lime and potash, does not need manuring to anything like the extent necessary in the south. The Godavari–Krishna deltas, indeed, approach optimum conditions, with ample cheap irrigation and rich alluvial soils; but here frequent cyclonic storms compel the use of some 5,000 bamboos per acre to protect the canes, and the

---

[15] The vegetable oil industry is discussed in Chapter 10, coconut culture in Kerala in Chapter 22.

[16] One ton per acre = 2,510 kg. per hectare.

cost of this in 1942 was Rs. 80–150 per acre, the latter figure being half the cost of cultivation. Further, although the main cane research station in India is at Coimbatore, work was originally on the thin varieties, improved strains of which were in general use in the north by 1938, when trials of new tropical canes were not complete. Finally there were few other cash crops suitable to Uttar Pradesh

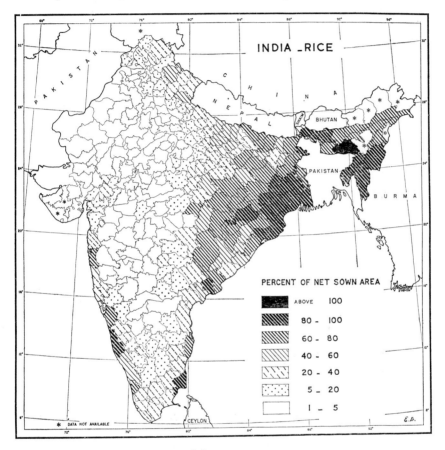

FIG 8.8 INDIA: RICE.

conditions, after the collapse of indigo cultivation, and hence cane is grown in solid blocks; the more sporadic distribution in the south has inhibited the growth of refineries, in turn restricting demand while the north was building up a great industry.

The main risk in the northwest, as far as eastern Uttar Pradesh, is frost; in Meerut losses of up to 20% are likely every five years or so, and in extreme cases losses of 50–80% have been reported. Frost is a menace as far south as Ahmadnagar and Nasik, at 1,600–1,800 ft. (490–550 m.) in the upper Godavari basin;

here also water-logging and saline efflorescences have put over a third of some canal-irrigated areas out of cultivation.[17]

Indian yields are generally low, averaging about 3,000 lb. of raw sugar per acre (3,363 kg./ha.); this is less than a quarter of Javanese and Hawaiian yields, though not very far below those of Cuba and Brazil. This figure is not so likely to be understated as cereal yields.

C. FIBRES

Here at last Pakistan holds a strong position, even if one rather less commanding than it used to be. In 1947 she had *c.* 80–85% of the area and output of jute, and about one-fifth of the area but one-third of the output of cotton. After an almost catastrophic war and post-war decline in the Indian cotton figures, there has been a considerable revival and they now exceed the immediate post-war acreage for both countries together. Pakistani yields, however, remain higher, producing about 2,000,000 bales a year against about 4,500,000 from India, but from less than a fifth of the Indian acreage, and including much of the higher quality fibre.

In jute, which is a notoriously fluctuating crop, there has been a striking change in the relative position of the two countries: whereas before Partition areas now in India had about one-third the area and little over one-quarter the output of East Pakistan, friction between the countries led to a remarkable expansion in India, as well as the introduction of *mesta*, which is now of considerable importance. Indian jute output is several times the pre-war average and, on a roughly equivalent area, is now about two-fifths that of Pakistan; the latter shows little expansion owing to the competition of paddy in the overcrowded Bengal delta.

Both raw cotton and raw jute are now overshadowed as Indian exports by their manufactures, and there is a large import of raw cotton, while Pakistan has made a beginning in the export of jute and cotton goods.

1. *Cotton* (Table IX)

The cotton of West Pakistan is entirely an irrigated crop, grown on about 3,500,000 ac. (1,400,000 ha.); in India only about 12·5% of some 17,500,000 ac. (7,100,000 ha.) is irrigated, it being essentially a rains-sown crop in the 25–30-in. (635–762-mm.) rainfall zone, usually grown on the deep, heavy, moisture-retentive black soils (regur) of the Deccan Lavas, the Gujarat alluvium, and pockets on the Archaeans. Cotton is again probably aboriginal to India, grown and woven from the earliest times. The indigenous (*desi*) cottons, of which the 'Tinnies' of the southeast and 'Oomras' of the Deccan are perhaps best-known, are short-stapled – only $\frac{1}{2}$–$\frac{7}{8}$ in. Efforts to increase staple have resulted in a considerable extension of the area under improved strains (especially Cambodia,

---

[17] This discussion is based on Chapters 8 and 9 of T. R. Sharma, *Location of Industries in India* (Hind Kitabs, Bombay, 3rd ed. 1954).

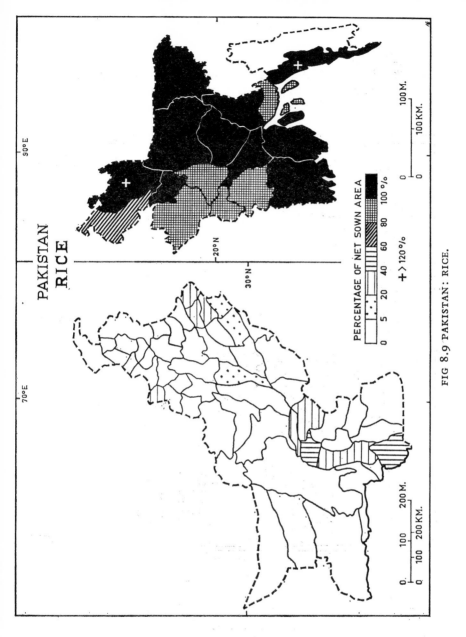

PAKISTAN
RICE

PERCENTAGE OF NET SOWN AREA

0   5   20   40   60   80   100 %

+ > 120%

FIG 8.9 PAKISTAN: RICE.

⅞–1 in.), but it is difficult to maintain standards owing to adulteration, especially in ginneries. On the whole, however, the proportion of long- or medium-staple is increasing. In West Pakistan development for export came later, with the Canal Colonies rather than with the American Civil War boom, and American varieties (staple 1–1 1/16 in.) predominate, accounting for the higher output in relation to area.

247

2. *Jute* (Table X)

Before Partition Bengal held practically a world monopoly of jute production: the nature and requirements of the crop are thus perhaps best dealt with in Chapter 19. The significant spread of jute in India since Partition is clearly a

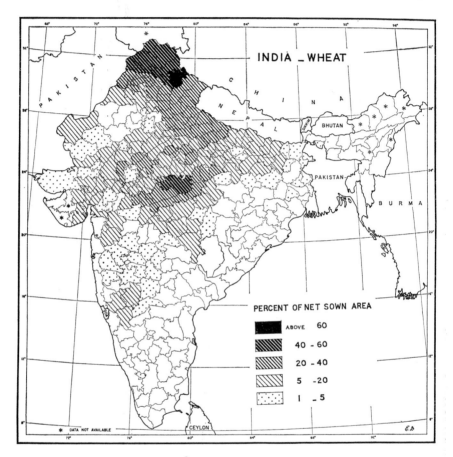

FIG 8.10 INDIA: WHEAT.

matter of nationalist rather than rationalist economics. It may be noted, however, that apart from the Orissa delta the main extension has been in Assam and along the terai in Bihar and eastern Uttar Pradesh. Here, on newly cleared land settled by refugees from East Pakistan, the claim that jute extension does not encroach upon the food area is doubtless justified; but it is difficult to think that this can be so in the other areas, and from the Indo-Pakistani ratio of area and yield it would seem that a good deal of this new cultivation is in rather marginal areas. But this is a part of the wider dilemma of food *versus* cash crops.

The indigenous grass *mesta* has been developed in India as a jute substitute or mixture: not shown in the *Statistical Abstract* before 1953–54, by 1961–62 it covered 950,000 ac. (385,000 ha.) and had an output of 1,700,000 bales, over 27% of the volume of jute output. It is grown mainly in West Bengal (35%), Bihar and coastal areas of Andhra and Maharashtra. It may be noted that the considerable linseed cultivation in India, as in other sub-tropical areas, is entirely for oil and not for fibre.

3. Wool

For the sake of a general view we may deal here with animal fibres. Of these wool is more important than silk. In 1961 India had about 40,000,000 sheep, half of them in Andhra, Madras and Mysore, and 7,000,000 in Rajasthan; some 10,000,000 must be added for West Pakistan. Kashmir, Rajasthan and West Pakistan produce nearly two-thirds of the annual clip, and it would seem that the Pakistani share would be fully 30%, and that again including most of the better grades from the hill sheep of Baluchistan and the Northwestern Hills. The northern wools are usually white, those of the south anything from off-white through red to black, and also coarse and hairy.

About half the clip was exported for coarse manufactures such as carpets, felt and rough blankets; for good woollens the Indian industry has to import most of its requirements from Australia.

4. Silk

It seems probable that the silkworms of ancient India were generally not mulberry-feeders (*Bombyx* spp.), though *Bombyx mori* from China is of old standing in Manipur. Mulberries are grown and the true silkworm reared along the western Himalayan slopes, especially in Kashmir, and on paddy-bunds in Bengal. In addition, 'India has three well-known purely indigenous silkworms: the *tasar*, the *muga*, and the *eri*. The first is widely distributed in the lower hills, more especially of the great central table-land, and feeds on several jungle trees. The second is confined to Assam and eastern Bengal, and feeds on a laurel. The third exists in a state of semi-domestication, being reared on the castor-oil plant'.[18] The EIC early took an interest in sericulture, exporting to England either fabrics or raw silk in accordance with changing economic or political circumstances.

A small proportion of cottage-produced tussore is of high quality, but the worms are generally badly cared for, and indeed much of the cocoon production is wild, collected in the forests. Nevertheless, the long decline in Indian sericulture seems to have been checked. Annual production of raw silk is about 3,300,000 lb. (1,500,000 kg.), and exports and imports in 1961 were of about equal value. About one-fifth of production is from the indigenous tasar, muga and eri.

[18] *Imperial Gaz.* III (1908), 208.

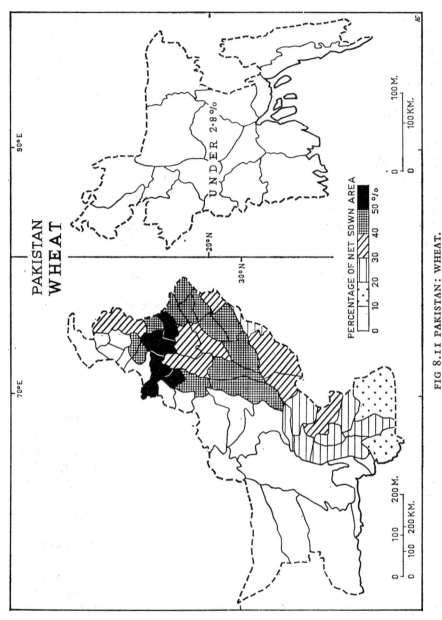

FIG 8.11 PAKISTAN: WHEAT.

D. MISCELLANEOUS PEASANT CROPS

It would be hopeless to attempt even to enumerate the enormous variety of interesting special crops, from the saffron of Kashmir to the senna of Tirunelveli. It may be noted, however, that two of the most famous of Indian products are now all but extinct: *indigo* and *opium*. In 1897 synthetic indigo became commercially practicable, and in fifteen years the area under the crop fell by 90%. It rallied in the First World War, but in 1939–40 only 40,000 ac. (17,000 ha.) were cultivated, mainly in Bihar, and it is no longer given in the returns. Opium had in 1939–40 about 7,000 ac., against over 600,000 before export to China was stopped in 1907; under 3,000 ha. against 243,000. The destruction of the industry was thus a deliberate, though not immoral, political act. Opium is consumed in India, especially in the Himalayas and the Assam Hills, but is rigorously controlled, though there is probably sporadic illicit cultivation in the hills. The social effects of opium smoking in Himalayan India, however, are hardly serious. Indian hemp (*ganja*) is far more dangerous.

Tobacco is grown in all Indian states, but mainly in Andhra, which has 40% of nearly 1,000,000 ac. (400,000 ha.); in Pakistan there has been a marked decline in the last 10 or 12 years, from 350,000 to 200,000 ac. (142,000 to 81,000 ha.), mainly in the east. Probably there is a good deal of unrecorded cultivation. Tobacco is grown to some extent all over the country, and in the north is a favourite crop on the rich silts of temporary alluvial islands; but Madras has over a third of the Indian acreage. Smoking is universal – cheroots, hookahs, English and American cigarettes (some manufactured in India with imported tobacco) or the appalling *bidis*, the cheap smoke of the masses. By and large Indian tobacco is poor stuff, and the divine if financially deplorable habit is far from playing the part in the national life that it does in Burma. The main cheroot-making centres are Dindigul and Trichinopoly in Madras, but even those brands which bear English (or Anglo-Indian) names are hardly as good as the humbler product of the petty shops of Burma, innocent of machinery or publicity.

E. PLANTATION CROPS

Plantations are almost confined to tea, coffee and rubber, with a little cinchona in the Nilgiris and Darjeeling. (Table XI.)

1. *Tea*

The wetter Himalayan slopes and their gravelly piedmont fans, and the hills of the extreme south, offer admirable conditions for tea; indeed when the EIC began planting with Chinese seed in 1834, a wild variety was found in the Assam Hills. Tea is grown in the south at elevations of over 4,000 ft. (1,200 m.) and in Darjeeling to 7,000 (2,135 m.), but generally speaking yields are smaller, though quality is better, on the higher plantations. Most of the larger plantations in Bengal and Assam are on the terai (here 'Duars') or its equivalent.

Of the total area of 865,000 ac. (350,000 ha.), which is about 40% of world area excluding China, East Pakistan has some 9%, Assam and West Bengal two-thirds, and most of the rest is in Kerala and the Nilgiris. Plantations in these areas are large, 450–550 ac. (180–220 ha.), but along the Himalayan slopes as far as East Punjab tea is grown on holdings of 4 or 5 ac. (2 ha.) or less; but their share of output is negligible.

The plantation economy is somewhat alien to the new India, but two-thirds of Indian tea is exported, and this amounts to about a fifth of the value of exports.

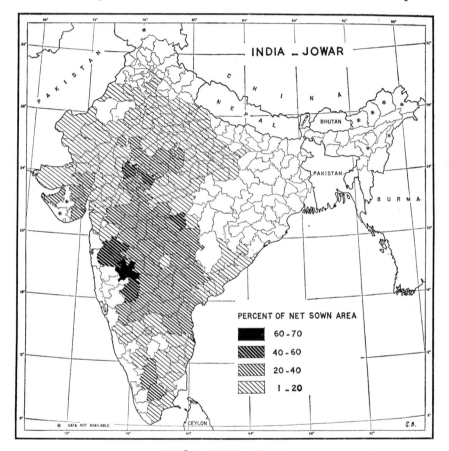

FIG 8.12 INDIA: JOWAR.

Owing to the static condition of the industry in Pakistan, and rising internal demand, Pakistani exports are not now important; with an export of 200,000–225,000 tons a year, India accounts for about half the world trade.

2. Coffee

Coffee was introduced by a 17th-century Muslim saint returning from Mecca, who gave the plant and his name to the Baba Bhudan Hills in Mysore; but real development began in the 1830s. By 1885 there were 237,500 ac. (96,000 ha.), but borers, leaf-blight and Brazil brought catastrophe, and in 1877–87 no fewer than 273 plantations were abandoned. Coffee estates are usually small, only about 50 ac. (20 ha.) and there are holdings of under 10 ac. which do not appear in the statistics. The area has increased since 1947 and is now about 250,000 ac. (100,000 ha.); about a third of the output of some 95,000,000 lb. (43,000,000 kg.)

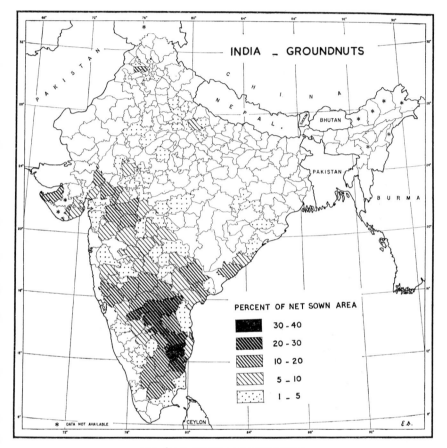

FIG 8.13 INDIA: GROUNDNUTS.

is exported. Coffee gardens are very narrowly concentrated in southern Mysore and adjacent uplands of Kerala and Madras; coffee is much drunk in the south.

3. Rubber

Only in Kerala, with high but equable temperatures and a dry season of only three or four months (and those not rainless) are conditions reasonably suitable for rubber, and even there they are not ideal. Yields are low, less than half those of Malaya, and this may be due as much to poor management as to environmental disadvantages; but there has been a remarkable increase in area, over 120% in the decade 1951–61. There are now about 264,000 ac. (107,000 ha.) with an output of about 24,000 tons. This expansion is probably due to the rising internal demand fostered by industrialization. Rubber is also grown, as yet experimentally, in the Chittagong area of East Pakistan.

III. ANIMAL HUSBANDRY

The cattle problem

The sub-continent, or even India alone, has to support the largest bovine population of the world: the 175,000,000 oxen and 50,000,000 buffaloes of India are nearly a quarter of the world's horned livestock. Altogether the sub-continent has at least 270,000,000 head of cattle. These numbers are undoubtedly excessive, perhaps by at least a third. *The First Five Year Plan* (1951, pp. 109–10) pointed out that there was probably roughage for only 78% of the (then smaller) cattle population, and of course a far smaller proportion of concentrates, and that only about 750 good stud bulls were bred annually, against a total need of about 1,000,000.

The agriculture of India differs fundamentally from that of Japan and most of China in that it is firmly based on the use of draught animals. Sacred as the cow is, the bullock is of more mundane importance; there are about five bullocks to every four cows, and they do most ploughing and almost all carting. 'The essential equipment of the peasant farmer includes a pair of bullocks or buffaloes to do the ploughing and draw the cart; a cow to propagate the species and quite secondarily to give milk.'[19]

Paradoxically enough, no branch of Indian agriculture is worse managed than animal husbandry. Except for the fundamental taboo against taking the life of the cow, this is not so much the peasant's original sin as the result of strictly geographical conditions. To take one example, Indian 'hay' is really dried grass which has lost its seeds and so is little better than straw, rather than hay in the European sense: it is too wet for hay-making when the grass (such as exists) is up towards the end of the rains, and after that the peasant is too busy with kharif harvest or rabi sowing. Where rainfall is too light to inhibit hay-making there is precious little to make hay with, and in any case – probably as a natural consequence of these conditions – the ryot 'has been a grass-cutter, but a hay-maker never, and he finds it hard to begin'.[20]

By and large the cattle, being essentially working rather than food animals, are where the men are, and in these areas pressure of population is so intense that often the village-site itself can hardly be squeezed into the sea of arable, and so

[19] L. D. Stamp, *Asia* (ed. 1944), 230.
[20] RCAI, 205–6; the whole of Chapter 7 remains of great interest.

obviously there is no meadow, no permanent pasture, no fodder crops: only the waste, which in the worst parts of the Ganga plains is reduced to mere wayside scraps. Elsewhere such fodder as there is – mainly paddy, wheat and millet stalks – goes mainly to the working cattle, the bullocks; the cow must fend for herself.

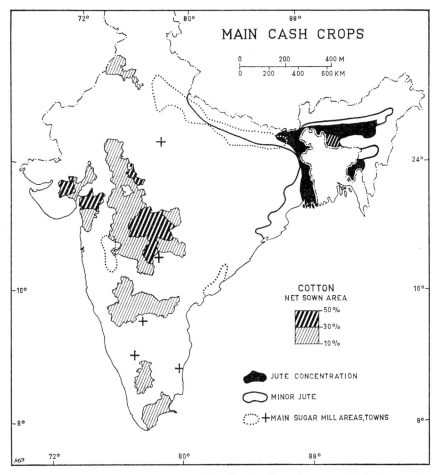

FIG 8.14 INDIA: MAIN CASH CROPS. The distribution of sugar mills indicates the main areas growing cane as a cash crop.

By April and May, the height of the hot weather, there is likely to be very little stalk left, the stubble has been grazed off, in many areas there is very little leafage on the trees, and finally the scanty vegetation of the waste, at best coarse, tussocky and of little food value – or guarded by a fierce array of thorns – has been reduced in effect to a mass of dry cellulose. The general appearance of the cattle in most parts of India is then simply horrible – skeletons wrapped in hide, tottering to whatever patches of shade may be.

Some areas, it is true, look at first sight as if they could support more cattle, farmed on pastoral lines: such are the less arid parts of Rajasthan, in Malwa. But soils are thin, rainfall irregular, grass poor except after flushes of rain; any considerable stocking would probably result in heavy erosion. Moreover pastoralism as such is at a discount; the long distances to wretchedly poor urban markets render dairying uneconomic, and there is obviously no sale for beef.

Such a state of affairs would be bad enough even were the stock healthy. But the country is unenclosed, there is still a great lack of eugenic practices, and too often feeble bulls beget at will upon diseased cows. Veterinary services, despite recent expansion, are terribly inadequate, and epidemic disease such as rinderpest still takes a heavy toll.

The over-population, however, is not solely the result of an irrational apotheosis of the cow. Paradoxically there is often an actual deficiency in the cattle-power needed to work the land; the numbers are there, but the bullocks are simply not strong enough for their work. Hence more are bred, which implies more cows and young stock – strictly speaking useless mouths – and the circle of starvation is complete. Yet, while one sizable and healthy animal will consume about half the food needed by two weaklings and may yet produce more dung, 'when it comes to the threshing of corn and the puddling of rice fields, eight feet are decidedly better than four. . . . [Again,] the chance of losing half of one's capital against an equal chance of losing it all, is one that would be preferred by any sound business man. The chance of one bullock falling down a well, or getting its leg broken, or being eaten by a tiger, is just half the chance of the same thing happening to two.'[21]

Since Independence, and against the views (however guardedly expressed) of central planning bodies, some States have enacted bans on cow slaughter. *The First Five Year Plan*, recognizing that wholesale slaughter was just not practicable, suggested (p. 111) that in areas 'where the fodder supply to-day is unutilised' (but where are they?), *gosadans* or camps of refuge for aged and infirm cattle might be set up, where they could end their days in peace and yet contribute something through arrangements for the collection of manure and the hides and bones of the carcasses. Some *gosadans* were created, but the experiment has not been very successful. Even without cattle slaughter, however, something can be done. The difficulty of diverting land from foodgrains to fodder is obvious, even though there would be an increase in milk supply; the Ford Foundation Agricultural Team, which estimated the annual loss from keeping useless cattle at Rs 70 crores, recommended a graduated tax on such animals and the control of open grazing. Steps have been taken to improve the breeding of bulls and to extend castration, sterilization, segregation and even artificial insemination. Progress has been made on these lines, but not nearly enough.

[21] G. Williamson, in U. N. Chatterjee (ed.), *Developing Village India* (Orient Longmans Bombay, 1951), 173–4.

However counter to average Indian opinion, the conclusion seems inescapable: the essential improvement of cattle cannot be attained without limitation and even actual reduction of numbers; but sentiment and policy act in a contrary direction. Even to a non-Hindu there may be something of a moral problem here; man has after all called into existence these millions of sentient beings for his convenience, to be liquidated when inconvenient. But on a different level we have the old dilemma of not being able to afford short-term what it is necessary to afford long-term: there are too many cattle in the gross, but most individual farmers may have too few to carry on with.

Better breeds

As so often, these malpractices are virtually forced upon the husbandman, either by the weight of immemorial social pressures, or by sheer necessitous poverty; and they are not universal. Indian cattle in normal conditions are well adapted to their trying environment in that they have amazing powers of endurance and recuperation, and the use of the zebu or humped ox for crossing as far afield as South America attests its inherent suitability to the leaner tropical grasslands.

When he is able to do so the ryot takes good care of his stock, and in some favoured localities really good strains have been evolved. These are mainly draught animals, such as the Kankrej of Gujarat, the Kangayam of Coimbatore, and the famous Amrit Mahal breed fostered by Haidar Ali of Mysore for military mobility. But they include milkers such as the Gir and Sindhi, and dual-purpose breeds such as the Hansi or Hariana of East Punjab. A few scattered groups are indeed pastoralists rather than cultivators: the few hundred primitive Todas of the Nilgiris, the Alambadi breeders of the Mysore forests. In the extra-Peninsular mountains, of course, a different type of pastoralism, based on sheep and goats, is common.

Dairying

Despite the enormous numbers of cows milk plays a pitifully small part in Indian diets; in Saurashtra daily consumption per head is about 19 oz., in the Punjab it is only 10, nowhere else consumes more than half as much, and in Madhya Pradesh the amount is under 1 oz.! The Indian average is 5·5 oz. (0·16 kg.), against 40 (pre-war) in Britain. The urban milk supply is almost everywhere entirely deplorable in quantity and much worse in quality, even when (if ever) not deliberately adulterated. Much of it is produced in foul conditions within city limits, the herds being driven out each morning to the ragged fetid waste found around all large towns. Climatic conditions are at least partly responsible for the low direct milk consumption, since it is obviously impossible to keep milk for long; over 40% of it is in fact converted into *ghi*, butter clarified over a slow fire, for which cowdung is the best fuel. Hence buffaloes are often preferred to cows as milch cattle, since their milk contains up to 50% more butterfat than that of the cow; buffaloes supply about 45% of total milk output. As might be expected, milk yields are almost incredibly low, except on a very few military or capitalist dairy-farms; in India they average 413 lb. (187 kg.) a year for cows and 1,100 (499 kg.) for buffaloes; with 61,000,000 milch cattle, nearly twice as many as all Europe outside the USSR, Indian milk output is only about one-fifth the European total.[22]

[22] *India Record* (London), II/39 (22/11/1950); improvement since 1951 is not likely to have affected relative and per capita figures significantly.

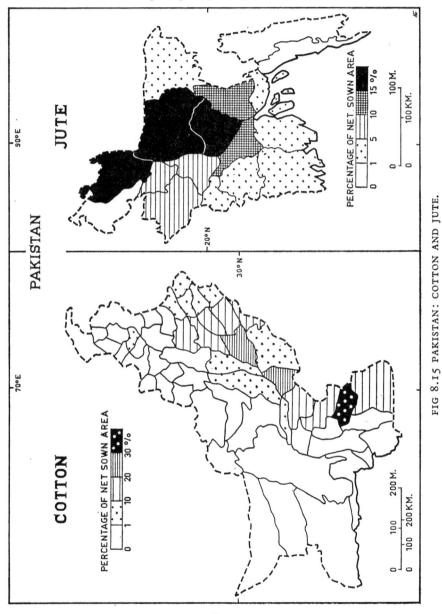

FIG 8.15 PAKISTAN: COTTON AND JUTE.

Hides and skins

Even though shielded from sacrilegious hands, the cow sooner or later dies and must be disposed of. This task is left to Muslims and the untouchable caste of Chamars or leather-workers. Something over 20,000,000 cow and 5,000,000 buffalo hides are produced annually, to which must be added 25,000,000 goat and sheep skins. Before 1939 some 40% of the hides and 50% of the skins were exported, about half the former as semi-tanned 'kips'. In the 11 years 1929–40 an annual average of 70,000 tons of hides, skins and more or less tanned leather was exported; 'for some time past India has been not only the most important exporting country for hides and leather but has constituted the only reservoir for the drawing of the large supplies of light hides by the world markets';[23] in 1960 the value of hides and skins exported was over Rs 10 crores.

Exports of bones were also very large, though their retention for processing (for bone-meal and so on) is increasing.

Other livestock

These need not detain us long. In addition to the 50,000,000 or so *sheep* there are over 61,000,000 *goats* in India and in Pakistan. Again Madras leads, followed closely by Uttar Pradesh, Bengal and the Punjab. Goat 'mutton' is probably the most widely consumed flesh food.

Horses are scarcely used for agricultural traction or indeed for any cartage, but they draw the light traps (*tongas* or *ekkas*), the taxis of the lower middle class, largely replaced in the south by the bullock-drawn *jutka*. *Donkeys*, in the mountains *mules*, and in the higher Himalayas even sheep, are used as pack animals; pack bullocks are also seen. *Camels* are still important in West Pakistan and Rajasthan, but hardly known elsewhere; in Karachi they do a good deal of the port cartage, hauling large rubber-tyred floats. *Poultry*, small and tough, are ubiquitous, but the *pig*, so conspicuous in China, is conspicuous only by his absence in most parts of India. Universally common to both countries are the village scavengers, lean mongrels of repulsive aspect: the traveller's entry into the village is invariably signalized by a clamorous reception committee of pariah dogs, and one thinks, not unreasonably, of rabies.

IV. OTHER RURAL OCCUPATIONS

It remains to glance briefly at other ways of life in the countryside. First in numbers and importance are the village artisans who, despite factory competition, in many lines still provide very essential services. Apart from these the most important rural occupations are those connected with the forests, sericulture (already discussed), and fishing.

[23] Sharma, *op. cit.* 168.

Forests and forest products

Forestry proper is almost entirely a government monopoly, either by direct exploitation or by licences. The most important timbers are noted in Chapter 3. Indian outturn is about 110,000,000 cu. ft. (3,125,000 m³), two-thirds of it from Madhya Pradesh, Maharashtra, Mysore, Kashmir and Uttar Pradesh; the accessible and exploited forests of Pakistan are mainly in the east, apart from small plantation areas in the Punjab. The recorded outturn of firewood is thrice that of timber. Pulp wood output is increasing, though bamboo and *sabai* grass are as yet the main bases of the paper industry. More important in the day-to-day life of those villagers who live within reach of woodland is the enormous range of 'minor forest products'. Many of these can be directly used or collected on payment of small fees; sometimes they are free by immemorial custom. Such items include foliage for use as fodder or leaf-manure; materials for thatching, mat-making and basketry; grass-cutting and grazing rights; fuel-wood; bamboos for individual use. The right to collect commercial products has naturally to be paid for, except in unreserved jungle: these include a multitude of dye- and tan-stuffs, drugs and nuts.

Among the more important, in which there is already some export, are acacia gum, artemisia (source of the vermicide santonin), beeswax, canes, cardamoms, cashew nuts, chaulmugra oil, cinnamon, cutch, Indian kapok, lac, lemon-grass oil, myrobalans, nux vomica, resins, sandalwood, senna and tamarinds.[24] Sugar and alcohol are obtained from the toddy and nipa palms and from the edible flowers of *mahua* (*Bassia latifolia*); this tree is so common and so luxuriously florescent in the northeast Peninsula that it has been suggested as a source of power alcohol.

Lac is no longer the most important of these products, but remains one of the most interesting. It is a gummy excretion from the body of the lac-insect, which infests several species of trees, notably dhak (*Butea frondosa*). The lac forms a crust on the twigs, which are collected and sold as 'stick-lac', and after processing shellac is produced. Shellac is an essential ingredient of some varnishes, of sealing-wax and similar compositions, and has also a wide range of uses in indigenous arts and crafts. Lac collecting is particularly important in Chota Nagpur and adjacent areas, where it provides a useful subsidiary income to a large number of villagers. Competition from plastics has caused decline.

Fishing

Even though the numbers of India's people are so great that it would seem that a large proportion of them would in any event be condemned to a poor life, the neglect of fisheries seems another striking example of what seems almost a masochistic tendency to make the worst of a bad world. Religious factors play a part:

[24] S. Krishna and R. L. Badhwar, 'Exploitation of Minor Forest Products' (5th British Empire Forestry Conference, Dehra Dun, 1947), 2.

the caste status of fishermen, who automatically take animal life, is very low. Climate also is obviously unfavourable to marketing any but dried fish far away from coast or river-bank.

The total production in India is not much over a million tons a year, a quarter of it fresh-water fish; this is under 6 lb. (2·7 kg.) per head of population. Obviously fish-foods can never attain the importance they have in truly maritime countries, but there is ample scope for expansion in both sea and inland fishing. The continental shelf in Indian waters is about 115,000 sq. miles (298,000 km^2), and the coast is dotted with fishing villages; but sea-fishing is rarely carried on beyond 5 or 6 miles offshore. In both India and Pakistan, however, steps are being taken to increase the number of powered boats and to expand and improve the generally very inadequate shore installations. Real deep-sea fishing is as yet in its infancy. Of the inland fisheries the most important and best-used are those of Bengal; many of the deltaic and estuarine fish are excellent, especially the *hilsa*.

Government assistance and co-operative marketing could probably lead to a great increase in the output of the inland fisheries by 'fish-farming', and this without undue difficulty; it is surprising that more has not been done in 'fish-farming' with such species as *Tilapia*; here East Pakistan has admirable opportunities, which are beginning to be taken up. The improvement of sea-fishing is a harder problem, though in some cases technological innovation has been acceptable, e.g. in the use of nylon nets. The Indian government is devoting considerable attention to fishery research and development, aiming at a four-fold increase in the catch under the Third Plan; but given the poverty of the fishing communities the lines of advance open would seem to be (*a*) large-scale capitalist fishing or (*b*) state working thinly disguised as co-operation. The former is socially undesirable and in any case unlikely as returns are at present problematical, and there is no real interest in it; the latter would probably be 'improvement from above', and unduly costly in relation to the nutritional gain. There might, however, be possibilities in canning, using wastes as fertilizer, and extracting shark-liver oil.

Apart from the delta fisheries of East Bengal, the situation in Pakistan is much the same as in India, but distinct progress is being made in both sea and inland fishing, the latter in West as well as in East Pakistan.

V. AGRARIAN PROBLEMS AND PROGRAMMES

Much more than in any Western country, the wealth of the sub-continent lies in its fields – fields often fragmented into mere rags of land, torn by erosion, tilled for so long without rest or fertilization that over large areas they seem to have reached the ultimate base-level of infertility; and yet ultimately responsible for the sustenance of some 550,000,000 souls. Advances in agricultural technique, while not entirely lacking, affect but a small fraction of the farming, and with increasing pressure on the land either sheer need or the reduction of cash crops has led, in some areas, to a lowering of standards in such matters as rotations. Until recently, the owner-cultivator was increasingly forced into tenancy, the small tenant to become a landless man. The pressure of the cattle population is as bad or worse, with results ultimately disastrous to man and beast. There can be no possible doubt, then, that the rehabilitation of agriculture is by far the most pressing problem facing both India and Pakistan; more important even than industrialization which has a vital part to play in that rehabilitation, yet cannot be truly successful without the markets of a thriving countryside. This at once suggests what is indeed the fact, that every step forward seems enmeshed, as in 'concertina wire', by a tangle of interlocking vicious circles.

This interlocking of the problems renders the writing of a coherent account extremely difficult. But we can, perhaps, get a reasonably articulated picture by separating out (i) problems of technique, (ii) problems of social organization and (iii) the general problem, resuming all others, of the ratio between food output and mouths to feed. Finally, in succeeding chapters, we may survey recent developments and plans. But it must always be remembered that this breakdown is arbitrary, all specific problems having both technical and social aspects, as is obviously true, for example, of fragmentation and the cattle position.

A. PROBLEMS OF TECHNIQUE

1. *Sub-division and fragmentation*

The average Indian farm is very small, probably uneconomic if we admit any element of welfare into economics. The position is complicated by the distinction (not always made) between ownership and cultivation holdings: the man who farms his own land, neither more nor less, is probably rare in the more settled regions. The following significant figures based on about 10,000 households are given by the National Sample Survey (Eighth Round, 1954-55):

*Acres occupied**	*% of households*	*% of cropped area occupied*
none	6·3	—
under 2·5	48·5	5·9
2·50–4·99	15·9	10·9
5·00–7·49	9·3	10·5
7·50–9·99	5·6	9·1
10·00–14·99	5·5	12·6
15·00–24·99	4·9	17·7
25 and over	4·0	33·3

[*5 ac.=2·02 ha.]

It will be seen that while 4% of rural families occupied a third of the cropped area, over 6% were entirely landless. On the other side it is possible to support a family on a very small area indeed of good rice land, and many of the tiniest cultivating holdings are worked by people whose main livelihood comes from some non-farming employment; are in fact allotments, not farms, tokens of attachment to the land rather than the main business of life.

Since overheads do not, of course, decrease proportionately as the size of holding goes down, the peasant with such an exiguous basis for his support is practically forced to overwork his land by neglecting fallows and by excessive double-cropping. Without venturing on the vexed and highly technical question of what an 'economic holding' might be, we may think it clear enough that the opening statement of this section errs if anything by moderation.

All this is the result of *sub-division* of property among all the sons, a practice sanctioned by both Hindu and Muslim laws of inheritance, but less invoked when the 'joint family' system was in full strength, or in old days when, in Jathar and Beri's phrase, 'it was land that ran after tenants'. Growing population and the substitution of the cash nexus for customary status have led to an insistence on individual rights which may reach fantastic extremes, and accentuates the allied, but distinct, *fragmentation* of one man's ground into scattered tiny parcels. In places this reached almost incredible proportions; to cite again some often-cited figures, in one Punjab village 12,800 ac. (5,184 ha.) were divided into 63,000 'fields'; in another 28% of holdings had each over 30 separate fields.[25] Even if physical division is impossible, partition between heirs has been insisted upon down to a half-share in a tree. To some extent this is understandable; he who has little must cling to what he has. But it is none the less deplorable, resulting, together with the multiplication of debt and tenancy suits, in a staggering burden of litigation. In 1939 nearly half the nearly 1,900,000 civil suits were directly concerned with the land, and over 1,000,000 were for Rs. 50 (£3. 15s.) or less. Unfortunately lawyers – and too often witnesses – must be paid, whence more debt. Recent land reforms may offer even more scope for litigation.

Fragmentation does not, of course, arise solely as an incident of sub-division. It is deeply rooted in the old communal principle of fair shares, and has sometimes still some economic justification, as for example to secure to each holding a balance of kharif flood-plain and rabi upland, to enable the farmer to plant two or more crops on different soils and so to insure against the weather, or to enable a better spread of working days than would be possible on a compact holding limited by soil and water factors to one or two crops in any one year. Nevertheless the general effects are often evil: waste of time in journeying to and from the fields, and of space in the boundaries; the prohibitive expense of fencing the small parcels, so that the cultivator is bound to follow the régime of his fellows or else see his standing crop destroyed by cattle grazing on the stubble; difficulties of

[25] See e.g. M. B. Nanavati and J. J. Anjaria, *The Indian Rural Problem* (Bombay, 3rd ed., 1947), 46–47; RCAI, 134.

water-supply. All these again give ample cause for dispute and litigation. Never-theless, as B. H. Farmer argues, to look only to inheritance laws and so on is to mistake the occasion of sub-division for its cause and to tackle the symptom, not the disease: 'The disease is an economic system . . . and the answer lies, if it lies anywhere, in economic development.'[26]

Consolidation of holdings is the obvious answer; a little too obvious. Clearly it applies to fragmentation rather than to sub-division; it is one thing to exchange enclaves, another to surrender land, and, in the absence of alternative employ-ment, compulsory formation of economic holdings could result only in an increase in the numbers of the most wretched rural class.[27] These are the landless labourers, condemned to work part of the year for minute wages and for the rest to exist in unemployment, from which the only 'escape' may be the acceptance of an extra-legal and unavowed, but in effect real, state of serfdom, in return for a pittance from better-off peasants. In some States a fair beginning has been made in the task of consolidation through co-operative societies; in East Punjab, where conditions are perhaps unusually favourable, rapid progress has been made in the last few years; from the air much of the area between Delhi and the Sutlej appears gridded into large squares, with the old irregular bound-aries showing up beneath the new. Altogether perhaps some 40,000,000 ac. (16,200,000 ha.) have been consolidated in India, and in West Pakistan about 7,000,000 ac. (2,800,000 ha.).

2. The fertilizer problem

Even if we follow the authority of Sir John Russell and add 25% to Indian yields, they remain pitifully low: rice 900–1,000 lb. per ac. (1,009–1,121 kg. per ha.; Japan 2,250 lb. per ac., 2,802 kg. per ha.); wheat 750–800 (760–785, about 40% of British yields, or equivalent to the yields of *extensive* farming in Aus-tralia); cotton 89 (102), against 300 (336 in USA). Moreover, if the figures mean anything at all, they show a marked fall in productivity in this century: the average rice yield was 982 lb. per ac. in 1909–13, about 840 in 1926–38; in kg. per ha., 1,101 against 942. It must be remembered that these are pre-Partition figures, and Pakistan took over some of the most productive areas. Recently, and on really comparable figures, there has been some recovery, but not nearly enough. For India, the average rice yield in the five years ending 1956–57 was only 740 lb. per ac. (830 kg. per ha.); in the next five years it was 838 lb. per ac. (940 kg. per ha.); for wheat the figures are respectively 642 (720) and 714 (800).[28]

[26] See his very important paper, based on Ceylon experience, 'On not controlling sub-division in paddy lands', *Trans. Inst. of British Geographers*, 28 (1960), 225–35, and also S. M. Ali, 'Field patterns on the Indo-Gangetic Divide', *Panjab Geographical Review*, 1 (1942), 26–35, for cases in which consolidation is either unfeasible or undesirable.

[27] Thus *The First Five Year Plan* admits (p. 102) that a main objection to rationalization is that it would throw large numbers out of work, and that 'hasten slowly' must perforce be the motto.

[28] *Statistical Abstract of the Indian Union*, 1962, Table 20; *Pakistan Economic Survey 1963–64*, Table 12.

Pakistani rice yields are much the same as India's, wheat rather greater, cotton twice as much (for mainly irrigated as against mainly rainfed cotton).

The main cause is simply failure to fertilize the fields; but again this is not mere stupidity or even ignorance. It is clear enough that the peasant with a tiny holding can hardly afford to grow a nitrogenous crop for the luxury of ploughing it in: the gain in output next year will not keep him alive in this. As a general rule he is far too poor to be able to buy artificials. Stubble may be burnt, but often it is needed for grazing. Where there is access to woodland, leaves and branches are burnt on the fields or leaf-mould collected; mud from tanks may be used; oilcake is sometimes applied. But in areas of greatest population and greatest need such resources, if available at all, are hopelessly insufficient. For social reasons it is unlikely that India will ever emulate Chinese thoroughness in the use of human waste-products, though around some large towns night-soil, poudrette and sewage have been exploited, and the universal use for natural purposes of the fields abutting upon the village-site has actually led to their up-grading in revenue assessments.

There seems little point in such picturesque impressionism as F. L. Brayne's remark that 'if we could rescue the cow-dung from the housewife' (whose duty it is to make it into flat fuel-cakes), then something like a third of India's agrarian poverty would be wiped out at a stroke.[29] As a matter of fact more cow-dung is actually used as manure than is generally realized; some 20% is simply lost, 40% burnt, and perhaps 40% spread on the fields;[30] the use of compost is spreading, if slowly. One factor in the burning of cow-dung is the preference for a slow-burning fuel for making *ghi*; but, quite apart from this, over much of the Indo-Gangetic Plains there is hardly any alternative fuel. Such 'forest' as exists is needed for grazing and produces very little wood, and it may be added that the lack of decent fodder in itself lessens the organic values of the cattle-manure. Sir Herbert Howard, in *A Post-War Forest Policy for India* (1944), pleaded for the planting of thousands of small fuel and fodder forests to meet this situation; but without a numerous police these might not survive human and animal assault during infancy, though perhaps with intensive propaganda co-operatives or *panchayats* (village councils) could give some protection. It is precisely where additional grazing and alternative fuel are most needed – in the Gangetic plain – that there is least room to provide them; indeed there is hardly room enough to expand the village-sites except at the expense of arable. And that expense can ill be afforded. It may be that there is promise in the use of cow-dung to produce combustible gas – the sludge would retain considerable manurial value; there are obvious problems in the organization and capital required, but in principle this is a fairly simple and even elegant operation.[31]

[29] Should we not rather wish to rescue the housewife from the cow-dung?

[30] *A Food Plan for India* (RIIA and OUP, 1945), 47n., 19, but cf. conflicting figures on p. 9.

[31] See S. V. Desai in *Developing Village India*, 140–3, and below, 291.

The conclusion seems inescapable that artificials must be supplied, and lavishly, even at financial loss to government; a loss which might in time be recouped financially by increased taxable capacity, but which would certainly be worth while in terms of welfare.

There has indeed been a great expansion in fertilizer output and use, but a disproportionate share has gone to plantations and special cash crops. A very much larger effort is needed, as is very obvious when the sale of 86,000 tons of fertilizer in nine months for the 26,000,000 (10,500,000 ha.) cultivated acres of East Pakistan can be officially described as 'a major break-through'. West Pakistan uses rather over 250,000 tons of artificials a year; India's use of ammonium sulphate amounted, in terms of nitrogen, to 230,000 tons in 1961, about half of which was home-produced, while superphosphate used was the equivalent of 70,000 tons of P_2O_5. The Third Plan would increase these four-fold and six-fold respectively; but these seem almost trifling beside the consumption of say Japan and Egypt on much smaller areas, and indeed are well below official estimates of needs.[32]

3. *Tools and seeds; roads and markets*
The manifold inefficiencies of Indian agriculture are probably less the responsibility of the peasant than of nature and of society: of precarious seasons and poor soils, of the immemorial load of exploitation. Doubtless the Indian farmer is on the whole conservative, and on the whole he has had need to be so: for ages past his farming practices have been so closely adjusted to their environment that there could be little need or possibility of change – until the whole fabric of his myriad little closed societies was shaken by the impact of the tightly-administered British Raj and of the world market. 'That in many places the system of agriculture followed has attained a very high standard is a matter of common knowledge; the cultivation of rice in the deltas, for example, has reached a marked degree of perfection, and the wisdom of many agricultural proverbs stands unchallenged by research.'[33] Now that change is imperative sheer poverty too often inhibits it, and perhaps more often than mere conservatism; but it must be admitted that, especially in the harder or more precarious areas, apathy and fatalism have struck deep and sapped away the vitality of the people precisely where change is most needed.

It is essential to see that innovation is really improvement; condemnation of 'the plough that merely scratches the soil', for instance, is too facile. The RCAI cites two widely held opinions to account for the cultivator's tenacious adherence to his ancient models: (i) a light plough is all that his bullocks can draw, and (ii) he prefers a plough which he can carry on his shoulders to and from his often scattered fields. These reasons are valid and important; but the RCAI itself held

[32] S. Thirumalai, *Post-War Agricultural Problems and Policies in India* (Indian Soc. of Agric. Economics, Bombay, and Inst. of Pacific Relations, NY, 1954), 170–1.
[33] RCAI, 14. A careful correlation of rural saws with the environmental conditions they reflect would be both fascinating and instructive.

that the main factor is a realization of the importance of conserving moisture. Whether this is consciously felt may perhaps be doubted, but the RCAI's conclusion is noteworthy: while deep ploughing is essential for some crops and soils, 'it has certainly not been established that it would pay the cultivator in all kharif conditions. Indeed, the contrary is more probable', as it might well lead to loss of moisture in areas of light rainfall, to the reverse in humid areas, in either case jeopardizing germination.[34]

Nevertheless many implements could be much improved, and some new ones are desirable: seed-drills, cheap threshing and winnowing appliances, better water-lifts, more efficient cane-crushers and oil-expellers. Mechanization in the normal sense is difficult, indeed probably impracticable while the farm unit, even if compact, is so small. The use of tractors is indeed increasing; in 1961 there were 34,000 used for agricultural purposes in India. These have been most successful on government clearing schemes, or preparing the ground for tillage in new irrigation areas such as the Thal; they are obviously beyond the means of most individual farmers, but can perhaps be made available by co-operatives. Except for actual tillage, indeed, there is not likely to be much need for mechanization, since harvesting machinery does not itself increase production; it may save a crop threatened by weather, but this is too slight a risk to be insured against at so heavy a premium. Tractors might also be used for transporting pumps, small presses, and so on. But if tractors are wanted for a part only of their possibilities, the question arises whether it is economic to use them.

Mechanization, after all, is labour-saving, and in the sub-continent it is not so much a saving of man-hours that is needed as an improved labour efficiency; by no means the same thing. And there is the problem of servicing: 'of the villages in which manufacturers would normally establish the chain of dealers and sub-dealers . . . not one in a hundred (and according to some estimates, not one in a thousand) has anyone capable of undertaking the responsibilities involved.'[35] Coming as it does in a generally optimistic survey, this admission has great weight.

On the other hand, a persuasive argument in favour of a large-scale shift from bullock to tractor farming has been put forward by K. W. Kapp; he discounts the effect on employment and points to the gains, financial and nutritional, from a change to milk cattle, as well as more general economic advantages. Here again reliance is placed on co-operative organization. It may well be questioned, however, whether all of Kapp's assumptions (e.g. on depreciation) are realistic.[36]

[34] RCAI, 110–12; a discussion of great importance. Those who condemn the light plough are not often in the habit of carrying agricultural machinery on their shoulders.

[35] *Report of the UK Industrial Mission to Pakistan* (1950), 31–40 (refce at p. 35). It should be noted that the Mission included no representative of agriculture; and the words 'soil erosion' do not occur in this most interesting discussion. Cf. G. Slater, *Southern India* (1936), 57–58, on 'labour-saving'. But for an opposite view, see W. Klatt, 'Agricultural planning in East Pakistan', *Pacific Affairs*, 25 (1952), 263–7.

[36] See his *Hindu Culture, Economic Development and Economic Planning in India* (Asia, Bombay, 1963), 144–62.

The application of cheap electric power to pumping (whether for irrigation or drainage), oil-pressing, and so on has great possibilities and has made a promising start. Great economies could be effected by improving bullock-carts; in some areas wheels are still all but solid and the weight of the cart ridiculously large compared with its capacity. The increasing use of rubber tyres is a notable advance.

Much research has gone into the production of improved crops; the most notable achievements are probably in sugar-cane and the introduction of Cambodia cotton and the development of strains from it. But there is substance in the frequent criticism that activities have been too much devoted to cash crops. However, since 1947 much more attention has been given, by both India and Pakistan, to improved seed for foodgrains, including jowar and maize. Many seed multiplication farms have been set up, but it is difficult to assess the actual results: as the Ford Team pointed out, it was 'unable to get what we felt was clear verifiable data on the extent to which improved seeds are actually used . . . in rice and wheat, a very high percentage is alleged to be planted to improved seeds. Yet only limited progress in some States has been made in increasing rice and wheat yields'.[37] It seems likely that there is a good deal of carelessness in distribution, and adulteration is probably widespread. It is difficult to reconcile the statement by the Grow More Food Enquiry Committee (1952) that 100% of rice land in East Punjab was under improved varieties, against 0·9% in West Bengal, with the higher yields of the latter State. Possibly double-cropping may account for this particular case, but there seems no relation at all between the ranking of States by 'improvement' and by yield, even where environmental conditions are not dissimilar.

A more vigorous attack on plant diseases, insects, fungi, wild pigs, rats and monkeys is urgently needed. Crops such as sugar-cane, grown more or less homogeneously, are of course especially liable to diseases and pests. Both India and Pakistan are devoting a good deal of effort to meeting the vital need for adequate storage godowns.

Rural communications are nearly everywhere inadequate: this is a major factor in the slight development of dairying and of fruit and vegetable crops, a large increase in which is exceedingly desirable to offset the excess of carbohydrates in Indian diets. Bad roads or rather tracks also impose a severe strain on bullocks, especially where kharif marketing coincides with rabi tillage. It is not surprising that the construction of feeder roads is often a main preoccupation of Community Development Projects, though if all the villagers contribute their labour, the lion's share of the returns is likely to accrue to the better-off farmer with a surplus.

Market facilities in India are in general poor. In some areas and for some crops (e.g. cotton in Maharashtra) there is a good network of officially inspected mar-

[37] *Report on India's Food Crisis and the Steps to Meet It* (Ministry of Food and Agriculture, ND, 1959), 194–5.

kets, though even so malpractices are not unknown. Elsewhere the peasant is often at the mercy of unscrupulous traders, and there are too many brokers and middlemen. As the farmer has usually very slight storage facilities and so no holding power, and is often without access to reliable market information, efforts to by-pass the broker can easily be broken by rings and boycotts, though here and there co-operatives have scored notable successes. But as a rule the peasant is exploited by secret bidding between the buying and the selling brokers, arbitrary deductions for alleged deficiencies, false weights, unwarranted commissions, and so on. Local governments are increasingly publicizing current prices, in part over village radios, in part by posters at markets; the importance of 'literacy drives' is obvious in this connection. Very much more remains to be done; there were only 978 regulated markets in India in 1962 – an increase of 248 over 1961.

B. PROBLEMS OF SOCIAL ORGANIZATION

1. Land reform in India

Land tenures and kinship systems are perhaps the most complex of all social phenomena; and when caste intricacies are interwoven with the vast variety of tenurial relationships produced by the diverse regional and local societies, histories and geographies of the sub-continent, it is obvious that any general account – even were half a volume rather than part of a chapter devoted to it – must be drastically simplified; yet some sketch is absolutely essential to any understanding of the agrarian *misère* of the countryside. Moreover, since Independence immemorial relationships have been, in theory at least, completely subverted by law – and not by a single body of central legislation, but by the many separate enactments of fifteen Indian States, not to mention Pakistan.

An officially optimistic article by a member of the Indian Planning Commission's Advisory Committee on Land Reform begins by remarking that 'It would be no exaggeration to say that never before in the world history of land tenure reform has so much legislative action, with such wide social and economic ramifications, been undertaken'; and this is certainly true if we exclude such totalitarian changes as those in Russia and China. The article ends, 'Hereafter, the major task . . . is to devise machinery for the effective implementation of the comprehensive legislation';[38] and that is even more certainly true, for the gap between enactment and enforcement is at the heart of the agrarian crisis. With all the vast literature, it is extremely difficult to evaluate what changes have actually taken place in the countryside, as distinct from changes in the law, and what their social and economic effects have been.

There was a distinction in British India between *ryotwari* areas, where the peasant held directly from the State, and *zamindari*, where the land was held by owners who were often absentees or, probably more often, resident but still exploiting gentry. Especially in areas under the Bengal 'Permanent Settlement' of 1793, which was designed to set up a class of 'improving landlords' on the

[38] M. L. Dantwala, in *Indian and Foreign Review* (ND), I/21 (15/8/64), 14–16.

contemporary English model, there developed a fantastic number of inter- mediaries between the rack-rented peasant and the final landlord who paid a fixed revenue assessment; and in many princely states, notably those of central India and Hyderabad, local notables held large grants or *jagirs*. Even in *ryotwari* areas there were often numerous petty tenancies; under the British Raj, land had become a market commodity for investment, and overwhelmingly investment of rentier rather than entrepreneurial type. With growth of population and ever- increasing land-hunger, the better-off, usually of higher caste, were able to build up estates. The variety of titles, tenures, rents and services was bewildering.

It is unfortunately not easy to have much confidence in the official figures on tenure. The 1954 Census of Landholding, so far as carried out, in effect eliminated joint-family holdings by simply instructing its officers to show separately the nominal share of each person; 'land under personal cultivation' included land not leased out for a year or more – and very much of this would be cultivated not personally by the owner but under oral arrangements, seasonal crop-sharing, and so on; while an area 'owned by A but worked under occupancy right by B will be shown as B's land'. The net effect was to inflate the number of 'owners' and to whittle away landlordism at one end of the scale, and to diminish the extent of sharecropping and tenancies-at-will at the other; but these are among the most important factors in the situation. Somewhat similar criticisms apply to the Census figures. In 1951 these showed 249,000,000 people dependent on agriculture; of these only 2·1% were rentier landlords, 67·2% were 'owner-cultivators', 12·7% 'tenant-cultivators', and 18% labourers. Labourers *and their dependents* num- bered 44,800,000; a figure difficult to reconcile with the total of 25,511,000 (1961: 31,482,000) just for labourers. All this before land reform; and as Daniel Thorner remarks, why, if these figures give a reasonably accurate picture, is there so strong and persistent a demand for reform throughout the country?[39]

Land reforms fall essentially under three closely related heads: the elimination of intermediaries between the cultivator and the State – this is often referred to as *zamindari* abolition; the setting of ceilings on individual holdings; and the protection of tenants by providing for security and fair rents. The history and details of legislation vary from State to State; in most cases, however, it is not unfair to remark that the length of the legislative process gave much time and opportunity for such evasions as the nominal splitting-up of joint holdings and securing the 'voluntary' surrender of occupancy rights. While the relatively few really large estates have been severely shorn (against compensation) and in some cases tenants have gained more security, the consensus of informed opinion seems to be that in many areas evasion took place on a large scale, and it seems quite possible that there has been an actual, though concealed, increase in share- cropping and what are in effect tenancies-at-will. These are matters difficult to police in any case, even were there no collusion by local officials, who are often badly underpaid or drawn from classes adversely affected by reform, or both.

[39] For all this, see D. and A. Thorner, *op. cit.*, Chapters 10–13, *passim*.

The big *zamindar* may be on the way out; but the *malik* or middling proprietor may have gained; and while a few *kisans* ('working peasants') may have improved their position and perhaps even graduated to the *malik* class, the *mazdurs* or labourers, often 'attached' by debt-slavery, are probably as wretched as ever.

The evidence for this view is scattered, but it comes from too many sources to be ignored.[40] Thorner, writing in 1955, was of opinion that there had been 'some perceptible change' in the then States of Bombay, Hyderabad, Madhya Bharat, Punjab and Punjab States Union, Saurashtra and Uttar Pradesh; the rest of India showed little or no change, with the significant exceptions of Kashmir and Andhra: here change was greatest, and here there were obvious political factors – the presence of Pakistan and the Communist agrarian rising of 1948–51 in Telangana.[41] On the other hand there has been more legislation since 1955, especially as regards rent fixing, though some of this is probably plugging of loopholes after the damage has been done; and a detailed survey of Saurashtra, while perhaps glossing over the amount of resistance and evasion, comes to definitely favourable conclusions.[42]

To what extent land reforms have actually improved production is an even more difficult question. One factor in the delays and changes of policy has been the apprehension, especially in bad years, that a too rigorous application of ceilings on the size of holdings might prejudice production by depriving the larger, better-equipped, and more commercially-minded proprietors of needed land, and also of incentives. Looked at in cold blood, it might indeed appear that a strengthening of the *malik* – or 'kulak' – class would, economically considered, be the best thing for production;[43] but this runs counter to the *mystique* of land reform, though as we have seen it may not be so unconformable to its *practice* in the countryside. Even setting aside more idealistic and humanitarian considerations, however, it seems unlikely that the rural masses can be enlisted for a really wholehearted economic effort without some vigorous reform, despite what Iyengar terms its 'cumulative diseconomies'.

2. Bhoodan, Gramdan and co-operative farming

The Bhoodan or 'land-gift' movement initiated in 1951 by the Gandhian idealist Acharya Vinobha Bhave has appeared to some as a way out. Vinobha based himself on a direct missionary appeal; he estimated that about a sixth of the land, 50,000,000 ac. (20,230,000 ha.) could meet the needs of the *mazdurs* and could be made available if only the landed would recognize their rightful obligation to

[40] Cf., for example, the essays (on widely scattered areas) in A. R. Desai (ed.), *Rural Sociology in India* (Vora, Bombay, 3rd ed. 1961), 489–505; and, in the same volume (424–6) an example of actual *loss* of land rights by low caste people in Madhopur village, UP.

[41] *The Agrarian Prospect in India* (Delhi Univ. Press, 1956), 29–53.

[42] R. B. Mishra, *Effects of Land Reforms in Saurashtra* (Vora, Bombay, 1961). Annual summaries of legislation are perhaps most conveniently found in *India: A Reference Annual* (Ministry of Information, ND), though in themselves they are not very revealing.

[43] See S. K. Iyengar, *A Decade of Planned Economy* (Indian Academy of Economics, Mysore, 1961), 114–15, 178–97, for a typically iconoclastic view.

the landless, and in the first few years the sincerity and emotive appeal of himself and his disciples elicited a remarkable response: by 1957 over 4,000,000 ac. (1,620,000 ha.) had been donated, half of them in Bihar. But he relied on a *continuity* of generous response which has not been maintained; often (and naturally enough) the land given was the most marginal in the village – and sometimes the gift was merely the surplus over the legal ceiling, which would have been forfeit anyhow; and Vinobha gave much too little thought to equipping the *mazdur* (with bullocks and so on) to become a *kisan*. There has been no increase – rather a slight decrease – in the cumulative totals of land donated, and although practically no new land came in after 1957, in the 10 years to 1962 only a quarter of the land given had been distributed.

The later phase of the movement is known as Gramdan, or the communalizing of entire villages; so far over 5,000 villages have accepted the movement, but nearly half of these are in the hill country of Orissa where there is plenty of land for shifting cultivation and the people are probably simply returning to tribal traditions. Gramdan may help in Community Development and have lessons for co-operative farming; but with all respect for the devotion of Vinobha and his followers, it is difficult to take their economic thinking seriously. Gramdan seems a desperate expedient to revitalize a movement which had already become stagnant.[44]

Faced with the general impasse, official thinking seems to be turning towards large-scale co-operative farming. It is admitted that even in rural credit, where most has been done, the achievements of co-operation have been disappointing, but it is hoped that with such strong government backing collective production, if not ownership, could be successful. Obviously much could be done on these lines in the way of supplying seeds and fertilizers and in running machinery; and some co-operative colonies have been established for refugees from Pakistan in East Punjab, the terai and Rajasthan. But clearly it is one thing to set up a collective of displaced persons on new land, backed by a definite government responsibility for rehabilitation; and quite another to reverse the strong and accelerating century-old trend towards individualism in the territorially and socially tight-packed villages of say the Gangetic Plains or Tamilnad, with their intense caste factionalism. Although financial provision is being made under the Third Plan for such development, detailed programmes do not seem to be readily available.[45]

[44] There is a large literature; statistics are given in the *Reference Annual*, and Desai, *op. cit.* 567–632, includes essays by both supporters and critics. It is perhaps significant that Srimati Kusum Nair does not so much as mention Vinobha, Bhoodan, or Gramdan in her excellent first-hand sketches of rural India, *Blossoms in the Dust: The Human Factor in Indian Development* (Praeger, NY, 1962).

[45] There is some discussion in Tarlok Singh's essay 'India's rural economy and its institutional framework' in J. P. Bhattacharjee (ed.), *Studies in Indian Agricultural Economics* (Indian Soc. of Agric. Economics, Bombay, 1958), 300–16, and *Towards a Self-reliant Economy* (Ministry of Information, ND, 1961), 186–92. For criticism, even more scathing than usual, see Iyengar, *op. cit.* 118–19, 186–90.

Readers of *Blossoms in the Dust* or of many sociological studies of Indian village life will not be optimistic; and yet this may seem the only way to render possible the application of those other necessities (which by themselves are but palliatives) such as improvements in technique and 'rural uplift'. As Wilfrid Malenbaum puts it, 'the devices proposed for closing the gap are exciting; as of the end of the second plan, they remained imprecise – and untested.'[46] They may have a hard time in what Thorner calls 'the world of organized subterfuge'.

3. *Debt, credit, co-operation*

Nearly all agrarian societies developed beyond subsistence level are debt-ridden, since (except for market-gardeners, dairy farmers and the like) the farmer's resources are liquid but once or twice a year, after harvest, while his outgoings recur throughout the year, often with peaks around sowing-time and at the harvest itself. Nowhere is debt so crushing as in the peasant societies of Asia.

After the depression of the 1930s the total volume of rural debt in British India alone was estimated to exceed Rs 1,200 crores or about £900,000,000.[47] Divided by scores of millions, the debt might seem small in terms of individuals, but it probably approximated to, if it did not exceed, the average annual income in the countryside. The high agricultural prices of the Second World War, together with the shortage of consumer goods, undoubtedly resulted in a considerable liquidation of indebtedness, but it seems highly probable that this affected mainly the middle and upper strata of rural society; there is evidence that since 1945 the volume of debt has again risen, and this time it is mainly the lower ranks that have been most adversely affected.[48] The All-India Rural Credit Survey of 1954–56 estimated that 69% of cultivating families were in debt to the average extent of Rs 526.[49] Most of the debt is non-productive; even for 'big cultivators', only about one-third is for capital outlay, and 'family expenditure' rises to nearly 60% for the smaller cultivators: the financial impact of the social conventions governing such expenditure does not fall proportionately with status.

The causes of indebtedness are manifold. Fundamental are the small holdings, the perversity of the seasons, the peasant's lack of information and of storage which compel him to a quick and blindfold disposal of his harvest. He has no reserves to meet sickness, drought, flood, cattle diseases; his savings account is in his wife's few poor rings and bangles, and when natural calamity comes and everybody is selling at once, these do not fetch much. The unco' guid and the well-to-do condemn his undeniable extravagance when his son is born or his

---

[46] *Prospects for Indian Development* (Allen & Unwin, London, 1962), 226. See also the balanced remarks in R. P. Sinha, *Food in India* (OUP, Bombay, 1961), 131–8.

[47] G. B. Jathar and S. G. Beri, *Indian Economics* (OUP, Bombay, 7th ed. 1942), I.283.

[48] Thirumalai, *op. cit.* 186, gives totals for both 1937 and c. 1953 of Rs 1800 crores.

[49] This vast report seems not to be available in Australia; there is a summary by V. M. Jakhade in J. P. Bhattacharjee, *op. cit.* 249–99. The sampling and general conduct of the enquiry are severely criticized by D. and A. Thorner, *op. cit.* 188–224.

daughter married: but in a round of drudgery and privation, these are the socially sanctioned opportunities for a little colour and gaiety, a few days of uninhibited projection of his personality, new clothes and good food; and it is hard to blame him over-much.

All this would be bad enough were the agents of credit impeccable; notoriously they are not. According to the Rural Credit Survey, about a quarter of all loans come from better-off agriculturalists, *maliks* and the like, and this often leads the poorer peasants and labourers into something very like almost permanent debt-slavery. Nearly half the total borrowings came from professional moneylenders. These people may also be the village grainbrokers and shopkeepers; they have funds for retaining lawyers and local officials, and command the services, as witnesses or strong-arm men, of numerous clients. Since the poorer borrowers are more likely than not illiterate, the cards are stacked against them. There is no doubt that the rigid legalism of the British Raj played into the moneylender's hands, and, despite much protective legislation (before Independence as well as since), it is not at all certain that things are greatly better now. In thirty-three of the seventy-five sample Districts covered by the Rural Credit Survey, over half the moneylenders' loans carried interest at over 18%.

The natural answer would seem to be co-operative credit societies. It is not a new one: the chequered history of such societies in India goes back to 1904. Their success has been by no means commensurate with the effort put into them; the Rural Credit Survey found that the 'utter insignificance' of the movement's share in rural financing – after fifty years, 3·1% – 'was perhaps the most startling revelation' from its enquiry. It is not easy to understand this surprise at what everybody knew, nor are the reasons obscure. The societies, bound by regulation, are faced always with the dilemma of too rigid management, or too lax; the moneylender is bound by no such rules, he is on the spot in almost the smallest village and knows his clients thoroughly, he imposes no formalities or delays, and he is as a rule quite content to receive interest to eternity rather than to foreclose or to be repaid. Co-operatives cannot – or at least should not – lend to support more borrowing; their rates are much lower than the moneylender's, but they are not nearly so obliging.

Perhaps nowhere is the gap between the official and the actual so wide as in this field. It is officially estimated that in 1961 about 39% of the population was served by the co-operative movement, but what this really means is hard to tell. It is claimed that 33% of agricultural production is covered by co-operative arrangements, and the Third Plan target is 60%; it is disconcerting to see a Third Plan target of 100% for coverage of villages, when no comparative figure is given for the end of the Second. Undoubtedly there has been a big increase in activity in the last ten years: all forms of co-operative societies rose from 185,630 in 1951–52 to 332,488 in 1960–61, membership from under 14,000,000 to over 34,000,000; and whereas before 1947 co-operation was almost overwhelmingly in the form of agricultural credit societies, there are now many for marketing, production (especially of sugar-cane), irrigation, fishing and so on. Two facts in relation to agricultural credit societies may be significant: though working capital per society rose from Rs 4,190 in 1952 to 14,808 in 1962, deposits per member were the same in both years – Rs 9; and while in 1960–61 such societies lent Rs 203 crores, outstanding loans were 218 and *overdue* loans over 44 crores.[50]

With all their shortcomings, credit societies have done something to keep interest rates down by providing an alternative source of credit. However, as so often, it is the bigger and stronger men who can best take advantage of them; the poor and weak, who need them most, are just those who cannot provide security and cannot afford the delays and limitations in their working. There is a complicated system of co-operative banks and other quasi-governmental financing agencies, and the Third Plan envisages very considerable expansion. Some critics appear to think that this will amount to throwing good money after bad,[51] and the Committee of Direction of the Rural Credit Societies itself was impelled to admit some truth in a definition of Indian co-operation as ' "a plant held in position with both hands by Government since its roots refuse to enter the soil." More than the roots of Co-operation, it is the tentacles of private economy that have acquired grip. . . .'[52] Yet it seems inescapable that, if there is a way out from the agrarian tangle, it will need massive financial assistance from government, and it is difficult to see any other practical method of deploying it. In Pakistan similarly, the *Five Year Plan Draft* summed up: 'Although it may be argued that co-operation has failed, it must nevertheless be resolved to make it succeed.'[53]

4. Community Development and Panchayati Raj

From all that has gone before, it will be apparent that the body social of the Indian countryside labours under a complication of ills; there is an appalling deadweight to be lifted. The agrarian problem seems hydra-headed; it is essential to establish priorities, and yet so many and so urgent are the tasks that there is always a danger of dissipating energy, or of 'solving' one problem at the price of raising up others: the history of land reform bears witness.

Before Independence, many attempts had been made to break through the cycle of rural poverty, rural apathy, rural poverty. . . . Notable among these were F. L. Brayne's village propaganda and M. L. Darling's co-operative work in the Punjab, Rabindranath Tagore's educational effort at Santiniketan, Mahatma Gandhi's village uplift in Gujarat. Such efforts, usually on a very local basis, lacked extension and continuity; often they tended to follow up one pet line. Striking results might be obtained, to be dissipated when the particular servant of the people departed and the village relaxed into the old comfortable ways.

---

[50] Figures in this paragraph from the 1963 *Reference Annual*, 225–31.
[51] Cf. Iyengar, *op. cit.* 141–74.   [52] Cited Desai, *op. cit.* 511.
[53] Cited in J. R. Andrus and A. F. Mohammed, *The Economy of Pakistan* (OUP, Karachi, 1958), 143.

Those carried out by British officials, however devoted and sympathetic, were still alien in inspiration; conversely, it is not unfair to say that many Gandhi-inspired efforts (of which Vinobha's Bhoodan is but the latest example) lacked a sense of the practical. Some residue of better living was usually left, but perhaps more important in the long run was that this experience produced a large literature on 'rural uplift', often indeed impractical enough, but in sum doing much to define problems and to evaluate techniques.

The Community Development Project, launched in 1952, set out to give large-scale government backing, organization, and continuity to what had been a sporadic movement. It was much encouraged by the very striking results obtained by an American-inspired project in Uttar Pradesh;[54] but pressures of opinion, internal and external, led to a pace of expansion which seems to have paid insufficient attention to the matter of diminishing returns ('what will happen when *every* village woman has been taught to make four-anna trinkets for sale to her neighbours?') and to the need for more careful observation and record of trial in diverse environments. The statistics of Community Development are impressive, but in that fact is hidden one source of weakness: the movement has of necessity evolved a sort of rural Welfare State bureaucracy, alongside or over-lapping with the normal administrative machine, with its own inevitable frictions and frustrations and a pressure to produce paper 'results'.[55]

Community Development is based on blocks of about 100 villages, say 60–70,000 people; there are now over 5,000 blocks covering practically the entire country. The aim is to enlist the effort of the people themselves in a wide variety of improvements – the use of fertilizers, better seeds, composts; better stock management, including castration; development of village industries; physical ameliorations such as properly lined wells, latrines, street drainage, school building, construction of feeder roads, provision of village radios and so on. The main agent is the *gram sewak* or trained Village Level Worker; unfortunately it is likely that only too often the multiplicity of interests which he – or she – is expected to encourage precludes really thorough training; on the other hand, undue specialization at this level could only increase bureaucratic stresses. At the next level, a Block Panchayat Samiti is in general control, formed of the heads of village panchayats and co-opted representatives of women and depressed classes, and assisted by the Block Development Officer and his specialist Extension Officers. The Presidents of these Block Panchayats, together with local elected representatives, form the Zila Parishad, which is in general control at District level, and the old officials in charge of sub-divisions (tahsils, taluks, or thanas), including the minor revenue officials, are brought into this set-up. This last point emphasizes that a great experiment in decentralization is in progress,

---

[54] See A. Mayer, *Pilot Project, India* (Univ. of California, Berkeley, 1958).

[55] Iyengar (*op. cit.* 124–5), critical as usual, makes the point that 'nothing is easier than boosting village figures for the simple reason that verification is impossible on account of area and numbers'.

which it is hoped will lead to Panchayati Raj, the long-desired revival of the old virtual village self-government by the Gram Panchayat. These were councils of five which, with the assistance of the headman and village clerk, in the past represented the main caste groupings, but are now to be enlarged and remodelled on elective lines, and also given the responsibility for expending a large share of the local land revenue.

The weaknesses and failings of Community Development are obvious. It has been over-extended and energies have been diffused into improvements which should be, but too often are not, co-ordinated. The dangers of bureaucracy have already been stressed; in some cases the new Panchayats, with their elected lower castemen, may really only rubber-stamp the behind the scenes decisions of the old petty oligarchies. Most serious is the fact, probably inherent in the nature of things (and by no means only in India), that a programme meant for the benefit of all, but especially the masses, in actuality plays into the hands of the already fairly well-off farmers. This is natural: the *malik* is the man with the resources to obtain the most benefit from better techniques and ameliorations such as feeder roads, to which, however, the whole village will have contributed, if only by its more or less voluntary labour. There are not wanting suggestions that this *shramdan*, or spontaneous labour contribution, sometimes tends to slide over into the old *begar*, or more or less forced labour at the behest of local magnates and officials. *Jis ke pas jitna hai, utana use milta hai*: precisely, To him that hath much, shall much be given.[56]

On the other hand, there have been undeniable successes, and the best blocks are surely inspiring. Whatever discounts may be made, it is surely no mean achievement that the people themselves have contributed, in cash, kind, or labour, some 40% (Rs 112 crores, to March 1962) of the total costs. Pukka wells, latrines, schools however poorly equipped, are at least tangible additions to the amenity of life. For this reason, doubtless, the official Evaluation Report of 1957 found that, while benefits varied greatly with such factors as the accessibility of villages and accrued more to those with bigger holdings and some financial resources, real understanding and active participation were stronger for the 'constructional' than the institutional aspects of the programme. These physical ameliorations are of course very good and very much needed, but they are not *directly* conducive to increased production; at best they offset the bigger direct dividend to the *malik* or kulak groups.

The true effect of Community Development on agricultural production is impossible to assess: there have been so many other factors, multipliers or depressors, at work; but in many places, at least, there has been some more general diffusion of improved techniques. Many communities remain sunk in

[56] Cited D. and A. Thorner, *op. cit.* 10. Good reviews from several points of view are given in Desai, *op. cit.* 531–66; Official evaluations and hopes may be found e.g. in *The New India* (Macmillans, NY, 1958, for the Planning Commission), 168–79, and *Towards a Self-reliant Economy*, 181–6. H. Tinker's 'Authority and community in village India', *Pacific Affairs*, 32 (1959), 354–75, underlines some fundamental assumptions and realities.

apathy and highly suspicious of all 'improvement'; in others, the major change as yet has been some acceptance of the concept that change of any sort is possible; in some there have been real self-help and even local initiatives. It is impossible to generalize. (Cf. pp. 342–3.)

It would be delusive to assume that techniques alone are the answer, or on the other hand, as the followers of Vinobha seem to believe, that only a spiritual revolution will help and that this is possible simply by appeals to conscience. Panchayati Raj, for example, is undoubtedly an appealing concept; sometimes it does open the way to real participation in affairs by the lowly and oppressed; too often it simply formalizes, on the local plane, the political intrigue to which caste factionalism, a culture very hospitable to that virus, gives such immense scope. To understand what is really happening in India one must penetrate behind the statistics and the official reports, behind the tendentious essays of the publicists, and fall back on such scattered samples as are available in the increasing number of scholarly studies in rural sociology, and in such honest reporting as Kusum Nair's *Blossoms in the Dust*. The picture is inevitably a confused one of success and failure, enterprise and frustration, hope and apprehension.

5. Agrarian reform in Pakistan

At Partition, the land situation in Pakistan was naturally as complicated as in India. Three-quarters of the cultivated land in East Pakistan was under the Permanent Settlement; in the Punjab, the Canal Colonies had a reasonably strong class of direct government tenants on sizeable holdings, but elsewhere *zamindari* was strong; Sind was officially *ryotwari*, but intermediaries had developed to such an extent that most actual cultivators were *haris*, tenants without occupancy rights and working on the *batai* share-crop system which gave them a nominal half, but often an actual third, of the crop. Partition led to a great exodus of non-Muslim landowners, but brought in many landless refugees; according to the 1951 Census, nearly half of the Punjab's 3,400,000 cultivators owned or claimed to own all the land they tilled, but this probably included many refugees resettled on evacuee land who 'regard[ed] themselves as owners, regardless of legislative definitions'.[57]

The objective in East Pakistan is the abolition of intermediaries altogether; *zamindars* are limited to a personal holding of 33 acres (13·3 ha.). One effect of the consequent strengthening of the position of former occupancy tenants, now in effect *ryots*, seems however to have been a weakening in that of non-occupancy tenants or *bargardars*, who are now in the position of landless labourers. Information on the full effects of legislation in East Pakistan is lacking.

In the West, Punjab legislation set a ceiling of 50 acres (20·2 ha.) for the landlord's personal cultivation, gave the option of purchasing proprietary rights to occupancy tenants and some security to non-occupancy tenants, and fixed a general proportion of 40% as the landlord's share of crop, water rate, and land

[57] Andrus and Mohammed, *op. cit.* 123.

revenue. In Sind, a certain amount of relief was given to *haris*. It was officially admitted that this led to more tensions than it allayed.

The Ayub Khan régime appears to have approached the problem in a manner at once more limited and more forceful. Individual ownership is limited to 500 acres (202 ha.) of irrigated or 1,000 acres of dry land; 2,200,000 acres (890,000 ha.) were resumed by government and by 1964 over half of this had been distributed to cultivators. When it is recalled that the cultivated area of West Pakistan is some 41,000,000 acres or 16,581,000 hectares, it is obvious that much remains to be done. At the same time, a vigorous programme of consolidation has been launched, and sub-division below 12·5 acres (5·1 ha.) in the former Punjab and 16 (6·5) in Sind has been prohibited.

One result of Partition was the disappearance of many non-Muslim money-lenders; although some Muslim groups, for example some Pathans, did practice usury, this was mainly in towns – before the war, as far afield as Rangoon. In Sind, the *hari* was entirely dependent on the *zamindar* for credit – on what terms may be imagined! – and the *zamindar* in turn on grain dealers; this was a factor in the extremely weak development of co-operation in the province, the Punjab being much stronger in this respect. In East Pakistan the number and membership of co-operative societies fell in the five years after Partition, and their working capital fell by a much greater percentage than their membership, which probably reflects the exodus of better-off Hindus. With the disappearance of many Hindu *banias* or moneylenders, the credit situation in East Pakistan thus became very serious, the only recourse of the small cultivator being sale or mortgage, a factor in the increase of *bargardars*.[58]

In West Pakistan, at least, there has been a considerable improvement. The Agricultural Development Bank, founded in 1961, works in both wings and is an important source of rural credit; in West Pakistan, rural credit co-operatives advanced Rs 11 crores in 1961–62, against 31·5 crores from the Bank and 1·8 as direct loans (*taccavi*) from the government. There has also been a considerable development of other forms of co-operation, including an experiment in co-operative mechanized farming covering 120 villages and 120,000 acres (49,000 ha.), of which over a third are already under mechanized farming.

The Pakistani equivalent of Community Development was initially the Village Agricultural and Industrial Development (AID) Programme; its methods and objectives were much the same, and it perhaps relied even more on (usually married) women helpers. With the institution of the Basic Democracies, AID has been subsumed into their activities, while many of its trained personnel have gone into the Agricultural Development Corporations of each wing: these are responsible for procuring and distributing fertilizers, implements, improved seeds, pesticides, and so on, as well as agricultural extension activities.

It is not likely that the results of such activities differ significantly as between Pakistan and India: against the general background of poverty, small holdings,

[58] See Andrus and Mohammed, *op. cit.* 136–56, for conditions in the mid-50s.

and backward techniques, regional differences within each country, the resultant of very diverse physical and social environments, are likely to be much more significant. For both countries, the general problem can be summed up by returning to the man/land or more precisely the man/food ratio.

V. THE GENERAL PROBLEM

Depressing as the agrarian picture is in both India and Pakistan, there are, especially in the former, some signs of more encouraging trends in what may be called the middle term, that is for the next ten or fifteen years, beyond which it would be useless to speculate. Fig. 8.16 suggests that the effort of the Indian Plans is at last beginning to show some results; the gap between targets and attainment is so far not desperately large. It must be remembered that, while the population curve has no actual dips and is likely to rise at a somewhat accelerating rate until the early 1970s (when the rate may begin to slacken off), the curve of food output is subject to marked ups and downs; even if the general prognosis is reasonably favourable, there may be very difficult spells, as for instance in the rainy season of 1964 and again 1965–66. The position is still generally marginal and sometimes critical. Nevertheless the fact that the area under foodgrains has risen less markedly (though more steadily) than that for output is in itself encouraging, bearing witness to an increase of productivity in the last few years, an increase not yet reflected in the available figures for unit yields. Better marketing and procurement may also have contributed to the gross apparent improvement.

It is however much too soon for optimism. The best of the possibilities for expansion have probably been taken up already; more and more the food for the ever-increasing population will have to come from intensification on already cultivated land. Both approaches, intensification by more fertilizers and better techniques, and expansion by irrigation and reclamation, are costly, and especially in the latter diminishing returns must always be reckoned with as more marginal options have to be taken up. Even before the shock of the 1961 Census, which showed a population well above most good projections, R. P. Sinha's careful study showed that only on very optimistic assumptions would there be any prospect of India reaching self-sufficiency in food by 1975–76; his conclusion after the Census was that, depending on the rate of rise of national income, the demand for food in the early 1960s would be between 94 and 115% greater than that of 1955–56.[59] This implies continuing food imports, which in the last resort must be paid for by exports, and it is clear that very careful adjustments must be made in the application of India's capital resources as between field and factory, private and public sectors. The machinery and the programmes for the development of India's mixed economy will be the subject of the succeeding chapters.

[59] *Op. cit.* 138–50, 183–5.

The prospect for Pakistan seems as difficult in the long term. Population increase is at least as great as in India; expansion of area has been much less proportionately, and it is very difficult to see how it can take place on any significant scale in the East, while in the West it must depend to a great extent on large and costly irrigation projects – and indeed on large-scale reclamation of waterlogged

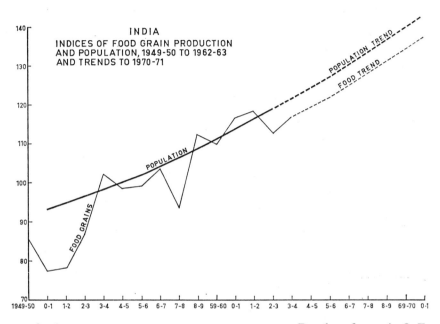

FIG 8.16 INDIA: TRENDS OF FOOD AND POPULATION. Based on figures in S. E. Johnson, *India's Food Situation and a Look Ahead* (Report to Ministry of Food and Agriculture, 1963).

and salinized land if it is not to remain static. On the whole Pakistan is much poorer than India in resources and, perhaps to a lesser extent, in know-how; and in both the situation is much worse in East than in West Pakistan. West Pakistan has the makings of a well-found if dominantly agrarian country; it is impossible to be very hopeful about East Pakistan, despite its recent (but, objectively considered, still slight) industrial development.

Industry has a great part to play, not only on its own account but in the rehabilitation of agriculture; it is not, however, a simple panacea. It is not likely to develop rapidly enough to be able to do much more than take off new surpluses, the new cohorts of job-seekers, without making very great inroads on the vast pool of un- or under-employed labour in the countryside; and, while in time urbanization may be expected to have a large effect on fertility, this effect does not come about, even in Japan, in decades so much as in generations. Moreover industrial development itself will depend to a considerable extent on rural

281

demand: its primary market is in the rural population, but one so far so depressed by poverty that industrial development itself must be inhibited if agrarian standards do not rise. The agrarian problem thus lies dead centre to all the workings of man in the sub-continent, and it is against an agrarian background that the drama of planning must be played out.

Postscript. Attention is drawn to two important recent articles. M. Harris, 'The cultural ecology of India's sacred cattle', *Current Anthropology*, 7 (1966), 51–66, is an authoritative discussion of many angles of this complex problem; J. G. Crawford, 'Planning under difficulties', *Australian Jnl of Politics and History*, 12 (1966), 155–76, talks of planning in general but pays special attention to the food/population problem.

CHAPTER 9

The Industrial Base: Power and Mineral Resources

INTRODUCTION

As long as agriculture directly supports 70% or more of the population, the agrarian problem will remain as the obvious and basic drag on progress towards a better living standard. Long term hopes and plans however lie as much – perhaps more – with industrialization. Agriculture and industry are symbiotic; the rural population provides both a market and labour supply, though limitless cheap labour does nothing to raise wages, efficiency or conditions. Conversely, industrial products are needed for the dams and power houses, fertilizers and machinery necessary for rural improvements. Equally important are the resources of power and minerals available. In assessing these, India and Pakistan are discussed separately with an analysis of power first, followed by minerals grouped according to their principal industrial users.

I. INDIA

A. POWER

1. *Coal*

With about 3% of world output, India shares eighth place with Japan. From a production of 500,000 tons in 1868, output increased to 6,000,000 tons by 1900, 30,000,000 tons in 1945 and has more than doubled since Independence; it is now over 60,000,000 tons a year and should reach 90,000,000 tons by the end of the Third Plan. Reserves are reasonable for the medium and poorer qualities (about 70,000,000,000 tons) but relatively low for the essential coking coals (2,500,000,000 tons), and of the total reserves, Fox's original estimate of only 20,000,000,000 tons less than 2,000 ft. (610 m.) deep and with ash content less than 25% still holds good, although it is now considered that workable coal goes down to 4,000 ft. (1,220 m.). In addition, there are reserves of about 10,000,000,000 tons of Tertiary coals. Most of the Lower Gondwana seams, which yield 95% of Indian coal, are fragments, preserved, by faulting, of four great Permian basins in the north of the plateau.[1] Linear series of exposures run along the Damodar,

[1] J. Coggin Brown and A. K. Dey, *India's Mineral Wealth*, (OUP, 3rd ed. 1955) is the source for most of the genetic information on minerals.

283

east-northeast/west-southwest to include minor fields in tributary valleys south of the Son, thence along the southern side of the Narmada structural valley where they are partly concealed by Deccan trap, but appear as small scattered coalfields. A second series, running southeast/northwest from Talchir in Orissa up the northern side of the Mahanadi valley, coalesces with the first in Baghel-khand. Westwards, a less well marked series, also trending northwest/southeast,

MINERAL-BEARING AREAS

FIG 9.1 MINERAL-BEARING AREAS. Based on Brown and Dey, *India's Mineral Wealth* (OUP, 1955).

gives the minor fields extending from Chanda in Madhya Pradesh along the lower Godavari to beyond the mining town of Singareni. The Damodar fields still dominate; the easily mined seams, often over 80 ft. (24 m.) thick, of the Jharia and Raniganj–Burdwan fields produce over 60% of the total; in the same area are the Bokaro, Ramgarh and Karanpura fields, the latter with important new coking reserves. Singareni, recently greatly developed by the National Coal Development Council, produces some 5% from relatively undisturbed beds. North-wards, the fields of Madhya Pradesh, yielding about 10% of the total, are also being developed partly by the NCDC to feed the new steel plants of Bhilai and Rourkela; one of these, Korba (discovered by Blanford in 1870), is now linked by rail to the main line 25 miles (40 km.) to the south near Bilaspur. One or two small fields are being developed in Maharashtra.

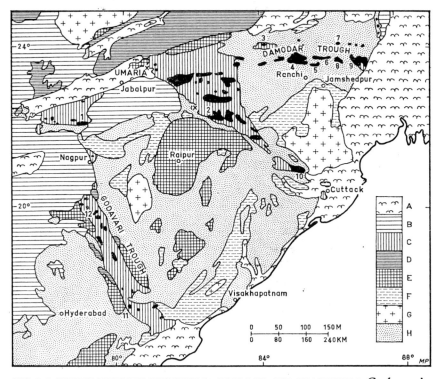

FIG 9.2 NORTH EASTERN PENINSULA: GEOLOGY AND COALFIELDS. Geology: A, alluvium; B, Deccan and Rajmahal Lavas (Cretaceous-Tertiary); C, Gondwana (Jurassic to Carboniferous, including marine Jurassic of coast and Umaria); D, Vindhyan, etc. (Cambrian to Algonkian; E. Cuddapah and equivalents (Algonkian); F, rocks of Dharwarian age (Huronian); G, Archaean crystalline and igneous rocks; H, mainly ancient gneisses and granites. X, X, occurrences of marine Jurassic in Peninsula. Coalfields in solid black; those mentioned in text: 1, Pench valley; 2, Korba; 3, Daltonganj; 4, Karanpura; 5, Ramgarh; 6, Bokaro; 7, Jharia; 9, Rani-ganj; 10, Talchir; 11, Singareni; 12, Chanda. Cf. Fig. 21.7.

Otherwise, there is some Eocene sub-bituminous and highly sulphurous coal in Assam, and some reserve but virtually no production from the highly faulted anthracite beds of Riasi in Jammu, and in the Rangit valley in Sikkim. Much more important than either of these are the lignites of Rajasthan, under Eocene limestones in Bikaner, which have been briquetted for railway use since 1898; and those of South Arcot in Madras associated with Miocene sandstones. Although discovered in 1934, exploitation only began here in 1961 as part of an integrated power, briquetting and fertilizer scheme at Neiveli. The *karewas* of Kashmir contain considerable low-grade deposits yielding some 5,000 tons a year.

Exploitation of coal began tentatively at Raniganj in 1774, but real development came only with the railways, still the main single consumer taking about 25% of output. But iron and steel plants are increasing their demand, and already take about another 18–20%. Power stations use 8% and other industries 20%, leaving the rest for bunkering, exports, and domestic consumption.[2] Development, apart from collieries owned by steel firms or the railways, was erratic and uncontrolled, with short term leases by the zamindars to inadequately capitalized syndicates. Some 80% of the output is still produced by the private sector, and the public sector concentrates on less profitable but strategically important developments. Efforts to rationalize some of the chaos of small workings have had only local and limited effect.

Labour problems remain acute, with the tribal people, who are an important element in the work force, returning to their fields at busy times. Housing conditions are only slowly improving, and mainly at the larger collieries, where provision of small holdings helps to stabilize the workers. On the physical side, problems of the industry stem from the shortage of coking reserves, and have led to attempts to conserve supplies – as well as to reduce subsidence: compulsory sand stowage instead of pillars in the thick, deep seams (fortunately with plenty of local raw material) and blending at the coke ovens; the Durgapur plant for instance uses only 20% of coking coal. The concentration of Indian coal in the northeast corner of the peninsula has always been a handicap, and today bottlenecks and storage, more than actual pithead output, appear as problems in attaining planned targets.

2. *Petroleum*

There appears considerable promise for oil potential in the general structural relations of the Indus–Ganga–Brahmaputra foredeep to the Himalayas, by analogy with Iran and Iraq, and with Burma; in the deltaic basin structures of the Indus and especially the Ganga–Brahmaputra, by analogy with the Gulf Coast of the USA, and to a lesser extent in various synclines of Tertiary rocks marginal to peninsular India.

The oldest exploited oilfield is in Assam. After one or two precocious and short-lived attempts at oil mining and even refining between 1879 and 1883, in the Upper Coal Measures near Jaipur and Makum, drilling was transferred to

[2] Figures throughout this section are averaged and approximated and are taken along with much useful information from the *Indian Minerals Yearbooks*, Indian Bureau of Mines, Nagpur.

the Digboi area in 1888; oil production began in 1892 in what has proved to be a very long-lived oilfield in an east-west anticline in Miocene impure sandstones, shales and clays.[3] The oil company opened a refinery at Digboi in 1900. Since Independence the company has continued exploration in the area under licence, and finding considerable further reserves at Nahorhatiya and Moran is developing these in partnership with the government, to supply the new refineries at Noonmati near Gauhati and Barauni in Bihar, by pipeline. Oil exploration in West Bengal from 1953 to 1960 added a great deal to geological knowledge, but no trace of oil was found.

In 1955, the government set up the Oil and Natural Gas Commission and widespread oil exploration has been carried out, with a good deal of technical collaboration from Roumania and particularly USSR. A further oilfield has been found in Assam, at Sibsagar, but the main new prospect opened out so far is in Gujarat. Geological and geophysical prospecting has revealed a down-faulted *graben* structure underlying the Tertiary sediments and alluvia of the plans around the head of the Gulf of Cambay; over a floor of Deccan Traps are some 5,700 ft. (1,900 m.) of alternating limestones and sandstones, shales and clays, from the Eocene to post-Miocene in date, within which are minor folds, including some oil or gas bearing anticlines, some slightly faulted. The Cambay or Lunej field appears likely to produce initially some 250,000 cu. m. of gas per day; reserves have not been estimated, though an early indication was of easy exploitation of shallow deposits rather than large reserves comparable to those of Sui in West Pakistan.[4]

The Anklesvar field may yield some 1,250,000 tons of oil per annum; reserves are not fully determined. The Kalol field contains oil and gas, but is not fully explored. A refinery has been built with Russian help at Koyali near Baroda.

In the Jurassic and Cretaceous shales, sandstones and limestones the slight anticlinal structure of Kutch are worth exploring further, though the probabilities seem to be against large accumulations of oil. But in Rajasthan the generally slight dip to northwest or westnorthwest is promising; hydrocarbons have been proved down-dip in Pakistan, and some may have migrated up-dip and may have been trapped in anticlines, etc., concealed by desert sands.

Exploration of the sea-bed off Kutch, Kathiawad and Cambay is regarded as well worth while, and several other possibilities on land and on the continental

---

[3] Legend has it that the Assam Railways and Trading Company was led towards buying up the oil rights from the earlier unsuccessful explorers by an elephant which returned to camp with traces of oil on its feet (*The Eastern Economist*, ND, 27 Dec. 1963, 133; this publication is a source for much of the quantitative data used). The Digboi field yielded some 1,558 million gallons of oil between 1892 and 1950 (Brown and Dey, *op. cit.* 100).

[4] United Nations, Proc. Second Symposium Development of Petroleum Resources of Asia and the Far East, Mineral Resources Development Series, No. 18, Vol. 1, New York, 1963, 239; this work is a major source for the following paragraphs. See also W. B. Metre and Y. Nagappa, 'Oil prospects in India', *India Quarterly*, 14 (1958), 154–65.

shelf may be considered together: (1) if the coast of Travancore was subject to down-faulting in mid-Miocene times, as Krishnan suspects, there may be a sequence of Upper Tertiary to recent sediments off-shore which may contain oil: (2) the sediments of the Thanjavur basin, Gondwana, Cretaceous and Tertiaries, thin on the western margin with the Archaeans, but up to 5,000 ft. (1,524 m.) deep on land, may continue under Palk Strait and the Gulf of Manaar and both land and sea-floor are worth exploring; (3) the continental shelf off Orissa may similarly include Cretaceous and Tertiary sediments worth exploring as also the whole of the submarine delta of the Ganga–Brahmaputra whose sediments may range from the Tertiary to the present.

To sum up, reserves at about the end of 1962 were some 45,000,000 tons in Gujarat and about the same in Assam. Production was just over 1,000,000 tons of crude petroleum, total home production just over 6,500,000 million, all petroleum-based products, i.e. including refining of imported petroleum mainly at dockside refineries; and total demand just over 9,000,000. Though demand is increasing about threefold per decade, production of crude oil is increasing at the moment a little faster, and the country's position is at least much stronger than might have been anticipated ten or fifteen years ago.

3. Electricity

The water power resources of the continent are considerable though not without limitations. The survey by J. W. Meares in 1918–24 arrived at an estimate of 12,680,000 kW as the potential at minimum flow; of this it was thought that 2,650,000 could be developed within twenty years. But by 1944 the total generating capacity was only 1,280,000 kW, and of this only 500,000 was hydro. Considering India's coal position this laggard pace is difficult to explain and perhaps not easy to defend.[5]

It is generally reckoned that Meare's estimate was less than half the real potential – current estimates range from 25,000,000 to 40,000,000 kW – and indeed schemes projected or under investigation already exceed his total.[6] Of course, it is not likely that all of these will be executed. Present total capacity is 6,030,000 (steam plant c. 3,500,000 kW, hydro-electric 2,000,000), the current target is 12,500,000 kW.

Since electricity was introduced to Bombay and Calcutta in 1899 over 2,000

---

[5] For a basic, even though dated, geographical account of high quality, see G. Kuriyan, *Hydro-electric Power in India* (Ind. Geog. Soc. Monograph No. 1, Madras, 1945); an up-to-date account is M. Datta, 'Electricity supply in India and its future', *Science and Culture* (Calcutta), 30 (1/1/64), 11–19.

[6] The Central Water and Power Commission's estimate is 40,000,000 kW at 60% load factor, or about 210,000,000,000 kWh annually, equivalent to 150,000,000 tons of coal. It is significant that one of the world's greatest single potentials is just within Tibet, at the Brahmaputra gorge and elbow through the Himalayas: it is estimated that an 11-mile headrace tunnel with a head of 7,500 ft. and a minimum unregulated flow of 30,000 cusecs (1 cusec=102m³ per hour) would yield about 130,000,000,000 kWh per year, or about six times the present Indian total (Datta, *loc. cit.*).

thermal stations, mostly very small, have been set up for town supplies. About 1943 Bombay and Calcutta alone used 42%, and adding Cawnpore and Ahmedabad, four cities with 1·5% of population accounted for over 50% of the total

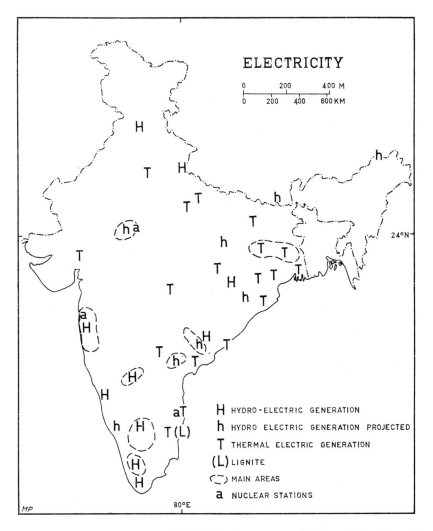

FIG 9.3 INDIA: ELECTRICITY. Hydel development so far is mainly along the Western Ghats and the Nilgiri-Annamalai group, and in montane Punjab; scheduled projects are largely in the Eastern Hills, with lower heads and larger rivers than on the Western Ghats. The very large potentials of the Himalayas present considerable engineering difficulties. Thermal power so far is related largely to urban markets, but location on fuel resources has begun in the Damodar and on the Neiveli lignite field in Madras (cf. Fig. 25.5).

electricity energy of India – which equalled a week's supply of the USA.[7] The concentration of coal in the Damodar kept costs high, on account of the long rail hauls, and it is not easy to generate centrally near the coal since water supplies are inadequate.[8] Hydro-electricity started fairly early. In 1902 Mysore opened the Sivasamudram installation, powering the goldfields 90 miles away – a notable achievement in its day. By 1915 about 130,000 kW were generated, 45,000 at Sivasamudram and 60,000 in the Tata schemes behind Bombay. Subsequent development and the main projects are shown on Fig. 9.3.

The main zones of hydro-electric potential are: (i) a belt along the Himalayas from Malakand to Assam (with an outlier on the Shillong Plateau); (ii) the Western Ghats; (iii) the Southern hills, especially on the Nilgiris and the middle Cauvery. In 1947 the three Tata plants above Bombay accounted for 47% of the total hydro-electric capacity of India, the Cauvery basin for 29%.

The main, and most obvious, limitation is the very pronounced seasonal variation of the rivers. All along the flanks of the Peninsular plateaus there are many sharp falls, some several hundred feet high, with an immense volume of water in the rains; but in the dry weather they are mere dribbles. Thus the Ken, a right-bank tributary of the Yamuna, varies from 300,000 to 5 cusecs, while even in sub-Himalayan Kumaon the Tons, with a maximum of 400,000, has fallen to 45.[9] Reservoirs must be large, and, as a rule, allow for a high rate of silting. In the Himalayas the slippery contorted shales which form much of the terrain are liable to slipping, and this is also the great seismic zone of India: earthquakes can be guarded against, but only by expensive specialized construction. In the Gangetic Plain, the deep Uttar Pradesh tube wells depend in part on thermal electricity but increasingly on that elegantly developed by concentrating the 146 ft. (44·5 m.) drop of the Ganga Canal into little falls of 8–12 ft. (2·4–3·7 m.); a principle which could obviously be extended at least in new canals.[10] When the first edition of this book was written, financial stringency was holding up developments and though there was obvious promise in the application of electricity to large and small scale industry, to lift irrigation and to village life, the general tone lay between caution and pessimism. Despite large development since then, the present position is of continued shortage of power. Plan targets have almost been fulfilled, but the generally dynamic tendencies of the economy tend to outstrip even this. The country has moved from using 'hydel' as a catch-word to a position where hydro-electricity must be considered in relation to new sources of thermal power, including lignite and nuclear energy. This broader strategy of power is better discussed under Planning (Chapter 11).

[7] P. J. Thomas, *India's Basic Industries* (Orient Longmans, Bombay, 1948), 134, 142.

[8] But half the electricity to be generated by the Damodar scheme will be thermal, using the great reservoirs of the project.

[9] T. R. Sharma, *Location of Industries in India* (Hind Kitabs, Bombay, 2nd ed., 1949), 213.

[10] For a useful regional account in detail, see A. S. Jahauni, 'Development of electric power in north west India', *NGJI* 2/1 (1956), 48–67.

4. *Total energy budget: domestic fuel; the burning of cow-dung; alternative sources.*[11]
The recent estimates of India's total energy budget give a total of 166,000,000 tons in coal equivalent. Commerce and industry consume 67,000,000 or 40%, (coal 55,000,000 or 33%, oil 10,000,000 or 6%, hydro-electricity 2,000,000 or 1%), while domestic consumers use 99,000,000 tons of coal equivalent or 60% (dung 46,000,000 tons or 28%, wood and charcoal 35,000,000 or 21%, various waste materials 18,000,000 or 11%). The total domestic use of energy for fuel, light, etc., is about 0·25 tons per capita per annum, and is similar to that in Latin America.

Wood and dung have the lowest thermal efficiency (17% and 11%), hence the highest real cost. Wood is derived from roadsides and wastelands, too often causing accelerated soil erosion, rather than properly maintained woodlands; if it could be properly controlled and charcoal manufactured so that the by-products are collected for use, this part of the pattern would be less wasteful. The dung used in this way is only 40% of the total dung: perhaps 30% is lost, though some of this may benefit the soil, while the 10% *systematically* applied as manure – increasingly composted with leaves and refuse – is much greater in areas with a good proportion of forests (which also have sources of green manure) than in largely treeless tracts. Taking the All-India average proportion burned as an index ratio of 100, well forested States like Madhya Pradesh or Himachal Pradesh may burn as little as 10 to 15%, ill-forested States like Uttar Pradesh or Bengal 180% to 220% or even more.

A satisfactory household plant for the production of dung gas for cooking and (less satisfactorily) for lighting, has been produced by the Indian Agricultural Institute in New Delhi. The cost is Rs. 350, though only Rs. 80 is for mechanical parts that could not be produced locally in a village. It will produce 100 cu. ft. (2·8 m³) of gas daily – ample for the needs of an average family – from the dung of four animals, and the manurial value of the dung is not lost. In the cities, the processing of sewage for gas production could yield similar results – for Delhi 90% of the fuel needs for cooking could be met in this way. It is estimated that if dung burned could be saved, the equivalent of the output of twelve Sindris in manurial value could be applied to the fields in ammonium sulphate equivalent alone, while there are also phosphates present. So considerable capital investment would be justified; the great difficulty is that twelve Sindris would be easier to control than a myriad family plants in over 500,000 villages. But it is difficult to think of a more constructive task for Community Development.

---

[11] This section is compiled from: P. Pant, 'The development of India', *Scientific American*, 209 (1963), 189–206; *Domestic Fuels in India* (Natl Ccil Applied Economic Research; Asia, Bombay, 1959); J. Kishen, 'Domestic fuel consumption in India', *Jnl Sci. & Indl Research* (ND), 18A/10 (1959), 458–66; E. G. Rao, 'Evaluation of the domestic fuel situation in India . . .', *Jnl Inst. Engineering India*, 44 (1963), 49–66. Cf. also fn. 30 to Chap. 8.

B. MINERALS

Apart from the serious shortage of coking coals India has a rich endowment for heavy metallurgy: not only reserves of high grade iron ore hardly to be matched anywhere in the world, but good resources of alloy minerals, fluxes and refractories. She is weaker in the non-ferrous metals as a group, especially copper, although bauxite resources are good. She has almost a monopoly of mica and holds a strong position in the sources for atomic energy.

Juxtaposition of down-faulted sedimentaries including coal, with the rich concentration of iron and alloy minerals in the Archaean metamorphics, gives the peninsula its dominant position, especially the plateau fringes of Chota Nagpur. It seems unlikely that the hegemony of the northeast quarter of the Peninsula will ever be seriously challenged, but prospecting and the development of power are producing important mining areas in the south and will eventually make much more of the mineral resources of the Himalayas.

1. Bases for iron and steel

The Dharwarian and Cuddapah rocks of the eastern half of the Peninsula contain some of the world's largest reserves of *iron ore*, mainly haematites and magnetites of high iron content – $60-70\%$ Fe. The most important exploitation lies on the northern flanks of the Orissa Hills, in what were the states of Keonjhar, Bonai and Mayurbhanj and in Singbhum District, Bihar.[12] Here 'there is what appears to be a range of iron running almost continuously for 40 miles', and this alone is estimated to hold 2,700,000,000–3,000,000,000 tons of metallic iron – 'thought to be the largest and richest deposits of iron perhaps in the world, surpassing in magnitude the Lake Superior ores.'[13] The ores occur in close association with banded haematite quartzites in the Dharwar schist series within the Archaean, probably because of secondary enrichment of the iron content of zones within volcanic series by re-arrangement of iron by later solutions.[14] This ironfield extends southwards into Chhattisgarh, Bastar (which jungly District has at least 600,000,000 tons), and southern Madhya Pradesh, where whole hills of haematite several hundred feet high are found; Madhya Pradesh has at least 1,100,000,000 tons. In the Damodar Valley the ironstone shales of the Raniganj coalfield have reserves of about 400,000,000 tons of lower-grade ore ($35-40\%$ Fe). Mysore has 250,000,000–600,000,000 tons, all over 42% Fe, and 100,000,000 about 65%. The magnetite ($35-40\%$ Fe) resources of Salem are unknown but at least to be reckoned in hundreds of millions of tons.

After this it seems an anti-climax to note the vast quantities of lower-grade

[12] The ores were discovered by a pioneer Bengali geologist, P. N. Bose, in 1904 (Brown and Dey, *op. cit.* 178); for a regional account, see below, 713–15, and also P. P. Karan, 'Iron mining in Singhbhum and Mayurbhanj Region', *Economic Geography*, 33 (1957), 349–61.

[13] G. B. Jathar and S. G. Beri, *Indian Economics* (OUP, Bombay, 7th ed., 1942), I.29–30; D. N. Wadia, *Geology of India* (Macmillan, London, 3rd ed. revised, 1961), 476.

[14] Brown and Dey, *op. cit.* 179–80, where other theories are also quoted.

(25–40% Fe) lateritic ores; the magnetite sands of the Konkan beaches, derived from erosion of the Deccan lavas and used for primitive smelting; the Dharwarian ores of Goa and Ratnagiri (Maharashtra); the large deposits of 40–60% Fe in Kumaon; and the association of poorer ores with the Tertiary coal of Assam.

Reserves of the major deposits of high grade ores amount to about 8,000,000,000 tons, but reserves of lower grade ores are very large and the Third Plan quotes total reserves of almost 22,000,000,000 tons. So superfluous is this richness that the Jamshedpur and Asansol furnaces for long did not use ore much below 60% Fe content, and some consignments are 69% Fe, 'the theoretical composition of pure haematite being 70% iron and 30% oxygen'.[15] However, the trend is towards less selective mining followed by careful mixing in the sintering process, to conserve resources. The main drawback of Indian ore is that much contains too little phosphorus for the relatively cheap Bessemer process, though some Deccan ores may have as much as 0·15% phosphorus. Fluxes are usually available. Large new ironfields are being developed, some for new iron and steel plants, others for ore exports mainly to Japan and Eastern Europe. Thus the Kiriburu field in Bihar and Orissa developed with Japanese aid has yielded ores for export, though it will be used eventually for Durgapur and Bokaro plants. It will be replaced, for export purposes, by a new field in Orissa where the Bailadila Range cliffs of haematite are being developed in association with a Japanese steel firm, and a rail link is being built to Visakhapatnam. It is possible that one of the new Fourth Plan steel mills may be built in this region; reserves here amount to some 3,500,000,000 tons with some limonite in addition. Similarly Mysore, which has rich reserves within 100–200 miles of the west coast ports, has recently explored new ones with reserves of 120,000,000 tons. The easily exploited ores of Goa, recently acquired by annexation, have a somewhat lower iron content. Again a future steel plant is being considered for either Goa or Hospet. Similar ores with a half million ton reserve are being developed at Ratnagiri. It is clear that even with the current output of 12,000,000 tons a year considerably increased, India's iron ore reserves can be reckoned in millennia rather than centuries.

Manganese, as Sondhi points out, has been an Indian export since 1891, second only to iron ore as an earner of foreign exchange.[16] With a production of well over a million tons she is equal to South Africa, and together they are second to USSR. Production has fluctuated with world demand and competition and still tends to do so in spite of increased home demands as steel making progresses. The chief problem is the reduction of the phosphorus content and the beneficiation of low grade ores to meet export standards under Indian conditions.

The ores are widely distributed in peninsular India in either tabular deposits in pre-Cambrian metamorphics, or subsequently formed or enriched deposits from weathering of manganiferous rocks or lodes. The Keonjhar Hills of Orissa

[15] A. M. Heron, *Mineral Resources* (OPIA, No. 28, 1945), 13.
[16] V. P. Sondhi, 'Manganese ores in India', *Indian Minerals*, 11/3 (1957), 167–84.

provide about a third, the northwest Districts of Mysore and Balaghat in Madhya Pradesh about a fifth each, Bhandara in Maharashtra and Rajasthan the remainder. Reserves are in the region of 185,000,000 tons of which under 50,000,000 are of high quality.

2. *Other minerals used in the engineering industries*

Unfortunately, the non-ferrous metals are not so well represented in Indian resources; some are completely lacking, such as tungsten, cobalt, and nickel, and others are inaccessible or difficult to work. *Lead and zinc* have largely to be imported. The only producing area is at Zawar in Rajasthan with an output of about 150,000 tons and reserves of 8,000,000–10,000,000 tons. Lead is smelted at Tundoo in Bihar and a little silver obtained in the process. The zinc, until now sent to Japan for refining, will be processed at the plant now under way at Debori near Udaipur. *Copper* too is a deficit mineral: only 10% of needs are produced from the 80-mile (129 km.) copper belt along the Subarnarekha southeast of Jamshedpur, where there are reserves of 3,000,000–4,000,000 tons. But there are reserves of 20,000,000 tons in Khetri and Dariba Districts in Rajasthan, and a smelter and refinery are under way. Some exploitation of the Sikkim copper is in progress as a joint venture with the Sikkim Government. Expansion of the existing refinery at Ghatsila in Bihar, with the new one at Khetri, may ultimately produce up to half India's needs for alloys and electrical industries; but these are always growing. It will also produce useful side-products of nickel, sulphur and selenium. Other, more doubtful, reserves have been found in Hassan (Mysore), and in the outer Himalayas. All Indian ores are low in copper content – about 2% only.

Of the abrasives, *corundum* is obtained from surface deposits in Sidhi District in Madhya Pradesh and to a lesser extent from Salem (Madras) and Hassan (Mysore), while *garnets* from Sikar District (Rajasthan) are still cheaper than the synthetic product; the Panna *diamonds* (Madhya Pradesh) provide only a quarter of needs, the rest being imported.

Chromite production also fluctuates with overseas demand, for over 95% of production is still exported to Japan and Europe for alloys. The bulk comes from ultra-basic intrusions in the Baula Hills of Cuttack and Keonjhar in Orissa, which also have the biggest proportion of a total reserve of 4,000,000–5,000,000 tons. Total output is in the region of 45,000 tons, the rest coming from Singbhum (Bihar), Bandhara (Maharashtra) and Hassan (Mysore). Within India chromite is only used at present for chemical (mainly tanning) and refractory uses. The main problem is the beneficiation of low grade ores to a marketable standard. *Vanadium* is not exploited although interest and exploration are increasing with the demand for alloys and atomic energy. There is a reserve of over 20,000,000 tons, along with the iron ores of Singbhum and bordering parts of Orissa; but it can also be obtained from steel slag and alumina sludge.

There are also adequate resources of refractory materials: *fireclays* are exploited in Sambalpur to provide Jamshedpur's needs, and there are significant quantities produced in the Damodar coalfields, Jabalpur (Madhya Pradesh), and South Arcot and Tiruchchirapalli in Madras. There is a small export to Pakistan and Burma. Production of *magnesite* has greatly increased to over 200,000 tons a year, from the open cast workings occurring as veins in the intrusive masses of the Chalk Hills near Salem in Madras; but there are big reserves here, in Mysore and in the Almora hills, the last to be opened up. Some 15% is exported, and the rest used for furnace linings and some chemical processes. *Asbestos* is however in short supply, all but 5% being imported; home supplies come from Rajasthan but there are fair deposits of chrysotile asbestos in the Andhra Cuddapah series. *Kyanite* from perhaps the largest deposit in the world, at Lapse Buru near Jamshedpur, is taken mainly from surface deposits and exported; only a little is used in India for high-grade refractory bricks, and for insulator and heater elements. *Sillimanite* is also a silicate of aluminium, and shares the very high heat resisting qualities of kyanite which make both suitable for purposes where fireclays break down. It is, however, a controlled export since the reserves in the only workings (in the Khasi Hills) are not large. Limestone for flux is plentiful and new deposits are being developed for instance in Durg District (Madhya Pradesh) for Bhilai, and Sandigarh's calcite marbles in Orissa for Rourkela (see also building materials, below). Quartz for ferro-silicon is also abundant.

3. Minerals used in the electricity industry

The chief user of aluminium is the electrical industry, especially since its substitution for the costly and scarce copper is desirable; it is important too for innumerable consumer goods including ubiquitous drinking vessels and plates. With plentiful reserves, in the region of 270,000,000 tons, of which some 73,000,000 are of high quality, India exports *bauxite* to Japan, Australia and Europe, while importing about two-thirds of her aluminium needs; such a situation reflects of course an early stage of development of an industry, in this case linked with the high power needs for the conversion of purified alumina to aluminium. Bauxite is obtained from the scarp faces of thick lateritic blankets on the peninsular plateaus; a situation making exploitation difficult. The main source of this type is in west Bihar, where workings feed the ore first by aerial ropeway and thence to the Lohardaga railhead. Similar deposits in Orissa await access, and in Madhya Pradesh those at Amarkanatak may be developed with Rihand power. The high level deposits of Kolhapur (Maharashtra) and the Shevaroy Hills (Madras) will be exploited with Koyna and Mettur power. Processing takes place at the integrated works at Jaykaynagar near Asansol, using thermal power; ore is also purified to alumina at Muri and converted by hydro electric power at Hirakud in Orissa and at Alwaye in Kerala, involving high transport costs in the latter case, in order to benefit from cheap power.[17]

[17] P. Dayal, 'Location and development of the aluminium industry in India', *NGJI* 4/2 (1958), 67–78.

Low level laterites, being more accessible, have been worked for many years at Katni in the Son Valley in Madhya Pradesh and still supply the cement and refractory industries; reserves are good. But the leading producer in this rapidly changing and developing industry is Gujarat; here low level laterites round Kaira provide bauxite for export from Okha port.

All the exploited peninsular bauxites have aluminium content between 50% and 60%; near Riasi and Poonch in Jammu are Eocene fossil laterites which reach 80%; unfortunately they are at heights from 2,000 to 5,000 ft. (610–1,525 m.), and lack at least existing power development; it seems Bhakra will have none to spare.

Bauxite production has expanded from under 20,000 tons in 1947 to over 500,000 tons. There is sufficient caustic soda for the alumina plants from the growing heavy chemical industry; the essential catalyst, cryolite, has previously been entirely imported from Greenland, but progress is reported in the home manufacture of a synthetic cryolite.

India produces almost 90% of the world's *mica* – one of the fundamentals of the electrical industry – and exports almost all her annual output of about 30,000 tons. About half of this comes from the Bihar mica belt, lying along the northern fringes of the Chota Nagpur Plateau in Hazirabagh; the other half comes almost equally from Nellore in Andhra and Bhilwara in Rajasthan. In Bihar, mica is obtained from innumerable primitive workings under difficult conditions along the forested scarps. Exploitation has shifted steadily eastwards over the last fifty years, echoing in a way the shifting cultivation of the hill tribes who comprise the work-force, and following similar laws of diminishing returns due to primitive exploitation.[18] There is increasing attention to quality control and export incentives to beat the potential competition from Brazil and from synthetics, not easy to bring home to the jungle miner or cottage worker splitting 'books' of mica.

India is very well placed for the raw materials necessary for atomic energy. Although known to exist for more than fifty years, it is only recently that workable deposits of *uranium* have been identified in Singbhum and Rajasthan, associated with pre-Cambrian thrust planes. More erratic sources are the mica-bearing pegmatites of Bihar. But her greatest strength lies in the *monazite* which is one of the minerals won from the black sands of the western littoral of south India.[19] *Thorium* from the monazite was first exploited by German, then British, interests for gas mantles; this use has now been superseded by the rise of thorium as an even more important factor in atomic power production than uranium itself.[20] Placer deposits in Bihar may double the known beach sand reserves of 1,500,000 tons in Travancore. Even higher amounts of thorium are

[18] P. P. Karan, 'The Bihar mica belt', *NGJI* 4/1 (1958), 16–34.

[19] P. Viswanathan, 'Beach sands of South India', *Science and Culture*, 27/1 (1961), 16–21, recounts the discovery of the Kerala beach sands in Kerala by C. W. von Schomberg, after walking in vain along the east coast from the Godavari to Tuticorin.

[20] D. N. Wadia, 'India and the Atomic Age', *Science and Culture*, 23/6 (1957), 264–70.

found in the rare *cheralite* also obtained from the black sands along with *zir-conium*. The latter, comprising some 6% of the sand, is essential in reactors as a refractory, as well as having ceramic uses; and resources which are the world's largest are now naturally jealously guarded. *Graphite* is also a strategic mineral now, because of its use in reactors; although it can be obtained from the chimney deposits of oil-fired power stations, research is going on along the Eastern Hills in the Khondalite series analogous to the graphite bearing rocks of Ceylon.

4. *Minerals used in chemical industries, and for glass and ceramics*

These are multifarious and only a broad review can be given; but from the humble but basic common salt, to the vital sources for fertilizers, they are of fundamental significance. *Salt* has historic associations and a wide range of modern industrial uses. It also is exported, mainly to Japan. Over 80% of the annual output of some 3,500,000 tons is from the evaporation of sea water in the tidal flats of Kutch and Maharashtra, with important contributions from Andhra and Madras coasts. The delta coast of Bengal is too wet for evaporation and the sea is too fresh; hence a small export to East Pakistan. Some 7% is produced from Lake Sambhar and the Pachbhadra beds of Rajasthan, and developments are planned in refining and even iodising to provide for the goitrous hill tracts. The magnesium chloride from the Kutch salts is also exported. There is a small output from the rock salts of Mandi (Himachal Pradesh), with further development planned.

Gypsum is used as an agent to retard the setting of cement, but two-thirds of the output are now used in the converting of ammonia to ammonium sulphate, and as a direct source for sulphuric acid; this is important since India lacks any sulphur resource. The pure gypsums of Jammu and Garwhal are used in plaster of Paris and as paint fillers, but production is negligible. Over 90% of the gypsum produced comes from the Bikaner, Barmer and Nagaur Districts of Rajasthan, and has increased by some 200% since supplies from the Salt Range were cut off in 1947. Reserves are good, but are becoming more difficult to work as the accessible manually quarried beds are depleted; the gypsum goes to Sindri, but a local fertilizer plant is planned. Tiruchchirappalli and Coimbatore, both in Madras, provide about 4% each of the total. In all, India is self sufficient, but there is some anxiety about the future as demands increase.

Sources for phosphatic fertilizers are much more deficient. India is able only to produce some 10% of her needs, and her twenty or more super-phosphate factories rely on imports from North Africa. Of the native output, over 90% comes from manually quarried lenses of *apatite* associated with the copper, uranium and magnetites of Singbhum; it is owned and chiefly utilized by Indian Iron and Steel in the making of the highly phosphorous pig iron. There is a small production from similar rocks in Visakhapatnam, and investigation is proving fair quantities of phosphatic nodules in Cretaceous clays in Tiruchchirappalli although little is exploited yet and there are problems of beneficiation. Some phosphate is obtained from monazite at the Rare Earth plant at Alwaye in Kerala. These sands too contain *ilmenite*, a major source of titanium oxide for pigment. Some 95% is exported, unlike the carefully guarded strategic monazite from the same source. The concentration is high – even the tailings from previous workings have a higher proportion of heavy minerals than the virgin sands exploited in Australia; yet poor methods and standards have led to economic difficulties in export.[21]

Several minerals are used as fillers in paper, textiles and paints; of these *barytes* (obtained from fissure veins associated with trap sills) from Kurnool has an export surplus, and a plant to produce barium chemicals is planned at Kothugudum in Andhra. *Steatite*, which is tending to replace kaolin and is used also in fertilizers, is also exported to Europe; the bulk comes from large pockets in the metamorphics of Anantpur and Chittoor in Andhra, which with Sirohi in Rajasthan also produces an increasing quantity of calcite as a filler and for insecticides. Adequate quantities of *Fullers earth*, used in bleaching and purifying oils, are found in Jaisalmer and Jodhpur and may even have a potential export value; it is of course the *dhobi* or washerman's main raw material, apart from a slab of stone or concrete. Another bleaching clay, with increasing demand in association with oil drilling, is *bentonite* found in Gujarat.

Felspar supplying the potteries of Jabalpur is mined from the pegmatites of Ajmer, and can be exported given better freight rates, and quartz has already been mentioned.

5. Building materials

The great majority of houses are built directly of mud (*terre pisé*) or of mud bricks, and stones may be set in mud-mortar or in lime derived directly from *kankar* concretions in the alluvium or from rock. The most important large scale exploitation is that of limestone for the cement industry rapidly expanding to meet the demands of today. There seem to be almost inexhaustible reserves in the Vindhyan limestones of the Son Valley; their relationships to steel needs have already been mentioned. In the south the deposits in Tiruchchirappalli are mainly used for cement. The bulk of the output, now in the region of 15,000,000 tons a year and planned to reach 30,000,000 tons by the end of the Third Plan, comes from the relatively small number of big concerns; but there is a multitude of small-scale quarries. India's building stones are justly famous: good *granites* and *slates* (the latter mostly Himalayan), the unique Porbandar *miliolite* and many meretricious *marbles*. *Deccan Lava* is a sombre material, giving dignity to even unimaginative architecture, and there is perhaps no more beautiful stone in the world than the Vindhyan *sandstone* of Akbar's rose red palaces. Nor should the humble *laterite* be forgotten, whether squared for tanks, temples or new village housing, or crushed to rubble and red dust on the local roads.

And so, finally to *gold*, impossible to class with any of our groups, but so

[21] P. Viswanathan, *op. cit.*

important to the Indian; for it is even – perhaps especially with today's anxieties – his personal bank. Its national importance is clear – and at times of crisis the government appeals to women especially to give gold jewellery to their country. It is mined solely from the Dharwarian quartz reefs of Mysore: at Kolar, which still produces three-quarters of the output, yields have been steadily decreasing as the mines extended to deeper and less productive levels; some go down 9,000 ft. (2,743 m.). The Hutti mines (Raichur District) are increasing output, and there is active exploration of the possibilities of re-opening the old fields of the Wynaad on the Mysore–Madras border and in Andhra.

It has been said that India is a rich land inhabited by poor people. The present balance sheet of India's power and mineral resources is given in the table below. The dominance of iron, manganese and mica in the export list, and of petroleum in the import list, is clear; but of course minerals can be vital even though not needed in large quantities, as with copper or nickel. Japan is the principal trading partner, followed by the countries of Eastern Europe, but USA and UK are important customers for manganese and mica.

INDIA'S MINERAL BALANCE SHEET

Self-sufficiency	Exportable surplus in order of value	Imports necessary in order of value
Coal	Iron ⎫ 60%	Petroleum (75%)
Limestones	Manganese ⎬	Copper
Bentonite	Mica (20%)	Zinc
Calcite	Coal	Lead
China Clay	Teminite	Asbestos
Fullers Earth	Kyanite	Apatite
Garnet	Magnesite	Tin
Ochre	Chromite	Diamonds
Vermiculite	Bauxite	Nickel
	Sillimanite	Tungsten
	Barytes	Wolfram
	Fireclay	Cobalt
	Felspar	

II. PAKISTAN

A. POWER

1. *Coal*

Coal reserves, estimated variously, but probably between 160,000,000 and 200,000,000 tons, are concentrated in West Pakistan.[22] Mainly sub-bituminous Eocene coals, they are friable, with high sulphur and ash content, and non-

[22] R. R. Platt (ed.), *Pakistan: A Compendium* (American Geogl Soc., NY, 1961). Although already partly out of date, this is a useful source used throughout this section along with J. R. Andrus and A. F. Mohammed, *The Economy of Pakistan* (OUP, 1958).

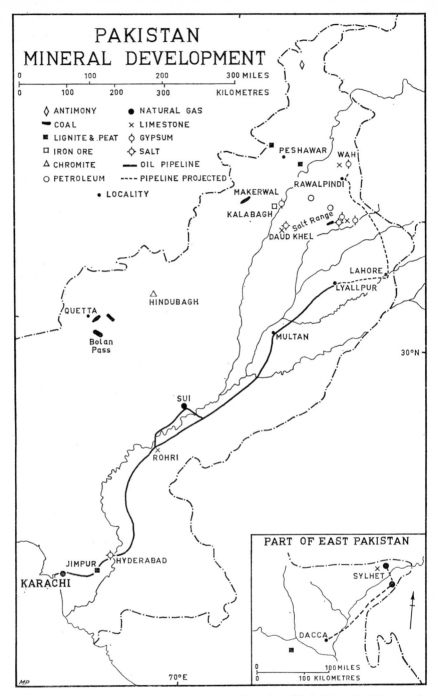

FIG 9.4 PAKISTAN: MINERAL DEVELOPMENT. Based on K. S. Ahmad, *A Geography of Pakistan* (1964). The pipeline should be shown as gas, not oil.

coking; exploitation is difficult because beds are thin and tilted, and the fields remote. Improved methods and intensive investigation of new reserves have almost doubled production in the last decade, to close on a million tons a year, but this is still only half of requirements, and higher grade coals are imported. Briquetting plants at Quetta and Rawalpindi produce fuel usable in foundry and factory from the poor quality lignites.

The highest production comes from Makerwal, the trans-Indus continuation of the Salt Range fields, themselves worked for over eighty years. But the biggest reserves are in Baluchistan, where the Khost–Sharig field along the Sibi railway has Pakistan's only coking coal, and her largest reserves. A newly developing field in the Sor Range, just east of Quetta, is seen as a useful asset to a backward region, and new roads and increased capacity on the Bolan railway are planned to meet its needs and those of the Mach field in the Bolan Pass area.[23]

Apart from these areas, there is some exploitation in the Kohistan region in western Sind, and of the poor lignites of the far northwest. East Pakistan has only the waterlogged peats and lignites of Sylhet,[24] Mymensingh and Faridpur, difficult to dry and of poor quality; coking coal is reported from Bogra too deep to mine, and there are high quality deposits in Paharpur which are thought to be extensive and economically viable, a continuation of the Bihar belt.

2. Petroleum

The most prolonged and expensive exploration by American and British companies, and now by the Pakistan Oil and Gas Development Commission which uses Soviet technicians, has failed to find commercial deposits beyond those of the small Potwar field; this in spite of the seemingly favourable geological conditions in the Tertiaries of the old 'Sind Gulf' in the west, and of Assam in the east. Drilling and access are difficult in the western deserts and the eastern jungles. Only a fifth of the country's quite modest needs (half of it used for diesel locomotives) are produced from the five small fields in the Punjab. The newer Bikasser wells produce more crude oil than the older Kaur and Dhulian fields, but it is of poorer quality and too thick to pipe to the refinery at Mogra; it is railed there. The Dhulian field has a small quantity of associated gas, now exploited.

One big refinery at Karachi will be joined by another within a short time; both relying on supplies from the Persian Gulf. East Pakistan so far imports all her oil ready refined.

3. Natural gas

In the course of oil prospecting in 1962, natural gas was discovered at Sui in the barren Bugti Hills 350 miles (563 km.) north of Karachi. Four other fields were

[23] F. Hussein, 'Structure and coal reserves of the Sor Range–Doghari Coalfield', *Oriental Geogr.* (Dacca), 5/2 (1961), 137–44.
[24] N. Ahmad, 'Peat deposits of the Faridpur District, East Pakistan', *ibid.* 5/1 (1961), 59–62.

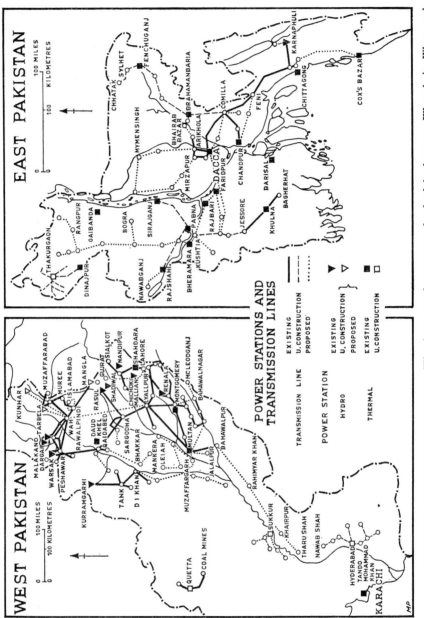

FIG 9.5 PAKISTAN: POWER DEVELOPMENT. The largest schemes are the hydel plants at Warsak in West and
Karnaphuli in East Pakistan (these are completed) and at Mangla in West Pakistan (projected); and the extended
thermal installation using Sui gas at Multan. Based on K. S. Ahmad op cit

soon found in the same region, and a big step was taken in solving Pakistan's fuel problems. Reserves would last four hundred years at present rates of consumption; even with vast increase, there is not less than fifty years supply.[25] A pipeline to Karachi, something of an engineering masterpiece as it crosses incredibly difficult terrain, began operating in 1955, serving industrial users at Hyderabad and Rohri. A branch goes to Multan 200 miles (322 km.) to the northeast from a point near the Gudu Barrage. At Karachi, the gas supplies both domestic and industrial needs as well as providing raw material for big new petro-chemical plants, and natural gas runs power stations at Karachi, Multan, Sukkur, Hyderabad and Lyallpur. The Multan branch will one day reach the new capital of Islamabad and serve the Punjab towns, supplementing the seasonably variable hydro-electricity and scarce coal reserves. The local tribal people in the new gas fields have benefited by lease payments and the new townships are bringing changes from a nomadic to sedentary way of life. In East Pakistan, natural gas has been found at four places in the Sylhet region; of purer quality but inferior quantity to the western supplies, the gas so far only supplies the Fenchuganj fertilizer plant (where again it is raw material as well as power) and the Chattak cement factory. There will be a pipeline to Dacca.

4. Electricity (Fig. 9.5)

From a very meagre consumption of power in 1947 (about half coming from Indian sources), Pakistan now has an installed capacity which is outstripping demand, although increasing industrialization and decreasing costs of production should soon reverse this position. There has been a big change too from almost complete dependence on thermal plants to the development of hydro-electricity and natural gas, but steam plants still play a very important part. West Pakistan again dominates, with an installed capacity of about 500,000 kW in 1963, three-fifths of which is accounted for in almost equal amounts by the Warsak multi-purpose project and the Multan natural gas plant which is now being doubled. Integrated development of water and power was undertaken in 1958, and great strides have been taken since then. Natural gas also supplies fuel for plants at Hyderabad, Sukkur and Karachi. The old hydro-electric plant at Malakand in the northwest has been doubled in capacity. And three new canal fall projects have been added to the Rasul scheme, on the Jhelum and Chenab Canals. All the stations are linked by a Primary Grid ensuring continuity of supply throughout the country.

East Pakistan has about half the installed capacity of the west, the biggest single contributor being the Karnaphuli project. But thermal plants still dominate in total output, the bulk being in the Dacca–Narayanganj region, and in other urban centres. There is as yet no widespread grid although one is planned to distribute Karnaphuli power.

[25] G. Whittington, 'Natural gas resources of Pakistan', *Tijdschrift voor Econ. en Soc. Geografie*, 53 (1962), 163–4; also Table XIII.

B. MINERALS

Unfortunately Pakistan's mineral resources can be quickly summarized; she lacks coal and iron in anything like the quantity needed for major industry, and remoteness is a serious drawback to developing such minerals as she has. There is, however, a good base for chemicals in the Salt Range complex. And the discovery and development of natural gas, first in the west and now in the east, has given tremendous impetus to power and industry.

The only known deposits of high grade *iron ore* lie in two extremities of the country – in Chitral and in northwest Baluchistan where they are too remote to exploit. Low grade ores (35–45% Fe) have been found in Mianwali District and experiments to determine their commercial value are in progress. *Chromite* is the only metallic ore mined in any quantity. The source is an ultra-basic intrusion in the Zhob valley worked since 1903, by primitive methods, and exported to Japan and UK. But production is a pathetic drop in the bucket of world output and it is subject to market fluctuations. The *antimony* mines of Chitral send small quantities across 175 miles (282 km.) of mountain road to a railhead. There are reported to be workable *manganese* deposits in the Las Bela region in the south of Baluchistan. *Fire clays* are being produced in increasing amounts from the Salt Range.

The chemical industry has a much firmer base: *salt* from the Salt Range and its trans-Indus continuation has been a government monopoly since Mogul times at least, and has been mined for over 1,000 years. The Khewra mine is the most mechanized of the three major workings which extract the salt from the vast, thick beds that stretch from Jhelum to Indus and beyond. Other centres are Warcha and Kalabagh, the latter now only of local importance; the layers here are thinner. Associated with the salt beds are large masses of *gypsum* mined for cement and also for the ammonium sulphate plant at Daud Khel (p. 502) further very large resources are as yet untouched in Sibi District in Baluchistan. *Magnesite* and *potassium* are found in workable amounts in the Salt Range and *alum* at Kalabagh. The *sulphur* in the volcanic craters of Koh-i-Sultan on the Afghan border is no longer worked; the Karachi refinery imports its supplies more cheaply. *Barytes* in Kalat (Baluchistan) and in Hazara District west of Rawalpindi now supplies all the needs of Pakistan's paint industry, and *bauxite* deposits in Hazara and in Azad Kashmir and Sibi are being assessed, and *silica* sand for glass comes from Sind. The lovely *marbles* of Peshawar region and the green *aragonite* marbles of Chagai are the basis of a small polishing industry, with a small export. But every one of these is in West Pakistan; the east has little but some glass sands in Mymensingh. And the position of the country as a whole offers little hope for new indigenous bases for industry, though those already exploited have considerable scope for expansion.

CHAPTER 10

The Evolution of Industry

I. FROM HANDICRAFTS TO FACTORY TECHNIQUES

The historical background

During those centuries when sailing ships, water-mills and handlooms were the most complicated machines in existence, India shared with China and Byzantium the leadership of the world in technical ingenuity, economic organization and volume of manufactures. Few finer textiles can ever have been produced than the 'woven wind', the diaphanous muslin of Dacca, and the wrought-iron pillar at Delhi, dated at latest AD 415, would rank as an outstanding technical achievement in any century before our own. For about 150 years after 1600 Indian textiles were a main staple of Eastern trade, and quite capable of capturing Western markets from local producers; so at least thought the London calico-printers when they rioted against the EIC's imports in 1721, and so secured protective legislation.

The decline from this position was abrupt, and with the rise of Lancashire and the fall of the princely Courts India collapsed into industrial insignificance, complete but for the hard-hit village crafts. In its external relations the whole Indian economy was geared to that of Britain, whether as market or as source of raw materials. The first steps towards a modern industry were indeed taken a century ago, but on the whole progress was irregular in time, space and the internal structure of industry. By 1957 India ranked about fifth among the industrial countries of the world, but this was a function of size rather than of development: coal and steel outputs were a fraction of those of the great industrial powers, output per head of population a fraction of that of minor industrial countries.

Yet perhaps only Brazil and China offer such scope for industrialization, and the technical bases have been laid. The main obstacles to advance are now probably social: low purchasing power, 'cheap' labour inefficient to the point of dearness. These are clearly linked factors, though unfortunately urban enthusiasm still seems to regard industry and agriculture as autonomous sectors of the economy, except that agriculture can be milked for raw materials.[1] Much Yamuna water has flowed past the Red Fort since Agarwala wrote, but residuals

[1] How strong this view is may be seen from the very odd arguments against it in A. N. Agarwala (ed.), *Position and Prospects of India's Foreign Trade* (Allahabad, 1947), 34-41.

of the controversy remain, and not entirely without reason: on the one hand, progress under the Five Year Plans has been imperilled by food shortages and other shortfalls in the agricultural sector; on the other, under existing conditions rural investment is very difficult to control, returns from it are *ipso facto* problematical, and yields are also vulnerable to monsoonal vagaries.

The crafts

It is hardly necessary to recount the dispossession of the artisan by the mill, whether the latter was British or, later, Indian – or Japanese;[2] in fact it is more to the point to indicate the limitations to this process. The town artisan, working for a market readily accessible to alien trade, suffered first and most; the village craftsman held out longer and in some areas, such as Assam, where communications are poor he has still a fairly strong position. Furthermore, distinctions must be made within the general category.

Those crafts with the highest survival value appear to be (*a*) services following population; (*b*) some luxury trades; (*c*) at the other extreme some crafts which have as it were a market sheltered by its poverty, or which deal in raw materials not worth processing by modern methods. Within all groups, in proportions varying with the technical cast of each trade, there is a wide range of organization, from the true independent artisan owning both tools and raw materials, through all the variants of piece-work for entrepreneurs, putting-out, and so on, to workers in what is in effect an embryonic factory. The pages of Lipson or Cunningham take on visible flesh and blood in this laboratory for the economic historian.

(*a*) The village servants include smiths, carpenters, tailors, potters. In the old days of self-sufficiency these were supported by a definite assignment of land or by a fixed annual payment in kind, in return for which they met all normal requirements through the year, but these customary arrangements have been largely superseded by payment for the job. Except where they do piece-work (knives, locks, etc.) for petty town entrepreneurs, the smiths are now less makers than fixers, and the same is true, to a less extent, of carpenters: they are the village repair and maintenance men, and 'it is the smith and the carpenter who make the Persian wheels go round'. The increasing use of simple machinery may actually improve their position, given some elementary technical education. Potters have to meet the demand for very cheap wares necessitated by the custom of smashing food-dishes after use (especially on ritual occasions) in order to obviate the risk of caste defilement; this is of course losing ground, but obviously no factory process could market at a sufficiently low price to meet the need. This custom is doubtless responsible for the striking lack of an important ceramic in Hindu civilization, perhaps alone among the great cultures of the world.[3]

[2] One of the most celebrated cases, if only on account of Marx's notorious onslaught on the EIC, is the decline of the once world-famous Dacca muslin industry; see N. Ahmad, *An Economic Geography of East Pakistan* (OUP, 1958), 94–102, and below 585.

[3] There is some attractive modern factory-made pottery, e.g. from Gwalior, but it is hardly equal aesthetically to the pots turned out in hundreds in any small Burmese town.

(b) The luxury crafts include the makers of the finest silk *saris*, of gold and silver-thread embroideries, really skilled jewellers, ivory-carvers, and so on. The old Court demand is all but dead, owing in part to the liquidation of the old aristocracies and in part to the apeing of bad European taste by the survivors, and only in a few places are classic standards more or less maintained. There is a strong tendency for these crafts to turn to workshop organization and the tourist market, with results more deplorable than describable.

(c) A vast demand at the lowest possible price-level is responsible for the survival of such trades as the making of *bidis*, the ersatz 'cigarette' of the masses; the units of sale are so petty as to be not worth much capital equipment so long as there is a reserve of cheap labour. *Bidi*-making is essentially a sweatshop industry using female and child labour; it could of course be put-out, but the entrepreneurs prefer the adulteration to be done for their own profit. The factory leather industry has made notable advances, and improved methods are found in some small rural tanneries and training centres, but the formerly untouchable Chamars still produce millions of half-tanned 'kips' from their crude vats; the hides of diseased and half-starved cattle, riddled by sores and ticks, are hardly worth tanning by modern methods. 'Like many other Indian handicraftsmen, the untouchable tanners remain because of the presence of low-grade materials and a market for cheap products.'[4]

The *charkha* or spinning-wheel and the handloom raise a number of difficult and much-canvassed questions: can they survive in the face of mill competition? if so, how? and is it really worthwhile to save them? The values involved are as much human as economic, and the answers therefore subjective; and the economic arguments are too technical to be discussed here. The whole question is studded with sociological man-traps, and the more sentimental devotees of the *charkha* simply ignore, or distort, the comparative costs of mill and home production. Nevertheless it would be socially very desirable to provide some relief to the seasonal un- and under-employment of the countryside, and perhaps even morally beneficial, as Gandhi held; this element in Gandhian thought was sufficiently strong for the spinning wheel to be placed centrally in India's national flag. Improvements to the *ambar charkha* and to handlooms are spreading, and a compromise solution may be possible by decentralising the machine spinning industry to provide cheaper yarn, and fostering cottage or small workshop weaving with electric looms.

Other rural crafts and trades, at present strictly speaking uneconomic, might be salvaged and become economically worthwhile given a sufficiency of *cheap* power; and since the expansion of large-scale industry cannot hope to take in all the increasing surplus of rural population, some such development, if attainable, might provide a way out of the impasse of an increase of population at a rate

[4] D. H. Buchanan, *The Development of Capitalist Enterprise in India* (Macmillan, NY, 1934), 94; his whole Chapter V is a very fair discussion of the craft *vs.* machine question and still valuable.

disproportionate to the expansion of agricultural and factory output. But obviously there are no short-cuts on these roads, and no easy salvation for India's ancient crafts.

Phases of industrialization

Broadly speaking, India's industrial revolution falls into five phases:

(i) *c.* 1854–1914: the provision of a railway net, the usual initial concentration on textiles;

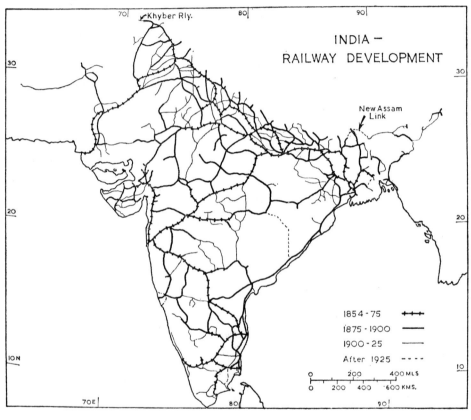

FIG 10.1 GROWTH OF THE RAILWAY SYSTEM.

(ii) 1914–21: (*a*) recognition of India's potential significance and actual insignificance to Imperial military economics; (*b*) political unrest and the attainment of fiscal autonomy;

(iii) 1921–39: experiments in protection, rise of iron and steel and of sugar industry, considerable but uneven progress generally;

(iv) 1939–50: involvement in a world war under the colonial power, the struggle for independence, the first uncertain years of a new nation;

(v) 1950 to date: India in the era of planning; it is a measure of the import-ance of this phase that it has been seriously claimed (though it might be difficult to substantiate the claim) that more progress has been made since the Plans began in 1951 than in the preceding half-century.[5] This last phase is the subject of the succeeding chapter.

1854–1914: Cotton is King. In the 19th century the EIC itself did virtually nothing for Indian economic development, except to foster opium cultivation for the China trade, to introduce tea-planting from China, and to give some support to the long-drawn-out attempts at exploiting Salem iron ores (below, 754); it left the field clear for private enterprise to flood India with Manchester goods, to extend tea and indigo plantations, and to build up a great export trade in cotton, jute, hides and oilseeds. Before 1850 a few steam-engines had been set up in docks, flour-mills and so on, mainly around Calcutta.

But the decade 1854–64 was critical. Politically the Mutiny led to the end of Company rule; economically two distant wars led to the founding of Indian factory industry: the Crimean War by cutting off hemp supplies to Dundee (which had been experimenting with power-woven jute since 1835) and so creating a great demand for raw jute; the American Civil War by producing an even more inflationary demand for raw cotton. With money pouring in and fibres pouring out it would have been strange indeed had nobody turned his mind to local manufacture. The major economic effect of the Mutiny was to render urgent, for military reasons, the extension of the two or three fragments of rail-way which existed in 1857, and this played a part in the general quickening of economic activity, not least by the establishment of railshops and collieries. But for sixty years at least railways rate policy favoured the export of cash crops and hampered industrial development away from the three great ports.

In 1854 a jute mill was opened at Calcutta, a cotton mill at Broach and another at Bombay;[6] the pioneers were respectively English, American and – significantly – Parsee. By 1861 Bombay had eight mills with nearly 200,000 spindles and a start had been made at Ahmedabad; the frenzied finance of the cotton boom was succeeded by merited catastrophe, but the Suez Canal (1869) was a stimulant and by 1877 there were fifty-one cotton mills with nearly 1,250,000 spindles, though only 10,385 looms. The jute manufacturing boom came later, with a jump from five to eighteen mills in 1873–75. From the first, however, weaving was important in Bengal, while Bombay devoted itself primarily to spinning, largely for the hand-looms of China. Apart from the local raw cotton – offset by the necessity of importing coal from England – the major factor in the lead taken by the west coast was historical. The sixty years which intervened between Plassey

[5] S. R. Sen, 'History of planning in India', *India 1962* (Information Service of India, London, 1962); the claim might be justified by the increase of 100% in the index of industrial production, 1950–60; only one index, but significant of achievement. See also P. Pant, 'The development of India', *Scientific American*, 209 (1963), 189–206.

[6] An unsuccessful cotton mill was set up at Bowreah, Calcutta, about 1818 (Buchanan, 128, 136). The Bombay mill is often dated 1851.

and the overthrow of the Marathas were those of the most ruthless economic aggression by the commercial oligarchs of Calcutta, seated in the entry to Hindustan and with their attention fixed on the richest plains of India. The very active trade of Bombay had a stronger element local to the Arabian Sea, and was hence more largely shared by indigenous groups such as Parsees and Khoja Muslims; indigenous enterprise was never so stifled as in the east. It is significant that the Managing Agency system is strongest in Bengal, where indigenous capitalists – quite rightly – showed an entire lack of confidence in their own managerial capacity. Hence while, except for the great Sassoon interests, British participation in cotton was from the start very slight, it is only in the last few years that British interests in jute have been bought out, and the executives of the industry are still in part Scots.

Apart from the growth of coal mining and of the service industries (foundries, etc.) of the ports, the last quarter of the 19th century was marked mainly by the spread of cotton mills to inland centres – Ahmedabad, Nagpur, Sholapur. By 1900 factories employed some 500,000 workers, of whom 160,000 were in cotton.

By 1900 also there was a significant hardening of nationalist feeling; Congress was soon to change its tone from 'we respectfully submit' to 'we demand'. A main part in this change was played by resentment against the government's adoption in 1883 of a virtually complete Free Trade policy; where the small revenue tariff could have assisted Indian manufactures (e.g. $3\frac{1}{2}\%$ on cotton goods) a countervailing excise was imposed. This certainly gave colour to suspicions that the whole policy was rigged in favour of Lancashire. The placing of India on the gold standard (1893–98) was a severe blow to the yarn trade with China, which adhered to silver; but this may have been a blessing in disguise since it impelled an increase of weaving and a better balance within the industry. There was neither disguise nor blessing in Lord Morley's doctrinaire refusal to sanction the Madras Government's industrial experiments. From the Indian point of view Free Trade was decidedly illiberal.

Yet despite all difficulties expansion continued: on the eve of the First World War coal output was over 12,000,000 tons, factories with over fifty hands employed some 900,000 workers, and few important towns had not been reached by a railway. And in 1911 the first pig iron had flowed into Jamshedpur moulds.

1914–21: the empty arsenal. The First World War brought an abrupt fall in imports from the warring countries and a boom demand for Indian raw materials, while the important campaigns in Mesopotamia and Palestine cried out for stores which could have been supplied by an integrated Indian industry, had that existed. The stage was set for large expansion, but the prime weakness of India's industrial structure was at once apparent: an almost complete lack of machines to make machines.

The growth of consumption industries had been favoured by untaxed machinery imports – some offset to 'Lancashire interference' – but this inhibited the development of production goods. As a result purely extractive industries boomed, Jamshedpur was sheltered at a critical phase, and existing industries worked to capacity; but except for jute, for which Calcutta engineering firms managed to produce some plant, very little expansion was possible. Government now paid heavily for its policy (in bland disregard of its own rules) of purchasing stores in England even when, with little inconvenience, they could have been had in India; a policy at once discriminatory and lacking discrimination. As it was, Britain's loss in the Indian market was only in small part India's gain; the lion's share went to Japan. Exports also were affected: in the Chinese yarn trade the India : Japan proportions of 77 : 23 in 1906 were exactly reversed by 1924. No better justification could have been found for the thesis that fiscal control from London was indefensible.

The post-war boom-and-slump was aggravated in India by violent fluctuations of the rupee. Nevertheless in 1922 factory employment was 1,360,000, and it is significant that the share of cotton had fallen from a third in 1902 to a quarter. At this point India gained fiscal autonomy.

1922–39: 'Discriminating Protection'. The new powers were exercised with discretion, rather strict interpretation being given, for instance, to the principle that an industry to receive protection should have such natural advantages as adequate home supplies of raw materials; this ruled out the glass industry for lack of soda ash, though matches, dependent on imported splints, received protection. The following figures illustrate the progress of the chief protected industries:[7]

	Steel	Sugar	Paper	Cotton Piecegoods	Matches
		1,000 tons		*1,000,000 yards*	*100,000 gross*
1922–23	131	24	24	1,725	8
1939–40	1,070	1,242	70	4,013	220
Increase %	717	5,075	192	132	2,850

The depression of the early 30s slowed expansion, but there was little actual retrogression, in part doubtless because there was so much leeway to make up. Cotton, for instance, added to both spindles and looms in every year until 1937.

Progress, however, was on a very ragged front, the most serious laggard being perhaps heavy chemicals. The leading developments of the inter-war years were: (i) changes in the cotton industry – an increased proportion of higher counts, especially in Ahmedabad; a relative decline in the position of Bombay Province, with an actual fall in the number of mills in Bombay Island; a rapid expansion in Mysore and Madras, especially at Coimbatore, consequent on the use of Jog, Nilgiri and Cauvery power;[8] (ii) the expansion of Jamshedpur as a metallurgical

[7] J. Matthai, *Tariffs and Industry* (OPIA No. 20, 1944), 9–12.

[8] In 1921 western India had 68·6% and southern India 9·3% of 280 mills; in 1937 the percentages were respectively 56·3 and 17·7 of 419 mills (T. R. Sharma, *Location of Industries in India* (Hind Kitabs, Bombay, 3rd ed., 1954), 30.).

centre; (iii) the rise of the sugar and cement industries; (iv) a proliferation of minor consumption industries. This last was in the nature of things, but was powerfully aided by the nationalist boycotts of British goods.

In 1939 coal output was 28,000,000 tons, steel had topped the million, and industrial employment (excluding government ordnance and railshops, and seasonal gins and presses) was 1,809,000. Cotton again accounted for nearly 33%, probably owing to Tamilnad's entry into the 'first phase'. Allowing for the multiplied mechanization of the second war, India was far better equipped in 1939 than in 1914, and this was reflected in a marked, if highly uneven, expansion not only in heavier industry – where, for instance, Jamshedpur developed some armament lines – but also, despite all difficulties of supply, of consumption industries.

Some general features

(*a*) *Mistries and Managing Agents.* The old territorial patchwork, the *morcellement* of the fields, the ladder of sub-tenancies from ryot to zamindar, the vivisection of society by caste – all these suggest that 'fragmentation' is a main motif in the life of India. Nor is even modern industry altogether exempt, despite such great integrations as the House of Tata. There seems a curious tendency to depute and re-depute responsibility: at one end of the scale labour is recruited and controlled by contractors, at the other executive functions are farmed out to Managing Agents, and exchanges in between are in the sticky hands of multiple hordes of middlemen.

There was originally, doubtless, good reason for this fragmentation of functions, just as there was for caste, but it can hardly be doubted that it is now a burden on industry, with endless delays, frictions and confusions, as well as the direct cash charge for services rendered. Thus the labour jobber or *mistry* – there are other names for him – who beat up a gang of labourers was useful enough in the earlier phases; he is now often an unscrupulous exploiter of both sides, at times even a strike-leader, more frequently a strike-breaker. He adds to legitimate commissions innumerable exactions from his workers, bound to him by initial advances, and thus secures his hold to the serious detriment of good and stable labour relations.

At the top is the Managing Agency system. This again was natural enough when Indian capitalists with no technical experience wished to start an industry; the importers who provided the plant would set it up and recruit technicians and managers; they would also buy stores and raw materials and market the product. This was, as it were, insurance against inexperience; but when in time one Agency came to run scores of firms, with perhaps a dozen of them in the same line, and was paid largely by commissions on both purchases and sales (or, much worse, on output sold or unsold) and took policy decisions for the 'directors' to rubber-stamp, the possibilities of abuse became enormous.[9] There are now

[9] See Buchanan, 165–72, and especially the extraordinary balance-sheet at p. 171.

Indian Agents, and there is still some case for the system. While the Government's commitment to a 'socialistic pattern of society' would not suggest this, it is also pledged to economic expansion, and meanwhile Managing Agencies further this by providing or attracting risk capital and by expanding existing businesses.[10]

(b) *Industrial psychology.* Indian industry has suffered from being initiated, as a rule, by men whose inherited aptitudes were commercial rather than industrial; hence a tendency to go all out for quick profits, often dissipated in speculative extensions. There is often a fantastic diffusion of energy and money into any number of petty unrelated projects – more fragmentation! Inflated optimism may be succeeded by as disastrous pessimism. In actual management there is often very loose costing; allowance for depreciation is often minimal; and there is a reluctance to cut losses and scrap antique plant: in 1886 Jamshedji Tata bought a mill 'which had a conglomerate mass of machinery operated by several steam engines and using twenty-three boilers. The mill's business had been wound up four times in twenty years. Tata literally threw the old machinery out of the windows.'[11]

It must of course be emphasized that these attitudes are receding into the past, though too slowly in some industries; and there are plenty of businessmen of quick and solid ability, and a small but rapidly growing managerial class.

(c) *Labour problems.* While direct comparisons of output per man-hour are usually very unfavourable to India, they leave out too many factors to be worth much. None the less it can hardly be doubted that much Indian labour is inefficient to an extent that goes far to offset its cash cheapness. The reasons are fairly obvious: bad physique, bad housing, bad food, bad working conditions, and as a corollary bad industrial and sometimes bad personal habits. Mills are often very insanitary – impure water has been used for humidifiers – and in any case the atmosphere is very exhausting in the hot weather. Overcrowding and bad water-supply, as in the great tenement *chawls* of Bombay or the *bustees* of Calcutta, negate the most elementary decencies. The worker is very often in debt, sometimes to the tune of a quarter's pay, and there were few nastier sights in India than the factory gates on pay-day, with tough Pathan moneylenders armed with heavy staves waiting for their prey.

Serious efforts have been made, both by governments and the better employers, to improve conditions, but the general level remains deplorably low, and legislation is too often evaded or corrupted.

It is not surprising, then, that absenteeism is rife and that there is a large labour turnover, in part owing to the instigation of jobbers anxious for a new round of bribes and commissions. To check desertion to other mills, or to the villages, payment is often by the month, sometimes with a regular fortnight's

[10] National Council of Applied Economic Research (non-official), *The Managing Agency System* (Asia, Bombay, 1959).
[11] Buchanan, 206.

313

arrear. But absenteeism and large turnovers will remain standard so long as a large proportion of industrial workers are really villagers supplementing their miserable incomes by a spell in the mills. Except where female labour is in demand, as in textiles, the worker is most properly unwilling to bring his wife; the urban sex-disparity is itself a social problem of the first magnitude. The worker's heart remains at home, whither he betakes himself at harvest or festival time. This constant interchange is a main factor in the sapping of the old village tradition, and owing to the large turnover a far higher proportion of the population is affected than would be indicated by the figures of factory employment at any one time. Only in a few places – notably Ahmedabad, Kanpur, Poona[12] – is the true urban proletariat more important than the migrant mass.

Trade unions are as a rule extremist and effective (e.g. the Bombay Girni Kamgar – 'Red Flag' – Union) or moderate and ineffective; often both extremist and inefficient; only in sheltered trades really stable. The illiteracy of the workers naturally makes them turn to outside organizers, often unemployed lawyers, some of whom have given devoted service while others have been amateurs in union methods but professionally skilled in exploiting their position, whether for politics or pay. While many unions are thus extremely irresponsible, little has been done to make easy the way of the properly-run registered union.

All this is not to say that the workers are without fault, nor that there are not good trade unions, good workers, and good managements. Where labour is well provided for and has become a real settled working-class it can fill the most skilled jobs, as Jamshedpur experience has shown. Moreover at present various 'welfare state' measures seem to indicate a general improvement, though unfortunately largely at the expense (through sales taxes, etc.) of the middle clerical classes, who also are subject to extreme exploitation. Nevertheless on the whole the labour situation is one of the prime weaknesses of Indian industries. Yet there is progress, in some cases very striking: '. . . workers who in 1955 took four or five times as long as their European counterparts to produce a given article – an Oerlikon lathe, a Mercedes truck, a railway coach – can now do the work in a little less than twice the European time, and the gap is still being narrowed.'[13]

II. DEVELOPMENT OF MAIN INDUSTRIES TO 1950

A. TEXTILES

1. *Cotton*

Cotton, first of India's modern industries in time, retained its premier position, and India's production of *c.* 5,000,000,000 yards a year was second only to that of the USA. To this mill capacity must be added 1,600,000,000 yards for handlooms.

[12] The Poona study of R. D. Lambert, *Workers, Factories and Social Change in India* (Princeton Univ. Press, 1963), suggests some modification of these generalizations.

[13] B. W. Jackson, 'India on the eve of its Third Plan', *Foreign Affairs*, 39 (1960–61), 259–70.

Its early location at Bombay was the result of the simplest geographical factors.[14] The raw material is 'non-localising', since it is not perishable and loses little weight in manufacture, but access to a wide range of grades is an advantage,

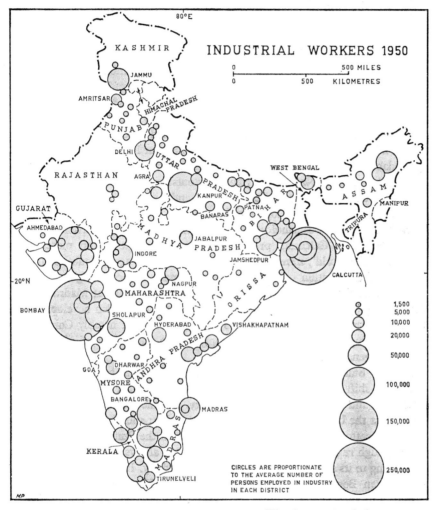

FIG 10.2 INDIA: INDUSTRIAL WORKERS, 1950. The largest symbols represent considerable absolute numbers of workers, even granting rather low efficiency and mechanization. Changes since 1950 are discussed in Ch. XI. From P. P. Karan and W. M. Jenkins in *Economic Geography*, 35 (1959).

and obviously most easily attained in the great export mart. Bombay was also favourably placed for the import of bulky machinery, stores and coal, and for the

[14] The discussion of cotton milling distribution which follows is drawn from the admirably lucid and stimulating analysis in Sharma, Chapter 2–3, *q.v.* for much further detail.

yarn export to China, the initial *raison d'être* of the industry. The rise of cotton manufacturing in Japan and China, however, enforced changes which after about 1905 began to react unfavourably on the relative position of the original base. Weaving for the home market became more important, and later the *swadeshi* movement against buying British, largely backed by the urban middle-class, led to a demand for finer counts than those adequate for the China trade. Apart from the increasing overheads – higher wages and charges natural to a great metropolis, Weber's 'deglomerative factors' – in Bombay Island, this shift in emphasis from foreign yarn to internal piecegoods markets added to Bombay's costs the charges on long rail hauls. Despite a railway rates policy which worked strongly in favour of the great ports, mills at the many internal raw cotton marts could save freight on both raw material and finished product, while the growth of coal mining in the Damodar or even locally (as near Nagpur) provided power. Ahmedabad, with old textile and financing traditions, was off the mark very quickly, followed by Nagpur and Sholapur; outside the Peninsular cotton tracts Kanpur, well placed between Punjab cotton and Bihar coal, led the way. Delhi shared slightly in this development, but beyond it even the great distributing market of Amritsar was handicapped by lack of power until the advent of Mandi hydro-electricity. Calcutta, 'probably the largest single cotton piece goods market in the world', nevertheless did not start until 1905, doubtless mainly because of the fixation on jute and the weakness of local indigenous entrepreneurs. In the south the Buckingham and Carnatic mills at Madras, established 1874–83, remained practically isolated until the sudden development in the early 1930s of centres served by Pykara power, most notably Coimbatore. Here spinning was still dominant, supplying the handlooms of Madura and Tamilnad generally.

Bombay State still had over half of Indian production, but the balance was tending to shift away from it: in Bombay Island the number of mills had actually decreased, and in Ahmedabad was stationary. But the spread was accompanied by at least the beginnings of regional specialization: spinning in Madras, light fabrics of cotton and rayon mixtures and so on in the Punjab, tent canvas and *durris* (rough rugs) at Kanpur, where industry has always had a certain military bias owing to its start as the centre for Army saddlery. In face of the increasing competition Bombay and Ahmedabad, like New England, have found their response in specializing in finer products: the percentage of yarn output in counts above 31 increased at Bombay from 2 in 1921–22 to 17·9 in 1941–42, at Ahmedabad from 7·4 to 35·6. This turn to higher-priced goods, in which freight was a lesser proportion of the final price, was the natural counter to the transport advantages of the inland centres.

In general the industry lacked well-integrated ancillaries. It is significant that Ahmedabad, which used a far higher proportion of foreign (i.e. longer-stapled) cotton than any other centre, and had a rather more stable labour force, was also ahead in this respect: starch, reeds and healds are made locally, and Tatas were already producing such essential chemicals as soda ash and bleaching powder at Port Okha, on the tip of the Kathiawad Peninsula.

2. Jute

'In 1940, 95·5% of the jute looms in India . . . were situated in a small strip of land about 60 miles long and two broad', up and down the Hooghly from Calcutta; and the 70,000 looms of this tiny area were actually about 54% of all in the world.[15] But at Partition 80% of raw jute output was in East Pakistan, which yet had not a single jute-mill.

The reasons for this anomaly are in part historical: capital and management were largely supplied by the Scots oligarchy of Managing Agents,[16] concentrated in the commercial metropolis of Gangetic India and the northeastern Peninsula. Calcutta in turn owed its trade hegemony to the physical character of the delta; poor as it is, the Hooghly is the best of the Ganga spill-ways until we reach the great conjoint Padma–Brahmaputra–Meghna estuary in the east, and this entry has a hinterland small in comparison with Hindustan, access to which is much more direct by the Hooghly–Bhagirathi or (for land routes) the western flanks of the delta.

Sharma's elegant analysis brings out a less obvious but beautifully geographical point. Calcutta, by its pull as the only port for seaborne trade,[17] was the hub of the internal waterways, and over half the jute arrivals were by water. Nevertheless 43% came by rail. But four Districts – Mymensingh, Dacca, Tippera, and Faridpur – supplied 70% of the Hooghlyside mill demand, and of these only the last and least lay west of the great unbridged barrier of the Meghna and its confluents. Transhipment was thus necessary; one ferry took loaded goods wagons, but on this route a break of gauge intervened. 'Under these conditions of transport, involving a good deal of terminal charges, if the jute mills were located in the main jute belt in Eastern Bengal, the transhipment hurdles would have to be crossed twice – once in moving the coal, mill stores, labour, etc., to the mills and again in moving the finished goods to Calcutta for export. . . . But in the case of mills in the Hooghly area the transhipment ordeal has to be faced only once – in moving the raw jute to the mills.'[18] In other words, the location of Calcutta was analogous to that of Bombay in the early days of cotton, not only for machinery from overseas, but also for Damodar coal which met the jute there just as if it had itself come oversea.

The splitting of the growing from the milling centres largely disrupted jute

[15] Sharma, 77, 89. This section based mainly on Sharma, Chapter V, and C. N. Vakil, *Economic Consequences of Divided India* (Vora, Bombay, 1950), 261–79.

[16] Scots executives are only now yielding their leading role in the Hooghlyside jute industry.

[17] Chittagong, at least until Partition, was too excentric to count in this discussion.

[18] Sharma, 84–86. Theoretically of course another port might have been developed, but even were physical conditions more favourable, the self-reinforcing hegemony of Calcutta was hardly shakeable by the 1870s; and the difficulty of coal movements from the Damodar to Dacca would remain.

movements. After Partition, strenuous efforts were made to increase raw jute output in India, and not without success, despite the need for self-sufficiency in food. Pakistan jute is usually of better quality than Indian; this again is largely a matter of the physical character of the delta, the more lively streams of the active eastern delta bringing their annual increments of silt to the fields, and providing much better conditions for retting than are found in the half-stagnant back-waters of West Bengal. It was clear that however successful the jute drive in India, considerable amounts would still be needed from Pakistan;[19] and as yet Pakistan had no jute mills, though they were not long delayed. As for India, the importance of the commodity may be judged from the fact that in 1948 about one-third of all her foreign exchange earnings – and two-thirds of hard currency – came from jute.[20] In these circumstances it was deplorable that jute should have become the terrain of continual economic skirmishing, culminating in the major engagement of the devaluation crisis of 1949, which for six months brought the Indo-Pakistani jute trade to a stop – except for smuggling, said to have amounted to over 85,000 tons (cf. pp. 594–5).

3. *Wool*

The woollens industry also suffered from Partition: a third or more of the clip came from West Pakistan, and again this was the better third in quality. In the 'continental' northwest were also the main markets for warm clothing; the Himalayas look after themselves with home-spun and sheepskin. Yet all but one of the factories were in India.

In 1939 the total employment in the 17 fairly important factories was 8,271; but Kanpur, Dhariwal near Amritsar, and Amritsar itself, with one mill each, employed respectively 2,311, 1,960 and 701 workers – together about 60% of the total. These locations are significant. Kanpur is on the border of the main wool-producing and wool-consuming zone, where it is nearest to Damodar coal. Here the first Indian mill was set up (1876) essentially for Army needs. Dhariwal and Amritsar were central to the main marts for the wools of the sub-continent and beyond – Peshawar, Multan, Fazilka and a string of contact-zone markets, from Kumaon to Kashmir, collecting central Asian and Tibetan wool. Once hydro-electricity was available the industry almost followed.

Demand was, and normally still is, seasonal; except when Army contracts are available working also is seasonal: labour turnover is too high for efficiency. Again market requirements are exceedingly varied, specialization almost impossible if mills are to work through the year, and administrative overheads (for supervisors, specialist technicians, etc.) correspondingly high. Most of the more skilled workers at Dhariwal and Amritsar were Muslims who went to Pakistan.

The handloom side remained strong, employment being estimated at anything from two to six times that in mills, despite the competition of cheap shoddies and

[19] Vakil, 264–5.
[20] *Report of Export Promotion Cttee* (1949), cited Vakil, 261 fn. 2.

mixtures from Japan, Italy and Poland; the cessation of these imports during the war, and the all-out working of the mills for Army clothing, gave the craft industry a great impetus. At Srinagar (Kashmir) a centrally organized cottage industry employs about 9,000 weavers; in the Himalayas spinning and weaving were family affairs, the producers owning everything from the sheep to the loom but elsewhere, and especially in the carpet branch, the weavers were in debt-bondage to petty entrepreneurs. Apart from carpets the main products were coarse blankets, at once cheaper and more resistant to hard usage than mill products. These matters at least are little changed.

4. *Silk, Rayon, Hosiery*[21]

Despite local supplies not only from mulberry-eating silkworms, but from other indigenous insects (see above, 249), the silk industry suffered from inadequate and irregular provision of raw material. The industry, located in Mysore, Madras, West Bengal, and Kashmir, was poorly organized, cocoon production unequal and generally inferior in quality. *Rayon* production was increasing rapidly: the main centres being Bombay, Ahmedabad and Surat – an interesting location, reminiscent of the early days of cotton when it also depended on imported yarn. The chief inland centre was Amritsar, associated with the general development of light industry consequent on electrification, and linked with cotton-rayon mixtures and knitwear.

Hosiery and *knitwear* works were found in the larger urban markets, but particularly at Rawalpindi and Lahore in West and Ludhiana in East Punjab. This probably stemmed from the migration of a craft industry from Kashmir, but one obviously particularly suited to electrification.

B. METAL INDUSTRIES

1. *Iron and Steel*

'The feature which stands out most prominently in a survey of the mineral industries of India is that practically nothing has been done to develop those minerals which are essential to modern metallurgical and chemical industries, while most striking progress has been made during recent years in opening out deposits from which products are obtained suitable for export, or for consumption by . . . direct processes.'[22] This statement accurately sums up the position in the first decade of this century, when it was generally held by (British) authorities that not much more was possible, and in particular that experience had conclusively shown that India was never likely to possess a large-scale iron and steel industry. The magnificence of the endowment of the northeastern Peninsula was hardly recognized, or was thought of in extractive terms only, and Free Trade meant that import of machines, constructional material, and semi-manufactured goods was possible at prices with which an unprotected industry starting from scratch could hardly compete.

[21] Vakil, 281–5. [22] *Imperial Gaz.* III (1908), 128.

As far back as the 1830s attempts had been made to exploit Salem iron, and the furnaces at Porto Novo (south of Madras) and Beypur (Malabar) were intermittently productive until 1866–67 (cf. below 753–4). In 1900 pig production from the iron-shales of Barakar in the Damodar was a mere 35,000 tons; the company concerned had just made the first profit since operations began in 1874, and was about to launch into a disastrous venture in steel. But in 1911 Jamshedpur's first blast-furnace was blown, in 1913 the first steel was made – and in 1914 the war provided a virtually protected market for the critical early years. Indian production was still small, especially in relation to population, but the Jamshedpur works were then the largest in the Commonwealth. Their history is a fascinating study in applied geography; Jamshedji Tata's success was due above all to three things: unflinching determination, adequate finance and meticulous geographical planning which resulted in the selection of a site with positional advantages possibly unequalled anywhere in the world: between Damodar coking coal and the mountains of Orissa haematite; with ample moulding-sand and water from the Subarnarekha; with fluxes, refractories, and the major alloys within 50 or 60 miles; and with the biggest single market in India – the general engineering trades of Calcutta – only 150 miles (241 km.) away.[23] These advantages are unique; but except for the charcoal-smelted works in Mysore, the industry in general benefited from the low cost of coke and there grew up a considerable export of pig iron, especially to Japan. But there was also some import of scrap to coastal foundries.

The location and nominal capacity (in 1,000 tons) of existing plants was as follows:

	Pig	Steel ingots
Tata I & S Co., Jamshedpur, Bihar	1,533	1,116
Indian I & S Co., Kulti, West Bengal	913	—
Steel Corporation of Bengal, Burnpur, West Bengal	—	5–600
Mysore (State) I & S, Bhadravati	30	20–40

This gave a total capacity of around 2,500,000 tons pig and 1,750,000 steel; but the plants suffered depreciation as a result of the unremitting production, with little replacement, of the war years, actual output was considerably less, though roughly equivalent to inter-war demand.

The wide range of products was notably increased by the demands of 1939–45. Around Jamshedpur and Asansol–Burnpur (on the Raniganj coalfield) clustered ancillary and associated industries: refractories, tubes and wires, heavy chemicals and so on. One of the most important was tin-plate, in which India became

[23] See Sharma, 98–101, and below, 713–15. J. L. Keenan's *A Steel Man in India* (Gollancz, London, 1945) gives an unorthodox but very lively view of a neglected aspect of Indian life.

almost self-supporting in ten years, with an output of over 80,000 tons. Considering the resources in alloys – manganese, chromium, silicon, titanium and vanadium are all available, mostly between the Damodar and the Subarnarekha – very little high-speed or other special steel was produced. This country on the Bihar–Bengal–Orissa border was really the only zone of primary heavy industry in the sub-continent, a concentration obviously due to the incomparable concentration of resources, facilitating linked development, but hampering distribution by the long rail hauls necessary to any markets but those of Hooghlyside.

2. *Aluminium and other non-ferrous metals*[24]

The production of aluminium smallware was one of the Madras Government's initiatives, as early as 1912, and in the inter-war period raw metal imports of 4,000–5,000 tons a year were the basis of a utensils industry located in the chief ports and exporting to Indian Ocean markets. In 1943 the production of aluminium ingots from imported alumina began near Alwaye (Travancore) and the actual production of alumina was begun at Muri and Asansol. Rolling into sheets (and foil for tea-chests) was mostly at Belur (Calcutta).

The war years saw a great expansion in miscellaneous light metal trades – brass and copper wire and tubes, lead piping and sheeting, brass sheets, expanded metal, and so on. Significantly enough most firms were in Calcutta, with Bombay second; the few up-country outliers included one at Jaipur presumably located with reference to Rajasthan zinc and copper. A small but interesting industry was the manufacture of plumbago crucibles for non-ferrous metallurgy, carried on at Calcutta, Bombay and Rajahmundry in the Godavari delta. Most Indian graphite is definitely inferior for this purpose, and imports from Ceylon were essential.

3. *Engineering: heavy, light and electrical*

The major concentrations in heavy engineering were, as we might expect, around Calcutta, at Jamshedpur, and on the Jharia–Raniganj coalfields, these areas accounting for 75% of output; lesser centres were Bombay, Madras and Kanpur. The Second World War saw a great expansion: steel used in bridges, for example, was 1,381 tons in 1940, 21,843 in 1943, and it is claimed that the largest floating dock in the world was constructed at Calcutta.[25] But such important lines as machine tools and textile engineering were in their infancy, the latter's capacity being only a fraction of the cotton industry's annual replacements of looms and spindles. While the war greatly increased demand for, and led to the introduction or expansion of the manufacture of, such things as jacks, road-making machinery and hand pumps, the existing small production of centrifugal pumps and oil-engines, so important in connection with rural

[24] The best readily accessible survey of the metal and engineering industries at this period is in P. J. Thomas, *India's Basic Industries* (Orient Longmans, Bombay, 1948), Chs. I–V and XIII–XX *passim*.

[25] Thomas, 165.

industry, was hampered or even reduced by the difficulty of importing essential tools and components, such as ball bearings. In 1950 demand for ball bearings was estimated at 900,000 – but of 2,500 different sorts and sizes – and 'any economical unit would produce India's total demand in a week or so'.[26] This illustrates the general lack of integration in Indian industry. Before the war precision instruments were made chiefly by the Government Mathematical Instrument Office, established over a century ago at Calcutta; the war saw a proliferation of private firms, but their products were not always very precise.

The production of most of the lighter types of electrical apparatus was either introduced or greatly increased during the war, and bulbs, fans, batteries, transformers, conduits manufactured on a fairly large scale.

4. Transport engineering, shipbuilding

(a) *Land transport*. Vehicle engineering was still largely in the assembly stage. Rail wagons and coaches were built mainly at Calcutta and Burnpur. Loco building, with imported components, began as early as 1896 in the Bombay Baroda & Central India rail-shops at Ajmer, but despite government's promise in 1921 to invite tenders and the consequent building of a plant at Jamshedpur, the Tariff Board refused protection – partly on the ground that electrification was pending – and not a single engine was produced.[27]

Motor vehicle assembly had been started at Bombay, and a beginning made on aircraft assembly at Bangalore. Bicycle demand included an unusually high proportion of tricycles, mainly for the 'trishaw' or pedal-bike-cum-sidecar which is replacing the man-pulled rickshaw.

(b) *Shipbuilding*. Some of the 'wooden walls' of Nelson's day were built not of British oak but of Indian teak, and the Parsee shipwrights of Bombay enjoyed a high reputation throughout Eastern seas. With the change to iron, however, only country craft were launched, except for tugs, launches and barges for the Bengal Delta, for which Calcutta was of course the main centre. Before the war a few sea-going tugs, up to 440 tons, were built there, and during the war a large number of motor-patrol boats and mine-sweepers were launched, though nearly all machinery had to be imported.

The only existing yards of any capacity were those of the Scindia Company – the premier Indian shipping line – at Visakhapatnam, which could build vessels up to 8,000 tons capacity. Though 'Vizag' is the nearest open-ocean port to Jamshedpur, costs are so high (nearly twice those of UK yards) that in 1949 the company suspended operations after launching only three ships; the yards were later nationalized. Delightfully, bananas were used instead of tallow for greasing the slipways, and the traditional bottle of champagne for the launch was superseded by the less expensive cracking of a coconut.

[26] Thomas, 189.
[27] Thomas, 205–6. There are still only 800 miles (1,285 km.) of electric railway, confined to suburban lines around Bombay, Calcutta and Madras.

C. CEMENT

The cement industry grew as modern methods of construction were adopted. Good limestone was available in quantity in many parts of India; gypsum is less abundant and the loss of that of the Salt Range to Pakistan caused some temporary difficulty. The need to use coal of low ash-content in the kilns meant that while the central Indian factories could use Rewah or Pench valley coal for power, half their requirements had to come from the Damodar. In 1947 there were about twenty-four plants with a total capacity of 2,800,000 tons. A quarter of this was in Pakistan and at least a third in central India, notably based on the Vindhyan rocks forming the northern flanks of the Son valley. Other important areas were Kathiawad, Telangana and East Punjab, while the largest single unit (220,000 tons) was in Bundi state, Rajasthan. Most of these were located with direct reference to limestone, e.g. the Shahbad factory in Hyderabad is on the narrow strip of Vindhyans, long worked for building stone, which intervenes between the Archaeans and the overlying Deccan Lavas.

The industry tended to be monopolistic, a good two-thirds of the 1947 capacity being controlled by Associated Cement Companies and two-thirds of the rest by Seth Dalmia, then perhaps the leading self-made magnate of India. Both these concerns controlled plants in what is now Pakistan, and there was some dislocation at Partition. Labour conditions were unusually good. Altogether capacity in India increased from 2,100,000 tons in 1947 to 2,960,000 in 1949, output from 1,400,000 to 2,100,000 (2,700,000 in 1950). There was still some import, but also export to Ceylon and Burma, and altogether the industry was one of the most flourishing in India.

D. CHEMICALS AND ALLIED INDUSTRIES

1. Acids and alkalis

The heavy chemical industry was one of the weakest sectors in India's industrial advance. Sulphuric acid, indeed, owing to the precautions needed in transporting it, and the fact that a ton of sulphur yields three of acid, must in general be made near its market, and this favoured home production; and consumption industries based on chemicals were expanding rapidly. But the highly important alkali side, despite a notable increase in production since the war, was still under-developed. Although the possession of the Salt Range gives Pakistan the largest single source of chemicals in the sub-continent, India's resources are by no means poor, and their uneven development reflected the general lack of co-ordination and balance.

Sulphuric acid was produced in the larger textile centres and at Asansol, Jamshedpur, Belagula (Mysore), and Alwaye. Alkalis were mainly from Saurashtra, at Drangadhra and Mithapur (Port Okha), where Tatas had the largest soda-ash and caustic-soda plant in the country; the localizing factor was the

323

proximity of limestone and sea-salt. There was also some production at Mettur. Ammonium sulphate was being produced at Sindri and Alwaye, with a small contribution from Belagula and from coke-ovens. There were thus three main areas of heavy chemical production: Kathiawad, the northeastern Peninsula and the electrified zone of the south.

2. Lighter chemical industries

The most important consumption industries based on chemicals were dye and tan-stuffs, paints and varnishes, soap and cosmetics, matches and drugs with fair natural resources, vegetable or mineral.

The indigenous production of vegetable *tan-stuffs* (avaram, babul, myro-balans, etc.) is supplemented by imports of wattle bark. Chrome alum (chromium/ aluminium sulphate) – important in dyeing and photography as well as tanning – was produced using bauxite and sulphuric acid; production in this group (including other alum salts for water purification, paper sizing and as mordants) more than doubled between 1939 and 1945, despite difficulties in transporting bauxite and other demands for sulphuric acid. *Dye-stuffs*, apart from primitive local production for use on the spot, were mostly imported. Output of *paints and varnishes* again more than doubled during the war, using the fair resource base in the oilseeds, the resins of the Himalayan forests, barytes in the south, and various other pigments and vehicles. The industry had the usual Bombay/ Calcutta localization.

The *soap* industry had ample supplies of vegetable oils, tallow and essential oils such as lemon-grass, citronella and sandal, though these last were still generally exported as crude oil and re-imported as distilled. Imports of some alkalis and of coconut oil were still necessary. The industry again developed mostly around Calcutta and Bombay, with important units in Kerala. *Match-making* was widespread as a cottage industry, but there were a fair number of factories, especially in Madras and West Bengal, though the largest concern, the West India Match Co., linked with Swedish interests, had its main factory at Kalyan near Bombay. *Drugs* again fall into two sections: the ancient remedies, largely herbal and with some elements of magic, used in the traditional medical systems and by village homeopathists; and factory-made pharmaceuticals, which had just made a beginning. The production of *plastics* themselves, as distinct from plastic goods, was in its infancy.

E. FOOD INDUSTRIES

Food processing came first of the major industrial groups in number of establishments, but third in employment. This is natural enough, since for the most part processes are relatively simple, needing little power or capital. Factories were (and are) often seasonal, and except for some concentration of larger units in ports and large cities their distribution followed that of the crop concerned.

Rice mills, for example, can be worked by cheap oil-engines or by steam-engines of no great power and often of antiquated design; fuel for steam plants is no problem, since fires once started can be fed on paddy husks. Hence their rickety corrugated iron sheds were scattered by rail or riverside through all the paddy-lands, with perhaps some tendency to thicken along the middle Ganga and the terai.[28] But flour mills were more urban in location, since the taste for wheaten bread instead of the unleavened *chupatti* (a tough but satisfying pancake) definitely goes with 'Western sophistication'.

1. Tea and sugar

Tea for Western markets needs immediate and relatively elaborate processing; hence tea factories were well organized and equipped capitalist units, serving either a single plantation or, as road transport improved, a group. A material factor is the need for adequate export packaging, and this led to a large, if ill-balanced, expansion of plywood production for tea-chests; even so, there were difficulties in reaching standards acceptable to dollar markets such as the USA and Canada.

The history of *sugar* production in India is one of marked vicissitude, dependent partly on imperial politics, as when British import duties were placed on East Indian sugar in West Indian interests. Again it must be remembered that beside the modern industry is the village production of *gur* or *jaggery*, the coarse unrefined sugar (rather like fudge) produced by boiling in open pans. This is of course much cheaper, and indeed gur normally took about half the cane supply. Other sugar, or at least sweetening, is still obtained from the estuarine nipa palms and *Phoenix paludosa* and, more important, the Palmyra (*Borassus flabellifer*); but this does not amount to much, and is mostly in the extreme south.[29]

For most of the 19th century India was either self-sufficient or a net exporter, but in the 1890s the competition of European beet-sugar and of cane from Mauritius (where it is grown by Indian labour) and Java practically killed Indian sugar as an organized trade, though of course the petty local production of gur carried on. There was some revival from about 1911, but after 1931–32 the grant of protection led to a sharp increase in factories, from 32 in 1932 to 145 in 1939, and in refined output, from 100,000 to 1,230,000 tons. By 1940 'India was the largest sugar-producing country in the world, and her sugar industry the second largest industry, next in importance to only the cotton textile industry', and employing over 120,000 hands.[30] There was usually an export surplus; the sugar industry of Burma, for instance, survived only on sufferance, and there were exports to the Indian colonies in Ceylon and Malaya, and to southwest Asia.[31]

[28] For a general discussion of rice-milling, cf. O. H. K. Spate, 'Beginnings of industrialization in Burma', *Economic Geography*, 17 (1941), 75–92.

[29] This section is based mainly on Sharma, Chapters VIII–IX; Jathar and Beri, I Chapter VI; Vakil, 297–303.

[30] Jathar and Beri, I.172 (7th ed., 1942).

[31] Indian exports 1948–49: 26,268 tons (but 22,000 as molasses); of this 3,377 to West Pakistan. Imports 10,576 tons.

Production fluctuated, however, and in later years imports were sometimes necessary.

As we have seen (Chapter 8), cane-growing was strongly localized in the north, and this was reflected in the concentration of the industry: in 1931–32/34–35 Uttar Pradesh and Bihar produced 90·8% of total refined output, in 1935–36/38–39 still 84·1%; but by 1943–44 their share had fallen to 79·4%,[32] indicating the start of a trend to a more even spread of the industry, which was desirable for several reasons.

In the first place, Indian cane as a whole is poor, output per acre being only a quarter of that in Java and Hawaii. But the disparity is much less for the thick tropical canes of the south, and greater reliance on these spells obvious economies, not to mention transport saving on the finished product. The extension of irrigation in the Deccan is likely to lead to an increase of cane-growing there, since the value of the crop renders it a favourite in irrigated areas; and the factories of the Deccan rely mainly on their own estates, instead of on 'gate cane' brought to the factory directly by independent growers, or on cane brought by rail. This had advantages – superior varieties are grown, and cutting takes place at a time to suit the refiner rather than the cultivator.

2. Oils

Oilseeds accounted for about 5% of the value of Indian exports, and there was a considerable import of vegetable oils. Manufacture of oil had begun, but the use of oil-cake as cattle food and fertilizer was negligible; it is significant, however, that there was a downward trend in exports of rape and mustard, which can be of direct food value without any processing beyond the crude extraction of oil by *ghani*, a great pestle-and-mortar, usually bullock-driven but sometimes mechanized, in which case a battery of *ghanis* might be connected to an oil-engine. The extraction rate is low, but this has at least the merit of leaving richer oil-cake. The loss of the European market in 1940 led to a marked increase in groundnut-crushing and the establishment of *vanaspati* or 'vegetable ghi' mills; while the increasing demand for coconut oil in the soap industry called for fairly large imports.

F. MISCELLANEOUS CONSUMPTION INDUSTRIES

1. Leather[33]

The leather industry of India suffers from peculiar social disabilities. Before Partition three-quarters of the 25,000,000 hides produced annually in the sub-continent came from animals which had died of disease, malnutrition or mere old age; and owing to the continuing bias against cow-slaughter, the proportion in India is probably still higher. Obviously this means a serious deterioration in

[32] Sharma, 152.
[33] Sharma, Chapter X; Thomas, Chapter XXX; Vakil, 348–52.

the quality of hides, and in fact good hides were in short supply. Moreover, those workers who were not Untouchables were mostly Muslims, and many – including the shoemakers of Agra – have migrated to Pakistan, which now has a superfluity of hides and of labour but a shortage of good tan-stuffs.

In India the raw material basis is obviously not quantitatively lacking, and there are plenty of vegetable tan-stuffs, especially in the south. 'The dry north-west and the wet north-east (including Bengal) are the poorest regions in the supply of local tanning materials', and this is one factor in the growth of chrome tanning at Calcutta.[34] It will be noted that both these deficit areas are now largely in Pakistan. The north in general, however, has to rely on babul (*Acacia arabica*) bark, which has only 12–14% tannin against the 16–18% of avaram (*Cassia auriculata*) which is widespread in the drier Deccan. Myrobalans (35%) and divi-divi (40%) also grow mainly in the Peninsula. None of these, however, is as valuable as wattle bark, which has 35% tannin and loses it far more slowly than any of the others. Wattle was imported from South Africa, and some grown in the Nilgiris.

Tanning and the production of leather goods were widely distributed, but with some interesting regional differentiation. Tanning was carried on at three levels: 'bag tanning', the production of kips, and modern factory tanning. In bag tanning the hide is sown up and, as it were, pickled from within; this is the standard method of the village tanner and accounted for 40–45% of the hides, but only the worst were used. Though any hides may be called kips, the word strictly applies to hides half-tanned in pits; no machinery is required, and little capital, but the scale of operations is larger than in bag-tanning. Over 40% of the hides were turned into kips, most of which were exported, especially to Britain. Madras was the leading centre, but kips were produced all over the Peninsula, and it is in this branch that wattle bark is most used. Modern methods accounted for about 15% of the hides; not all in large factories, since there was a considerable output of chrome-tanned leather around Calcutta, in small or even cottage units owned and mainly worked by Chinese. Most of the large modern tanneries are in the north, especially in Uttar Pradesh where Kanpur is the chief centre. Not only had this area a larger proportion of better hides than the south – perhaps in part owing to the stronger Muslim element – but here, for climatic reasons, are the main markets for solid footwear; the southerner can walk on sandals or bare feet. Hence too the north was far more important for finished leather goods, much of the demand being military. Apart from the Chinese craft industry at Calcutta, only a few tanneries – two dozen – used the chrome method, and these were Kanpur, Calcutta and Madras.

The production of finished goods, still mostly by hand, either by individual shoemakers or in small shops, was estimated at 100,000,000 pairs of various indigenous types and 30,000,000 of European shoes and boots; on the 1941 population this is one pair a year for one person out of three. All sandals and

[34] Sharma, 164–7, 173.

80–90% of European shoes are handmade; Agra was the chief centre with nearly 150 small 'factories'. There were only nine modern factories – two each at Agra, Kanpur and Calcutta (including Batanagar), one each at Madras, Bombay and Bangalore. But the enormous increase in Army demand, from c. 100,000 pairs a year pre-war to 6,600,000 in 1943, 'involved a sudden expansion'; one Kanpur firm is said to have had the largest self-contained footwear factory in the world, and the Government Harness and Saddlery Factory, also at Kanpur, took on ten times its pre-war number of workers.[35] The localization at Kanpur stems largely from its old importance as a depot for military stores of all kinds.

2. Rubber

The rise of rubber industries in India was due to the international restriction scheme of 1934, which meant that much India-grown rubber could not be exported and so was available at prices well below the artificial world level. West Bengal and Bombay developed the great majority of the factories. Pre-war demand for tyres was met mainly by plants owned by Dunlops and Firestone, which by 1942 together produced 390,000 car and nearly 1,900,000 cycle tyres; the war as usual intensified production, which by 1949 had risen to 1,400,000 motor and 7,700,000 cycle tyres, together with nearly 18,000,000 pairs of rubber shoes.

3. Glass

Of the 232 glass factories in India in 1947, no fewer than 92 were entirely devoted to the making of bangles, which was also a cottage industry. The great centre for the factory production of bangles was Firozabad (Uttar Pradesh), with hundreds of small workshops to which finishing and decorating was put out by the factories. Japanese competition nearly ruined the cottage industry, to the benefit of Firozabad.

Of the remaining 141 factories, Uttar Pradesh, West Bengal, and Bombay had respectively 58, 31 and 21, but the value of output was in reverse order, though not differing greatly. In Uttar Pradesh the industry developed mainly along the flanks of the Vindhyan sandstone plateaus, mostly in Agra District and near Allahabad; the Province accounted for nearly half and the District for nearly a third of Indian employment. About two-thirds of the cost of raw materials was for soda ash, formerly obtained from Khewra (West Punjab) but now from Indian sources. About half the output, by value, was contributed by bottles. The war saw a marked expansion in range as well as output, and thermos refills, electric bulbs and a small amount of scientific glassware were produced. The industry, formerly using mainly crude pot-furnaces, made much technical progress, but suffered from a tendency to plunge into any line which looked lucrative: as a result the sheet-glass capacity was three to six times actual output in 1946–49.

[35] Vakil, 350; Thomas, 305.

4. *Paper and other wood-based Industries*[36]

(a) *Paper*. The classics of Sanskrit literature were usually written on palm-leaves, in the north sometimes on birch-bark; paper-making seems to have come from China via the central Asian Muslims, and the indigenous hand-workers were mainly Muslims. Paper-making by hand, usually from fibrous plants, lingered on in a few places but was of no importance. A few mills were set up in 1870–90, on the Hooghly and at Lakhnau, Poona and Raniganj; but supplies of softwood are limited to the Himalayas, and no mills were added until bamboo pulping became commercially practicable, about 1922; a protective duty was placed on imported pulp in 1931, and in five years the utilization of bamboo pulp rose by 280%. The war once more checked imports and increased demand.

Bamboos supplied about 55% of the raw material, grasses 22%, waste paper 10–12%, wood pulp only 1–2%. *Sabai* grass is better than bamboo, but yields are lower and more erratic. Obviously regeneration of cut-over bamboo areas is essential, but growth is rapid (only 4–5 years) and supplies at the rate of 600,000 tons of canes a year can be maintained indefinitely given proper conservation. Capacity was 135–150,000 tons of paper a year, but hitches in the supply of chemicals were keeping current production down to about 130,000 tons, a third of it boards. This was about half the demand; the bureaucracy naturally received priority, and supplies to schools were short. Whatever the planned expansion, the increasing official mania for *papierasserie* will probably continue to tax the industry to the utmost.

As usual West Bengal and Bombay led with 4 and 3 of the 12 larger mills; but West Bengal, which produced over 50%, drew largely from the Chittagong Hill Tracts and Sylhet (East Pakistan) and farther afield, into the Orissa Hills, for a product bulky in proportion to weight. This may lead to a shift to the areas with the most ample bamboo forests, roughly the hill borders of the Peninsula. The industry in Uttar Pradesh and East Punjab relied largely on *sabai* grass from the Siwaliks.

(b) *Plywood* is especially useful in Indian conditions of temperature and humidity, in which ordinary woodwork readily cracks and swells. Madras and Assam led in the production of plywood, which rose during the war (when Japanese and European imports were cut off) from 13,000,000 to 50,000,000 sq. ft. in 1944. The latter figure was much less than capacity, another example of plunging after quick returns. West Bengal had now 40 and Madras 30% of capacity (162,000,000 sq. ft.); output in 1952 was 90,500,000 but in 1953 had fallen to 60,800,000 sq ft.[37]

Timber supplies are adequate, and India usually produces sufficient casein and protein glues. But it is significant that the tea demand, which pre-war took over 80% of output, fell to less than half the 1944 figure as soon as imports were

[36] Thomas, 290–302; Vakil, 306–10; M. P. Bhargava, 'Review of the pulp and paper industry in India' (*5th British Empire Forestry Confce*, Dehra Dun, 1947).
[37] See Thomas, 295; cf. Vakil, 292–3.

resumed. Plywood production is highly skilled, and get-rich-quick expansionism resulted in very poor chests being put on the market; some of them did not even survive to leave India. The industry is potentially very important, with a wide range of uses apart from tea-chests.

(c) *Distillation, etc.* The 'collier' of the European Middle Ages survives in the person of the Indian charcoal-burner, whose primitive kilns, dotted about the vast scrub-forests, produced about 9,000,000 tons of charcoal a year. But all the valuable distillation products were wasted. There was so far only one wood-distillation plant, part of the charcoal-smelted iron and steel industry at Bhadra-vati (Mysore). This indeed was one of the biggest in Asia, producing daily 30,000 gallons (136,000 litres) of distillate, from which calcium acetate (main source of acetic acid), methyl alcohol, and formaldehyde are extracted. Rosin and turpentine were formerly made chiefly at Jalo (West Punjab), but there is little industrial demand in Pakistan as yet, and as most of Punjab coniferous forests went to India production became concentrated at Hoshiarpur (East Punjab).

CHAPTER 11

India in the Planning Era

India entered the second half of the 20th century still on the crest of the wave of confidence and jubilation following Independence, with a stable political scene, a good administrative system and an adequate rail-net (the two steel frames bequeathed by the British Raj), as well as an amount of industry considerable in absolute figures, even if but small in relation to the large population. Under Pandit Nehru's leadership of the ruling Congress Party, the Central Government passed a number of measures to turn the country towards 'a socialistic pattern of society', with a mixed economy as between the 'public sector' of nationalized or government-controlled establishments) and the 'private sector' under private capital, and a series of Five Year Plans aimed at speeding up and directing the rapid economic development, and especially the industrialization, of the whole country and its federal states.[1]

In most countries with modern economies, under whatever political system, government policy has become a factor in economic and particularly in industrial location, a factor of equal moment with – though not necessarily counter to – the factors of raw materials, markets and the like; it was only to be expected that government action should assume paramount importance in the 1950s and 60s, particularly in industrial location. This phase of rapid change under the influence of new forces is almost revolutionary, though not to the extent of rejecting and tearing up the foundations presented by the *fait accompli* of history. It is fortunate that Karan's valuable study of industrial distribution patterns presents a synoptic picture at the crucial watershed date of 1950, at the very beginning of the planning era. Figs. 10.2 and 11.1, founded on his work, are in a sense both the culmination of the discussion in the preceding chapter, and an essential beginning to this one.[2]

[1] The principle of the mixed economy was established by an Industrial Policy Resolution of 1948, and further spelled out by a Resolution in 1956. The public sector is mainly industries of basic or strategic importance, or public utilities – steel, coal, strategic minerals, heavy engineering, defence production, rail and air transport and communications; though even here some undertakings, such as the Tata steelworks, are in the private sector. Other industries like machine tools, essential drugs, and basic chemicals are undertaken by the government 'to the extent necessary', though vigorous private sector activity is encouraged. Consumer industries of all types are in the hands of private capital, including co-operatives to some extent. See Planning Commission, *Towards a Self-Reliant Economy: India's Third Plan 1961–66* (Delhi, 1961).

[2] See also G. Kuriyan, 'Industrial development in India since Independence', *Proceedings of IGU Regional Conference, Japan 1957* (Science Ccil of Japan, Tokyo, 1959), 374–81, and his 'An analysis of the spatial distribution of industry in India . . . ', *IGJ* 37/1 (1962), 1–7. Also Karan's more up-to-date account in *Ann. Ass. Amer. Geog.*, 54 (1964), 336–54.

Even granting the low productivity per worker discussed in Chapter 10, the distribution pattern of Fig. 11.1 is impressive, and it is interesting that an Indian worker should have concluded that industrial regions were beginning to form at the close of the colonial phase. He notes the generally small size of undertaking, and it should be added that even in his major regions there are considerable tracts of terrain which are completely untouched by industry or even

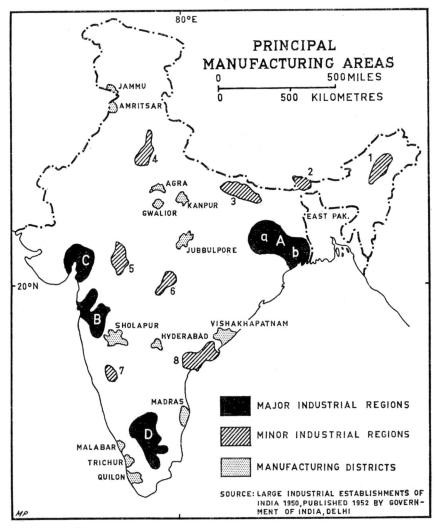

FIG 11.1 INDIA: PRINCIPAL MANUFACTURING AREAS. Most of these nascent industrial areas of 1950 were (and are) characterized by a sprinkling of industrial foci in rural tracts otherwise relatively little affected by urbanization or industrialization; changes since 1950 are noted in the text. *Source:* P. P. Karan and W. M. Jenkins in *Economic Geography*, 35 (1959). See expanded key opposite.

FIG 11.1 PRINCIPAL MANUFACTURING AREAS

Major Regions

	A. Bihar-Bengal Industrial Belt	B. Bombay-Poona	C. Ahmedabad-Baroda	D. Madurai-Coimbatore Bangalore
Main industries	(a) *Hooghlyside* Jute, cotton, electricals, light engineering, chemicals. (b) *Chota Nagpur* Iron and steel, wire, rolling stock, vehicles	Cotton (over one-third of workers), chemicals, engineering, food processing, printing, light engineering, consumer goods	Cottons, chemicals pottery	Cottons, light consumer goods, light engineering
Coal	Damodar	Originally UK, S. Africa by sea, now long haul from Bihar	Long haul from Bihar (recently some oil and gas strikes)	Long haul from Bihar
Hydro-electricity	(Recently a little from Damodar Valley project)	Important supplies from Western Ghats	—	Cauvery, Jog, Nilgiris
Iron ore	Singhbum	—	—	Small iron and steel works at Bhadravati using ores from Bababhudan hills
Other raw materials mainly from agriculture	Bengal jute, by water meeting Damodar coal (but much of best jute area to East Pakistan)	Cotton, ground-nuts on regurs of Plateau to east	Cotton surrounding regur soils. Salt from salt-pans	Some cotton on Madurai and Coimbatore regur
Port and commerce	Calcutta (including European managing agencies)	Bombay (including Parsees and Gujaratis)	Local commerce (Marwaris and Gujaratis)	Madras as port with own commerce and industries, though some distance away
Markets	Largest urban market, Hooghlyside	Early exports China then large local urban market	Local markets of some importance	

Minor Regions

1. Assam Valley — Processing of local tea and rice and oil-seeds, some petroleum
2. Darjeeling terai — Processing of local tea
3. North Bihar-Uttar Pradesh — Manufacture of local sugar-cane
4. Delhi-Meerut — Manufacture of local sugar-cane, some textiles, chemicals, engineering
5. Indore-Ujjain — Local cottons for local markets, handicrafts (former courts)
6. Nagpur-Wardha — Small textiles, foundries, railway and general engineering, glass and pottery

333

7. Dharwar-Belgaum — Cotton textiles, local cotton and markets, railway and general engineering

8. Godavari-Krishna Delta — Local tobacco, sugar-cane, rice and oil, cement, small textiles

Manufacturing Districts

Agra: very important for shoes and leatherware, made in a few large and many small factories and workshops, glass, tourist bric-a-brac, some cottons and woollens

Amritsar: woollens, carpets, embroidery

Gwalior: china and pottery, cottons, leather, light-engineering, quarrying, cigarettes

Hyderabad: food processing including biscuits, light engineering, handicrafts (formerly for the court)

Jammu: woollens, cottons, dyeing and printing, pottery

Jabalpur: railway workshops, textiles

Kanpur: textiles and clothing, large modern tanneries, leather works, boots and shoe factories, founded on military clothing and equipment

Madras: textiles, light engineering, consumer goods of wide variety

Malabar-Quilon-Trichur: cashew processing, coconut and other oil pressing, associated industries (coir manufacture, soap), some textiles, numerous handicrafts in very densely peopled coastal tract

Sholapur: important textile and engineering centre on regur soils

It should be noted that most of these areas are really nascent rather than developed; see text.

by strong industrial influence, even today. It seems best to adopt the phrasing of our caption and call these nascent rather than accomplished industrial regions. And one should also note again the small proportion of the population involved or benefited, and the low per capita incomes and marked socio-economic disparities. These have naturally been very bitterly criticized by nationalist writers;[3] it is already becoming possible to review this period in the perspective of history, and Nehru himself possessed this perspective to a remarkable degree, even when writing from gaol. Later, Buchanan points out how India might well have progressed *pari passu* with Japan, but for the obstacles to leadership inherent in the colonial relationship (even if added to by some features of Indian character and social structure);[4] and Malenbaum points out how the nascent industrial regions or foci of the geographer were also economic enclaves, not diffusing economic stimulus to surrounding regions to any extent.[5]

The character of the Five Year Plans

The first Five Year Plan was relatively small and mainly oriented to agriculture; for example, the fertilizer plant at Sindri is of this period. Its modest demands on foreign exchange for capital goods were well within the country's means – India had, for instance, considerable sterling balances on account of war-time expenditure by Britain. Thinking about growth rates was based on a very simple general model. Immediately after Independence a series of poor monsoons caused widespread hardship and locally actual famine, particularly in the south, but there were good rains during the Plan period, and a series of good harvests,

[3] J. Nehru, *The Discovery of India* (Doubleday, Anchor Books, NY, and London, 1946), Chapters 7–9.

[4] D. H. Buchanan, 'Differential economic progress . . . Japan versus Asia', *American Economic Rev.* 41 (1951), 359–66.

[5] W. Malenbaum, *Prospects for Indian Development* (Allen & Unwin, London, 1962), 32.

and good demand for export of Indian primary products due to the Korean war resulted in a very fair measure of success for a relatively unambitious Plan.

The Second Plan (1956–61) was much more ambitious, based on more complex macro-economic growth models (though based largely on assumption, rather than available data). It involved considerable reliance on foreign aid, but in this Plan period the government overhauled the taxation system and introduced varied measures to make resources for development available from internal finance.[6] Without neglecting agriculture it emphasized the need to cope with unemployment on the one hand, and on the other stressed the long term benefits of developing heavy and basic industry as a foundation for more complex industrialization later. (It should be noted that this latter 'heavy industry' policy is not necessarily the best way to increase employment, at least in the short term; this was at least largely accepted, but with some reliance on the development of labour-intensive consumer goods industries, light in capital needs, as noted presently.) An econometric model incorporating differing proportions of producer-goods and of consumer-goods industries over a twenty-year period was used, deliberately at hazard, in order to demonstrate an approach to resolving the competition between these two sectors in India's particular circumstances. In detail something of the conflict was resolved by recommending that increased effective consumer demand should be met, and inflationary pressure arising from the capital-intensive developments of heavy industry, etc., should be partly met, by light investment in labour-intensive consumer-goods industries during this Plan period; this would enable the country to step out far more boldly than at any previous period in the development of heavy and basic industry.[7]

The Third Plan (1961–66), while continuing to emphasize industrial development including farther developments in heavy industry, also shows some return to giving a high priority to agriculture, as a *sine qua non*. Again it involves a good deal of foreign aid.

Both the Second Plan and the Third Plan have encountered serious difficulties. The Second Plan was hampered early on by a serious foreign exchange crisis,

[6] See *inter alia* D. L. Spencer, 'India's planning and foreign aid', *Pacific Affairs*, 34 (1961), 28–37, and V. K. R. V. Rao and D. Narain, *Foreign Aid and India's Economic Development* (Asia, Bombay, 1963); for share of foreign capital, P. K. Srivastava, 'Foreign participation in Indian industry', *Eastern Economist* 27/12/63, 1487–1513; D. L. Spencer, 'New sources of industrial finance in India', *Pacific Affairs*, 31 (1958), 261–74; for taxation, etc., N. A. Khan, 'Resources for India's Third Five Year Plan', *Indian Jnl Economics*, 40/156 (1959), 65–72.

[7] Here, as elsewhere, it would be easy to have more footnotes than text; some guidance to the vast literature is given in the Bibliographical Note. Useful insight into these problems may be derived from: P. C. Mahanalobis, 'The approach of operational research to planning in India', *Sankhya* (Calcutta), 16/1–2 (1955), 3–130, and from critiques from different angles in: D. R. Gadgil, *Planning and Economic Policy in India* (Gokhale Inst., Poona, 1961); W. Malenbaum, *op. cit.*, especially 88–91; H. W. Arndt, 'The Balance of Payment argument for priority of heavy industry', *Sankhya*, Series B 24/2–3 (1952), 265–76.

population growth was more rapid than had been expected (see p. 145), and many of its targets were not fulfilled. The Third Plan was upset by the need to quadruple defence spending from October 1962 onwards following the Chinese aggression against India's far northern borders; and there was perhaps underestimation of the lag effect of some of the capital-intensive development, and over-estimation of the extent to which the Community Development investment was oriented, or effective, towards measures to improve agricultural productivity. Nevertheless there is considerable determination to improve the performance during the remainder of the Plan period, and to prepare for a Fourth Plan which will not only provide for improved standards of living, but also bring the economy to Rostow's 'take-off point' of a self-generating economy, not dependent on foreign aid, by the end of that Plan period (1966–71). Meantime crucial achievements may be summarized: in spite of a population increase of 80,000,000, per capita income has increased by 19%; agricultural output has increased by 37% and industrial production by 100% during the first two Plan periods.[8]

The influence of the Five Year Plans on industrial location, employment and urbanization

In the Five Year Plans, a key place is occupied by the building of large plants, mainly in the public sector, for heavy and basic manufacturing processes – iron and steel making, heavy machine tools, fertilizers and the like. Fig. 11.11 shows both concentration and dispersion in the distribution of major industrial units under the Plans.

There is a marked concentration of iron and steel plants in and around the northeastern part of the Peninsula, though this is a very large tract of country within which there has been some attempt to disperse industry into backward areas and to develop new resources of coal and iron ore. There has been expansion of the steel industry on the Damodar coalfield with an increase in the capacity of the private sector plant at Burnpur, the new public sector plant at Durgapur and a very large new one planned for Bokaro. The fertilizer factory at Sindri is also in this area, and both the public sector and the private sector contribute to some growth of nascent 'industrial complex' type within this general region, e.g. the public sector heavy machine tool factory at Ranchi, alloy steel plants at Jamshedpur (private sector) and Durgapur (public sector), the private sector wire manufacturing and vehicle assembly plant at Jamshedpur–Tatanagar and public sector locomotive factory at Chittaranjan north of the coalfield. There has been planned expansion of the Tata steel plant at Jamshedpur, increasing its

[8] See the refreshingly frank *Third Plan Mid-Term Appraisal* (Govt of India, Planning Commission, Delhi, 1963); V. V. Bhatt, 'A decade of planned development', *Economia Internazionale*, 15 (1962), 347–66; P. Pant, 'The development of India', *Scientific American*, 209/3 (1963), 189–206; and for a very cool critique, not unfriendly but rather anxious, Malenbaum, *op. cit.*, and his 'India and China: contrasts in development performance', *American Econ. Rev.* 49 (1959), 284–309.

capacity to 2,000,000 tons, with further expansion projected. Meantime coal production has been left mainly in the private sector under government control and supervision, but the National Coal Development Corporation produces an appreciable proportion of the output from the Damodar area, and is responsible for the development of new fields like the Korba field near Bilaspur, or expansion at Singareni, which might not be attractive to private capital but ought to be undertaken in the national interest.

So far there is expansion in well-tried broad regional locations, discussed in Chapter 9: precise siting is influenced by existing plant, water and transport facilities and the like, so far as is publicly known. The plant at Rourkela in Orissa is producing steel by the Linz–Donawitz process, particularly suitable for rolling steel sheets, e.g. for the Visakhapatnam shipyards, and is located on the main broad-gauge railway line between the Damodar coal and Singbhum iron and the distant but great industrial market for steel products in Bombay; it obtains ore from Barsua about 50 miles (80 km.) away, and brings large-scale industry to almost virgin territory in forested plateau country. This is also true of the plant at Bhilai in Madhya Pradesh near the railway junction of Raipur; this project has also involved the development of a new ironfield at Rajhara some 60 miles (97 km.) to the south, and was planned to draw some of its coking coal from a new coalfield at Korba, development of which, however, appears to have been a little slow and beset by difficulties. The location was, however, chosen partly to supply the shipyard at Visakhapatnam.[9]

Other developments within the field of heavy and basic industries are relatively small: there is some expansion including ferro-manganese plant at the small Mysore Government iron and steel plant at Bhadravati (see p. 330), foundry development at Bombay and at various steel plants and engineering works including defence establishments and railway workshops. So that so far there is some impetus towards industrial complex formation in the Damodar and Jamshedpur areas, with which is closely linked the Hooghlyside area. Hooghlyside has meantime been developing quite buoyantly in chemicals, light engineering (electrical apparatus, typewriters, etc.) in the private sector while the older-established jute industry has been re-equipping and adjusting to the difficulties following Partition. Elsewhere there is large-scale iron and steel development in new and relatively isolated areas mainly in the northeastern plateau, the new fertilizer plants at Varanasi (Benares) in the private sector, and at Nangal, Neiveli and Rourkela (public sector), and relatively small developments elsewhere mainly in older industrial towns and cities.

Some public sector developments in engineering industries have already been

[9] For a good account of these earlier planned developments, see N. N. Sen, 'The development of the iron and steel industry in India', *Science and Culture* (Calcutta), 26/2 (1960), 58–67, and *ibid.* 25/2 (1959), 112–20; also S. R. Ahsan, 'A note on the development of the Indian iron and steel industry', *Oriental Geogr* (Dacca), 1/2 (1958), 178–89, and D. Mookerjee, 'Durgapur, West Bengal's new steel plant', *Geography* 44 (1959), 127–8. Visakhapatnam may get its own steel plant under the Fourth Plan.

mentioned in order to fit them into their regional context. There are many other developments. At Bangalore there is quite a significant grouping of aircraft factory (expanded from a wartime repair and maintenance plant for the USAAF), aero engine factory, telephone factory, electronics factories for civil defence purposes, machine-tool plant and watchmaking establishment. Locational factors probably include existing Mysore Government factories (electric lamps, soap, ceramics) and private sector textile industry on all scales of production, an equable climate and much pleasant garden-city development, as well as some political pressure to take substantial industry to the south. Other developments are more scattered – expansion as a public sector project of the struggling private sector shipyard at Visakhapatnam, and a new shipyard at Cochin, aluminium and carbide plants at Alwaye, a rolling stock factory at Madras, a heavy electricals plant at Bhopal, and various ordnance factories for defence purposes. The oil refinery at Gauhati in Assam is between Assam's modest oilfields with their own refinery at Digboi and the huge markets of Hooghlyside and industrial Bihar. The plant at Barauni is being linked by pipeline to the Assam oilfields on the one hand, and to Kanpur and Calcutta on the other;[10] we can see in the allocation between Assam and Bihar the Central Government's need to compromise. These developments are much more scattered and isolated, with some attempt to disperse benefits of industrial development through the country.

Several of the nascent industrial regions of Fig. 11.1 have not or have barely been mentioned in this account of public sector activity. Meantime there has been considerable buoyancy and development in the private sector – e.g. in engineering industries around Bombay (including motor vehicle assembly and progressive manufacture), in Madras (again including motor vehicles and bicycles), in the Ahmedabad area, in Kanpur, in the relatively new but active textile centre of Coimbatore, and in Punjab, largely under the stimulus of refugees. As an example, Ludhiana and its environs produce sewing machines, bicycles, motor vehicles and spares, and small tools, in addition to traditional textile industries.

In comparison with Karan's 1950 map of industrial regions, the current picture after well over a decade of planning naturally includes intensification in nearly every one of the nascent industrial regions or complexes he described, while there are also considerable new nuclei brought mainly by the public sector into relatively backward areas which may act as catalysts in their regions. There have been signs of the formation of a congeries of small-scale ancillary industries round major engineering factories, e.g. in Bangalore which admittedly has a whole group of such large engineering units, and this tendency may grow. On the other hand regional interactions between expanding industrial towns and the surrounding region have been rather slight, and on a disappointingly narrow front. There has been a local response to the market, say for vegetables, or milk,

[10] *Third Plan Mid-Term Appraisal,* 136.

but not much general quickening of economic life and the better side of urban based culture.

One of the main objectives of the Plans has been to increase employment, and while this need not necessarily be urban and industrial employment, the large scale industries are mainly of this type. A rough estimate of the additional employment becoming available during the Second Plan is 8,000,000 (6,500,000 outside agriculture). Unfortunately, the backlog of unemployment at the end of the Plan period was some 9,000,000, with an additional 15–18,000,000 under-employed.[11] For the first two years of the Third Plan, i.e. 1961–63, employment was known accurately to have risen by 1,300,000 in the public sector and in the private sector establishments employing twenty-five persons or more (40% in services, 30% in manufacturing and 17% in transport and communications); other non-agricultural employment is thought to have added almost another 2,000,000, ascribed to Plan expenditure, with in addition some additional agricultural employment (the target for 1961–66 is 3,500,000 in agriculture). The total may amount to 5,000,000, almost half the target for the whole Third Plan period.[12] So there may be a slow gain, even with rapid increase in population (and labour force offering).

We now turn to small-scale industrial development, certainly more dispersed though naturally including considerable development in the nascent industrial regions as auxiliary industries to large scale units.

Small-scale industry

The Second Five Year Plan, as we have noted, set out to stimulate small scale and handicraft industry. Some picture of the regional distribution patterns may be gained from the National Atlas of India (Fig. 11.2), and in more detail region-ally in the insets. It is much more difficult at present to show the regional differences in trends, but for the country as a whole published data permit an assessment of the degree of success attained in stimulating small-scale industry.

In 1950–51 employment in small-scale industry was estimated at 11,000,000, per capita earnings at Rs. 659. Investment in this sector during the first two Plan periods was Rs. 218 crores (some £260,000,000).[13] In 1960–61 employment was almost 16,000,000, per capita income about Rs. 515. Despite the drop in per capita income, this is probably satisfactory progress in a country with such severe unemployment. Just over 9% of the labour force contributed almost 6% of national income, which again seems satisfactory for a generally labour-intensive sector.[14]

[11] *Third Five Year Plan*, 156.
[12] *Third Plan Mid-Term Appraisal*, 52–3.
[13] T. R. Sundaram, 'Utilisation of idle man-power in India's economic development', *Pacific Affairs*, 34 (1951), 131–40.
[14] Unpublished paper by Planning Commission, Perspective Planning Division, Notes on Perspective of Development in India, April 1964.

As examples, the *khadi* (coarse homespun cotton) industry, admittedly emphasized because of association with Gandhian ideas, produced 843,000,000 yards in 1951, 1,865,000,000 in 1958–59, worth Rs. 13·75 crores and employing 1·4 people. More modern products are included – small industries producing sewing machines, electric fans, bicycles, builders' hardware and handtools have increased production by 25 to 50% in the Second Plan period, and provided an additional 300,000 jobs.[15]

By and large, traditional handicrafts and small rural industry remain significant – though not necessarily prosperous – in the more backward and inaccessible areas; they account for 10% or more of the total employed population in eastern Assam, Kutch, Jaisalmer in the Thar Desert, and the Kanara Districts. Another type of concentration, however, is associated with 'putting-out' around industrial centres, or in the diffusion of small workshops into the countryside in developing industrial regions, as around Hooghlyside and in the Damodar valley. A combination of immemorial tradition and the resettlement of post-Partition refugees is probably responsible for a remarkable concentration (over 10% of the total work force) around Delhi. The spread of village electrification may be expected to strengthen this component.

Many rural crafts naturally go with population; carpentry, smithery, and so on, as we have seen (above, p. 306) and minor mechanization in the countryside may actually result in an increase of demand for artisans in metal, as repairmen rather than as craftsmen in their own right. Apart from these almost ubiquitous trades, there are of course some interesting regional variations: metal- and leather-working, carpetry and rug-making in the Punjab; khadi in Kutch and Kathiawad, tobacco in southern Tamilnad, coir, soap and other coconut-based products in Kerala. In many cases primitive production carries on in the villages, with increasing difficulty, side by side with – or in face of – factory production for wider markets: the aggregate unorganized production of vegetable oils and *gur* from sugar-cane and other sources (such as *nipa* palm) must be very large; and, with Prohibition the general law of the land, one important consumption industry, the manufacture of toddy, must *ipso facto* be a village occupation.

With improvement in communications, there is of course a tendency for small-scale crafts to retreat; under-employment may turn into unemployment. It is difficult to envisage any really substantial rescue of the crafts from this process, though palliatives are possible such as the better organization of the trade in toys and souvenirs around pilgrim and tourist centres. There may be more hope in workshop production of small consumer durables – bicycles, tools, small electrical gear, and so on.

It is perhaps these more modern industries which are particularly associated with the move to spread small industrial estates – with hutted workshops rather than the medium to large industrial sheds of industrial estates say in Britain – and which justify some even if guarded optimism about possible increases in

[15] *Towards a Self-Reliant Economy*, 242.

dispersed industry particularly as electricity spreads into small towns and villages (see p. 290). Fig. 11.2 shows how these industrial estates are fairly evenly spread through the country.[16]

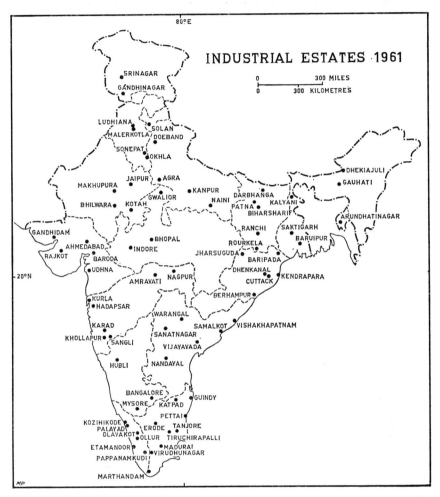

FIG 11.2 INDIA: INDUSTRIAL ESTATES. By March 1962 there were 71 estates with 138 factories, employing 19,000 people and producing Rs 160,000,000 worth of goods a year. *Source:* G. Whittington in *Tijdschrift voor Econ. en Sociale Geografie,* 54 (1963).

Before leaving the small-scale sector, we may note the high proportion of retail and distributive trade carried out by household traders – about 5,000,000 of just over 8,000,000 total businesses, but contributing only some Rs. 200

[16] G. Whittington, 'New features in the Indian industrial landscape', *Tijdschrift voor Econ. en Soc. Geografie,* 54 (1963), 193–4.

crores of the Rs. 1,200 crores contributed by distributive trades to the national income.[17]

Rural development: large-scale irrigation and multi-purpose projects and minor irrigation works; Community Development

These have already been discussed in Chapter 8 from an agrarian point of view. Figures 11.9 and 11.10 summarize a good deal concerning the areal distribution of the various projects.

From the planning point of view, the larger-scale projects have been satisfactory on the whole. Techniques are established, supervision and evaluation are relatively easy and effective; the Table shows the varying but by no means despicable degree of attainment of targets.

There have been problems locally. For instance, there was a period of lag in the Tungabhadra irrigation and hydro-electric project when there was difficulty in finding local farmers to take up irrigated plots, adapt their methods, and pay the water dues; since this project was to help the long notorious Bellary famine tract, the authorities were reluctant to bring in people from other areas overpopulated in relation to available resources and techniques, possible social difficulties apart. But large irrigation projects, such as the Punjab Canal Colonies of last century, have often shown a marked lag in full growth of benefits, and some such lag may bring more heartening news in the second half of the Third Plan period, and in general it seems that these medium to large projects are a good planning risk. There have been disappointments in food production, but due rather to vagaries of the monsoon on unirrigated plots.

In Chapter 8 there is also a full discussion of many problems of Community Development. Summarizing from the planning point of view, there has been very rapid expansion, evenly spread throughout nearly all parts of the country. Though probably politically inevitable, expansion was probably too rapid from both the technical and the human points of view, which must be inseparable in Community Development. Granting almost irresistible political pressures, internal and external, what has gone wrong so far?

There was probably too much reliance on the universality and effectiveness of the upsurge of dynamic forces expected from the Indian people when they were freed from the colonial yoke (in part justifiably as the achievements since 1947 show); linked with this there was probably too much hoped for from officials: from being tools of colonialist oppression – or at best of excessive emphasis on the negative qualities of law and order – the same individuals were expected to become leaders of these released dynamic forces, no barriers now separating them from the people. This was certainly expecting too much of a whole body of men, however devoted, whether old-style Revenue Officers turned Block Development Officers, or new style *gram sewaks* whether recruited from within

[17] *Report on Household Trade* (NSS 7th–9th Round, Govt of India Cabinet Secretariat, Delhi, 1960).

the village as in Uttar Pradesh or from outside as in Maharashtra. This rapid expansion was subject to scrutiny and evaluation, at its best honest, disinterested and valuable; but it was probably too little controlled in the sense of being subject to constant review by skilled practitioners of the social sciences as well as officials and technologists, too little based on expansion from a firm core of locally or regionally relevant experimental success from villages selected for the purpose very early in the programme, and actually attaining self-generating development growing out of locally felt needs and aspirations. Above all, from one vital viewpoint, it was surely too little productivity-oriented, too much amenity-oriented – or at worst, as has been pointed out earlier, oriented to merely paper victories.

Published tabulations of the results of the Plans as a whole show reasonably satisfactory entries under Community Development. In real gains, in socio-economic advancement of the most underprivileged, and also in the vital matter of agricultural activity, too little has been achieved. The Chinese aggression in the north in the second year of the Third Plan period, and a series of droughts in the wheat-eating northwest causing local famine (controlled with some difficulty) and a very widespread food shortage which had to be handled 'on a war footing' in 1964, were factors in bringing to a head a growing dissatisfaction with this part of the Plans. But the effect may be to concentrate effort on the pressing problem of food supply, delaying progress in social reform or directing it along lines not hitherto foreseen.

The Mid-Term Appraisal of the Third Plan, of November 1963, reports that henceforth 'the village level workers should be assigned only one set of duties, namely, those pertaining to agricultural extension, supplies and demonstrations and assistance to co-operatives and Panchayats in drawing up and implementing village production plans'. The national emergency apart, the emphasis on productivity was overdue; the dilemma of a community development programme not accompanied by really drastic socio-economic reform remains. The landholder is likely to benefit, especially the owners of larger plots even following land reform (above, 270, for a critique). Therefore the underprivileged, especially the landless labourers, will be benefited only marginally by slightly increased availability of work and perhaps marginally higher wages. Perhaps as some palliative to this, there is also instituted a very rapidly expanding programme of rural works, for which in the first two years expenditure of Rs. 1·5 crores in perhaps 20,000 (of over 500,000) villages was responsible for providing some 7,500,000 man-days of employment at Rs. 1 to Rs. 2·50 per day.[18] Expanded rapidly, this programme may well be significant in relieving local pockets or severe seasonal incidence of unemployment or underemployment (see p. 131).

It is intended to be used to build roads, especially to markets, to set up soil conservation works, to carry out afforestation and drainage, and even to dig field channels, subject to eventual recovery of the cost from the farmers benefiting

[18] Planning Commission, *Mid-term* Appraisal, Manager of Government Publications, Delhi, 1963, esp. pp. 96–98.

from them. The two programmes together may at last turn the scale in securing widespread improvement in crop yields and reliability, especially if co-operation can also gain real momentum, particularly co-operative agreements about land-use to permit of consolidation of holdings where fragmentation at present prevents soil conservation measures or other rational land-use. They are likely to bring but palliative benefit to the economically vulnerable classes, to whom they may seem a rather pale benefit from 'a socialistic pattern of society', but the great hope – assuming the desirability of victory for the planning programmes while preserving democracy of more or less Western type – is that they may enable the society of rural India to survive, not necessarily unchanged, but evolving gradually, against the time when urban-industrial development can absorb many more of its people, and the standards of living especially among landless labour can be upgraded by higher, perhaps legally defined wages. The scale of the problem to which this is a palliative, however, is that according to the Second Plan (p. 14) about 40% of the agricultural population should be drawn elsewhere to make farming more economic, and that the agricultural labour force should be reduced to 60% of the total labour force by 1975–76.

The Five Year plans have now been considered in relation to large- and small-scale industry, and to the Community Development programmes – politically vital and potentially crucial in the success of the whole. Equally important and interrelated sectors remain to be reviewed: power, transport and trade.

The strategy of electric power generation

The available bases for power generation have been discussed under the appropriate headings in Chapter 9. The over-all strategy and the allocation between different sources of generation of electricity are considered here, in relation to recent demands and probably short term future demands for power. The tables summarize recent trends in demand and in generation, with short term targets as amended up to the Third Plan mid-term review and subsequent to the adjustment of targets following the Chinese threat in 1962, which are very likely to be fulfilled on recent performance in this industry (p. 363).

Beyond 1966 very large increases in demand are anticipated, and the strategy of power generation includes these factors:

(a) poor quality coal (including much from coal washeries needed to keep the iron-and-steel works supplied with adequate coking coal while conserving the scarce reserves) is available and can be used, given adequate protection from atmospheric pollution; this is a cheap method of generation, at present needing a large proportion of foreign exchange, though one that is falling as heavy electrical equipment comes into home production;

(b) the first five units, totalling 250,000 kW capacity, of the integrated scheme based on Neiveli lignite have come into production in Madras, to produce power, fertilizers and domestic fuel; this source of power will probably play a large part in the growing Southern Grid;

344

(c) hydro-electricity is at present somewhat more expensive to produce than that from well-sited and well-designed thermal plant, because of high capital cost, and it involves considerable lag because of long construction time; but a lower proportion of the capital goods requires scarce foreign exchange and generation costs are low since there is no cost for fuel; moreover, hydro-electric projects tend to be conservative of water, to be very useful for a variable load, and (at the price of less than optimal generation costs) to fit in with irrigation projects – but on the other hand to be located in out-of-the-way places where demand is low or only gradually built up;

(d) India's resources of nuclear material, and her skilled man-power, give her a leading position among the less developed countries in nuclear power generation.

As yet, however, the capital costs of nuclear generation are so heavy that despite the saving in fuel costs (especially on transport), the over-all cost lies between that of thermal and that of hydro-electric power, while much of the capital goods at present needs foreign exchange, and nuclear stations are not suitable for widely varying loads. It is thus difficult to decide whether a country like India should import nuclear power stations at their present stage of development, tying herself to some extent to this technological stage, or should wait until much cheaper methods of generation have been evolved, as no doubt they will be within a few years. Even at present, however, nuclear power stations are justified in places remote from fuel sources or with very large markets for power, and stations are under construction for Tarapore near Bombay (400,000 kW capacity), and in prospect for Rana Pratap Sagar in Rajasthan and Kalpakkam near Madras.[19]

The general picture is of flexibility in an attempt to reduce the local power famines of the most industrially developed areas at the present day, and to keep ahead of demand in order to maintain electric power as a major catalyst in industrialization. For ten or fifteen years ahead the main target will be industry – still accounting for 75% of consumption – but the spread of electricity into tens of thousands of the larger villages (some 30,000 by late 1962) for lift irrigation, small industry and street and house lighting, is also giving experience and spreading a demand which may be quite crucial in raising living standards.

Transport

At the time of Independence, India's legacy from the colonial phase included, as we have seen, a kind of transportation panoply of imperialism: the major ports, the related 'steel frame' of broad-gauge railways, feeder lines of metre and

[19] Sources include: *Third Plan Mid-Term Appraisal*; M. Datta, *op. cit.*; H. J. Bhabha, 'The promise of nuclear energy', *Science and Culture*, 29/12 (Calcutta, 1963), 574–6 (and Editorial), and his 'On the economics of atomic power development in India', *Advancement of Science*, 14 (London, 1957–58), 159–75. Dr. Bhabha's tragic death in an air crash early in 1966 represented the loss of a "modern Leonardo" (Yehudi Menuhin, in a letter to the *Guardian*).

narrow gauge. The road net-work included distinct if not always good trunk roads (of decreased military importance for a time, during the peak of the railway age), and important feeder roads, totalling under 100,000 miles (161,000 km.) of

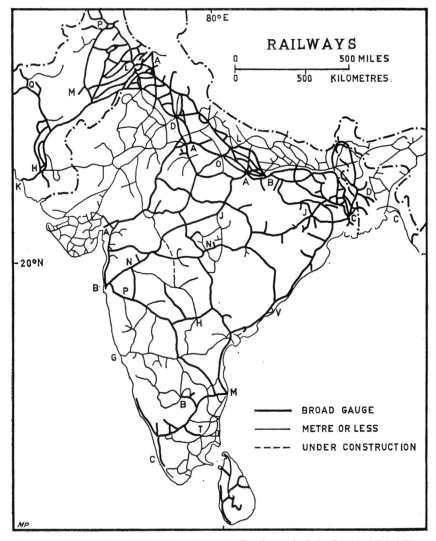

FIG 11.3 INDIA AND PAKISTAN: RAILWAYS. By the end of the Indian Third Plan all major cities should be linked by double-track lines.

surfaced road (generally with 9–10 in., 23–25 cm., of road metal), beyond which were the dirt roads and the village tracks. Inland transport by country boats was important in the northeast, supplemented by steamboats and steel barges, and survived in some other areas such as the southwest. Coastal traffic by steamship and sailing craft survived and was locally important (see the figures for Mangalore, p. 672 below), with some of it in foreign hands, while Indian overseas lines were in existence and growing. Privately-run internal airlines already had several years of honourable experience. The pattern of imperialism is plain, but changes had already begun, and moreover military routes were also channels of imperial trade, with notable exceptions such as the railways in the North-West Frontier Province and Baluchistan, now in West Pakistan. And the Nagpur Road Plan of 1943, still the basic document in the field, shows the importance attached to transport in forward thinking.

From the First Five Year Plan onwards, the Indian Government has constantly given a high priority to developments in transport. In railway development the main initial tasks were to overcome the backlog caused by excessive war-time strain on the system – inadequate maintenance, obsolescence of locomotives and rolling stock, etc. – to regroup and rationalize the railway companies as nationalized groups (completing the long-standing tendency to government subsidy and control), and to make adjustments consequential upon Partition. Then there was the task of forward planning in relation to a developing and industrializing economy. Up to now the demand for rail transport of passengers and goods has been so buoyant that railway planning has been able to take place in an atmosphere of confidence, of planning an enterprise profitable to the government, in contrast say to the problem of cutting down all but the essential and profitable services in Britain. So far road services are complementary rather than competitive, although competition does exist even on quite long hauls because of the normal advantage of lorry transport in flexibility (see Fig. 11.5). Inland waterways are of some importance in Bengal and Assam, and in the southwest, but mainly by means of small 'country boats'. The trade by river steamer and steel barge on the Brahmaputra seems not to have recovered from the earthquake of 1950 while the main steam navigation company on the Ganga ceased business in 1950. There is an attempt to reactivate inland navigation under the Five Year Plans, but this progresses extremely slowly.[20] Airlines also are complementary and highly specialized; Fig. 11.7 shows an exception – the heavy traffic between Calcutta and the extreme northeastern areas (Assam and Tripura, etc.) across East Pakistan. Major developments in the rail system include the elimination of bottlenecks especially by bridging to replace ferries (e.g. the Ganga road-rail bridge at Mokameh), electrification of the busiest lines (Calcutta–Kanpur eventually – some busy lines near Bombay have long been electrified), limited dieselization (probably increasing as manufacture of diesel locomotives replaces the making of steam locomotives), and the construction of multiple tracks over lines unable to take the increasing traffic without causing hold-ups and bottlenecks.

Since the war, road development has come a long way from a fairly low starting

[20] *Third Plan Mid-Term Appraisal*, 144; see also *Ganga Traffic Survey* (National Ccil Applied Econ. Research, Bombay, 1960) which estimates that there are modest potentialities (perhaps 200,000 tons per annum) for revival of steamship traffic on that river.

point. By the end of the Second Plan, surfaced roads were about 144,000 miles, unsurfaced over 250,000 (232,000 and 402,000 km.), but in places they remain unbridged, too narrow or poorly maintained. The main objectives of the Third

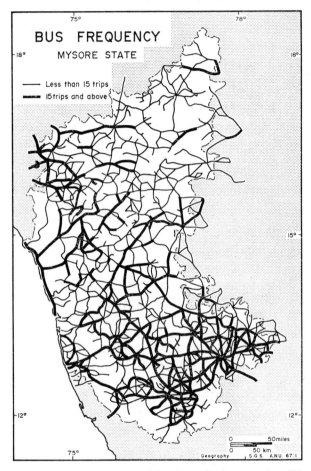

FIG 11.4 MYSORE: BUS FREQUENCIES. Number of trips per day. The local bus, ploughing through clouds of dust, is a powerful factor in social change. Road densities are low compared with developed countries, but considerable compared with many undeveloped countries, though there are still regions of isolation in the heart of India, especially the tribal country of central India and the northeastern Peninsula. Mysore services, partly State-run, may stand as representing the pattern in a reasonably developed region; the relative poverty of most of the Malnad and of the far north, adjacent to backward Telangana, will be noted. *Source:* A. T. A. Learmonth and L. S. Bhat (eds.) *Mysore State I. An Atlas of Resources* (Indian Statistical Institute, Calcutta), 1960.

Five Year Plan in relation to road development are based on a twenty-year road development plan (1961–81) drawn up by the Chief Engineers of the State and Central Governments: no village in a developed and agricultural area should

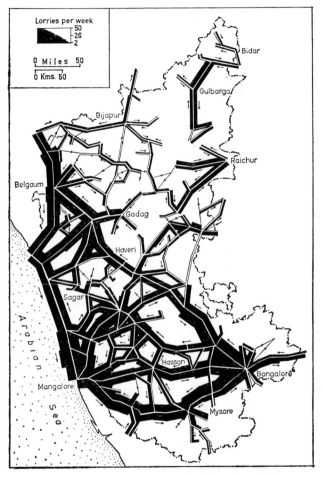

FIG 11.5 LORRY MOVEMENT IN MYSORE. On the Bangalore–Belgaum route, which continues to Bombay, lorry transport runs alongside the metre-gauge rail; in the coastal tract, it is competing successfully with shipping; along the east–west routes, it is gradually replacing the bullock cart. *Source:* A. T. A. Learmonth in *Geographers and the Tropics: Liverpool Essays* (Longmans, 1964).

remain more than 4 miles from a metalled road and 1½ miles from any type of road, while undeveloped and underdeveloped areas will receive special attention appropriate to their needs. The target for 1981 is 200,000 miles of surfaced and 405,000 miles of unsurfaced roads (322,000 and 652,000 km.).

The priorities given in the Third Plan are indicative of the picture underlying Fig. 11.5: (a) bridges should be provided on all arterial routes, and the road surfaces improved to at least one lane of black-topped type, (b) the main roads in the vicinity of large towns should be widened to two lanes or more, and (c) the major arterial routes should have at least two-lane carriageways. The Chinese threat of October 1962 onwards has brought speeding rather than slowing of this particular part of the plan, though naturally mainly in the northern part of the country.

In some areas there is nationalized road transport for passengers and/or goods, elsewhere there are large and well-organized operating companies. But over much of the country road transport for both passengers and goods is carried on by excessively small-scale entrepreneurs. Numbers of commercial goods vehicles as yet are relatively small (in 1961, 171,000 out of a total of 675,000), but manufactures are increasing (28,000 in 1960–61). No doubt there is a place for small entrepreneurship with low capital investment (coupled with inspection of vehicles!) for purely local and spasmodic transport. But for longer distance work some measures of rationalization, whether by nationalization or no, are surely long overdue.

The table shows the expansion in coastal and overseas shipping achieved, and contemplated in the Third Plan period.

Thousands of Gross Registered Tons

	1950–51	1955–65	1960–61	1965–66
Coastal	217	240	292	425
Overseas	174	240	613	855
	391	480	905	1,280

The overseas shipping, in the hands of both public sector corporations and private sector companies, is given a high priority in order to conserve foreign exchange, while a committee on transport co-ordination is endeavouring to plan the best use of coastal shipping to complement the railways, notably in carrying bulk cargoes like coal.

Fig. 11.6 shows the main ports of the country. The great ports built up during the British phase retain their paramountcy, but Cochin is rising, and Kandla – built as a replacement for Karachi under the First Plan – carries appreciable traffic.[21] At times port congestion and delays are very serious and the Second Plan provided additional berths and facilities at Calcutta, Madras, Visakhapatnam and Cochin, while under the Third Plan preparations are at various stages to convert several minor ports for all-weather operations. Of these Haldia is 65

[21] See D. R. Gadgil, *op. cit.* xiv for an interesting questioning of the decision to make Kandla a free port; Cochin, in over-populated Kerala and with a great need for expansion of trade and industry, would have been a more rational choice for a free port.

miles (105 km.) downstream from Calcutta, so that ships may lighten before going up to Calcutta, have a quick turn-round there and load additional outwards cargo again at Haldia; this involves a rail link from Kharagpur to Haldia. The

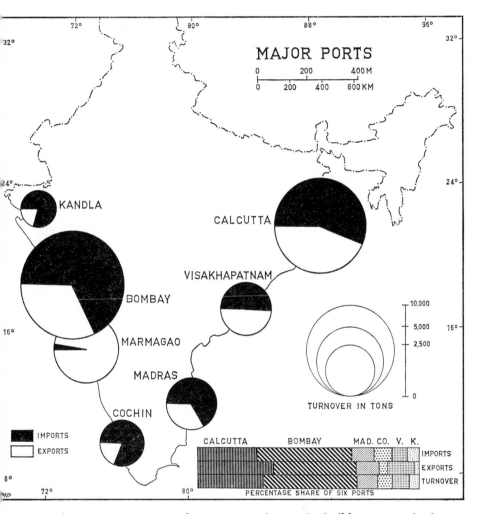

FIG 11.6 INDIA: MAJOR PORTS. Averages 1959–60 to 1963–64 (Marmagao 1961–62 to 1963–64). The great colonial ports of Calcutta and Bombay are still dominant, but Cochin rivals Madras and the new port of Kandla has already a fair turnover. The striking contrast between Marmagao, with its iron ore exports, and the general import/export pattern will be noticed. *Source: Statesman's Year-Book.*

others are Tuticorin in Madras, Mangalore in Mysore and Paradip in Orissa. A barrage on the Ganga at Farakka is to be built to send additional water down the Hooghly to decrease silting on the Hooghly and reduce tidal bores.[22]

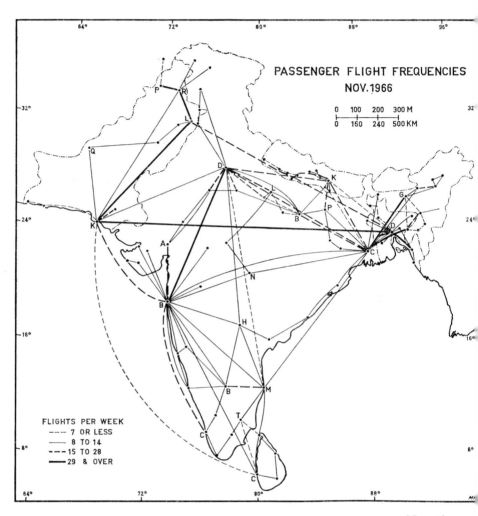

FIG 11.7 INDIA AND PAKISTAN: PASSENGER FLIGHT FREQUENCIES. Note the importance of the Karachi–Dacca and Calcutta–Gauhati services. *Source:* compiled from data in *ABC World Airways Guide*, Nov. 1966 (T. Skinner, London).

[22] *Third Five Year Plan*, 558–9; *Third Plan Mid-Term Appraisal*, 145; note in *Science and Culture*, 27/1 (1961), 31. Progress of port capacity (in million tons turnover) is: 1951, 20; 1956, 24; 1961, 37; 1965–66 target, 49.

Trade

The era of the Five Year Plans has naturally brought marked changes in India's trade position, large imports of capital goods reversing the generally favourable balance of trade of the British period. Yet recent changes in direction of trade, with less close relations with Britain, continued trends which started several decades ago. There is a growing tendency to state and inter-government trading, largely by bi-lateral agreements.

Exports and imports during the era of the Five Year Plans

During the First Five Year Plan, avowedly modest in scale, imports were relatively low at an average of Rs. 724 crores per annum, while exports at Rs. 609 crores included very high figures for 1951–52 because of the Korean war. The much more ambitious Second Plan brought a sharp increase in imports from Rs. 746 crores in 1955–56 to Rs. 1,099 crores in 1956–57 and Rs. 1,233 crores in 1957–58. This increase was unexpectedly sharp, draining foreign exchange reserves, notably the sterling balances resulting from British spending in India for war-time purposes. Moreover, various factors have invalidated the foreign exchange control system so that much of the foreign exchange was spent on imports not scheduled in the Plan, not even in the large estimates allowed for private sector imports of capital goods, etc. This foreign exchange crisis, particularly sharp and peculiarly vexing to the government because it showed lack of acceptance of the Plan by officials and politicians as well as businessmen – not to mention corruption – was nevertheless inherent in this phase of planned economic development. It was met by further import restrictions, imports falling to Rs. 920 crores by 1959–60. Such restrictions are likely to continue in some form at least until the end of the Fourth Plan in 1971. The table shows the changing emphasis on imports of raw materials and capital goods, and also the need to import food from time to time though this may not drain foreign exchange because of the special provisions of the American P.L. 480 legislation.

Meantime, exports have remained comparatively stagnant, though in the middle of the Third Plan period an improvement was seen, following years of effort to promote exports, and encouraging successes were gained for individual products and exports, such as iron ore (to Japan and Eastern Europe), manganese ore (to Japan), coal (to Pakistan), and mica (to many industrial countries); and jute fabrics, vegetable oils, electrical and electronic equipment, engineering goods, iron and steel castings, metals and metal manufactures (mainly of iron, steel and aluminium), chemicals and soap, rubber manufactures, drugs and medicines. Cotton and jute fabrics and tea are tending to stagnation or decline and manufactured goods generally to be less promising than appeared likely a few years ago – largely because Japanese competition is too powerful in most likely markets. The export campaign during the Second Plan period may have been affected by the 1958 economic recession in North America and Europe, but the tables below show how difficult the problem is. Exports of agricultural commodities and related manufactures tend to fall, within which the separate figures for cotton and jute manufactures should be noted; the fall in these goes far to offset the increase in other manufactures, including new lines, and also in mineral exports, notably iron ore to Japan and Eastern Europe.

PATTERN OF EXPORTS 1951–60

(Rs. crores)

	1960–51	1955–56	1958–59	1959–60
1. Agricultural commodities and related manufactures	496·5	489·3	453·5	473·6
Cotton and jute manufactures (included in item 1)	250·5	181·7	153·4	180·5
2. Other manufactures	58·4	61·0	53·3	105·0
New manufactured products (included in item 2)	8·9	8·61	12·5	25·0
3. Minerals	23·4	34·4	46·2	53·0
Total	578·3	584·7	553·0	631·6

DIRECTION OF INDIA'S FOREIGN TRADE

(Per cent shares)

Country/area	Exports			Imports		
	1952	1956	1960	1952	1956	1960
1. ECAFE countries	25·7	16·3	17·0	13·6	12·4	13·1
Japan	4·1	4·9	5·5	2·4	5·2	5·4
2. West Asia	5·7	5·8	6·5	7·7	10·8	7·5
3. Africa	3·6	3·9	2·5	3·8	4·0	4·4
4. Western Europe	29·6	39·8	38·5	30·1	50·1	40·4
UK	20·5	29·8	27·5	18·5	25·0	20·0
European Economic Community	7·5	8·3	8·0	8·8	20·0	18·0
5. Eastern Europe and China	1·3	3·5	8·0	2·2	4·2	3·7
6. North America	21·1	17·0	18·7	37·3	12·4	25·2
USA	19·0	14·7	16·0	33·6	11·3	23·7
7. Latin America	1·4	1·0	2·5		0·1	0·1
8. Oceania	4·3	4·4	3·1	2·0	1·7	2·3
9. Others	7·3	8·3	3·2	3·3	4·3	3·3
Total	100·0	100·0	100·0	100·0	100·0	100·0

The table shows the decreasing but still considerable proportion of trade with Britain, which takes more from India than India takes in return, in contrast to the rising proportion of trade with Japan, with a relatively even trade balance, and with USA and the countries of the European Economic Community with both of which the trade balance tends to be distinctly adverse to India, and where export promotion campaigns may be particularly needed.

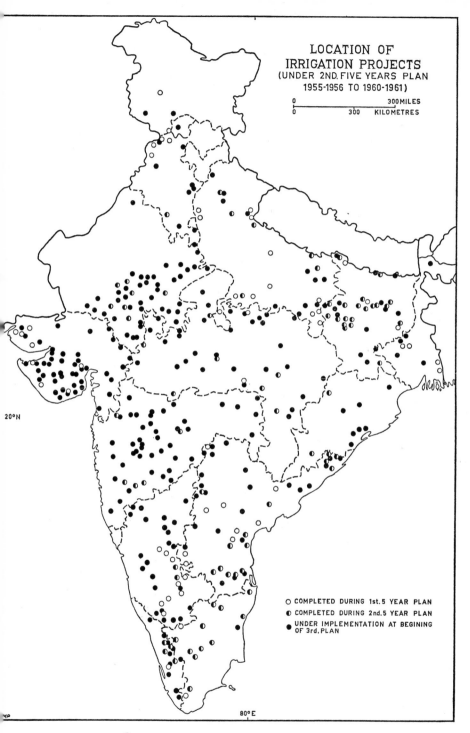

FIG 11.8 INDIA: SECOND PLAN IRRIGATION PROJECTS

FIG II.9 INDIA: MULTIPURPOSE AND MAJOR IRRIGATION PROJECTS.

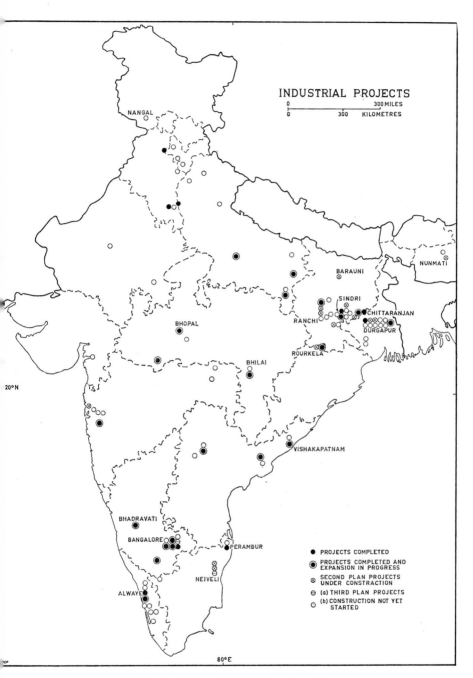

INDUSTRIAL PROJECTS

| 0 | | | 300 MILES |
| 0 | | 300 | KILOMETRES |

NANGAL

NUNMATI

BARAUNI

SINDRI

CHITTARANJAN

RANCHI

DURGAPUR

BHOPAL

ROURKELA

BHILAI

20°N

VISHAKAPATNAM

BHADRAVATI

BANGALORE

PERAMBUR

NEIVELI

ALWAYE

80°E

● PROJECTS COMPLETED
◉ PROJECTS COMPLETED AND EXPANSION IN PROGRESS
⊗ SECOND PLAN PROJECTS UNDER CONSTRUCTION
⊖ (a) THIRD PLAN PROJECTS
○ (b) CONSTRUCTION NOT YET STARTED

FIG 11.10 INDIA: INDUSTRIAL PROJECTS.

Conclusion : Indian society in the era of Five Year Plans

These paragraphs must reflect personal experience and even prejudices, must be subjective in judgment. What yardsticks shall we use? The reports of the National Sample Survey give some quantitative data, interestingly analysed by Malenbaum. There is probably a slow rise in 'consumer expenditure' – a useful general indicator of standards of material living. The Survey has for some years now made available data about the higher standards of consumption in the towns and generally towards the north and west of the country, and indicated the tendency for rural dwellers experiencing a rise in consumption to increase their non-food items, while town dwellers moving from the lower levels tend to diversify their consumption. Fig. 11.11 gives some, though subjectively based, indications of regional variations in economic development according to Schwartzberg;[23] there is evidence of higher consumption levels in the four largest cities, and the increases may also be concentrated there and in other major foci of economic development under the Five Year Plans – in both the public and the private sectors. The Second Plan target of providing new jobs for 11,000,000 people was not fulfilled – only 8,000,000 were found in the event. Even so the direct effects and the indirect influence on the economy have effected some improvement of standards of living, even taking groups among the most difficult and vulnerable classes, the landless labour of the countryside and the very poor, often rootless, casual labouring groups of the towns and cities. The improvement was but slight, but it was carried out despite a sharp upsurge in rates of population increase, much higher than were anticipated at the beginning of the Plan period.

How does the present picture compare with the later part of the British period on the one hand, and on the other with the declared objective of the Congress Party Government of a socialistic pattern of society?

As the Indian nationalists predicted, Independence has brought a much more positive approach to many problems than was possible under a colonial régime, and this has been done while preserving and continuing many of the more worthy legacies of the British period. This has allowed the best of the politicians, professional men, administrators and business men to fulfil themselves and to serve and advance their country in a way unthinkable before Independence. Nepotism and corruption have possibly increased, at least at certain levels; it probably affects some in all the classes mentioned, yet many individuals are completely beyond reproach or suspicion, and it may well prove possible to control this plague, particularly if the Plans as a whole do succeed. There is a new and wider prosperity and confidence among middle class people, accompanied by very much freer and more confident social and professional exchanges with Europeans. The need for controls for restrictions on imports and on internal consumption in order to promote exports makes for a certain grey

[23] A revised version of this map may be found in W. Norman (ed.), *India, Pakistan, Ceylon* (Univ. of Pennsylvania Press, 1960); there is little substantive change, but the map includes Pakistan and Ceylon.

monotony reminiscent of the later part of the Second World War and immediately post-war years in Britain, and with similar results in causing a certain amount of dissatisfaction or rebelliousness especially among young people. There is a very much larger and more widely dispersed class of industrial workers – middle class rather than working class in many respects. The respectable lower middle class of clerks, school teachers, and so on have often a bitter struggle in these times of inflationary pressures, even more or less controlled.

The very poor urban groups have relatively stable social standards and *mores* so long as they can survive as family and preferably as village or hamlet-type groups within the city; even if they are living under slum conditions their individual houses are clean and preserve some vital traditions of hearth and home. They may be subject to appalling health risks, especially high infant and child mortality, and the pressure to moral degradation may be strong, but often a local social organization preserves their culture and *mores*. There is a more serious problem of a largely male, temporary migrant, rootless, homeless, poor urban proletariat in northern industrial cities especially. Underemployment is rife, and as the old hymn observed Satan finds mischief for idle hands to do. These masses contain unstable groups, quick to unrest and at times to seemingly meaningless, randomly cruel violence – a potential threat to the society and culture in which they live, and yet hapless victims, needing steady work, but too often scarcely able to grasp it when it offers. These two groups of urban poor are largely recruited from the vulnerable rural class of poor landless labourers. All these very poor groups of people are among the most difficult, the least helped by the Five Year Plans, the most likely to destroy by violence the attempt to reach higher standards of living and a socialistic pattern of society by planning within a free, multi-party parliamentary democracy. Massive as the efforts have been, industrialization simply has not proceeded fast enough to create jobs, directly or indirectly, to mop up the pool of urban unemployment and underemployment, constantly rising by drift from rural areas – here pushed by drought, there by small size of holdings, and so on. The attempt has been massive; conceived on a scale to meet a great backlog of poverty, ignorance and unemployment with a modest improvement in standards of living, it has in the event rather more than kept pace with the rise in population. But it has not been able as yet to convince all men, including the grossly underprivileged, that unemployment and poverty can be mastered within one or two further Plan periods. To win the masses from extreme poverty to modest standards of living, education, and population stability is a matter of urgency, if the present pattern of development is to succeed.

How does the present picture compare, again, with the government's declared objective of a socialistic pattern of society? What is envisaged apparently includes parliamentary democracy and a mixed economy of public and private undertakings in industry and commerce; rural land farmed mainly by individuals – subject to ceiling limits of landholding varying from state to state – who are to be encouraged to form producers' and marketing co-operatives, but not compelled nor even put under excessive pressure to collectivize agriculture. Therefore the present vulnerable landless labour class must be largely drawn off to the cities by industrialization and urban growth, preferably without further development of shanty-town slums, and those remaining as labourers must be protected

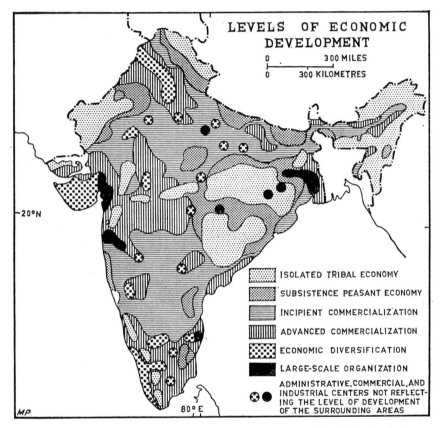

FIG II.II INDIA: LEVELS OF ECONOMIC DEVELOPMENT. By 'subjective integration' approach, one of three methods discussed in the source, J. E. Schwartzberg in *Annals Assoc. American Geographers*, 52 (1962).

by control of wages and conditions, and agriculture must be such that farmers or co-operatives must be able to afford to pay accordingly. Regional development of resources to the utmost possible extent is avowed policy, according to both the Second and Third Plans. Within this socio-economic pattern the general educational, social and political pattern must ensure equality of opportunity for all. These are large demands, even in the perspective of the next fifteen or twenty years. But India does have some considerable natural and human resources – minerals, water, land, a stable government and society, a culture that has recently undergone something of a renaissance, an experienced and on the whole a devoted and relatively incorruptible civil service, and considerable experience of the planning process. Success is probably attainable. Conditions of success include widespread confidence in eventual success, more widespread active participation, freedom from external pressure, and more foreign aid over the next fifteen years at least. Internally there is relatively little controversy that planning is needed in India. But should planning be less direct, more directive, as in France, or tighter, as in the communist countries, with nearly all agents of production in the public sector? There are, of course, differences of opinion both within and outside India. Whether controls be more or less tight, or more or less direct, the geographer may well feel that on the one hand the blots in the present picture, despite great advances, and on the other hand the serious problems of redeployment of resources and manpower involved in looking ahead, call alike for regional integration in development. The planning of town and country together will be necessary, if only to fulfil the undertakings in the Plans about evening out regional disparities in development, and to control rural migration to urban slums, so that the inevitable urban expansion can take place at a standard worthy of the new India and her imaginative series of Plans within a parliamentary democracy.[24] It remains to be seen, also, whether the federal structure can take the new strains imposed by the 1967 elections, when Congress lost control of States as important as Madras and Uttar Pradesh.

ADDENDA TO CHAPTER 11

A. FIRST FIVE-YEAR PLAN

	Planned		Achieved	
	Rs million	% of total	Rs million	% of total
Agriculture and Community Development	3,610	18	2,910	15
Irrigation and power	5,610	27	5,700	29
Transport and communications	4,970	24	5,230	27
Industry	1,730	8	1,170	6
Social services and miscellaneous	4,770	23	4,590	23
Total:	20,690	100	19,600	100

[24] On the broad regional aspects of planning see M. N. Pal and A. T. A. Learmonth, 'An appraisal of the regionalisation of economic development in India', oral paper to Australian and New Zealand Association Adv. Sci., Canberra meeting, January 1964, at present in mimeographed form; for physical planning in the sense of town and country planning see J. Wood, 'The development of urban and regional planning in India', *Land Economics*, 34 (1958), 310–15.

The financial basis of this outlay was as follows:

	Planned	Achieved
	Rs million	
Internal resources (other than deficit financing)	12,580	13,520
External assistance	5,210	1,880
Deficit financing	2,900	4,200
Total:	20,690	19,600

In addition, the private sector was expected to invest Rs 14,000,000,000, later revised to 18,000,000,000.

B. SECOND FIVE-YEAR PLAN

	Planned		Achieved	
	Rs million	% of total	Rs million	% of total
Agriculture and Community Development	5,680	12	5,300	11
Irrigation and Power	9,130	19	8,650	19
Industry and mining	8,900	18	10,750	24
Transport and communications	13,850	29	13,000	28
Social services and miscellaneous	10,440	22	8,300	18
Total:	48,000	100	46,000	100

The financial basis of this outlay was as follows:

	Planned	Achieved
	Rs million	
Internal resources (other than deficit financing)	24,000	25,620
External assistance	8,000	10,900
Deficit financing	12,000	9,480
Gap to be met	4,000	—
Total:	48,000	46,000

In addition, the private sector was estimated to make an expenditure of Rs 24,000,000,000, later revised to Rs 31,000,000,000.

C. KEY TARGETS OF THE THIRD FIVE-YEAR PLAN

	1960–61	1965–66
Foodgrains (million tons)	79·3	100·0
Cotton (million bales)	4·5	7·1
Power: installed capacity (million kW)	5·6	12·7
Railways: freight carried (million tons)	154·0	245·0
Steels, finished (million tons)	2·4	6·8
Aluminium (000 tons)	18·2	80·0
Machine tools (value Rs million)	72·4	300·0
Industrial boilers (value Rs million)	4·0	250·0
Automobiles (000 Nos.)	53·5	100·0
Coal (million tons)	55·5	98·5
Fertilizer (N) (000 tons)	97·1	800·0
Sulphuric acid (000 tons)	354·0	1,500·0
Petroleum products (million tons)	5·7	9·9
Electric motors (000 h.p.)	700·0	2,500·0
Cloth (million yards)	7,476·0	9,300·0
Pupils in schools (million nos.)	43·4	64·0
Engineering students – intake (000 Nos)	39·4	56·5
Hospital beds (000 Nos.)	186·0	240·0
Increase in national income (plan period)	20%	30%
Per capita income (Rs at 1960–61 prices)	330·0	385·0

The financial basis of outlay is as follows:

	Rs million
Internal resources	30,400
Additional taxation	17,100
External assistance	22,000
Deficit financing	5,500
	75,000

D. THE GROWING DEMAND FOR POWER, 1950–65
(In millions of kilowatt hours)

	Over the First Decade 1950–60			By the end of Third Plan	
	1950	1960–61 (estimated)	% increase 1950–1960–61	1965–66 (anticipated)	% increase over 1960–61
For domestic light and small power	525	1,492	184	3,400	128
For commercial light and small power	309	870	182	1,900	118
For industry	3,984	12,314	209	28,400	131
For traction	308	449	46	1,800	301
For public lighting	60	192	220	400	108
For irrigation	162	836	416	1,900	127
For public water works etc.	189	455	141	900	98
For auxiliaries, transmission losses, etc.	1,038	3,242	212	6,300	94
	6,575	19,850	202	45,000	127

E. ELECTRIC POWER GENERATION
(*In million kW*)

	1950	*1955*	*1961* estimated	*1966* estimated
Hydro plant	0·56	0·94	1·93	5·1
Steam plant	1·59	2·27	3·46	7·08
Oil plant	0·15	0·21	0·31	0·36
Nuclear plant	—	—	—	0·15
Total	2·3	3·42	5·7	12·69★

★ Amended to 12,500,000 in the Mid-Term Appraisal, *op. cit.*, p. 106.

F. INDIA – PHYSICAL TARGETS AND OUTPUT
(*Million tonnes u.o.s*)

	Third Plan Mid-Term (*Appraisal*) 1965–66	Expected Production 1965–66	Fourth Plan-Target 1970–71
AGRICULTURE			
Foodgrains	100·0	74·0	125·0
Cotton	7·1	5·2	0·85
Sugar and gur	10·0	12·0	13·5
Jute (lakh bales)	62·0	50·0	80·0
Nitrogenous Fertilizer – Consumption	0·8	0·6	2·4
Phosphatic Fertilizer – Consumption	0·25	0·2	1·0
INDUSTRY			
Inputs for Agriculture			
Fertilizers-N_2	0·51	0·25–0·3	2·2
Fertilizers-P_2O_5	0·2	0·13–0·2	1·0
Power driven pumps (1,000 units)	180·0	160·0	300·0
OTHER			
Newsprint	0·03	0·03	0·17
Steel ingots	7·9	6·6	16·8
Pig iron for sale	1·2	1·2	4·1
Aluminium	0·07	0·07	0·25
Cement	12·2	11·0	30·0

Sources: Memorandum of the Fourth Five-Year Plan. Government of India, Planning Commission, Oct., 1964; Annual Plan 1966–7, Government of India, Planning Commission, Mar. 1966; Report of Committee on Fertilizers, Government of India, 1965; J. G. Crawford, 'Planning Under Difficulties', *Australian J. Pol. & Hist.*, 12/2, Ang. 1966, 155–76.

CHAPTER 12

Economic Development in Pakistan

General features of Pakistan planning

Pakistan has a shorter history of planning than India. Almost immediately after Partition, a list of projects was drawn up, necessary to begin the long process of economic rehabilitation. A Planning Board (later the Planning Commission) then drew up a six-year plan under the Colombo Plan, for the years 1951 to 1957, giving priorities to agriculture, transport and communications, industry and mining, fuel and power, and social uplift in that order; this was modified to stricter priorities in 1953, and a First Five Year Plan was formulated to begin in 1955. This was largely frustrated by political instability (the Plan was not even officially approved until 1957) and by indiscipline in the administration. The target of a 7% increase in *per capita* income fell sadly short, and only 3% was attained. Agriculture, water development and education came nowhere near their targets although some industrial development succeeded in doing so, notably in the cotton and sugar industries. There were signs of gathering momentum towards the end of the period which, with the experience gained, has allowed the Second Plan to go ahead with more hope and evidence of success for its more ambitious aims in the struggle 'to find some way towards the liberation of the people from the crushing burden of poverty – mainly through inducement . . . less through direction'. The net national product has increased by some 9% and progress has been greatest in those sections using foreign aid and technology such as power and communications. It has been much less in what might be called 'boot strap' operations such as agriculture and social uplift. And the whole problem is bedevilled by the alarming population increase beyond all forecasts, so that targets aimed at improvement turn into targets that, even if achieved, will only prevent actual decline. The targets might be attainable, but only with considerable acceleration.[1] The approach is avowedly pragmatic – a compromise based on evaluation of the first plan, desirable aims and inspired guesswork.[2]

The burden of poverty can only be raised by increasing national and individual income: the Second Plan aims at increasing these by 24% and 12%

---

[1] *Mid-Plan Review* (Planning Commission, Karachi, 1963); this is analysed by J. H. Power, 'Two years of Pakistan's Second Plan', *Pakistan Development Review*, 3/1 (1963), 118–33.

[2] F. C. Shorter, 'Planning procedures in Pakistan', *Pak. Dev. Rev.* 1/2 (1961), 1–14.

respectively, and the Third by 30% and 15%; and the 1960 standards should be doubled at the end of the Fourth Plan in 1985. This can only be done by increasing the country's dependence on the outside world, by industrialization, and by increased agricultural efficiency. Agriculture and industry, with the associated developments of water and power must have the lion's share. But health and education are creeping up, from 9% of the First to 20% of the Third Plan's expenditure. Just as the Second Plan aimed at an 'agricultural breakthrough', an 'educational breakthrough' is the keynote of the Third Plan. The swing from agriculture to capital goods industry in the Third Plan shows trends similar to India's.

There is government control of vital sections of the economy, or those too costly and widespread to be capable of private development: communications, power, irrigation, reclamation, social services, defence. The Second Plan introduced a 'semi-public sector', a group of central agencies of which the chief are the Pakistan Industrial Development Corporation (now with a separate group in each wing), with the object of developing vital industries for which private capital had not been forthcoming in sufficient amount, and the Small Industries Corporation. The system is flexible; in some cases the government supplies only the foreign exchange element required, in others it may finance all initial development before private investment is invited; or again, only supply the unsubscribed remainder of investment required. There is also heavy reliance on foreign aid, mainly from USA, but also from UK, Canada, Australia, New Zealand, West Germany and Japan. The result has been to achieve more rapid industrialization following the very slow progress during the First Plan period.

To the ordinary citizen, however, the progress which may seem impressive to the observer as yet means very little. Of the scant 2% increase a year in income, a quarter is taken back in taxes to provide the balance needed beyond the massive contributions of foreign aid and investment. The Second Plan is brutally frank – 'the provision of adequate houses, water supply and sanitary facilities for the nation's population is a gigantic task well beyond the foreseeable resources of the government' – small comfort in spite of the rising splendours of Islamabad.

Agriculture in general

In order to achieve the aim of conserving and, if possible, earning foreign exchange, the twin objectives are self-sufficiency in food crops and the increase of cash crops, notably jute, cotton and tea, which can be exported raw or fed to local industry, either for local markets or ultimate export. Along with self-sufficiency in food crops, improved diets are aimed at, involving more consumption of fish, vegetables, pulses, fats and oils and sugar. The First Plan failed to make great headway, partly through inefficient application, but aggravated by the continuing problems of re-settlement of refugees, most of whom were peasants. Again there is a two-fold attack: increasing the yields from existing farmland, and the opening up of new areas. The former rests on the increased use of fertilizer and seed improvement (which together account for almost half of the 13% of the total investment allocated to agriculture) and on reclamation of waterlogged and saline lands. The remainder will go into longer-term improvement of grazing lands, forests and fisheries, the furtherance of land reform, social projects and the colonization of new canal areas. The costs of fertilizer factories, and the major water and reclamation schemes are budgeted for separately, but of course are ultimately of great benefit to agriculture. The Second Plan shows much more hopeful signs of success, especially in foodgrains where the target had been almost achieved by 1963. But favourable weather had largely accounted for big agricultural increases, which can be nullified by drought or flood; the 1962 Bengal floods for instance were a setback.

The use of fertilizers has increased rapidly, and is well on the way to the target for 1965. The nitrogenous group, which at Partition was the only type used, and that in pathetically ineffectual amounts, had grown from 43,000 tons in 1955 to 282,000 tons in 1962 and was being widely distributed instead of being confined to limited destinations such as the tea gardens. The need for a more balanced diet for crops as well as people had led to increased use of phosphates and potash. Credit facilities and heavily subsidized prices have put them more within reach. It is claimed (Second Plan, p. 144) that subsidies can gradually be withdrawn, since the value of fertilizers is now sufficiently appreciated (for fertilizer production, see Table XIV).

Organic sources are scarce; yet even in 1960, bones and oilcake appeared on the export list. The Plan condemns this and advocates expansion of the programmes to compost that evil scourge of East Pakistan, the water hyacinth, and the growth of green manure.

Plant protection both by chemical coatings of seed, and aerial spraying of the growing crop, has had American help; it seems possible that an insecticide can be developed from waste at the Daud Khel fertilizer factory, and two special factories were planned to replace imports. Even more fundamental however is the improvement of the seeds themselves; a necessarily lengthy process from the original government farm, through registered growers to the final distribution with at first subsidies and credit to the farmer; and involving cold storage plant.

Mechanization is seen as applying largely to the initial development of new land (and reclamation of old) rather than to everyday husbandry, since people are plentiful and in need of work. The government hires out tractors for specific tasks such as rapid ploughing of desert soils after rain. As in India, soil survey is in its infancy, although a rapid fertility survey was carried out during the First Plan, and a survey of deficiencies is in progress. For individual crops, of course, improved varieties will help, such as the crossing of *indica* and *japonica* strains of rice, the development of longer-stapled cottons and the valued short stapled Comilla cotton grown by shifting cultivators in East Pakistan (hence a very fluctuating total!). Four new varieties of jute have been developed; it would now seem that research is needed on new uses for the fibre, presumably a reflection of the invasion of paper and plastics into the packaging industry. A hybrid maize has been grown successfully in Peshawar, and potatoes are considered a commercial possibility in the lower hills; it is to be hoped that the soil erosion following similar developments in the Nilgiris will be avoided by supervised terracing.

Towards a better human diet, little has yet been done. It is gratifying enough that food grains are 'on target'; the rest must await education and finance which in all its forms is of course as basic as water. From a period of fairly tight control, both wings have gone on to an open market for the basic food grain – rice in the East and wheat in the West, with some misgivings, for the hoarder and speculator can send prices soaring in times of shortage.[3] Storage facilities to cope with such periods are therefore part of the plan; the need is greater in the East where 'in normal years domestic production is satisfactory' but with only an occasional surplus. But storage is not one of the rapidly advancing projects, and little was done to conserve the good harvests of 1960 and 1961.

The objective in financial policy and marketing is to provide the maximum incentive to the farmer to increase his production and income. While irrigation, fertilizers and incentives play their part, much can be done to improve methods of cultivation. The Second Plan sees this as a long term measure which will yield slow results, as against the quick ones it has emphasized, and one that will stem from the adoption of methods seen to be effective on demonstration farms and from the success of various methods used for communication.

The primary function of livestock in Pakistan is to provide motive power; meat, milk, hides and skins are of secondary though not insignificant importance. The livestock pictures in the two wings are in contrast. Thus the excess of poor quality cattle of East Pakistan, where fodder is almost non-existent and Hindu influences have some bearing, need to be slaughtered, while the West had an estimated deficit of 1,500,000 at the beginning of the Second Plan, likely to double as new irrigated land is opened up. In the West, goat keeping is now prohibited except for stall-fed animals and the all-consuming wandering herds are being slaughtered, while in the East the need is to improve and multiply the beast. Sheep are found only in the West and come far short of supplying the woollen industry; improved breeding on special farms is seen as the only way. There is a good basis for improving cattle stock based on excellent native breeds like Red Sindhi and Sakarwal, actually in demand for export.

Land reform and AID

In January 1960 the government of Pakistan brought into effect an important policy of land-holding reform for West Pakistan. There are two problems: the

[3] A. R. Khan and A. H. M. Chowdhury, 'A study of behaviour of West Pakistan farmers in relation to marketing', *Pak. Dev. Rev.* 2/3 (1962), 354–76.

large estates and the extreme fragmentation of the small holdings.[4] As we have seen (Chapter 8), it placed a ceiling of 1,000 ac. (202 ha.) on unirrigated land and 500 on irrigated, future fragmentation is forbidden below 12·5 ac., and consolidation of the present fragmented pattern is being tackled, not without difficulty on account of Islamic laws of inheritance. The Land Reform Commission recommended a definition of a 'subsistence holding' as 12·5 to 16 ac. (5–6·5 ha.) and an 'economic holding' as 50 to 64 ac., according to locality; in East Pakistan, an inherited unit below a (smaller) subsistence figure may be resumed and added to others to make a new holding. On the consolidation front, the *Mid-Plan Review* stated that by 1963 just on half of the 9,200,000 ac. (3,723,000 ha.) target had been consolidated in West Pakistan, in the East a 90,000 ac. pilot scheme completed on time. It is, as usual, difficult to evaluate real progress on the other front – the break-up of large estates – but according to some reports it has been remarkable, not least in view of the political influence of the big landowners who virtually controlled the votes of their tenants.

One might, however, query whether some of the provisions are entirely realistic; as in India, there seems a certain conflict between welfare policy – 'the land to the people' – and economic advance. One might query whether limits of 12·5 ac. for subsistence and 50 for economic holdings are consistent with the capital demands of new production; for instance, the tube-wells which are recognized as a necessary adjunct to canal irrigation, to prevent waterlogging probably cannot be financed from holdings of this size.[5] There is also uncertainty in East Pakistan, where the ceiling of 30 ac. (12 ha.) imposed in 1952 was proving too small for the type of cultivator described above; a limit of 100 ac. (40·4 ha.) was recommended in 1959, and reassessment is still in progress.

The *jagirs* – lands carrying hereditary rights to revenue collection – were abolished in Sind, Bahawalpur and Baluchistan in 1960; the system had been progressively eroded by governments during as well as since the British period. Many remain in areas not fully reported in the west and north, but their days are numbered.

Security of tenure has been strengthened, although it was recommended in 1959 that the retired soldier could eject his tenants (after due notice) if he wishes to cultivate his own land; thus, it is hoped bringing leadership and example to the countryside. It may even be extended to other retired professionals!

Communication with the eight out of every ten Pakistanis who live on the land has presented the same problem as has faced all developing countries. 'High impact devices' are used in areas where success seemed hopeful, and

[4] A Planning Commission estimate of holdings, quoted in *PGR* 14/1 (1959), 42, gives both ends of the scale: 3,300,000 people (65%) of all landowners) held 15% of the total cultivated land in holdings under 5 ac.; 6,000 people (0·1% of owners) also held 15% of cultivated land in holdings of over 500 ac.; these are the people affected by the new laws.
[5] C. Beringer, 'Welfare and production efficiency: two objectives of land reform in Pakistan', *Pak. Dev. Rev.* 2/2 (1962), 173–88.

include co-operative farming on a scale calculated not to inimicize the individualistic peasant: that is, he was left as owner of his land and co-operated only with the buying of seeds, fertilizers and tools, and the marketing of his products. 'Area concentration' has been used too, and has been carried out as an agricultural 'crash programme', in seven Districts of each wing, again chosen for their likelihood of success (a policy open to criticism though understandable) and involving intensive application of every known method of crop and livestock improvement.

Community development, aimed at raising the entire sordid standard of village life, took the form of the Village Agricultural and Industrial Development movement, known as Village AID. Owing much to the energy and drive of the emancipated Muslim women who emerged from purdah with the birth of their country, to help with the enormous problems of caring for and settling the refugees, the movement began very modestly in 1953. Village workers were trained and sent out to live with the villagers; one worker to about seven villages in the east and to five in the west. A married couple often shared the task, the wife trained in home economics, child care and hygiene, her husband in improved farming methods, elementary sanitation and cottage industries.

The programme was fairly successful, even penetrating to the tribal areas of Zhob, Loralai, Kurram and Malakand in the northwest and notably in the remote areas of Gilgit and Baltistan. Although operated on a small scale financially it seems to have achieved the aims of 'self help' among the villagers. About 150 villages made up a Development Area, and a Development Officer controlled a group of areas. Training at a higher level, for people concerned with rural development, takes place at a Village Development Academy at Peshawar or Comilla (East Pakistan).[6]

In 1961 Village AID was wound up except in Azad Kashmir and Baltistan and its functions absorbed at two levels: by 'Basic Democracies' which train village workers, and the Agricultural Development Corporations in each wing which handle the practical matters of tools, seeds, fertilizers, etc.

Water : too little and too much

Agricultural development depends more on proper utilization of water resources than on any other factor. Industrial power can be obtained cheaply, after a heavy initial investment, from the fall of water in the mountain fringes or from canal-falls in the plains. Planned developments in water can therefore be considered together.

Large parts of West Pakistan have too little rainfall for agriculture at any time, and the rest has too little for year-round cultivation. East Pakistan has high totals, but rainfall is concentrated in the monsoon months, and there is a con-

[6] Evaluation has, however, been lacking except for occasional papers, such as J. J. Honigmann, 'A case study of community development in Pakistan', *Economic Development and Cultural Change*, 8/3 (1960), 228–304.

siderable dry season. Yet there is too much when the waters of the Brahmaputra surge down through the delta channels, and the waters of the Bay of Bengal bank up in a cyclone. Flooding is not unknown in the arid West, when the monsoon rains follow the snow-melt; and man-made obstacles get in the way. Even the canals, when they cross the natural lines of drainage, can both accentuate flooding and in the process receive serious damage. But much worse, there is too much water in those very areas where irrigation was brought fifty years ago to the Canal Colonies of the Punjab. Inadequate drainage has led to a steadily rising water-table until the surface layers where roots must grow are water-logged; and the intense summer heat draws up the salts until the soil is poisoned and a white efflorescence marks the former fields. It is estimated that 100,000 ac. (40,500 ha). are going out of production every year, and that a total of over 16,000,000 ac. (6,470,000 ha.) has been totally lost and a further 10,000,000 (4,050,000 ha.) requires urgent treatment, in West Pakistan.[7] This represents about 40% of the irrigated total (see Fig. 17.5 A and B).

The Canal Colonies were developed as a unit, which Partition cut apart, leaving the bulk of the headworks feeding them in India. Not surprisingly, there followed years of negotiation and wrangling, followed at length by the Indus Water Treaty in 1960, something of a triumph in compromise, patience and engineering investigation. Broadly, it gives the waters of the three western rivers, Indus, Jhelum and Chenab to Pakistan, and the three eastern rivers, Ravi, Beas and Sutlej to India (Fig. 17.6). During the transition period, while great works are carried out in Pakistan to bring water from the west to her lands formerly watered from the eastern rivers, India will continue to supply water.[8] India also will contribute to the cost of the necessary works in Pakistan, which involve two great storage dams and seven link canals at a total cost of about 1,300,000,000 dollars (174,000,000 from India, 749,000,000 from foreign aid, and the rest from Pakistan). In planning expenditure, therefore, Pakistan is faced with competing and sometimes conflicting demands on three fronts; the works essential under the treaty, the development of completely new irrigated areas, and the reclamation of the waterlogged and saline lands of the old colonies.

New irrigation is fairly limited in possibilities: the Thal scheme is the biggest, and this scorched doab between Indus and Chenab had been left to the last by the British because it *was* the most difficult. Also a system of five barrages along the Indus will make about maximum use of its fluctuating waters. One object is to make perennial irrigation available in areas hitherto watered only by inundation canals: the Ghulam Mohammed (Lower Sind) barrage opened in 1955, the Gudu Barrage (Upper Sind) in progress, the Taunsa (1959) and the Jinnah projected. The turbulent western tributaries can be trapped to irrigate parts of the western borderlands; Kohat, Kabul and Swat all have their dams, but the

[7] G. Whittington, 'The irrigated lands of the Indus Plain in West Pakistan', *Tijdschrift voor Econ. en Soc. Geografie*, 55 (1964), 13–18.
[8] This principle had already been applied in the Triple Canals Project of 1905–17.

areas gained are not large. Small schemes like the Miriot dam in Potwar can all contribute to new farmland or to improved yields from existing fields. A third of the planned increase in food production from 1961 to 1965 is expected to come almost equally from new and from improved irrigation. In the East, it will take the form of lift irrigation from existing waterways and from the new ones of the Ganges–Kobadak scheme, to extend the cropping season into the dry months. There is a likelihood of underground water resources up to ten times greater than the total Indus discharge; while its quality varies it may well be capable of supplementing canals.[9]

The programmes to combat waterlogging and salinity have been carefully worked out on the basis of the findings of the exhaustive Huntings Survey under the Colombo Plan.[10] The answer to waterlogging is tube wells which serve the dual purpose of lowering the water table, and providing further irrigation water or water simply to flush out the salts. A scale of priorities has been decided on, and the results of the first period of working the tube wells in the Rech Doab (Ravi-Chenab) are very encouraging – the water table was lowered 5 ft. in fifteen months. But the cost is prodigious; the total programme almost equals the *total* to be spent in Pakistan under the Water Treaty!

Four-fifths of the money allocated to flood prevention will go to East Pakistan, mainly to open up congested channels to build new or strengthen old embankments, including some tidal defences.[11] It is ironic that there are the makings of a new Waters Dispute in this area, for both countries have plans to divert Ganges floodwaters to the useful purpose of flushing the delta channels.

It may be worth while looking at several of the individual schemes, although of course they will be mentioned again in regional contexts.

The Thal

The headworks at Kalabagh, for which the British had done preliminary work, were almost ready in 1947. The need to resettle refugees added urgency to the project, and a Thal Development Authority was set up in 1949 (it includes a statute prohibiting 'politicians and criminals' from serving on its board!). One main canal from Kalabagh trifurcates taking out 6,000 cusecs – the maximum allowed because of the needs of Sind – although it is capable of more. A million and a half acres (607,500 ha.) are now irrigated along the piedmont sandy plain and in a long strip down the left bank of the Indus (the Daggar, see p. 518). The dunes and 'pattis' of the heart of the Doab are not commanded, although three 'national parks' devoted to a twenty year forestry rotation are located here. Plantations are made using basin irrigation in the sand-hill tract, with a tilth of canal silt and sand; but despite the cutting by half of the proposed 10% forest

[9] Note on 'Indus Plain ground water reservoir', *PGR* 18/1 (1963), 44.

[10] K. Ahmad, 'Reclamation of waterlogged and saline lands in West Pakistan', *PGR* 16/1 (1961), 1–19.

[11] B. L. C. Johnson, 'Technology and the economic development of Pakistan', *Oriental Geogr* (Dacca) 6/1 (1962), 71–78.

cover, and the need for trees both for timber and to counter erosion, the foresters have difficulty in securing enough water.

The irrigated areas are divided into 1,000 ac. (405 ha.) units called 'chaks', which includes 50 ac. of trees and 50 of communal grazing land. A family holding averages 15 ac., which seems perhaps rather low (a 'subsistence unit' has been defined as 12·5) and leaves little to spare, especially as crop yields are considerably lower than in the Punjab colonies.[12] The proportion of rabi to kharif crops is 2 : 1, and these depend on rainfall, again introducing a chance element in a marginal economy.

The loss of water by evaporation and percolation is very high; Murphy quotes a figure of only 43% of water in Punjab canals at the headworks actually reaching the crop roots. But, *horribile dictu*, salinity and a rising water table are already in evidence, especially in the northeast where heavy runoff from the Salt Ranges is a factor, coupled with an intermediate water-table caused by a layer of hard impervious sodium clay. Pressure to make land available, along with the costs involved, made it impracticable to instal proper drainage at the beginning. It was thought that the general slope would make it unnecessary. The suggested remedy of using canals in summer and tubewells in winter would solve the problem but at great cost.

Five new market towns have developed, aimed at absorbing labour in agriculturally based industries. They are meeting some difficulties: cotton is not a popular crop (it is too demanding and prone to disease), and there is more profit in making *gur* in the village and taking it to town to sell, than in taking the bulky raw cane to the nice new sugar mill!

Ganges–Kobadak scheme

This is a multi-purpose project in East Pakistan and only a part of a very ambitious possibility stretching over decades and involving barrages over the Teesta, Surma, Meghna and Brahmaputra, with canal networks to give lift irrigation and communication and drainage schemes. Comprised, realistically, of independent units, only the first of which is under way, the Ganges–Kobadak scheme covers the Districts in the dying delta of Khulna, Jessore and Kushtia south of the Ganges; the first unit to irrigate 100,000 ac. (40,500 ha.) by diesel-driven lifting devices. The second phase envisages a 60-mile (97 km.) canal to divert Ganges water into the moribund Kobadak, and the third, the empoldering about a million acres of land in Khulna District irrigated from the new canal and the dredged Kobadak.

Warsak in the west and *Kaptai* (Karnaphuli) in the east are multi-purpose projects now completed, while Mangla, under construction, is of interest as part of the Indus Settlement works, and involves the removal to a new site of the town of Mirpur. It will benefit Azad Kashmir through power and irrigation, as

[12] See P. J. H. Murphy, 'The agricultural development of the Thal Desert', *PGR* 13/2 (1958), 55–87, for fascinating account of a particular village in the Thal.

well as the Punjab. Both Warsak and Kaptai have involved tribal people of the country's fringes. At Warsak, watchtowers had to be maintained to control the sniping tribesmen in the early stages; but their labour was enlisted, and the whole project, with its attendant irrigation of tribal areas does seem to be helping Pakistan's frontier problems.[13] The power will add to local industrial development although the bulk is transmitted to the Punjab towns. Tribal people in the Chittagong Hills had to be resettled as a result of the Kaptai scheme completed in 1962, which has improved navigation right down to Chittagong as well as providing power for industry.

Power

The development of hydro-electricity is bound up with energy planning in general, which in turn is closely linked with the bases of coal, gas and oil (see p. 299 and Fig. 9.5). It is impossible to separate the review of these elements, especially since the discovery of natural gas in both wings has led to reappraisals. For example, the Mianwali hydro-electric project may be abandoned in favour of extending the gas pipeline from Sui to the Punjab. This will further affect the development of coal in the region, and water power developments in the mountains of the northwest. The planned developments in coal are mainly in the Sor Range fields in Baluchistan where access roads and increase in capacity of the Bolan railway are under way. Further exploration may confirm resources of good quality coal in East Pakistan on an extension of the Bihar belt; the potentialities of the peats of Faridpur seem very limited. The plans emphasize the need for further exploration for oil and gas with an emphasis on the Dera Ismail Khan and Potwar areas of West Pakistan and the Sylhet region in the east. A pipe line is projected to Dacca to carry Sylhet gas. For the rest geological investigation has a share of funds: iron beds of dubious quality in Makerwal and barytes in Kalat are the only yield of any significance so far.

The revised figures for the Second Plan show a target of 1,271,800 kW which is well within sight with the completion of the Warsak and Karnaphuli Projects. This will increase the *per capita* figure from 30 to 50 units a year. There is a wide disparity again between the two wings, for 75% of the installed capacity in 1965 will be situated in West Pakistan. The biggest single outstanding project is the Mangla Dam, a multi-purpose storage dam, being developed under the Indus Water Agreement, which will supply 300,000 kW of power eventually. Meantime the Multan gas plant is doubling output to 260,000 kW and Warsak is capable of similar expansion. The Sui pipeline may be used to generate power at Lyallpur to fill the gap in supply until Mangla is complete. With the completion of Karnaphuli, East Pakistan can only develop further on the use of peat, timber and natural gas, all difficult to exploit and transport. There is no grid as yet and rural electrification is even further behind than in the west. An Institute of nuclear science and technology is the first major undertaking in Islamabad

[13] L. F. Rushbrook Williams, *The State of Pakistan* (Faber, London, 1962), 68–76.

and a training and research centre has been begun in Dacca; the use of atomic energy is still at the stage of 'feasibility surveys'.

Industry in general

Pakistan began with few industries; those she had were largely concerned with

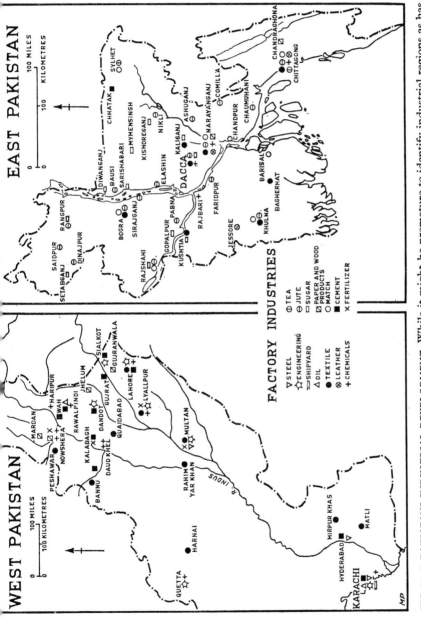

FIG 12.1 PAKISTANI INDUSTRIAL DEVELOPMENT. While it might be premature to identify industrial regions as has been done for India (Fig 11.1), there is at least one nascent region in the belt Peshawar–Lahore, and industrial districts around Karachi, Hyderabad and Dacca. Based on K. S. Ahmad, *A Geography of Pakistan* (1964) and M. R. Brearey and B. S. Connock in *Geography*, 46 (1961).

processing agricultural resources for export; cotton ginning, jute baling, tea factories, flour, rice and oil mills, and innumerable cottage industries serving local markets. Karachi was poorly developed, and East Bengal was served by Calcutta. Industry was largely in the hands of Parsees or Marwaris, who migrated at Partition. And, of greatest significance to the future, she lacked adequate resources for the development of heavy industry. The picture has brightened in this respect with recent discoveries of natural gas and coal deposits. The division of the country into two wings, with 1,000 miles (1,610 km.) between them, is a serious factor, leading to increased costs in transport, or alternatively in duplication.

Yet industrialization must increase if the national income is to rise and the increasing population be absorbed. The main industrial objectives in the Plans are the fundamental ones of (1) saving the money hitherto spent abroad, by home production and even export, and (2) laying a broad foundation of basic industries on which others can build: steel and chemicals. Thus a quarter of the State investment in industry in the Second Plan goes into chemicals and a fifth into engineering and metallurgy, including a steel plant in each wing (an example of the duplication referred to). There was an initial development after 1947 of consumer goods, by private enterprise to fill important needs of food and clothing. Then came very rapid planned development in those sectors using local materials or heavily protected, notably textiles. The pace is slackening now, and future industrialization lies more with capital goods industries; the easier prospects having been exhausted, improved technological education and efficiency are now desiderata.

'Resources cannot be wasted by promoting at all costs an industrial pattern dominated by small enterprises' (Second Plan, p. 224). At the same time, small industries still employ by far the bulk of industrial workers, making everything from envelopes to revolvers and shoe laces to surgical instruments; and labour-intensive as opposed to capital-intensive projects are seen as a partial solution to rising numbers of job seekers. The Plans try to steer a middle course, by encouraging (through the Small Industries Corporation) those small-scale enterprises which can do better or as well in small as in large units (e.g. specialized textiles from woven rugs to embroidered saris) or those which are ancillary to factory industry, such as bobbin makers. It is hoped that small workshops will grow into bigger units. It is tacitly implied that many will complete the decline which started during the British period and has gone on as a result of decrease in efficiency and the stranglehold by the middleman. Increased productivity is assisted by loans and technical help in modernization, using one-eighth of the state investment in industry to do so. Sweated labour workshops are successful at present, and show well in capital-output ratios compared with larger establishments, and also in the capital-labour ratio so useful in a populous under-developed country. But it is scarcely possible for a government today to encourage their spread, while on the other hand the owner of a sweatshop seldom tends to invest in more machinery or better conditions of his own volition, and so under-mine the very basis of his profits.[14]

Trading estates as a means of combining some of the advantages of small industry and large scale facilities of power and transport, and at the same time spreading industrial location are being developed round Karachi, Kotri, Sukkur and at Rajshahi, Comilla and elsewhere in the east.

The PIDC which assists in large-scale industry has increased its initial list of jute, paper, fertilizers, heavy engineering, chemicals and shipbuilding, to include cement, sugar, cotton, wool, iron and steel and pharmaceuticals; inevitably it receives a larger share of the total investment.

Although, at first, limitations were placed on the further industrial develop-ment of Karachi in favour of less industrialized areas, the tug of war between idealistic and realistic solutions that we have already seen in the decisions about size of unit, is now pulling towards realism, and the advantages of port facilities, capital and skill, and now the availability of power from Sui gas, are combining to give Karachi an overwhelming lead in industry in spite of the water problem.

Eddison[15] in reviewing the effects of locating industry for purely social and political reasons points out the failure of this policy – as in the cotton mills of Quetta and the Thal towns. A more successful development is likely to come from location of new industries in urban centres of medium size with some industry already, such as Hyderabad, Nowshera or Sylhet; thus further swelling of the really major cities can be avoided. The old industrial centres of the north and west, however, are showing considerable development in textiles, wood products and engineering, in the belt from Peshawar to Lahore, where hydro-electricity is available as well as the coal deposits of the Salt Ranges. Sui gas will eventually reach here also. East Pakistan, limping behind in *per capita* income and industrialization, is to receive a bigger share of Third Plan Resources. Karnaphuli power, and now possible coal and natural gas resources, will help. At present industry concentrates largely in Chittagong and the Dacca area, with timber, sugar and cement locally important in the delta, the north and the hills respectively.

Steel

Steel is the yardstick of industrial development; but to use it as a measure in Pakistan would be a discouraging exercise. The Kalabagh iron is the only indigenous source capable of being worked; the Chitral deposits are too in-accessible as yet (Fig. 9.4). Steel production is confined to small installations in Lahore and Karachi: re-rolling mills are more numerous and found in both wings and there is a new one at Karachi. Small-scale mills are primitively in-efficient, although they are gradually being improved. Planned increase, aimed

---

[14] J. H. Power, 'Small industrial enterprises in Bombay, Delhi and Karachi', *Pak. Dev. Rev.* 2/3 (1962), 433–43.
[15] J. C. Eddison, 'Industrial location and physical planning', *ibid.* 1/1 (1961), 1–21.

at supplying 70% of the needs by 1965, rests heavily on the use of imported pig iron and local and even imported scrap in two new steel mills, one in Karachi yet to be financed, and the other in Chittagong due to be in production by 1967 at the latest, using Japanese assistance. From an initial output of 150,000 tons, it will increase to 1,500,000 tons over twenty years. But an integrated steel plant is a long way off.

There is as yet no manufacturing of the industrial machinery, electrical equipment, railway stock or vehicles, that are basic to development; these are imported, or at best assembled. The engineering industries are mainly small scale, carried out in innumerable workshops and largely concentrated round Lahore, making a variety of tools. Small factories produce agricultural equipment, Batala Engineering Works at Lahore, for instance, making tube well pumps, and others making oil expellers and sugar crushers, even Persian wheels. The simpler parts of the ubiquitous sewing machine and bicycle are made and the rest imported; the whole to be assembled in Lahore, Karachi or Dacca. Realising that if a machine-making industry is to be established the basic need is skill, the plans emphasize technical education and assistance more than immediate increase in capacity. Although no large-scale electrical equipment is made, light bulbs, fans and switch gear are made in Karachi, as well as the kerosene lamps that are still of greater importance; but in both cases much is still imported. Some plugs, sockets and switches are made by cottage industries. East Pakistan will likely benefit from new development in this type of industry. Telephone and telegraph equipment made at Haripur, north of Rawalpindi, and Kotri supply almost the entire needs.

Chemicals

The agricultural programme demands increased use of fertilizers. A third of industrial investment in the public sector is devoted to the chemical industry. The country has good resources for the development of chemical fertilizers at least, the tragic irony being that they are mainly in the west, while the most desperate need is in the east. However, the natural gas from Sylhet is now piped to Fenchuganj to make urea, a concentrate equivalent to large amounts of ammonium sulphate, and a much needed source of nitrogenous fertilizer. A similar plant has opened at Multan in the west, using Sui gas. There is a new and expanding ammonium sulphate plant at Daud Khel on the Indus, sited here to use the Indus waters, Makerwal coal, and gypsum from the Salt Ranges; the chemical complex here is to be increased by the addition of a dye works, and a plant extracting ammonium sulphate from natural gas. A former sulphuric acid plant at Lyallpur has been converted to make superphosphates, but does not work to capacity because costs are too high and prices to the farmer too high. Even so, another superphosphate plant is being built at Chittagong; a reflection of transport costs between the two wings. Sulphur deposits exist but are fairly inaccessible; a refinery was opened in Quetta in 1956.

Soda ash at Khewra, close to rock salt and limestone, supplies a small glass industry (as well as legions of dhobis) and may be refined for a viscose rayon industry in Karachi. Caustic soda is made in the East for the paper factory at Chandhragona (Karnaphuli) and at Nowshera in the northwest, in association with DDT production, but has still to be imported for other industrial uses. There are plans to make it from sea salt at Gharo in West Pakistan. There is a new sulphuric acid plant at Lyallpur. There have been developments in the petro-chemicals groups, using Sui gas at Karachi to make acetylene and PVC; and even polythene, for the ubiquitous polythene wrapping, to be made from sugar bagasse in Karachi. Another modern development is the drug factory at Dacca while there are still industries based on medicinal herbs (*Artemesia ephedra*) at Rawalpindi and Quetta.

Textiles

The biggest group of industries, textiles, has developed rapidly from very small beginnings. Cotton leads, employing about a third of the industrial work force, with quite spectacular developments in yarn production and weaving that have eliminated imports and begun to build up useful exports of yarn and piece goods. Local demand was expected to be 14·5 yards per annum per person by 1965. Karachi is the leading centre; though it had no mills at Partition, the rail link with the cotton-growing area, local capital, port facilities, and unlimited power supplies from the Sui gas field have led to the establishment of mills here. Hyderabad too has a new cotton industry, lying as it does in a developing cotton producing area in Sind, while the former centres at Lyallpur and Multan have expanded and the industry is developing in relation to the Thal cotton as well as in northwestern towns like Tank, Kohat and Mardan. In East Pakistan, the industry is concentrated in the Dacca–Narayanganj district, once the famed centre of fine muslins; the huge local market and the general need for industrial development here have led to the new mills at Kaliganj northeast of Dacca and in Rajshahi which will supply the heavy local demand by handweavers. In the East raw cotton of course must virtually all be imported.

A quarter of the yarn produced is retained to feed the factories and the important handloom cottage industry making both coarse cheap cloth and high grade specialities; it accounts for 40% of total production. There was a period of rapid expansion in handloom weaving after Partition, which included pavement 'factories' set up by refugees. But the small handloom factory is giving way to power looms set up with loans and technical help through the Small Industries Corporation.

The larger-scale factory industry, which as we have seen developed at prodigious rates in the early years of Pakistan, has been mainly run by private enterprise; partly no doubt because the capital investment was relatively low, and profits good. The supply of refugee labour was also a factor here. The success of this, Pakistan's first venture into large-scale industry, must be measured in more than statistics however, for it had a very useful moral effect. The table shows the rate of increase. Another feature is the predominance of the composite mill.[16]

	Spindles	Looms	Mills
1947	177,148	4,824	17
1959	1,927,470	29,104	87
1961	1,998,000	30,000	93
1965 (Planned)	2,500,000	40,000	121

Since the Partition guillotine cut the Calcutta factories from the growing areas, jute mills have been built in East Pakistan with a capacity of 200,000 tons; more are planned, including one at Kotri in West Pakistan, using jute grown in the irrigated area of Sind, and the target, likely to be achieved, is of 14,000 looms by 1965. Jute earns about half of Pakistan's much-needed foreign exchange, for only about a quarter of her production need be retained for her own needs in bagging sugar, cement and fertilizer. Most of the export is as raw fibre, but this too required considerable effort in providing jute baling plant, for 'pucca' baling had also been done in Calcutta. Both branches of the industry are tending to concentrate near the port and transport facilities of Chittagong, round Dacca (especially Narayanganj) and at Khulna, rather than in the heaviest growing areas farther north. Reluctance of private capital to invest, because profits are low, has meant that development has been done largely by the PIDC. The cottage weaving of jute has declined and little remains.

Sufficient wool yarn to meet internal requirements is produced from mills, mostly built since 1950 in West Pakistan. The largest in Karachi also spins worsteds from imported finer wool; the others lie in the main sheep areas of the northwest and have been developed in co-ordination with producers on the one hand, by helping in flock improvement, and the handloom workers on the other (who may be the same people) by a supply of yarn. Raw wool is still exported for carpet and felt making in UK and USA, and yarn production for export is planned. Such weaving as has developed on a factory scale is restricted to blankets and suitings which do not compete with handloom products so important in the northwest. Dera Ghazi Khan and Multan are still important for weaving of rugs and carpets.

The relatively minor importance of artificial silk is not likely to increase, since yarn must be imported; indeed the Second Plan talks of converting the existing looms to cotton production. However, an acetate rayon plant at Lyallpur in the west and an expanding weaving industry is to be fed by yarn from new plants at Okara and Kairi. A viscose rayon plant at Karnaphuli is to be established by private enterprise. Kapok from the silk cotton tree (*Eriodendron anfractuosum*) is extracted at Chittagong. While sericulture is encouraged by the Small Industries Corporation, reeling and filature development is only of minor importance, using largely imported silk from Japan.

[16] K. Ahmad, 'Cotton textile industry of Pakistan', *PGR* 17/2 (1962), 1–16.

Paper, wood, leather

East Pakistan has the lead in resources and development of paper and wood products, and self sufficiency is attainable, even export of newsprint, in spite of increasing home demands. Bamboo floated down to Chadhragona on the Karnaphuli is processed with power from the new dam; and at Khulna the newsprint factory is fed by bargeloads of *gewa* (*Exeocaria agallocha*) pulled upstream with the tides from the Sunderbans. There is an associated caustic soda plant, and a projected particle board factory. West Pakistan makes enough wrapping paper for its own needs, as well as some paper and hardboard from local grasses (at Nowshera), rice straw (Rahwali), firs from the Kaghan Valley (at Mangarh) and paper mulberry (at Lahore).

Left by Partition with the basic resource, but not the tanneries, leather imports had to continue until the industry developed – slowly because tanning materials are not plentiful, and the low caste Hindu skill had largely gone, though Hindu influence remains in East Pakistan where fewer cattle hides come from slaughtered animals than in the West. Hides remain important as an export, about a third of them now tanned using *Acacia arabica* and *Terminalia chebula* in the West, and mangroves in the East. Muslim craftsmen from Kanpur have helped to establish shoe and leather factories; western style shoes are made in Karachi and Lahore, and at Narayanganj in the East, but the traditional sandals of the country are a cottage industry.

Agriculture-based industries

The bulk of planned investment in food industries is going into wheat mills in the western wing and rice mills in the East wing respectively, by expansion and modernization; not only will mouths increase, but tastes are demanding more refined products. But austerity is maintained in sugar consumption, with little allowance for import of the preferred white sugar, and emphasis placed on increased production and local milling. Mardan in the West, said now to be the biggest refinery in Asia, has been followed by others in the northwest Punjab located near production areas because of the bulky nature of the raw material. Efforts to meet the huge demand in East Pakistan have been handled by PIDC with several new mills, which face the difficulties posed by scattered production and poor quality of the crop and transport. The bulk of the crop is still handled as a cottage industry – producing the sticky yellow 'gur' – crudely and wastefully produced by press and iron pan. Vegetable oils must still be imported, although efforts to increase and modernize, and educate tastes (especially with *vanaspati*, blending the hitherto unpopular cotton seed-oil with sesame and coconut) are slowly raising production at home. The modest soap consumption is met by cottage industry and one modern factory making toilet soap at Bahawalpur.

Tobacco growing is confined to the West, and the handmade *bidis* produced in innumerable homes and workshops in both wings come nowhere near demand.

381

A substitute made from *khumbi* leaves to replace imported *bidis,* coupled with more sophisticated cigarette manufacture by foreign firms at Karachi, Chittagong and Mardan are the main planned developments. Tea is slowly climbing from a serious financial slump after Partition, and is of course confined to the East; in addition to the estate factories, there are blending and packing plants in Chittagong, and in West Pakistan. Development of more luxury foods like canned fruits receives scant encouragement, although private enterprise is raising production for sophisticated and wealthy urban customers particularly in the West. The more vital milk industry struggles along on a local (unhygienic) basis except for the military dairy farms bequeathed by the British and since expanded, and some urban bottling plants at Karachi: although in the form of ghi, curds and other products, dairy produce finds its way to the urban markets as well as village use. The problem is one of transport, to get milk to the urban centres; at Karachi a plant is planned to combine local milk with imported powdered milk. Dacca and Lahore will have peripheral dairy farms. And condensed and dried milk factories are planned in areas of rural surplus.

Cement

Having lost both its source of fuel and its market at Partition, the cement industry of West Pakistan, based on local limestone, declined. As development has got into gear, however, the demand has increased rapidly, and the providential discovery of natural gas has partially solved the fuel problem. Canadian help has established the Maple Leaf factory at Daud Khel, and New Zealand's 'Zeal Pak' unit at Hyderabad, and a new one also at Rohri. Two more are planned along the Sui pipeline as well as increasing the existing plant at Wah. But East Pakistan suffers again, through lack of fuel and has only one plant, at Chattak; the Sylhet gas has replaced the Indian coal imported to run the plant.

Trade (Tables XVII, XVIII)

The foreign and inter-wing trade of Pakistan reflect the economic diversity of the two wings as well as the country's development as a whole. As an exporter of a limited number of agricultural products and an importer of consumer and development goods, Pakistan trade is vulnerable to fluctuations in world commodity prices. The need actually to import foodgrains at times of crop failure has further retarded trade. Since 1950, imports have increased steadily, controlled by Plan requirements and with the emphasis changed from consumer to capital goods and to industrial raw materials (Table XVIII). Machinery, iron and steel, vehicles and oil account for the majority of imports now, with the USA as the major source of supply, followed by UK, West Germany and Japan. Under a trade agreement, USA supplies mainly wheat and rice but with increasing amounts of development goods. Exports have fluctuated, and on the whole declined, partly at least due to increased demand at home. The most significant thing is the increasing importance of cotton and jute manufactures. Jute is by far the major export. Hides and skins and raw wool from the West, and decreasing tea exports from the East are also important. India is second only to UK as a market (but Pakistan does not import from India to any extent), followed by USA, Japan, Benelux and West Germany. Exports have failed to keep pace with imports by a steadily decreasing margin. Overall trade has increased with the EFTA countries rather than ECM, with America and with Japan.

Inter-wing trade shows an interesting pattern. Ahmad points out that the distance, costs and economic contrasts between the two zones give it more the character of international than intra-national trade.[17] But the artificial controls inherent in the division of the country, and the efforts to replace foreign imports with Pakistani products, have an important bearing. West Pakistan finds an important outlet in the East for cotton (raw and manufactured), oilseeds and cement; indeed almost half of East Pakistan's total imports come from the other wing. But the West gets a relatively small proportion of her total imports such as jute and paper, since the East has not the items she needs, unfortunately. Conversely, East Pakistan sells a bigger proportion of her exports to outside countries than to the West, with jute of course dominating.

In absolute terms, West Pakistan has something like double the total trade of the less developed East; a familiar conclusion.

Ports and shipping

There are three ports; Karachi of course reigns alone in the West, and has been modernized from the export-orientated wharves fed by railways, which had existed for over half a century, to make an all purpose port. Land reclamation for oil refineries has been carried out, and facilities for storage, shipbuilding and repair, and also a fishing harbour. Karachi now imports twice as much as she exports (Table XVI) and the allocations under the Second Plan underline the port's dominance. Three hundred miles (483 km.) farther west there is a possibility of developing Pasni as an outlet for Baluchistan and the not insignificant Afghan transit trade. Chittagong was only a minor port in 1947, and had to be developed rapidly to meet the needs of East Pakistan. This is being done, in the face of difficulties such as the 1963 cyclone, with new wharves, oil installation and dredging; and the Karnaphuli project has the useful effect of regulating the river flow and reducing silting. There are special facilities for handling and storing both jute and tea. But congestion is still serious because of the lack of facilities to move cargoes back from the port area. To relieve the concentration at Chittagong, an anchorage was sought west of the Brahmaputra–Ganges. While the final choice of site has been delayed by the vagaries of river currents, there has been considerable development at Mangla, 30 miles (48 km.) down the Pussur River from Chalna, the original choice. Goods are trans-shipped and taken to Khulna railhead. Unlike Karachi and Chittagong, exports dominate at

[17] N. Ahmad, 'Some aspects of interwing trade in Pakistan', *Pak. Dev. Rev.* 3/1 (1963), 1–36.

Mangla; the planners are concerned about the empty trucks that arrive at Chittagong, and the empty ships which reach Mangla.

Shipping was vestigial at Partition (Table XVI), but has received considerable attention because of the separation of the two wings, and the increased overseas trade, the bulk of which is carried in foreign vessels. The importance of river traffic in the east has led to the expansion of the small boat-building yards at Narayanganj and Khulna. Karachi now builds as well as repairs ocean-going ships. By buying abroad second-hand ships (such as the railway flotilla that came from the Philippines and brings jute from Narayanganj to Chittagong, involving 20 miles (32 km.) of storm-prone open sea) Pakistan now has rather more capacity than she can use.

Transport and communications (Table, XV)

Inter-wing transport is by sea and air, involving the development of shipping and the improvement of facilities at the terminals. Karachi is a key international airport, with a jet air strip completed in 1961; while Lahore and Dacca will have them in a few years. The major urban centres are linked by frequent flights; a helicopter service for the delta has been initiated.

Internally there is a contrast between the road and rail networks of West Pakistan and the domination of waterways carrying three-quarters of the traffic in East Pakistan. While inheriting important strategic and commercial lines in the Punjab and the northwest Frontier, Pakistan got only one repair workshop of size, and the deterioration of the war and early years of Independence left a legacy of rundown stock and track only gradually being overcome. The plans emphasize repair units and the purchase of rolling stock rather than indigenous manufacture. In West Pakistan, broad gauge predominates – 1,000 miles (1,610 km.) of it double-track from the convergence of Punjab and northwestern lines at Lodhran, to Karachi, built to tap the agricultural surpluses of the Punjab for export, and to penetrate and control the northwest through the Khyber and Bolan Passes. The metre gauge line in Sind, part of the old Hyderabad–Jodhpur line, was severed at Partition like the broad gauge between Lahore and Amritsar; both are now restored; the Sind railway serves the cotton region. Narrow gauge lines in the hills include the little-used line from Quetta west to Iran and the line north to Chaman, now being extended to the Afghan border. Some new track has been laid in the Peshawar Basin to feed the sugar refineries.

There are two separate systems under the control of Pakistan Eastern Railways, linked by ferries over the unbridged Brahmaputra. One rail ferry comprises barges with rails onto which goods trucks are manoeuvred down rails at three different inclines to cope with the fluctuations of river level, while vagaries of its course have involved shifting the whole railhead at times; a sufficient comment on the difficulties of the largely metre gauge lines of the east. The small amount of broad gauge was oriented to Calcutta from collecting points like Goalundo: a metre gauge served and serves Chittagong. A new line has been pushed up from Sylhet to the cement and fertilizer factories, and another to the Karnaphuli dam site.

While the East has the higher total of roads (Table XV), the figures for miles of surfaced as against kachcha tracks reveals the lack of development, again largely because of difficult terrain. A mile of road costs four times as much to build in East Pakistan as it does in the West. The building of 200 miles (322 km.) of good road south from Chittagong to Arakan has been a major achievement. The three great trunk roads in West Pakistan include some 300 miles (483 km.) of the Grand Trunk Road from Afghanistan to Calcutta, the Karachi–Lahore road and the Lahore–Quetta road, which are being augmented by a road along the Makran and another up the west side of the Indus, which is bridged at several points over the barrages and by the famous boat bridge of Dera Ismail Khan. Local roads and the bullock carts radiating from district headquarters are controlled by local governments.

Water transport was once significant in West Pakistan but was killed by railways and the irrigation schemes. In the East, inland waterways extend from about 3,000 to 4,500 miles (4,830–6,520 km.) in the monsoon; the bulk of the shipping is by unmechanized country boats, but two British companies operate steamer services in addition to the railway flotilla mentioned above. Silting is tending to reduce the mileage; but on the other hand the Karnaphuli project is helping in the Chittagong River, and the Ganges–Kobadak scheme will help in the western region, as well as canalizing some of the stretches.

Conclusion : some comparisons between India and Pakistan

Like most countries attaining independence after a period of colonial rule, or arousing themselves after a period of economic stagnation of different emphasis and cause, India, Pakistan and Ceylon have all adopted five year plans, ten year plans, or five year plans complemented by longer-term 'perspective planning' of about the order of fifteen years. In this they have followed the general ideas of countries with governments of widely differing political ideas ever since the First Five Year Plan of the USSR of 1928–33. India's approach is pragmatic rather than doctrinaire in the sense of rigid attachment to Marxist theory, even though borrowing from it a good many ideas and ideals; there is more attempt to use macro-economic models, and with growing confidence and attachment to actual data rather than inferred levels. There is a mixed economy, with defined spheres for the public and private sectors within a wider aspiration towards a 'socialistic pattern of society', and much emphasis on the phased development of industry, building up from basic industries like steel and chemicals, heavy machine tools, heavy electricals and the like, through lighter machine tool, electrical and engineering industries, towards a considerable range of light consumer goods industries in twenty years or so. Compared with most underdeveloped countries, however, the starting-point included much more in the way of textile, engineering, chemical and food processing industries – with all that is implied in managerial, and entrepreneurial skill and adjustment of factory labour.

Irresistible political factors have enforced a very rapid, possibly too rapid, progress in Community Development programmes, and these have been accompanied by changes in grass-roots democracy and allocation of revenues; there is a marked tendency towards excessive emphasis on amenity-oriented rather than production-oriented development, but also a reaction against this. There have been declarations of intention to secure the greatest possible regional spread of development, since the Second Five Year Plan; these have been partly implemented through the federal state structure and the democratic representation of local interests within the State legislatures, and there are some signs that more integrated regional development plans may be in use at least experimentally in the Fourth Plan period, much more widely as compared with limited projects like those of the Damodar Valley Corporation (see p. 636). Foreign capital in industry lasting over from the colonial period, as in the plantation and jute industries, is somewhat uneasy, not nationalized or expropriated but prevented from leaving the country by foreign exchange regulations; even the Managing Agency system remains relatively unchanged. On the other hand, new foreign capital continues to enter the economy, on conditions acceptable to the government, though on rather too slender a scale in relation to the country's enormous needs. There are hazards – the upward trend in population increment, the Chinese invasion of the far north as a direct threat and as diverting investment from general and productive investment to defence and destructive devices – and possibly a phase of political instability or a change of direction at the end of Pandit Nehru's long period of dominance. But it seems certain that India's economic development will follow along the lines of Five Year Plans, not less Marxist and possibly more so than at present.

Pakistan, sharing with India the two 'steel frames' – the carry-over of efficient civil administration from the Indian Civil Service, and the railway links so vital to the British Raj – had greater initial difficulties because of the splitting of the two wings, the poorer endowment of industrial resources and development accentuated by the greater proportionate disturbance by the chaos, slaughter and population movements following Partition, and also, in the opinion of much Pakistani opinion, by Indian hostility, overt or covert. There was a period of political instability unmatched in India after Independence: the tentative Six Year Plan associated with the Colombo Plan, the period of military government under General Ayub Khan, the supersession of the Six Year Plan by the modest but latterly successful First Five Year Plan, and following Village AID the beginning of the 'Basic Democracy' programme which takes a somewhat different approach from India in relation to a largely common heritage of administration and many aspects of village culture and land tenure, the legacy of the Mogul and British periods. The basic democracies are somewhat analogous to the modern rather than the traditional *panchayats* of India, while the Indian *gram sevak* corresponds to the Village AID, the leaders often a man and wife (advantageous in the presence of the Muslim *purdah* but hardly less so potentially in conservative and husband-venerating rural India). The Basic Democracies have been made the fundamental unit for the election of representatives to vote at 'electoral colleges' in the new house of representatives, the present indirect form of democracy that replaced the military government, with Ayub Khan as elected President, in 1962. Initially more lacking in industrial resources and establishments than India, and less afraid of foreign (meaning particularly American) military and economic aid than of Indian mass and menace (as it has seemed to Pakistan), Pakistan has been ready to join the South East Asia Treaty Organization, and to accept a much larger proportion of American advice on economic development on the one hand, to strike a bargain (at some hazard) with China on the other. The modest First Five Year Plan of Pakistan, and the Second Five Year Plan so far, have shown very rapid progress in relation to targets. Pakistani thinkers are less given to demi-official macro-economic analysis and theorizing. From very low, sometimes negligible starting points, there has been a notable build-up of industrial units, including import of complete factories, techniques and technical assistance, as compared with India in much more consumer-oriented fields like textiles. (Of course India had more of these industries to start from.) The result has been that Pakistan's plans show a very gratifying speed of development; India's much larger plans, with a much more complex web of inter-dependence between parts of the Plans, have suffered much more from lags and frustrations. Pakistan, however, is now turning towards the basic type of industrial development like iron and steel works in both wings. On the other hand India's initial endowment of consumer goods industries was greater, and moreover if her plans are even within reach of their targets she may be ready to turn afresh to the development of the lighter type of industry which affords some of the most striking growth points to western economies. So the contrasts in the development plans of the two countries may lessen in time, though for long India is likely to have the more complex and sophisticated industrial development. One measure of this may be that the account of Pakistan's industries in the third edition of this book is somewhat comparable to that of India's industries in the previous editions; it is still possible and rewarding to give an industry by industry account for Pakistan, with only some auguries of future development of industrial regions, whereas for India it is now only possible and relevant to give an account of industrial regions of various orders, even while stressing that none of these as yet attain the massing or the complexity of a Ruhr or a Black Country.

BIBLIOGRAPHICAL NOTE FOR PART III

It is difficult to do more than indicate different approaches from a literature large enough and often heavy and viscous enough to float a new Gondwanaland. If a country's index of economic development were the amount of documentation about it, India would outstrip most countries on the globe.

Comprehensive works on Indian economic affairs discuss matters common to all the chapters of Part III; many of the older ones cited in earlier editions of this work are still useful, and mention may be made especially of D. H. Buchanan, *The Development of Capitalist Enterprise in India* (London, 1934) on the industrial side and the *Report of the Royal Commission on Agriculture in India* (1928) on the agricultural. A very comprehensive book, covering political as well as economic developments, is Charles Bettelheim, *L'Inde indépendante* (Armand Colin, Paris, 1962).

Official sources. There is a plethora of these, including the successive Draft Outlines and full-scale Five Year Plan volumes, Mid-Term or other Reviews and Assessments, e.g. the Evaluation Reports on Community Development prepared by the Programme Evaluation Organization of the Indian Planning Commission. They are of great value, and while they do present the official line, most of their quantitative data are to be regarded seriously, even where their accuracy must be viewed critically; this last point applies especially to some of the huge official surveys cited in the text, e.g. those on land holding and agrarian credit (see D. and A. Thorner, *Land and Labour in India*, Asia, Bombay, 1962). It applies also to data on Community Development, though even here some of the Evaluation Reports are of considerable candour.

For India these official publications are normally issued by the Manager of Publications, Delhi.

Non-official critiques. Like official reports, their name is legion. Some follow a more or less official line, by no means uncritically, e.g. B. G. Tandon (ed.), *The Third Five Year Plan and India's Economic Growth* (Chaitanya Publishing House, Allahabad, 1962) and W. B. Reddaway, *The Development of the Indian Economy* (Allen & Unwin, London, 1962), which is largely an exercise in model building. Some are farther from the official view, and it should be noted that association with the Plans at some stage does not preclude a critical viewpoint, as in D. R. Gadgil (ed.), *Planning and Economic Policy in India* (Gokhale Institute, Poona, 1961) or P. C. Mahanalobis, 'The approach of operational research to planning in India', *Sankhya* (Calcutta) 16/1–2 (1955), 3–130. Among foreign commentaries the authors have found particular value in W. Malenbaum, *Prospects for Indian Development* (Allen & Unwin, London, 1962); and the same could have been said of Bettelheim's book had it come to hand at an earlier stage of the revision.

For more hostile reviews see S. K. Iyengar, *A Decade of Planned Economy* (Indian Academy of Economics, Mysore, 1961), which is amusing, at times erratic, but makes many very palpable hits, or P. T. Bauer, *Indian Economic Policy and Development* (Allen & Unwin, London, 1961). A shorter critique in a journal accessible to many Western readers is W. Letwin, 'What's wrong with planning: the case of India', *Fortune* (June 1963), 118 – not quite as hostile as the title and source would suggest and, as in the larger publications cited, the arguments and criticisms are worthy of consideration and not necessarily unhelpful in the long run.

Material is spread through an astonishing gamut of learned journals in various countries and languages. Among Indian publications in English, *The Eastern Economist* of New Delhi, *The Economic Weekly* of Bombay, and major newspapers such as *The Hindu* of Madras, are all worth-while sources.

Pakistan. The Pakistani development has not attracted so much attention as the Indian. A substantial debt is owed to R. R. Platt (ed.), *Pakistan: A Compendium* (American Geographical Society, NY, 1961); this, while already becoming out of date in part, does exactly what it sets out to do by presenting 'a picture of Pakistan as it was in the decade of the 1950s'. Of the same era is J. R. Andrus and A. F. Mohammed, *The Economy of Pakistan* (OUP, Karachi, 1958). Though small, K. S. Ahmad's *A Geography of Pakistan* (OUP, 1964) is a welcome and handy work, and N. Ahmad's older *Economic Geography of East Pakistan* (OUP, London, 1958) is also very useful. In addition to works cited in footnotes, and to the two periodicals *Pakistan Geographical Review* (Lahore) and *Oriental Geographer* (Dacca), mention should be made of a relatively young economic journal of good quality, *The Pakistan Development Review* (Karachi).

Postscript. An immense quarry of factual information will be found in the two volumes (text and tables) of the Census of India 1961, Volume I Part I-A (i and ii), by Ashok Mitra, Registrar-General of India, on *Levels of Regional Development in India.* This was unfortunately received in the very last week of revision.

STATISTICAL TABLES

TABLE I

THE INDIAN SUB-CONTINENT AND CEYLON

AREA AND POPULATION, 1951 AND 1961

	Area sq. mls	Population, millions 1951	Population, millions 1961	Density to sq. ml. 1951	Density to sq. ml. 1961	Females to 1,000 males 1961	Increase % 1951–61
I. India							
A. States:							
Andra Pradesh . .	106,286	31·115	35·983	293	339	981	15·65
Assam	47,091	8·837	11·873	188	252	876	34·45
Bihar	67,196	38·784	46·456	577	691	994	19·78
Gujarat	72,245	16·263	20·633	225	286	940	26·88
Jammu and Kashmir	86,024	3·254	3·561	379	414	878	9·44
Kerala	15,002	13·549	16·904	903	1,127	1,022	24·76
Madhya Pradesh . .	171,217	26·072	32·372	152	189	953	24·17
Madras	50,331	30·119	33·687	598	669	992	11·85
Maharashtra . . .	118,717	32·002	39·554	270	333	936	23·60
Mysore	74,210	19·402	23·587	261	318	959	21·57
Nagaland	6,236	0·213	0·369	48	58	933	14·07
Orissa	60,164	14·646	17·549	243	292	1,001	19·82
Punjab	47,205	16·135	20·307	342	430	864	25·86
Rajasthan	132,152	15·971	20·156	121	153	908	26·20
Uttar Pradesh . .	113,654	63·216	73·746	556	649	909	16·66
West Bengal . .	33,829	26·302	34·926	778	1,032	878	32·79
B. Union Territories, etc.							
Andamans and Nicobars	3,215	0·031	0·063	10	20	617	105·19
Dadra and Nagar Haveli	189	0·041	0·058	220	307	963	39·56
Delhi	573	1·744	2·659	3,044	4,640	785	52·44
Goa, Daman and Diu	1,426	0·637	0·627	447	440	1,070	−1·66
Himachal Pradesh .	10,885	1·109	1·351	102	124	923	21·78
Laccadives, Minicoy, Amindivis . . .	11	0·021	0·024	1,912	2,192	1,020	14·61
Manipur	8,628	0·578	0·780	67	90	1,015	35·04
N.E.F.A.	31,438	n.a.	0·336	n.a.	11	894	n.a.
Pondicherry . . .	185	0·317	0·369	1,715	1,995	1,013	16·34
Sikkim*	2,744	0·138	0·162	50	59	904	17·76
Tripura	4,036	0·639	1·142	158	283	932	78·71
Total India	1,265,019	361·130	439·235	312	370	941	21·50
II. Pakistan							
West Pakistan . .	311,406	33·780	42·880	107	138	868	26·8
East Pakistan . .	54,501	42·063	50·840	773	922	930	20·1
Total Pakistan	365,907	75·843	93·720	207	256	901	23·4
III. Other countries							
Nepal	54,600	8·470†		155		n.a.	n.a.
Bhután	18,000	0·700†		39		n.a.	n.a.
Ceylon‡	25,332	8·098	9·896	320	391	—	22·2

* Sikkim is 'connected to India by special treaties'. Some small discrepancies may be found in totals an d densities between this and similar tables in other works arising from the inclusion or exclusion of Sikkim and of Jammu and Kashmir, 'because the 1961 census in that State did not cover portions currently under foreign occupation'.
† Estimates only.
‡ Ceylon figures for 1953 (Census) and 1960 (estimate).

390

TABLE II

CLASSIFICATION OF AREA, 1958–59

(In million acres/hectares. Discrepancies due to rounding off)

I. India		Acres	Hectares	% SG area	% VP area
Area, Village Papers		726·1	293·8	90	100
Area, Surveyor-General's estimates		806·3	326·3	100	111
Forests		130·1	52·7	16·1	17·9
Not available for cultivation		114·7	46·4	14·1	15·8
Permanent pasture and grazing		32·4	13·1	4·0	4·5
Misc. tree crops and groves		14·1	5·7	1·75	1·9
Culturable waste		50·9	20·6	6·3	7·0
Fallow, other than current		30·3	12·3	3·75	4·2
Current fallows		29·4	11·9	3·65	4·0
Net area sown		324·1	131·2	40·2	44·6
				89·85	99·9
Area sown more than once		48·6	19·7	6·0	6·7
Total cropped area		372·8	150·9	46·2	51·3

II. Pakistan				% total area	% area reporting
Total area:	WP	198·7	80·5	100·0	173·5
	EP	35·3	14·3	100·0	102·0
	Pak.	233·9	94·7	100·0	156·9
Area reporting:	WP	114·5	46·4	57·6	100·0
	EP	34·6	14·0	98·0	100·0
	Pak.	149·1	60·4	63·7	100·0
Forests:	WP	3·2	1·3	1·6	2·8
	EP	5·5	2·2	15·6	15·9
	Pak.	8·7	3·5	3·6	5·8
Not available for cultivation:	WP	50·3	20·4	25·3	43·9
	EP	5·6	2·3	15·9	16·2
	Pak.	55·9	22·7	23·9	37·5
Other uncultivated, excluding current fallows:	WP	20·0	8·1	10·1	17·5
	EP	1·9	0·8	5·4	5·5
	Pak.	21·9	8·9	11·0	19·1
Current fallows:	WP	9·6	3·9	4·8	8·4
	EP	1·3	0·5	3·7	3·8
	Pak.	10·9	4·4	4·7	7·3
Net area sown:	WP	31·3	12·7	15·75	27·4
	EP	20·3	8·2	57·5	58·7
	Pak.	51·6	20·9	26·0	34·6
Area sown more than once:	WP	4·5	1·8	2·3	3·9
	EP	5·6	2·3	15·9	16·2
	Pak.	10·1	4·1	4·3	6·8
Total cropped area:	WP	35·8	14·5	18·0	31·3
	EP	25·9	10·5	73·4	74·9
	Pak.	61·9	25·0	25·9	41·5

For discussion of terms, see text, p. 227. The 'reporting' and 'Village Paper' areas may be taken as the *oecumene*; the contrast between East and West Pakistan is instructive.

TABLE III

INDIA: AGRICULTURAL SUMMARY BY STATES, 1958–59

(In thousand acres)

		Total area by village papers	Forest	Rice	Wheat	Jowar and bajra	Gram	All food grains	Sugar	Ground nuts	Oil seeds	Cotton	Fodder	Irrigated	NSA	TSA	Area sown more than once	
1	Andhra Pradesh	67,452	14,614	7,610	53	8,003	252	23,036	204	2,034	1,545	673	371	7,287	26,907	29,521	2,614	1
2	Assam	35,764	12,042	4,479	10	4	4	4,736	70	—	335	36	—	1,533	5,449	6,436	987	2
3	Bihar	42,823	9,287	12,335	1,613	24	1,428	24,021	443	—	800	—	84	4,464	19,718	27,010	7,292	3
4	Bombay (incl. Gujarat)	121,263	15,924	4,564	3,931	25,752	1,578	44,323	373	7,446	2,691	9,850	4,166	4,065	67,247	70,997	3,750	4
5	Jammu and Kashmir	11,993	7,465	533	415	50	9	3,754	4	—	95	3	32	745	1,652	1,973	321	5
6	Kerala	9,535	2,610	1,900	—	4	—	2,041	22	32	1,285	21	—	879	4,706	5,698	992	6
7	Madhya Pradesh	108,360	34,293	10,061	7,821	4,937	4,113	37,615	99	1,077	3,560	1,770	106	2,289	39,555	44,932	5,377	7
8	Madras	32,135	4,613	5,721	4	3,190	4	12,220	145	2,066	455	1,004	208	5,631	14,574	17,403	2,829	8
9	Mysore	46,362	6,671	2,466	727	8,320	377	18,233	157	2,383	1,012	2,550	437	1,991	25,247	26,182	935	9
10	Orissa	38,401	8,799	9,173	11	147	61	11,248	69	61	780	23	251	2,414	13,854	14,958	1,104	10
11	Punjab	30,286	915	980	5,318	2,820	6,190	17,775	590	151	640	1,329	3,047	7,409	18,479	23,997	5,518	11
12	Rajasthan	83,624	1,921	248	3,041	12,458	4,312	27,901	69	213	2,273	588	3,363	3,571	32,656	35,748	3,092	12
13	Uttar Pradesh	73,131	9,531	10,351	9,579	4,912	6,657	46,176	2,944	458	724	160	1,759	12,734	42,341	53,705	11,364	13
14	West Bengal	21,874	2,646	10,533	87	6	477	12,751	66	—	353	—	—	3,339	12,929	15,055	2,126	14
15	Delhi	366	4	3	70	—	36	218	12	—	—	1	24	93	216	275	59	15
16	Himachal Pradesh	6,962	1,959	112	352	87	19	1,021	3	—	12	1	5	97	670	1,085	415	16
17	Manipur	347	20	223	—	—	—	223	—	—	17	—	—	168	223	224	1	17
18	Tripura	2,634	1,573	426	—	—	—	429	7	—	4	18	—	20	511	611	100	18
19	Andamans and Nicobars	1,655	1,600	4	—	—	—	14	—	—	—	—	—	—	20	21	1	19
20	Laccadive Islands	7	—	—	—	—	—	—	—	—	—	—	—	—	7	7	—	20
	Total India	734,974	136,487	81,632	33,032	70,710	25,517	285,735	5,277	15,921	16,591	18,033	13,859	58,729	326,961	375,838	48,877	
	thousand hectares:																	

TABLE IV

PAKISTAN: AGRICULTURAL SUMMARY BY DIVISIONS, 1959–60

(In thousand acres)

	Total area	Rice	Wheat	Maize	Barley	Sugar-cane	Jute	Cotton	Irrigated	NSA	TSA	NSA % total	TSA % NSA	
Dacca	7,395	5,650	35	—	16	65	760	—	92	5,244	6,891	70·9	131·4	1
Chittagong	10,616	5,307	8	1	—	16	214	51	107	4,670	6,345	44·0	135·9	2
Rajshahi	8,431	5,558	73	52	47	136	322	—	106	5,692	6,946	67·5	122·0	3
Khulna	8,208	4,636	22	—	4	63	78	—	8	4,273	5,060	52·1	118·4	4
East Pakistan	34,650	21,351	138	53	67	280	1,374	51	313	19,879	25,242	57·4	127·0	
thousand hectares	14,023	8,641	59	21	27	113	556	21	127	8,045	10,215	—	—	
Peshawar	18,018	28	749	564	233	147	—	7	926	1,695	1,939	9·4	114·4	5
Dera Ismail Khan	7,124	6	616	48	27	10	—	2	271	1,033	1,047	14·5	101·4	6
Rawalpindi	7,235	74	1,732	132	52	30	—	72	625	3,310	3,555	45·7	107·4	7
Lahore	5,701	801	1,438	98	86	188	—	168	2,204*	3,559	4,177	62·42	117·4	8
Sargodha	10,957	67	2,253	186	58	260	—	562	4,362*	6,118	6,470	55·8	105·8	9
Multan	15,897	227	2,415	94	42	181	—	939	5,726*	5,518	6,546	34·7	118·6	10
Bahawalpur	11,206	40	945	49	15	112	—	540	2,777*	2,902	3,210	25·9	110·6	11
Khairpur	12,987	872	750	5	9	28	—	205	2,978	3,365	3,365	25·9	100·0	12
Hyderabad	23,460	767	730	10	10	21	—	801	4,244	4,143	4,405	17·7	106·5	13
Quetta	33,993	54	324	12	15	—	—	—	n.a.	397	431	1·2	108·6	14
Kalat	46,684	c.5	114†	—	—	—	—	—	n.a.	153	153	0·3	100·0	15
Karachi	5,379	n.a.	n.a.	n.a.	n.a.	n.a.	n.a.	n.a.	n.a.	109	109	2·0	100·0	16
West Pakistan	198,581	3,041	12,066	1,198	547	977	nil	3,296	24,113	32,302	35,407	16·2	109·61	
thousand hectares	80,366	1,231	4,883	485	221	395	nil	1,334	9,758	13,073	14,193			
Total Pakistan	234,231	24,392	12,204	1,251	614	1,257	1,347	3,347	24,426	52,181	60,649	22·3	116·2	
thousand hectares	94,389	9,872	4,942	506	248	508	556	1,355	9,885	21,118	24,408			

* 1958–59.   † 1962–63, inserted for comparative purposes. The statistics for Quetta, Kalat, and to a less extent Dera Ismail Khan, are imperfect.

TABLE V

IRRIGATION

(In thousand acres/hectares)

	Canal, ac.	Tank, ac.	Well, ac.	Other, ac.	Total, ac.	Total, ha.	% of total	Total as % of: TCA	NSA
I. India, 1959–60									
Andhra Pradesh	3,168	3,101	734	284	7,287	2,951	12·4	24·7	27·1
Assam	899	—	—	634	1,533	621	2·6	23·8	28·1
Bihar	1,473	734	644	1,613	4,464	1,808	7·6	16·5	22·6
Bombay*	762	805	2,658	140	4,065	1,646	6·9	5·7	6·0
Jammu and Kashmir	716	—	7	22	745	302	1·3	37·8	45·1
Kerala	450	79	35	315	879	356	1·5	15·4	18·7
Madhya Pradesh	1,067	334	794	94	2,289	927	3·9	5·1	5·8
Madras	2,083	2,058	1,394	96	5,631	2,281	9·6	32·4	38·6
Mysore	524	861	303	303	1,991	806	3·4	7·6	7·9
Orissa	556	1,223	94	541	2,414	978	4·1	16·1	17·4
Punjab	4,977	7	2,342	83	7,409	3,001	12·6	30·9	40·1
Rajasthan	818	774	1,944	35	3,571	1,446	6·1	10·0	10·9
Uttar Pradesh	5,005	1,935	5,977	717	12,734	5,157	21·7	23·7	30·1
West Bengal	1,992	910	39	468	3,339	1,352	5·7	22·2	25·8
Total, acres	24,420	11,621	16,965	5,345	58,351	—	99·4	15·6	18·0
Total, hectares	9,890	4,706	6,871	2,165	—	23,632			
II. Pakistan, 1957–58 to 1959–60									
West Pakistan	16,482	29	1,619	1,350	19,480	7,889	97·0	55·8	61·4
East Pakistan	217	38	28	347	630	255	3·0	2·5	3·1
Total, acres	16,699	67	1,647	1,697	20,110	—	100·0	33·1	32·5
Total, hectares	6,763	27	667	697	—	8,144			

* Bombay is now divided into Maharashtra and Gujarat. 'Other' includes tubewells in the Indo-Gangetic plains, elsewhere *pynes*, *ahars*, and various minor inundation channels. There is of course some yearly fluctuation, part statistical and part real.

TABLE VI

MAIN CROPS, 1950–51 AND 1960–61

(In thousand acres/hectares and tons/bales)

	Area 1950–51 ac.	Area 1950–51 ha.	% NSA	Area 1960–61 ac.	Area 1960–61 ha.	% NSA¶	% increase	Output 1950–51	Output 1960–61	% increase
I. India										
Net Sown Area	293,400	118,740	100	327,902	132,700	100				
Rice*	76,135	29,598	24·9	82,947	33,569	25·3	13·4	20,251	33,658	66·2
Jowar	38,477	15,571	13·1	42,683	17,274	13·0	10·9	5,408	9,215	70·4
Bajra	22,296	9,023	7·6	28,230	11,425	8·6	26·6	2,554	3,177	24·4
Maize	7,807	3,159	2·7	10,774	4,360	3·3	38·0	1,702	3,952	132·2
Wheat	24,082	9,746	8·2	32,047	12,969	9·8	33·1	6,360	10,818	70·1
All foodgrains and pulses	240,489	97,326	82·0	279,825	113,245	85·3	16·4	50,022	78,566	57·1
Sugarcane*	4,217	1,707	1·4	5,789	2,343	1·8	37·3	56,150	102,482	82·5
Groundnuts*	11,106	4,495	3·8	15,461	6,257	4·7	39·2	3,426	4,682	36·7
Other main oilseeds§	15,402	6,233	5·3	17,925	7,254	5·5	16·4	1,650	2,129	29·0
Cotton*†	14,536	5,883	5·0	18,871	7,637	5·8	29·8	2,910	5,390	85·2
Jute*†	1,411	449	0·4	1,512	612	0·5	36·3	3,283	3,982	21·3
Mesta*†	—	—	—	689	279	0·2	—	—	1,131	—
Tea†	777	314	0·3	818	331	0·2	5·4	271	347	13·7
Coffee†	224	91	0·1	272‖	110	0·2	20·9	25	n.a.	84·0
Tobacco	883	357	0·3	989	400	0·3	12·0	257	307	19·5
Rubber†	144	58	0·1	318	129	0·3	122·4	13	25	92·3
Coconut††	1,598	647	0·5	1,700	688	0·5	6·3	358	464	29·6
II. Pakistan										
Net Sown Area				53,063	21,475	100				
Rice*	22,399	9,065	46·0	24,804	10,038	46·7	10·7	8,195	10,533	28·5
Jowar	1,256	508	2·6	1,177	476	2·2	6·3	244	218	–10·7
Bajra	2,404	973	4·9	1,844	746	3·5	23·3			
Maize	948	384	1·9	1,207	488	2·3	27·1	384	439	14·3
Wheat*	10,893	4,408	22·4	11,603	4,696	21·9	6·5	3,950	3,786	–4·2
All foodgrains and pulses	41,367	16,741	84·9	44,052	17,828	83·0	6·5	14,094	16,048	13·9
Sugarcane*	694	281	1·4	1,238	501	2·3	78·3	8,817	15,412	74·8
Rape and mustard	1,628	659	3·3	1,791	725	3·4	10·0	285	308	8·1
Cotton*	3,071	1,243	6·3	3,242	1,303	6·1	4·8	1,413	1,657	17·3
Jute*	1,711	692	3·5	1,518	614	2·9	11·3	6,009	4,708	–21·7
Tea†	75	30	0·2	78	32	0·1	6·7	17	19	11·8
Tobacco	179	72	0·4	198	80	0·4	11·1	72	84	16·7

* Cleaned rice, cane, lint, dry fibre for rice, sugarcane, cotton, jute (and mesta) respectively.
† In bales of 392 lb. (=177·8 kg.) for cotton and 400 lb. (=181·4 kg.) for jute and mesta.
†† Coconuts in crores (ten millions) of nuts.
§ Other main oilseeds are castor, sesamum, rape and mustard and linseed.
‖ 1958–59.
¶ % of NSA under 'Principal Crops'; this figure is usually 0·5–2·0% below the total NSA.

TABLE VII

NUTRITIONAL VALUES OF SELECTED FOODGRAINS

	Moisture %	Protein %	Fats %	Mineral Matter %	Carbo-hydrates %	Vitamins units/100 grams AA	B	Iron mgs/100 grams	Calories per 100 grams
Wheat. . . .	12·8	11·8	1·45	1·5	71·3	108	230	5·3	345
Rice (1) . . .	12·2	8·5	0·35	0·7	78·3	—	100	2·75	350
Rice (2) . . .	13·0	6·85	0·55	0·5	79·1	—	26	1·0	349
Jowar	11·9	10·4	1·9	1·8	74·0	136	—	6·2	353
Bajra	12·4	11·6	5·0	2·65	67·1	220	110	8·8	360
Ragi	13·05	7·1	1·3	2·2	76·3	70	140	5·4	345
Millets (minor) . .	11·75	9·55	2·75	3·5	64·9	trace	100–300	6·7	320
Maize. . . ('tender')	79·4	4·3	0·5	0·65	15·2	42	—	0·7	82
Oatmeal . . .	10·7	13·55	7·6	1·8	62·9	trace	325	3·8	374

Note.—Rice (1) home-pounded in mortar, (2) factory milled; minor millets average of six (low carbohydrate due to high fibre content, average 7·5%). Cf. especially bajra and oatmeal.
Source: *Health Bulletin No. 23*, Nutrition Research Laboratories, Coonoor, Madras (1937), 18–21.

TABLE VIII

'NUTRITIONAL DENSITY'

(Population by 1961 Census related to nearest available area figures)

	Net Sown Area density per 100 ac.	100 ha.	Foodgrains density per 100 ac.	100 ha.	Crude density per sq. mile	Foodgrains density per sq. mile
I. India						
Andhra Pradesh	132	326	160	395	339	1,024
Assam	232	573	267	660	155	1,708
Bihar	236	583	193	477	691	1,235
Gujarat	89	220	175	432	286	1,120
Jammu & Kashmir	223	551	226	558	n.a.	
Kerala	369	912	829	2,048	1,127	5,306
Madhya Pradesh	83	205	86	213	189	550
Madras	235	581	282	697	669	1,805
Maharashtra	90	222	130	321	333	832
Mysore	94	232	137	339	318	877
Orissa	127	314	144	356	292	922
Punjab	110	272	114	282	430	730
Rajasthan	65	161	74	183	153	474
Uttar Pradesh	182	450	163	403	440	1,043
West Bengal	270	667	264	652	1,032	1,690
India	135	334	156	385	370	998
II. Pakistan						
West Pakistan	134	331	190	469	138	1,216
East Pakistan	250	618	240	593	922	1,536
Pakistan	183	452	212	524	256	1,357

TABLE IX

COTTON AREA AND OUTPUT, 1958–59 AND 1961–62
(*In thousand acres/hectares and bales**)

	1958–59 Area: ac.	ha.	Output	1961–62 Area: ac.	ha.	Yield: lbs/ac.	kg/ha.	Output
I. India								
Andhra Pradesh	831	336·0	116	816	330·0	61	68·0	116
Gujarat	4,565	1,847·5	1,297	4,033	1,631·0	122	138·0	1,254
Madhya Pradesh	2,117	857·0	380	1,957	792·0	38	42·5	192
Madras	1,123	454·5	356	995	402·5	152	170·0	386
Maharashtra	6,352	2,570·5	1,184	6,226	2,519·5	57	64·0	913
Mysore	2,537	1,027·0	441	2,347	950·0	74	83·0	441
Punjab	1,485	601·0	711	1,459	590·5	254	285·0	944
Rajasthan	619	250·5	145	584	236·0	113	127·0	168
Uttar Pradesh	197	80·0	34	188	76·0	94	105·0	45
Rest of India	98	40·0	22	103	42·0	n.a.	n.a.	29
Total India	19,924	8,064·0	4,686	18,708	7,568·5	94	105·0	
II. Pakistan								
West Pakistan	3,273	1,324·5	1,443	3,449	1,396·0	203	228·0	1,830
East Pakistan	51	20·5	17	39	16·0	173	194·0	17
Total Pakistan	3,324	1,345·0	1,460	3,488	1,412·0	190	213·0	1,847

* 1 bale of cotton = 392 lb. = 177·8 kg.

TABLE X

JUTE AREA AND OUTPUT, 1959–60 TO 1961–62
(*In thousand acres/hectares and metric tons*)

	1959–60 ac.	ha.	Area 1960–61 ac.	ha.	1961–62 ac.	ha.	Output 1959–60	1960–61	1961–62
I. India									
Assam	334	135·0	299	121·0	363	147	202	148	205
Bihar	399	161·0	363	147·0	565	229	174	152	229
Orissa	75	30·0	100	40·5	114	46	33	43	55
Tripura	20	8·0	15	6·0	35	14	11	7	19
Uttar Pradesh	33	13·0	32	13·0	38	15	17	16	21
West Bengal	824	333·5	720	291·0	1,144	463	394	360	608
Total India	1,685	680·5	1,529	618·5	2,259	914	831	726	1,137
II. Pakistan (East)	1,375	556·5	1,518	614·0	2,061	834	1,008	1,021	1,264

TABLE XI

TEA AND COFFEE: AREAS AND OUTPUT
(*In thousand acres/hectares and metric tons*)

	Tea (1960–61) Area ac.	ha.	Output	Coffee (1958–59) Area ac.	ha.	Output
Assam	401·1	162·3	157·5	—	—	—
West Bengal	204·1	82·5	81·5	—	—	—
Tripura	12·5	5·0	2·1			
Madras	80·8	32·6	30·9	63·7	25·8	5·0
Mysore	4·5	1·8	1·6	160·5	65·0	34·0
Kerala	98·1	39·7	37·2	47·7	19·3	7·2
Punjab	9·6	3·9	1·0	—	—	—
Rest of India	7·5	3·0	1·1	0·3	0·1	0·4
Total India	818·2	330·8	312·9	272·2	110·2	46·6

Tea ha. brackets: Assam, West Bengal, Tripura = 74·1%; Madras, Mysore, Kerala = 22·4%. Tea Output brackets: Assam, West Bengal, Tripura = 77·0%; Madras, Mysore, Kerala = 22·3%.

TABLE XII
INDIA: CENSUS LIVELIHOOD CATEGORIES AND CLASSES

	1951 Population, millions	1951 % total population	1961 Population, millions	1961 % total population
Cultivator	100	22·78	70	19·6
Agricultural labourer	31	7·06	28	7·8
Mining, quarrying, etc.	5	1·14	4	1·1
Household Industry	12	2·73	—	—
Manufacturing other than Household Industry	8	1·82	13	3·6
Construction	2	0·46	1	0·3
Trade and Commerce	8	1·82	7	2·0
Transport, storage and commerce	3	0·68	2	0·6
Other Services	20	4·56	15	4·2
Non-workers	250	56·95	217	60·8
	439	100·00	357	100·0

TABLE XIII
MINERAL PRODUCTION

I. India

Output:	1957	1962 (In thousand metric tons)	Status	Major producing areas
Barytes	13	n.a.	A	Andhra Pradesh
Bauxite	110	573	A	Bihar, Madhya Pradesh
Chromite	80	66	A	Orissa
Coal	44,196	61,548	B	Bihar, Bengal (Damodar)
Copper	410	492	C	Bihar
Gold (kilograms)	5,568	5,076		Mysore
Gypsum	937	1,124	C	Rajasthan
Ilmenite	301	138	A	Kerala
Iron ore	5,172	13,188	A	Orissa, Bihar
Magnesite	90	217	A	Madras
Manganese	1,680	1,212	A	Mysore, Madhya Pradesh
Mica	31	28	A	Bihar
Petroleum, crude	440	1,077	C	Assam
Salt	3,672	3,864	C	Rajasthan, Gujarat and Madras (brine)

A=normal export; B=adequate for domestic consumption; C=imports necessary.

II. Pakistan

In long tons (units)

A. Solid minerals

Output :	1959	1962 (provisional)
Antimony	152	105
Barytes	508	2,677
Chromite	16,223	30
Coal	723,000	947,000
Gypsum	97,000	128
Iron ore	2,250	3,804 (1961)
Limestone	927,000	1,515,000
Marble	2,796	2,222
Salt (rock)	157,000	192,000
Silica sand	22,000	14,000

Source: *Pakistan Basic Facts* (Govt of Pakistan, 1963). The small scale and violent fluctuation of production are significant.

B. Oil and Gas

Output :	1959	1962
Oil (millions Imp. gallons)	82	117
Gas (million cubic feet)	22,365	42,076

Gas reserves (in thousand million cubic metres);

West		East	
Sui	170*	Sylhet	7·9
Mari	99	Chattak	0·5
Uch	71		
Dhulian	48·1		8·4
Other	16·3		
	404·4		

* Equivalent to 127,000,000 tons of coal.

TABLE XIV

PRODUCTION IN SELECTED INDUSTRIES

(In thousand metric tons, unless otherwise stated)

	1951	1956	1960	1961	1962	1963	% increase 1951 to 1963
I. India							
Cotton yarn (million kg.)	592	758	788	863	859	893	50·8
Cotton cloth (million m.)	3,727	4,853	4,616	4,702	4,560	4,423	18·7
Jute manufactures	889	1,111	1,085	971	1,183	1,236	39·0
Pig iron	1,829	1,961	4,175	4,987	5,796	6,604	261·1
Steel	1,034	1,270	2,150	2,798	3,564	4,272	313·2
Sulphuric acid	109	168	354	422	468	568	421·1
Cement	3,247	4,972	7,844	8,245	8,587	9,355	188·1
Sugar	1,170	1,985	2,591	2,842	2,786	2,316	98·0
Soda ash	48	78	145	177	223	264	450·0
Paper	134	196	348	364	388	463	245·5

	1950	1955	1959	1960	1961	1962	% increase 1950 to 1962
II. Pakistan							
Cotton yarn (million kg.)	19·5	125·0	178	185·5	187·5	196	1,000
Cotton cloth (million m.)	97·0	414·0	565	575·0	639·0	663	684
Jute manufactures	—	105·0	238	269·0	254·0	291	177 (1955–62)
Steel ingots	3·0	11·0	9	7·0	9·0	3	133
Cement	420·0	692·0	1,002	1,138·0	1,242·5	1,395	332
Sugar	33·5	96·5	170	147·0	125·0	194	578
Phosphate fertilizers	—	—	44	49·0	57·0	60	—
Paper	—	20·0	n.a.	58·0	61·0	n.a.	—

TABLE XV
INTERNAL TRANSPORTATION

I. India, 1960–61

A. Railway routes by gauge:

	Broad		Metre		Narrow		Total	
	miles	km.	miles	km.	miles	km.	miles	km.
	16,566	26,676	15,629	25,168	3,178	5,118	35,353	56,962*

* Break-up of 317 miles (510 km.), mainly in Madhya Pradesh, not available.

B. Railway working

Passengers, millions	1,616†	Freight, million metric tons	158
Passenger miles, millions	48,475	Net metric ton-kilometres, millions . .	87,833
Passenger kms, millions	78,060	Average metric ton haul . 346·5 miles (558 km.)	
Average journey . . . . 28 miles (48 km.)			

† Of whom 7,600,000 were detected travelling without tickets.

C. Roads:

black-topped		cement/concrete		water-bound macadam		unsurfaced		total	
miles	km.	miles	km.	miles	km.	miles	km.	miles	km.
44,903	72,308	2,604	4,194	51,698	83,249	182,961	294,623	282,363	454,691

II. Pakistan, 1962

A. Railway routes: by gauge:

	Broad		Metre and narrow		Total	
	miles	km.	miles	km.	miles	km.
Western Railway.	4,636	7,459	693	1,115	5,329	8,574
Eastern Railway	599	964	1,113	1,791	1,712	2,755
Total	5,235	8,423	1,806	2,906	7,041	11,329

B. Railway working

Passengers, millions	193	Freight, million metric tons	20
Passenger miles, millions	7,431	Net long ton-miles, million	4,859
Passenger kms, millions	11,956	Average ton haul . . . . 243 miles (391 km.)	
Average journey . . . . 38 miles (61 km.)			

C. Roads

	'high type motorable'		'low type fair weather'		total pukka roads	
	miles	km.	miles	km.	miles	km.
West Pakistan	9,510	15,302	32,483‡	52,265‡	41,993	67,567
East Pakistan	1,833	2,949	27,495	44,239	29,328	47,189
Total	11,343	18,251	59,978	96,504	71,321	112,756

‡ For climatic reasons, in West Pakistan many of these roads in arid areas are in fact motorable all the year.

D. Inland Waterways, East Pakistan

Mileage of perennial waterways 2,700 (4,345 km.), monsoon waterways 4,000 (6,440 km.).
Steamers 172, motor vessels 887, total 1,059; capacity 100,000 passengers, 160,000 tons.
Country craft: estimated number 300,000, capacity 1,500,000 passengers, 1,200,000 tons.

TABLE XVI

PORTS AND SHIPPING, 1961–62

I. India

(In lakh (100,000) GRTs and metric tons)

Major Ports	Ships entering: No.	Gross tonnage	Imports	Exports	Turnover	% turnover of major ports
Calcutta	1,806	123·5	48·8	44·2	93·0	27·4
Bombay	3,156	202·9	104·1	41·3	145·4	42·9
Madras	1,230	85·3	22·7	12·0	34·7	10·2
Visakhapatnam	613	43·8	14·0	14·6	28·6	8·4
Cochin	1,342	72·7	18·8	4·9	23·7	7·0
Kandla	230	17·3	11·1	2·7	13·8	4·1
Total	8,377	545·5	219·5	119·7	339·2	100·0

In addition about 225 minor ports, of which 150 are 'working ports', handle about 6,000,000 metric tons per annum.

Shipping: In 1960, 173 ships of over 150 GRT were on the Indian register, 91 (279,000 GRT) in coastal and 82 (573,000 GRT) in overseas trade. By the end of 1962, GRT had risen from 952,000 to 1,014,000.

II. Pakistan

Major Ports	Ships entering: No.	Gross tonnage	Imports	Exports	Turnover	% turnover of major ports
Karachi	n.a.	n.a.	36·17	17·25	53·42	57·7
Chittagong	n.a.	n.a.	24·54	4·42	28·96	31·5
Chalna	n.a.	n.a.	3·25	6·76	10·01	10·8
Total	n.a.	n.a.	63·96	28·43	92·39	100·0

Shipping: In 1962, 45 ships (29 coastal), of 405,941 Dead Weight Tonnage, approximately 600,000 GRT.

TABLE XVII

SHARE OF SELECTED COUNTRIES IN TRADE, 1958–62
(*As percentage of values*)

I. *India*

		UK	USA	USSR	W. Germany	Japan	Pakistan
1958	Imp.	17·1	15·6	2·0	10·5	4·5	0·6
	Exp.	29·1	15·3	4·8	2·6	5·0	1·1
1959	Imp.	20·2	21·7	1·8	12·1	4·0	0·9
	Exp.	27·3	15·2	4·8	3·3	5·5	1·1
1960	Imp.	19·4	29·2	1·4	10·9	5·4	1·3
	Exp.	27·0	15·8	4·6	3·0	5·5	1·5
1961	Imp.	18·4	23·4	3·7	11·3	5·5	1·3
	Exp.	24·4	17·6	4·9	3·0	6·2	1·4
1962	Imp.	16·6	29·3	5·1	9·0	5·8	1·5
	Exp.	23·7	17·0	5·6	6·6	4·9	1·4

II. *Pakistan*

		USA	UK	W. Germany	Japan	Iran	India	Belgium-Luxb'g
1957–58	Imp.	25·7	18·8	8·1	5·1	2·0	4·0	4·0
	Exp.	11·6	18·1	9·7	10·0	0·9	6·2	5·1
1958–59	Imp.	22·7	17·5	10·5	4·9	3·3	4·9	4·0
	Exp.	10·5	16·3	5·8	8·1	1·1	3·2	5·6
1959–60	Imp.	23·5	17·5	10·0	8·0	6·2	3·3	1·8
	Exp.	8·9	17·5	5·4	10·8	0·7	5·2	3·6
1960–61	Imp.	23·9	18·6	8·6	7·9	4·8	4·1	3·2
	Exp.	9·2	15·6	5·1	6·9	0·2	5·9	4·1
1961–62	Imp.	30·8	20·4	9·4	8·0	3·7	3·4	2·0
	Exp.	9·5	15·9	5·5	5·9	0·4	5·5	6·0

TABLE XVIII

CHANGES IN IMPORT/EXPORT STRUCTURE, 1957–62

(As percentages of total imports/exports. Indian year ends 31.3, Pakistan 30.6)

	Commodity Groups	Imports				Exports			
		1957	1961	1962	1963	1957	1961	1962	1963
1	Food	8·17	13·49	15·86	14·19	27·24	32·66	34·50	31·44
2	Beverages and tobacco	0·18	0·15	0·15	0·09	2·49	2·29	2·78	2·75
3	Crude materials, inedible, except fuel	9·72	11·92	11·24	10·67	18·61	17·69	16·37	16·62
4	Total mineral fuel, lubricant and others	9·62	8·79	7·77	9·10	2·16	0·90	0·95	0·98
5	Animal and vegetable oils and fats	0·53	0·70	0·50	0·42	1·84	0·99	2·01	2·59
6	Chemicals	6·96	8·23	8·87	7·69	0·85	1·19	1·15	0·83
7	Manufactured goods	23·81	20·29	18·02	17·02	41·23	41·11	39·31	37·79
8	Machinery and transport equipment	28·31	33·72	34·24	36·69	0·31	0·60	0·64	0·64
9	Miscellaneous manufactured articles and transactions	12·70	2·62	3·35	5·27	5·27	2·57	2·29	6·31
	Total	100·00	100·00	100·00	100·00	100·00	100·00	100·00	100·00

II. Pakistan

		Imports					Exports				
		1957–58	1958–59	1959–60	1960–61	1961–62	1957–58	1958–59	1959–60	1960–61	1961–62
1	Food, drink and tobacco	33·5	24·5	17·5	19·9	13·1	3·3	6·4	8·7	7·2	11·3
2	Raw materials	13·3	17·1	21·3	18·7	17·8	85·4	75·8	62·5	64·6	63·3
3	Manufactured articles	52·3	57·4	60·9	61·4	69·1	10·5	17·3	28·7	28·2	25·4
4	Postal articles and baggage	0·9	1·0	0·3	—	—	0·8	0·5	0·1	—	—
	Total	100·0	100·0	100·0	100·0	100·0	100·0	100·0	100·0	100·0	100·0

PART IV

The Face of the Land

CHAPTER 13

The Regions of the Sub-continent

I. BASIS OF THE DIVISION

The independent pioneer work of Baker and Stamp resulted in a remarkably close agreement on a working regional division of India;[1] and the more detailed break-down here presented will show a strong family likeness to these early efforts. Agreement on the main outlines is perhaps not surprising, since the broad fundamentals are clear enough, but in detail the problems are by no means simple, especially if a strict delimitation based on one master-principle is attempted. Indeed, this is an unattainable ideal. Structure is perhaps the most obvious guide, at any rate on the macro-scale; but it is clear that in an area like the Indo-Gangetic Plains landforms are of little help, since the divisions are as a rule either too broad or too much a matter of local detail, such as the distinction between *bet* and *doab*, *khadar* and *bhangar*; these may be of great importance in local life, but are in practice useless as bases for regional description on a sub-continental scale – and in descriptive writing, scale is of the essence. Yet the physical landscape and the life of Sind are obviously greatly different from those of Bengal, imperceptible as may be the gradations between these two extremes. In such a vast area, some sort of division other than micro-morphological must be made, and in the absence of strong physical lines climate may be accepted as a guide, though obviously in an open plain climatic transitions are also gradual.

On the human side, another possible approach, and perhaps in strict theory the best approach, would be to relate the regional network to the spheres of influence of towns; but the data are as yet lacking, except perhaps in a handful of cases, to educe such 'functional' regions; nor can it well be assumed *a priori* that methods and concepts appropriate in the United States can be carried over into the very different polity of India. Historic identities, such as those evoked by such names as Tamilnad, Maharashtra, Malwa, cannot be ignored; while not precisely coincident with physical divisions, they are often by no means divorced from them. With the new linguistic States, some traditional linkages have been revived; others of a functional nature, associated with the territorial structure of the British Raj, have been to some degree weakened – the orientation of Karnataka, for example, is changing now that it is entirely within Mysore, with its own

[1] J. N. L. Baker, 'Notes on the natural regions of India', *Geography*, 14 (1928), 447–55; L. D. Stamp, 'The natural regions of India', *ibid.* 502–6.

access to the coast, and no longer split up between old Mysore, Bombay and the protrusion of Madras into Kanara. The difficulty of following a political criterion, however, will be clear from the heterogeneity of Andhra Pradesh or Bihar. Such considerations will often recur in our regional chapters.

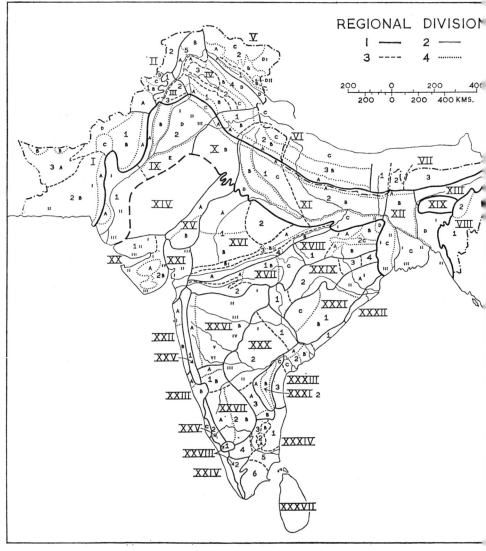

FIG 13.1 THE REGIONS OF THE SUB-CONTINENT.

Not all political divisions are arbitrary, however, and it is convenient to use political units as major regions where possible, as in Madras State, practically coincident with the Tamilnad region delimitable on other grounds, or best of all in Kerala; but normally the use of administrative boundaries is not so easy. There have been a number of attempts to divide India into economic regions for planning, adhering to State boundaries, and this is certainly not quite so difficult as it was with the more arbitrary Provinces, in part merely historic accidents, of British days. Plotted on a physical map, however, these do not seem to produce a satisfactory pattern, even when District breakdowns are used.[2] Nor does the 'Zonal' division into groups of States seem to have made much progress or, geographically considered, to have much point. One of the more interesting of these essays, apart from Thorner's, is that of Sen Gupta, which on the whole keeps to State boundaries, with some divergences, but has some rather odd sub-divisions within States, and some sub-regions spanning State boundaries and apparently simply physical in basis.[3] This problem is easier on the scale internal to a given State, and a notable experimental survey was carried out in Mysore by a Regional Survey Unit under the auspices of the Indian Statistical Institute.[4]

Conversely, a mechanical but very real difficulty in the organization of a regional treatment on physiographic lines lies in the fact that some definite physical regions, such as the Siwaliks and other sub-Himalayan zones, are ribbons hundreds of miles long and only a few wide. To treat them as wholes would involve an intolerable amount of cross-reference. Some sort of splitting-up is essential here, and it may have to be more or less arbitrary; the difficulties may be illustrated from Dehra Dun and Hardwar, only a few miles apart, closely associated, and yet divided by one of the primary physical divisions, that between the mountain wall and the plains. In practice a semi-political grouping across the physical trend is as convenient as any: the avenues of human activity run transversely to the physical strike. Again, there are areas with strongly differentiated topography but with affinities far from clear, as for example in the great triangle between the Aravallis, the Vindhya–Kaimur scarp and the Gangetic alluvium.

The division here adopted is, then, in the empirical tradition of Baker and Stamp. At this stage, it seems needless to enter the critique of some ostensibly single-factor divisions included in earlier editions of this book. It may be simply remarked that some element of hierarchy is needed, and that the factors to be considered are far too multiplex to 'drape themselves completely' in accordance with an *a priori* division, be it on physical or political lines. The *practising* regional geographer cannot bind himself in advance to so rigid a statute; our study is far too rich, varied and subtle to be tied down easily by rule and line.

Landforms are the first factor to be consulted, but climate and position can

---

[2] This was done for the scheme set out in the chapter 'Agrarian Regions' in D. and A. Thorner, *Land and Labour in India* (Asia, Bombay, 1962), 39–47, q.v. for an interesting discussion of other attempts.

[3] P. Sen Gupta, *Planning Regions for Resource Development in India* (Registrar General's Office, ND, 1964).

[4] A. T. A. Learmonth et al., *Mysore State: I. An Atlas of Resources, II. A Regional Synthesis* (Indian Statistical Institute, Calcutta, 1960, 1962).

never be ignored. A metaphysical dubiety may surround the whole concept of 'the region', but for practical purposes regions exist, and if they did not they would have to be invented to obtain manageable units of study. Rigid definition is however impossible; it must ever be remembered that 'in a large country like India, it would perhaps be impossible to choose factors which have a universal application, but understanding is more important than classification'.[5]

It is of course true that some preliminary cutting-out is necessary before even a start can be made, but this can be only a first empirical approximation. Many more regional studies, and (perhaps even more important) many more studies of the sub-continental distributions of specific phenomena, will be needed before that division can be drawn which satisfies the greatest number of criteria while doing least violence to any one of the fundamentals. At this stage, certainly, we must delimit our regions in a hypothetical way before we study them, otherwise we fall into the fallacy of complete induction; but it will be suspicious if we find, after studying them in detail, that they survive unchanged, fitting with mechanical convenience into our preconceived scheme. Nor, considering the immense totality of the phenomena, distributed perhaps with correlation but hardly ever with coincidence, can we hope to escape doubtful affiliations and overlaps. After all, even in political geography there are frontier zones as well as boundary lines; and in this sphere the most meticulous efforts at precise definition are made.

This avowed empiricism may well shock purists, whether they be adherents of physiographic regions or functionalists of 'Regional Science'. In fact, some of the 'regions' listed below – e.g. the upper Mahanadi basin – are simply what is left over when more definite regions have been sieved out: 'though . . . regions exist, it by no means follows that a whole continent can be divided up into well-marked areas.'[6] Although the most constantly recurring factor will be structure, the division cannot be based on any one touchstone – 'understanding is more important than classification.' Moreover, while in the broad organization of the regional chapters the threefold macro-division of mountains, plains and peninsula is paramount, as a matter of working convenience some groupings based essentially on positional or even political factors are adopted, bringing the treatment of regions belonging to two or even three of the primary regions into juxtaposition: thus the hills of Assam are treated with the plains, since the two cannot be intelligibly treated separately without much repetition and cross-reference. After all, regions *are* so juxtaposed in nature, on the map, and in human activity.

II. THE REGIONAL DIVISION

The regional scheme set forth below is empirical, having been arrived at in the actual process of writing the regional descriptions. The credentials of each region

[5] G. Kuriyan, in discussion of schemes by M. B. Pithawalla and K. S. Ahmad, *IGJ* 17/1 (1942), 71.
[6] L. R. Jones and P. W. Bryan, *North America* (Harcourt Brace, NY, 9th ed., 1950), 41. For the specific Mahanadi problem, see below, 685, 707.

are set out in the text, and no attempt is made to justify the division here. Obviously many regions and sub-regions might be further divided, and some of the minor units listed are not treated in the text under separate heads. Hierarchy has been kept in mind, but can obviously be only approximate, since a ridge which might rank as a sub-region in the Peninsula would be hardly more than a feature in the Himalayas; variations in geomorphological texture and intensity of human activity compel variations of scale.

It would be fascinating and instructive to attempt a detailed division in Unstead's terms, but this is obviously a task for the regional monographer working in India. However, some of the more significant stows and features found within the minor regions (which correspond approximately to Unstead's 'tracts') are indicated.

The order of the list is not strictly adhered to in the text; thus the Western Borderlands and the Indus Plains are juxtaposed, which has the advantage of bringing all West Pakistan in one place; and it would obviously be absurd to treat Assam in three places – as part of the Mountain Rim, of the Indo-Gangetic Plains, and (for the Shillong Plateau) of the Peninsular Block.

This scheme is tentative, but with 34 regions of the first order (under the three macro-regions, and excluding islands), 74 of the second order, and about 225 sub-divisions of these, it may fairly claim to represent a refinement on previous divisions.

Abbreviations:

Hs	.	. Hills
P	.	. Pass
pl	.	. plateau
rs	.	. ranges
vy	.	. valley

Ss	.	. Stows
Fs	.	. Features
@	.	. transitional
Ø	.	. outlier
Delhi	.	urban area receiving separate treatment

A. THE MOUNTAIN RIM

I. BALUCHISTAN

1. *Northern Ranges:*
   (*a*) Sulaiman r
   (*b*) Loralai–Zhob arcs
   (*c*) Toba–Khakar rs
   @(*d*) Quetta node: Ss – Quetta basin, Harnai and Bolan Ps, Khalifat massif
2. *Southern Ranges:*
   (*a*) Kirthar: Ss – Kalat pl, Hab vy; Fs – *tangis*
   (*b*) Makran:
      (i) En limestone/lava folds and pls
      (ii) Wn flysch: Ss – Hingol, Dasht, etc. vys

3. *Interior Plateaus:*
   (*a*) desert basins:
   (i) Mashkel
   (ii) Lora } Fs – *hamuns* (playas), *dasht* (desert floors)
   (*b*) Chagai Hs: Ss – Koh-i-Sultan volcanoes

II. NORTHWESTERN HILLS
   1. *Southern Transverse Zone:*
      (*a*) Waziristan (@ from I.1(*b*))
      (*b*) Kurram vy
      (*c*) Safed Koh
         (i) Safed Koh r
         (ii) Kabul vy: F – Khyber P
   2. *Northern Longitudinal Zone:*
      (i–iii) Chitral, Panjkora, Swat vys (@ to IV.5)

III. SUB-MONTANE INDUS
   1. *Trans-Indus Basins:*
      (*a*) Vale of Peshawar
      (*b*) (i) Kohat vy } Ss – *daman*; old lake floors
         (ii) Bannu
   2. *Potwar Plateau:* Ss – Kala Chitta Dhar, etc.;
                        Chach
   3. *Salt Range:*
      (i) Cis-Indus
      (ii) Trans-Indus: Fs – Kurran water-gap,
         Pezu windgap

   Fs – *khuddera* badlands; piedmont fans

         [*Regions I–III = Western Borderlands (Ch. 16)*]

IV. KASHMIR
   1. *Punch and Jammu:*
      (*a*) Siwalik zone
      (*b*) sub-Himalayan zone:
         (i) foothills: Ss – Jhelum gorge, Tawi vy
         (ii) mid-Chenab vy
   2. *Pir Panjal Range*
   3. *Vale of Kashmir:*
         (i) border rs and vys
         (ii) Vale: Fs – *karewas* terraces, Jhelum marshes
   4. *Main Himalayan Mass:*
      (*a*) Nanga Parbat massif
      (*b*) Great Himalaya
      (*c*) upper Chenab vy (@ to VI. 1(*b*))

(*d*) Zaskar Range:
    (i) range proper
    (ii) Deosai Plains
    (iii) Rupshu
5. *Gilgit-Hunza:*
  (*a*) (i) Astor vy
      (ii) Indus Kohistan: S – Indus gorge
  (*b*) (i) Gilgit-Hunza vys
      (ii) Hindu Kush

V. KARAKORAM
  1. *Ladakh:*
      (i) Indus furrow: Fs – fans
      (ii) Ladakh Range
  2. *Karakoram:*
    (*a*) Baltistan (Nn Shigar vy)
    (*b*) Shyok-Nubra vys:
      (i) main vys; F – Shyok dam
      (ii) Chang-chenmo vy
      (iii) Harong vy
    (*c*) Karakoram massif: Fs – glaciers
    (*d*) Tibetan pls:
      (i) Depsang and Lingzi-tang Plains
      (ii) Pangong rift
        [*Regions IV–V=Kashmir and Karakoram (Ch. 14*)]

VI. CENTRAL HIMALAYA
  1. *Himachal Pradesh* (montane Punjab):
    (*a*) Siwalik zone: Ss – *duns*
    (*b*) sub-Himalayan zone:
      (i) main vys: Chandra (Kulu), Beas (Mandi and Lahul)
      (ii) main rs: En Pir Panjal, Dhaoladhar
      (iii) Sutlej vy
    (*c*) upper Sutlej
      (i) Spiti
      (ii) Hundes: Fs – Rakas and Manasarowar lakes
  2. *Kumaon* (montane UP):
    (*a*) Siwalik zone:
      (i) Siwaliks
      (ii) Dehra Dun
    (*b*) sub-Himalayan zone: Yamuna, Ganga, Kali vys
    (*c*) high Bhotiya vys

3. *Nepal:*
   (*a*) Siwalik zone: Dundwa, Sumesar, Churia Ghati rs
   (*b*) Pahar: Ss – Katmandu vy, minor *duns*
   (*c*) high Himalaya

VII. EASTERN HIMALAYA
   1. *Kosi basin:*
         (i) Siwaliks and longitudinal vys
         (ii) Arun gorge
         (iii) Everest massif
   2. *Darjeeling–Sikkim:*
         (i) Tista vy: Fs – Singaliya ridge, Darjeeling Hs, Tista vy proper, Dongkhya r
         (ii) Chumbi vy
   3. *Bhutan and Assam Himalayas*
                     [*Regions VI–VII = Ch. 15*]

VIII. ASSAM–BURMA RANGES
   1. *Border Hills:*
         (i–v) Patkoi, Naga, Chin, Lushai, Chittagong Hs: Ss – Manipur basin, Kabaw vy (Burma)
   2. *Barail Range:* S – Cachar gap (@ between XII and XIII) (@ to XIX)
         [*Region VIII grouped with XIII and XIX as Eastern Borderlands (Ch. 20)*]

B. THE INDO-GANGETIC PLAINS

IX. INDUS PLAINS
   1. *Sind:*
         (*a*)   Sindi Kohistan (@ to I. 2(*a*))
         (*b*) lower Indus Vy:
               (i) Sewistan (Sibi or Kacchi): S – Manchar
               (ii) Indus/Nara Doab: Ss – Rohri (Sukkur) and Hyderabad uplands; Fs – *dhands*
               (iii) Indus Delta
               Karachi
   2. *Punjab Plains:*
         (*a*) Derajat: Ss – *daman*, Indus floodplain
         (*b*) Thal (Sind Sagar Doab)
         (*c*) Sub-Siwalik (winter rain) zone

(*d*) central Doabs:

    (i) Jech   ⎫ S – Kirana Hs (Ø of XV); Fs – *bet* floodplains, *dhaya*

    (ii) Rechna   ⎬ bluffs, *bar* uplands

    (iii) Bari   ⎭

(*e*) Bahawalpur (@ to XIV)

                 [*Region IX = Ch. 17, Indus Plains*]

X. INDO-GANGETIC DIVIDE

  1. (*a*) sub-Siwalik zone: S – Bist Doab; Fs – *chos* torrents

     (*b*) Sirhind (Hariana): S – Ghaggar *wadi*; F – Delhi Ridges (Ø of XV) **Delhi**

XI. GANGA PLAINS

  1. *Upper Ganga Plains:*

    (*a*) Sub-Siwalik zone: Ss – bhabar, terai

    (*b*) Yamuna/Ganga Doab: Fs – Jumna badlands

    (*c*) Rohilkhand–Avadh doabs: Fs – *bhur* sands

    (*d*) Trans-Jumna alluvial veneer (@ to XVI, XVII)

  2. *Middle Ganga Plains:*

    (*a*) as for XI. 1(*a*)

    (*b*) Tirhut: S – Kosi floodplain

    (*c*) trans-Ganga alluvial veneer:

       (i) Son delta

       (ii) S Bihar: Fs – Gaya Hs (Ø of XV)

(The boundary between XI. 1 and 2 is climatic. For IX–XI in general bhangar (old) and khadar (new) alluvium might be considered Ss.)

          [*Regions X–XI = Ch. 18, Gangetic Plains*]

XII. BENGAL

  1. (*a*) Duars (= terai)

    (*b*) Nn Paradelta (Ganga/Brahmaputra Doab): Ss – Barind, Tista floodplain

    (*c*) Western Margins:

       (i) Rarh (@ to XVIII. 2 (*b*)): Fs – lateritic doabs, paddy floodplains

       (ii) Damodar deltaic area

       (iii) Contai coastal plain: Fs – old beach-ridges

    (*d*) En Margins:

       (i) Surma–Meghna vy: S – Madhupur Jungle

       (ii) Chittagong coastal fans

    (*e*) Delta proper:

       (i) moribund: Fs – *jhils*, etc.

       (ii) mature

       (iii) active: S – Sundarbans; Fs – new islands

    Calcutta and Hooghlyside

          [*Region XII = Ch. 19*]

XIII. ASSAM VALLEY

1. *Brahmaputra vy:* Ss – Kapili/Dhansiri re-entrants; Fs – detrital terraces, floodplains

[*Grouped with Regions VIII and XIX as Eastern Borderlands, Ch. 20*]

C. THE PENINSULA

XIV. THAR DESERT

1. (*a*) Pat

(*b*) Thar proper: Ss – Bikaner irrigated area, Luni *wadi*, Aravalli *daman*; Fs – dunes, monadnocks

(The numerous hills of old rock protruding through the aeolian veneer indicate that the Thar is part of the Peninsular mass; but most of it is covered with superficial deposits, and the boundaries are hence ill-defined except where the desert is banked against XV. 1.)

XV. ARAVALLIS

1. *Aravalli Range:* Ss – Delhi Ridges (Ø), Jodhpur–Jaipur saddle; Godwar (*daman*); Fs – Mt Abu, Lake Sambhar

2. *Udaipur Hills:*
   (i) Mewar
   (ii) Bagar

XVI. CENTRAL VINDHYAN COUNTRY

1. *Malwa:*
   (*a*) Vindhyan *rock* zone: Ss – scarplands, Dholpur – Karauli pl
   (*b*) Deccan Lava zone:
      (i) Malwa pl
      (ii) Vindhyan *Hills* scarp (overlap with XVI. 3 (*b*) (i))

2. *Gneissic Bundelkhand*

3. *Vindhyan 'Ranges' and Plateaus:*
   (*a*) Rewa pl
   (*b*) scarps:
      (i) Vindhyan *Hills* (= XVI. 1 (*b*) (ii))
      (ii) Bhanrer–Kaimur Hs

4. *Narmada-Son furrow:*
   (*a*) Narmada vy:
      (i) lower gorges
      (ii) rift floor
   (*b*) Son vy

XVII. SATPURA–MAIKAL
  1. *Ranges:*
    (*a*) Satpura rs:
      (i) Satpuras proper ⎫ F – Burhanpur gap @ to XVII. 2 (*a*) (ii))
      (ii) Gawilgarh Hs ⎭
    (*b*) Mahadeo rs: Ss – intermont basins (Pench, etc.), Jabalpur gap; F – Marble Rocks
    (*c*) Maikal dissected pl: Ss – upper Narmada vy, Maikal scarp; F – Amarkantak
  2. *Khandesh* (@ to XXVI. 1 (*b*)):
    (*a*) Tapti-Purna vy:
      (i) lower Tapti gorges
      (ii) rift floor: S – Purna/Wardha watershed (@ to XXVI. 1 (*b*) (i))

XVIII. CHOTA NAGPUR
  1. *Upper Son-Deogarh uplands* (@ to XVII. 4 (*b*) and XVII. 1 (*c*))
  2. *Chota Nagpur:*
    (*a*) Hazaribagh Range
    (*b*) peneplains:
      (i) Hazaribagh
      (ii) Ranchi
    (*c*) Gondwana trough (Koel–Damodar basins): F – Parasnath
    (*d*) Rajmahal Hs: Fs – *daman*, upper valleys
    [*Regions XIV–XVIII grouped as Aravallis and Central India (Ch. 21)*]

XIX. SHILLONG PLATEAU (Ø)
  1. *Shillong Plateau* (Garo, Khasi and Jaintia Hs)
    [*Grouped with Regions VIII and XIII as Eastern Borderlands (Ch. 20)*]

XX. KUTCH AND KATHIAWAD
  1. *Kutch:*
      (i) Rann mudflats
      (ii) lava/sandstone pls
      (iii) alluvial/aeolian margins
  2. *Kathiawad:*
    (*a*) central platform:
      (i) Drangadhra–Wadhwan sandstone pl
      (ii) Nn and Sn lava pls: Fs – Gir Hs, Girnar (Ø)
    (*b*) lowland margins:
      (i) Halar coast: Fs – creeklands
      (ii) Dwarka foreland: F – Okha Rann
      (iii) Sorath coast: Ss – Bhadar–Ojat and Shetrunji vys (Fs – *gher* lands); miliolite zone; Cambay coast
      (iv) Gohilwad (@ to XXI. 1): S – Nal depression

XXI. GUJARAT

1. *Gujarat Plains:*
    (i) Cambay coastal marshes
    (ii) central alluvial shelf: S – Charotar
    (iii) En alluvial veneer (@ to XV. 2 (ii) and XVI. 1 (*b*))

XXII. KONKAN

1. *Konkan coastal lowland:*
    (*a*) N Konkan:
        (i) Nn lowland: Ss – longitudinal ridges and vys (Vaitarni, Amba); Fs
           – coastal alluvium and mangrove
        (ii) Ulhas basin (@ XXII. 1 (*a*) and 1 (*b*), and to XXV. 1) Ss – foot-
           hills (@ to Ghats (F – Matheran mesa (Ø)), Kalyan lowland,
           Salsette Is. (Fs. – dune and rock coast, alluvial lateritic shelf,
           central hills, creeklands)
        Bombay
    (*b*) Kolaba–Ratnagiri:
        (i) indented coast: Fs – mangrove flats
        (ii) hilly lowland: Fs – paddy valley-floors, lateritic interfluves, Chiplun
           amphitheatres (@ to XXV. 1)
(The distinction between XXII. 1 (*a*) and 1 (*b*) is essentially that the trends
of the former are longitudinal to the coast, of the latter transverse.)

XXIII. GOA AND KANARA

1. *Konkan–Kerala transition:*
    (*a*) Goa:
        (i) Ilhas deltaic zone: S – Ilha de Goa
        (ii) lowland: Ss = Bardez, Marmagão peninsula
        (iii) foothills: F – Braganza Ghat (@ to XXV. 1–2)
    ((ii) and (iii) = approximately Velhas and Novas Conquistas respectively.)
    (*b*) N Kanara:
        (i) discordant coast: Fs – paddy valley-bottoms, lateritic interfluves
        (ii) Ghats breaches zone (@ to XXV. 1–2): Fs – gorges (Sharavati,
           Kalinadi), high interfluves
    (*c*) S Kanara:
        (i) Netravati (Mangalore) lowland: Ss – alluvial coast, lateritic shelves;
           Fs – Ghats outliers
(The whole Region is transitional between XXII and XXIV, and also displays
a marked softening of the contrast between the Western Littoral and the
Deccan.)

XXIV. KERALA (MALABAR)

1. *Kerala coastal plain:*
    (i) littoral: Fs – dunes-and-lows, backwaters
    (ii) alluvium/laterite shelf
    (iii) gneissic lowlands (@ to XXV. 2): Ss – Palghat approaches (@ to XXXIV. 4), Nagercoil valleys (@ to XXXIV. 6 (*d*) (ii))
    [*Regions XX–XXIV grouped as Western Littoral (Ch. 22)*]

XXV. WESTERN GHATS

1. *Deccan Lava Ghats, scarp and crest:* Ss – Dangs and Peint forests, Koyna and upper Krishna vys; Fs – Thal and Bhor Ghats (@ to XXVI. 1 (*a*))
2. *Archaean Ghats, scarp and crest:*
    (*a*) Ghats breaches zone (repeat of XXIII. 1 (*b*) (ii))
    (*b*) higher Sn zone:
        (i) contact zone along crest (@ between XXIII. 1 (*b*) and XXVII. 1)
        (ii) Coorg coulisses (@ to XXVII. 2 (*a*))
        (iii) Wynaad pl (@ to XXVII. 2 (*a*))

XXVI. MAHARASHTRA

1. *Deccan Lava country:*
    (*a*) Maval (@ to XXV. 1)
    (*b*) plateau:
        (i) Wardha vy
        (ii) Ajanta Hs
        (iii) Godavari vy: S – Nasik basin
        (iv) Balaghat 'Range'
        (v) Bhima vy
        (vi) Bijapur dry zone
(Northern limits ill-defined; culturally Khandesh (XVII. 2) is Maratha.)

XXVII. KARNATAKA (SOUTH DECCAN PLATEAUS)

1. *Northern Karnatak:*
    (*a*) Belgaum marginal zone (@ to XXVI. 1 (*b*) (vi)): Fs – Kaladgi scarps
    (*b*) Dharwar peneplains: Fs – Dharwarian synclines
    Mysore Karnatak:
2. (*a*) Malnad: Ss – sub-Ghats strip (evergreen forest (@ to XXV. 2 (*b*)); Fs – Babu Bhudan Hs
    (*b*) Maidan: Ss – peneplains, Mysore Ghat (@ to XXXIV. 3 (i)); Fs – *drugs* (tors)
(Also Ss – longitudinal valleys of Tungra, Bhadra, Hagari, upper Penner in both (*a*) and (*b*)).

XXVIII. SOUTHERN BLOCKS

1. *Nilgiris:* Ss – Moyar trench, Nilgiri pl; Fs – *sholas*, downs
2. *Anaimalais,* etc.:
    (i) Anaimalai/Palani Hs
    (ii) Cardamom Hs: S – upper Periyar vy
    (iii) Varushanad/Andipatti Hs
    (iv) Comorin Hs: F – Shencottah gap (@ between XXIV. 1 (iii) and XXXIV. 6 (*d*) (i))

XXIX. NORTHEAST DECCAN (MAHANADI BASIN AND ANNEXES)

1. *Wainganga vy* (En flank, off Lavas) (@ between XXVI. 1 (*b*) (i) and XXIX. 2): S – Wainganga/Mahanadi watershed; Fs – haematite monadnocks of S
2. *Chhattisgarh:*
    (i) Nn (sub-Maikal) margins (@ to XVII. 1 (*c*))
    (ii) Seonath/Mahanadi doab
    (iii) Raigarh basin
                ((i) and (ii) should rank as Ss?)
3. *Sankh/S Koel/Brahmani basins* (@ in all directions)
4. *Jamshedpur basin:* Ss – Sanjai gap (@ to XXIX. 3), Subarnarekha vy (@ to XII. 1 (*c*) (i))
    Jamshedpur
(Region XXIX, except for its Chhattisgarh core, is the most ill-defined of the whole sub-continent.)

XXX. TELANGANA

1. *Lower Godavari trough* (@ to XXIX. 1 and XXXIII. 2 (i))
2. *Telangana proper:*
    (i) Hyderabad
    (ii) Bellary peneplains   } Fs – *drugs*
    (iii) Raichur (Krishna/Tungabhadra) Doab
3. *Anantapur/Chittoor basins:*
    (*a*) interior basins:
        (i) Chatravati
        (ii) Papagni
        (iii) Cheyyur – Bahuda
    (*b*) transitional zone:
        (i) Suvarnamukhi vy (@ to XXXIV. 1 (i))
        (ii) Nagari Hs: Ss – intermont basins
(XXX. 3 is shut in between XXVII. 2 (*b*) (Mysore Maidan) and XXXI. 2 (*a*) (Palkondas) and is really another left-over; all of it really transitional between Telangana and Tamilnad.)

XXXI. EASTERN HILLS

1. *Orissa Bastar mass:*
   (*a*) Orissa Hs:
      (i) hill massifs
      (ii) Brahmani/Mahanadi trough (@ to XXXII)
   (*b*) khondalite zone:
      (i) dissected peneplains
      (ii) Tel/Sileru trough
2. *Cuddapah ranges and basins:*
   (*a*) Western arcs (Erramalai–Seschalam–Palkonda Hs): Fs – Palkonda
      scarp, gorges (Cheyyur, Papagni)
   (*b*) central (Kunderu) basin:
      (i) Kurnool–Cuddapah plain
      (ii) Razampeta corridor: Fs – lateritic piedmont, Cheyyur shingle-
      spread
   (*c*) En ridges:
      (i) Nallamalais
      (ii) central (Sagileru) vy
      (iii) Velikondas
      [*Regions XXV–XXXI grouped as Peninsular Interior (Ch. 23)*]

XXXII. ORISSA DELTAS

1. *Mahanadi/Brahmani Deltas:* Ss – Baitarni vy; Fs – Balasore gap (@ to
   XII. 1 (*c*) (iii), delta seaface, Lake Chilka, Mahendragiri gap (@ to
   XXXIII. 1)

XXXIII. ANDHRA DESA

1. *Vizag-Ganjam lowland:* Ss – Rushikulya, Languliya, Vamsaḍnara vys;
   lateritic foothill zone (@ to XXXI. 1 (*b*) (i)); F – Waltair Highlands.
2. *Godavari/Krishna Deltas:*
      (i) Godavari/Krishna breach (@ to XXX. 1 and 2 (i))
      (ii) Godavari delta: Ss – sub-deltaic margins, delta proper; Fs – sea-
      face, Colair Lake
      (iii) Krishna delta: Ss and Fs as for Godavari delta
3. *Nellore* (@ to XXXIV. 1)*:*
   (*a*) *Nellore lowlands:*
      (i) Archaean low peneplain
      (ii) coastal alluvium: Fs – cuestiform marine deposits, Pulicat lagoon
      [*Regions XXXII and XXXIII grouped as Eastern Littoral (N), (Ch. 24)*]

XXXIV. TAMILNAD

1. *Coromandel coastal plain:*
    (i) Archaean low peneplains: Fs – monadnocks, Cretaceous–Eocene inliers
    (ii) Cuddalore/laterite shelf: Fs – Red Hs, Capper Hs
    (iii) young alluvial zone: Ss – embayments, strandplain; Fs – Korteliyar, Cooum, Adyar, Palar vys
    Madras

2. *Tamilnad Hills* (Ø of Mysore Maidan):
    (a) Javadis: Fs – Agaram – Cheyyur through vy, Yelagiri (Ø), Ponnaiyar gap (@ between 1 (i) and 3 (ii))
    (b) Sn group: Ss – Shevaroys, Kalroyans, Pachamalais, Salem monadnocks (Ø)

3. *Palar/Ponnaiyar trough:*
    (i) lower shelf of Mysore Ghat (@ to XXVII. 2 (b))
    (ii) Baramahal
    (iii) Sn margins (Salem area, @ to 4): Fs – Chalk Hs, magnetite monadnocks

4. *Coimbatore plateau (Kongunad):* Ss – Bhavani, Noyil, Amaravati vys, Palghat sill (@ to XXIV). 1 (ii), Coimbatore Hs; F – Kangayam interfluve

5. *Cauvery delta:*
    (a) delta head (@ to 3 and 4)
    (b) delta proper:
        (i) Velar/Coleroon doab (@ to 1 (iii))
        (ii) Coleroon/Cauvery doab: Fs – Srirangam Island, floodplains
        (iii) main delta plains: Ss – higher Western margins (F – Vallam Tableland), older irrigated area
        (iv) seaface: Fs – marshy low, dune belt, Pt Calimere, Veddaniyam salt swamp

6. *Dry Southeast :*
    (a) upper Vaigai:
        (i) Varushanad vy
        (ii) Kambam vy
        (iii) Dindigul col (@ to 4)
    (b) Madurai/Ramanathapuram shelf:
        (i) colluvial piedmont zone: Fs – monadnocks (Sirumalais, etc., Ø)
        (ii) laterite/old alluvium panfan (from Varshalei to Vaippar): Ss – tank country, coastal strip, Pamban Island (Fs – old reefs, Adam's Bridge)
    (c) Black Soil area
    (d) Tirunelveli:
        (i) colluvial zone
        (ii) red soil zone: Fs – *teris*, coastal dunes

(iii) Tamprabarni basin: Ss – foothills (@ to XXVIII. 2 (iv)), Chittar
vy, Tamprabarni vy
[*Region XXXIV = Ch. 25, Tamilnad*]

D. THE ISLANDS

XXXV. MALDIVES AND LACCADIVES
[*In Ch. 22, Western Littoral*]

XXXVI. ANDAMANS AND NICOBARS
1. *Andamans*
2. *Nicobars*

[*In Ch. 25, Tamilnad*]

XXXVII. CEYLON
See separate division in Ch. 26; but it may be noted here that the main
divisions of Ceylon essentially reproduce those of the southern Peninsula:
central massif (cf. XXVIII, perhaps genetically connected), surrounding low
gneissic peneplains with alluvial embayments (cf. XXXIV. 1), dry zone (cf.
XXXIV. 6); the Jaffna area, despite lithological differences, is essentially a true
coastal plain (cf. XXXIV. 1 (ii–iii) and 6 (*b*)–(*d*)).

CHAPTER 14

The Himalayas: Kashmir and Karakoram
(Regions IV and V)

Methodological difficulties

The vast system of ramparts and fosses which girdles India on the north presents all but insuperable difficulties to regional treatment on our sub-continental scale. Some of the physical regions are narrow belts hundreds of miles long, and to work through and along these *seriatim* would be intolerably tedious and confusing to writer and reader. From another angle the whole area is a mosaic of small regions, similar but not merely standard repetitions; this is reflected in the richness of the *pays* nomenclature.[1] Even a simple topographic description of this multitude of little worlds, Gilgit, Rupshu, Spiti and the rest, would fill a volume of Himalayan dimensions; while structure and genetics are known either in excessive detail (for our scale) for small areas, or in excessive vagueness for vast areas. Adequate climatic data are lacking over much of this huge area, where obviously micro-climates are of the highest importance; in ecology and pedology the site may be as important as the zone. Fragmentation, indeed, is the ruling theme. The human adjustments to a complex and difficult environment are nice and minute, and here, too, justice cannot be done within the limitations of our scale.

The compromise adopted is imperfect, but perhaps the most reasonable one available. In the west, where the width of the mountains proper is close on 300 miles (483 km.), it is possible to discuss the main longitudinal units individually and to synthesize in terms of the political unit of Kashmir. Farther east the true longitudinal regions will be broken up and reassembled into transverse segments treated as far as possible as wholes. Convenience of handling dictates this allowance to locational, and even to political, factors of a weight to which they are not entitled on physiographic grounds; but this is not without justification since by and large the broader human divisions of the centre and east tend to run transverse to the physical. The whole Himalayan area may thus be divided as follows, premising that each 'unit' is in fact made up of longitudinal belts, except in the west where the more massive build renders treatment on longitudinal lines more feasible:

[1] 'Nowhere in the world are the small natural regions more sharply separated than in the Himalayas.' A. G. Ogilvie, 'The technique of regional geography', *JMGA* 13/12 (1938), 109–24, refce at 123.

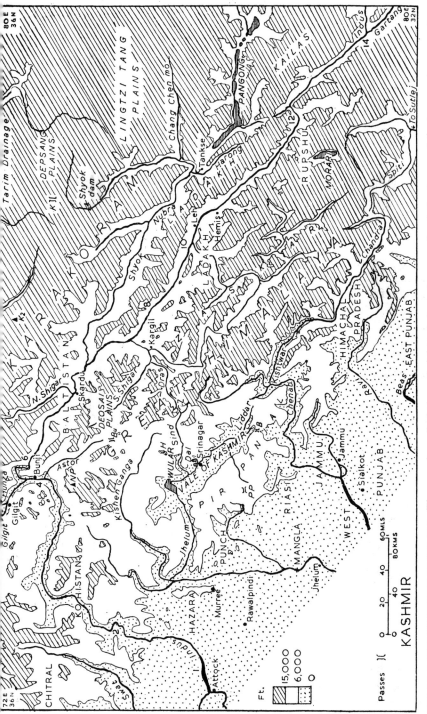

FIG 14.1 THE KASHMIRI HIMALAYA. Figures along Indus are height of river above sea-level (in thousand feet): note the steep drop above Bunji. Passes: K, Karakoram; Bu, Burzil; Z, Zoji La; PP, Pir Panjal; B, Banihal. NP Nanga Parbat; H, Haramukh.

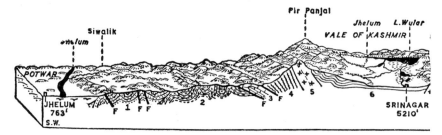

FIG 14.2 POTWAR TO LADAKH: BLOCK SECTION OF KASHMIRI HIMALAYAS. Line
Shyok confluence; vertical exaggeration 8.3. Geology (based on de Terra) dia-
and 'Tethys' formations (U. Permian-Cretaceous) in northeast; 4, older Palaeozoic;
granites. F, major faults and thrusts.

1. Sub-Himalayan Kashmir   ⎫
    (Punch and Jammu) |
2. Pir Panjal   ⎬ IV
3. Vale of Kashmir |
4. Indus Kohistan and Gilgit |
5. Main Himalaya   ⎭

1. Ladakh and Baltistan   ⎫
    (the Indus furrow)   ⎬ V
2. Karakoram   ⎭

1. Himachal Pradesh   ⎫
    (sub-Himalayan Punjab) |
2. Dehra Dun and Kumaon   ⎬ VI
3. Nepal   ⎭

1. Kosi basin (E. Nepal)   ⎫
2. Tista basin (Darjeeling and |
    Sikkim)   ⎬ VII
3. Bhután and Assam Himalayas   ⎭

This chapter will be confined to the western regions, which by fortunate chance
do correspond very nearly to the territorial limits of Kashmir.

The Himalayas in general

The general structural outlines have been set out in Chapter 1, and as far as may
be will be taken as read: there is no general account of the Siwaliks throughout
their length, for instance. But we may recall briefly the great Northwestern
Syntaxis, the overthrust boundary faults on the inner edge of the younger sub-
Himalayan terrain, and the great nappes of the Himalaya proper.

The barrier function of the mountain wall is obvious. Climatically the monsoon is as it were banked up against the Great Himalaya, and but thin trickles of
monsoon air lip over the few notches in this stupendous dyke: the Vale of Kashmir is intermediate in this respect, with a definite rain-shadow from the Pir
Panjal, but with wet and cloudy weather in the monsoon months. The snow
supply of the Himalaya, especially in the west, comes mainly from troughs in the
westerly air-movement of the upper troposphere (above p. 50).

From the human point of view, the Himalayas are far from impenetrable, but
for long there was not much point in penetrating them, at least in a military and
political sense as against cultural and trade movements: the negative values

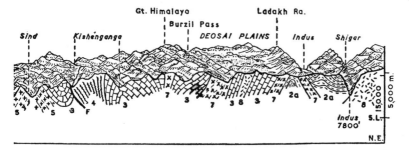

of section on bearing 38° for 430 miles (690 km.) from Jhelum town to Indus below grammatic: 1, Siwaliks; 2, Murree; 2a, Flysch; 3, Permo-Carb. (thrust on to 2), 5, younger Palaeozoic igneous; 6, Karewas Beds; 7, Cret.-Eocene eruptives; 8,

concerned are as much a matter of what lies beyond as of the terrain difficulties, great as these are. Beyond the Vale of Kashmir transport was entirely human and animal, and not even draught animal: mules, yaks, even sheep carry the little trade that exists. Except in the height of the monsoon, flying is now possible over practically the whole area, despite difficulties in take-off in the rarefied air. The use of aviation, including helicopters, is increasingly important in a civil as well as a strategic sense.[2]

Yet the Himalayas have a high human interest. Where armies have rarely penetrated, Chinese pilgrims seeking the land of Buddha, Hindus the source of sacred Ganga and the hidden mountain Kailas, have left the impress of their faith in shrine and temple. Here indeed three mighty empires of the mind meet: Islam in the tangled valleys around the Indus and in the Vale; Hinduism in the Vale and the sub-Himalayan borders; the Mahayana Buddhism of Tibet and Ladakh spilling down the glacis to mingle with Hinduism in the peculiar culture of Nepal. Ethnically, too, though ruling groups may be often Rajputs, most of the Himalaya are probably Mongol or at least Mongoloid; and in Ladakh and Sikkim we are no more in an Indian or an Islamic environment. Not only is the cultural landscape of monastery and prayer-wheel different, but the economy itself, though agriculturally based, is remarkable for the high development of transhumant pastorialism. So too the social world is different; the polyandry universal in Ladakh is rarely found south of the mountains. Over against the dwellers in the vast Indian plains these people are not even hill-men; they are mountaineers.

Finally, this land of difficulty and mystery has in all ages powerfully impressed the mind of India: around Kailas and the sources of Ganga cluster the beautiful legends of Siva and Parvati, and the eternal snows have always stood as symbols of an ideal serenity, attainable, if at all, only by indomitable patience and

[2] K. Mason, 'The Himalayas as a barrier to modern communication', *GJ* 87 (1936), 1–16; cf. R. R. Rawson, in W. G. East and O. H. K. Spate (eds.), *The Changing Map of Asia* (4th ed., 1961), 307, 312.

427

resolution. What the Himalayas have meant to India may be glimpsed from the lovely verse of Kalidasa:[3]

> God of the distant north, the Snowy Range
> O'er other mountains towers imperially;
> Earth's measuring-rod, being great and free from change
> Sinks to the eastern and the western sea. . . .

Kalidasa's view of the functions of Himalaya, 'who steadies earth, so strong is he and broad', is not of course in accordance with the views of modern geomorphology:

'Both from within and from without, the Himalayas are in a condition of extremely active change. . . . If we contemplate the Himalayas as a whole, we come to regard them as representing a mighty upward flow of the earth's crust. . . . Angara got the better of the thrust, so that the mobile mountain masses flowed over the sinking lowlands of Gondwana. Thus to the eyes of the geologist, who is used to thinking in great periods of time, the Himalayas seem a mobile organ of our planet which is not merely rolling on its course through the universe, but within its own framework is continually undergoing the throes of an active life.'[4]

SUB-HIMALAYAN KASHMIR: PUNCH AND JAMMU

Very broadly speaking, Kashmir consists of two huge mountain masses – the Karakoram in the far north, the Himalaya/Zaskar to the south, with the Indus entrenched between them; and, on the southern flanks of the main Himalaya, the famous Vale, walled in by the Pir Panjal which in turn gives way to the lower but highly dissected Tertiaries of the Punjab border hills (Figs. 14.1, 14.2). In actual fact the detail is exceedingly complex and the breakdown into seven units of study rather arbitrary, though not entirely so.

Kashmir includes a narrow strip, up to 15 miles (24 km.) wide, of the Punjab plains, here at 1,100–1,200 ft. (335–366 m.); this tract is badly ravined and of little significance except for the inclusion of the Mangla headworks of the Upper Jhelum Canal. North lies a belt of Siwalik terrain, hills up to 2,000–4,000 ft. (610–1,220 m.), largely anticlinal and overlooking a series of *duns*-longitudinal valleys – succeeded in turn by the Miocene Murree sandstones and Eocene Nummulitic limestone at 6,000–8,000 ft. (1,823–2,444 m.). The Siwalik zone, a 'pile of rock waste' up to 20,000 ft. thick, has undergone very recent folding and faulting, including early Pleistocene thrusting. In the earlier Tertiary zone strike-faults have disrupted anticlines and brought in massive Permo-Carboniferous limestones forming the higher ridges. The upper Murrees are preserved on the down-throw (southern) side, while to the north the lower Murrees and the Nummulitics, resting with a great unconformity on the Permo-Carboniferous,

[3] A. W. Ryder, *Translations from Kalidasa* (Everyman ed., n.d.), 157.
[4] A. Heim and A. Gansser, *The Throne of the Gods* (1939), 220.

are greatly disturbed and the terrain correspondingly confused; yet, 'although dissection is intense, their heights display unmistakable signs of an older topography. Levelled spurs and plateau remnants, valley flat and abrupt terminations of high valley floors along master streams, indicate a mature relief which underwent rejuvenation.'[5] This sub-Himalayan zone ends in the great boundary thrust-faults, beyond which the Pir Panjal rises steeply.

Rainfall varies with aspect, but in general lies between 35 in. (635 mm.) in the west and 28 in. (528 mm.) in the east, with a fair contribution in January–March; temperatures are of course affected by altitude and aspect. The low outer ridges carry a sparse dry scrub, the inner rather better forest, largely of *chir* or *chil* (*Pinus longifolia*). This is the basis for an important resin-tapping industry, exporting throughout southeast Asia for paper and soap making. Forest management is hampered by the Cease Fire line as much as by the goats and landslides.[6]

The Siwalik and Murree terrain, with thin thirsty soils, very liable to erosion and often degenerating into pebble-spreads, is agriculturally poor, as are the limestone slopes. Here and there, in *duns* and in a piedmont belt at the foot of limestone scarps, conditions are better. Irrigation is limited, as the water-table is generally deep for wells, and channels are liable to be overwhelmed by spates from the numerous transverse gullies; while some lower areas are so fever-ridden that cultivation is largely carried on by a seasonal immigration of hillmen. Wheat, barley and rape are grown as rabi, maize and bajra as kharif. Higher up, in wider, better-watered valleys, bajra gives way completely to maize. Irrigation is difficult here also, as streams are incised, but it is not so necessary as in the lower valleys.

The unexploited mineral resources of the region are important. In Riasi District the Nummulitics contain three or four small fields with seams of anthracite (carbon 60–82%) up to 20 ft. thick; farther west the coal is very friable and the thin seams too disturbed to be workable. The pisolitic limonites and ironstone of the same area and formation were exploited by indigenous methods in the past. The basal Eocene beds are fossil laterites, an old land-surface on the Permo-Carboniferous, and contain patches of pure bauxite forming a large reserve of aluminium ore.[7]

The region is fairly well peopled: recent district figures are not available, but densities are over 300 in Jammu and between 150 and 200 in Riasi and Kathua, which contain definitely mountainous areas. The southeast is strongly Hindu: this is the home of the Dogras, the dominant minority in the state. Jammu (102,738) was the original base of the ruling house, whence the official title of the state is 'Jammu and Kashmir'. To the west Punch is mainly Muslim, a feudatory generally on bad terms with its Kashmiri overlord in the past.

The whole region is of less significance in itself than in relation to the western

[5] de Terra (1939), 8, 18. Until further notice, citations to de Terra are from this very admirable work.

[6] G. S. Mathauda, 'A brief survey of the post-war resin-tapping industry in India', *Indian Forester*, 85/8 (1959), 458–67.

[7] D. N. Wadia, *Geology of India* (Macmillan, London, 3rd ed. revised, 1961), 335.

Punjab, with which its links were close, especially as a supplier of timber to a region desperately short of it. At least the Mangla headworks are secured to Pakistan as part of the Indus Waters Agreement.

Finally we may note the essentially similar, though rather higher, country across the Jhelum, which forms much of Rawalpindi and Hazara Districts in West Pakistan. Murree, a hill station at the usual 6,500–7,500 ft. (1,980–2,255 m.), was chiefly noted for brewing; the high barley acreage of the region may have been significant as cause or more likely effect.

THE PIR PANJAL

The Pir Panjal is in a sense a bifurcation from the main Himalaya farther east. Structurally and lithologically it is most complex; thrusting is important and Wadia considers it as the front of a great Kashmir nappe. The massive Permo-Carboniferous limestones, metamorphics, and intrusives form a broad swelling platform at about 13,000 ft. (3,960 m.), on which lies a serrated residual crest, the highest monadnocks reaching 15,500 ft. (4,725 m.). The passes lie as a rule at 11,000–12,000 ft. (around 3,500 m.).

The contemporary glaciation presents interesting features. Most of the thirty-odd small glaciers are on the northern slope, in contrast to the Himalayas farther east where there is relatively little ice on the arid Tibetan side. The Pir Panjal snow, however, comes mostly in winter, from west or northwest, and the southern aspects are more exposed to warm air-currents from the plains. Only one or two of these glacierets have real valley tongues, the lowest at 11,600 ft. (3,535 m.); most of them are simply cakes of ice in wide cirques which form the collecting grounds. The river-pattern is very striking, with the great bends of Chenab and Jhelum (the latter controlled by the syntaxis), the tributaries at these bends on the line of the lower main streams, and a general layout of feeders suggesting that the drainage was originally to the southeast.

The southern flank is wetter than the northern, but slopes here are so often too steep for soil formation that the larger coniferous forests are mostly to the north; here a sparse population of Gujar herdsmen lives in large huts with flat earth-and-turf covered roofs designed to support the weight of winter snow, even among the deodars.[8] The SOI 1/2,000,000 maps carry the Pir Panjal across the Chenab, the upper (Chandra Bhuga) valley being closely inset in the angle of the Pir Panjal and the main Himalaya. The lower levels of this high basin (6,000–12,000 ft., 1,830–3,660 m.) in the west carry a fair population. The climate here is definitely cold, 'the mango-tree gives place to the apple'; but terraced irrigation is not too difficult, and rice is important.[9]

The region, is however, essentially negative, a barrier. Of the routes into the

[8] S. C. Bose, 'Morpho-ecology in and around Pir Panjal', *GRI* 23/4 (1961), 55–67.

[9] See Bose, *op. cit.*, for interesting details on other intermont basins; their isolated populations, though declining in numbers appear well adjusted to local resources; the more inaccessible are still polyandrous.

Vale the most direct is the old Mogul road from Rawalpindi by the Pir Panjal Pass (11,400 ft., 3,475 m.), which gives its name to the range; this old route is now only a mule track, having been superseded by the motor road up the Jhelum valley – excellent engineering but costly to maintain and now disrupted by the Cease Fire line. At the other end of the Vale access from India through Jammu is by a road which tunnels under the Banihal Pass to minimize interference by snow.

THE VALE OF KASHMIR

The physical setting

Between the Pir Panjal and the main Himalaya lies the famous Vale of Kashmir, a great basin about 85 miles by 25 (135 by 40 km.) with a floor which in the Jhelum floodplain is only 5,200 ft. (1,585 m.) above sea-level. Wadia and de Terra agree in regarding it as a great synclinal, which according to Wadia is seated on the back of a vast nappe.[10] The southern flanks fall relatively regularly and gently from the Pir Panial crest, but the Jhelum thalweg lies close to the northern side of the Vale, and here facetted spurs give a clear indication of faulting; similar features on the Pir Panjal slope are as a rule masked by the Pleistocene deposits. The stream pattern is interesting. The northern wall is dissected by the Sind and other rivers which are antecedent to the immediately bordering hills; but beyond the ridge crowned by Haramukh (15,999 ft., 4,846 m.) the northwestern end of the valley shows a well-adjusted synclinal pattern, significantly 'rather suggestive of an ancient headwater portion of a master stream'.[11] On the Pir Panjal side the upper valleys are incised and dendritic, but farther down the rivers have developed on parallel courses, consequent on the uplift of the Karewas Beds and antecedent to the folds in them. As we are about to see, the geomorphological evolution is extremely recent.

Among the most striking features of the Vale are the flat-topped terraces known as *karewas*, which term is also applied to the Pleistocene sediments of which they are composed. These deposits consist of clays, sands and silts of undoubted lacustrine origin, in which bands of marl and of loessic silt, together with lenticles of conglomerate from old deltaic fans, bear witness to many fluctuations of level. The sequence of events suggested by de Terra[12] is: (i) capture by the Jhelum of an original subsequent flowing to the southeast, probably along the longitudinal course of the Chenab;[13] (ii) Pir Panjal uplift blocking this exit; (iii) filling of the lake and overspilling; (iv) alternate draining and deepening of the lake in response to glacial changes and changes in the ratio

[10] Cf. Fig. 42 in Wadia, *op. cit.* (1961), 423.

[11] H. de Terra and T. Paterson, *Studies on the Ice Age in India* (Carnegie Inst. of Washington, Pubtn No. 453, 1939), 23 (cited as 'de Terra').

[12] de Terra, 116–18. In this section, *karewas* = topographical, Karewas = geological.

[13] Note in this connection the directions of the Liddar and the tributaries joining the Chenab at the Kishtwar bend.

of uplift and erosion at the spill; (v) continued uplift accompanied by cutting-down of the Jhelum and complete drainage of the lake. It should be noted that the various existing lakes, of which Wular is the largest (area 12–100 sq. miles,

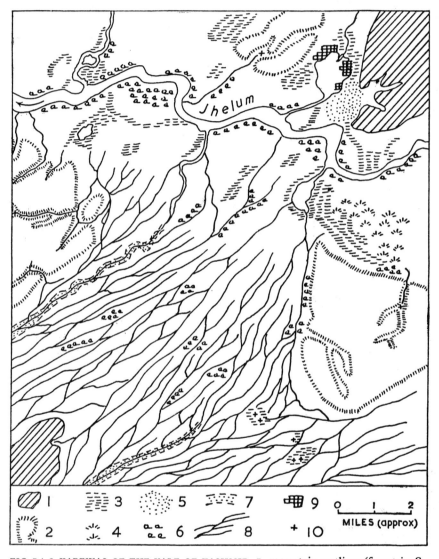

FIG 14.3 KAREWAS OF THE VALE OF KASHMIR. 1, mountain outliers (forest in S, grass or rock in N); 2, karewas; 3, marsh; 4, grass; 5, alluvial cone; 6, willows, poplars, orchards; 7, stream beds; 8, irrigation channels (kuls); 9, demb cultivation; 10, springs. All blank areas cultivated except ravines and flanks of karewas (cf. Fig 66). Altitude about 5,200 ft. along Jhelum, 5,800 on upper margins of karewas, 6,000–7,000 on hills. This map does not represent any specific area.

31–259 km², according to season and flood) are not strictly relics of the ancient lake, but rather enlarged old oxbows and abandoned courses of the Jhelum; in some cases ponding by detrital fans from the hills seems to be responsible.

In places the *karewas* have been eaten into great bluffs by the Jhelum, and the terrace lies at 450 ft. (137 m.) above the river. On the south Karewas Beds extend from about 5,400 up to 9,000 ft. (1,645–2,740 m.), and are quite steeply tilted. With the Pir Panjal uplift the deposits were folded and in places faulted, another striking testimony to the persistence of orogenic process into recent, perhaps even contemporary, times. To summarize, we have:[14]

First interglacial   Lower Karewas deposition (*c.* 2,000 ft. 610 m.), lake beds, fluvial inwash and aeolian drift.

Second glaciation   Karewas gravel (*c.* 400 ft., 122 m.), glacio-fluvial outwash fans.

Second interglacial   Upper Karewas, (*c.* 200 ft., 61 m.) – 'topmost beds of aeolian and fluvial origin; lower beds lacustrine; also fluvial outwash (partly varved).'

The word *karewa* applies strictly to the level surface between the incised streams dissecting the terraces, the flanks of which are generally steep (Fig. 14.4). They are usually permeable and soils tend to be poor, though pressure of population enforces their cultivation. Lower down finer alluvium fills the marshy valley-floor, and where streams debouch from the hills fans of coarser material are formed. These relations are suggested by Fig. 14.3, which it should be noted does not represent any actual area, though all features shown are found on each of the several SOI 1/63,360 sheets.

The climate is naturally continental, the severity of the winter being increased by drainage of cold air down the encircling slopes, and by radiation. Srinagar lies at 5,200 ft. (1,585 m.) and its climate is more extreme

[14] de Terra, table at 224; for general glacial sequence see above, 37–39.

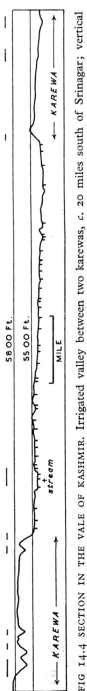

FIG 14.4 SECTION IN THE VALE OF KASHMIR. Irrigated valley between two karewas, *c.* 20 miles south of Srinagar; vertical exaggeration 5·28. Ticks below section indicate kuls (40 within 6 miles); horizontal bars above, areas not cultivated.

than that of hill stations lying 2,000 ft. (610 m.) higher on the outer Himalayan ridges:

Temperature, °F

J.	F.	M.	A.	M.	J.	J.	A.	S.	O.	N.	D.	
30·7	33·0	45·1	55·7	63·9	69·9	73·0	70·8	64·0	53·2	44·0	36·3	Ra. 42·3 (23·5° C.)

Precipitation, inches

J.	F.	M.	A.	M.	J.	J.	A.	S.	O.	N.	D.	
2·7	2·8	3·6	3·8	2·3	1·5	2·2	2·3	1·6	1·2	0·4	1·5	Total 25·7 (653 mm.)

While the difference between the annual means at Simla (7,200 ft., 2,135 m.) and Srinagar is very small indeed, the January temperature at Simla is 8·1°F. (4·5°C.) higher than that at Srinagar, and those for February and March show little less excess; in July and August the position is almost exactly reversed, the range at Simla being only 28·1°F. (15·6°C.). Much of the precipitation is snow, and the régime shows a marked winter westerly influence, with a higher total in January–March than in the usual rainy season. It must be remembered that Srinagar is in the very bottom of the Vale, which as a whole receives 32–35 in., (813–889 mm.)

There is naturally a strong vertical zoning of climate and vegetation, and differences in exposure to insolation are most important. Immediately below the forest maize is the most important crop and walnut trees are numerous; at 7,000 ft. (2,135 m.) 'hardy and stunted' types of paddy come in, to be succeeded by the better paddy of the lower terraces and the marshy tracts where the streams wind along through groves of willows.

> 'The side valleys . . . have certain features in common. At the mouth of the valley lies the wide delta of fertile soil on which rice, plane-trees, mulberries and willows grow luxuriantly; a little higher up the land is terraced and rice still grows, while the slopes are ablaze with the wild indigo, till at about 5,000 feet the plane-tree gives place to the walnut, and rice to millets. On the south bank of the river endless forests stretch from the bottom of the valley to the peaks; and on the north bank, wherever a nook or corner is sheltered from the sun . . . pines and firs establish themselves. Further up . . . millets are replaced by buckwheat and Tibetan barley. Soon after this the useful birch-tree appears, and then come grass and glaciers, the country of the shepherds.'[15]

Agriculture

Agricultural figures are lacking for over four-fifths of Kashmir; of the remaining area about a quarter is cultivated, and a third of this quarter is in the Vale. Rice at lower and maize at higher levels are dominant. Wheat is also important, and the only other crops of much areal significance are linseed and rape.

Farming methods are very distinctive. Not much care (except the use of a rough rotation) is given to crops other than rice and garden produce. Rice is intensively

[15] *Kashmir Gaz.* (1909), 6. As a corrective, we may note a recent paper describing the fir and deodar forests as 'a sorry sight', with the *margs* ('alps') above and *karewas* below severely gullied through overgrazing. H. Singh, 'Land erosion in the Kashmir Valley', *Indian Forester*, 84/10 (1958), 617–22.

manured, sometimes by piling farmyard refuse at the irrigation entry, so that it is distributed over the field as liquid manure. The droppings of the animals in the winter, when they are kept indoors, are kept for the fields; in the spring sheep are folded on the fields, and turves cut from the marshy stream-banks are particularly useful. Near Srinagar the market gardeners use poudrette from the city's refuse. Rice seeds are pre-germinated in water; the labour of transplanting rice is rendered even more arduous than usual by the necessity of weeding out various hill grasses which only an expert can distinguish from paddy seedlings; four weedings are needed in broadcast sowing. Maize is grown in association with grazing, high yields being obtained by folding buffaloes and cattle on the fields; at lower levels it is grown mainly on the heavy peaty soils along the Jhelum. Dry crops, including a little cotton, are grown on the *karewas*, rape or mustard on soft reclaimed swamp soils. Near the limit of cultivation buck-wheat and *grim* – the naked Tibetan barley – are the only reliable food-grains; the former is also a useful stand-by lower down, as it can be sown late on almost any soil if the season seems likely to be unfavourable.

About half the cultivated area is irrigated. Practically all irrigation is by *kuls*, leats led off from the *karewas* streams, made and maintained by landowners or villagers; these are difficult to keep in good order where they run along the steep and erosion-liable *karewas* flanks or cross ravines in wooden aqueducts. Their numbers are astonishing (Figs. 14.3, 14.4). The mountain streams bring down good silt from the snow-melt, except where deforestation, as in the Sind valley, has led to sand-spreads. Springs are sometimes used for irrigation, but they bring no silt and their waters may be cold enough to affect plant growth adversely.

Agricultural rhythms are, of course, differentiated from those of the sub-continent as a whole by the cold winters, which also affect tillage. 'In March . . . the soil has perhaps been worked by the frosts and snow; but if, as is sometimes the case, no snow has fallen, it will be difficult work for the plough-bullocks, thin and poor after the long winter, to break up the soil.' With this dependence on the spring melt the aspect of the snow on the mountains is the cultivator's anxiously observed guide to the chances of the ensuing season. The agricultural calendar is roughly as follows:

March: ploughing, manuring with dung of winter
April: fertilizing with turves from stream-banks; paddy, linseed, and
             sesamum sown (kharif)
May–June: rape harvest; *grim* sown (above 7,000 ft., 2,135 m.)
June–July: paddy weeding; barley and wheat harvest (rabi)
July–Aug.:   linseed harvest
Aug.–Sept.: ploughing for rabi wheat and barley; *grim* harvest
Sept.:   ploughing for rape; rape sown
Sept.–Oct.: paddy and sesamum harvest; wheat sown
Oct.–Dec.:   barley and later wheat sown.

January and February are dead months. The shortness of the *grim* growing season will be noted.

The lakes have a peculiar economy of their own. 'They bear innumerable boats, from which fish are caught in skilfully manipulated throw-nets. Weeds are dredged up to provide fodder for the cattle, and water chestnuts and lotus roots for human food. And, as if such fertility were inadequate, sods of marshy earth are bound together into rafts heavy with manure, and these are moored in rows across the swamp to form floating gardens, so that the boundary between earth, air and water is made fruitful and bears the fiery red fruits of tomato plants.'[16]

More important, if less picturesque, is the formation of new land on the shallow lake-margins by planting willows in the water and filling up the compartment so formed with boatloads of lake-mud and weeds. These *demb* lands are used not only for fruit and vegetables, but even for rape, maize and tobacco.

The orchards of Kashmir provide the most valuable of its exports after timber; most temperate and sub-tropical fruits and nuts are grown. The most important fruit is probably the apricot, and the walnut is a source of lighting and cooking oil as well as a food. One of the main attractions of Kashmir to hard-drinking Moguls like Babur and Jahangir was its wine, but the vine has no longer its ancient fame, despite the establishment of a state vineyard with Bordeaux stocks. Finally we may note the cultivation of one or two *karewas* of the saffron crocus, in demand as a condiment and as a pigment for Hindu sect-marks. Minor crops include opium poppy and the recently introduced pyrethrum.[17]

Other occupations

Supplementary to agriculture proper are sericulture and pastoralism. By 1900 the former activity was decrepit as well as ancient, but the introduction of modern filatures has led to a wide extension of mulberry culture. The industry is now state-controlled to ensure quality. There is also, of course, a good deal of hand-loom weaving of silk, cotton and wool; silk is a major export.

The main pastoral activity is sheep-rearing; this is transhumant, the sheep live in winter beneath the human dwellings – adding to their warmth – and in summer are taken by professional shepherds to the high pastures above the tree-line; this is the *marg* common in place-names and strictly equivalent to the Swiss *alp*. Winter feed is willow and dried flag (Iris) leaves. After agriculture, wool production is probably the chief means of livelihood in Kashmir, employing full- or part-time some 300,000 people. The famous Cashmere shawl industry died a languishing death in the 1870s, but there is naturally a large cottage production of woollen clothing, blankets and rugs; felting is important also, though the Chinese occupation of Tibet has cut off supplies of the important

---

[16] G. E. Hutchinson, *The Clear Mirror* (1936), 102.

[17] Most of the details in this section are drawn from the full and fascinating account in the *Gazetteer* (41–63); and cf. C. D. Deshpande, 'Pampore: a reconnaissance study in land-use in the Kashmir Valley', *Bombay Geog. Mag.* 6–7 (1959), 81–88.

pashmina goat hair, and Srinagar has a large woollens factory. Mineral exploitation is insignificant, though a start has been made on the commercial exploitation from some of the *karewas* of lignite, which has been used locally by the villagers for years. Kashmiri wooden craft products are famous, but supplies of seasoned walnut, their main base, were largely destroyed in the fighting. The small cricket-bat industry relies largely on imported English willow; the plentiful local trees are diseased and degenerate, though new plantations are being made for fuel, fenceposts and honeycombs as well as bats. But tourist exploitation is still perhaps more lucrative than any other trade.

Srinagar

For this, of course, the capital Srinagar (295,084) is the centre: 'quaint' in itself, with its carved wooden architecture, immediately surrounded by the beautiful Mogul gardens and magnificent lake and river scenery, central for hunting and mountaineering, it is – on the surface – one of the most attractive cities in all Asia. But it has always been liable to fire and to flood, at times to earthquake; its site obviously leaves much to be desired from a sanitary point of view.[18] Nor, if report be true, are its citizens any more virtuous, in any direction, than they need be.

The factories of Srinagar are largely due to state enterprise, and make it the only industrial centre of the slightest note in Kashmir. But craft industries are important. Neglecting the obvious tourist lines – silver and copper work, wood-carving, papiermaché and lacquer – the leading crafts are probably carpet-weaving, embroidery and leather work: leather gear of various sorts is essential to transport in the mountains, and the products have a high standard of durability. The supply of hides and skins was large, as the Hindu orthodoxy of the ruling house prohibited cow-slaughter and so inflated the numbers of cattle. The production of high-grade rag paper was once important, but has declined before the growth of the Indian mill industry. Finally we may note the importance of water-borne traffic: much of the provisioning of the city is done by flat-bottomed boats which can carry up to 30 tons of cargo. The boatmen, particularly those who man the tourist house-boats, have a reputation for supplementing licit earnings by following the world's second oldest trade.

Much of the importance of the Vale, and hence of Srinagar, lay in its function as a staging-base on the Himalayan routes. The southern entries have already been mentioned; to the northwest the track to Gilgit and the Oxus by the Raj Diangan and Burzil Passes has been virtually blocked by the Cease Fire line. But the most important trade route, at least in normal times, leading either up the Indus into Tibet or across the Karakoram into Sinkiang, is that to the north-east by the Zoji La. At 11,578 ft. (3,545 m.) this is the lowest col on the main

[18] In the 1892 cholera epidemic 600 people died in one day 'and the only shops which remained open were those of the sellers of white cloth for winding sheets'. The total mortality was 5,781 of a population around 120,000 (*Gazetteer*, 119).

West Himalayan axis, a pass of the Maloja type with the steep ascent on the south: this is due to the Sind cutting back into the headwaters of the Dras, which lies on the drier side of the mountains and has much farther to go before it reaches 5,200 ft. (1,585 m.), the local base-level of the Sind. The route is now followed by an all-weather road to Kargil and Leh.

If anywhere on earth presents the semblance of the Happy Valley of *Rasselas*, it is the Vale of Kashmir; but however pleasant the prospects, the human history of the region has been less attractive. To begin with, it is probably over-populated; density in Anantnag (Srinagar) District is over 400 (and of course far higher in relation to cultivated area), and it is significant that sugar and grain come next to cotton goods in the Kashmiri import list. Beyond this it is hardly an exaggeration to say that the whole history of Kashmir for the last few centuries has been one of misgovernment and oppression, often deliberate, of the peasantry for the benefit of narrow Court cliques; nor was this tradition dead in this century. Now, however, India is pouring aid into Kashmir; Community Development is intensive. A new road from Jammu to Srinagar has helped to revive tourism. But lack of power resources – the *karewas* lignites are difficult to exploit – and isolation coupled with over-population are still the major problems. And a political question mark still hangs over the area, despite India's present political control and economic effort.[19]

'The trouble in Kashmir' stems finally from the simple fact that a population 77% Muslim was ruled by a family of the strictest Hindu orthodoxy, descendants of a particularly able and ruthless condottiere under the Sikhs, Gulab Singh of Jammu, who 'mediated' between British and Sikhs to his own profit. It is safe to say that at no time in the century's existence of the state have relations between the dominant Dogra Rajputs of Jammu and the Muslim majority been other than those of exploiters and exploited, to such an extent that until quite recently agricultural progress was still inhibited by the peasant's simple reflection that, if any profit resulted, the tax-gatherer would seize it.

With the removal of British rule the throne of Kashmir became more than shaky. Legally the ruler's right of adherence to India was unquestionable, and this is the basis of the Indian claim. The respective proportions of looting and liberation in the tribal incursions of 1947 cannot be evaluated, and the situation was worse confounded by the virtual war-within-a-war of the Punchis in support of their own ruler against the Dogras of Jammu. At present there is an uneasy truce, under United Nations supervision, along a cease-fire line which leaves India holding Jammu and part of Punch, all the Vale, and most of Ladakh, the rest being under a Pakistani 'Azad [Free] Kashmir' Government. It is impossible to assess fairly the work of the rival governments; either territory is in the full swing of rehabilitation and social reform, or stagnant and starving, according to the source of information so liberally supplied by either party.

[19] J. Dupuis, 'Les bassins intérieures du Kashmir et du Nepal', *Annales de Géographie*, 71e année, No. 384 (1962), 156–66; a stimulating comparative study.

Leaving the legal and moral issues aside, the economic disruption caused by the *de facto* partition along the Cease Fire line has been deplorable. The importance of Kashmir water to West Punjab, for both irrigation and power, has been stressed already; Kashmiri timber was also very important to West Punjab, and conversely had its main outlet there, since exploitation depended largely on rafting down the rivers which all flowed into the *western* Punjab. The Sialkot sports goods industry used Kashmir willow and resin. The import of salt for the Kashmir tanneries is also more costly from India than from the Salt Range mines, and Pakistan would probably find it easier to supply the food deficit than would India. Oil is essential for transport into the Vale, and Pakistanis claim that the natural supply would be from Attock or southwest Asia through Karachi.

The natural links of Kashmir are mainly with West Punjab. All roads are difficult to maintain, but the Jhelum route is really the only all-weather one. It is only 185 miles (298 km.) from Srinagar to Rawalpindi, but 250 (402 km.) to Amritsar, and the Indian route is partly impeded by snow while its sub-Himalayan stretch lies athwart the drainage of an area notoriously liable to gullying and landslips. Fruit and timber were the largest exports from Kashmir, and while Pakistan has far more potential resources in temperate fruits than has India, she is poor in timber.

The Kashmir assembly in 1957 declared the State an integral part of India; this action was specifically stated to be without prejudice to the claim for the entirety of Kashmir, and is regarded by the Indian Government as *chose jugée*, an internal affair on which the United Nations can and should have nothing to say. Eighteen years after the stormy events of 1947, the situation might be described as a stalemate, with India in effective control of much the larger and better-found part of Kashmir, and doing everything possible to emphasize her *de facto* government (as well as her claim *de jure*), especially her economic effort. Kashmir remains a poisonous irritant in Indo-Pakistani relations, costly and dangerous to these two great nations and (especially since the Chinese intervention and the apparent Pakistani acquiescence in Chinese claims) with implications of wider menace.

INDUS KOHISTAN AND GILGIT

Nanga Parbat and the gorges

Nanga Parbat, the mighty northwestern pillar of the Great Himalaya, is almost separated from the main mass by the valleys of the Kishen Ganga and the Astor, between which lies the Burzil Pass; and to the north and east it is moated by the deep gash of the Indus gorges. In several ways it differs from the main mass. 'Located at a structural interference of two major geanticlines, both of which have undergone repeated uplift in the Quaternary', it consists of a core of granitoid gneiss with a 'massive envelope' of sedimentary gneisses; the strike is north/ south (probably the result of its situation on the syntaxis) instead of the normal northwest/southeast of the Kashmir Himalaya. There are no signs of nappes here, but to the north late Tertiary and even early Quaternary sandstones are folded in a steep syncline along the Indus valley: 'thus this very young folding appears here locally in the crystalline inner zone.'[20]

The massif carries about 100 sq. miles (259 km²) of snow-fields, draining into small glaciers descending nearly 8,000 ft. (2,440 m.) below the snow-line. Several erosion platforms can be traced, especially notable at just over 13,000 ft. (3,960 m.) 'where the rounded and flattened ridges and broad rudimentary valleys, cut short in front, resemble the old morphology of the Deosai plateau'.[21] Yet perhaps no mountain in the world is quite so impressive; certainly not Everest, perhaps not even K2. This is due to the intense erosion around it: the land falls to the north by 23,100 ft. in 14½ miles, 7,041 m. in 22·6 km., and the falls to west and east are of nearly the same order. Vast moraines and talus slopes hardly soften a relief which includes precipices of 12,000–13,000 ft. (3,660–3,960 m.) nicked by tiny hanging valleys and glaciers.

Round this massif the Indus flows in gorges 15,000–17,000 ft. (4,572–5,182 m.) deep and only 12–16 miles wide. The floor itself is relatively wide and flattish, hot and arid, 'a desert embedded between icy gravels'. It was formerly fairly peopled, but ruined by the great flood of 1841 when the gorge was blocked by a landslide on the Hattu Pir cliff near the Astor confluence: the burst swept away a Sikh army on the river-bed at Attock. The Hattu Pir is 'scarred with the remains of the many difficultly aligned and skilfully built paths, most of which have fallen hundreds of feet into the river below. . . . A heavy rock, stone shoot, or sharp shower of rain, any one of these is enough to destroy the tenderly cared-for road.'[22] Round Bunji there are three to five gravel terraces lying on sands which seem to indicate a former lake – a point of some importance in connection with the Potwar erratics problem (below, 497).

This is Indus Kohistan – emphatically the 'land of mountains' in a mountainous land. In the tributary valleys are a few isolated villages, dependent on buckwheat and *grim*; in much of the gorge the walls are too steep to carry a track except at 4,000–5,000 ft. (1,220–1,525 m.) or more above the river, and communication – impossible in winter – is easier (*le mot juste?*) over the shoulders of the mountains.

The Astor valley marks the transition from the vivid colours of rock, field and wood in the Vale to the desolate outer marches of Kashmir. Agriculture in this dry valley is carried up to 9,000 ft. (2,745 m.) by little irrigation channels, but low temperatures render it precarious: wheat, barley, pulses, maize, buckwheat, lucerne, and other fodder crops are grown.

[20] de Terra, 231; P. Misch and W. Raechl in 'Scientific work of the German Himalaya Expedition to Nanga Parbat, 1934', *Himalayan Jnl* 7 (1935), 44–52.

[21] Raechl, *loc. cit.* 47–48.

[22] R. C. F. Schomberg, *Between the Oxus and the Indus* (London, 1935), 16–17; see pp. 29–30 for an amusing account of the difficulties of managing the swinging bridges – up to 100 yards long – made of birch- or willow-bark ropes.

Gilgit

Beyond the Indus lies Gilgit, and around it the Frontier Illaqas, which were more or less feudatory to Kashmir. Although we have it on the high authority of Holdich that where small parties of Buddhist pilgrims 'made their way with infinite pain and difficulty to the great monasteries of the Peshawar plains, no military force of any consequence ever has, or ever could, follow their foot-steps',[23] nervousness about Russian intentions led to the preservation of the long panhandle of Afghan territory, 15–25 miles (24–40 km.) wide, in Wakhan, the valley of the Ab-i-Panja branch of the Oxus, and at no point did the two great Empires actually touch.

Outside Gilgit itself the area is held by a congeries of petty tribal republics and chieftaincies of which Hunza is the most important; Schomberg gives them all (except Hunza and Yasin) a bad name for turbulence, murder, intrigue, avarice, dishonesty, laziness, stupidity, and general backwardness. The population is very slight, in Gilgit and the frontier some 120,000 in all on 18,000 sq. miles (46,620 km²); the density in Astor is 10, Gilgit proper 15, Frontier Illaqas 4. But in relation to cultivated area it is a different story – in 1901 the Gilgit density was 1,295. These are old figures, and probably little better than notional, but more recent data seem not to be available.

Settlement is usually on little terraces in the better valleys; one such is occupied by Gilgit itself, a nodal centre near the junction of the Gilgit and Hunza Rivers, which between them drain nearly the whole area between the Indus and the 20,000–22,000 ft. (6,095–6,705 m.) peaks of the Hindu Kush. At Gilgit rice and cotton are grown as well as the usual montane crops and fruits; higher up Yasin has even a tiny export of wheat and barley. Hunza is even better: 30–40 sq. miles (78–104 km²) of tiny terraced fields, orchards and poplars, and 'curling along the bleak stony hillsides' carefully engineered *kuls* provided with little tunnels for the escape of scree from the slopes above. 'All are of dry masonry, all have been built without scientific aid, with nothing more than industry, common sense, and the usual tools of a peasant; ibex horns were chiefly used.' Fruit culture is of the utmost importance to life in these valleys, and above all the apricot, according to Schomberg the sole diet for weeks on end.[24]

THE GREAT HIMALAYA AND THE ZASKAR RANGE

The Great Himalaya may be taken as commencing in the Indus bend; across the river, in Swat, the strike is swung round by the syntaxis and is practically at right

---

[23] *India* (1904), 105; but cf. Sir Aurel Stein, 'A Chinese expedition across the Pamirs and Hindukush, AD 747', *GJ* 59 (1922), 112–31. Lord Ronaldshay (*Lands of the Thunder-bolt* (London, 1923), 141) aptly calls Gilgit and Chitral 'listening-posts in the vast system of natural defences which keep silent and eternal watch over the teeming plains of Hindu-stan.'

[24] Schomberg, *op. cit.* 59–60, 112–13.

angles to the northwest/southeast trend of the main range. From the Zoji La to the Indus the really high ground (over 15,000 ft., 4,570 m.) is broken into a number of distinct massifs, of which Nanga Parbat is by far the most conspicuous; east of the Zoji La the passes are nowhere below 15,000 ft. until the great break of the Sutlej/Spiti valley – a distance of 250 miles (402 km.) in which there are several peaks over 21,000 ft. (6,400 m.). To the south is the eastern continuation of the Pir Panjal (here 15,000–18,000 ft., 4,572–5,486 m.) beyond the Chandra-upper Chenab valley, and south again the Dhaoladhar (10,000–15,000 ft., 3,048–4,572 m.) with the upper Ravi between it and the Pir Panjal; the Beas itself as a whole cuts across the trend, with longitudinal stretches. Between the Great Himalaya and the Indus the same lines are well shown in the Zaskar Range[25] and its reticulate drainage pattern, e.g. the Southern Shigar, the headstream of the Zaskar River, and the valleys of inland drainage in Rupshu.

'As a tectonic unit, the Great Himalaya is made up of the roots of the Kashmir nappe, the principal geanticline within the main Himalayan geosyncline, consisting of the Archaean and pre-Cambrian sedimentary rocks together with large bodies of intrusive granites and basic masses.'[26] The granitic intrusions are post-Cretaceous, perhaps associated with the actual orogeny, and the thrusts of this area are not comparable with the great nappes of the central and eastern Himalaya, so far as is yet known.

The area north of the main axis is more interesting. The higher Zaskar peaks are seated upon a broad plateau-like range, much dissected, at about 19,500 ft. (5,945 m.). More definite erosion surfaces are found in Rupshu, round the enclosed basin of Tso Morari, at 16,600 ft. (5,060 m.), and in the northwest the Deosai Plains lie at about 13,000 ft. (3,960 m.). It is probable that these areas of rolling mature or late-mature terrain are merely the clearest expression of platforms of much greater extent – in Deosai the country intermediate between the deeper valleys and the 15,000-ft.-plus massifs from Nanga Parbat to the Zoji, and possibly connected with the Pir Panjal surface south of the Vale.[27]

The human geography is naturally almost nil. In the wide open valleys of Rupshu – the lowest are around 13,500 ft. (4,115 m.) – some barley is grown, and here, above Tso Morari, is Korzok, at 15,000 ft claimed as the highest agricultural settlement in the world.[28] A little borax is produced from the saline lakes. Zaskar also has its patches of cultivation, and is noted for its hardy ponies. The Deosai Plains 'are mournful stretches of grass and stones, with many a bog

[25] Range nomenclature as on SOI 1/1M sheets 43 (Srinagar), 52 (Leh), 53 (Delhi); but Zaskar is often spelt Zanskar, Dhaoladhar Dhauladhar (both the latter in SOI.).

[26] D. N. Wadia, op. cit. (1961), 426.

[27] de Terra, 'Physiographic results of a recent survey in Little Tibet', GR 24 (1934), 12–41; refces at 21, 34. From now on citations from de Terra refer to this paper.

[28] According to S. D. Pant (The Social Economy of the Himalayans (London, 1935), 9, 41) the highest settlement of any description is the pastoral steading of Lwan, north of the Kumaon Himalaya at 19,000 ft. (5,791 m.).

difficult to cross, and uninhabited but for the marmots, an occasional bear, and swarms of big black gnats. The absence of wood for fuel, the distance from human habitations, and local superstitions regarding "the devil's place" prevent the people from using the pastures.' Such population as there is in the Himalaya/ Zaskar region is largely nomadic, and the shepherds of Rupshu 'complain bitterly of the heat of Leh' – average annual temperature 40·9°F. (9·9°C.)![29]

LADAKH AND BALTISTAN: THE INDUS FURROW

The Indus and the Ladakh Range: 'Little Tibet'

The Indus rises on the northern flanks of the Kailas Range, and flows in a great northerly curve until it breaks through that range to the Gartang confluence in the narrow Gartang–Indus corridor continuing the line of the main river through Kashmir between the Kailas and eastern Ladakh ranges. This long stretch is generally on a straight southeast–northwest course and in a longitudinal valley, but south of Lake Panggong it makes a sharp bend and cuts through the Ladakh Range,[30] which it pierces again above the Shyok confluence. Then the Gilgit joins it at Bunji and it turns south to round Nanga Parbat. This great furrow is on the whole fairly graded; from the Gartang confluence to Bunji (*c.* 450 miles, 724 km.) the fall is only from *c.* 13,800 to 4,600 ft. (4,205–1,400 m.) or about 20 ft. per mile. Alluvial flats are found in the extreme east of its Kashmir course, at about 13,800 ft. In the east – Ladakh proper – the whole catchment as well as the immediate valley is narrow, constricted between the closed basins of Pang-gong and Morari; but in Baltistan the catchment widens somewhat. At Skardu where the Northern Shigar comes in a few miles below the Shyok, the Indus is often over 500 ft. (152 m.) wide and 9–10 ft. deep even in winter.

The Ladakh Range between the two Indus gaps forms a remarkably straight wall for some 190 miles (306 km.): Indus and Shyok flow parallel 25–30 miles apart, and between them the range rises 10,000 ft. or more to a rather even crest at 19,000 ft. (5,790 m.). Again the flanks, gentler on the north, carry evidences of a pre-glacial mature relief: 'at 17,450 ft. [5,450 m.] a rolling surface with valleys one to two miles in width separated by low divides . . . head-waters moving sluggishly around sand bars until they break through the terminal moraine walls and fall at a rate of 1,600 ft. per mile through boulder-choked gorges.' The relations between the abrupt steps – often of 1,000 ft. (305 m.) – in the valley floors and the moraines indicate that these are old erosion levels, independent of ice action, but affected by inter-glacial uplift. The pre-glacial Indus valley floor 'must have been at the level of the flat spurs, which now are 3,000 to 4,000 ft. [915–1,220 m.] above the valley'.[31] The valley and foothills are

---

[29] *Kashmir Gaz.* 3, 105.
[30] de Terra, however, thinks that the Range bends sharply from northwest/southwest to west/east just here (18–19, 22, 40 and Fig. 6), and his arguments seem valid. But for convenience the accepted nomenclature of the SOI maps is retained.
[31] de Terra, 33–36.

largely formed of Eocene beds, dissected into sharp ridges which contrast strongly with the bolder granite forms of the mountain wall.

Climate

The climate of Ladakh may be illustrated by the figures for Leh, on a fan in the Indus valley at 11,500 ft. (3,505 m.):

Temperature, °F

J.	F.	M.	A.	M.	J.	J.	A.	S.	O.	N.	D.	
17·3	18·8	30·9	42·9	49·8	57·8	62·6	61·0	53·7	42·7	32·1	22·1	Ra. 45·3 (25·2° C.)

Precipitation, inches

J.	F.	M.	A.	M.	J.	J.	A.	S.	O.	N.	D.	
0·4	0·3	0·3	0·2	0·2	0·2	0·5	0·5	0·3	0·2	0·0	0·2	Total 3·2 (81 mm.)

The absolute minimum is about −19°F. (−28·3°C.); mean annual pressure 20 in.; mean relative humidity *c.* 40% from May to November, *c.* 70% in winter.[32] Farther west, around Skardu, conditions are a little less extreme. In the thin atmosphere insolation and radiation alike take place at an extreme tempo; mechanical disintegration of the rocks is rapid, and the saying that a bare-headed man with his feet in the shade can get sunstroke and frostbite simultaneously is hardly an exaggeration. Aspect and diurnal variation are of the greatest importance; many streams even in summer flow for only a few hours a day when the ice melts in their gravel beds. Vegetation is extremely thin: a few bushes, a kind of furze (*burtse*), stunted cedars, willows, alpine pasture: 'timber and fuel are the most pressing wants of the people.'

But it must be remembered that here climate, like nearly everything else, is 'vertical' and the mountains receive a fair precipitation: 'the vertical diversity of the climate makes human life possible in Indian Tibet. To the east, where the mountain ranges die out, the country is too dry for any permanent settlement.'[33] Without the glaciers and snow-fields even the west would be a desert; and even so the life of the region is in a sense an oasis and caravan life.

The human response

Culturally, this is Tibetan rather than Indian or Pakistani: Baltistan, it is true, is mainly Muslim, but Ladakh proper is solidly Buddhist, and Buddhist culture extends as far west as Kargil in the Dras valley.

The Indus furrow is in general broken, rocky, barren and dry. But every snow-fed tributary builds its fan, and where there is enough water the stream is split into radiating channels: 'the living greens of apricots, willow trees, and little fields of barley make the surrounding desert appear uniformly parched and brown.' East of Leh the Indus flows for 20 miles along a fault which brings it against the softer Eocene rocks; here there is a little alluvial plain and the fans 'end abruptly against swampy fields, so that a man can stand with one foot in a desert and the other on damp green grass'. This is perhaps the best-peopled part

[32] W. G. Kendrew, *The Climates of the Continents* (1937 ed.), 150–1.
[33] G. E. Hutchinson, *op. cit.* 127–8.

of the region, which has an average density of 4. The plain is dominated by Hemis Gompa, the most important Buddhist monastery of Little Tibet.

Beardless *grim* barley is the dominant crop, and can be grown to nearly 15,000 ft. (4,570 m.); at lower altitudes two crops a year may be possible, as the plant matures very quickly. Wheat, buckwheat, pulses, roots and lucerne are grown in sandy carefully-manured soils; new soil is brought to the fields from hillside pockets, or sprinkled on the snow to melt it when it lies late. Ploughing and transport are mostly by the *dzo*, the offspring of the cow and the yak bull. The grain is ground by water-mills of rough but ingenious construction.[34]

The people are in part nomadic – the Champa herders of sheep and yaks – but the Ladakhis proper are for the most part settled agriculturalists. Although they are often in debt to the monasteries, these are apparently very amenable creditors, and the peasantry is on the whole much more prosperous than the Muslim Baltis down-river; there seems little doubt that this is mainly due to the check on population provided by polyandry and monasticism. The whole atmosphere is Mahayana Buddhist, and the most prominent features of the cultural landscape, after the irrigated fans, are the monasteries, the innumerable *chorten* shrines, prayer wheels, fluttering streamers to affright the demons, and the long piles of *mani* stones on the approaches to villages: 'heaps of rubble, shaped like sheds, with a width of twenty feet, a height of five or six, and a length of from fifty to a thousand . . . covered with hundreds of flat stones on each one of which the lamas had inscribed the universal *om mani padma hum*.'[35] Hard as life is, swayed by the most fantastic demonolatry, the people have their full share of the usual Buddhist – or Mongol – cheerful good-fellowship, and are not without amenities: festivals in the winter and in the short slack season as the barley grows, a living and intricate religious art of painting and dance.

In normal times the transit trade was an important source of income: through Skardu lies the trail to the Muztagh Pass and Kashgar; at Leh, a pleasant little caravanserai town, converge the roads from the Zoji La and the high Himachal Pradesh passes, the Indus road into Tibet itself and eventually to Lhasa, and the route via the Saser and Karakoram Passes (17,480 and 18,290 ft., 5,335 and 5,580 m.) into Sinkiang. Leh owes its importance mainly to the unusual size of its fan – 5 miles wide and 1,000 ft. thick; purely Tibetan in aspect, it is dominated by the palace of the old Ladakhi kings, a miniature of the Potala at Lhasa.[36] But the Sinkiang trade has been declining for years with the increasing pull of Soviet Asia, and the war in Kashmir and the Chinese occupation of the Karakoram glacis have disrupted the external contacts of this remote and fascinating little world.[37]

---

[34] Details and illustration in Hutchinson, *op. cit.* 91–94.
[35] E. Huntington, *The Pulse of Asia* (NY, 1907), 58–60; cf. G. Dainelli, *Buddhists and Glaciers of Western Tibet* (London, 1933), 41–90, an admirably vivid description.
[36] See plate at p. 74 of Dainelli, *op. cit.*
[37] This is dealt with in M. Geary, 'Western Tibet' (London Ph.D. thesis, 1948) – a full and admirable study which I have regretfully refrained from using for reasons of space.

THE KARAKORAM

Here, rather than on the Pamirs, is the Roof of the World, a mass of rock and ice extending for 250 miles (402 km.) from the Shyok to the Hunza, with the greatest assemblage in the world of giant peaks – 33 over 24,000 ft. (7,315 m.) – culminating in the tremendous keeps of the three Gasherbrum summits, all over 26,000 ft. (7,925 m.) and finally K2 itself (Fig. 14.5). K2 (Mt Godwin Austen) is an almost regular cone of ice and limestone on a granite/gneiss base; at 28,250 ft. (8,610 m.) it is exceeded only by Everest, but the latter has no such spectacular

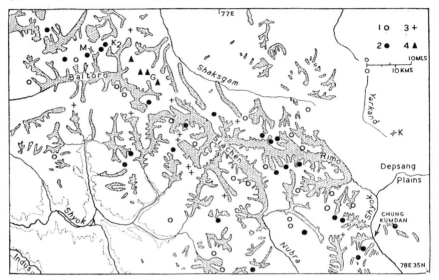

FIG 14.5 KARAKORAM: PEAKS AND GLACIERS. Glaciers dotted, dotted line 10,000 ft. contour. M, Muztagh Pass; K, Karakoram Pass; G, Gasherbrum peaks. 1, peaks 20–22,000 ft.; 2, 22–24,000; 3, 24–26,000; 4, 26–28,000; K2, 28,250 ft. Based on RGS map *The Karakoram* (1/750,000, 1939).

company of high peaks around it, and 'above all it does not display such an immensity of silence and desolation'.[38] The very passes are rarely lower than the summit of Mt Blanc and several are over 18,000 ft. (5,485 m.); though some of those shown on the map are probably topographical cols rather than passes in a real sense, the West Muztagh, at 19,030 ft. (5,800 m.) is certainly the highest trade route in the world. The name Karakoram means 'black gravel' and has been extended from the relatively subdued terrain – at 18,000–20,000 ft.! – around the Karakoram Pass in the east.[39] Geomorphologically the region is intensely interesting; its human geography is scanty, but what there is may fairly be called heroic.

[38] F. Grenard, *Haute Asie* (*Géographie Universelle*, Colin, Paris (1939) T. VIII), 343.
[39] Heights and range-names in this section from the beautiful map of the Karakoram (1/750,000) published by the Royal Geographical Society.

As we have seen (Chapter 1, pp. 29–35), the Karakoram is probably much older than the Himalaya, as shown for example by the absence of Tertiary sediments between Ladakh and the northern flank of the Kun Lun. Its actual relations with the other ranges of the great orogeny remain obscure; to the northwest the Karakoram Ranges abut on to the Pamir/Hindu Kush in a country of very confused topography, while their continuation to the southeast is still debateable, but probably via the Panggong Range into the Kailas. The divergence of Himalayan and Karakoram trends is most clearly seen north of the Shyok, but de Terra, who regards the Ladakh Range as the first member of the Karakoram system, draws attention to the swing from northwest/southeast to west/east about 78° 35′ E in all four of his Karakoram Ranges – Ladakh, Panggong, Karakoram/Chang-chenmo and Karakoram/Lingtzi-tang. This is in some degree paralleled by the Great Himalaya itself, and is shown very clearly in the outline of Panggong Lake, which apparently occupies a rift. The whole may well be controlled by the hidden margin of Gondwanaland.

Huntington noted that 'the deep young inner gorge of the Shyok River grows shallower [to the north] and finally merges into the upland plain of Depsang',[40] and de Terra and others have refined on the earlier concept of a vast peneplain dissected as a result of one major uplift; at least four erosion levels may be traced between the Muztagh peaks (c. 23,800 ft., 7,255 m.) and the Deosai/Pir Panjal platforms. The present drainage pattern is distinctly peculiar, especially in the Shyok, Nubra, Chang-chenmo and Harong valleys; the Chang-chenmo in particular is a misfit, and there is also the through valley from Panggong to the Indus with its summit only 1,600 ft. (488 m.) above the lake at 13,900 (4,240 m.). Biological observations strongly support de Terra's view that all the valleys originally drained out to the southeast; Hutchinson draws attention to the distribution of the hill barbel in the headwaters of Oxus, Indus, Tsang-po, Mekong, Yangtse, Hwang-ho, and the streams of the great enclosed basins of central Asia:[41]

> 'But a grander event than simple river-capture must be sought . . . to explain the similarity of the inhabitants of the Indus and the Tsang-po. The flat-edged shoulders of the Chang-chenmo mountains, where butterflies circle around pinnacles of rock, suggest the nature of this occurrence, though they lie aridly in the air, far above the homes of the few fishes that inhabit the stream below. Such flat ridges represent the levels of the valley floors before the last upward movements of the mountains. . . . The remains of such valley floors may be found throughout Indian Tibet. They all record the same history. All the rivers of the land ran toward the Tibetan plateau. . . . Not until quite recent times, when the mountains rose high enough to cut off the rain from the inner deserts of Central Asia, were the more northern of these streams

[40] Op. cit. 78; de Terra (1934), passim.
[41] G. E. Hutchinson, 'Limnological Studies at High Altitudes in Ladakh', Nature (New Series), 77 (1933), 497–500; but less technically and more vividly in The Clear Mirror (Cambridge, 1936), 148–52, from which I quote.

dried up. Then across the ever-growing Himalayas, gorges were cut . . . draining away the waters of the older rivers. In this manner erosion and earth movements have moulded the pattern of the present Indus and have cut out the path by which the traveller enters the western confines of Tibet.'

The physical characteristics of the Karakoram glaciers have already been discussed (above, 37–38); we may note further the contrast between the generally clear ice of the eastern Himalayan glaciers, girdled by forest and alp, and the Karakoram icestreams set in barren disintegrating rock and hidden beneath a mass of debris and wind-borne dust. The rivers emerging from their snouts flow over, or more often through and under, great ribbons of shingle. In winter, of course, the entire landscape is frozen, rigid, dead; in summer the streams wake only when the weather is clear. Cloudiness reduces evaporation, and the cold drizzly rain melts little snow; but with a few hours' sun the streams come down in sudden dangerous freshets. The Shyok itself, 'a clear rushing stream thirty feet wide', is intermittent in this fashion: 'We looked again, but there was no river. Yet even as we were talking about it, a new stream came pouring down a dry channel, a red muddy flood of freshly melted snow'.[42]

There is, however, much evidence, morainic and other, of significant climatic change. Panggong at present consists of several lakes separated by deltaic fans, and for the most part is saline; there is no outlet. But beaches at various levels up to 200 ft. (61 m.) bear witness to great oscillations, the most notable of which (in the Riss-Würm interglacial) must have allowed it to drain into the Shyok; the tendency has been to desiccation, not without fluctuations. Thus the patina on a palaeolithic artefact from Kargil speaks of aridity, while the representation of deer (with yaks and ibexes) on the sculptured rock at Tankse in the Harong valley suggests that within very recent times conditions have been more favourable to human activity; no deer are now found nearer than the Vale. There was a drier period at Panggong in the last century, but in other places there seems to have been no significant change, to judge from patches of dead ice which have not altered much since 1848.[43]

Baltistan, the country between the Northern Shigar and the Nubra, is slightly more favoured than Ladakh, with c. 6 in. (152 mm.) precipitation and more glaciers; but it is still very harsh. The valleys at 8,000–10,000 ft. (2,440–3,050 m.) have a few patches of pine and deodar on the slopes, willow and poplar along the streams. Agriculture depends on the snow, which lies from mid-December to mid-March; in winter many villages are reached by the sun for barely an hour or two a day, but in summer the heat in the narrow rock-walled valleys – especially around Skardu – is intense. The usual crops, with ordinary and naked barley prominent, are grown, a spring and an autumn crop where water is sufficient. Lucerne, carefully tended, is important, but except for intensive manuring of the sandy soils farming is extremely primitive, and rotations unknown. The hot

[42] Huntington, *op. cit.* 74.
[43] Cf. also T. Longstaff, *This My Voyage* (1950), 165.

summer enables a wide variety of fruits – peaches, melons, grapes, above all apricots – and even a little tobacco to be grown. But the absence of the demographically restrictive social institutions of Ladakh keeps the Baltis miserably poor. Here and there washing for alluvial gold ekes out incomes a little, or at least enables revenue demands to be met.

To the east conditions get progressively worse. Around Panggong there are a few fields of barley and peas on the fans at 14,000 ft. (4,265 m.) or a little more; at Tankse 'the few houses that constitute the village seem to hide behind a little grove of willow trees planted on one side of a stream, as if these trees were the greatest treasure of a place that wished to put up a brave front, a green and damp façade, to the hostile dry world before it'. But on the plateaus northeast of Panggong even pastoralism is difficult. The Chang-chenmo valley has some vegetation: tamarisks on the floodplain, *burtse* on the slopes, and just below the snowline some flower plants and patches of grass, shared by tame yaks and wild asses. Here and there hot springs 'water the gravelly plains into producing a little green grass . . . so precious that each patch has a name'.[44]

Yet this most negative of regions has its place in human history; and today, alas, more than ever. The old trade to Yarkand and Kashgar is dead or dying, but at the hands of man himself: politics in Sinkiang and Kashmir are responsible for its decay, not the desolate leagues of rock and ice nor the murderous winds of the Karakoram. The passes are open for only five or six months of the twelve; but over them, carried on yaks or even sheep, travelled jade, hemp and silk from China; from India goods from the bazaars of Srinagar and Amritsar, sugar and salt; borax from the dead lakes of Rupshu. Goods of less bulk, but to many of highest value, also traversed this, one of the strangest pilgrim routes of the world. Chinese disciples of the Enlightened One, seeking the shrines of Peshawar and Sarnath and Buddh Gaya or the libraries of Taxila, fought their bitter way over these savage gables of the world; and here too came Christian men, perhaps fleeing from the tide of Islam, perhaps couriers of long-forgotten churches. The great boulder of Tankse bears cryptic testimony to other changes than those of climate. A cross and a long inscription in Soghdian tell of the passage of a Nestorian Christian on the road to Tibet; two words, one unique and untranslateable, of Tokharian also carry the sign of the cross. On another face of the rock the name of Jesus lies among the symbols of Buddhism, dated in the Tibetan manner 'the year of the earth-tiger'; but what year, what century even, cannot be told. Can there be in the world a monument more moving than this rock, in solitude and mystery eternally spelling out its riddle of men who came this way on errands for ever unknown, and rested awhile, and are no more?

And it is in Aksai Chin, the northern glacis of the Karakoram itself, that what is probably the most serious Chinese encroachment has taken place. The area involved is about 15,000 sq. miles (38,850 km²) and in itself is obviously about as desolate a tract as could be found on the earth's surface. It has, however, a very

[44] Hutchinson, *op. cit.* 106–7, 128–38. For the facts of the next paragraph, *ibid.* 108–11.

material value to China, since it forms a salient breaking across a possible link between Sinkiang and Tibet; and here indeed the Chinese have constructed a military road. Whatever the strictly legal aspects of the dispute, it seems clear that this material fact of geopolitics lies at the origin – at any rate the proximate origin – of the whole conflict.

BIBLIOGRAPHICAL NOTE

The Himalayas have attracted a voluminous literature, and this is especially true of Kashmir, the Karakoram, and the greater peaks. Much even of the mountaineering narratives is of little geographical value; exception must be made for the records of the Italian expeditions, especially that of de Filippi on which Dainelli did his admirable glaciological work; but this I know only through de Terra. It is regrettable that, except for Heron's geological contributions, the official *Sketch of the Geography and Geology of the Himalaya Mountains and Tibet* (Hayden, Burrard, and Heron, n.d., 2nd ed., 1933) shows a less than modest acquaintance with modern geographical ideas, and, while it contains an immense mass of facts, is perhaps the most incoherent scientific work ever put out by authorities of repute.

Of the travel books, those of Huntington and Dainelli are perhaps the most useful. *The Geographical Journal* contains many papers, of which those dealing with the Karakoram are the most important (see note to Chapter 1 above). In the *Himalayan Journal* Professor Kenneth Mason's glaciological studies are especially valuable. Among papers not cited in the text are D. N. Wadia, 'The geology of Poonch' (*Mem. GSI* 51 (1928), 185–370), and 'Note on the geology of Nanga Parbat' (*Rec. GSI* 66 (1932–33), 212–34); and de Terra's important general paper, 'Himalayan and Alpine Orogenies', in *Report of the XVth International Geological Congress*, Vol. 2 (1936), 859–72.

A special word is due to two remarkable books. H. de Terra and T. T. Paterson, *Studies on the Ice Age in India* (Carnegie Institution of Washington, 1939) is indispensable, not least for its splendid series of 56 plates and 193 text figures. In an unclassifiable class is G. E. Hutchinson, *The Clear Mirror: A Pattern of Life in Goa and in Indian Tibet* (Cambridge, 1936): a mannered but beautiful style, an extraordinary range of allusion, and careful scientific observation combine to form a strange but wholly satisfying work of art.

On the Kashmir problem, see M. Brecher, *The Struggle for Kashmir* (Univ. of Toronto Press, 1953), and on the Sino-Indian boundaries, M. W. Fisher, L. E. Rose, and R. A. Huttenback, *Himalayan Battleground* (Pall Mall Press, London, 1963) and A. Lamb, *The China-India Border* (OUP/RIIA, 1964), and the review of both books by Sir Olaf Caroe, *GJ* 130 (1964), 273–5.

CHAPTER 15

The Himalayas: Central and Eastern
(Regions VI and VII)

For reasons discussed at the beginning of the previous chapter, any division of the Himalayas on a workable scale is likely to be to some extent arbitrary. Once the more massive zoning of Kashmir and the Karakoram is left behind, the arc of 1,300 miles (2,090 km.) from the Ravi to the Brahmaputra gorges is built up of longitudinal belts, some very narrow, cut across by the human groupings: some compromise between the human and the physical is thus necessary, and it is convenient to use even political criteria, of course within the major frame of the mountain mass. Two excursions are necessary. The Tibetan boundary in Ladakh cuts across physical trends, but southwards it often lies south of the crest; the Sutlej valley, for example, cannot be understood if cut short at Spiti. In the south the terai/bhabar strip can by no stretch of the imagination be considered montane, yet it is genetically the creation of the mountains, the boundaries of the Himalayan political units generally lie within this formerly very negative tract, and its life has intimate links with both plain and mountain. It must thus receive consideration both as the glacis of the Siwaliks and the selvedge of the plains, and we must transgress in the north the political, in the south the physical boundary.

In strict theory these procedures may be only doubtfully legitimate, but the succeeding pages attempt, at least by implication, a pragmatic justification.

Before turning to our *ad hoc* divisions, we may note their place in the general human setting. Between the Buddhism of Ladakh and that, much modified, of Nepal is a broad salient of almost completely Hindu territory. Himachal Pradesh was a congeries of petty states, the holdings of Pahari (= hill) Rajput chiefs driven there when the Muslims forced the Delhi gate and so split the Rajput domain. In Kumaon the ethnic complex is more strongly tinged by Mongoloid strains, but except in the extremest north the whole texture of life is Hindu. In Nepal Buddhism still lives, whether surviving from the days when Asoka held sway there, or creeping down from Tibet; this is perhaps a function of the agricultural bases offered by large longitudinal valleys, together with the defensive curtain of the exceedingly malarial terai. In Sikkim and Bhután Buddhism is the ruling faith. Beyond, in the Himalayan fringe of Assam, the pattern of life is culturally tribal and animist, the ethnic stocks Mongol.

451

We may then divide the whole area as follows:

Central Himalaya		Eastern Himalaya	
1. Himachal Pradesh	VI	1. Kosi basin (eastern Nepal)	VII
2. Kumaon		2. Tista and Chumbi Valleys	
3. Nepal		3. Bhután and Assam Himalayas	

For convenience, the Assam Himalayas are treated in Chapter 20.

CENTRAL HIMALAYA

HIMACHAL PRADESH

Despite recent simplifications, the territorial arrangement of this area remains annoyingly complex, owing mainly to the separation of Chamba from the main area of Himachal Pradesh by the hour-glass shaped East Punjab District of Kangra; the region also includes a narrow Siwalik strip of Hoshiarpur District, East Punjab. The total area is about 18,000 sq. miles (46,620 km²) with over 2,500,000 people.

Physical features

There is the usual longitudinal arrangement dependent on the parallel Himalayan structures: the Siwaliks, here with a remarkably even crest at 2,000–3,000 ft. (610–915 m.) but largely deforested and savagely eroded, feeding the *chos* torrents which bring ruin to the plains below (Fig. 18.1); the tangled mass of intermediate spurs up to 7,000–9,000 ft. (2,135–2,745 m.); the 'Lesser Himalaya', here forming a definite range, the Dhaoladhar (12,000–15,000 ft. 3,660–4,570 m.) which separates the longitudinal sections of Beas and Ravi, the latter in turn walled off by the continuation of the Pir Panjal from the long northwest/southeast extension of the Chenab in the Chandra valley; finally the Great Himalaya, which on the whole is lower and more broken here than in eastern Kashmir or in Kumaon.

South of the crystalline core in the Great Himalaya the rocks are exceedingly varied: slates, phyllites, schists, quartzites, crystalline limestones, for the most part, probably, of Dharwarian and Vindhyan (Huronian and Torridonian) age. They are arranged in a great series of nappes: 'Four over-thrusts are noted which have trespassed over the 64 miles (103 km.) broad Upper Tertiary area of Kangra and restricted it to 16 miles at Solon' south of Simla. Simla itself lies on a klippe, with the Tertiaries exposed in a great window to the north, between Simla and the Sutlej.'[1] Confused as the topography is in detail, old erosion levels are everywhere perceptible.

The layout of the Ravi and Beas valleys is similar to that of the Chenab, and, presumably, so is their genetic history, whatever it may be. At the head of the Beas, however, the Kulu valley is nearly transverse to the main trends.

[1] D. N. Wadia, *Geology of India* (Macmillan, London, 3rd ed. revised, 1961), 421–5 and Fig. 43.

The Sutlej

Very different from these rivers is the Sutlej, which breaks right through both the Great Himalaya and the Zaskar Ranges,[2] thus forming perhaps the most striking physical feature of the region (Fig. 15.1). As we have seen (Chapter 1), Davies holds that the Sutlej is a young river, developed by collapse along a line of weakness – a Gondwana trough continued by the line of the Ghaggar (below, 536) and doubtful as some of his arguments seem, the great cleft, 5,000–7,000 ft.

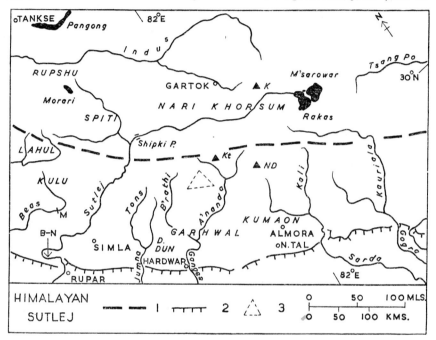

FIG 15.1 THE HIMALAYAN SUTLEJ. 1, Gt Himalaya; 2, Siwalik front; 3, Gangotri–Kedarnath–Badrinath peaks. K, Kailas; Kt, Kamet; ND, Nanda Devi; M, Mandi; B-N, Bhakra–Nangal dams.

deep and 100 miles long (1,525–3,570 m., 161 km.) in a straight line from north of Simla to Shipki, bears all the marks of youth, in strong contrast to its upper valley in Hundes or Nari Khorsum (Tibet). This is a broad arid basin at 14,000–16,000 ft. (4,270–4,880 m.) filled with detritus in which the glacier-fed river has cut a canyon said to be 3,000 ft. (915 m.) deep in places; at one point the Sutlej/Karnali watershed is reported to be level alluvium. The fall of the river itself is steep enough and it has cut 600–700 ft. (180–215 m.) deeper than its neighbours Beas and Giri (Yamuna). Despite the fact that Heim and Gansser claim that 'it has long been known that the Sutlej has ceased to derive any of its water' from Rakas Tal and Manasarowar, owing to depression, it seems almost certain that the

[2] And the Ladakh Range also, if Gurla Mandhata is taken as its southeast culmination.

feeders of these lakes are in fact its sources. The large aggraded basin with the obvious youthful incision of the Sutlej itself certainly looks very much like capture of old Indus waters.[3]

Between the Zaskar and Great Himalaya crossings the Sutlej has cut a gorge up to 3,000–4,000 ft. (915–1,220 m.) deep, narrower in quartzose granites, opening out into inhabited basins on weaker schists;[4] in this stretch it receives the Spiti from the northwest, which leads us back to Rupshu. Here, too, the river is sunk deep between alluvial terraces; 'the upper basin of the Spiti, in Rupshu, has been separated by local uplift combined with the accumulation of detritus: it has only enclosed lakes', of which the most important is Tso Morari.[5]

Climate

The montane climates are extremely diverse according to aspect and elevation. In Kangra the Dhaoladhar has over 100 in. (2,540 mm.) of precipitation, but a little to the north 'two or three weeks of mist and drizzle represent the monsoon'. Kulu has 30–40 in. (762–1,016 mm.), but the Sutlej gorges, transverse to the monsoon currents, are very dry, and in Spiti the scanty precipitation is almost entirely snow. Simla, at 7,250 ft. (2,210 m.), represents fairly well the outer hills:

Temperature, °F.

J.	F.	M.	A.	M.	J.	J.	A.	S.	O.	N.	D.	
38·8	40·6	51·5	59·3	66·0	66·9	64·3	62·8	60·9	56·7	50·1	43·4	Ra. 28·1 (15·6° C.)

Precipitation, inches

J.	F.	M.	A.	M.	J.	J.	A.	S.	O.	N.	D.	
2·5	2·7	2·7	2·3	2·8	7·2	17·0	17·4	5·9	1·0	0·5	1·0	Total 63·7 (1,618 mm.)

Economy and settlement

Most of the population consists of settled agriculturalists, with pastoralism and caravan trading becoming progressively more important to the north.[6] Agricultural rhythms in the higher areas are largely controlled by snowfall: in Lahul

[3] On the Sutlej problem see: Burrard, Hayden and Heron (1934), 227–32; L. M. Davies, 'Geographical changes in North-West India', *Proceedings 6th Pacific Science Congress* (1940); Heim and Gansser 'Central Himalaya', in *Mem. Soc. Helvetique des Sciences Naturelles*, Zurich, 73 (1939), 96, 212; Swami Pranavananda, 'The Sources of the Brahmaputra, Indus, Sutlej and Karnali', *GJ* 102 (1939), 126–35, an admirable paper full of good logic and convincingly circumstantial detail. For the Beas (Kulu), see S. L. Kayastha, 'The Himalayan Beas Basin: A hydrographical study', *NGJI* 1/1 (1955), 11–25.
[4] G. S. Puri, 'Soil and water conservation problems of the Bashahr Himalaya', *NGJI* 2/1 (1956), 7–13.
[5] F. Grenard, *Haute Asie* (*Géographie Universelle*, Colin, Paris (1939), T. VIII), 349.
[6] For various cultural groups in the region, see S. D. Misra, 'Social groups in Himachal Pradesh', *Bull. de la Soc. de Géographie d'Egypte*, 35 (1962), 217–62 – the nomadic Gaddis, suffering from rural depopulation among their youth, the pastoral Gujars, turning to sedentary cultivation, the Bohras, traders and moneylenders who have lost their wool trade with Tibet; S. L. Kayastha, 'Ghirths of the Kangra Valley', *NGJI* 5/1 (1959), 12–24; S. C. Bose, 'Nomadism in high valleys of Uttarakhand and Kumaon', *GJI* 22/3 (1960), 34–39.

(the uppermost parts of the Chenab valley) and Spiti sowing takes place as soon as the ground is free from snow, about the end of April. Lower down, two crops are grown in some areas, such as the Kangra (Beas) valley: wheat, barley and gram as rabi (sown September–December) and maize and rice as kharif (sown April–July). Agricultural practices vary enormously, from precarious fields on tiny river-terraces in Spiti (where 2 sq. miles, about 0·1% of the area, are cultivated, solely under barley) to the fairly intensive cultivation of the Kangra valley, and the Kiarda and Jaswan *duns* behind the Siwaliks. Animal manure is widely applied, and transhumant flocks are folded on the fields in winter; but fragmentation is intense.[7] In Kangra District the fields are:

> 'generally unenclosed, but in some parts surrounded by hedges or stone walls. In the Kangra valley, where rice cultivation prevails, the fields descend to successive terraces levelled and embanked, and where the slope is rapid they are often no bigger than a billiard table . . . where the country is less broken, the fields are larger in size, and the broad sloping fields, red soil, and thick green hedges are charmingly suggestive of a Devonshire landscape.'[8]

Apart from subsistence crops, there are a few very small tea plantations (9,000 ac. in Kangra) and, of growing importance, market-gardening both for hill stations and for the cities of the plain: potatoes are especially widespread.

Forestry is of great importance; timber includes deodar from the higher forests, *chir* from the outer hills (cut even up to the high morainic ridges, thus accelerating soil erosion), bamboo and *sabai* grass, for fodder and paper, in the Siwaliks. Soil conservation has been successfully pioneered in the Siwaliks from the 1930s and its extension is essential, if only to prolong the life of the Bhakra reservoir. It may even be necessary to curb local irrigation by hillside channels which lead to landslips in the deep alluvium now precariously perched above the rivers. The local planting of orchards on river deposits is useful in checking erosion.[9]

Mineral resources are widely scattered and include lead, copper, antimony and zinc. But it is not likely that they will ever be of much importance: the antimony and zinc, for example, are found in 'deposits of considerable size', but the location at the end of a Lahul glacier is rather against them.[10] The most important mineral output is slate from quarries at Kangra.

The major industrial resource of the region is not of local importance: this is hydro-electricity. Water from the Uhl is dammed at Barot and drops 3,000 ft. (915 m.) by a tunnel through the Ghogar Range to Jogindernagar, to generate 48,000 kW. This power supports the industries of Amritsar.

[7] S. D. Misra, 'Agricultural geography of Himachal Pradesh', *Oriental Geogr* 7 (1963), 46–58.
[8] *Punjab Gaz.* (1908), I. 363.
[9] R. M. Gorrie, 'Countering desiccation in the Punjab', *GR* 38 (1948), 30–40; Puri, *op. cit.*
[10] Wadia, *op. cit.* 471.

The population is remarkably dense for so mountainous an area, though of course it is markedly concentrated in the *duns* of the south, and in Spiti and Lahul the density sinks to 4 or 5. But Kangra as a whole has over 200 and Himachal Pradesh 125. In 1951 agricultural densities for all but one District ranged from 800 to 1,200 per sq. miles cultivated. But settlement is hamletted rather than nucleated: two-thirds of the people live in groups of under 500 souls. Indeed, between Simla and the plains the unit is often an isolated farmstead, its fields occupying the sunnier sides of a little valley left hanging by the rapid erosion of the main stream, or a fragment of terrace, or the end of a little spur: below the centrally-placed square-built stone farmstead is contour-bunded paddy, with maize on unirrigated slopes, and perhaps one or two field-huts. Building, while not reaching the massive solidity of Ladakh, reflects the rigours of winter and the availability of good timber and stone.

Apart from the hill stations of Simla (see Chapter 7) and Dalhousie, and former petty state capitals, urbanization is negligible, less than that of any other units except perhaps NEFA and Nagaland. There are, however, two mountain railways (2 ft. 6 in. gauge), to Simla and to Jogindernagar; and the war in Kashmir has forced on the construction of the Kangra–Kashmir road. A motor road clings to the steep sides of the Larji gorge, giving access to the remote Kulu valley; tourism is of growing importance. Apart from the economic strategy of power production, the region has a locational strategic value, athwart routes into Tibet, flanking those into Kashmir.

The Far North

To the north the cultural landscape of agriculture and Hinduism gradually gives way to that of pastoral Tibet: in northeastern Bashahr polyandry is prevalent, and religion and language are transitional. In Lahul January *means* are below freezing and most of the country is 'entirely uninhabited, except for a few weeks in summer, when the Kangra shepherds bring up their flocks'. The summer pastures are excellent, but deep snow from December to April (or even June) makes it impossible to keep sheep and goats out of doors, in contrast to more arid Ladakh. The Lahulis are notable caravan traders.

Spiti is even poorer, and more purely Buddhist, a remote canton walled in by red and yellow cliffs; the mean elevation of the valley is 13,000 ft. (3,960 m.). In 1908 there were no schools, police or dispensaries; these services were no doubt adequately fulfilled by the three monasteries. The shortest route into Spiti, from Kulu, involves the traverse of a glacier and two passes at 14,200 and 14,900 ft. (4,330 and 4,540 m.) 'so that this is beyond question the most inaccessible part of the British dominions in India'.[11]

Hundes lies beyond the confines of India, 'a vast little-articulated plateau' walled in by Ladakh and Kailas on the north, the great peaks from Badrinath to

[11] *Punjab Gaz.* I. 378. These two paragraphs are based on *ibid.* 371–8 – the unacknowledged source of Grenard's account in the *Géographie Universelle.*

456

Gurla Mandhata on the south. There are a few half-bandit nomadic clans, a handful of monasteries and villages up to 14,500 ft. (4,420 m.). But around the remote lakes and desolate ravine-scored terraces 'where'er we tread is haunted, holy ground'. Due north is Kailas itself, which 'seems to present the highest Tertiary conglomerate series of our globe still in the position of deposition. The accumulation must have been made possible during subsidence at low levels' followed by an uplift of at least 23,000 ft. (7,010 m.).[12] This is impressive enough; but the superbly symmetrical mountain is also the holiest of all the sacred places to both Tibet and Hindustan. Here Ganga divides, like the waters of Paradise, into four rivers: Indus, Sutlej, Brahmaputra, Karnali. The sacred way around Kailas is an avenue of cairns bearing the *mani* formula; the circuit is made clockwise,[13] and many pilgrims make it by repeatedly measuring their length on the craggy path; at the highest point are votive piles of their hair and teeth. Yet, bizarre as these expressions of devotion are, it is no ignoble instinct which places 'the axis of the world' on this peak of serenest beauty.

KUMAON

The general setting

Although the general culture of Kumaon is not dissimilar to that of Himachal Pradesh, it seems yet to have an individuality of its own. Perhaps this merely reflects the greater fame of an area which holds the sacred sources of Mother Ganga and so, despite a rather stronger Mongoloid ethnic infusion, is more deeply impregnated with Hindu tradition. Broadly speaking Kumaon is the country between the Tons feeder of the Yamuna and the (Maha) Kali feeder of the Sarda, which is the western boundary of Nepal. The region thus includes the Himalayan basins of the Yamuna, Ganga, Ramganga and Sarda.

Politically, it consists of the Kumaon Division (Almora, Garhwal, Naini Tal, Chamoli and Uttarkhasi Districts) of Uttar Pradesh, with Dehra Dun District and the state of Tehri Garhwal, now merged with Uttar Pradesh. Covering about 10,500 sq. miles (27,195 km^2) with some 2,500,000 people in 1961, the over-all density is 115, reaching 222 in Dehra Dun. The whole area was wrested from the Gurkhas of Nepal after the war of 1814–15. Physically it rises from the sub-Siwalik bhabar to a magnificent series of glacier-garlanded peaks: the Kedarnath/Badrinath group (22,000–23,000 ft., 6,710–7,010 m.), of peculiar sanctity as feeding the Bhagirathi and Alaknanda headwaters of the Ganga; Kamet (25,447 ft., 7,756 m.) across the Alaknanda; and farther east Trisul, Nanda Kot and Nanda Devi, the last at 25,645 ft. (7,817 m.) being the highest peak in India outside of Kashmir.

Apart from the Dehra Dun and the deeper valleys, most of the region consists

---

[12] A. Heim and A. Gansser, *The Throne of the Gods* (London, 1939), 224.

[13] A heretical sect, maintaining pre-Buddhist animist traditions, perversely travels widdershins. See Grenard, 349, and the vivid description in Heim and Gansser, *ibid.* 95–106.

of highly dissected country at 6,000–12,000 ft. (1,830–2,135 m.) formed of 'an anticlinorium consisting of several anticlines of normal and of fan-shaped type' with twisted strikes, and of great nappes.[14] The pattern of relief and structure has been described in Chapter 1. We may note once again, however, the extra-ordinarily late date which seems necessary for these movements, tangential as well as vertical. Ten miles northwest of Dehra, Upper Siwalik boulders are 'so shattered that it is impossible to obtain a hand-specimen of them'. It is true that the *major* movements were earlier – probably in Helvetian times – and the upper nappes were then dissected to such an extent that they were 'divided off into separated outliers, unable to translate the stresses as a unit'. The Garhwal movement was at least 50 miles (80 km.); later, intrusive granites were involved in a movement of several miles towards the southwest.[15]

Superimposed, as it were, on this recently mobile and highly complex base are the effects of intense contemporary physiographic activity. It is true that the present glaciation is but the shadow of what it was: on the Alaknanda and Kali the outermost moraines are at 7,050 and 6,550 ft., 2,150 and 1,995 m., while today the main valleys are ice-free and the lateral glaciers do not fall below 13,000 ft., 3,960 m. 'The glaciers in the larger valleys, such as . . . the Milam, are not only covered with detritus for several miles (three to ten), but float, so to speak, on their moraines, which they are no longer capable of sweeping away.' But the intensity of water erosion is striking: Heim cites a hanging valley, filled with moraine, the floor of which is at least 160 ft. (49 m.) above the present level of the Kali, and this post-glacial erosion is in micaceous schists and quartzites.[16] The reverse is seen in the tremendous detrital terraces on the edge of Dehra Dun, which has been filled up to a height of 1,000 ft. (305 m.) above the plains.

The climate shows the usual montane variations. The lower valleys, and still more Dehra Dun, are climatically depressing: hot and sultry in summer, hung with heavy mist until nearly noon in the cold weather, when ranges are extreme. May–June maxima reach 110°F. (43°C.) in the valleys, the ridges going up to 94°F. (34°C.); at 6,000–7,000 ft. (1,830–2,135 m.) the winter mean is c. 40°F., (4·4°C.), but 3,000 ft. higher it is around freezing point. But at Almora and Ranikhet, on 6,000-ft. ridges, summer maxima are 85–90°F. (29–32°C.). Precipitation is 40–50 in. (1,016–1,270 mm. at these towns, rises to twice this on the outer ranges at 10,000 ft. (3,050 m.) and falls off somewhat behind them, apparently rising again towards the snow-line, generally at 16,000–17,500 ft. (4,880–5,335 m.). Snow falls as low as 4,000–5,000 ft. (1,220–1,525 m.). The rainfall régime is normal, the rains beginning in the second half of June, with slight winter falls coming from the north and west. Run-off is of course extremely rapid wherever the ground is not blanketed by forest.

[14] Heim and Gansser, *op. cit.* in fn. 3, 221.

[15] J. B. Auden, 'The structure of the Himalayas in Garhwal', *Rec. GSI* 71 (1936–37), 407–33; refce at 429–32.

[16] Heim and Gansser, *ibid.* 219, 36–37.

Much of the area below 12,500 ft. (3,810 m.) is forested, largely on the northern slopes with their less direct but more effective precipitation. In ascending sequence we have the sal forest of the terai/bhabar and the Siwaliks; a belt of *chir*, then at 5,000 ft. (1,525 m.), evergreen oak/rhododendron, with ash, yew, ilex and bamboo; then the coniferous zone from 9,000 to roughly 11,000 ft. (2,745–3,355 m.). This is succeeded by birch/rhododendron forest (up to 13,000 ft. (3,960 m.) at the highest), and finally alpine scrub and steppe. Isolated rhododendrons are found at 15,400 ft. (4,695 m.) and on the Tibetan border 'adventurous grass-patches' up to 16,400 ft. (5,000 m.).

In the region as a whole pastoralism and various trading activities are of less significance than agriculture, but in the higher north they may be said to predominate. Lower down the forests play an intimate part in the life of the people. Roots of *Jurinea macrocepahala*, the chief source of *dhoop* (incense) are collected in autumn from the alpine meadows and marketed at Amritsar, and resin collecting employs 10,000 people in Kumaon.[17] Mineral deposits are patchy: iron, copper, alum, gypsum, lead, graphite, but none are of any economic significance at present.

It will be convenient to discuss the human geography by the sub-regions: the Dehra Dun, Kumaon proper, the Bhotiya valleys.

Hardwar to Mussoorie: the Dehra Dun

Hardwar, where the Ganga breaks through the Siwaliks,[18] is a typical contact mart, with the added attractions of the holy river: up to half a million pilgrims may attend the specially sacred twelve-yearly Kumbh Mela, presenting serious problems to police and sanitation. Behind the Siwaliks, as far as the Yamuna breach 45 miles (72 km.) to the northwest, stretches the great Dun, 15–20 miles wide and rising from 1,200 ft. (365 m.) along the two rivers to 2,200 ft. (670 m.) in the middle. The Dun drains pretty equally to Yamuna and Ganga, and Dehra town lies on the low swelling interfluve. To the north the Mussoorie Hills rise abruptly to 7,000–7,500 ft. (2,135–2,290 m.) (Fig. 15.2).[19]

With a rainfall of *c.* 90 in. (2,286 mm.) agriculture should be secure enough, but the edaphic factors are not too favourable. The Dun is floored by gravelly detritus with light, thin top-soils; erosion is very active indeed, and losses by lateral shifting of the mountain torrents, by gullying, by sand and shingle spreads, are serious. The water-table is naturally low, irrigation is by short canals. On the whole, also, farming methods are poor. The staple crops are wheat, rice, ragi (locally known as marua or madua) and barley, and there are fair acreages of maize, oilseeds, orchards (especially of mangoes), sugar-cane and

[17] M. D. Upadhjay, 'Progress of the resin industry in Uttar Pradesh', *Indian Forester*, 83/1 (1957), 26–33.
[18] In some Hindu literature this water-gap appears as a mighty cleft in Himalayan fastnesses. Merit can be obtained with less exertion than by making the really strenuous pilgrimage to Badrinath – or Kailas.
[19] E. Reiner, 'Das Dehra Dun', *Petermanns Geog. Mitt.* 97 (1953), 1–12.

rather poor tea plantations. There are large compact villages, and also dispersed settlement associated with irrigation from wells and along canals.[20]

Dehra itself (156,341) is not an attractive town: there is a small Anglicized core and around it a big straggle of loose urbanism. Nor are the immediate surroundings any better – a tangle of ravines, pebbly or ankle-deep in fine dust in

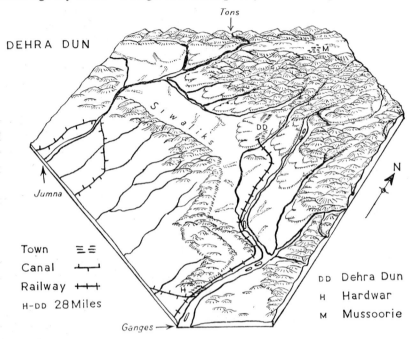

FIG 15.2 DEHRA DUN – BLOCK DIAGRAM.

the dry weather. The Survey of India headquarters are at Dehra, and to the northwest, on rather higher and more solid ground, are the National Defence Academy and the Forest Research Institute. All around Dehra the most prominent features of the cultural landscape are connected with forestry: saw-yards, piles of sleepers and fuel-wood, furniture shops, and charcoal kilns. Mussoorie (9,879) is a hill station of some importance as an educational centre.

Kumaon

The basis of life in Kumaon is an elaborately organized agriculture. It is impossible to summarize adequately the mass of detail in S. D. Pant's *The Social Economy of the Himalayans*, but the following tabular statement[21] gives some faint idea of its complexity and, though there are of course large local variations,

[20] S. D. Kaushic, 'Types of human settlement in the Jaunsar Himalaya', *GRI* 21/2–4 (1959), 1–17.

[21] Based, with succeeding paragraphs, on Pant, Chapters VI–XIII *passim*. Madua is marua or ragi.

is probably fairly representative of 'intermediate' Himalayan conditions as a whole; specialized sub-types are in parentheses.

KUMAON CULTIVATION TYPES

Local Name	Position	Nature	Crops (K=kharif, R=rabi)
1. Katil	Forest edge	'Intermittent' – 2–3 crops in 12 years to 3 in 5; first step to terracing	K: madua, horse gram, buckwheat, turmeric, potatoes; no R.

((a) *kharak* – intensive manuring on garden plots near temporary (pastoral) living-huts)

2. Upraon	Hillsides	High stone terraces	K: madua, dry rice, millets, sugar cane buckwheat, chillies, turmeric; R: wheat, barley, mustard

((a) *talliya* – level, alluvial, unirrigated, 'buffer' between 2 and 3)

3. Talaon	Valleys	Irrigated, low mud terraces	K: paddy only (3 types of cultivation)*; R: wheat, barley, lentils, mustard, flax

*((a) *sera* – fine alluvial clay, always plenty of water;
(b) *panchar* – coarser soil, water-supply may be precarious;
(c) *shimar* – waterlogged, only one crop yearly but best paddy.)

A few points may be expanded. The terracing is often most elaborate, covering entire hillsides with steps 5–8 ft. high (1·5–2·5 m., occasionally up to 20 ft., 6·1 m.) and 10–20 ft. wide: 'in some places as many as five hundred of these terraces can be counted in continuous flights. In some villages there are more than six thousand terraces.' Since it takes a day for one man (assisted by others to fetch the stones) to build a wall a foot thick, six long and three high, the cumulative labour involved is enormous. Maintenance also is arduous in a region where even properly built roads are often swept away by landslips; usually 25–40% of the cultivation terraces give way during each rains.

Rotations are elaborate and ingenious. On the *upraon* the village lands are divided into two compact blocks, the rice and the madua *sars*, and these have an alternating rotation; the sequence is the same on each *sar*, but they differ in phase:

Rice sar			Madua sar
paddy, chillies, oilseeds, or buckwheat	1 K	3	madua, pulses or buckwheat
wheat, pulses or mustard	2 R	4	fallow
madua, etc.	3 K	1	paddy, etc.
fallow	4 R	2	wheat, etc.
	(K=kharif, R=rabi)		

In *talaon* land the three very different systems of paddy cultivation enable the same area to grow kharif rice for years, rotating the type of tillage and introducing different rabi crops.

Soils are generally poor, shallow and stony, and manuring is very important. Ample fuel-wood permits the storage of cattle dung, and during winter the litter of pine-needles in the cattle-sheds accumulates to form thick layers of compost. Folding of cattle and sheep is extensively practised, and when the Bhotiyas pass through with their flocks there 'is sometimes a regular scramble to secure their services'.

Irrigation is limited – *c.* 8% of cultivated area – and is mainly by leats (*guls*) from the smaller streams; the larger are too turbulent and too variable to be easily harnessed. Long flumes take the *guls* across ravines. Mills similar to those described in Ladakh are aligned along leats, and on some exceptionally favourable streams they may be stepped as closely as 12 in half a mile.

With the opening up of the outer ranges, as far as Almora and Ranikhet, to the motor-bus, the traditional transhumance is declining, while on the other hand there is a marked extension of market-garden and potato cultivation. But there is still a drift to the bhabar in the severe and agriculturally slack winter; petty trade and forestry work, particularly resin tapping, provide useful supplementary income, but a powerful motive is simply the desire of 'eating sunshine'. The importance of sunshine is also emphasized by the distinction between cultivated *tailo* slopes – the sunny or *adret* side of the valleys – and the forested *saylo* (= Alpine *ubac*). Scattered iron, copper, and asbestos deposits are as yet too inaccessible to be economically exploited.[22]

Villages are usually along spurs low enough to avoid the bleakness of the ridge-tops, but well above the valleys, sultry in summer but frosty and foggy in winter; the village lands often extend in 'strip-parish' fashion, from irrigated valley floor to forested or grassy ridge-top. There are traces of an original tribal settlement in the dialectal and cultural homogeneity of the chain of villages along a spur.

The towns are essentially petty marts: contact points of hill and plain in the bhabar, or nodes of valley- or ridge-ways. Almora (16,602) and Ranikhet (10,642) are no longer isolated but retain considerable charm, largely owing to their high tradition of artistic wood-carving, and, with other centres, have factories extracting resin and making toys and packing cases from softwoods. Naini Tal (16,080) remains a favourite hill station.

The Bhotiya valleys

At the highest level live the Bhotiyas,[23] among whom pastoralism and trading are more important than agriculture. Their alpine pastures lie at 10,000–14,000 ft. (3,050–4,270 m.), in valleys with little rain but much winter snow: here are the summer villages, of which Milam, with some 600 families, is the largest.[24] The fields are too small and irregular for ploughs to be much used, and hoe culture is far more common. The growing season is only about four months;

[22] B. S. Negi, 'Mineral resources of Kumaon and Garhwal', *GRI* 22/3 (1960), 40–48.

[23] Bhotiya, Bhot, Bhoti, Bhutia, etc., all=Tibetan and are applied to different tribes from the Punjab to Bhután.

[24] See Heim and Gansser, *The Throne of the Gods*, Chapters VI, IX, XI, XIV; Pant, Chapters II, III, XX–XXII.

madua, wheat, barley are chief crops, often irrigated by primitive methods on little outwash cones. The junipers and furze-like bushes of the hillsides are carefully preserved to check snow- and land-slips, and before flocks and goods can be moved up from the winter villages advance parties of pioneers are sent on to repair paths and bridges.

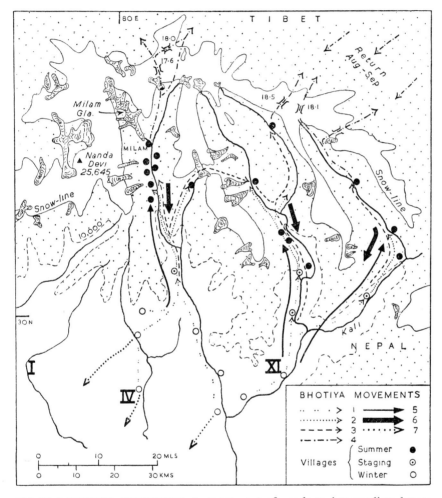

FIG 15.3 BHOTIYA MOVEMENTS. I, movement of goods to intermediate bases; 2, advance pioneer parties to summer villages (both April–May); 3, goods to summer villages (May–June); 4, traders to Tibet (July–August); 5, families and flocks to upper valleys (June); 6, general descent (October); 7, trading trips to plains (usually 2 trips in September–April). I, IV, XI – sites and months of fairs. Heights of passes in thousand feet. Based on text of S. D. Pant, *The Social Economy of the Himalayans* (1935), 50–60, 195–201, 240–2. I am indebted also to Mr Gurdial Singh of Dehra Dun for comments on Kumaon.

The highly mobile life of the Bhotiyas is summarized in Fig. 15.3: even in winter the Bhotiya men range far afield, generally making two trips to the bhabar market-towns and sometimes going as far as Kanpur; to the north, before the border hostilities, the range was as far as Gartok. During the long absences of their menfolk the women weave fine woollens, most of the yarn being produced by the men spinning as they walk. The trade into Tibet was mainly in grain, sugar, tea, small metal and general 'bazaar goods'; imports thence were salt and borax, furs, ponies, yak-tails and above all wool. The main baggage animals are sheep and goats, which can carry up to 40 lb. at 5 miles a day, mules, yaks and various yak/cattle crosses: these can carry 2–3 maunds (160–240 lb., 72–180 kg.). The sturdy little Bhotiya ponies are also in much demand in the winter fairs at the upper series of contact marts (I, IV and XI in Fig. 15.3). But man himself is the most reliable beast of burden on these all but impassable ways, where the local proverb has it that 'it takes ten goat-herds to drive nine goats'.

A notable contrast with the rest of Kumaon is provided by the higher and more independent status of the Bhotiya women, left for long spells in charge of home and fields, with only the children and the aged to help them; environmental factors and Mongolian affinities are probably jointly responsible.

NEPAL

Nepal 'remains the last [independent] survivor of those Indian communities which stood for civilization, learning, and culture when Europe was still in the darkest period of her history. She alone among Asiatic Powers has never suffered either the galling triumph of the Moslem or the political and commercial results of Christian expansion'.[25] This statement emphasizes the strong cultural individuality of Nepal which in turn warrants its treatment as a separate region; though the extreme east (roughly the Kosi basin) is better taken with its Tibetan approaches by Sikkim and the Arun. History and culture enter so intimately into any regional discussion that it seems better to deal with them first.

Generalities: cultural

The heart of Nepal is the Valley around Katmandu; indeed this *is* Nepal to the Nepalese, the rest being either Terai or Pahar (= Hills). The earlier history is very obscure, but it is at least certain that in the Mauryan era the Valley was a centre of Buddhist culture: here, at Patan, Asoka built four great *stupas*, and at Rummindei, just inside the terai boundary, he erected a still surviving pillar to mark the exact site of the Buddha's birth. After the Muslim invasions and the final decay of Buddhism in Hindustan, Rajput infiltration weakened and overlaid, but did not completely supplant, Nepalese Buddhism, which by this time had taken on a pronounced Mahayanan tinge.[26] In the 17th century the Valley

[25] Landon, *Nepal* (1928), preface. For 'Christian' read 'European'.
[26] A very clear account of the divergence of the two great Buddhist schools will be found in Lord Ronaldshay, *Lands of the Thunderbolt* (1923), Chapters VII and XII.

was divided between three petty princedoms – their capitals are still the chief towns of the whole country, the centres of two of them, Katmandu and Patan, only 2 miles apart, and the third, Bhatgaon, a bare 6 miles away. To the west the Rajputs were consolidating around the little base of Gurkha – whence the name Gurkha loosely applied to all the fighting-men of Nepal. Around 1769 the Gurkha prince, Prithwi Narayan, subjugated the Valley, more perhaps by intrigue, terrorism and a ruthless blockade than by battle. This was the foundation of the present state, which at first was in an expansionist mood. By the 1780s Gurkha power extended to the Kangra valley, where it was turned back by the Sikh leader Ranjit Singh. On the northeast expansion was checked by an unsuccessful war with Tibet, and infiltration into Oudh led to the Anglo-Nepali war of 1814–15.

This was decisive in the sense that neither side cared to try again – a unique phenomenon in British wars with the 'country powers'. Nepal lost Kumaon and some of the Terai (later in part retroceded in return for effective assistance in the Mutiny) and had to accept a Resident at Katmandu. In effect, however, the Resident was rather an Ambassador and Nepal remained independent. Perhaps more important, the Court of Katmandu accurately assessed the probable effects of 'peaceful penetration' – not perhaps a difficult assessment – and would have none of it. Europeans were admitted only by permission of both the Nepali and Indian governments in every individual case, and permission was not lightly given. The terai was gradually opened to commercial development, but only a favoured few could penetrate to the Valley, and beyond the Valley remained forbidden territory. Paradoxically, Nepal is now more open than ever before.

Behind the curtain of the malarial terai jungles, Nepal evolved an extraordinary polity, not without much palace intrigue and murder. As in pre-Meiji Japan or Merovingian France, the monarch became a virtual nonentity, all power being in the hands of the Rana family, shoguns or Mayors of the Palace, whose hereditary offices of Prime Minister, Marshal, and Supreme Commander-in-Chief descended in the agnatic manner – i.e. to all brothers of one generation in order of birth, then to the eldest surviving son of the eldest brother, and so on. On the whole the Ranas, if not progressive in the usual sense, were remarkably efficient; those who were not were deposed. A little economic development and social reform took place, but the former was more or less confined to the Terai and the Valley, and social stability was preferred to rapid advance.

The resultant was apparently a well-knit state, combining the peasant and the military virtues, and until recently notably free from communal discord despite the fact that the rulers are Rajputs and the mass of the people more or less Mongoloid.

This is probably due in large part to the fact that Nepali Buddhism and Hinduism, while not fused, at least interpenetrate: most observers incline to think that Buddhism is declining, but it has certainly not left its rival unaffected. The pantheon consists of animist nature-spirits and demons, Buddhist boddhisatwas, and definitely Hindu gods; the most popular deity, Machendranath, the bringer of rain, appears to combine all three.[27] This unique culture is reflected in the mingling in Nepali architecture of Hindu and 'Chinese' elements, though there seems at least a possibility that some typical features of Chinese and Burmese building – the superimposed roofs, the bell-shaped pagoda – actually stem from Nepal, which has handed on the ancient traditions of Indian wooden building and of the *stupa*.[28]

The area of Nepal is about 54,000 sq. miles (13,390 km²) and the population was estimated in 1962 at 9,500,000. The main tribes are Mongol: Gurungs, Magars, Bhotiyas; the first two provide the bulk of the 'Gurkha' soldiery, though the Rajput Gurkhas proper naturally preponderate among the officers. The Terai, of course, has a considerable Indian admixture, and the Valley is largely Newar. The correlation of 'Newar' with the Nairs of southern India is far-fetched and unconvincing, but there do seem to be persistent and peculiar links with the south in the earlier religious history. The official language – Nepali (or Gurkhali or Eastern Pahari) – is akin to Kumaoni and thus belongs to the Hindi branch of Indo-Aryan speech; but much of the peasantry speaks one or other of the Tibeto-Burman tribal tongues.

Generalities: physical[29]

Nepal lies along the southern glacis of Tibet, from the Sarda (Kali) to Kangchen-junga, a distance of 550 miles (885 km.); its breadth is 100–150 miles (160–240 km.). The northern boundary lay by tradition along the watershed north of the Great Himalayan Range, but until the 1962 China–Nepal Boundary Agreement was undefined; Everest itself is still in dispute. The southern boundary lies mainly in the terai, though in places it is formed by the Dundwa and Sumesar Hills. Structurally, three zones are distinguished (Fig. 15.4). In the south, the Tertiaries of the Siwaliks are continued in the Churia Hills and their *duns*. The Midland Zone of Hagen comprises two great nappes, separated from the Tertiaries by a reverse fault (the Great Boundary Fault). It includes the markedly east–west Mahabharat Lekh, with a steep south-facing escarpment, and gentler forested slopes to the north; with other ranges, this encloses the tectonic depression of Katmandu, now filled by lacustrine deposits. Other marked longitudinal features are occupied by sections of the Rapti, Kali, Ganadki and Sun Kosi. Hagen sees the Midland Zone as one of the final collapse, as it were, of the nappe fronts which formed the Mahabharat, trapping the rivers in these longitudinal valleys. The Great Himalaya are the region of nappe roots; their great height and transverse gorges the result of earlier horizontal thrusts squeezed 'like toothpaste

---

[27] Landon, II. 216, and, for a careful mapping of cultural indices, J. Kawakita, 'Influence of the Himalayas in the human geography of Nepal', *Proc. of the I.G.U. Regional Conference, Japan 1957* (Science Council of Japan, Tokyo, 1959), 357–62.

[28] See Landon, Appx. XX; S. Levi, *Le Népale* (1906).

[29] The main sources for modern knowledge of Nepal are P. P. Karan and W. M. Jenkins, *Nepal: A Cultural and Physical Geography* (Univ. of Kentucky, Lexington, 1960) and T. Hagen, *Nepal: The Kingdom in the Himalayas* (Kümmerley and Frey, Berne, 1961).

from a tube'. They tower above the Midlands and include such giants as Anna-
purna (26,492 ft., 8,075 m.) and Dhaulagiri (26,795 ft., 8,167 m.), only a little
over 20 miles (32 km.) apart but separated by the deep gorge of the Kali Gandak.
North of the main range is a zone of high wide valleys on softer sedimentaries,
between the gneisses of the Great Himalaya and the granite hills of the arid
Tibetan borders on the watershed.

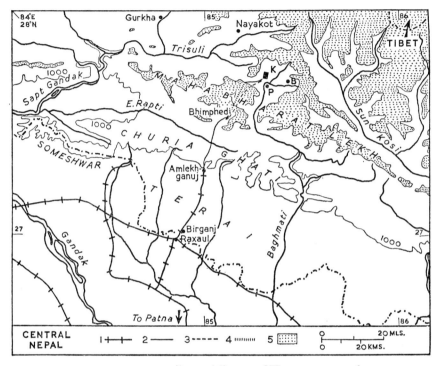

FIG 15.4 CENTRAL NEPAL. 1, railways (all metre ST); 2, motor road; 3, ropeway;
4, track (2–4 on Katmandu Road only); 5, over 5,000 ft. approx. K, Katmandu;
P, Patan; B, Bhatgaon. The all-weather motor road now runs through from Birganj
to Katmandu.

Although altitude and aspect provide intricate climatic variations, there are
clear distinctions between (a) the subtropical Terai, with rainfall decreasing
from 80 in. (2,032 mm.) in the east to 40 in. in the west, and also away from the
mountain foot; (b) the Midland zone (Katmandu 58 in. (1,473 mm.) and a
January–July range from 50 to 77°F., 10 to 25°C.), which merges into a colder
but occupied zone at 10,000–15,000 ft. (3,050–4,570 m.). Beyond lie the per-
petual tundra or ice of the high peaks; north of these, rainfall drops sharply
except where the transverse gorges allow the access of monsoonal air. Here are
the longest glaciers, for the southern slopes are too steep to nourish the nevé
necessary for excess ice accumulation.

467

The vegetation sequence is as follows:

under 4,000 ft. (terai and Siwaliks)	tropical deciduous (sal), riverain (sissoo), savannah
4,000–8,500 ft. (1,220–2,590 m.)	oak, maple, pine
8,500 ft.	spruce, fir, cypress, larch
10,000 ft. (3,050 m.)	alpine (rhododendron, juniper).

A point of some interest is the occurrence of deodar in the Karnali basin, an outlier 150 miles (240 km.) east of the normal limit of deodar in Garhwal.[30]

The Terai

This, the least Nepali part of Nepal, is economically perhaps the most important; the policy of exclusion was not so rigorously enforced, and in any case did not apply, in general, to Asian peoples. Hence, despite its limited area – a discontinuous strip 10–20 miles (16–32 km.) broad – its notorious climate and malaria, and its large areas of savannah and sal forest, the Terai holds about one-third of the population, mainly in the southeast.[31]

Until malaria control was perfected, the Terai remained exceedingly unhealthy in the rains, and no traveller spent a night in the junglier parts if he could help it. Only the Tharus, a tribe of carters, seemed more or less immune from the dreaded *awal* fever.[32] The dangers of the Terai, including its wild animals, lost nothing in the telling, and have undoubtedly contributed to the seclusion and security of Nepal.

Much is still undeveloped; this includes the large areas of 'elephant grass', often 15 ft. (4·6 m.) high and so thick that elephants can hardly push through it. There is a good deal of timber exploitation, mainly sal, and much land has been cleared for crops – rice, rabi wheat on the paddy-fields, grain, some sugar and tobacco. Karan distinguishes the dry over-grazed Terai, with only isolated patches of cultivation; the uncertain but increasing cultivation in the central area; and the east with its intensive cropping of jute and rice, largely for export to India. Nepal's only railway (narrow gauge) runs for 29 miles (47 km.) from the border at Raxaul to Amlekhganj, through Birganj which has some rice mills and match factories. The jute and chemical factories of Biratnagar, in the southeast, account for most of Nepal's industry.

The little towns of the Terai were places of trade and transit rather than of residence, with godowns and booths of brick and corrugated iron, almost empty in the hottest weather and the rains. The permanence of these marts is secured by their 'position on the high road just where the under-features of the Himalayas burst up through the Terai, and further progress must be by one track alone'.[33]

---

[30] For a beautiful vegetation transect, see Hagen, *op. cit.* 48.

[31] Karan, *op. cit.* 47–62, gives a detailed and well-mapped survey of population and settlement. As a regional name, 'Terai' is capitalized.

[32] L. R. Singh, 'The Tharus: a study in human ecology', *NGJI* 2/3 (1956), 153–66, describes the Tharus' migration from the Uttar Pradesh terai into that of Nepal as agricultural colonization proceeds.

[33] Landon, II. 7–10.

The Valley

The heart of Nepal is the central Valley, where lies the capital, Katmandu. Before 1956 the journey over the Mahabharat Lekh was on foot or by animal transport, but in that year an all-weather road was opened from Raxaul. Some goods must still be transported over these mountains by an electric ropeway, which can take loads up to 10 cwt. (508 kg.) and is to be extended southwards to railhead at Amlekhganj; an all-weather road from Lhasa to Katmandu is being built with Chinese aid. Air transport is increasingly important both into and within the country; Pokhara has a regular air link with Katmandu, but no road.

The Valley itself, an amphitheatre about 15 miles (24 km.) across, around the headwaters of the Baghmati, is an old lake-bed. With a density approaching 2,000 to the square mile, it is intensively cultivated; on the valley floor rice predominates, rainfed or irrigated by simple devices, with barley and millets higher up, and wheat in winter.

The Valley is concentrated history. The three old capitals are rich with temples, pagodas and a domestic architecture in which wood-carving has been carried to the highest pitch. Katmandu (1955: 105,000) is naturally the most important, and has what little industry there is away from the Terai, including plywood and mica processing. The focus of the town is the Hanuman Dhoka or temple square, where there are 'more gods than humans'. It is surrounded by narrow alleys and bazaars; the town is now expanding eastwards towards the airport. Some of the great, but architecturally undistinguished, palaces of the Ranas are now government offices and hotels. Of the other Valley towns, Patan is chiefly notable for its Asokan *stupa*, Bhatgaon the least modernized and perhaps the most attractive of the three. In spite of modernization and the technical and financial aid that is pouring in to this key area between India and China, the colour of life is still much as it was in the golden days of classical Indian culture.

The Pahar

Most of the hill country (Pahar) lies in three great basins: those of the Ghaghra headstreams, the Sapt (seven) Gandak and the Sapt Kosi. Here and there are fertile vales: Dumja on the Sun Kosi, growing rice and barley, Pokhara on the Seti Gandak mainly rice; Jumla, high up on the Karnali headstream of the Ghaghra, mainly barley. Maize is widely grown. Around Palpa and Nayakot are extensive orchards; at Nayakot mangoes, pineapples, oranges and some temperate fruits. Potatoes are increasingly important, with export by air to India. Outside the Terai and the Valley, the only towns of any size are Palpa and Pokhara, each with only about a tenth of the population of any of the Valley towns.

North of this longitudinal belt the country rapidly becomes very wild; beyond Nayakot the Trisul Gandak and the Tadi descend some 8,000 ft. in 30 miles, 2,440 m. in 48 km. Trade with Tibet has always been important locally, carried over difficult passes and notorious suspension bridges in the wild gorges. Agricultural produce was exchanged for salt and yaks, with the outpost town of Mustang as a main collecting centre. Now this flow has been checked and there is real hardship in the northern valleys.

Nepal: present and future

A century of stability but stagnation ended in 1951 when the Ranas were deposed by a palace revolution and a constitutional monarchy declared. For almost a decade Nepal struggled towards democracy, and a general election was held early in 1959. But King Mahendra, dismayed it seems by the success of the Nepali Congress, dismissed the government at the end of the year and assumed absolute power. In 1962 a new constitution provided for indirect elections from local through zonal *panchayats* up to a national body, with various advisory boards and a Council of Ministers appointed by the King from the national *panchayat*.

There can be no better commentary on Nepal's strategic position in the Cold War than a review of some of the projects and their donors under her Development Plans. Over 80% of the finance is from foreign aid, with USA in the lead, next India, then China.[34] The main emphasis is on transport, starting with the road from India in 1956, followed, significantly enough, by the road from Lhasa being built with Chinese technical and financial aid. The Americans have provided airstrips, including one at Mustang on the Tibetan border, and the Russians have surveyed an east–west road to link the Midlands terminals of the trans-montane routes.

Industry, which employs less than 5% of the population, has a bigger share of investment than agriculture. The concentration in the Terai will be increased by the Russian-built sugar and tobacco factories at Biratnagar; there will be a Chinese-financed cement plant at Hetuera, headquarters of the American Rapti Valley Development which has opened up for agriculture a formerly malarial hunting estate of the Ranas; the Indian firm of Birla will build a textile mill; and so it goes on. . . . Two industrial estates are being developed outside Katmandu, to foster and improve the old handicrafts and new light industry. But the industrial bases are slight; so far agricultural raw materials (jute, sugar) predominate, although there is probably a greater potential in the forests. So far the only mineral of any significance is the mica east of Katmandu, but there may be commercial deposits of cobalt and marble.

According to Hagen, Nepal has the biggest hydro-electric potential of any country in the world; but it will be long until she needs much of it herself. India has developed the Trisul project for the Valley and central Terai, and the Russians have developed Panauti for the same region. But the bulk of developed

[34] The Three Year Plan, 1962–65; total Rs 670,000,000 (foreign aid component, 460,000,000); allocations: transport 38%, industry and tourism 20%, agriculture and irrigation, 14%; expenditure 1950–61, USA Rs 63,000,000, India 40,000,000, China 5,000,000.

power seems destined for Indian markets, from the Kosi scheme in the east to the Karnali and Gandak in the west; not without much gain to Nepal, both in revenue and such power as she needs, and irrigation in the Terai.

The seemingly smiling valleys conceal poverty, ill-health and population pressure which has led to the emigration of cultivators to India and Sikkim. Indebtedness and feudalism still oppress, despite tentative efforts at land reform, which include the attempted abolition of the *birtas*, the huge holdings of the Rana families. Karan sees little scope for agricultural expansion, except on a limited scale in the Terai and the western valleys, and indeed much is cultivated that should be left under forest; erosion is widespread. He points out that while much Indian and American aid is aimed at the basic problems of agriculture and education, the Chinese contributions – which include Buddhist temples – are more obvious and spectacular.

Yet there is strong anti-Indian feeling, which has led to flirtations with the Communist bloc, including a rather ambiguous Boundary Agreement with China. Nepalis resent the very real Indian economic domination: over 90% of trade is with India. The chief source of outside income is still the Gurkha mercenary, or migrant labourers.[35] With internal unrest following the suppression of directly-elected government, and external pressures from the giants north and south, the gates of Nepal are indeed open as never before, and the outcome of the flood of modernization, social and political as well as economic, is incalculable.

THE EASTERN HIMALAYA

Between 86 and 88° E the general character of the Himalayas changes to such an extent that a new division is warranted. The northwest/southeast trend is replaced by an east/west line, and beyond 92° E the strike is more southwest/northeast. Further, for some 140 miles (225 km.) (87° 45′–90° E) the mountains are exposed to the direct impact of the monsoon across the open gap between the Rajmahal Hills and the Shillong Plateau. Rainfall is high and the dense, wet tropical jungle extends eastwards along the Assam Himalaya, where the funnel-shaped valley also acts as a rain-trap. Opposite the gap the Siwaliks, rocks and hills, simply disappear, whether overriden by thrust-masses or eroded out of existence by the intense rainfall; Siwalik rocks reappear again east of 90°; but hardly form so marked and persistent a topographic feature as they do from Jhelum to Kosi. Finally the drainage is now, in its main lines at least, directly transverse, as shown by the Arun–Kosi, the Tista, and the rivers of Bhután.

The bold lines and the human importance of the Tista basin, leading to the main gateway into Tibet, justify the treatment of Darjeeling and Sikkim as one unit. This leaves as the others eastern Nepal, and Bhután with the Assam Himalaya.

[35] J. T. Hitchcock, 'A Nepalese village and Indian employment', *Asian Survey* 1/9 (1961), 15–20; this analysis indicates how very dependent the Nepali peasant is on outlets in India for his sons.

EASTERN NEPAL

Paradoxically enough, the parts of this area which are best known are the mountain fastnesses of the north, mapped by the Everest expeditions, though the Kosi scheme is leading to fuller knowledge of the basin. The Kosi is an example of de Martonne's schema of a mountain torrent with its 'cone of deposition' on a vast scale: on the 3–5-mile wide Chatra gorge – site of the main dam of the project – converges the drainage of an area 150 miles (240 km.) wide, most of this being taken up by the longitudinal course of the Sun Kosi; while from the north the Arun rushes straight down to this narrow exit. Work on hydrology, soil erosion, and conservation for the Kosi project reveals such gross movement of landslides that the original scheme may have to be much modified (see below, p. 564). Small wonder that in Bihar the Kosi is the most devastating of all the swinging rivers of the paradeltaic fans.

Much of the Sun Kosi drainage is developed on Hagen's Nawakot nappe, with remnants of the overlying Katmandu nappe forming the immediately enclosing ranges, north and south; northwards again the vast ramparts of the High Himalaya spring from the largely crystalline nappe roots, except for the Everest massif itself and Cho Oyu. Five peaks exceed 26,000 ft.: Gosainthan 26,305; Cho Oyu, 26,867; Everest, 29,002; Makalu, 27,790; and, across the Arun, Kangchenjunga, 28,146.[36]

The Everest Massif

The world's highest point, known to the Tibetans as Chomo-Lungma,[37] 'Goddess-Mother of the Land', is in itself not so impressive as many less famous peaks, including its neighbour Makalu with 11,000-ft. (3,355 m.) sheer cliffs and buttresses of black rock and dazzling ice. Everest is a 'lumpy pyramid' of geosynclinal sediments (Permian to Tertiary) with gneisses and schists, resting on a plinth formed by an anticlinal thrust-mass with a granitic core and a cover of originally sedimentary para-gneiss; modern work stresses recent nappe formation, rather than isostatic uplift, as responsible for the vast height.

The glaciers of Everest and Kangchenjunga may once have spilled over the cols of the 'Trans-Himalaya' along the south of the Tsang-po. Of the existing glaciers the most interesting is the Rongbuk, which descends to the north from Everest itself. This is some 12 miles long, falling from 22,000 to 16,500 ft. (6,705 to 5,030 m. in 19 km.); transverse to the mountain axis, it is practically as long as the longitudinal glaciers – a marked contrast to Karakoram conditions.

---

[36] Respectively 7,988, 8,189, 8,840, 8,470, 8,579 m. For a good tectonic block-diagram see Hagen, op. cit. Fig. 52. Correcting for gravity anomalies, the height of Everest is often given as 29,141 ft. (8,882.5 m.); but cf. J. de Graaff-Hunter, 'Various determinations . . . of the height of Mount Everest', GJ 121 (1955), which arrives at 29,080 ft., 8,863.4 m.

[37] 'Or words to that effect', Tibetan transliteration being notoriously one of the world's major impossibilities (see Ronaldshay, op. cit. 67–68, where 'Songa Chelling'='Gsang-Sngags-Chlosgling').

Apparently peculiar to the higher Himalayas are the tremendous curtains of nearly vertical and beautifully fluted ice encasing many peaks almost to their summits, especially on northern faces.

Between the Everest/Makalu and Kangchenjunga massifs lies the great gash of the Arun, with two very remarkable gorges, ascribed by Heron to cutting-back and by Wager to antecedence. In the lower gorge, below Kharta, the river is over 100 yd. (90 m.) wide and falls 4,500 ft. in 20 miles (1,370 m. in 32 km.); the

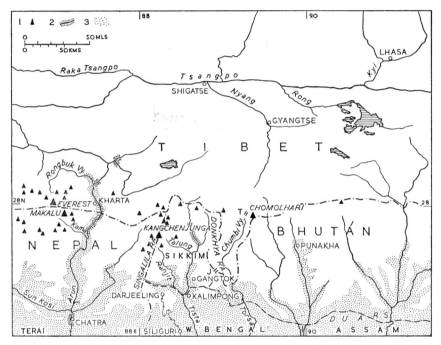

FIG 15.5 EVEREST AND THE GATEWAY TO LHASA. 1, peaks over 22,000 ft.; 2, main Arun and Tista gorges; 3, below 6,000 ft. J, Jelep La; T, Tang La. The Assam/Bhutan boundary conforms much more closely to the plains/hill margin than the 6,000-ft. contour indicates.

trade-route abandons the 5,000-ft. precipices of the valley for a switch-back over the lateral spurs. On the Doji La, north of Kharta, is the Indo-Tibetan climatic divide. In the arid open valleys and hollows above there is little vegetation but sparse grass and dwarf junipers, and at the upper entrance of the gorge 'a sweet-smelling land of juniper and wild-rose thickets'; the gorge itself has pine and birch woods. But the Arun lies directly facing the monsoon, and a little lower down, in the superlatively beautiful Kama valley, it seems always raining, with forests to 12,000 ft., almost reaching the glacier snouts; forests of pines, rhododendrons, and giant junipers covered with long streamers of grey lichens.

From a human point of view interest is concentrated on the Tibetan side

473

'characterized by somewhat soft sedimentary rocks, predominantly shales, with rolling, lumpy, rounded hills . . . alternating with open flat-bottomed valleys occupied by lakes or by swamps through which meander mud-laden rivers'.[38] The sombre colours of the hills are relieved by multi-coloured lakes, blue, purple, green, yellow, even red. Some of these valleys have villages only a few miles apart, ringed with irrigated barley fields up to 15,500 ft. (4,725 m.), and groves, also irrigated, of poplar and willow. Sheep, goats, oxen, yaks and horses are kept in the swampy meadows and moved to higher pastures in the summer. The staples of diet are barley meal (*tsamba*), mild sour beer, and the notorious tea mixed with salt and rancid butter, probably not much improved by being served (at wealthier monasteries) in agate and silver cups.

Over all is the peculiar impress of Tibetan Buddhism. The magic *mani* invocation is written on huge rolls of fine paper, encased in great prayer wheels so that with each revolution – and it takes only a second or two – several hundred thousand prayers are automatically registered. Elsewhere water-wheels and wind-mills provide mechanically for prayer without ceasing.[39] There is a far finer side: high in the sombre cliff-shadowed Rongbuk Valley are the cells of religious solitaries, women as well as men, spending years in devotion and protecting by their presence the birds and animals which have never learnt to fear man – or perhaps have learnt not to fear him *here*. It is fitting that such should be the last representatives of our race on these stairways to the stars. More lowly forms of life struggle higher: wild sheep, hares, foxes and wolves at 17,000 ft.;[40] 'grass-hoppers at 18,000, near the farthest limit of vegetable growth'; bees and butter-flies at 21,000. Choughs have been seen at 27,000 ft., perhaps following up the Everest climbers for scraps of food. The last permanent outposts of organic being are still the spiders which live on the mites of dead vegetation blown up to 22,000 ft., or on each other:[41] surely an ironic comment on existence. Beyond lie the elements: rock, ice and wind.

THE TISTA VALLEY

Directly opposite the Ganga Delta, the Tista valley, like the Kosi, reproduces on a vast scale de Martonne's schema of a mountain torrent. The upper basin is 50 miles (80 km.) wide and occupies easily eroded slates, phyllites and schists along the axis of an overfolded anticline at the core of which lies Kangchenjunga.[42] The river cuts through the Darjeeling ridge (7,000–8,000 ft., 2,135–2,440 m.) in a narrow gorge, to spill on to the plain in a vast fan seamed with old courses.

[38] A. M. Heron, 'The Everest neighbourhood, Tibet', *Calcutta Geog. Rev.* 1/1 (1936), 5–13.

[39] See Ronaldshay, 78–80, for comment on this mathematical piety.

[40] Their tracks have been reported at 21,000 ft., 6,400 m. The extremes in this paragraph are 5,180 and 8,230 m.

[41] R. W. G. Hingston, 'Animal life at high altitudes', *GJ* 65 (1925), 185–98.

[42] P. P. Karan, 'Sikkim and Bhután: a geographical appraisal', *Jnl of Geography*, 60 (1961), 58–66, quoting E. H. Pascoe.

With a rainfall of 120–180 in. (3,046–4,572 mm.) erosion is intense; the head of the gorge at the Ranjit confluence is only 750 ft. Sikkim is in effect the all but enclosed basin, the hills portion of Darjeeling District the retaining wall; and the range of relief in Sikkim is 750–28,141 ft. (230–8,579 m.) or over 5 miles.

To the west the little state is shut in by the Singalila ridge; to the east the Donkhya Range (15,000–17,000 ft., 4,570–5,180 m.) is the Tibetan boundary. But this is crossed by several easy passes into the Chumbi (upper Torsa) valley, which forms a salient of Tibet between Sikkim and Bhután. This is by far the shortest and easiest route into Tibet, leading direct to Gyantse and Lhasa; the Tang La (15,200 ft., 4,635 m.) at the head of the Chumbi is two or three miles wide and the gradients on both sides are very gentle. The Chumbi carried as much trade as all the rest of the Indo-Tibetan routes put together.

Darjeeling, at 7,376 ft. (2,248 m.), may be taken as typical of the climate of the outer hills:

Temperature, °F.

J.	F.	M.	A.	M.	J.	J.	A.	S.	O.	N.	D.	
40·1	41·6	49·7	56·2	58·3	59·9	61·5	60·9	59·4	55·2	47·8	41·8	Ra. 21·4 (11·9° C.

Precipitation, inches

J.	F.	M.	A.	M.	J.	J.	A.	S.	O.	N.	D.	
0·6	1·1	1·8	3·8	8·7	24·9	32·3	26·1	18·4	4·5	0·8	0·2	Total 122·7 (3,117 mm.)

Higher up, Gangtok has 133 in. and Gnatong, on the Donkhya Range, 180 in. (3,378 and 4,572 mm.). Of course, aspect and exposure are main determinants of vegetation and cultivation.

(a) *Darjeeling* was secured from Sikkim in 1833, 'a worthless uninhabited mountain'; the adjacent terai eleven years later. But by 1873 there were 15,000 ac. (6,045 ha.) of tea; today Darjeeling and Jalpaiguri Districts have about 190,000 ac. (7,690 ha.), much of course in the terai of the Duars. Much of the labour is Nepali. Subsistence agriculture is marked by the dominance of rice – half the acreage of foodgrains. Tea acreage is about equal to rice, and maize comes next. But the cultivated ground is barely a quarter of the total area, the rest being mainly magnificent forest with the whole range from sal to pine. Even here, however, soil erosion is serious.[43]

Already at Siliguri, in the terai 8 miles (13 km.) from the foot of the hills, we are in the contact zone: 'Siliguri is palpably a place of meeting', evidenced by the appearance of Mongolian faces, the large iron-roofed tea godowns, different types of rolling stock, long lines of bullock-carts and lorries. The town, which doubled in size in ten years (1951: 34,840), has gained impetus from the new Assam rail link, bringing timber for new sawmills, from the strategic importance

[43] S. Sinha, 'Influence of physiography on the location and land-use of tea gardens of Darjeeling Dt', *Indian Geogr* 1/2 (1957), 114–21; V. S. Rao, 'Some problems of soil conservation and proper land use in a Himalayan Region of West Bengal', *Indian Forester*, 87/6 (1951), 339–48 – a fine study; even the tea gardens are not immune from erosion, and recently planted cardamom along river banks is a causative factor. See also B. Banerjee, 'Economic geography of tea in West Bengal', *Indian Geogr* 2/2 (1957), 246–70.

thrust upon it by the border troubles, and from its university; but it has been described as a slum town, overcrowded with refugees from East Pakistan. Here the railway is succeeded by two mountain lines, one up the Tista to a point opposite Kalimpong (12,000), the starting-point for the road to Tibet, the other a mountain railway to Darjeeling itself. Apart from its importance as a centre of the tea-trade, Darjeeling (25,873 (in March)) has obviously a most favourable site for a hill station serving the greatest conurbation of India; April–May mean temperatures are 27–29°F. (15–16°C.) below those of Calcutta. Like most hill stations, it has many schools; mist-enshrouded for half the year, on clear days the skyline is climaxed by the magnificent peak of Kangchenjunga.

(b) *Sikkim* had a 1961 population of 167,000 on 2,818 sq. miles (7,532 km²) of deeply dissected highland. The state has a special protected relationship with India. In the north it is practically Tibetan in character, and the State religion is Buddhist, though owing to Nepali and now Indian immigration the majority of the people is now probably Hindu; the original inhabitants, the Lepcha or Rong, are now only about 10%; a mixture of Mongoloid and non-Mongoloid, of herdsmen and farmers, they are now almost submerged.

Geoffrey Gorer's description of Zongu, between the Tista and the Talung in the heart of the country, may be taken as representative of the intermediate levels. 'Except for a few artificially levelled places, there is probably not a hundred square yards of level ground', and tracks are too steep even for mules. Rain is 'almost continuous' from June to September, at least on south-facing slopes; only October and November are dry. Above 8,000 ft. (2,440 m.) snow lies every year, and there are often powderings of snow at much lower levels; but oranges and peaches can be grown in the valleys, and only once in the last fifty years has snow fallen by the rivers at about 2,000 ft. Mean temperatures vary between 40 and 86°F. (4·4 and 30°C.) and diurnal ranges are high:

> 'The river valleys are hot, steamy and somewhat malarious, and consequently there are no houses right on the river. . . . Most of the houses are between 3,500 and 7,500 feet above sea level (1,070 and 2,285 m.), a relatively narrow band between the two rivers. . . . Above the cultivated land is the forest in which wild produce is gathered, a decreasing amount of hunting done, and to which the cattle are sent up to pasture in the winter months. Above the forest level comes first the rhododendron forest, and then the snows, rarely visited except by hunters searching either for ibex or musk-deer or for the wild aconite which forms the basis of their arrow poison.'[44]

The northern part of the country remains pastoral, sheep, yaks and the zomo (a cow/yak cross) providing wool, leather and milk. The southern half of the tiny country is more open, and here cultivation becomes important. Since the turn of the century Nepali settlers have introduced rice on alluvial flats and terraced lower slopes; the Lepchas, confined more and more to their cleared patches in secondary jungle, grow mainly maize, but with some buckwheat and millets.

[44] G. Gorer, *Himalayan Village* (London, 1938), 51–54.

Nutrition is marginal, although the Lepchas eat meat – any meat – when they can. Fragmentation is excessive, and the gulf between landlord and cultivator great; alcoholism, based on fermented grains, is widespread.[45]

Settlement is essentially dispersed in hamlets of two to four homesteads, strung loosely along the hillsides above the fields, or even athwart the ridges; the stilted Lepcha houses can be distinguished from those of the Nepalis, direct on the ground and, near roads, roofed with corrugated iron rather than thatch. Only those villages which have a monastery have any sort of focus. Even in Lingthem, the second biggest village in Zongu (population 176) and one of the most coherent, eight houses are the most that can be seen from any one point: 'I should reckon that there were quite three miles and three thousand feet between the lowest house to the east and the highest house to the west in the village.'

There are potentially useful deposits of copper, associated with bismuth, antimony and galena; attempts have been made to exploit them but transport difficulties are so far insuperable. Except for the capital, Gangtok, with its little Court nucleus, the 'towns' of the map are simply staging-points on Tibetan routes, with a few trading and administrative functions. Across the Tista from Zongu the little settlement of Mangan has half a dozen Indian shops, belonging to Marwaris who exploit (in every sense) the cardamom trade; a dispensary, post office and school, some liquor shops, and 'a couple of Tibetan prostitutes for the use of the muleteers'. In Lepcha society these last probably give Mangan an urban cachet.[46]

In the far north and under Kangchenjunga even this thin film of life frays out into a tattered edge. Above the forests is a different world, not to be entered without charms and incantations: 'Not far beyond the last of the thickets of rhododendrons stands a rough shed of stone, the home of two yak-herds who tend their charges in these high places during the summer months, a fact which entitles the spot to a definite location on the map under the name of Jongri. We had reached the threshold of the snows.'[47]

BHUTÁN

Bhután (18,000 sq. miles, 47,000 km²) is a country of the wildest mountain and forest, of drab rolling yak-pastures, of fantastic monasteries wedged into the clefts of huge precipices, of massive castles where life is almost as feudal as it looks.[48] In the northwest it is dominated by the superb cone of Chomo Lhari, 'Divine Queen of Mountains' (23,930 ft., 7,263 m.), guarding the Tang La col on the Brahmaputra/Tsang-po watershed.

From its conquest by Tibetan freebooters in the 16th century until some fifty years ago, Bhután was nominally governed by a temporal and a spiritual lord, the

---

[45] J. Dupuis, 'Le Sikkim', *Acta Geographica*, 29 (Paris, 1959), 17–35; Karan, *op. cit.*
[46] Gorer, *loc. cit.*
[47] Ronaldshay, *op. cit.* 171.
[48] See the plates in Ronaldshay.

Deb and Dharma Rajas, who were in fact the puppets of rival magnates. In 1907 one of the latter established a definitive monarchical régime; the country remained poor, remote and aloof, but at least peaceful. Now, however, it finds itself on the marches of the Sino-Indian conflict.

Inheriting British control, India finances the country and guides its external relations. Following the Chinese claims to part of the north of the country, Bhután has opened her doors southwards: a 'jeepable' road links Hasimar in West Bengal with Paro, the old, and Thimbu, the new capital. Neither is much more than a palace, a monastery, a few houses and a few shops started by Tibetan refugees. Four more routes from India are under construction, to be linked by an east–west road over the high Black Mountain range which divides the country into an essentially Assamese east and a Tibetan west. South of the mountains, Nepalis who have settled in the Bhután Duars comprise about a quarter of the population, though they are as yet second-class citizens.

Karan estimates the population at about 8,500,000. Entirely agricultural, they grow rice on valley floors and stone-faced terraces, up to 4,000 ft. (1,220 m.), along with some buckwheat; above this altitude wheat and barley are the main crops. The yak dominates the pastoral scene, and, apart from rice, its hair provides the only commercial export – for Guardsmen's bearskins! Rice was bartered with Tibet for salt, but now goes over the new road to India. Although the country is poor and the people live under semi-feudal conditions, illiterate and unhygienic, there is not the crushing burden of starvation or, as yet, of overpopulation. The forests offer the only industrial resource, and a Swedish company may start their exploitation; meanwhile Bhután gets a small share from the new Jaldhaka power project on the India border, primarily designed for the tea gardens of West Bengal.[49]

BIBLIOGRAPHICAL NOTE

The general references given at the end of Chapter 14 are relevant here also. On Kumaon, S. D. Pant's excellent *The Social Economy of the Himalayans* (London, 1935) is marred only by bad maps; the 220 plates of A. Heim and A. Gansser, *The Throne of the Gods* (London, 1939) cover both human and physical aspects. More technical papers by Heim and Gansser and by J. B. Auden are cited in the Bibliographical Note to Chapter 1 above.

On Nepal the old standard work, P. Landon, *Nepal* (London, 1928), which always presented a sort of Never-never land, is now completely superseded by the admirably illustrated books of Toni Hagen, *Nepal: The Kingdom in the Himalayas* (Kümmerley & Frey, Berne, 1961) and P. P. Karan and W. M. Jenkins *Nepal: A Cultural and Physical Geography* (Univ. of Kentucky, Lexington, 1960); the maps in the latter are very instructive. The latter authors have a

[49] See P. P. Karan and W. M. Jenkins, *The Himalayan Kingdoms: Bhután, Sikkim and Nepal* (Van Nostrand, Searchlight Books, Princeton, 1963); I. Brinkworth, 'Bhután: The Unknown Kingdom', *Geogr. Mag.* (London), 36 (1963), 320–35.

smaller book, *The Himalayan Kingdoms: Bhután, Sikkim and Nepal* (1963), in Van Nostrand's Searchlight Books, while Karan has published 'A land use reconnaissance in Nepal by aero-field techniques and photography', *Proc. Amer. Phil. Soc.* 104/2 (1960), 172–87. An excellent study is J. Dupuis, 'Les Bassins intérieures du Kashmir et du Nepal', *Annales de Géographie*, 71 (1962), 156–66. Increasing attention is naturally being paid to Himalayan questions in the Indian geographical journals.

CHAPTER 16

The Western Borderlands
(Regions I–III)

This chapter treats all the extra-Himalayan territory between the alluvial plains of the Indus and the Afghan and Iranian boundaries. These boundaries, except for short stretches in the extreme north and along the Safed Koh, pay little attention to physical features; there is little or no natural difference between the Kabul and Kunar valleys east and west of the border, between the desert basins of northwest Baluchistan and of Seistan, or between Iranian and Baluchi Makran; and for the most part the frontier peoples straddle the actual boundary. Yet, at least along the great routeways, decades of British administration have left a distinctive imprint on the land – the military symbol of the cantonment.

Regionally the whole area falls into three main divisions: the hills of the Northwest Frontier; the sub-montane Indus region, including the Vale of Peshawar and the Bannu Plain, the Potwar Plateau and the Salt Range; Baluchistan. Politically, it lies within the Peshawar and Dera Ismail Khan Divisions (these two=the old Northwest Frontier Province) of West Pakistan, the Quetta and Kalat Divisions (=most of Baluchistan); Las Bela in the south is attached to Karachi and the Potwar Plateau is in Rawalpindi Division. These administrative divisions include a number of Tribal Agencies from Chitral to Makran.

BALUCHISTAN

The arid basins and hills of Baluchistan form the eastern portion of the great Iranian plateaus, sharply marked off from the Indus Plain by the Kirthar and Sulaiman ramparts. In the northeast the Gomal River may be taken as a rational limit; beyond this the strongly trellised drainage patterns of Baluchistan are replaced by transverse valleys direct to the Indus, giving a distinctly different human – or strategic – emphasis. The lowland of Kachhi (in the Sibi re-entrant) is treated as part of the Lower Indus region.

Relief and structure (Fig. 16.1)

The mountain skeleton of Baluchistan consists of two great virgations, knotted together in the complex Quetta node, where Zarghun and Khalifat attain over 11,000 ft. (3,355 m.) – a culmination probably associated with a concealed extension of the Peninsular Block controlling the Sibi re-entrant (cf. Fig. 1.1).

Between the Kundar and the Zhob tributaries of the Gomal the 9,000-ft. (2,745 m.) Toba Kakar Range trends southwest towards Chaman, with a slight convexity to the southeast. South from the Gomal runs the great series of echelonned ridges, known collectively as the Sulaiman Range, which rise to over 11,000 ft. in Takht-i-Sulaiman, only 30 miles (48 km.) from the Gomal, but have

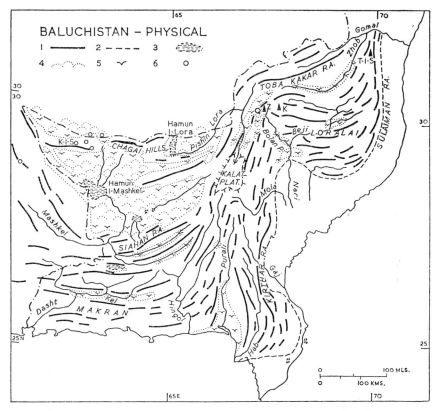

FIG 16.1 BALUCHISTAN, PHYSICAL OUTLINES. 1, main trends of ranges; 2, boundary of Indus alluvium; 3, hamuns (playas); 4, sand desert; 5, alluvial basins; 6, recent volcanoes. T-I-S, Takht-i-Sulaiman (11,100 ft.); Z, Zarghun (11,730); K, Khalifat (11,430); K-I-S, Koh-i-Sultan (7,654). Q, Quetta.

summits generally at 6,000–7,000 ft. (1,830–2,135 m.). At about 30° N the Sulaimans begin to swing westwards, until finally their continuations in the Bugti Hills are pointing towards the Quetta node. Looped between the Toba Kakar and Sulaiman Ranges lie the trellis-patterned basins of the Zhob and the Beji: nested folds of Cretaceous and Eocene limestones and sandstones producing in Loralai an extraordinary landscape of innumerable scarps and hogsbacks, small plateaus and mesas, steep craggy outcrops with the talus-slopes littered with boulders half the size of the fields (very small fields, it is true); and set in

481

these arid hills, grey and dun and ochre, a few greener patches in small alluvial or detrital basins.

Southwest of Quetta, Baluchistan includes but a portion of the vaster Iranian loops; but something of the same pattern can be discerned, ranges trending north/south in the east and swinging round east/west in Makran. This pattern is broken across by the Arabian Sea, probably fairly recently subsided, and most of the coast is longitudinal, with many hammerhead peninsulas, one of which – Gwadar – belonged until 1958 to the Arabian state of Oman; but in the east the ranges run out transversely in Ras Muari (Cape Monze).

There is a marked contrast between the ranges on either side of 66° 15′ E. To the east massive limestones, Cretaceous to Oligocene with some intrusions of Deccan Lava age, form great anticlinal bulges; erosion has opened up the anticlines, but in this arid climate and thirsty rock it has not progressed to the stage of inversion of relief: anticlines are still ridges and synclines valleys. The most striking feature is the Kirthar wall, rising from 4,000 ft. (1,220 m.) in the south to nearly 8,000 in the north, and broken only by a few gorges such as those of the Mula and the Gaj now useless for any but local traffic, though the former is relatively easy and was used by one division of Alexander's withdrawing army. The capping of the Kirthar is the massive Spitangi limestone (Eocene), which also forms the Kalat plateau at 7,000–8,000 ft. (2,135–2,440 m.). In the south the ranges break down into the little scarps behind Karachi, and the triangular alluvial lowland of the Purali, occupied by Las Bela state, is set into them.

In the west the ranges are formed mainly of Oligocene flysch, weak sandstones and shales which (except in more massively built coastal Makran) fold more sharply. A rainfall rather less scanty, impermeable clays instead of calcareous masses, sharper folding, all combine to permit the more normal development of synclinal hills. The landscape of southern Makran is bizarre: 'that brazen coast washed by a molten sea', and inland 'gigantic cap-crowned pillars and pedestals are balanced in fantastic array about the mountain slopes . . . with successive strata so well defined that they possess all the appearance of massive masonry construction . . . standing stiff, jagged, naked and uncompromising'[1] above the confused ravine-riddled lower hills of clay.

North of the great longitudinal valley of the Kej, in Pangjur, these parallel wall-sided or knife-edged ranges are higher than in coastal Makran, but beyond the Siahan Range they sink into the great desert depression (1,500–3,000 ft., 455–915 m.) of the Hamun-i-Mashkel (*hamun* = playa), flanked on the north, along the Afghan border, by the remarkable recent volcanoes of the Chagai Hills. Round this interior drainage basin, and that of the smaller Hamun-i-Lora, the hills are skirted by great coalescing talus-fans. The basins are floored by wide expanses of bare sun-cracked clay, spreads of black oxidized pebbles (*dasht*), and shifting reddish dunes; there seem to be terraces possibly indicating former levels of lakes which are now, except in flood-time, nothing but salt incrustations

[1] T. H. Holdich, *The Gates of India* (1910), 285, 289, 317.

with a few marshy patches and fewer of more or less permanent water.[2] Small wonder that the local proverb considers Baluchistan as the dump where Allah shot the rubbish of Creation.

Climate and vegetation

Great aridity and great temperature ranges are the leading features of the climate. Quetta, in an intermont basin at 5,500 ft. (1,675 m.) has mean temperatures of 39·6° F. in January and 77·8° in July (4·2–25·4° C.), and the mean diurnal ranges for these months are respectively some 20° and 28° (11° and 15·6° C.); variations of 80° (44·4° C.) in 24 hours are said by Holdich to be not uncommon. The country is not sheltered by the Himalayan wall and winds are very strong, whether on the open desert plains of the northwest or in the narrow corridors of the border valleys; prevailingly from the northwest, they are scorchingly hot in summer, filling the air with dust from the Iranian deserts; in winter bitterly cold, 'like a keen-edged blade, to the dividing asunder of bones and marrow'.[3] Annual rainfall is hardly anywhere over 10 in. (Shahrig has the maximum, 14·7 in. (3,734 mm.)), and it is of course extremely unreliable, falling when it does fall in intensely violent storms which send vast spills of detritus into the desert basins, or sudden spates, dangerous to travellers, through *tangis* or transverse clefts, often only a few yards wide, by which the streams penetrate the longitudinal ranges; at other times most rivers are mere trickles and pools in their stony beds. Over most of the plateau precipitation (often snow) is brought mainly by shallow west-moving winter depressions, but in the lower highlands (Loralai–Zhob) it has the usual monsoon summer maximum, and Quetta is near enough to the eastern edge to show a slight secondary maximum then:

J.	F.	M.	A.	M.	J.	J.	A.	S.	O.	N.	D.	Total
2·1	2·1	1·8	1·1	0·3	0·2	0·5	0·6	0·1	0·1	0·3	0·8	10·0
												(2,540 mm.)

The naturally xerophytic vegetation has been destroyed or reduced by over-grazing; protection brings dramatic regeneration to hillsides of thorny scrub, poor grass and bare rocky soil. On the higher northern Sulaimans there are forests of juniper and wild olive, with pistachio, laurel and myrtle. In the north-west these grade into true desert, utterly barren but for the reedy wetter patches of the *hamuns* and thin lines of tamarisk along the bigger wadis or *loras*.

The desert pediments of the interior and the wild gorges of the bordering hills bear witness to the intermittent but intense spells of erosion, the natural consequence of the few downpours and the thin vegetation cover. Intense heat and cold, savage winds, rare but violent floods, in summer dust insidious everywhere; a surface largely rock, pebble or sand; scanty and unreliable rainfall, earthquakes – a harsh environment, brightened to brief beauty in the spring, and enclosing but few green islands of fertility.

[2] See M. Abu Bakr, 'Physiography of Chagai-Kharan Region', *PGR* 18/2 (1963), 1–12.
[3] Holdich, *The Indian Borderland* (2nd ed., 1909), 112.

The peoples

The population of Baluchistan, excluding the lowland areas, was 1,300,000 in 1961 – about 10 to the square mile, and obviously much less in the western deserts. Four main indigenous groups are generally recognized: the cultivating Jatti of Las Bela and Kachhi; Pathans, north of Quetta; Brahuis in the mountain border in Sarawan and Jhalawan, separating the Baluchis of the Marri–Bugti country from those of the west. All these are of course much intermingled both territorially and ethnically; all are tribal and there are a variety of kiths,[4] sometimes overlapping tribal and linguistic divisions; while in Makran some of the stocks, such as the Med fishermen and the Lori gypsies, seem to be very ancient. Perhaps the only common factor is Islam of no advanced kind, riddled with atavistic beliefs and customs. The Baluchi and Pathan languages are Iranian, but Brahui is definitely Dravidian, an outlier removed by 1,700 miles (2,735 km.) from the main Dravidian mass: a fascinating riddle, yet perhaps not so strange as appears at first sight, since the Dravidians presumably entered India by the land-gates, perhaps picking their way southwards when the Indus was still joined by the Sarasvati and the Thar Desert was much more restricted. This conjecture of Holdich's is perhaps strengthened by the recognition of Dravidian elements in the Indus civilization, and by the evidence of a more humid climate in Sind in Mohenjo-daro times.

Under Arab domination in the first centuries of Islam Makran seems to have reached a high pitch of prosperity; thereafter Baluchistan was a debatable land, constantly changing masters, between Moguls, Afghans and Iranians. For obvious political and topographical reasons the north has a strong pull towards Afghanistan, Makran to Iran. In the 17th and 18th centuries the Khans of Kalat built up a strong Brahui confederacy, nominally (and perhaps sometimes really) subject to Delhi or Kandahar. They fell under British domination between 1840 and 1875 – largely as an incident in relations with Afghanistan, whence the northern districts were annexed by the Treaty of Gandamak after the Second Afghan War of 1879–81.

Economic life

The economic activity of the great mass of the population remains primitive; as a rule no hard and fast line can be drawn between agriculturalist and pastoralist, and many add a variety of petty trading, carrying or handicraft activities to their primary pursuits. Nomadism, both regular and enforced by bad seasons, largely accounts for the great fluctuations in rate of increase of population (e.g. in Chagai) and is still of importance, though declining. Even among the settled groups the scanty amount of useful land enforces shifts of hamlets, and the dwellings themselves are often impermanent – matting or felt tents, summer shelters of reeds and branches.

[4] In the sense used in E. Huntington's *Mainsprings of Civilization* (Wiley, NY, 1945), 102.

Much of this nomadism, indeed, is rather transhumance: Brahuis moving into Kachhi or Sind with their families and flocks, to escape the winter cold; Pathans and Baluchis, half farmers and half shepherds, moving on a restricted round

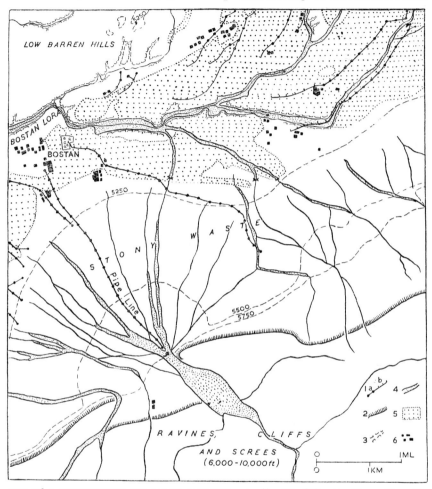

FIG 16.2 SETTLEMENT ON A FAN, BOSTAN. 15 miles N of Quetta (A on Fig 76). 1a, karez; 1b, open irrig. channels; 2, abrupt edge of hills; 3, ravines; 4, stream beds (only permanent water channel shown in Bostan Lora); 5, cultivation; 6, settlement. Only karez in flow shown; numerous dry karez on fans omitted, as are Quetta–Zhob road (along 5,250 ft. contour) and railway just below it. *SOP* 34 N/3. *Courtesy* SOP.

between flocks and fields; influx into the fertile valleys of Kej and Pangjur for the date-harvest. True pastoral nomadism yet survives in the inhospitable north-west. There is also the transit of the Afghan Powindahs who winter in the plains, trading in cloth and dried fruits for bazaar goods, or engaging in casual labour such as canal digging. Even Quetta is not unaffected by this seasonal mobility: the population is perhaps 50% greater in summer than in winter, plains dwellers coming to escape the hot weather, families of quasi-permanent residents leaving to avoid the rigorous winter.

Pastoralism is obviously of great importance. Goats and fat-tailed sheep probably account for over 80% of the stock, and much of the petty local traffic is still carried on camels and donkeys, despite the rapid inroads of lorry and bus. Agriculture, equally obviously, is dependent on the most careful use of such water as exists. About 5,000 ac. (2,025 ha.) are irrigated near Pishin by canals, with wheat as the main rabi crop and lucerne and melons in the summer, and there is also some irrigation on the Zhob, though for much of its course its banks are too high and steep to permit its use.

The most remarkable indigenous irrigation method is the *karez*: shafts are sunk in the great fans skirting the hills, and these shafts are linked by galleries to form a tunnel, sometimes tapping a spring but more often collecting the sub-soil water (Fig. 16.2). The *karez* has the great advantage of avoiding loss by evaporation, and where hydrographic conditions are suitable it may remain productive a long time.[5] Elsewhere, rough bunds on hill-slopes and across valleys retain the soilwash of the rainstorms, forming a trap for the saturated soil; *karez* irrigation is mainly in the Quetta region, as in the south the *daman* is usually too gentle in slope to retain much water or give much head. Wheat, barley and millet are the chief crops, with potatoes increasingly important in the eastern valleys. Apricots, peaches, apples and grapes are grown in the valleys around Quetta, and the Harnai valley is thought suitable for citrus fruit. Makran has two distinctive occupations: date-growing in the relatively well-watered central valley, now being extended by irrigation to supply a packing plant at Turbat, and fishing along the coast. Future progress in Baluchistan probably depends on the improvement of stock-breeding, range improvement (already begun in a pilot area), the development of fruit culture and processing, and a more scientific development of indigenous irrigation methods and possibly of sub-artesian water. In the southeast the Las Bela plain is an agriculturally undeveloped zone, whose water resource potential is likely to be developed now that Baluchistan is better integrated with West Pakistan as a whole.[6]

Industrial development remains slight. There is some new textile industry, cotton at Quetta, wool at Harnai. Pakistan's only coking coal is mined, mainly by adits, at Khost in the Harnai Pass, and the thin steeply-inclined seams of the Sor Range east of Quetta are now being developed (above, 301). A briquetting plant

[5] See R. D. Oldham, *Rec. GSI* 25 (1892), 36–52. For a detailed and beautifully illustrated account of *karez* irrigation, see J. Humlum, *La géographie de l'Afghanistan* (Gyldendal, Copenhagen, 1959), 212–14, 223–35, with a map on the scale 1:2100.

[6] Cf. H. K. Thirlaway, 'The need of . . . integrated survey in Quetta-Kalat Division', *Oriental Geogr* (Dacca), 3/2 (1959), 63–70, and the note on pistachio in the same issue, 70–73. On Las Bela, A. H. Siddiqi's article (*ibid.* 47–62), and D. E. Sopher, *Annual Summary Report: 1959* to US Office of Naval Research, NR 388–041.

and a thermal power station are also being built at Quetta. The sulphur of Koh-i-Sultan is no longer worked, but green marble is exported. The Bolan railway will have increased capacity to serve the coalfields in the Pass and the Sor Range.[7]

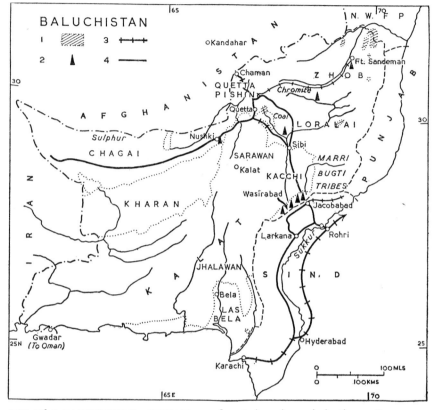

FIG 16.3 BALUCHISTAN, GENERAL. 1, forest (open); 2, irrigation railways; 3, BGDT; 4, BGST; east of the Indus only the main line to the Punjab is shown. Gwadar has now been ceded to Pakistan.

Communications and towns (Fig. 16.3)

Alexander the Great's privations in Makran appear to have given Baluchistan an undeservedly bad name. The country has not been unimportant as a passageway; but although access to the Indus is relatively easy by Quetta or Makran, the barrier of the Thar Desert blocked further advance, and the greater movements into India have generally been in the north. Ancient dams and cultivation terraces (perhaps early Arab) in widely separated areas suggest a more favourable

[7] F. Husain, 'Structure and coal reserves of the Sor Range–Daghari coalfield', *Oriental Geogr* 5/3 (1961), 137–44.

climate; the Arab invasion of Sind in the 8th century, the first Muslim irruption into India, used the Makran route, where the long Kej corridor is less inhospitable than the coast, and in Arab times agricultural prosperity and town life seem

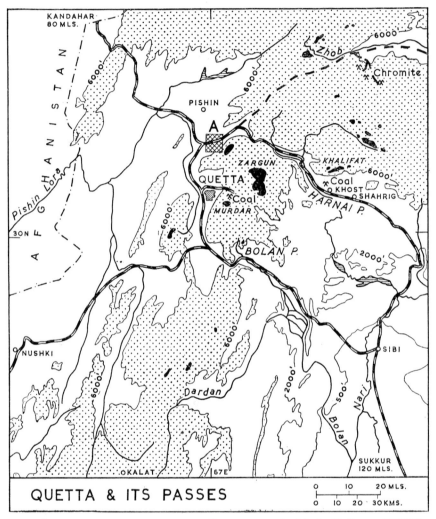

FIG 16.4 QUETTA AND ITS PASSES. Over 10,000 ft. black. Railways BGST; broken line Zhob valley road. Note the great joint fan of the Dardan and Bolan Rivers. A = Fig 16.2.

to have been well diffused there. In the 19th century British interest in Baluchistan was motivated by the desire to control routes to Herat and Kandahar, the keys to Afghanistan on the west and south.

The eastern border hills are pierced by two broad-gauge railways, via the

Bolan and the Harnai Passes; strategic lines reach out to New Chaman on the Afghan border, railhead for Kandahar (only 80 miles, 129 km. away), and for over 400 miles (644 km.) west to the Iranian border: obviously this latter line is hardly justified by local traffic. In any case motor transport has largely superseded even the strategic functions of this long finger of rail. On the other line, however, there is talk of continuing the rail link into Afghanistan, and with increasing economic development in that country the transit trade may be expected to expand, despite political difficulties. The chief items to Afghanistan are bazaar goods, sugar, motor and lighting oils, with dried fruits, carpets and wool as Afghan exports.

Quetta is really the only big town of Baluchistan, and it is entirely extraneous – an administrative and strategic centre which, as the only concentration of population in the country, has added to itself some commercial and now industrial function; it is also a hill resort. It is hardly necessary to emphasize its strategic value, commanding as it does both routes up from Sibi (Fig. 16.4). It was largely rebuilt after the very destructive 1935 earthquake, and in 1961 had a population of 107,000, an increase of 27% from 1951 when the population had already been swollen by the influx of refugees from India.[8] The other towns – Fort Sandeman, Kalat, Bela – are little more than bazaar villages, of military origin in the first case, grouped round the palace or fort of the local Khans in the other two.

THE NORTHWESTERN HILLS

In a broad sense the hills of the old 'North-West Frontier' are but the ragged fringe of Afghanistan. The clear trends and massive structures of Baluchistan are absent north of the Gomal, and to some extent there is a corresponding human fragmentation. Although the vast majority of the people of the Northwestern Hills are of one ethnic stock, one language and one faith – Pathan, Pakhtu or Pushtu, and Sunni Islam respectively – their political development is more amorphous, a congeries of petty tribal republics and clans. The western boundary of the region is of course arbitrary – the Durand Line, the political boundary between Afghanistan and (until 1947) India: the eastern boundary from the Vale of Peshawar southwards is taken as the *daman* where the hills sink under the basins along the Indus – roughly the old Sikh border. Except in Kohat this corresponds fairly well to the boundary between the Administered Districts and the Tribal Agencies (Fig. 16.5), between the 'settled' Pathans and their untamed fellows of the hills. In the north, in the spurs running down from the Hindu Kush/Pamir/Karakoram node, it is impossible to draw any hard and fast boundary: the political boundary with Kashmir is as suitable a line as any, and the 'no man's land' nature of this transitional area is emphasized by the serio-comic difficulties of integrating such states as Chitral into Pakistan. Chitral

---

[8] See K. U. Kureishy, 'Quetta: a study in urban landscape', *PGR* 14/1 (1959), 14–25.

is definitely within the framework of Basic Democracy; to the north, Gilgit, Hazar and Hunza remain in effect quasi-feudal.[9]

The physical setting

The great change of direction between the Karakoram and the Hindu Kush is presumably controlled, at a distance, by the hidden outlines of the Peninsular block. The long tongue of Afghan territory in the Oxus valley – Wakhan, the buffer-strip between Russia and the Indian Empire – runs west/east along the top of the arch. Here the northern boundary lies at 16,000–24,000 ft. (4,880–7,315 m.) actually on the Hindu Kush, the watershed between the Yarkhun and Chitral Rivers and the Gilgit. Of the several passes which cross the Hindu Kush, here described by Holdich as 'flat-backed', the most important is the Baroghil (only 12,460 ft., 3,798 m.) which can be used by laden animals for eight months of the year, a comparatively easy crossing.

South from this high watershed, as far as the Kabul River (220 miles, 354 km.), the general trend is northeast–southwest with a northerly component, falling from the 25,263 ft. (7,700 m.) of Tirich Mir in the north of Chitral to 5,000–6,000 ft. (1,525–1,830 m.) in the Mohmand Hills and the Malakand ridge which separates the Swat valley from the Vale of Peshawar. The far north is geologically Himalayan territory: the rocks of upper Chitral are Permo-Carboniferous and Jurassic with large areas of gneiss and granite; but all the human links are with the south. This mountain area is gashed by deep narrow valleys – the town of Chitral itself, only 30 miles (48 km.) from Tirich Mir, is under 5,000 ft. The striking parallelism of the Yarkhun, Chitral-Kunar, Panjkora and Swat Rivers to the middle Indus, and their relations to the Kabul River into which they flow, seem to call for a large-scale tectonic explanation.

South of the Kabul River the northeast/southwest trend is interrupted by the strong west/east line of the Safed Koh Range, which reaches 15,620 ft. (2,543 m.) in its western culmination, Sikaram, falling under to 5,000 ft. in the Kohat Hills in the angle between the Kabul or Landai River and the Indus (Fig. 16.5). This trend is perhaps a continuation of an outer Himalayan arc from the neighbourhood of the Jhelum gorges by the Kala Chitta Dhar south of Attock. The whole area between the Safed Koh and the Tochi River is a tangle of arid hills up to 5,000 ft. (1,515 m.), largely Eocene nummulitic limestones and Siwalik sandstones, with a general west/east trend cut across from northwest to southeast by the more favoured upper Kurram valley. In the Bhittanni country, between Bannu and Jandola, there seems to be an arcuate arrangement convex to the west; the spurs of the Northwestern Hills and of the Salt Range nearly meet in the Pezu gap between Bannu and Dera Ismail Khan. In the extreme south, Waziristan, the north/south trends of the Sulaimans begin. The sinuous

[9] W. A. Wilcox, *Pakistan: The Consolidation of a Nation* (Columbia Univ. Press, NY, 1963), 153–62; see this study also for the Baluchistan states. Cf. R. D. Campbell, *Pakistan: Emerging Democracy* (Van Nostrand, Princeton, 1963), 18.

strikes of this area between the Kabul and Gomal Rivers express 'the buckling caused by the meeting . . . of the Himalayan, Hindu Kush, and the other more western systems of crust movement, setting in from three sides against the rigid

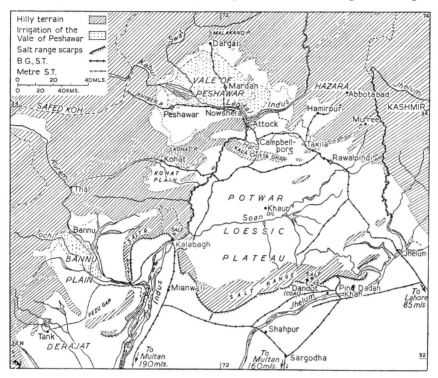

FIG 16.5 THE NORTHWESTERN HILLS AND SUB-MONTANE INDUS REGION. Dotted line is boundary between administered and tribal areas. Khewra (salt, gypsum) lies between Dandot and its rail junction. The new capital of Pakistan, Islamabad, lies just north of Rawalpindi.

peninsular mass', and are the habitat of the ever-warring tribes whose political fragmentation corresponds to the extremely broken terrain.

As on the Baluchistan plateau, westerly climatic influences are important. On the whole the region is better watered than is Baluchistan, although the difference is naturally very little in the south. Rainfall is generally 12–25 in. (3,810–6,350 mm.), depending of course greatly on altitude, exposure and aspect; in the north winter precipitation predominates, while farther south the westerly and the monsoonal influences are of approximately equal strength:

	J.	F.	M.	A.	M.	J.	J.	A.	S.	O.	N.	D.	Total
Chitral	1·2	1·6	3·2	3·9	0·7	0·3	0·1	0·2	0·2	0·7	0·3	0·9	13·3 in. (3,378 mm.)
							2·2						
Peshawa	1·7	1·5	2·0	1·5	0·7	0·5	2·2	3·3	1·2	0·3	0·4	0·6	15·9 in. (4,039 mm.)
							8·2						

491

Both sources are precarious and droughts are not infrequent either in winter or in summer.

Temperatures tend to extremes and are again much affected by topographical situation. Peshawar (in the plains, but very close to the hills) ranges from under 50° F. in January to over 91° in June (10–32·8° C.), and in the intermont valleys extremes are of course much more marked: Chitral, in its narrow wind-swept valley, has had temperatures as low as 5·4° F. and as high as 108° (−14·8 and +42·2° C.), and to the south in Waziristan the more or less enclosed plain between 4,000 and 5,000 ft. at Wana has had *minus* 13° F. (−25·0° C.).

There is naturally a considerable variation in the vegetation cover. The lower hills, as in Waziristan and the Mohmand country, do indeed conform to the usual impression of the Frontier: a land of bare jagged ridges carrying little but infrequent bushes, acacia, dwarf palms, coarse grasses. But in the higher west there are forests of pine, deodar and ilex (evergreen oak), and those on the southern flanks of Safed Koh form good tall stands of timber. On the Kurram River 'more or less all along are cornfields and fruit gardens, mulberry groves and fertile glades, passing up to ridges crested by oak and olive, yew trees and pines.' The northern mountains have plane, poplar, and ilex, and great forests of pine and deodar, as well as extensive mountain grasslands; but in the far north altitude and exposure inhibit vegetation and many of the valley sides are rocky and barren.

The peoples and their life

The population of the hills is almost solidly tribal and Muslim. Strictly speaking, 'Pathan' implies tribal status rather than race, but in normal usage it is applied as a generic term to most of the tribes – Afridis, Mohmands, Mahsuds, Orakzais, Waziris, etc. – and the last few decades have seen the growth of something like a Pathan national sentiment. This is, however, complicated not only by the inherent particularism of the tribes and clans, but also by the political separation of the Pathans into three distinct groups: the settled tribes (over 1,000,000) in the Pakistani Divisions; the 3,000,000 hillmen in the Tribal Agencies; and their fellows in Afghanistan, estimated at 3,000,000–7,000,000. Nearly all speak dialects of Pushtu, an Iranian tongue, and culturally the region is in broad outline remarkably homogeneous.

For the most part the tribesmen are intensely democratic, eking out from scanty patches of arable land a hard living, supplemented by less licit but more exciting acquisitive processes; riddled with tribal, clan and family vendettas; easily aroused to religious fanaticism, sometimes mitigated by susceptibility to hard cash. The cultivator goes to his fields with spade or plough on one shoulder and rifle on the other, and in some areas where village watch-towers are within range of each other cultivation is mutually inhibited by sniping. *Zar, zan, zamin* – gold, women, land – are at the root of most of the feuds, but politics and intra-Muslim sectarianism play their part. The Afridis 'are so distracted by intestine quarrels that they have little time for carrying on feuds with the neighbouring tribes'; a truly appalling thought. Anarchic as this tribal society appears at first sight, it is not without principles of conduct and rules of intercourse: the code of revenge enforces the wiping out of insult with blood, but it is to some extent offset by the obligations of hospitality and asylum.

Much of this should now be in the past tense: it is yielding, perhaps rapidly, to a more civil polity. Responsible observers[10] agree that Pakistani policy has been at once resolute and enlightened: the Tribal areas have representation without much taxation; Afridis and Shanwaris are running buses and trucks up the Khyber; 'the Wazirs are becoming farmers and the Mahsuds entrepreneurs'; the Warsak multi-purpose project is giving direct employment and the benefits of irrigation. The Afghan irredentist demand for 'Pakhtunistan' would seem to have little support from the Pakistan side of the border, unless the closing of the frontier to nomads should rouse old resentments.

It seems possible that the differences in British border policy – and the kind and degree of Pakistani integration – are related to the physical background – more massive in Baluchistan, more fragmented in the Northwestern Hills – and it is perhaps significant that in the north, which although higher is again rather bolder in its topographic outlines, the tribes are more oligarchic and something like feudal organisms – Chitral, Dir, Swat, Buner – have grown up. Other factors are involved, however, and the Chitralis at least are not Pathan, whatever their origin may be.

Agriculture is carried on throughout the hill country – mainly dry crops such as wheat, barley and maize, with some rice in the valley-bottoms which, however, can be malarial. In some areas the tribal lands are interchanged among the cultivators every few years. Large numbers of sheep and goats are kept, and winter transhumance to the plains is very important; the camel of Baluchistan is naturally replaced by the mule in this broken country. There is also a good deal of petty trading with the plains in wood, charcoal, fodder-grass and mats and ropes made from the ubiquitous dwarf palm (*Nannorhops*). Some areas are particularly favoured: the upper Kurram has rich irrigated fields and excellent orchards – grapes, apples, apricots, peaches – and, like the Gomal, is the site of a new irrigation and power project. Some spots in the northern valleys are likewise noted for fruit, but despite their perennial streams, their groves of poplars and mountain forests, they are for the most part poor: in Chitral even the upper classes are said to have generally a hungry look. Mineral wealth is not likely to be great, though there are deposits of iron and magnetite, and the antimony of Chitral – 175 miles (282 km.) from railhead by mule-track and road – yields up to 100 tons a year. Building stones await demand; the only effective mineral exploitation is that of salt from the Kohat anticlines.

In fact the whole border from Chitral to Makran has been called a distressed

[10] L. Rushbrook Williams, *The State of Pakistan* (Faber, London, 1962), 62–69; A. J. Toynbee, *Between the Oxus and the Jumna* (OUP, 1961), 151–60.

area. There was a vicious circle of poverty, anarchy and more poverty; even on low standards the region cannot support its relatively dense population by local resources alone. Hence the necessity for outside income, in the past largely derived from raiding the plains or trading caravans. Under the British régime these activities were severely restricted, but to a large extent replaced by subsidies, military employment, road and rail contracts. There was also a considerable migration to Indian cities of Pathans as petty traders, mechanics and labourers: their remittances home were a not unimportant contribution. The costs and technical difficulties of developing the area make progress slow, but the Pakistan Government is making relatively large investments in power, irrigation, light industry and education.

The historical significance of 'The Frontier'[11]

The importance of this northwestern angle as the great entry into India is a commonplace of historical geography. British tradition placed most emphasis on the Khyber Pass itself, which in fact was often by-passed, by Alexander and Babur among others; the earlier importance of Makran has been noted, and when the southwestern flanks of the Punjab were better watered Multan and the Tochi and Gomal routes were correspondingly more significant. Nevertheless the Vale of Peshawar has probably been the most usual first objective of invaders.

This great belt of semi-arid country between the Afghan mountains and the Indus has always been a shatter-zone, incapsulated rather than assimilated in the great empires which have reached from the Iranian plateaus into Hindustan; its tough uncivilized hillmen offered little in the way of taxable capacity and much in the way of administrative strain; strategic roads and key nodal points were firmly held, and formed bases for punitive action, but in the interstices the tribes governed or misgoverned themselves. Policing was easier when 'saddle-states' spanned the whole border, with bases on the Kabul–Kandahar line and in the Punjab; but such a layout had its own elements of instability. For states based in the Punjab, such as the Sikhs (the immediate precursors of the British), the boundary was the *daman-i-koh* – the 'skirt of the hills', the sharp break between plain and hill which did not, however, correspond to any ethnic, linguistic, or religious division.

The problem became far more than local with the growth of Russo-British rivalry in the 19th century. British policy was divided between the view that any advance beyond the *daman-i-koh* (unless confined to mere 'influence') was a dangerous over-extension, and the 'forward school' which emphasized the importance of controlling both flanks of the difficult transition zone, by holding Kabul and Kandahar, or even a border on the Hindu Kush. The Second Afghan War of 1879–81 put Kabul and Kandahar into British hands – briefly, for the costs and risks of holding down so tough and bitterly hostile a population were

[11] A fuller discussion of the evolution of the Frontier is given in earlier editions of this book, 438–44.

obviously excessive. Policy concentrated on maintaining Afghanistan as a strong buffer-state, under definite and if possible exclusive British influence. In Baluchistan, with its generally more open terrain and the greater status and power of its chiefs, it did prove possible to control both sides of the hill belt; the Treaty of Gandamak (1879) interposed a belt of British-administered territory between Afghanistan and the mountainous Sind border. In the north, however, the Administered Districts lay back from the border and the intervening 'Agency' territory could scarcely be said to be governed by the British, except in so far as outrage outside tribal limits was liable to be visited by overwhelming force within them.

Failing a firm control on both sides of the border zone – Kabul and Kandahar as well as Peshawar and the Derajat – it was necessary to come to some arrangement with Afghanistan for a delimitation of the spheres of the Amir and the British Raj. This was accomplished by Sir Mortimer Durand's negotiation in 1893 of the 'Durand Line', the present international boundary, which represents the balance reached, by waiting on events rather than by conscious policy, between the old concept of a tightly closed boundary on the *daman* and the 'forward school's' demand for a 'scientific' frontier to include Kabul and Kandahar. The Durand Line is demarcated south of the Safed Koh, between that range and the Kabul River (i.e. across the Khyber), and east of the Kunar. It bisects some tribes – notably the Mohmands, 'as convenient neighbours as a nest of hornets' – and there is thus the potentiality of trans-border intrigue, but on the whole it has worked reasonably well.

However, since the Raj was replaced by Pakistan, there have not been wanting signs of an opportunist attitude on the part of Afghanistan, a solicitude for Pathan interests (expressed as support for a 'Pakhtunistan' separatism) which might become very inconvenient should the waters become sufficiently troubled for Kabul to fish in them.

THE SUB-MONTANE INDUS REGION

The area here described as the Sub-montane Indus Region consists of:

(a) the three plains of Peshawar, Kohat, and Bannu, all west of the Indus;
(b) the Potwar Plateau, east of the Indus;
(c) the Salt Range, marking off the southern boundary of the region both in Bannu and Potwar, and cut through by the Indus at the head of the remarkable Kalabagh re-entrant.

The southern boundary is taken as the foot of the Salt Range scarp, the north-eastern as the edge of the foothills of sub-Himalayan Kashmir.

This is not, it must be confessed, a very satisfactory division, and other arrangements are possible; the three plains might, for instance, be included within the Northwestern Hills Region. But the Indus cuts across some of the most prominent structures and is in no sense a geographical division, and although the Salt

Range has very different values from those of the other components, it is after all intimately connected with the Potwar Plateau behind it. To elevate each unit to the rank of a region, while theoretically tenable, would be practically difficult and distinctly out of scale with the regional scheme as a whole. Moreover, the Indus does at least form a link in the complex structural history of the whole area.

Structural history

In Miocene times the whole region was an area of 'foreland sedimentation' from the newly risen or rising Himalayas, whether this was by alluviation in the Indobrahm of Pilgrim and Pascoe or, as de Terra suggests, by the fans of transverse rivers – 'such slope drainage, when repeatedly rejuvenated by intermittent uplift, is able to accumulate vast quantities of sediment.'[12] At the end of the Pleistocene uplift took place, and by the Lower Pleistocene (Upper Siwalik) this foreland sedimentation was replaced by alluviation in basins and valleys formed by the increasing uplift and warping of the Potwar Plateau, now traversed by northeast/southwest or east/west ridges – generally limestone anticlinals, such as the Cretaceous–Eocene Kala Chitta Dhar and Khair-i-Murat.

On the Indobrahm view, the rejuvenation caused by this uplift contributed to dismemberment of the middle Indobrahm by its own tributaries cutting back from the southwest. At any rate it is agreed by all that the present River Soan, the master stream of Potwar, is a complete misfit, far too small for the erosion of its great and very mature basin. A small stream entering the Jhelum very near its debouchment from the Sub-Himalayan foothills (Fig. 16.5), and pointing upstream, may indicate the old course by which the Jhelum flowed southwest on the present Soan line. This great, and doubtless braided, stream probably contributed to the extensive peneplanation of the break between the Middle (Mid-Pliocene) and Upper (Lower Pleistocene) Siwaliks. Relics of the peneplanation are found in the Kala Chitta Dhar and elsewhere, but the relief has been generally much altered by later erosion and deposition.

A strong erosive phase followed, during which the Jhelum was diverted, probably by a small anticlinal uplift north of Panjar, through a great boulder-fan of one of its own braided channels. Meanwhile, in the north, compression and faulting elevated yet further the Kala Chitta Dhar. The Indus abandoned its old course by the Haro River – a course along which it is probable that the muchcontroverted erratic blocks of Campbellpur were swept by immense glacial floods and mud-flows.[13] It now cut a channel across the eastern end of the Kohat

[12] H. de Terra and T. T. Paterson, *Studies on the Ice Age in India* (Carnegie Inst. Pubtn No. 493, Washington, 1939), 300. The following, greatly foreshortened, summary is based mainly on de Terra. For the Indobrahm, see above, 39, and earlier editions of this book, 28–33, and the original papers of E. H. Pascoe, 'Early History of the Indus, Brahmaputra and Ganges', *Qly Jnl Geol. Soc.* 75 (1919), 138–59, and G. E. Pilgrim, ' . . . History of the Drainage of Northern India', *Jnl Royal Asiatic Soc. of Bengal* (New Series) 15 (1919), 81–99.

[13] For the theory of their strictly glacial origin, see A. L. Coulson, 'Pleistocene Glaciation in North-Western India', *Rec. GSI* 72 (1938), 422–39; for another view, de Terra, *op. cit.* 266–68.

Hills; it seems plausible that the erosive force needed was provided by the ponding-up of a great lake in the Vale of Peshawar. In late Pliocene times most of western Potwar drained direct to the Indus, until uplifts broke up the old drainage system; there is at least one clear case of antecedence, the Nanda Kas tributary of the Haro, which cuts right across the eastern Kala Chitta Dhar.[14]

This erosive stage appears to correspond to the 2nd Interglacial in Kashmir, and was succeeded by the deposition of the Potwar loess or loessic silt, probably mainly in the 3rd Glacial of Kashmir. The later Pleistocene saw continuing deposition of loess, but probably more re-sorting of it by streams, with extensive terrace formation and gullying.

The Salt Range itself has an excessively complex history. The lowest – by no means necessarily the oldest – rocks are the Saline Series, which are overlain by several hundred feet of Cambrian sandstones and shales. From Cambrian to Upper Carboniferous times the area was apparently dry land; after this break deposition seems continuous in one part or another of the range except for gaps in Triassic–Jurassic and Oligocene times. The sequence begins again with the Carboniferous (Talchir) Boulder Bed, undoubtedly glacial and of great interest owing to the analogies with similar deposits in the Gondwana blocks of the Southern Hemisphere. The included boulders are largely rhyolites and granites of Vindhyan age from the Aravallis. The Carboniferous tillites and sandstones are succeeded by the massive *Productus* limestones, all together forming a Permo-Carboniferous (Lower Gondwana) sequence. The early Eocene Ranikot and Laki beds are of great importance, the Sakesar (Laki) nummulitic limestone forming the great upper cliff of the scarp from the eastern range almost to Kalabagh. Near Kalabagh the limestone is altered to massive gypsum, and associated with important salt deposits; here the Saline Series seems definitely of Laki age. Overlying the Eocene beds is the Murree–Siwalik–Potwar loess sequence.

The whole of the Salt Range has been subjected to intense faulting, thrusting, and block-dislocation. The general structure would appear to be that of a mono-clinal uplift overwhelmed by lateral pressure from the Himalayan orogeny, so that the southern portion has been depressed under the Punjab Plains and over-ridden on low thrusts by the northern part, leaving a truncated monocline with gentle rises from the Potwar Plateau and the great dissected scarp overlooking the plains. The striking horseshoe bend round the Indus at Kalabagh may be controlled in part at least by the underground topography of the Peninsular block and eaten out, as it were, by the Indus.

The great stratigraphical problem concerns the Saline Series, which in places appears in a definitely Tertiary position, in places overlain in a complicated and irregular, but quite natural, manner by undoubted Cambrian. It contains organic dust – including remains of angiosperms, conifers and insects – which, if not

[14] de Terra, *op. cit.* 259.

alien in origin, put a Cambrian age out of the question. The highly disturbed upper boundary has been variously interpreted as the result of buckling and yielding of the incompetent Saline Series beneath the massive sandstone overburden; of solution of the salts and consequent slumping and brecciation; and of great overthrusts bringing Cambrian over Eocene. The evidence and arguments of the leading protagonists, Gee and Sahni, are fascinating but almost indescribably intricate, and cannot be summarized here. The debate is far from concluded, and the Salt Range has the distinction of being probably the only place in the world where there can be serious and long-continued controversy as to whether a series with included organic remains should be placed in the pre-Cambrian or the Eocene.[15]

There is thus, if not an underlying structural unity, at least a unity of structural history for the whole region; the Salt Range cannot be separated from the Soan synclinal trough, 'there is a gradual passage from the complex folding and over-thrusting of the northern limestone ranges (Kala Chitta Dhar, etc.) into the low-dipping Soan basin',[16] and the events which produced the great open synclines of Potwar and the tightly-packed little anticlines of the Kala Chitta Dhar doubtless also played their part in the formation of the alluvial and detrital floors of the trans-Indus basins.

THE TRANS-INDUS PLAINS

(i) *The Vale of Peshawar* forms a semi-circle of lowland of some 2,200 sq. miles (5,698 km²), hill-girt except in the east where only a low sandstone ridge separates it from the Indus. The basin floor consists of Attock slates, Vindhyan in age, but mainly buried deep in gravelly or clayey alluvium at a general level of 1,000–1,100 ft. (305–335 m.); the weight of the detritus may have been sufficient to depress the floor, or down-warping may have permitted deep accumulation. The deposits show some doming due to recent earth movements, and the region's liability to earthquakes is perhaps linked with this.

Rainfall averages some 20 in. (508 mm.) in the centre, decreasing south and west, increasing east and north. Perennial water from the two main rivers, Kabul and Swat, has long provided irrigation; so much so, in fact, that formerly seasonal streams have now a permanent flow from seepage and discharge, and waterlogging and salinity are problems towards the east. The central basin is watered by the Upper and Lower Swat Canals, the former fed by water brought by tunnel under the Malakand Pass and supplying power to Malakand. The Peshawar area is supplied by the Kabul Canal and now by the multi-purpose

---

[15] The account in the text is based mainly on the scattered references in D. N. Wadia, *Geology of India* (Macmillan, London, 3rd ed. revised, 1961, especially 138–45 and 330–2). The controversy on the Saline Series is the subject of two symposia in the *Proceedings of the National Academy of Science of India*, Vols. 14 (1945) and 16 (1947), conveniently summarized by E. B. Bailey in *Nature*, February 21st, 1948, 265–6.

[16] E. S. Pinfold, *Rec. GSI* 49 (1918), 140.

Warsak Dam on the Kabul River, which will ensure perennial water; previously canals were dependent on uncertain summer floods.[17] Mardan and Peshawar Districts have the greatest concentration of irrigated land; double-cropping increases the NSA by up to 50%. Rabi wheat followed by kharif maize dominate, but rabi fodder crops, kharif sugar-cane and tobacco (irrigated by wells towards the east) are important, the last two as major cash crops. Sugar beet is now being grown in winter to extend the working season of the refineries at Mardan and Charsadda.[18]

The Vale, with its irrigated fields and famous orchards, its groves of willow, mulberry and tamarisk, is a great oasis in the generally arid Northwest. Wetter conditions in earlier times may have been responsible for Alexander the Great's approach from the north, skirting the then marshy centre; but the fans of the perennial streams on this northern flank must always have attracted settlement, and the area was one of the most flourishing centres of Graeco-Buddhist culture. Today it has a considerable concentration of population; Peshawar District in 1961 had 1,213,000 people, Mardan 814,000, the Malakand Agency 1,537,000. Peshawar City (1961: 219,000) has a key strategic position controlling the debouchment from the Khyber Pass; it is of increasing industrial importance, mainly for textiles, and with its large university is an educational centre for the whole Northwest. Power from Malakand and now Warsak is fostering industrial expansion in Nowshera (cotton, wool, chemicals, a big newsprint and hardboard factory), and there is a new sugar mill at Charsadda as well as that at Mardan (78,000) reputed to be the largest in Asia.

(ii) The *Kohat* valley lies higher than Peshawar and Bannu, around 1,500 ft. (460 m.), and is much broken by west/east limestone ridges. The filling of the uneven limestone floor varies from lacustrine clays to gravel and boulder fans; there are many springs in the limestone, and the water-table is generally high. The Tanda Dam on the Kohat, started in 1952, will allow perennial irrigation and supplement the small tanks formed by bunding the rivers. Wheat, watered by the relatively high rainfall (16 ins., 406 mm.), dominated in the past, but summer crops will be possible with extended irrigation.

(iii) The *Bannu* lowland (about 500 ft., 152 m.) covers some 1,700 sq. miles (4,400 km²) and is entirely enclosed by hills except for the Kurram gorge through the section of the Salt Range west of the Indus and the Pezu gap in the south. Into this basin converge the Kurram, the Tochi, and many hill streams, all much braided and with broad boulder-strewn channels, dry for much or most of the year but eroding when in flood. Here again it is difficult not to postulate earlier lacustrine conditions, but soils are in general sandy or gravelly, except for the rich silts below Bannu town. Rainfall is an evenly distributed 10 in. (254 mm.), allowing some year-round cropping, but with the emphasis on winter wheat;

[17] Geographical knowledge of this region, and indeed of the Indus basin generally, has been greatly increased by the work done for the Pakistan Government by Huntings Aerial Surveys, but their reports are not generally available, at least outside Pakistan.

[18] H. Kampf, 'Sugar Beet in Pakistan', *World Crops*, 13 (London, 1961), 106–9.

there is much fallow and scrub, and even sand-dune country. Perennial irrigation is almost confined to the Tochi/Kurram doab, an oasis like the Vale of Peshawar, and supplied by a dam on the Kurram above Bannu which was finished in 1962.

In the unirrigated parts of Kohat and Bannu, fat-tailed sheep, camels and donkeys are reared, and wool is perhaps the most important commercial crop. There are few real towns, though power from Kurram is allowing industrial development in Bannu (1961: 32,000) where woollen mills have been established to provide a local market for the wool-growers and yarn for the important cottage industry; there is some factory weaving of coarse woollens, mainly blankets. The railways to Thal and Bannu, built originally for strategic purposes, are helping the economic quickening of the region, both agricultural and industrial.[19]

The population densities of Peshawar, Mardan, Kohat and Bannu Districts were in 1961 respectively 740, 670, 180 and 200, remarkably high for the scanty resources. Conscious of economic and political dangers, the Pakistan Government is applying much effort to the intensification and extension of agriculture throughout the northwest, as well as encouraging industry. Pride of place goes to the multi-purpose Warsak Dam, completed in 1962. This has a positive role beyond its economic value; initially watch-towers were necessary to keep off tribal snipers, but 7,000 tribesmen were eventually employed and 11,000 ac. (4,450 ha.) of tribal land is included in the new irrigation; the power capacity is 240,000 kW.

POTWAR

The Potwar Plateau covers an area of 4,000–5,000 sq. miles (10,360–12,950 km²) at about 1,200–1,900 ft. (366–580 m.); there are a few outlying spurs of the Salt Range in the south, and in the north the Khair-i-Murat and the Kala Chitta Dhar with a very open cover of wild olives and bush. But in general it is open undulating country developed on the mainly sandstone Siwaliks and mantled by varying thicknesses of loessic silt which erodes easily into deep canyons; most of the hills and rivers are bordered by belts of intricately dissected ravine lands, locally *khuddera*. The streams are generally deep-set owing to rejuvenation, and of little or no use for irrigation: agriculture is thus almost entirely dependent on the rainfall of 15–25 in. (381–635 mm.), between a quarter and a third of which falls in January–March, especially in the less arid northern strip near the hills; the southwest is of course very arid at all seasons. Temperatures are extreme and snow, though rare, is not unknown. Soils are often sandy, or stony near the *daman*, and wind-blown sand from the stream-beds is a menace to agriculture. On the whole it is a hard land: symptomatic of the general poverty is the fact that donkeys are often used for ploughing instead of bullocks. Most of the area is insecure; in 1920–21 in one tehsil only 7% of the sown area matured and there was not even enough grain for seed.

The chief rabi crops are wheat (easily leading) and barley; kharif crops are jowar, bajri and pulses; in most favoured areas onions, melons and tobacco are

[19] See 'Tribal Areas of West Pakistan', *West Pakistan Year Book* (Karachi, 1963).

grown. Irrigation is almost non-existent, but in many areas fields are carefully embanked to conserve soil-moisture. The most favoured area is the Chach, a strip some 20 miles by 10 (32 by 16 km.) along the Indus northeast of Attock, and really perhaps a continuation of the Peshawar Vale. Here the soil is generally a rich loam and wells are numerous; wheat, maize, sugar-cane and vegetables are grown, and snuff-tobacco is an extremely valuable cash crop. Chach tobacco is also used for the *bidi* industry developed, mainly in Karachi, since Partition. Farming is good and intensive, heavy manuring being the rule: unfortunately soil variety and tribal individualism have led to extreme fragmentation, the land being divided into strips half a mile long and only 20 to 30 yd. wide (800 by 18–27 m.).[20]

Pressure on resources is severe and the population by no means sparse: deducting the urban centre of Rawalpindi, that District has still a density of almost 400. Cultivators readily take up alternative occupations; labour on canals or in towns, cartage, military service. Pakistan's only oil-field is worked in five areas in the Khaur–Dhulian neighbourhood, and now has some natural gas production. The most recently developed wells at Bikasser yield oil too thick to be piped to the Mogra refinery, and it must be railed. At Wah is one of the largest cement-works of the sub-continent, using Hazara limestone, and now ordnance and tractor plants. Rawalpindi and Lawrencepur have an expanding textile industry, and timber from Azad Kashmir supplies sawmills and newsprint plants at Rawalpindi, Jhelum and Manghar.

The strategic importance of Attock, a site of great historic importance at a relatively easy crossing of the Indus, has been superseded by those of Peshawar and Rawalpindi, the 'interim capital' of Pakistan. The latter town owed its original importance to its control of the route into Kashmir up the Jhelum gorge; with 340,000 people in 1961, it remains (for the time being) the only really big town, important industrially, with an oil refinery and textile mills, and as an educational centre. Some 30 miles (48 km.) away are the ruins of Taxila, greatest of the Buddhist universities of India; and three miles to the north of Rawalpindi the new capital of Pakistan, Islamabad, is being built on the southern slopes of the Murree Hills. Islamabad is being planned by the Doxiadas group; the metropolitan area (including Rawalpindi, the Cantonments, and a National Park) will be designed for a population of 2,500,000 within two generations; it will be supplied with water and power by the Rawal Dam on the Kurang River, which will also irrigate 10,000 ac. (4,047 ha.).[21]

THE SALT RANGE

The ramparts of the Salt Range, sinuous in outline and exceedingly complex in detail, sharply mark off the region from the Punjab Plains. They reach nearly

---

[20] M. L. Darling, *The Punjab Peasant in Prosperity and Debt* (London, 1928), 89–91.
[21] For Islamabad, see R. L. Heinecke, *GR* 51 (1961), 437–8, and a note in *PGR* 14/2 (1959), 93.

5,000 ft. (1,525 m.) at Sakesar but in general are not much over half that height. The southern face is remarkably steep and dissected into jagged spurs and crests separated by wild ravines; for the most part an intensely arid and forbidding country, even though rainfall is higher than in the surrounding plains, reaching 20 in. (508 mm.) at Sakesar. Northwards the hills sink more gently beneath the Potwar loess; between the great south-facing scarps and the indeterminate northern edge is a narrow belt of isolated plateaus and basins, filled with graded deposits and fertile enough near such streams as are perennial, though the lower courses of these are usually brackish; agriculture is rain-fed, relying on the summer maximum and the winter depressions. There are a few picturesque lakes in solution or aeolian hollows, often very saline. The north is diversified by scattered oleanders and wild olives, but in the south vegetation is sparse, stunted and xero- or halo-phytic. The Salt Range is flanked by the most intensely gullied *khuddera* badlands; alternating with the over-grazed interfluves are patches of torrent-watered rabi crops in a zone transitional to the Thal.

Between the outermost Kashmiri hills and the Salt Range is the convenient gap followed by the lineal descendants of the great military routeway from the northwestern passes into Hindustan – the Grand Trunk Road of the British Raj, running from Calcutta to Peshawar, and the main railway. The river-crossing is guarded by Jhelum town, said to have been founded by Alexander. The Indus gorge at Kalabagh a little to the southeast, at Daud Khel, is used by the Multan-Attock railway, and 18 miles (29 km.) farther southeast the range narrows to a mile and Potwar and the plains are practically in contact (Fig. 16.5). West of the Indus the metre gauge railway from Kalabagh to Bannu crosses a sandy piedmont plain before penetrating the Kurram breach.

There is some agriculture in the little intermont basins, but the human interest of the sub-region is centred on the enormous deposits of rock-salt – perhaps the most massive in the world – which are worked at several points, notably at Kalabagh at the southern end of the Indus gorge, and at Khewra north of Pind Dadan Khan.

Kalabagh, built in close-packed hillside tiers, the roofs of one tier forming the street of the next above, is probably the thirstiest place in the world; the air is salt-impregnated, roads cut through walls of salt, and the town is built on, one might almost say of, masses of rock-salt. Exploitation from the great open quarries has declined before the competition of the more scientifically run government mines at Khewra, and is important only locally and down the Indus, the trade with Afghanistan and India having dwindled.[22] The Khewra mines have better rail connections and are now the chief producers; there are five seams, totalling 275 ft. in thickness, of practically pure salt. Some potash salts and large quantities of gypsum form the basis of one of the largest soda-ash factories of the sub-continent. Coal, mostly Tertiary and lignitic (carbon content only 40%), is widespread and is worked at Dandot in the Salt Range and

[22] Asrar Ullah, 'Rock salt resources of Pakistan', *PGR* 18/1 (1963), 19–33.

Makerwal west of the Indus, the chief producer in Pakistan. There is an ammonium sulphate factory at Daud Khel and a cement plant at Mari Indus. Altogether the Salt Range is an area which may well become of vital importance in a country so poorly endowed in non-agricultural resources.

BIBLIOGRAPHICAL NOTE

Under the British Raj, the strategic interest of the Northwest Frontier gave rise to a large literature of very unequal value. The older works of Sir T. H. Holdich, as good a writer as he was an observer, are still worth reading:

India (Regions of the World Series, 1904) – a general work but with very strong emphasis on this area;
The Indian Borderland (1909) – largely a personal record but full of information;
The Gates of India (1910) – a broad historical survey.

On Baluchistan, see also:

R. D. Oldham, 'On the recent and sub-recent deposits of the valley plains of Quetta . . .', *Rec. GSI* 25 (1892) – important for *karez*, etc.;
E. Vredenburg, 'Geological sketch of the Baluchistan Desert . . .', *Mem. GSI* 31 (1904);
Idem, 'Report on geology of Sarawan . . .', *Rec. GSI* 38 (1909) – much geomorphological information.

For *karez* irrigation in itself, however, the best account is probably in the lavishly illustrated work of J. Humlum, *La géographie de l'Afghanistan* (Gyldendal, Copenhagen, 1959), Chapters XV and XVI, with a coloured plan of the oasis of Pirzada (near Kandahar) on a scale of 1/2100.

For the Frontier in a more limited sense, C. C. Davies, *The Problem of the North-West Frontier, 1890–1908* (London, 1932) is wider in scope than its title suggests.

On the Sub-Montane Indus Region, the work of de Terra and Paterson, already cited, is important on the physical side; see also:

D. N. Wadia, 'Geology of Poonch State and adjoining portions of the Punjab', *Mem. GSI* 51 (1928).

There seems to be no comprehensive recent work on the human side, though material can be gained from the Pakistani geographical journals and official reports such as the *West Pakistan Year Book*. The work done by Huntings Aerial Surveys (Photographic Survey Corporation of Toronto) has been mentioned, but is not freely available.

CHAPTER 17

The Indus Plains
(Region IX)

THE LOWER INDUS (SIND)

The area treated here (*c.* 48,000 sq. miles, 124,320 km²) corresponds nearly to the West Pakistan Divisions of Khairpur and Hyderabad, with Karachi District, but includes the Sibi lowland or Sewistan, i.e. the plains portion of Kalat (now included in Quetta Division). Most of it formed the old Sind Province. Sind lives by the Indus, which has indeed given its name not only to the Province but also to the sub-continent.

The physical background: hydrography

The region may be divided, following Pithawalla, into three major and seven minor divisions (Fig. 17.1):

    1. Western Highlands: (*a*) Kirthar, (*b*) Kohistan.
    2. Lower Indus Valley: (*a*) Western, (*b*) Eastern, (*c*) Delta.
    3. Desert: (*a*) Pat, (*b*) Thar.

Sewistan is included in the Western Valley section.

    The hydrographic history – really the history of the Indus – is extremely complex, and there have been many changes in historic times. In common with many great rivers of the Northern hemisphere, the Indus shows a strong tendency to work into its right bank, but from Sehwan, east of Manchar Lake, to below Hyderabad its movements are to some extent limited by its impingement on to the more or less solid Tertiaries of Kohistan, and in the north the channel is as it were pinned down by the Sukkur/Rohri limestone outliers, forming a fixed point of the highest significance (Fig. 17.2). Between 1911 and 1930 the minimum discharge at Sukkur varied between 17,568 and 39,907 cusecs, the maximum between 430,445 and 885,165.[1] High flood is usually in August or September, lowest stage between January and March; the time-lag as compared with the Punjab needs no explanation. The average annual discharge at Sukkur is over 5,000,000 cu. ft., carrying nearly 10,000,000 cu. ft. of silt. It has been estimated that in the twenty-nine years 1902–30 the silt deposited between Sukkur and

---

[1] One cusec is equivalent to rather over 100 (actually 101.9) cu. m. per hour.

Kotri amounted to about 1,300 sq. mile-ft.[2] Excessive levee-building and many shifts of course are the inevitable consequences, and it is said that hardly a

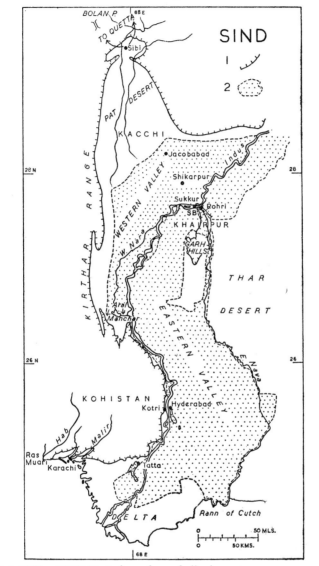

FIG 17.1 SIND: GENERAL. 1, boundary of alluvium; 2, areas commanded by irrigation works. SB, Sukkur Barrage. Regional division after Pithawalla.

square mile of the Eastern Valley section has not been traversed by an Indus channel at some time. North of the limestone outcrop at Rohri-Sukkur a similar

[2] M. B. Pithawalla, *A Geographical Analysis of the Lower Indus Basin (Sind)*, Part I (Karachi, 1936), 329–35. I have drawn heavily on this work for physical details.

area of past and present Indus floodplains, watered by inundation canals and flanked by the desert edge of the Thar, forms a transition to the perennially irrigated Bahawalpur plains and the beginning of the Punjab.

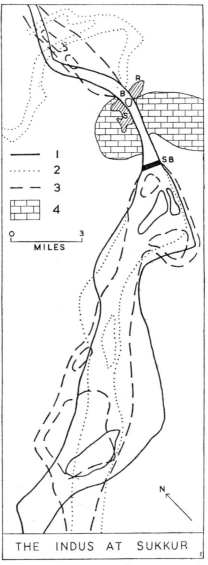

FIG 17.2 THE INDUS AT SUKKUR. 1, course in 1900–1; 2, in 1908–9; 3, in 1916–17; 4, approx. limestone outcrop. S, Sukkur; B, Bukkur I.; R, Rohri; SB, site of Barrage. Adapted from M. B. Pithawalla.

From a point east of Sukkur the East Nara parallels the Indus at a distance of 60–75 miles (97–121 km.); now fed mainly by a cut from the Indus, this stream possibly represents the lower course of the now dry Hakra or Ghaggar (Chapter 18). It effectively divides the desert from the sown, the bulk of Sind's cultivated land lying on the Indus/Nara doabs.

Kohistan ('mountain country') consists of an arcuate mass of Tertiary anti-clinals, forming low (1,200–3,300 ft., 305–840 m.) scarps, hogsbacks and plateaus, of which the most prominent are associated with the massive Kirthar Limestone. The only permanent stream is the Hab on the Baluchistan border, but in the south the large underground reservoir of the Malir supplies part of Karachi's needs.

The *Western Valley* section is formed mainly of older alluvium (bhangar). The Kalat and Kirthar Ranges are flanked by alluvial fans on which incised, sporadic torrents feed strips of kharif jowar and rabi wheat, before losing themselves in the desolate clay desert (*pat*) between Jacobabad and Sibi. Soils are finer towards the south, with many small lakes; fertile in itself, this is one of the worst areas of Pakistan for waterlogging and salinity. There are plans to dam the Bolan and Nari Rivers, and the West Nara, probably an old Indus course, is canalized for irrigation. The marshy Manchar Lake is alternately drained and fed by the Aral as the Indus is high or low; it is fished in summer by the Mohanas, who in winter grow rabi crops on the dry bed.[3]

The *Eastern Valley* is in a sense the older delta, a great doab of recent alluvial sands and clays, falling from 250 ft to 50 ft. in 200 miles (76 m. to 15 m. in 322 km.) and crossed by innumerable meander-scars and long narrow depressions (*dhoros*), apparently fragments of old drainage systems now disrupted by shifts of course, desiccation, and sand encroachments. Along the East Nara small alkaline lakes (*dhands*) are especially numerous. Very important features are the two Kirthar Limestone outliers, the larger in the north reaching 400 ft. (122 m.) and providing the emplacement for the Sukkur Barrage, the smaller carrying at its northern end the old capital, Hyderabad, and the sites of yet older cities.

The *Delta* merges southwards into the great mud and salt wastes of the Rann of Kutch (Chapter 22). Changes in the distributaries have been numerous; according to Pithawalla they are facilitated in the north by a sandy micaceous surface. The coast is fringed with dead creeks and dead ports. When high tides and Indus floods coincide the littoral is flooded for 20 miles (32 km.) inland. In from the shore mangrove-flats are old sandy beach-ridges succeeded by clayey silts; the streams are fringed by tamarisk thickets. There are great stretches of tall grass and a few cultivable patches; but on the whole the Indus Delta is a savage waste: a marked contrast to that of the Ganges, or even more strikingly to the more comparable Nile.

It is hardly necessary to stress the dominant features of Sind climate, heat and aridity. At Shikarpur 'ice forms as late as February; yet in summer, for weeks

---

[3] There is a good account in M. M. Memon, 'Manchar Lake: a study of its fish industry', *PGR* 18/2 (1963), 13–24.

together, the readings *at midnight* do not fall below 100° F.' (37·8°C.), and Jacobabad holds the Indian, and nearly the world, record with 126° F. (52·2° C.).[4] As the local proverb well remarks, 'O Allah, why, having created Sewistan, bother to conceive of Hell?' As for aridity and its concomitant variability, Drigh Road (Karachi), with an average annual fall of about 8 in. (203 mm.) recorded in five successive years 13·52, 0·69, 9·41, 20·82 and 6·97 in. – *c.* 343, 18, 528 and 177 mm. Almost it never rains but it pours; Karachi has recorded 12 in. (305 mm.) in 24 hours. The rivers of Kohistan, normally great trails of gravel and boulders, then come down in turbulent flood; even around Karachi it is often hardly worth while to build permanent bridges, and roads cross the wadis on broad concrete aprons flush with the bed.

The natural vegetation of thorn scrub merges into thickets of babul (*Acacia arabica*) and tamarisk along the inundable riverain tracts. These supply fuel to Karachi, and even some Punjab towns, and timbers for Kalat collieries. Their use as fuel is decreasing with the development of natural gas and electricity.[5]

Agriculture

It is a commonplace that the Lloyd Barrage at Sukkur transformed Sind. The Barrage takes advantage of the narrowing and fixing of the Indus by the lime-stone hills of Sukkur (right bank) and Rohri; between the two the anciently fortified island of Bukkur carries the railway to Quetta. The Indus flows higher than the surrounding country, even in the gap, and careful river-training is necessary. Four canals take off from the left bank, two to irrigate the northern half of the Eastern Valley, where rabi wheat and fodder lead over kharif millets and cotton; rice is important only below the Barrage. The other two canals take water well to the south, one of them using the depression of the Nara Dhor, a former Indus course; here the summer kharif crops are more important. The water-table is now within 8 ft. (2·4 m.) of the surface, and rising over more than half the irrigated area; hence waterlogging leading to salinity and to epidemic malaria succeeded by severely endemic conditions.[6]

Farther down, at Hyderabad, the Lower Sind (Ghulam Mohammed) Barrage has a perennial canal from each bank and two seasonal ones from the left. Rice growing in the perennially watered area is prohibited, to avoid waterlogging, and wheat, cotton and sugar are grown. Further extensions of the irrigated area, and forest plantations, are planned, and a pilot project to settle East Pakistani families on newly opened lands is meeting with some success. North of the Sukkur the Upper Sind (Gudu) Barrage, completed in 1963, brings irrigation to a wide area which will be extended into the *pat* deserts of the west. Altogether,

[4] *Bombay Gaz.* (1909), II. 176.

[5] T. A. Ansari, 'Riverain forests of Sind – Hope or Despair?', *Empire Forestry Rev.* 40 (1961), 228–33; A. H. Husain, ' . . . Vegetational resources of the Lower Indus Basin', *Oriental Geogr* (Dacca) 1/1 (1957), 43–50.

[6] B. L. C. Johnson, 'Technical and economic development of Pakistan', *Oriental Geogr* (Dacca) 6/1 (1962), 71–78; A. T. A. Learmonth, *op. cit.* (1957) above, 149.

the three Barrages will irrigate over 10,000,000 acres (4,050,000 ha.) and account for 40% of Pakistan's irrigated land.[7]

Most of the land was in large estates, farmed by share-croppers (*haris*) under a system by which say all the cotton, all the wheat and all the fallow of an estate for any one year was in a compact block, parcelled out to the tenants year by year and rotated annually. This did help a few progressive landlords to introduce modern techniques such as tractor ploughing; but the system in itself was open to all the normal abuses of *métayage*. With the limitation in size of estates, some land is now being distributed to tenants on a better basis.

Settlement in the better-irrigated areas is largely in nucleated villages, but in part of Kacchi (the Sibi re-entrant) there is a tendency for homesteads to be lined out along irrigation channels. Elsewhere, among the *dhands* of the East Nara, in the Delta patches of cultivation, or where precarious cultivation is carried on by bunding *daman* nullahs (Fig. 17.3), hamlets rather than villages are the rule. The camel is still an important transport animal, even in Karachi, where it draws long floats; goats and fat-tailed sheep are numerous, and buffaloes are pastured in large numbers in the Delta. Sea-fishing has been carried on in a very primitive manner, but a good deal of attention is being given to its improvement.

Sind in general

Sind was the first part of India to come under Muslim domination, being over-run by the Arabs from Makran in the 8th century. Its subsequent history was local and tumultuous until it was conquered by Napier in 1843 as a sort of by-blow of the First Afghan War; he is said to have announced his unauthorized addition to the Raj in the one-word despatch *Peccavi* – I have sinned. It was then administered as a part of Bombay until 1936, an historical accident which became an indefensible anomaly; perhaps partly as a result of this, and partly of the exceptionally large share of Hindus and Parsees in the towns and trade of the Province, Sindi politics remained local and tumultuous, becoming a bye-word for corruption and intrigue, and the habit was not lost with Independence and the departure of the non-Muslims.

Apart from the Barrages, Sind is not wealthy. There is some poor haematite and poorer lignite in the hilly fringe of Kohistan, and this is now worked; otherwise solid minerals are confined to limestone, basis for an important cement industry; clays, glass-sands, and in the Delta salt deposits. Hopes of a big oil-strike, reasonable in view of the geological structures of Sibi, have not material-ized, but Sind's position has been greatly improved by the discovery of natural gas at Sui in the barren Bugti Hills above Sibi (above, p. 301). As well as revolutionizing the nomadic life of the Bugti people, the gas has provided power for industry at Karachi and along the pipe-line: cement at Rohri and Hyderabad;

[7] L. H. Gulick, 'Irrigation systems in the Former Sind Province', *GR* 53 (1963), 79–99; for a detailed study, see his 'A cotton-wheat farm in Hyderabad District, West Pakistan', *PGR* 16/1 (1961), 25–34.

shoes, cigarettes and other consumption goods at the Sui Trading Estate outside the latter town. There are cotton spinning and weaving mills here and at Khair-pur, and jute mills are being set up at Kotri. Elsewhere there are widespread

FIG 17.3 BUNDED CULTIVATION ON THE DAMAN. 10 miles west of Karachi. Low scarp in north is last ridge of Kohistan, running out to Ras Muari (C. Monze), 8 miles to W. Contours at 250 and 500 ft. Note settlement in hamlets. *SOP* 35/13. *Courtesy* SOP.

but primitive agrarian industries such as oil-pressing, sugar-crushing and rice-milling.[8] But Karachi dominates the industrial scene, no doubt thanks largely

[8] A. H. Siddiqi, 'Industries in the Lower Indus Basin', *Oriental Geogr* 4/2 (1960), 96–109.

to the immense piling-up of people (including of course scores or hundreds of thousands of refugees) since Partition.

In the old days ports and trade centres flourished or decayed by favour or disfavour of the shifts of the Indus; thus Tatta, on firm ground at an old head of the Delta, was said in 1742 to have no fewer than 40,000 weavers and 60,000 dealers; gross exaggeration, but symptomatic. Already in the 18th century decline began, and it is now an insignificant market village. Shikarpur was long a trading centre with wide connections with southwest and central Asia, but has now been largely superseded by Sukkur (103,000), with its more advantageous railway position and its increasing importance as the site and service-centre of the Barrage. The only pre-British town of real importance, Hyderabad (435,000) dates only from 1768, though the site at the northern end of the limestone outlier has had permanent significance. The Indus crossing and nodality ensure considerable commercial activity, and Hyderabad is a growing industrial centre. But the only really important city is Karachi itself.

KARACHI

In a century Karachi (Fig. 17.4) has risen from a mere local port of 14,000 people to become the first capital of almost the largest Muslim state by population in the world, with a 1941 population of 359,492. By 1961 the city had a population of 1,912,598, an increase of 432% in twenty years.

The set of the Arabian Sea currents is to the east: Karachi lies just off the eastern extremity of the Delta, sheltered from the Makran longshore drift by Ras Muari (Cape Monze). It occupies a peninsular site between the Kohistan rivers Lyari and Malir. The harbour is formed by the Lyari mouths, sheltered by the long Manora spit and the little island of Kiamari, which is connected to the mainland by the 3-mile-long Napier Mole with its railway; the whole area has of course been greatly altered by port development. The surrounding area is practically semi-desert, with a mangrove-fringed coast; the more densely populated areas towards the tip of the peninsula are subject to flooding, but to the east the usual open suburbs and cantonments extend along a 50–100-ft. (15–30 m.) ridge, and to the south the raised beach at Clifton provides an attractive lung. Strong sea-breezes in the wide suburbian avenues give exceptionally invigorating conditions for a town with mean summer minima a degree or two on either side of 80° F. (26·7° C.).

Sind was the favourite, if illegitimate, child of Sir Charles Napier, to whose energetic (though far from modest) initiative the early development of Karachi owed much. It owed more to the boom when the American Civil War cut cotton supplies; by this time steamer navigation on the Indus was in full swing, and in 1863–64 the value of trade was about 28 times that of 1857–58. A 50% slump followed, but the railway tapping the Indus traffic at Kotri (one of the earliest in India, opened in the mid-1860s) was extended through to the Punjab in 1878, and by 1884 trade was nearly double the 1863–64 peak. Since then the development of the Punjab and the rise in Karachi trade have been symbiotic, while with the opening of the Barrage exports again rose by 40–50%. Exports formerly greatly exceeded imports, but this structure was altered as Karachi developed to become the entrepôt of a new political entity.

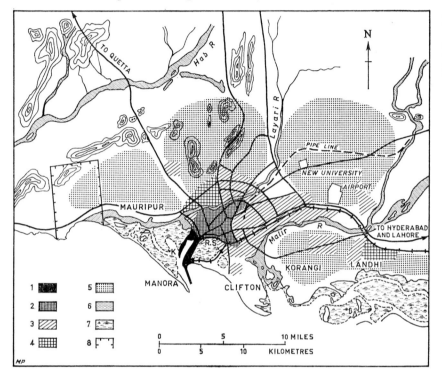

FIG 17.4 KARACHI. 1, port area; 2, built-up area c. 1947; 3, built-up area in mid-1960s. 4, industrial areas mid-1960s; 5, future residential areas; 6, dry streambeds; 7, tidal marsh; 8, area of Fig 17.3.

Imports are now double the value of exports. Cotton remains the leading export, and raw cotton is still thrice the value of manufactured, but the proportion of piece goods and yarn is increasing; hides and skins and oilseeds are also important. The inter-wing trade with East Pakistan accounts for a high proportion of manufactured exports, and hence the share of piece goods in Karachi's trade, as distinct from Pakistani exports, would be larger than stated above. Imports are dominated by development goods, fuels, and prime movers – oil, manufactured goods and construction material, vehicles. To handle the increasing trade, the original Kiamari wharves have been reconstructed and new ones built; there are now twenty-one berths handling 5,500,000 tons a year. Further land reclamation and deepening and widening of channels are being planned. The former dominance of the Punjab export trade, rail-hauled direct to the dock-side, is weakening, and new installations are made necessary by the change in function to that of a port handling imports for storage and redistribution.

Planned efforts to divert industry to other areas have now largely been abandoned in face of overwhelming and self-reinforcing metropolitan concentration,[9] and Karachi now dominates Pakistan industrially. To some extent at least the fearful problem of the refugee influx has been met by new townships, including Korangi to the southeast, a model town with its own transport system and industry; one oil refinery has been built here and another is planned. Such improvements have in turn attracted more newcomers. Port-based industries include steel re-rolling from scrap, and there will be a steel mill in a few years; others are vehicle assembly and ship repairing. Sui gas is an increasingly vital factor and is becoming the basis for a growing petrochemical industry. The largest of the country's woollen mills is in Karachi, and cotton spinning and weaving have mushroomed. Water supply is still a problem, despite the supplementing of the Malir tubewells by piping from the Indus 120 miles (193 km.) away.

It may be doubted whether any city in the world, anywhere and at any time, has shown such a sustained growth rate from such a high base; most of the 432% was in the fourteen years 1947–61. The problems were, and still are, immense; it is difficult to imagine how a scratch bureaucracy, working with the most make-shift accommodation and equipment, managed to avoid disaster in the early years; but it did. There have been little time or money for architectural frills – they will be reserved for Islamabad; and Karachi is unlikely to rival Lahore as an Islamic cultural centre. But with its first-class jet airport, it remains Pakistan's window on the world, and the dynamism of recent years is unlikely to be checked by the shift of the central administration to Islamabad; Karachi will continue indefinitely to be Pakistan's major commercial and industrial centre.

THE PUNJAB

The area described here is smaller than the old Punjab Province of British India; it consists of the West Pakistan Divisions of Lahore, Sargodha, Multan and Bahawalpur, with the Gujrat District of Rawalpindi, a total area of about 70,000 sq. miles (181,300 km²). The area northwest of the Salt Range is obviously excluded, as is the montane part of the old Province. In the western, trans-Indus, area the boundary again lies on the *daman*. But for the rest, in the Indo-Gangetic alluvium, there are no clear physiographical breaks. The climatic transitions are

[9] The percentage shares under the Second Plan for Karachi/Rest of Pakistan are:
Housing, 40/60
Water Supply and Sewage, 28/72
Improvement Trusts and Development Authorities, 38/62
Road Transport, 27/73.
See J. C. Eddison, 'Industrial location and physical planning', *Pak. Dev. Rev.* 1/1 (1961), 1–21.

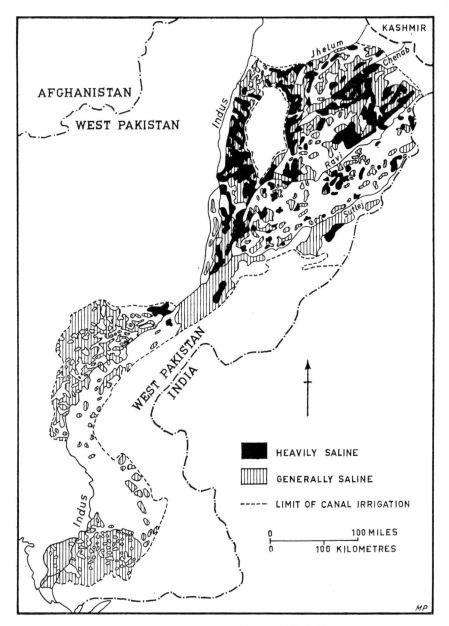

FIG. 17.5A THE INDUS VALLEY: SALINITY.

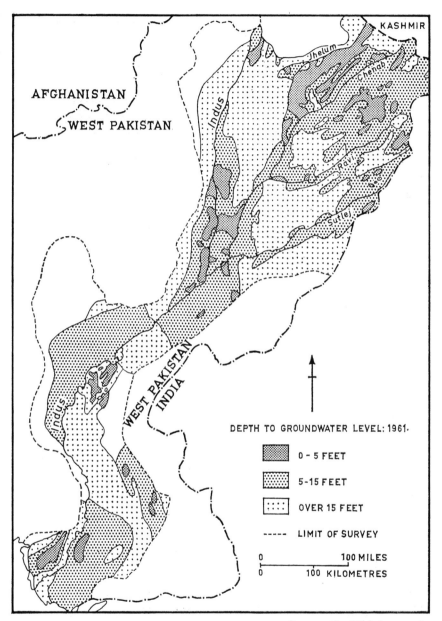

FIG 17.5B THE INDUS VALLEY: WATERLOGGING. *Source:* G. Whittington in
Tijdschift voor Econ. en Sociale Geografie 55 (1964).

inevitably gradual and any boundaries must be arbitrary, at least until more detailed soil and crop mapping has been carried out, and then of course they will not be the boundaries of natural regions. In the circumstances it is most convenient to accept the fact, in a physical sense arbitrary, of the political division and to take the Indo-Pakistan boundary as the limit. This involves detaching the upper portion of the Bari (Beas/Ravi) Doab, the Amritsar area, and treating it with the Indo-Gangetic Divide in the next chapter. In Bahawalpur the boundary lies largely in the sandy wastes of the Thar; farther north it is formed for a considerable distance by the Sutlej, which in the past was sometimes regarded as the traditional boundary of Hindustan.

The old Province really consisted of a central core – the doabs of the Five Rivers – and two wings, of which the eastern, the Bist (Beas/Sutlej) Doab and Sirhind has been separated, here and by the 1947 Partition. The western wing, more arid and for local physical reasons less easily irrigated, consists of the Sind Sagar Doab, between Jhelum-Chenab and Indus, and the trans-Indus Derajat, mostly in Dera Ghazi Khan District. Another extremely important differentiation is the sub-montane belt of greater rain, with an appreciable amount in winter, and a high water-table from seepage from the hills.

Topography (Fig. 17.6, inset)

The whole area forms an immense plain, some 350 miles northwest/southeast by 450 northeast/southwest (565 by 725 km.). All of it (with a tiny exception to be noticed) is under 1,200 ft. (366 m.) most of it under 600, while in the extreme southeast, along the Indus, it falls to under 250 ft. (76 m.). The fall is naturally steepest (about 15 ft. per mile, rather under 1 m. per km.) in the sub-montane strip; over most of the area it is 1 ft. and in the extreme southwest only 6 in. The region is a great mass of alluvium brought down by the Indus and the Five Rivers – from west to east Jhelum, Chenab, Ravi, Beas and Sutlej – which give the province its name and unite in the southwest to form the Panjnad or Five Streams.[10] The interfluves – doabs or 'two waters' – are given names compounded from those of their confining streams – in the same order Jech or Chaj, Rechna, Bari and Bist. Near the Kashmir foothills the country is to some extent undulating and diversified, and numerous smaller streams and torrents (mostly dry except in rains) descend from the hills. Most of these are dissipated in the fields – it must be remembered that the natural drainage has been greatly interfered with by canal construction – but the Degh parallels the Ravi for 150 miles (241 km.) before entering it.

The only breaks in the alluvial monotony of the plains are the little groups of arid broken hills near Sangla and Kirana, on either side of the Chenab. These are very small in extent but rise in jagged pinnacles 1,000 ft. above the plains (their highest point is 1,662 ft., 512 m.) and are geomorphologically of great

[10] The joint course of Jhelum, Chenab and Ravi above the Panjnad is the Trimab – 'Three Rivers'.

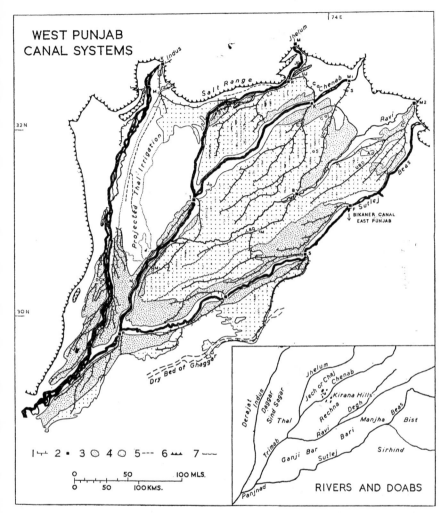

FIG 17.6 W PUNJAB: CANAL SYSTEMS. 1, canals; 2, headworks; 3, inundation,
4, perennial, canal areas; 5, projected canals; 6, alluvium/hill margin; 7, old river
banks. Canals: C, Chenab, UC, Upper Chenab; U (L) J, Upper (lower) Jhelum:
U (L) BD, Upper (Lower) Bari Doab. Headworks: K, Kalabagh (Indus); M,
Mangla; R, Rasul; T, Trimmu; P, Panjnad; M₁, Marala; K, Khanki (Chenab);
M₂, Madhopur; B, Balloki Weir; F, Ferozepore; S, Sulemanke; I, Islamabad.
Other initials are District headquarters. With the Thal and other developments,
this map is now of largely historical interest, but is retained as giving an idea of the
physical layout of the irrigation system.

interest, as they are Aravalli outliers of quartzites, slates and rhyolites and indicate the concealed extension of the Peninsular Block postulated by Wadia as controlling the Northwestern Himalaya syntaxis: they lie within 40 miles (64 km.) of the Salt Range.[11]

For the rest, the sole topographical differentiation is that provided by existing or abandoned river-courses. Hydrographic changes have been complex and far-reaching: 'The Chenab used to flow east of Multan. . . . Ancient Multan stood on two islands in the Ravi, and in Tamerlane's time the Ravi joined the Chenab below Multan.'[12] The riverain belts are of course of great importance for human settlement, an importance reflected in their detailed local nomenclature. The great rivers are countersunk in broad floodplains of newer alluvium (the khadar, locally *khadir*) bounded by steep scalloped bluffs (*dhaya*) which may be 20 ft. (6 m.) or more high and are often intricately gullied. The actual banks of the rivers are naturally a little higher than the *khadir*, owing to silt-deposition in floods; the immediate riverain or *bet* lands are agriculturally valuable but exposed to flooding. Villages are generally perched on top of the *dhaya* or occupy minor terraces, the bluffs of old meander-scars, in the *khadir* itself. Away from the rivers the higher and more arid parts of the doabs – often mere waste where not irrigated – are known as *bar*; the most notable is perhaps the Ganji or 'bald' Bar (so called from its patches of bare hard clay) lying west of the well-marked old course of the Beas, which formerly extended as far as the Trimab-Sutlej confluence and gave more point to the name of the Panjnad.

The old unreclaimed Punjab still persists (not, perhaps, for much longer) in the intractable and unirrigated steppes of the Sind Sagar Doab between Jhelum and Indus, and especially in the wind-blown sands of its central section, the Thal, the heart of which at least approaches true desert conditions. Once past the Jhelum–Chenab *bet* there is an abrupt cessation of cultivation along the scalloped edge of the Thal, which from the air is a sea of sand with a remarkably even (and very light) stipple of bushes and low acacias and a very occasional village, alive or dead a mere pattern in the sand. In years of good rain there is a thin grass cover, and there are scattered patches of precarious cultivation in the lows. But in the western half the Thal irrigation scheme (above, p. 371) is transforming the landscape. Westwards again a strip of level ground, the Daggar, runs parallel to the Indus at a distance of 20–25 miles (32–40 km.); its centre is a narrow level depression in which the water-table is high enough for well-irrigation; this probably represents an abandoned channel of the Indus. The broad and braided present river is bordered by the Powah, an upland strip some three miles broad and in places 40 ft. above river-level, for long a settlement-line for villages farming the *bet* below. Beyond the Indus, in the Derajat, the *bet*,

[11] See A. M. Heron, 'The Kirana and other hills in the Jech and Rechna Doabs', *Rec. GSI* 42 (1913), Pt. 3, 229–36.
[12] W. H. Arden Wood, 'Rivers and man in the Indus-Ganges alluvial plain', *Scottish Geographical Magazine*, 40 (1924), 1–15; reference on p. 13. The Sutlej problem is discussed below (pp. 536–7).

irrigable by inundation canals, is called *Sindhi* after the river, and is narrower or absent, the main channel often abutting directly on to a high bank. Beyond lies the *daman* of the Sulaiman Ranges. East of the Sutlej, the old Bahawalpur state borders the Thar, with a fringe of irrigable *khadir* 5–25 miles wide between the desert and the river.

The soils of the area are for the most part sandy loams (brown or grey semi-steppe soils), with patches of clay and larger areas of almost pure sand. In places limestone concretions and useless expanses of alkaline efflorescence – *reh* or *kallar* – are found. Over most of the area precipitation is too small for leaching to have occurred, and the almost virgin soils respond generously to irrigation, at least initially.

Climate and vegetation

The influence of the Westerly depressions extends right across the Punjab, dying down around the Yamuna: Peshawar has 5·2 in. in January–March, Lahore only 2·7 (132 and 69 mm.). But the sub-montane strip is narrow: while the immediate foot of the hills gets around 35 in. (889 mm.) this has fallen to about 20 in. (508 mm.) at Lahore, only 25 miles from the hills, and the whole of the southern half has under 10 in. and that, of course, very unreliable and often torrential. Lahore has 5–6 in. in both July and August, but the average of rainy days is only about six in each of these months.

Temperatures are extreme for the plains. Lahore ranges from under 55°F. (January) to nearly 94° in June (12·8–34·4°C.); and the mean of the minima for January is only 34·7°F. (1·5°C.); the corresponding maximum figure for June is 115·2°F. (46·2°C.). Frosts are normal in January in the north and not uncommon even at Multan. Dust-storms are a prominent feature of the hot weather, less distressing than might be assumed since they are accompanied by a marked and very welcome drop in temperature (by as much as 20°F., 11·1°C.) and rise in relative humidity.

The weight of modern opinion appears to be against desiccation in the true sense of an actual climatic change; but prolonged human interference with natural drainage, deforestation on the Siwaliks, and so on have undoubtedly led to marked deterioration in ground-water conditions and so in vegetation. The accounts of Alexander's campaigns and Mogul hunts bear witness to considerable forest growth; and today on the more arid margins strong winds and frequent but torrential rains have led to a serious spread of shifting sands and more serious if less spectacular deterioration of good cultivated land.[13] It is probable also that Multan and the southern routes from the Gomal Pass to Hindustan were of more importance in the later Middle Ages than they are today; here hydrographic changes in Sirhind may have been decisive (see below, pp. 535–

[13] See R. MacLagan Gorrie, 'Countering dessication in the Punjab', *GR* 38 (1948), 30–40; and for the contribution of the montane catchments, N. Ahmad, 'Soil erosion by the Indus and its tributaries', *PGR* 15/2 (1960), 5–17.

37). But away from the streams it does not appear likely that the south can ever have carried more than very open acacia scrub and bush, with scattered low trees, saltworts, much bare ground, and thin grass after rain; west and east, in the Thal and the Thar, this thorn 'forest' shades off into what is to all intents desert country. It is interesting to note a strong 'European' element in the annual herbs of the west, which include poppies, vetches, thistles, chickweed and so on.

The *bets* carry stretches of tall 'pampas' grass and streams are often lined with tamarisk: large areas of scrub, locally dense, remain in the unreclaimed western *bars*, but there is practically no real natural forest. Along the Lower Bari Doab Canal trees (mostly sissoo) are grown by irrigation: this Changa Manga Reserved Forest was originally planted to increase the rainfall, but has more undoubted value as conserving soil-water and supplying local fuel. The central areas of the Thal are also being afforested. The cultivated areas are by no means treeless: much of the sub-montane strip has almost a parkland appearance, and even in the Canal Colonies the scattered trees appear to close in towards the horizon.

The natural conditions over much of the Region have been vividly described by E. S. Lindley:

> 'A typical *Bar* of the western Punjab was a desolate place; the surface mostly bare, in places hard and smooth and almost impervious to water when rain fell, in places powdery with saltpetre, and in places growing some grass after rain. Belts of such open ground alternated with belts dotted with small hardy trees or shrubs, which tended to collect the moving sand and dust to form sand-hills that in places formed a miniature Sahara. . . . Animal life is represented by snakes, lizards and a few gazelles . . . a few pastoral and nomad tribes lived a free but hard life, living precariously by their camels which could eat anything, and their cattle that seem able to exist on the smell of grass roots, finding sport and occupation in stealing cattle from each other and from riverain neigh-bours. The water-table was 80 to 120 ft. (24–37 m.) below the surface; in the shallow valleys of a plain that is perfectly level to any but a trained eye, the collection of the annual rainfall of less than 6 inches gave better grazing, and and these Janglis ("jungle folk") had their regular camping places, at wells they had made . . . holes, up to four feet in diameter and going into the bowels of the earth . . . the huts were made of reed screens. . . .'[14]

Very much of this unpromising area has been transformed by the canals into one of the most prosperous agricultural areas in Asia, a feat of bold and imaginative planning which can have few parallels in the world, in spite of the unforeseen after-effects in waterlogging and salinity.

Agriculture: the development of canal irrigation (Fig. 17.6)

Agriculture is the mainstay of the Punjab, and before 1947 it was no exaggeration to regard the Indus Plains (including Sind) as the granary of India.[15] This strong

[14] From an unpublished paper on 'The canal system of the Punjab', kindly communi-cated by the author.

[15] In this section, the historical treatment naturally must transgress the boundary of the 1947 Partition.

position was temporarily weakened by the economic and social dislocations consequent on Partition; but there can be little doubt that a primary function of West Pakistan, of which the Punjab is by far the most important section, will remain the provision of a grain and cotton surplus. Figures for the 'industrial' labour force seem large, but much of it is small-scale craft production, and much of the organized industry is closely based on agriculture, either as a supplier of materials for processing or as a market for agricultural necessities.

Agriculturally three main divisions may be recognized:

(i) the sub-montane strip with appreciable winter rain and a high water-table from seepage from the Siwaliks; well-irrigation supplements rainfed cultivation and is more important than canals;

(ii) the main mass of modern canal irrigation between Jhelum and Sutlej;

(iii) the arid margins: the west beyond Jhelum, in which such agriculture as is possible has been dependent mainly on inundation canals, really modern irrigation being as yet little developed; and Bahawalpur, southeast of Sutlej; in both areas the old systems are being gradually modernized and extended.

These three divisions are brought out on Fig. 17.6. The NSA is around 19,000,000 ac. (*c.* 7,700,000 ha.), and irrigation adds about 10% to this; altogether, counting double-cropping, the total area irrigated by 1960 was over 16,500,000 ac. (6,670,000 ha.). Food crops account for most of the acreage, wheat leading with about 7,500,000 ac. (3,035,000 ha.); cotton covers about one-third the wheat area; rice, oilseeds and sugar-cane are also important. Rice is grown mainly on the sub-montane strip or in the west by irrigation, sugar is predominantly a sub-montane crop under wells, although some is grown by canal irrigation in Lyallpur District. A feature of great importance is the relatively high acreage under fodder crops. Before discussing the divisions it is convenient to consider the development of canal irrigation.[16]

The régime of the Punjab rivers, though irregular (the normal summer discharge is about 20 times the winter minimum) is more favourable to irrigation than that of the Peninsular rivers, since the spring snow-melt in the Himalayas makes the high-water stage begin earlier, and the winter precipitation in the sub-montane strip and the foothills gives a minor rise at the end of the year. The main rise usually begins about the middle of March (the Peninsular rivers are dry for a full three months after this date) and by July the monsoon rains bring a greater but more fluctuating volume; this discharge begins to fall off in September. Some idea of the scale of irrigation is given by the facts that the rivers take off only about one-third the summer discharge and that for half the year they would be dry were it not for the considerable seepage return from the irrigated land.

Small inundation canals have of course been made from time immemorial.

[16] For this section I have drawn very heavily on Mr Lindley's article, with his courteous permission.

Inundation irrigation remains very important, however, beyond the commond areas of some of the major canals, and more especially in the west and Bahawalpur (cf. Figs. 17.5 and 17.6). In the southwest many inundation canals were constructed by Diwan Sawan Mal, the remarkably able governor of Multan under the Sikhs. Inundation canals, however, are useless when most needed – in the dry weather – and being dependent on the current river flow, are liable to run low in a bad rainfall year, again when irrigation is most vital. 'The limit of irrigation under an inundation canal is restricted to the lower land and such canals reach their maximum development where the rivers of the Punjab converge to form the lower Indus and the *khadir* widens at the expense of the bhangar' or older alluvium of the doab.[17] The earlier canals were of inundation type, but all the greater schemes are now perennial, with headworks designed to give an assured supply throughout the year.

The first canal of any size to reach an upland, as distinct from the *khadir*, was constructed from the Yamuna in AD 1351, extended and improved by the Moguls, and renovated, at first very ineffectually, by the early British administration. But modern canal development really began with the construction in 1859 of the Upper Bari Doab Canal (in part on a Mogul alignment) with headworks at Madhopur on the Ravi. In 1886 the Sidhnai Canal, from the lower Ravi in Multan District, was opened, and this was the first 'colony', although Sawan Mal had earlier introduced settlers into some of his reclamations. The Ravi, however, is perhaps the most unreliable of the great rivers (it has a relatively small mountain catchment) and these works hardly gave a full perennial service. The Upper Bari Doab (as its Mogul pre-history implies) served an already settled countryside, a fact reflected in its settlement and field patterns and the aspect of the villages. The Sidhnai irrigated only a small and not particularly inhospitable area, and topographically it was favoured in that the ridge of the doab, giving command of a wider area, was quickly reached. Later schemes were far bolder and have effected far more striking transformations.

Parts of the Rechna and Jech Doabs were irrigated in the early and later 1890s respectively. By 1900 the area east of the old course of the Beas was only partly irrigated by inundation canals, while the Ganji Bar was dry; the Multan area was irrigated by the Sidhnai and inundation canals. The upper Rechna Doab stood in great need of irrigation and so did much of the Jech. Of these as yet untouched areas the Ganji Bar was most promising; but the Ravi had been reduced to a relative trickle of water, the Chenab was fully utilized. The first proposal was to use the Sutlej and Beas; but major canals so far constructed had run eastwards, the western banks lying higher as a result of the tendency of Northern hemisphere rivers to work into their right banks; and the Sutlej water would be needed in Sirhind, Bahawalpur and Bikaner. There remained the distant Jhelum.

[17] G. Kuriyan, 'Irrigation in India', *Journal of the Madras University*, 15 (1943–44), 46–58 and 161–86; refce on p. 161.

Consideration of these facts inspired the great Triple Project (1905–17). The Upper Jhelum Canal irrigates 350,000 ac. (142,000 ha.) in the Jech Doab and discharges into the Chenab above the Lower Chenab Canal (1887–92) headworks at Khanki; the Lower Chenab irrigates some 2,500,000 ac. (1,012,000 ha.) and has an average discharge four or five times that of the Thames at Teddington. The upper waters of the Chenab are thus free to be taken off by the Upper Chenab Canal, which after supplying 650,000 ac. (263,000 ha.) in the Rechna Doab passes its remaining water across the Ravi by a barrage. This feeds the Lower Bari Doab Canal on the Ganji Bar. In the great Canal Colonies of these three doabs the land was empty and everything could be, and was, planned in advance on a generous scale, even if the results on the map look a little inhuman. The land is divided into *chaks* or blocks fed by a single outlet, of about 2 cusecs, from a main distributary, and so far as possible villages conform to *chaks*; hence the repulsive numbers on the maps, though fortunately on the ground human nature softens the severe rectilinear patterns with some minor untidiness, and insists on giving the *chaks* a local, often a personal, name: the village in Fig. 17.7, for instance, officially Chak 73 G.B., is more humanely known as Kala Gaddi Thamman.

The colonization of these areas was a remarkable phenomenon in itself. The allotments were high – as much as 55 ac. (22·25 ha.), more to men of substance – and the attractions for cultivators and larger landholders obvious. Contingents came especially from the over-populated plains beneath the sub-montane strip; some selectivity was exercised, but they included, as well as the more enterprising spirits, not a few induced by pressure or reward to leave their village for that village's good. But on the whole the human material was good and amply demonstrated that, where uninhibited by age-old population pressure on scanty plots of soil, the Punjab peasant is no mean farmer. Early conditions were hard enough to weed out incompetents: scrub had to be cleared, fields banked and levelled; marketing was difficult, and the lack at first of accustomed village social amenities was not compensated by the attitude of the local *janglis*, who saw in the settlers' bullocks an admirable supplement to their own herds. But the reward came in crops far superior to those on the overworked soils of the north. The descendants of the original colonists – if not Sikhs – remain the dominant groups in today's villages.[18]

The increase in population has been remarkable; in Lyallpur and Montgomery Districts from 60,306 and 416,669 respectively in 1891 to 2,684,000 and 2,134,000 in 1961; in density terms, from 17 to 763 and 99 to 502 to the square mile. Despite this, holdings (at least in the Colonies, covering over half the irrigated area) remain large and standards consequently high. Elsewhere the traveller's eye becomes wearily accustomed to the manifold distressing make-

---

[18] For an account of a Canal Colony village today, see J. J. Honigmann, 'A case study in community development in Pakistan', *Econ. Devpmt and Cultural Change*, 8 (1959–60) 288–303.

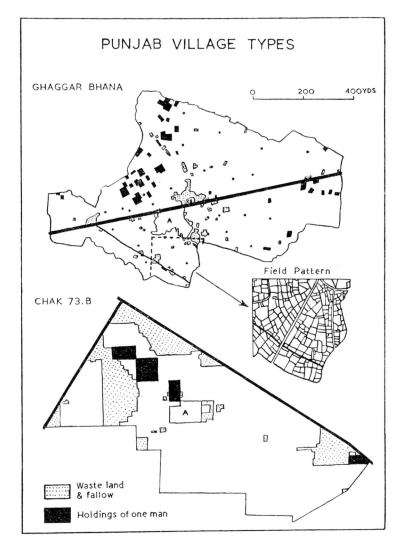

FIG 17.7 A CONTRAST IN VILLAGES: Gaggar Bhana, 25 miles east of Amritsar, and Chak 73 G.B., 11 miles southeast of Lyallpur, respectively in long-settled well-and-canal zone and new Canal Colony. A, Abadi (village site); CB, Canal Bungalow. Uncultivated land includes cemeteries, cremation grounds, cattle pounds, etc.; wells small circles. The most fragmented holding in Chak 73 (4 plots) and in Gaggar Bhana (32 Plots) in black – cultivating holdings show similar pattern.

Inset (twice scale of main map) shows field pattern for part of Gaggar Bhana; that of Chak 73 is severely rectangular.

Area, cultivated area, population (1921) and density of Gaggar Bhana and Chak 73 respectively: 1,644 and 1,856 ac.; 1,386 and 1,362 ac.; 1,468 and 964 persons; 571 and 332 to sq. ml.

Based on maps in Punjab Board of Econ. Inquiry, *Village Surveys*, Nos. 1. (1928) and 4 (1932).

shifts or slacknesses which bespeak an unequal struggle with a too narrow environment, or a mere fatalistic apathy in the face of overwhelming difficulties, the whole vicious circle of agrarian poverty; here it is rejoiced by numerous evidences of good farming and, by Asian standards, very good living. To the community at large the gains have been immense; canal income represents a high proportion of local revenues. The large-scale transfers of population after Partition, which replaced the solid Sikh yeomen by destitute refugees, caused something of a crisis, only slowly overcome, in the Canal Colonies. The Thal has absorbed many refugee families.

The Indus Water Treaty of 1960 gave the waters of the three western rivers (Indus, Jhelum, Chenab) to Pakistan, the three eastern (Ravi, Beas, Sutlej) to India, which undertook to allow unrestricted flow in the western rivers subject to some carefully specified projects upstream. The necessary works in Pakistan include a dam at Mangla on the Jhelum, which is well advanced, and one at Tarbela on the Indus, not yet precisely sited. There will also be seven link canals and five barrages, taking water eastwards across the doabs as far as Ferozepore on the Sutlej. India will provide part of the cost and in the meantime will allow water from her eastern rivers to flow into Pakistan.

Apart from this great readjustment, the technical problems of waterlogging and salinity will cost as much as Pakistan's share of costs under the Treaty. Thousands of acres have been lost under *reh* or saline efflorescences, notably in the *bets* and in much of the Rechna Doab, which has a smaller proportion of *bar* and more of past or present floodplain. Here tubewells have been installed and have demonstrated their efficiency in reducing the water-table; they are to be installed also in the Jech Doab.[19] Loss from canals by percolation and evaporation is very high, and lining them to stop seepage is so costly that, even today when the dangers of waterlogging are known, it can only be applied on a few main channels.

Agriculture: sub-regional variation and settlement patterns

(i) *The sub-montane strip.* This belt of varying width, with decreasing slope away from the hill-foot, has alternating coarse alluvial cones and flat floodplains. Rainfall, between 30 and 40 in. (762–1,016 mm.), increases hillwards and eastwards, and comes mainly from the monsoons, though with important winter falls. Land use changes accordingly: on the coarser deposits of the wetter rim, it shares many of the features of eastern Potwar, including the rotation of rabi wheat with kharif millets followed by a year of fallow; the cropped and fallow fields are in compact blocks despite the fragmentation of holdings. Well irrigation, by Persian wheel or ramp (*mhote*), is largely concentrated on the old floodplain of the Chenab; both methods make great demands on the labour of the cultivator

[19] On these points, see M. Badaruddin, 'Drainage by tubewells in Rechna Doab', *PGR* 16/2 (1961), 27–45; a note on the Indus Water Treaty, *ibid.* 16/1, 53–57; and *ibid.* 17/1 (1962), 50; also above, 371–2.

and his animals, and hence are often associated with intensive market gardening, as well as cash crops like cotton and sugar-cane.[20]

A rich, smiling countryside, with many trees, especially the dark village groves of mangoes; but it has the defects of its qualities. It has suffered severely from malaria, and the fertile soil and ample water-points have led to great population pressure. Holdings are very small and densities very high; in 1961 Sialkot, the most purely sub-montane District, had 772 to the square mile. Fragmentation is or was extreme, and in such conditions the practice of grazing cattle on the stubble hampers attempts at introducing new crops or rotations. Loss of land by sand-spreads and erosion in the streams debouching from deforested foothills is serious.

(ii) *The canal areas.* Within the great irrigated doabs a distinction must be made between the northern zone, transitional from the sub-montane strip, and the zone of newer colonies to the south. These are in turn succeeded by the inundation areas of the Sutlej khadar and the Multan/Muzaffargarh borders. The northern zone was well-peopled before modern canal irrigation, though density has of course increased greatly. To the south, though population has increased with great rapidity, the evil effects of population pressure were scarcely felt. Since settlement was planned in a practically new land, the pattern of villages and farms is mathematically rectilinear, a very striking contrast to the irregular patchwork of the north, where irrigation was superimposed on existing close rural settlement (cf. Fig. 17.7).

Rainfall is 20–25 in. (508–635 mm.) along the northern margin, but falls off very rapidly, in both amount and reliability, to the southwest, and *barani* (rain-fed) cropping tails off very markedly in this direction. The great staples – rabi wheat and kharif cotton, maize and fodder – are the same for both areas; and there is also some rice and sugar-cane, the latter mainly for local consumption. The Colony areas have naturally a strong emphasis on cash crops, growing longer-stapled Punjab–American varieties of cotton. In the north, market gardening is of increasing importance to supply Lahore, and other large towns; this of course is specially associated with well-irrigation in the *bet.*

In the north, with tehsil *rural* densities usually between 400 and 700 (up to 785 in Kasur), pressure on land is high and holdings correspondingly small and fragmented, though rather larger in the sub-montane strip. In the south the primary division of land was into squares of 25–27·5 ac. (10–11 ha.), and although tenancy increased with population, and ownership holdings tended to decrease in size, the cultivating holdings are still large. There is thus some possibility of using more advanced farming methods; co-operation is fairly strong in the Colonies and some capital is available for implements and fertilizers. Fig. 17.7, though based on old data, brings out some basic points: it should be noted that fragmented holding in Gaggar Bhana was only *one* of the worst in the village and

[20] Once again, the Huntings surveys are adding greatly to our knowledge. See K. S. Ahmad, 'Land use in the semi-arid zone of West Pakistan', *PGR* 18/1 (1963), 1–18.

had thirty-two plots; in Chak 73 G.B. the *most* fragmented holding was in four plots only, of which only one was really outlying. The great distance between isolated plots in Gaggar Bhana is an obvious drain on time and energy, and the inset suggests another form of wastage – that of land in field boundaries.

Fig. 17.8 is a highly typical section. The doab is canal-irrigated, but below, in the Ravi *bet*, wells, almost absent on the doab, are very numerous. This suggests good soil and intensive culture; the braided course of the river, the patches of tall grass, suggest the persistence of marshy conditions and the liability to flood.

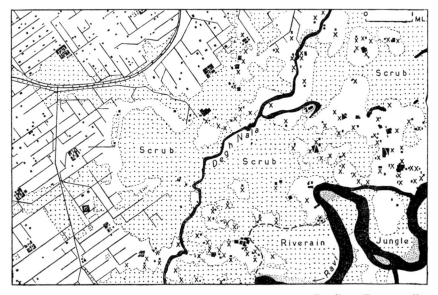

FIG 17.8 A CONTRAST IN SETTLEMENT: DOAB AND BET. Lyallpur Dt, 70 miles southwest of Lahore. Continuous lines, canals; crosses, wells; stipple, land not cultivated. Contrast between planned settlement pattern of L. Chenab Canal Colony and amorphous settlement in Degh and Ravi bets, irrigated by wells. *SOP* 44 E/8 (1915-colonization incomplete). *Courtesy* SOP.

In general the importance of the *dhaya* as a settlement-line is striking; the houses are mud-walled, flat-roofed, incredibly tight-packed, and the village generally occupies a slight rise formed of debris of generations of settlement. In the *bet* most wells have a field-hut, in itself an indication of the intensity of well-cultivation.

In the newer canal areas everything is rectangular or at least rectilinear; a Roman pattern. From the air a chequerboard of square fields, wheat and cotton, with much fallow, ominous patches of sand towards the arid margins, and sometimes of salt incrustation in heavy-soiled hollows; and neatly-planned rectangular villages like Roman *castra*, the major squares outlined by distributaries and roads. On the ground, a thriving countryside, on the whole drier in aspect than the north. Except for those in the centre of the village (the social equivalent of the British housewife's queue) wells are virtually absent; the numerous dispersed huts are generally for cattle. It would be unfair to deny imagination to the Canal Colonies; after all the Triple Project has a boldness of scope which is aesthetic as well as scientific; but the Roman comparison is a good one, and there was a completely British lack of imagination in the detail planning of the villages. One feels the point of Darling's comment: 'The Canal Colony with its rectangular fields, its straight roads, its interminable avenues of shisham trees, and its trim four-cornered villages, speaks of a new order of things. But here [in the north] was the old order – melodious, plaintive, prodigal, prickly, above all warm-hearted.'[21] Also, it must be added, often unspeakably squalid. Another corrective to Darling, here a little rosy, is afforded by the Sandal Bar, named for a famous cattle lifter of *jangli* days – a waste as hot as hell and certainly prickly, but hardly warm-hearted. When all is said, the Canal Colonies were a great achievement in civilization and human welfare; no mean part of Britain's legacy.

(iii) *The arid margins.* Conditions west of the Jhelum–Panjnad line were summed up by Darling in Zolaesque phrases: 'Half the country is burnt up by the sun and the other half drowned by the river, and the whole is waterlogged by debt.' A year of torrents may be followed by one almost rainless; 'so valuable, in fact, is water that property in it arose before property in land.' Agriculture depended on natural floods, unreliable inundation canals, wells in floodplains and abandoned river courses, and the gamble on an inch or two of rain at the right time: '. . . . where nothing can be sown, nothing can be lost. But in this area [outside the then empty Thal itself] a crop can almost always be sown and almost always be lost . . . the monsoon may abruptly end and the river sink before it has done its work. Then must the cultivator choose between losing what he has already sown and not sowing the winter wheat, the biggest crop of all, since there will not be enough water for both.'[22]

While much of this still holds for areas not reached by the new developments, it is no longer a fair assessment. The Sind Sagar Doab differs for the worse, in both aridity and soil composition, from the more favoured eastern doabs, and it is not surprising that it was the Cinderella of Punjab irrigation in British days. The northern strip, the Salt Range piedmont, has supported a fair population for some decades, and the riverain tracts of Indus and Chenab had their wells and inundation canals; and now the Thal itself is being largely transformed by the great project designed to irrigate 1,500,000 acres (607,500 ha.), as well as providing some afforestation (above, p. 371). Across the Indus the Gomal project will give irrigation and flood control to an area now dependent on bunding to trap the flow from occasional storms and stream flow. Wheat and gram, with kharif millets, are the chief crops; cotton is not important except in a few favoured

---

[21] M. L. Darling, *Wisdom and Waste in the Punjab Village* (London, 1934), 55.

[22] Darling, *The Punjab Peasant in Prosperity and Debt* (London, 2nd ed. 1928), Chapter VI.

parts of Muzaffargarh District. Dates are grown, and in bad years their stones may be ground for flour.

Although in some Canal Colonies horse-breeding for the Army was fostered by government, and goats and sheep are kept as well as draft bullocks and milch buffaloes, the open pastoralism once characteristic of the central doabs is now significant only in these arid marginal steppes. Camels are still of some importance in transport.

Away from the new farming frontier of the irrigation developments, the crude population density is very low; the heart of the Thal and the Derajat are almost empty. But in terms of available resources, pressure is acute, and the precarious subsistence agriculture must be eked out by labouring and emigration.

On the other side of the Sutlej–Panjnad line, Bahawalpur lies for some 300 miles (483 km.) between the rivers and the Thar: one is conscious that the desert margin is near at hand, but a wide belt near the rivers has been revivified by inundation and some perennial canals. Millet dominates the kharif crops, with cotton less important than in the central doabs, though in the south it ranks nearly with the main rabi crop, wheat; sugar and the less demanding oilseeds and gram are also significant.

It is clear that the prosperity of the Punjab is in the strictest sense artificial, dependent on the efficient working of an extremely intricate man-made machine; and for such working, political stability is an obvious essential. The settlement of the canal waters dispute gives hope of stability, but the threat of political troubles has been replaced by the unforeseen technological difficulties of water-logging and salinity;[23] and the continued growth of population threatens to eat up all the increased production, and to demand more.

Industry

The Pakistani Punjab is even now relatively little industrialized, nor can it well be claimed that its potentialities for large-scale industrialization are great, except perhaps in textiles. But craft production is still considerable, and in some cases – e.g. small metal goods – the craft tradition is adapting itself to small-scale factory methods; and there has been an encouraging start with bigger enterprises, based in part on old resources and skills, in part on the experience and desperate initiative of refugees, in part on new power resources.

There are no large power resources actually within the border of the old West Punjab, except the limited and inferior coal of the Salt Range and some sub-montane hydro-electricity. But Attock oil and Sui gas (which has reached Lyall-pur) are important, and a Primary Grid now links hydel, gas and thermal power stations in West Pakistan, and the power situation has greatly improved.

Before Independence, the low humidity and the export demand for the longer-

[23] For a general review, see K. S. Ahmad, 'Reclamation of waterlogged and saline lands in West Pakistan', *PGR* 16/1 (1961), 1–18. For the entire Indus plains (including Peshawar) he gives 18,783 sq. miles (48,648 km²) as waterlogged or poorly drained, and 7,850 (20,337 km²) as severely saline – 17 and 7% of the total area. Cf. Fig. 17.5.

stapled Punjab cottons hampered the development of cotton mills, though some existed at Lahore and at Lyallpur, Montgomery and other Canal Colony towns. There has been a big expansion in both spinning and weaving in these places and farther south in Multan and Bahawalpur.[24] Woollen mills have been built at Gujranwala, Lyallpur, and Multan, largely to provide yarn to invigorate cottage weaving, but also producing blankets and suitings. There are probably more factories in hosiery and knitwear than in any other single line, while Punjab *durris* (rugs), carpets and blankets, still largely craft-produced, have a wide reputation. Owing to the severity of the cold weather there is a considerable local demand for woollens, and the important Kashmir and Punjab hill supplies of raw wool are supplemented by the import of better grades from Australia. The woollen and silk industries to some extent represent an evolution from the old crafts for which Lahore and Multan were famous; montane Punjab produces some raw silk, and experiments have been made with sericulture in the irrigated Changa Manga forest.

Heavier industry is lacking, except for the foundry and engineering trades essential to a great city like Lahore, railway workshops and so on. One interesting development is the manufacture of tubewell and other pumps by the Batala plant in Lahore, a much-expanded version of a small industry originally near Amritsar, now in India. There are also new ventures in chemicals, such as the manufacture of filament yarn or the projected urea factory, using Sui gas, at Multan.

The only other Punjab industry of any individual note is the manufacture of sports goods, especially cricket bats, hockey sticks and tennis rackets, at Sialkot: Changa Manga timber is used and there is some overseas sale. Near Sialkot also paper is made, as a cottage or small-scale industry, from gunny bags and waste. For the rest, better power supplies have led to a considerable growth of light consumption industries – shoes, soap, paints, varnishes, matches, cosmetics, electrical fittings, sewing machines and so on – in and around the larger cities, especially Lahore.

There is scope for the expansion of such lines as cottonseed oil and cake (for which there are two new factories at Bahawalpur), jam canning and so on; the large production of hides and skins and the various salts of the Salt Range await better organized production. But on the whole industrial resources are not great, especially without free access to Kashmir; Pakistan is naturally reluctant to remain too exclusively a primary producer, but it seems that development would be most soundly based on industries ancillary to agriculture.

Communications and towns

Until about 1880 the Punjab rivers were of importance for navigation, Pind Dadan Khan and Wazirabad, for example, having boat building and repair yards

[24] See J. W. Macnab, 'The Pakistan cotton industry', *Pacific Viewpoint* (Wellington), 2 (1961), 85–97.

and steamboats ascending the Sutlej, at high water, as far as Ferozepore. But railway competition and the abstraction of water for irrigation killed this navigation (except for small craft on the lower Indus), and early projects for using the canals for country boats met too little demand to make the costs of special construction, and the interference with the primary object of irrigation, worth while. Only the upper reaches of the rivers and of canals above the first railway crossing are now used for rafting timber from the Kashmir foothills.

The railnet, except west of the Jhelum, is one of the best in the sub-continent, and the Punjab is also fairly well supplied with roads. The main physical trends of the region – the northwest/southeast sub-montane strip and the northeast/southwest run of the doabs – are reflected in the orientation of the railways. The whole area is in the hinterland of Karachi, and all lines converge on Lodhran, between Multan and the Sutlej, whence there is only the one line southwards; and although, in contrast to the other lines, this is double-tracked, congestion at the height of the cotton harvest is serious.

The north, of course, has for centuries been the great highway for armies and peoples from central Asia into Hindustan: the Aryans, Alexander the Great (who reached the Beas), the earlier Muslim invaders, Babur the first of the Moguls, the Afghans and Persians in the post-Mogul anarchy, to mention but a few. The highway is marked by a string of towns commanding river crossings or central positions on doabs: Jhelum, Gujrat, Wazirabad, Gujranwala, Lahore, Amritsar. Away from this routeway the only really large town was Multan (358,000), in the Middle Ages the commercial and military key to the middle Indus and the southern route into Hindustan. A centre of craft production – textiles, pottery, leather, enamel – it is also an exchange centre for the semi-nomadic Ghilzai traders from Afghanistan, and is rising industrially. Muslim merchants in other parts of India are, or at least were, generally known as Multanis. The two Colony towns, Lyallpur and Montgomery, are, as their names imply, entirely new creations: Lyallpur rose from 13,483 inhabitants in 1906 to 425,000 in 1961. Primarily administrative and commercial centres, great cotton marts, they have the rigid rectangular plan of the Colonies, and the brand of newness sets them apart. Lyallpur has growing textile industries and a factory is being established to make corn products – dextrose, sucrose and corn solubles for penicillin.

Of the northern towns Sialkot (164,000) is the least. Lying off the great route, nearer the hills, it was the capital of the Punjab under the White Huns (6th century AD) and lost some importance when Wazirabad, on the main route, was planned (on rectangular lines) by the Italian general Avitabile for Ranjit Singh; but as already noted it has a certain industrial individuality. Sargodha (129,000) is rising in importance through its function as headquarters of the new Sargodha Division, which includes most of the Thal irrigation.

But the queen of the Punjab is beyond all doubt Lahore: the fifth city of undivided India, the second of Pakistan, it had 1,296,477 people in 1961. The city lies on the eastern edge of the floodplain of the Ravi, which once washed the

Fort walls; across the river is the magnificent tomb of Jehangir at Shahdara. Lahore was the capital of the Punjab from early Muslim times and, despite decay, retained that position under the Sikhs, while the tremendous development of the Province in the century of British rule gave it a new lease of life. There are the usual components of a great Indian city: the Fort, and under it the incredibly crowded and irregular walled town, a bazaar area (Anarkali) between the walls and the great spread of bungalows for the bureaucracy and lawyers[25] and their hangers-on, the Civil Lines and government offices and the Cantonments, the railway suburb. Its commercial hegemony was to some extent weakened by the rise of the Colony towns, but as the seat of government of an historic and proudly self-conscious Province and as an educational centre (incidentally with more and better bookshops than are to be found in comparable English cities) Lahore was supreme. With the loss of much of the area which formerly looked to it as a cultural and political centre, and with the far more serious loss of its non-Muslim traders and industrialists (who controlled the great bulk of its economic activity), Lahore declined seriously – though not in numbers – in the troublous times after Partition, and recovery was slow. With about 10% of Pakistan's industry she is a poor second to Karachi; the Moghalpara railway shops are still dominant, but there has been an increase in textiles, steel re-rolling and consumer production of many sorts. A new industrial suburb extends along the Rawalpindi road; factories (or workshops) are small on the average and there is still much craft production.[26] But it is not likely to lose its pre-eminence as the leading cultural centre of Islam in the sub-continent.

BIBLIOGRAPHICAL NOTE

The Punjab produced what was probably the best regional, though not avowedly geographical, literature of British India, though much of it was naturally and properly concerned with agrarian economics, following the lead of Thorburn's *Musalmans and Moneylenders in the Punjab* (1886). Some of this literature is still of value: H. K. Trevaskis, *The Land of the Five Rivers* (1928), an admirably written economic history to 1890, with much essential geography; and especially the delightful books, full of vivid pictures and keen insights, of M. L. Darling: *The Punjab Peasant in Prosperity and Debt* (2nd ed., 1928); *Rusticus Loquitur* (1930); *Wisdom and Waste in the Punjab Village* (1934). Out of date as these are in detail, much of their background remains valid. The Board of Economic Enquiry (Lahore) also published valuable village surveys in the 1930s.

There are many good articles in *The Punjab* [now *Pakistan*] *Geographical Review* (University of Lahore). Attention may be drawn to K. S. Ahmad,

[25] No small contingent: in 1922 H. C. Calvert estimated that 2,500,000 persons – equivalent to 40% of the male population – annually attended courts as parties or witnesses (*The Wealth and Welfare of the Punjab* (1922), 206).

[26] See M. K. Elahi, 'Some aspects of the development of factory industries in Lahore' *Oriental Geogr* 4/1 (1960), 37–46.

'Economic holding in the Panjab', *IGJ* 18/1 (1943), 24–29, which brings out some very suggestive points.

Between 1952 and 1956 an aerial survey, backed up by field-work, of the Indus plains was made by the Photographic Survey Corporation of Toronto, on contract for the Canadian Government as a Colombo Plan contribution. The resulting maps, aerial photographs and reports are in the hands of the Pakistan Government, but have been used for a number of papers, e.g. K. S. Ahmad, 'Land use in the semi-arid zone of West Pakistan', *PGR* 18/1 (1963), 1–19, and a note on 'Land use of the Indus Plain', *ibid.* 16/2 (1961), 59–63. See also R. C. Hodges, 'Canadian Colombo Plan Resources Survey of Pakistan', *Jnl Soil and Water Cons. India* 2/2 (1956), and the Canadian Government's *Summary of Canadian Colombo Plan Survey Operations 1952–61.*

There is unfortunately no equivalent of Nafis Ahmad's *Economic Geography of East Pakistan*, but Kazi Ahmad's *Geography of Pakistan* (OUP, Karachi, 1964) is useful.

CHAPTER 18

The Gangetic Plains
(Regions X–XI)

THE INDO-GANGETIC DIVIDE
(Bist Doab, Sirhind and the Ghaggar, Delhi)

In a very real sense all the regions lying between the Indus and the Ganga Deltas are transitional, but the area between Sutlej and Yamuna is peculiarly so, both physically and culturally; if the correspondence is not causal, it is at least significant. Primarily it is the actual divide between the two great river-systems, but it also includes two important climatic limits: in the north that of the sub-montane strip receiving really significant winter rain, in the south that between the area where any large agricultural development is possible only by irrigation, and the area where rainfed agriculture can precariously persist. The transition between the definitive aridity of the central Punjab doabs and the relatively humid mid-Gangetic area is fairly rapid between Sutlej and Yamuna, and in the old undivided Punjab the southeast, the area within the sphere of Delhi rather than that of Lahore, had a distinctive nuance, in the east more closely akin to Uttar Pradesh than to the Punjab proper. Communally and culturally it was the great marchland between Islam and Hindustan: Muslim culture today probably finds its highest expression at Lahore, while on the other side of the region Mathura (Muttra) is rich in Hindu tradition; between them Delhi was until very recently a Muslim outpost, yet with deep roots in the remoter Hindu past: the history of the northern part of the sub-continent is summed up and symbolized in Delhi to the highest degree.

The region is bounded on the north by the sharply-rising and straight Siwalik Hills, east by the Yamuna; on the south it grades into the Thar, and its limits here may be taken as the Ghaggar and, in the southeast, the low broken Aravalli ridge which reaches out to Delhi. With some violence to strict geographical logic, the northernmost portion of the Bari Doab, where Indian territory extends west of the Beas-Sutlej around Amritsar, is included for convenience. The area is about 35,000 sq. miles (93,240 km²).

Topography and hydrographic changes: the 'Lost Sarasvati'
Apart from a few scattered and broken Aravalli outliers in the southeast, and the topographic discontinuities of the river courses, the terrain is simply the usual

alluvial monotony. Most interest attaches to the sub-Siwalik strip in the north and to the hydrographic history of the Ghaggar. Between Beas and Sutlej the Siwaliks are on the whole more sharply defined than they are to the west, and for climatic and historical reasons more deforested than they are to the east. The result has been erosion on a spectacular scale. The Siwaliks in this area are formed for the most part of 'barely coherent' sandrock, with occasional clays, gravels and conglomerates, an ideal lithology for gullying. In the 80 miles

FIG 18.1 SUB-SIWALIK CHOS EROSION. About 6 miles north of Hoshiarpur
SOI 44 M/14. *Courtesy* SOI.

(129 km.) of the Siwaliks in Hoshiarpur District nearly a hundred streams debouch on to the plains. These *chos* are dry except in sudden spates, when they come down armed with masses of sand and are agents of rapid erosion on the plain below, itself sandy and with a perceptible slope near the hills. The *chos* country is really an immense 'pan-fan', in which individual detrital cones are hardly perceptible, while erosion is so violent that the *chos* are graded from two to four miles (3–6·4 km.) back into the hills – a marked contrast to the usual torrent profile (Fig. 18.1). On a vastly greater scale the *chos* belt is not unlike a beach crossed by runnels, each *cho* is a broad river of sand, with a shallow ever-shifting bed, and with banks which, where defined at all, 'are composed of unstable sand . . . or of scarped cultivation liable to be washed away by any flood'.[1] Except in the Salt Range *khuddera* and the great Yamuna-Chambal ravines, nowhere in India has erosion been so devastating as on this Siwalik front, where e.g. Rupar town is islanded in a broken sea of troughs and ridges.

[1] A. P. F. Hamilton, 'Siwalik erosion', *Himalayan Jnl* 7 (1935), refce. p. 95; see also R. Maclagan Gorrie, 'Countering desiccation in the Punjab', *GR* 38 (1948), 30–40. There is a large literature, summed up in Sir H. Glover, *Erosion in the Punjab*, and R. Maclagan Gorrie, *Soil and Water Conservation in the Punjab* (both Lahore, 1946).

Except for a few streams at each end, the drainage of the 100-mile (161 km.) long Siwalik ridge between Sutlej and Yamuna is either dissipated into the fields, or converges into the Ghaggar. The identification of this stream with the Saras- vati, the lost river of the Vedic hymns and other early Sanskrit writings, seems secure enough, and the ancient name still appears on the maps as that of a Ghaggar tributary. But the old records tell of a mighty stream, 'rich in lakes' and the mother of cities, and the Ghaggar of today, although the only river actually piercing the Siwaliks between Sutlej and Yamuna, is rainfed only, and at a short distance from the hills it becomes non-perennial, a monsoon river merely. Even its rainy season flow normally ceases at Hanumangarh, about 290 miles (467 km.) from its source and 15 miles (24 km.) within the Bikaner border; occasionally it extends for another 16 miles or so. Its dry course, the Hakra, in Bikaner and Bahawalpur, is impressive enough: for over 100 miles the flat bed is nowhere less than 2 miles wide, in places over 4 miles, bordered on either hand by steep and continuous lines of dunes. These are not true river banks, but as it were aeolian levees, accumulations of windblown sand trapped by vegetation on the riverain strips once seasonally flooded: 'The gradually rising accumulation of driftsand, usually protected by some growth of scrub, has prevented the on- ward march of the dunes and thus preserved the dry bed from being smothered.'[2] But it is unlikely that this broad bed was ever completely filled with water; the fertility of its loamy levels when water can be brought to them, and its striking definition between the bordering sand-ridges, are responsible for the local belief in the existence of a river of the first magnitude. This is very unlikely, but that water once flowed well down into Bahawalpur is attested beyond doubt by numerous ancient settlement-mounds, and it is often held that the East Nara in Sind is the continuation of the Hakra, beheaded by the Sutlej.[3] The reality is unknown, but in all probability less dramatic. The confused evidence and exceedingly controversial interpretations of the ancient tradition, the magic of the name Sarasvati, a complete failure to discriminate between prehistoric and mediaeval sites (natural enough before any serious archaeological investigation was attempted) – all have fostered exaggeration of the changes in historic or pseudo-historic times. Theories of extensive climatic change have been generally succeeded by theories of sweeping recent river-diversions; the annexation of the Yamuna drainage by the Ganga has been referred to historic or at least proto- historic times, while the line of the Sutlej above the Rupar elbow has been projected to the convergence of the present Ghaggar tributaries.[4] The balance of

---

[2] Sir Aurel Stein, 'A survey . . . along the "Lost" Sarasvati River', *GJ* 99 (1942), p. 175; this interpretation, based on Tarim analogues, is now generally accepted but not always acknowledged as to source.

[3] See W. Arden Wood, 'Rivers and man in the Indus–Ganges Plains', *Scottish Geo- graphical Magazine*, 40 (1924), 1–15.

[4] So far as I understand him, Siddiqi appears to hold both views simultaneously. See also A. Geddes, 'The alluvial morphology of the Indo-Gangetic Plains', *Trans. Inst. British Geogrs* 28 (1960), 253–76; an important paper relevant throughout this chapter.

evidence seems to be against this. Stein, whose views are based on first-hand fieldwork rather than on dubious documentation, does indeed hold that a branch of the Sutlej along the line of the Desert Branch Canal (see Fig. 18.2) built a deltaic fan in the Hakra south of Bahawalpur town, and so made possible the

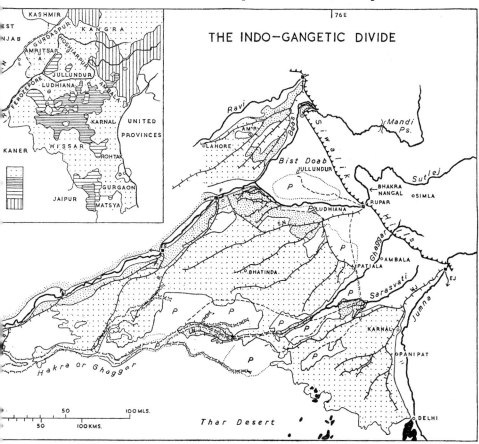

FIG 18.2 THE INDO-GANGETIC DIVIDE. Black, outlying Aravalli ridges; irrigation symbols as on Fig 85. Canals: B, Bikaner; DB, Desert Branch; H. Hariana; SN, Sutlej Navigation; W (E) J, West (East) Jumna. Headworks: F, Ferozepore; S, Sulemanke; I, Islamabad. P, projected irrigation areas. Again as in Fig 17.6, much of the 'Projected' irrigation has now been carried into effect, and irrigation now extends well south of the Hakra into Rajasthan (cf. Fig 8.1).

Inset: 1, E Punjab; 2a Patiala 2b, other states of Pepsu (all now Punjab); 3, Himachal Pradesh. The inset gives some idea of the complexity of the old princely states.

extensive prehistoric settlement there, and according to the *Punjab States Gazetteer* some Sutlej water still enters the Hakra. 'But it may be considered as certain that the riverine belt along the Hakra in this area knew no settled agricultural life during historical times. What small settlements existed near the Hakra before the modern canal system reached it were those of a very scanty pastoral population, maintaining itself partly by the supply of camel transport for caravan traffic following an old route . . . from Multan and Sind towards Delhi. . . .'[5]

In his very balanced review of the problem S. M. Ali holds that at least during historical times the Ghaggar has been an independent non-perennial river; he neatly turns the interpretation of Sarasvati as 'rich in lakes' by pointing out that after the monsoon such streams naturally form large pools or 'lakes'. The diversion, natural or artificial, of some upper Ghaggar tributaries into Yamuna and Sutlej is a contributory factor in the dwindling of the river. The Indo-Gangetic Divide has been settled (fairly densely in the north) for three millennia, and main communication lines lie athwart the drainage: the cumulative effect of their interference with the drainage lines is probably not small. The destruction of the plains forests in the north, generations of cultivation and over-pasturing, irrigation diversion, not to mention the Siwalik deforestation (perhaps too recent to affect the main issue) have resulted in too-rapid run-off and the familiar alternation of 'frequent floods during the rainy season and little or no water during the rest of the year'.[6]

To sum up: it is certain that a larger stream penetrated more deeply to the southwest, but it is very unlikely that this was the main Sutlej, and still less likely that the Yamuna has followed this course since human occupance of the region began. River diversion has had some part, but according to Ali's view – which seems to be borne out by Stein's facts and general conclusion – the main action in the Ghaggar drama has not been by way of catastrophic changes in the river-pattern but by slow, unspectacular, but cumulatively decisive deterioration in ground-water conditions, largely aided by human activity. And there is the menace of the spreading Thar.

Agriculture

Agriculturally the three-fold aspect of the Punjab proper is repeated: sub-montane strip, canal-irrigated area, arid margins. But there are significant differences: the rainfall from the westerly depressions is tailing off; canal irrigation is at once older and on the whole less well developed; and the arid margins, except along the Ghaggar, have not the topographic mitigations of the Indus riverain: there are no great streams to fill inundation canals, no *daman* to be bunded, and the water-table is very low.

By far the best-favoured area is the Bist Doab, as is shown by its District densities of 919 for Jullundur and 558 for Hoshiarpur (which includes part of the sparsely populated Siwaliks). The Sutlej riverain is also densely populated,

[5] Stein, *loc. cit.* 180.
[6] S. M. Ali, 'Population and settlement in the Ghaggar Plain', *IGJ* 17/3 (1942), 157–82; cf. S. I. Siddiqi, 'River changes in the Ghaggar Plain', *IGJ* 19/4 (1944), 139–48, and 'The physiognomy of the Ghaggar Plain', *IGJ* 20/10 (1945), 87–92.

as is the Amritsar area across the river; but the arid south falls to 287 in Hissar.

In the sub-montane strip well irrigation is more important than canal; the water-table is high and this is a rich parkland country, except where waterlogged (as in the Beas bend in the northwest corner) or where it has been torn to pieces by *chos*. Losses of good land by erosion and sand-spreads have been very serious. Before British rule the Siwaliks had been under petty feudal lords and the forests were on the whole preserved for hunting; this society was largely broken up by the conquest, and legal titles were secured virtually by squatting. No control was exercised over land use, and at the same time the general economic development of the plains called for much constructional timber. The forests were gutted by reckless timber-felling, charcoal burning and the all too intensive grazing of goats. The results are shown in Fig. 18.1. Erosion has now been checked, to a considerable extent, by forest control and afforestation, contour bunding, and more systematic fodder exploitation, but it remains a serious problem. Settlement patterns and crops are similar to those in the sub-montane strip in West Punjab, but sugar-cane becomes more important as the great sugar belt of western Uttar Pradesh is approached.

In Sirhind or Hariana, the Sutlej/Yamuna or 'Delhi Doab', soils are lighter than in the sub-montane strip – 'a great wedge of light loam and sand which Rajputana pushes northwards almost to the Sutlej'. In the north, well-irrigation is still important in light fertile loams; in the Jangal Des – 'jungle country' – to the southwest the water-table is too low. Nevertheless the sandy loams are remarkably drought-resistant and crop failure is less frequent than might be expected considering the low rainfall (*c.* 12–17 in., 305–432 mm.). Gram, wheat and barley are the chief rabi, millets the chief kharif dry crops. Irrigation is mainly for wheat. Villages are fairly large, nucleated, evenly spaced.

The real south – especially Hissar – is in worse case, except in the Sutlej and Yamuna riverains and where the Ghaggar brings a belt of irrigation across it (Fig. 18.2). The water-table is too deep for wells, rainfall is scanty (10–12 in., 254–305 mm.) and unreliable, yet most of the crops must depend on it. Insecurity is the dominant note. Density is relatively low, though probably high enough in relation to resources, and holdings are of necessity large – 7·5 to 10 ac., and in places up to 60 (3–4 and 24 ha.). Owing to the paucity of water-points villages also are definitely large and rely on tanks for their domestic supply; this is rare in northern India. In a really good year – say one out of five – the large holdings provide large surpluses of wheat and barley; more normally kharif bajra and rabi gram are the chief crops. Stock-rearing is of great importance, the Hissar or Hariana cattle being among the best Indian breeds, and camels are used for transport and even for the plough. But here too a run of two or three bad years means ruin.

> 'I remember a year in Hissar when we had less than four inches, and a man could ride for fifty miles and see nothing greener than the poisonous akk. . . .
> At such a time fodder is so scarce, that any bit of scrub that cattle will eat is

guarded as jealously as if it were a crop of valuable sugar-cane. Every tree, too, is lopped to the bark, and there is no more desolate sight than the long roadside avenues raising flayed, twisted arms to a bare, pitiless sky. After a bad famine there are villages where not a cow, buffalo, or calf is to be seen.'[7]

Much has already been changed by the completion of the Nangal Dam on the Sutlej, while a few miles farther upstream, in a narrow gorge in the Siwaliks, Bhakra is the highest straight dam in the world (700 ft., 213 m.). Ultimately the project should irrigate 6,500,000 ac. (2,630,000 ha.) and generate 954,000 kW.[8] As for industrial resources, East Punjab possesses Bhakra, Mandi and other hydro-electric sites in the montane area, as well as its timber; otherwise, except for hides and skins, its resources are even less than those of West Punjab: minerals, except for patches of *reh* salts of doubtful economic value, are non-existent in the plains. Industry was of little importance in 1947, and the Kashmiri Muslims who provided skilled labour for woollen and silk weaving in Amritsar and Ludhiana left for Pakistan. But cotton production is increasing, and with wool from the Indian Himalayan regions, silk and artificial silk, provides the basis of a small textile industry at these towns and Jullundur. Ludhiana has important bicycle and sewing machine factories, and fascinating roadside workshops producing spare parts for vehicles – in good weather, with the lathe under a shady fig-tree. Paper-making (using *sabai* grass) near Ambala, a few agricultural processing mills, a few foundries in the railway towns, practically exhaust the list of factories. The availability of *kikar* (Acacia) bark, an important tan-stuff, the large supplies of hides and skins, and the large number of Chamars (untouchables who have no caste to lose by handling dead cattle) has led to a fairly marked concentration of petty village tanneries in the southeast; although of course it is a question whether tanning is responsible for the numbers of Chamars or vice versa.

Since Partition the rosin and turpentine industry, and some firms from Sialkot, have migrated from West Pakistan.

The great highway and its towns

The cities of the region are mostly route centres, associated with the great highway from the northwest into the gates of Hindustan at Delhi: four times has a great struggle for power been decided at Karnaul or at Panipat, respectively 75 and 55 miles northnortheast of Delhi. Of these battles the most far-reaching in their effects were Babur's victory at Panipat in 1526, which gave Hindustan to the Moguls and the complete overthrow of the Marathas by the Afghans near the same town in 1761, which, although leaving the Marathas as the greatest power in central India, ended their hopes of complete dominion in the north and left

---

[7] M. L. Darling, *The Punjab Peasant in Prosperity and Debt* (1928 ed.) 92. There was a sharp famine in 1939 and a widespread dearth in 1964 after two years' failure of both winter and summer rains.

[8] See *Eastern Economist* (ND), April 3rd, 1964, 804.

the field open to the British power advancing up the Ganga. On or near this historic highway lie four important cities, Amritsar, Jullundur, Ludhiana and Ambala, as well as Delhi itself, which deserves separate treatment. Urbanization increased greatly with the influx of refugees, and about 3,000,000 people, mainly with urban backgrounds and traditional skills, have settled in and around the older towns.[9]

Amritsar (265,000) grew up round the main centre of Sikh devotion, the Golden Temple (actually a copper-gilt dome of doubtful architectural merit) built on a site presented – by the Moguls! – to the fourth Sikh *guru*. It is now a leading industrial town, with historic craft industries, though woollens have declined with the exodus of the Kashmiris and cotton with the competition of Bombay.[10] Jullundur (265,000) lies central to the Bist Doab, an important rail centre with sports goods and small metal industries. Ludhiana (244,000) owes its initial importance to the Sutlej crossing, much of its recent growth to refugee industry; Ambala (182,000) is an 'economic border' town between plains and hills. Other towns such as Ferozepore, Bhatinda and Patiala are mainly railway towns and minor administrative centres, except for the new capital, Chandigarh. Planned and largely built by Le Corbusier, with some very exhilarating architecture, tempering the harsh sunlight by colour and 'sun breakers', it has had a great influence on style, despite some criticism of its social planning.[11]

Many of the small princely states which once occupied this marchland were ruled by Sikhs, and the transfer of populations after Partition greatly strengthened the concentration of Sikhs, and resulting militancy, in what until 1966 was the Indian Punjab State. After much disturbance, a Punjabi-speaking basically Sikh State was conceded in 1966 (cf. p. 172), leaving the poorer southeastern rump to the new Hariana State.

DELHI

It is hardly necessary to emphasize the larger nodality of Delhi: the gateway between the Thar-Aravalli barrier and the Himalaya; the marchland position between the northwest, ever accessible to new waves of invasion and cultural intrusion, and the shock-absorbing Gangetic Plains; the convergence of the routes from the ancient Cambay ports and the Deccan by Rajputana and Malwa. Few sites enjoy such long-sustained significance: to the north lie the fields of Karnaul and Panipat where the fate of India has four times been decided. But not only is the general area thus marked out as the great crossroads of the subcontinent: the pattern is reproduced in detail by the famous Ridge, the worn

[9] I. N. Chawla, 'Urbanization of the Punjab Plains', *Indian Geogr* 3/1–2 (1958), 29–48. For an interesting central place study, see R. C. Mayfield, 'The range of a central good in the Indian Punjab', *Annals Ass. Amer. Geogrs* 53 (1963), 38–49.
[10] J. P. Singh, 'Prosperity of textile industry in Punjab', *IGJ* 38/2 (1963), 1–35.
[11] O. H. K. Spate, 'Aspects of the city in South Asia', *Confluence* (Cambridge, Mass.), 7 (1958), 16–28.

and arid last spur of the Aravallis, pointing like a lean but wiry finger straight to the Yamuna.

A triangle of some 70 sq. miles (181 km²) is strewn with the ruins of old capitals (Fig. 18.3): New Delhi is commonly reckoned the eighth. Delhi proper is Shah-jahanabad, founded by the Mogul Emperor of that name (reigned 1628–58), on

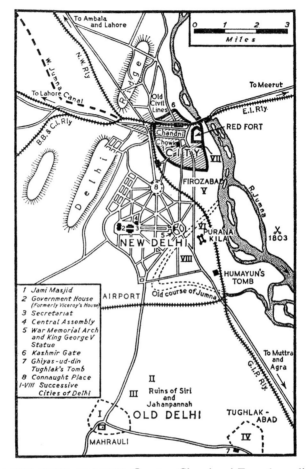

FIG 18.3 THE CITIES OF DELHI. *Courtesy* Chambers' Encyclopaedia (*1950*).

the low bluff overlooking the Yamuna floodplain; on the landward side its red sandstone walls extend for 3¼ miles (5 km.), while on the river front the vast enceinte of the Red Fort encloses the Mogul palace, still magnificent despite barbarous usage by Persians, Afghans, Marathas and British. West from the Fort runs the long, straight Chandni Chowk, 'Silver Street', the bazaar of the goldsmiths and other craftsmen; and across the broad, open space surrounding the Fort walls lies the finely proportioned Jama Masjid or Friday Mosque.

Beyond the city walls the nearer suburbs and the immense and ill-planned Civil Lines (the administrative headquarters of Delhi Division until 1911) sprawl across the northern end of the Ridge. There are a few light industries (flour-milling, cotton textiles, printing, small metal goods), and such industry (mainly cotton-milling) and commercial importance as Delhi now possesses is to be found in the teeming tight-packed lanes of Shahjahanabad and in its formless nearer suburbs. New Delhi, for long administrative and nothing else, still has almost half its workforce in government service; perhaps no other city in the world – almost certainly no other of its size – is more bound up with the business of governing. In the old city the ancient arts carry on the Mogul inheritance, much degraded by pandering to tourist taste, real or alleged. Against this are modern industrial estates, including a sulphuric acid plant, and light industry started for or by the refugees. Over all lingers a Muslim imprint; Shahjahanabad is a town of the northwest, and this was nowhere more apparent than in the shabby fore-courts of the absurdly castellated railway station, where camels, pack donkeys, mules and herds of sheep and goats give the air of a dusty market town.

South of Shahjahanabad lie both New Delhi and the ancient cities. The oldest site, going back perhaps to the beginning of the Christian era, is Indarpat, traditionally Indraprastha, one of the five cities of the epic Mahabharata War. But the visible remains, the Purana Qila of Humayun and his supplanter Sher Shah, are early 16th century. Beyond New Delhi the countryside is a litter of mouldering walls, the domes and cupolas of innumerable tombs, kiosks, enclosed tanks and gardens, culminating in medieval Mahrauli and Tughlukabad, capitals of the earlier Muslim dynasties. These two form an impressive contrast. At Mahrauli is the towering Qutb Minar (AD 1220), its 234 ft. (71 m.) making it the highest free-standing stone tower in the world, and the richly beautiful tomb of Altamsh (c. 1230), the faces of its masonry a maze of interlacing calligraphic ornament. Near it stands the famous iron pillar, a Gupta monument of the 4th century AD and an astonishing metallurgical achievement, being in effect a single piece of wrought iron 23 ft. long; and here too is the stump of the minaret which the megalomaniac Ala-ud-din began in 1311 and planned to be twice the height of the Qutb. Three miles away the massive sharply-battered walls of Tughlukabad crown a rocky outcrop, grim beyond expression; even the tomb of the first Tughluk ruler, austerely beautiful as it is, is simple to the point of severity. Mahrauli appears sophisticated, even decadent, beside this puritanic and cyclop-ean architecture, and it is difficult to realize that chronologically Tughlukabad is a century later.

So much for the past. The transfer of the capital of India from Calcutta to Delhi in 1911 was conscious historical imitation: the Moguls were to be matched on their own ground. A new Province was created mostly from the Punjab but with a few trans-Yamuna villages; since the Government of India Act (1935) and the achievement of Independence the Province has taken on the character of a federal district. Its population has more than quintupled, rising from 413,851 in 1911 to 2,359,408 in 1961, of which 261,545 were in New Delhi. Old and New Delhi together form the third city of India, and by far the biggest inland city in the sub-continent.[12]

New Delhi naturally affects the monumental, and not without success: at least the gulf between New Delhi and the barbarous generality of Indo-British official architecture is far wider than that between New Delhi and its Mogul precursors. On the whole it is fine planning, though the distances are too magnificent: in the common Indian phrase, fitted For Princes and Rich Men Only. The main axis runs east–west, from the huge but dull First World War Memorial Arch (which carried in gigantic letters the single but superfluous word INDIA) to the rise on which stand the immense buildings of the Secretariat and the former Viceroy's House, now used by the President of the Republic. This triple avenue, with its long canals and lines of trees, is flanked by the houses of the chief Princes; fortunately its mirror-symmetry is broken by two small ruined mosques, and now the canals are humanized. Splendid as it all is, the artifice is too apparent; the houses of high officials nicely proportioned to their several statuses, the side-avenues named after Hindu and Muslim rulers in strict communal balance, the oppressive symmetry –

> Grove nods at Grove, each Alley has a brother,
> And half the platform just reflects the other.

As for the architecture proper, it is perhaps no disgrace if it fails in the competition with its near-by rivals the Jama Masjid and Humayun's Tomb, since these are two of the noblest of Mogul buildings, which is as much as to say two of the really great architectural achievements of the world. . . . But although New Delhi does achieve its monumental ambitions it lacks as a rule the final touch of imagination needed for greatness, and in places it is positively inept – as for example in the unrelieved monotony of the exterior circular colonnades of the huge Assembly building, with a skyline broken only by the meanest of puny finials. The most modern-looking building in New Delhi – not excepting the modernistic All-India Radio building, with its clover-leaf plan – is the open-air observatory built by the astronomer-prince Jai Singh of Jaipur in the 18th century, immense dials and gnomons with beautifully clean lines which make the mean and shallow architecture of the shopping centre, Connaught Place, look even shoddier than it really is.

Yet with all its faults New Delhi has undeniably an imperial as well as a merely bureaucratic impress: a tribute to the Mogul tradition, a costly monument to the British Raj, but beyond that the always busy (if not always perhaps purposeful) governing centre of one of the world's greatest states. Nor does it seem likely that this site, so rich in historic association and so magnificently placed in relation

---

[12] For some details, see Spate, *loc. cit.*; A. Bopegamage, *Delhi: A Study in Urban Sociology* (Univ. of Bombay, Pubtn No. 7, 1957); and for planned projects, G. Cullen 'IXth Delhi', *Ekistics* (Cambridge, Mass.), 9 (1960), 399–408, and M. Anand, 'Master plan for Delhi', *ibid.* 11 (1961), 361–72.

to the sub-continent, can easily be displaced as the central focus of Indian political life.

THE UPPER GANGETIC PLAINS

Regional divisions

The rational regional division of the Gangetic Plains is extremely difficult; physiography is of no help, since there are no marked physical breaks other than river courses, and the surface variations that do exist, such as the *bhur* tracts, are

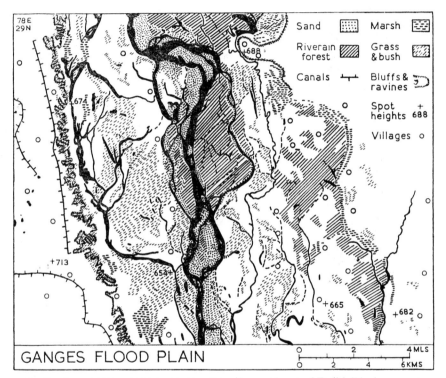

FIG 18.4 THE GANGA FLOODPLAIN, *c.* 65 miles northeast of Delhi. Black = perennial water; all blank areas cultivated. 3 village-names in floodplain have 'khadar' as one component. *SOI* 1/126,720 53 L/NW. *Courtesy* SOI.

only local. Climate would seem the obvious alternative principle, but the isohyets trend diagonally northwest/southeast across the lie of the land, cutting the rivers, the topographic master-features, at acute angles, and it seems absurd to put places a few miles apart into separate regions on the basis of a line which is strictly speaking hypothetical and does not correspond to any marked ecological change. J. N. L. Baker heroically treats the whole area from the Yamuna to the deltaic margins as the Indo-Gangetic Plain East, which is reasonable physiographically but takes no account of the big difference between the dry Delhi–Agra country and the wet jute-growing east of Bihar, a difference big enough to enforce some division. It seems best to follow Stamp and make a rather imprecise division on a line running roughly from the Ganga–Yamuna confluence at Allahabad across the northnorthwest–southsoutheast section of the Ghaghra. This does not correspond very well to the 40-in. (1,016-mm.) isohyet, as Stamp implies, but it does conform quite closely to an area of more mixed main crops to the west – our Upper Gangetic Plains – and the Middle Gangetic Plains where rice predominates, with an acreage at least double that of wheat; and the former region also contains the great bulk of the irrigated area of the Gangetic Plains (Fig. 18.6 and inset).

An unsatisfactory solution, it must be confessed, but perhaps in as much accord with the intractable facts as is possible pending the production of more, and more detailed, local studies. The region includes three areas of some historic individuality:

(i) *The* Doab, that of the Yamuna and Ganga, commanding the northern approaches to the Malwa passage into the Deccan; this was the core of the pre-Mogul Delhi Sultanate;

(ii) the greater part of the Kingdom of Oudh (Avadh), a successor-state set up by a governor nominally under the Moguls in their 18th-century decline, and later a British client-state until its suppression in 1856 – one of the proximate causes of the Mutiny;

(iii) between these two lies Rohilkhand, so named from the Rohilla Afghans who were dominant here in the post-Mogul anarchy. Rampur state (now merged into Uttar Pradesh) was a survival of their power.

Politically the Upper Gangetic Plains occupy the western two-thirds of the United Provinces of Agra and Oudh (renamed Uttar Pradesh), excluding the montane districts (Chapter 15) and in the south most of Jhansi and those parts of Banda and Hamirpur Districts lying on the Peninsular foreland. Agra was the old 'North-Western Provinces', separated from Bengal in 1834–36, of which the western portions were acquired in 1801–3 when Rohillas, Marathas and the Nawabs of Oudh had cancelled each other out. The distinction between Agra and Oudh has long ceased to have much but a formal administrative significance. As statistics by Districts are not always available the treatment of some topics below refers to the whole Uttar Pradesh rather than to the restricted region, but where this is so it is clearly stated and the general argument is not greatly affected.

Land and climate

The lie of the land is simple; a great plain built up of detritus from the Himalayas, and traversed by the great rivers Yamuna, Ganga and Ghaghra, which show a very marked parallelism, with the main drainage-line naturally pushed well over to the south. The northern limit is marked by the very smooth curves of the Siwaliks (which east of the Sarda lie within independent Nepal); but on the south the boundary is very irregular, as the old rugged surface of the Peninsular Foreland has been smothered by the Gangetic alluvium and that of the southern tributaries of the Yamuna (Chambal, Betwa, and Ken), leaving, of course, much-broken peninsulas and islands of older rock rising out of the alluvial flatness. The main physiographical variation within the great mass of the plain is that between the upland bhangar alluvium of the doabs and the fingers of khadar along the main streams and their sub-parallel tributaries such as the Ramganga and Sarda and the Gumti, which last is wholly a plains river. There is of course a great development of dead arms, deferred junctions and *jhils* in the broad floodplains, which on the greater rivers are several miles across and in the rains have almost the aspect of arms of the sea, with a great expanse of water extending right to the horizon up and down stream. The right banks are generally the higher, with bluffs and some ravining, though nothing comparable to the great belts of bad-lands which border the lower Chambal and the Yamuna in the arid southwest, where one knows by the gullies that one is coming to a river when still three or four miles away (cf. Figs. 18.4 and 18.5).[13]

In these all but featureless alluvial expanses there are, it is true, what may be called micro-regional differences of slope and aspect, in some areas undulations faintly perceptible to the eye. These are tracts or facets rather than sub-regions, though they may be associated with soil or water-table variations by no means without agricultural significance. But broadly speaking there are only three really important variations from the norm: *bhabar, terai, bhur*.

The first two may be treated together. The bhabar (='porous') is simply the great detrital piedmont skirting the Siwaliks, where the stream profiles suddenly flatten out and the coarser detritus – boulders and gravels is deposited. In this tract, 20 miles (32 km.) wide in the west but narrowing eastwards, the smaller streams, except when in spate during the rains, are lost in the loose talus, to seep out again where the slope is still flatter and finer material is deposited in the marshy and jungly terai below. Originally the terai covered a great zone perhaps 50–60 miles (80–97 km.) wide and extending in Oudh as far south as the middle Ghaghra.[14] But much of this has been so altered by settlement that the true terai is now confined to a relatively narrow strip parallel to the bhabar. Its practical absence west of the Yamuna (where the immediate sub-montane belt is occupied by the *chos* country) may be due to the fact that between Yamuna and Sutlej the Siwaliks stand well away from the Himalayas and so have developed their own purely rainfed drainage system to a greater extent than is possible where the Siwaliks are as it were impacted into the Lesser Himalaya and are cut through by snow-fed rivers; the significance of the gap between Yamuna and Sutlej has been discussed above in connection with the Ghaggar problem. Farther west in the

---

[13] See the discussion in A. Geddes, *op. cit.*, and also A. B. Mukerji, 'Alluvial morphology of the Upper Yamuna–Ganga Doab', *Deccan Geogr* (Hyderabad), 2/1 (1963) and 2/2 (1964), 1–36 and 101–26.
[14] M. H. Rahman, *L'Oudh : Étude de géographie économique* (Paris, 1940), 18–21.

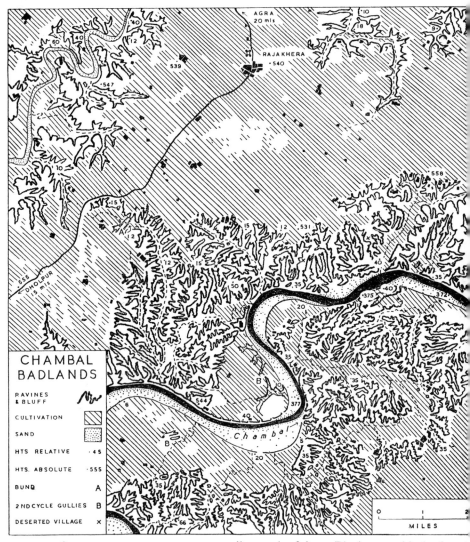

CHAMBAL
BADLANDS

RAVINES & BLUFF	
CULTIVATION	
SAND	
HTS RELATIVE	·45
HTS. ABSOLUTE	·555
BUND	A
2ND CYCLE GULLIES	B
DESERTED VILLAGE	×

AGRA
20 mls

RAJAKHERA ·540

DHOLPUR
15 mls

Chambal

0   1   2
MILES

FIG 18.5 CHAMBAL BADLANDS, *c.* 30 miles south of Agra. Blank areas thin bush
and tussocky grass, much bare ground in ravines; settlements black. Note unsuccessful attempt to protect road at A; cultivation on floors of larger ravines
(probably enlarging laterally) and slip-off slopes, with suggestion of second-cycle
gullying in latter. Since the date of original map (1922) some contour-bunding
and afforestation have probably taken place; properly controlled the area might be
a useful fodder reserve; to this end the Chambal Valley Project is under (rather
slow) implementation. *SOI* 543/I, *Courtesy* SOI.

Punjab, where the Siwaliks again abut on to Himalayan ranges, it is too dry for a terai development and the *daman* corresponds to the bhabar; farther east in turn, where the Siwaliks are again separated from the snow-mountains by the longitudinal valleys of Nepal, the rainfall itself is much greater and there is an ample water-supply for the terai.[15] Both terai and bhabar are jungly, and malarial, but population pressure has led to increasing colonization (with strict anti-malaria measures) and rice and wheat are grown in equal proportions with maize, oilseeds and jute. There are some really large government farms and a little canal irrigation.[16]

Bhur is a generic term for patches of sandy soil, in places sufficiently extensive to form low but undulating sandy uplands. The Bhur proper is a belt on the east bank of the Ganga in Moradabad and Bijnor Districts; generally rather arid but waterlogged in the depressions, especially in wet years, it was until recently a somewhat negative tract, but most of it has been reclaimed by tubewells.

The general landscape is admirably described in the *United Provinces Gazetteer*,[17] although over much of the region irrigation has now somewhat softened the seasonal contrast:

' . . . a level plain, the monotony of which is broken only by the numerous village sites and groves of dark-olive mango-trees which meet the eye in every direction. The great plain is, however, highly cultivated, and the fields are never bare except during the hot months, after the spring harvest has been gathered, and before the rainy season has sufficiently advanced for the autumn crops to have appeared above the ground. The countryside then puts on its most desolate appearance; even the grass withers, and hardly a green thing is visible except a few patches of garden crops near village sites, and the carefully watered fields of sugar-cane. At this time the *dhak* trees burst forth with brilliant scarlet flowers. . . . With the breaking of the monsoon in the middle or end of June the scene changes as if by magic; the turf is renewed, and tall grasses begin to shoot in the small patches of jungle. Even the salt *usar* plains put on a green mantle, which lasts for a very short time after the close of the rains. A month later the autumn crops – rice, the millets and maize – have begun to clothe the naked fields. These continue to clothe the ground till late in the year, and are succeeded by the spring crops – wheat, barley, and gram. In March they ripen and the great plain is then a rolling sea of golden corn, in which appear islands of trees and villages. . . .'

The soils of the plain range from the very heavy *usar* clays – towards the west with alkaline *reh* efflorescences in the more arid areas – through the very generally distributed loams (*dumat*) to the sandy bhur; the reasonably heavy *matiyar* clays of the khadar are the best paddy-land.

Regional differences in temperature are relatively unimportant – January means

[15] I owe the original hint for this view to a remark of my former student, Dr Enayat Ahmad. Cf. also A. Geddes, *op. cit.* 262–5.

[16] Y. D. Pande, 'Agriculture in the Naini Tal Terai and Bhabar', *GRI* (Calcutta), 23/2 (1961), 19–39 – an excellent quantitative study with dot maps.

[17] Vol. I (Calcutta, 1908), 8.

range from 55 to 64° F., May from 90–95° F. (13–18, 32–35° C.) with extremes of 115° F. (46° C.) or more. In the northwest, however, the cold season has special features of significance approximating to the more extreme Punjab winter; night frosts in January, hail-storms in February and March, are not uncommon and are sometimes severe enough to damage the rabi crops, and especially sugar-cane.[18]

Rainfall, as universally in India, is of prime significance. Only in the extreme northwest is winter rain worthy of note, with one or two inches in January and February together – enough to account for the large proportion of unirrigated wheat in Saharanpur and Muzaffarnagar; unirrigated wheat is also associated with the high rainfall (over 45 in., 1,143 mm.) of the northern tier of Districts. The 40-in. (1,016-mm.) isohyet slants across the region: north and east rainfalls of 50 in. (1,270 mm.) or so are attained in the immediate sub-montane strip, south and west they sink to 30 in. (762 mm.) and in Agra and Mathura to under 25 in. Some of the agricultural correlations will be immediately apparent from Fig. 18.6, which while statistically out of date presents a picture which is basically still true.

Along the northern border there is still a strip of sal forest in the bhabar and terai; on the plains the natural vegetation has largely disappeared but survives in riverain strips, mainly of the khair/sissoo type which is an early colonizer of new detrital spreads. The trees named are the most important economically: sal (*Shorea robusta*) and sissoo (*Dalbergia sissoo*) for construction, khair (*Acacia catechu*) also for timber but perhaps more important as a source of tanstuffs. Much of the floodplains is occupied by tall coarse grasses or tamarisk brakes. 'Two well-marked features are observed in the annual herbaceous species. Those appearing in the cold season on waste ground, or as weeds in cultivation, are mostly of European origin and are more abundant in the wheat-growing Districts of the northwest; while the annual herbage which springs up in the rains is composed mainly of species which have come from the east or from Central or Southern India'[19] – an interesting point emphasizing the transitional nature of the Gangetic trough.

The agricultural foundations: crops and irrigations

The region is one of the most cultivated in India, with well over half the total area of some 40,000,000–45,000,000 ac. (16,000,000–18,000,000 ha.) cultivated, and double cropping adds 20–25% to this figure. Forests are under a million acres and current fallows (nearly half in the dry southwest) show a marked decline as compared with the Indus Plains; so also, unfortunately, do fodder crops.[20]

[18] See R. N. Tikkha, 'Persistence probability of cold spells in Uttar Pradesh', *IGJ* 36/4 (1961), 140–51.

[19] *UP Gaz.* I. 13. There is a detailed description in A. B. Mukerji, 'Vegetation of the Upper Doab', *IGJ* 37/1 (1962), 8–16.

[20] The omission of detailed crop figures, here and elsewhere, is regretted, but detailed breakdowns are not available in Australia.

Foodcrops as usual predominate, wheat being easily first, followed by rice, barley, jowar and bajra; gram and maize are also important. Of cash crops sugarcane, especially in the moister north, is the most important, followed by oilseeds. Cotton, mainly in the drier west, is of declining importance before the competition of sugar. A considerable quantity of tobacco is grown, but opium and indigo are now practically negligible. Fig. 18.6, although based on old figures, still shows the salient features; we may note: (i) the high proportion of un-irrigated wheat and *per contra* of irrigated rice in the northwest, associated with the small but useful winter rainfall for rabi wheat and the relative falling off of monsoon rainfall for rice; (ii) the virtual disappearance of sugar and rice in the arid or unreliably watered southwest: (iii) the increasing importance of rice *vis-à-vis* wheat as we go eastwards and beyond the limits of the region. The high proportion of wheat irrigated is striking – some 60% against 15% for rice – and it must be remembered that wheat is a winter (rabi) crop and rice kharif, relying on the monsoon; of course this does not imply that paddy-fields are not flooded, but except in the khadar this is mostly by the local rain. Finally we may note the universal village mango-groves and the production of market-garden crops (especially melons, gourds, and the like) in the fertile floodplain silts near the greater towns.

Although irrigation is not such a *sine qua non* of agriculture as it is in most of the Indus Plains, the actual cultivated area, and still more the security of agriculture and the proportion under cash crops, has been greatly increased in the last few decades by irrigation.

The older canals are mainly in the Doab: the Eastern Yamuna (an improved version of an 18th-century original), the Upper Ganga taking off at Hardwar, the sacred portal where the Ganga cuts through the Siwaliks, and the Lower Ganga. The major works for these were mostly constructed between 1850 and 1880, but there have been many improvements and a full perennial supply was not attained on the Upper Ganga Canal until 1926. The Ganga and Yamuna have not such large mountain catchments as the Punjab rivers (except the Ravi) and occasionally shortages occur; these are being increasingly met by tubewell pumping into the more distant tails. The Lower Ganga headworks contains a special passage to allow sufficient water always to pass through for Hindu ritual bathing. These canals irrigate some 50% of the Doab; on the Yamuna right bank is the smaller Agra Canal.

In Oudh the most important work is the Sarda Canal, first mooted in 1870 but held up for decades by the short-sighted opposition of local landlords. A proposal to take Sarda water right over to western Uttar Pradesh, however, not unnaturally produced a sudden change of front, and they then petitioned for the original project. The canal was opened in 1928, extended in 1941, and now irrigates well over 1,000,000 ac. (404,700 ha.).

Besides the canal systems a considerable area in the dry southern margins is irrigated from large reservoirs in the valleys of the Peninsular foreland. But most

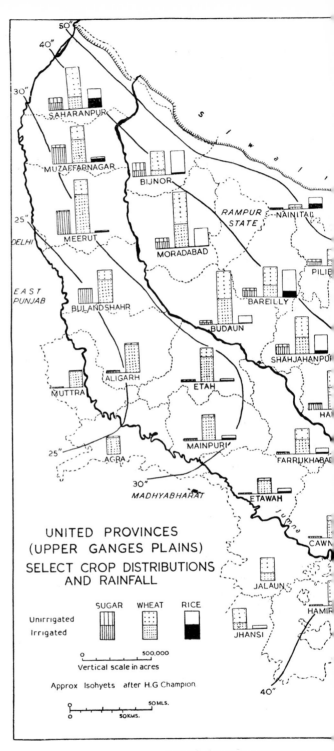

FIG 18.6 UTTAR PRADESH: SELE

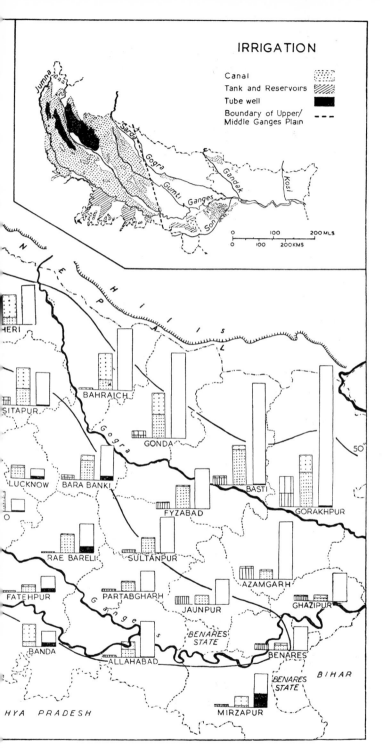

Canal
Tank and Reservoirs
Tube well
Boundary of Upper/
Middle Ganges Plain

0   100   200 MLS
0   100   200 KMS

NEPAL HILLS

HERI

SITAPUR

BAHRAICH

GONDA

Gogra

50°

LUCKNOW   BARA BANKI   BASTI

FYZABAD   GORAKHPUR

RAE BARELI   SULTANPUR

AZAMGARH

FATEHPUR   PARTABGHARH

Ganges

JAUNPUR   GHAZIPUR

BENARES
STATE

BANDA   BENARES   BIHAR

ALLAHABAD

BENARES
STATE

HYA   PRADESH   MIRZAPUR

BUTIONS, RAINFALL AND IRRIGATION.

interest attaches to the remarkable recent tubewell development, tapping the underground resources of the Gangetic alluvium. Experiments were made with oil-pumped tubewells, but these proved on the whole uneconomic, and attention was turned to hydro-electric possibilities on the small artificial falls which adjust the slopes of the canals to those of the country they traverse and promote an even flow. The natural fall of the Upper Ganga Canal is about 146 ft. (44·5 m.) broken into 13 vertical falls of 8–12 ft. each. Some of these have been utilized for small hydel stations, linked into a grid, with supplementary and stand-by thermal stations, and provide the power for about 2,000–3,000 tubewells. These are located on the higher parts of the doabs on each side of the Ganga, and have been especially valuable in the great *bhur* tract in Moradabad and Bijnor, which is unsuitable for canal irrigation. Each well commands an area of up to 1,000 ac. (405 ha.) of cultivable land. The water-supply, held up in lenticular aquifers at depth, seems to be well in excess of any likely withdrawals and there is still great scope for extension of the method. In addition to working the wells the grid brings electric light to many villages, and there is an increasing demand for power for small agricultural processing industries such as sugar-cane crushing; the application of electricity to such purposes represents an important reduction in the usually exorbitant demands on the energies of underbred and underfed cattle. Power pumping also enables water to be lifted from the Ramganga, otherwise useless for irrigation owing to the enormous variation in discharge (from 20 to 100,000 cusecs) which would make ordinary canal methods utterly uneconomic.[21]

It is hardly too much to say that the success of the tubewell scheme bids fair to revolutionize rural life in its area; not the least promising aspect is the supply of cheap power for badly needed light rural industries; and, perhaps most important of all, the scheme has led the way to the exploitation of the vast potential resource of underground water at depth.

Agricultural life

In many ways the region provides a type-section of Indian agrarian life and problems. As usual cultivating holdings are small; for Uttar Pradesh as a whole over 80% are under 5 ac. (2 ha.). This is too small for really efficient farming and the evil is made worse by fragmentation.[22] Uttar Pradesh in general, and Oudh in particular, were largely the domain of big landlords, often absentees; but the Partition obviously weakened the Muslim *taluqdars* of Oudh, zamindari has been

[21] Most of these facts are drawn from P. K. Dutt, *Power Resources and Utilization in the UP* (London, M.A. thesis, 1947); see also A. H. Siddiqi, 'A regional study of the Budaun District,' *IGJ* 25/1 (1950), 16–33.

[22] There are two important studies by M. A. Shafi bearing on productivity: 'Measurement of agricultural productivity in Uttar Pradesh', *Economic Geography*, 36 (1960), 296–305, and *Land Utilization in Eastern Uttar Pradesh* (Dept of Geography, Muslim University, Aligarh, ?1962); this is based on twelve detailed village studies, but has a useful general introduction.

abolished and the land is now vested in the State as in *ryotwari* provinces. At least some of the increased cultivation has been ascribed to the supersession of the zamindars, many of whom have left the countryside for Lucknow and other towns.[23] Despite, or rather because of, the fertility and good rain of most of the region, population presses very hardly on resources; between the Yamuna and the Ghaghra almost the entire area has District densities of over 650, reaching 1,170 in Meerut, and this without much urbanism. Farming methods, except in the northwest, are primitive, debt is high, and the cattle problem is perhaps the most serious in India. The cultivator has very inadequate storage and market facilities and is still the prey of the moneylender, retail seller and grainbroker, often one and the same person.

The division between kharif and rabi is of great importance; the chief kharif crops, besides rice, are maize, millets and cotton; wheat, barley, gram and oilseeds are rabi. The agricultural year begins with the onset of the rains and has the following rhythm:

mid-June to mid-July	kharif sowing
August through September	tillage for rabi
early October to early November	kharif harvest, rabi sowing
December to mid-February	weeding and irrigation of rabi
March to mid-April	rabi harvest
mid-April to mid-May	threshing and sale of rabi
mid-May to June	culture of cane in irrigated land.

The most striking development of recent years has been the supplanting of cotton by sugar-cane as the chief cash crop. Uttar Pradesh dominated the increasing production of sugar after protection was introduced in 1931 and normally has over half the Indian cane area. Cotton on the other hand has seriously decreased, and in recent years the sugar acreage has been about ten or twenty times that of cotton.

The cattle population of Uttar Pradesh is very heavy. Except in the extreme north and the extreme south, the terai and Peninsular margins, there is very little grazing – the human population is far too thick on the ground. Cattle are grazed on stubble fields after the harvest (in itself a practice inhibiting improved husbandry in hedgeless and fenceless fields); but otherwise they are as a rule left to pick up what they can get on roadside verges and meagre patches of waste, generally carrying more weeds than grass, and quite burnt up in the hot weather. By May most of the beasts look like tottering skeletons, and in the southwest even in mid-rains the buffaloes present a shocking appearance. Eugenic practices are at a discount in the heart of Hindu India; the cattle are thus individually

---

[23] U. R. Singh, 'Changing land use around Mirzapur Town', *NGJI* 5/4 (1959), 212–19; S. P. Singh, 'Demographic features of Lakhnau', *ibid.* 5/3 (1959), 157–75; and the searching discussion in J. W. Elder, 'Land consolidation in an Indian village', *Econ. Devpmt and Cultural Change* 11 (1962), 16–40.

weak in proportion to their excessive numbers, in many places not strong enough to draw a modern plough. The cultivator, looking for a tangible return, either in food or in cash, from his crops, is generally loath to 'waste' time and space – still less irrigation water which has to be paid for – on fodder crops. The large jowar stalks do provide fodder, but the use of oilcake is as yet neglected. Significantly enough, it is only in Saharanpur, Muzaffarnagar, and Meerut Districts, with winter rain and better farming (and perhaps Punjab influence), that fodder crops account for more than 10% of the TSA. Except near the terai and the riverain jungles there are few or no fuel reserves and little or no space in which to create them, and in consequence cattle dung has to be used for fuel rather than manure. The reclamation of some of the Yamuna badlands with quick-growing grasses and bushes may do something to relieve this joint fodder-fuel problem locally. But on the whole the region is thoroughly typical of India in its interlocking vicious circles of agrarian poverty and inefficiency.

Settlement, communications

Settlements are generally nucleated in large and remarkably evenly spaced villages, though there are of course interesting variations in detail, among them the common preference for new or old river-bluffs as settlement-lines; in some cases a large village on the *dhaya* will have an offshoot in the fertile but insecure silts of the floodplain below. The general characteristics of the villages are well described by Rahman, with specific reference to southern Oudh:

> 'These villages form large enceintes of sun-dried brick huts. In the centre one sometimes finds a few masonry houses and the Pukka Haveli, a small burnt-brick house belonging to the landlord or moneylender. The huts of the lower castes are found on the outskirts of the village. There are generally two or three entrances to the village, but the absence of main roads shows that it is self-sufficing. Each village has one or two temples or shrines. Where water is sufficiently abundant, the village pond is surrounded by groves of neem, pipal and plantains, a splash of green pleasantly breaking the monotony of the grey and drab houses.'[24]

In the terai and the arid margins the villages are usually smaller and poorer; in more intensively cultivated areas there is severe competition for space between fields and houses, and villages 'reach the densities of industrial towns, sometimes 600 to the acre'. In the extreme west and southwest the flat roofs of southwest Asia still predominate – here 'the sun is more to be feared than the rains'; farther east brushwood covered with mud is used for roofing, and in the more humid extreme east huts are gabled and thatched; a very significant transition.

True urbanism is modest, though there are a very large number of 'towns' of

[24] *Op. cit.* 84–85. Unfortunately space does not permit even a summary of the important work of Enayat Ahmad: *Settlements in the UP* (London Ph.D. thesis, 1949). This fascinating study is the best and most detailed known to the writer on any large Indian area. See also R. L. Singh, 'Evolution of settlements in the Middle Ganga Valley', *NGJI* 1/2 (1955), 69–114.

the 5,000–10,000 class; but as Rahman remarks, 'all the towns, except the largest, have something of the aspect of village life'. There can be no more striking testimony to the broad homogeneity of the plains than the approximation of the distribution of smaller towns and larger villages to Christaller's hypothetical diagram of the service-centre and its region, although owing to the very different conditions of northern India and southern Germany the analogy must not be

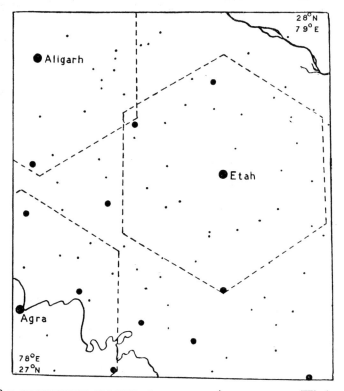

FIG 18.7 SETTLEMENT SPACING ON YAMUNA/GANGA DOAB. Whole area of *SOI* 54, I. Largest circles are District capitals, medium tahsil headquarters, dots larger villages. Broken lines represent Christaller 'service regions' for the three large towns; the distinct approximation of this theoretical construct to the actual spacing of larger and smaller centres will be noted. Distance between centres and angles of hexagons, 22·5 miles (36·2 km.).

pressed too hard. Nevertheless in Fig. 18.7 Etah and Aligarh at least correspond well in size and function to the county town of 30,000 to 100,000 inhabitants.[25] The five great cities of Uttar Pradesh, Kanpur, Lucknow, Agra, Varanasi and Allahabad, have a distinctive individuality; below them come the more generalized bigger administrative and commercial centres. Many of these grew up around the forts (*garh*) of petty magnates playing their own hands in times of

[25] Cf. R. E. Dickinson, *City, Region and Regionalism* (Kegan Paul, London, 1947), 30–35.

trouble, Rajputs, Rohillas, Marathas; others are later creations, nodal points on road or rail, and the eponymous headquarters of Districts or tahsils – of the fifty-three Districts of Uttar Pradesh, only six do not bear the same name as their 'county town'.[26] The larger have attracted some industry, generally in strict association with the agricultural milieu: such are the great wheat, sugar or cotton commodity markets Meerut, Muzaffarnagar, Aligarh, Bareilly, all occupying central sites on their doabs. Such towns generally have populations between 50,000 and 200,000, and even in the smaller ones they often display a fascinating tapestry or socio-territorial associations, some strands of which may be very ancient, others dating from the times of the Moguls or the Nawabs, yet others stemming from the socio-economic changes of the Raj and its railways; but these cannot be gone into here.[27]

There is a good railnet, but road development is inadequate. Until the railways came, river traffic was of great importance and exercised a strong influence on the siting and layout of towns; but apart from local traffic by country boats carrying up to 70 tons of weight, this has long declined, though there are some thoughts of reviving it in association with better river control. Animal transport is still very significant in the aggregate – bullock and buffalo carts (often waste-fully heavy in build, mechanically inefficient and ruinous to roads), pack donkeys, and in the extreme southwest even camels.

Industry

The region is devoid of significant mineral resources. The most important power projects under the Third Plan are for dams on the Yamuna and on the Son at Rihand and a thermal station at Singrauli; these are in the 350,000–325,000 kW class and altogether existing and planned installations would produce about 1,200,000 kW. Apart from the great industrial centre of Kanpur, treated separately, and the usual foundry-and-consumption trades of larger regional centres, industry is mainly: (i) agricultural processing and textiles; (ii) small consumption goods (especially glass), whether survivals of old luxury trades or to meet modern urban needs; (iii) the standard village maintenance crafts – tanning, carpentry, pottery and the like – and handloom weaving.

(i) The chief processing industries are naturally sugar-refining and oilseed-pressing. The refineries have the advantage of producing their own fuel in the refuse of the cane, bagasse; there are over seventy modern vacuum-pan factories, but less advanced open-pan works are still numerous, and much *gur* (unrefined brown sugar) is produced by still more primitive methods in the villages. Nearly a quarter of the industrial workers of Uttar Pradesh are employed in sugar-refineries, but many of these are seasonal. Cotton ginneries and presses give some employment, but cotton mills are more important, especially of course in

[26] The administrative practice goes back at least to Mogul times, and is common to most of India; see above, p. 208.

[27] For examples, see R. L. Singh, 'Faizabad-Ayodhya', *NGJI* 4/1 (1948), 1–6; S. D. Misra, 'A note on the socio-historical geography of Mathura', *ibid.* 4/4 (1958), 189–99.

the west – Kanpur, Aligarh, Meerut, Bareilly, Agra, Moradabad and Hathras, with an outlier at Varanasi.

(ii) The chief centres for luxury trades and for arts such as brassware, ivories, silks and gold- and silver-thread embroideries and jewellery, and for the finer craft-produced textiles such as shawls and printed calicoes, are Agra, Varanasi and Lakhnau. The associations are clear: the patronage of the extravagant Court of the Nawabs of Oudh at Lucknow, the tourist attractions of Agra, the great flow of pilgrims to Varanasi. More modern trades, mainly in the five great cities but with outliers in such towns as Meerut and Aligarh, include paper, matches, paints and chemicals, soaps and cosmetics, hosiery and a variety of small metal goods. Perhaps the most individual and important is glass, in which Uttar Pradesh holds a commanding position,[28] with a strong concentration in Agra District. Glass works are mainly over towards the Vindhyan margins whence they get their sand; Firozabad is the centre of the important bangle trade, in part a cottage industry.

(iii) Village industries, such as silk,[29] play a very important part in the life of the people, but despite much official encouragement their part in wider trade currents is small. It is of course possible, and much to be desired, that the introduction of hydro-electric power will lead to an increasing development of light rural industries.

The Five Cities

Uttar Pradesh had the largest Muslim minority of any non-Muslim province of the Indian Empire – over 15% in 1941 – and, as the intrusive community, an unusually high proportion (30·6%) of the Muslims were urban, while as landowners and officials they had a larger share of influence than their numbers would account for, again an inheritance from the Kingdom of Oudh. It is noteworthy that the Muslim University was established in Uttar Pradesh, at Aligarh, not in the more Muslim Punjab.

Of the five great cities of Uttar Pradesh one, Varanasi, is in the Middle Ganga Plain region; but together they form a curious cross-section of Indian cultural history and for that reason it is more interesting, if admittedly not very logical, to treat Varanasi with the rest. Varanasi, then, and Allahabad represent the heroic and medieval ages of Hindu civilization; Agra is a relic of the Mogul heyday, the apogee of Islam in India, Lucknow conversely of the post-Mogul Muslim decadence; while Kanpur typifies Indo-British civilization, in both its earlier John Company phase and that of the modern economic revolution.[30]

The origins of Varanasi or Benares or Banaras or Kasi (1961: 489,864) are

[28] For a local study, see R. L. Singh and S. Pannu, 'The Saryupar Plains – A study in agro-industrial relationships', *NGJI* 3/3–4 (1957), 109–16.

[29] S. A. Majid, 'Silk production and weaving in Bihar', *NGJI* 5/2 (1959), 57–66, has a good analysis of this important industry.

[30] For fuller treatment, see O. H. K. Spate and E. Ahmad, 'Five cities of the Gangetic Plain: a cross-section of Indian cultural history', *GR* 40 (1950), 260–78. All quotations in this section are from *UP Gaz.* See also R. L. Singh, *Banaras* (Nand Kishore, Banaras, 1955).

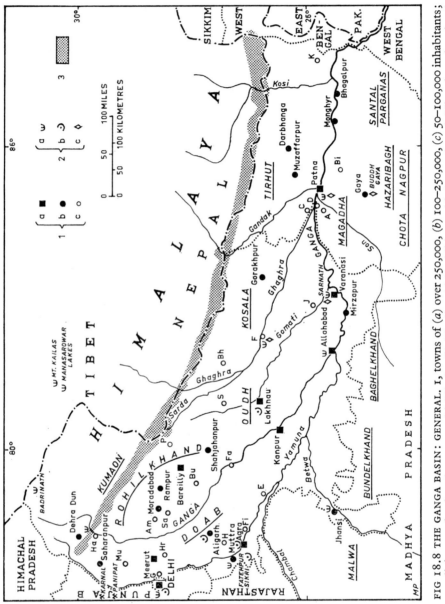

FIG 18.8 THE GANGA BASIN: GENERAL. 1, towns of (*a*) over 250,000, (*b*) 100–250,000, (*c*) 50–100,000 inhabitants; 2, religious and cultural centres – (*a*) Hindu, (*b*) Muslim, (*c*) Buddhist; 3, bhabar and terai. Historic and regional names underlined.

unknown but very ancient; at its old site, Sarnath, a few miles to the north, is the deer park where Buddha commenced his mission. But during the Muslim invasions so notorious a centre of idolatry fell on evil days, and most of the temples are relatively recent, many being built by Maratha princes in the 18th century. The city lies along the Ganga, on a *kankar* ridge, for about 4 miles; and the curving riverfront is lined by great flights of steps, the bathing ghats, and by massive temples, in turn tawdry and splendid. Behind these is a labyrinth of narrow fetid alleys, overhung by tall galleried houses, with innumerable shrines 'ranging from a shapeless fragment of stone smeared with vermilion to magnificent temples'. The streets are crowded with priests, mendicants and touts, and their pilgrim prey, and through the turmoil the sacred bulls of Siva lounge arrogantly. In Christian countries the odour of excessive sanctity has not infrequently a commercial taint, but in Varanasi it is all-pervading. The resort of Hindu princes and rich men, either on pilgrimage or to end their days, brings much trade, and Varanasi is noted for fine silks and embroideries and for cheap brassware, which last is largely intended for the tourist trade and of suitably atrocious design. There is also a certain amount of modern industry; but essentially Varanasi lives parasitically on its past and on the exploitation both of genuine piety and of superstition. It is appropriate that the sacred city of Hinduism should be the seat of the Hindu University which, however, owes its origin at least partly to Mrs Annie Besant.[31]

Allahabad (430,730), the ancient Prayag, is at the junction of Yamuna and Ganga – obviously a sacred site, and made more so by the legendary underground confluence of the Sarasvati; at Varanasi the lack of confluence (other than that of the insignificant Barna) is compensated by the meeting of five rivers at the Panchganga Ghat, of which 'the Ganges alone is visible to the gross material eyes' of geographers. The great Fort in the angle of the rivers was built by Akbar; beneath it, on the dry sandbanks, is held the annual Magh Mela fair, which attracts about 250,000 people; every twelfth year the Kumbh Mela gathers together perhaps the greatest known assemblies of human beings on one site, over a million people sometimes attending. This poses great medical problems (above, p. 141) and there have been tragedies when even a slight loss of control in such vast crowds has caused many deaths by crushing and suffocation; but these can happen with say football crowds in the West. The old city lies along the Yamuna; northwards, on a long-terrace-like tongue of higher ground between the rivers, extend the rectilinear Civil Lines and the Cantonments. Allahabad is primarily an administrative and legal centre, but there is increasing

---

[31] Lest these remarks be ascribed to Western materialism (the great Aunt Sally of Indian publicists) and offensive British insularity, I may mention that they are largely based on, and a faint reflection of, Mahatma Gandhi's disgusted description of the greed with which the pious are despoiled and of the revolting fakes – such as five-legged cows – produced by the allegedly religious for their edification. See his admirable autobiography, *My Experiments with Truth* (Ahmedabad, 1927, and other eds.; Pt III, Chapter XX, and Pt V, Chapter VII). I trust that this is an untainted source.

industrialization, including cotton mills, bicycle making and other light metal lines, and furniture.[32]

Agra (508,680) lay originally on the left bank of the Yamuna, but Akbar moved it to the strategically better western side, where the route into Malwa and the Deccan diverges from the great arc of the Yamuna. Much of the city is filthy, squalid and ruinous, and even the Civil Lines are shabby and ill-planned; the suburbs are in places made hideous by ravines used as refuse dumps. But central Agra contains some of the glories of Mogul architecture: the serene strength of Akbar's Fort, the exquisite Pearl Mosque and the little kiosks looking from the Fort walls to the Taj; less successful is the Jama Masjid with its bizarre zigzag striped domes. For thousands the Taj Mahal symbolizes India; by the time (1631–48) that Shah Jahan was building this sumptuous mausoleum for his favourite wife Mumtaz Mahal there was some decline from the strength of Akbar's building, and the dazzling white marble is less beautiful than the rich reds of the Vindhyan sandstone favoured in the preceding century; but despite serious defects the Taj remains a beautiful building, not least in its setting, a great red-walled formal garden by the river. Few visitors go on to Akbar's soon-deserted capital at Fatehpur Sikri, 22 miles away; those who do are the richer by an unforgettable aesthetic experience.[33] In its originality and daring ingenuity, in the combination of the towering magnificence of the great Gate of Victory with the charming fantasy of the smaller buildings, Fatehpur undoubtedly represents the peak of Mogul architecture, at its best one of the most satisfying styles in the world. Looking out over the populated and yet in appearance lonely landscape, it is a far cry to the squalor of modern Agra, with its crafts degenerated to supplying shoddy alabaster models of the Taj to the tourist trade. Agra has some cotton mills, a declining craft production of woollen carpets and *durris*, and great hide and wool markets.

If in Agra and Fatehpur we are in a rich dreamland, in Lucknow we have entered the realm of lunatic fantasy. Like the Mogul centre, Lucknow was built on the sordid exploitation of the peasant masses; but at least the Mogul dignity and splendour show tangibly their imperial standards of culture and catholicity of interests; the clumsy and garish provincialism of Lucknow, the bastard progeny of debased Oriental and debased European models, reflects an appalling decadence. There are a few solid and relatively restrained buildings, and it must be admitted that the Nawabs of Oudh have had a bad press; but all allowance made, their private morals, their public administration, and their taste seem to have been all on one level, and that depraved. 'Buildings, which look like marble by moonlight, are shown by the disillusioning sun to be degraded examples of stucco and brick. Flying buttresses to support nothing but one another, copper

[32] See R. L. Dwivedi, 'Allahabad – A study in industrial development', *National Geogr* (Allahabad) 4 (1961), 53–60, and 'Replanning an existing city – Allahabad', *ibid.* 5 (1962), 93–107; and see Bibliographical Note to this chapter.

[33] There is a spirited interpretation by Naomi Mitchison, 'Fatehpur Sikri: City of the Angry Young Man', *Geogl. Magazine*, 31 (1958), 367–8.

domes gilt from top to bottom, burnished umbrellas and balustrades of baked clay' form a gallery of architectural horror perhaps matched only in the Indo-British buildings of Bombay. The city was of little importance until the 18th century; modern Lucknow (655,673) sprawls over an immense area mainly south of the Gumti, but increasingly also on the north bank with a refugee colony and the University. The central zone is separated from the river by open spaces and more open residential development; the old Cantonment to the southeast retains its military aloofness as an army headquarters. Lucknow is the capital of Uttar Pradesh and has a considerable industrial development, including rail shops, paper and cotton mills, sugar-refineries, and a wide range of light consumption trades.[34]

Kanpur (Cawnpore) in the 18th century was a mere village, but between 1931 and 1941 it outstripped Lucknow and in the latter year had 487,324 inhabitants; it has since grown rapidly to 971,062 under the stimulus of the war industrial demand. In Company days a military and trade station – like Lucknow a Mutiny storm-centre – its real rise also began under war conditions, when the American Civil War created a sudden demand for Indian cotton. Kanpur had then just been linked by rail to Calcutta and promptly became a boom town. 'Lands covered with the mud huts of camp-followers were hastily taken up by the authorities. Commissariat elephants were brought out to push down the frail erections in order to clear space for the bales of cotton which, piled up level with the roofs, had been blocking every lane in the city. At the same time the ordinary country produce of the Doab and of Oudh began to pour in here instead of passing along the river.' Unlike most of the riverain cities except Lucknow, Kanpur has its older close-built core a mile back from the Ganga; between it and the river is a western industrial and an eastern administrative zone. One of the leading industrial centres of India, its industries are more varied than Ahmedabad's, yet cotton is still predominant, then leather and woollens, in both of which it is the leading Indian producer.[35] It has also flour and vegetable oil mills, sugar refineries, small chemical works, and many minor industries, among which the manufacture of brushes (associated with its importance as a tanning centre) may be mentioned. The first cotton mills were built between 1869 and 1882, so that Kanpur ranks as one of the older of the factory cities of India. There is a true proletariat here, and in many cases living conditions are little better than those of the first boom days, so it is not surprising that labour disputes have been bitter.

THE MIDDLE GANGETIC PLAINS

Reverting to the discussion of the regional division of the Ganga lowland, we may define the Middle Gangetic Plains as simply what is left between the Upper Gangetic Plains and Bengal: roughly the eastern third of Uttar Pradesh and the

[34] M. N. Nigam, 'Evolution of Lucknow', *NGJI* 6/1 (1960), 30–46.
[35] U. Singh, 'The origin and growth of Kanpur', *ibid.* 5/1 (1959), 1–11.

northern half of Bihar. The only real difficulty (once we have settled on the boundary in the indeterminate passage-zone of Oudh) is in the east, where there is no marked difference between Purnea District of Bihar and adjoining Bengal. However, the set of rivers, communications, and life in northern Bengal is so distinctly to the south that it is better to detach the doab between the great bends of Ganga and Brahmaputra and regard it as a sub-region of Bengal; we may thus make a virtue of convenience and take the state boundary as our eastern limit. The Middle Gangetic region thus defined is very comparable to the Upper Gangetic Plains in area – about 62,000 against 65,000 sq. miles (160,000 and 168,000 km²) – and also in topography; as already stressed, the major variable is climate.

Climate and topography

In both these respects the region is obviously transitional between the relatively dry, mainly bhangar, doabs of the Upper Gangetic Plain, and humid, largely khadar, Bengal. About 90% of the rainfall is from the monsoon, except in the extreme northeast, where the hot weather 'Nor'-wester' thunderstorms of Bengal bring some 6 in. (152 mm.) to Purnea in March–May inclusive; but even here the monsoon proportion falls only to 87%. Spatially the rainfall shows a steady decrease from 70 in. or more on the eastern to a little over 40 on the western margins (1,778 to 1,016 mm.); and there is also, as in the Upper Gangetic Plains, marked decrease from the Himalayas to the Ganga: while the main mass of the region receives 45–55 in. (1,143–1,387 mm.), the extreme north has around 60 (1,514 mm.). Mean minimum and maximum temperatures in December–January are around 50 and 85°F., (10 and 29.4°C.), and there are no frosts; mean maxima in May exceed 100°F. (37.8°C.).

Rainfall is intense in incidence, the average fall on a rainy day being 0.75–1 in. (19–25 mm.); although real droughts are rare, the monsoon is sufficiently variable to introduce insecurity. The rains tail off in October and variability is then most likely and on the whole most serious, since a premature cessation may involve both failure of standing kharif and very unfavourable sowing conditions for the rabi.

The whole area, with very minor exceptions, lies below 500 ft., falling to under 100 (152–30 m.) in the east. Physiographically it is of course much the same as the Upper Ganga Plains, but still there are some broad differences. Foremost of these is naturally the greater development of khadar, though most of northern Bihar is still bhangar; or it is perhaps better to regard it, with Geddes, as essentially built up of vast alluvial cones.[36]

The monsoon rainfall on the Himalayas becomes increasingly heavy as the Bay of Bengal is approached, and the rivers draining them are consequently subject to extremely violent fluctuations in volume and course. In the east the Kosi is especially notorious, with rises of 30 ft in 24 hours. From its montane

[36] See A. Geddes, *op. cit.* 262–4 and his Fig. 1.

catchment of about 24,000 sq. miles (62,000 km²) largely in shales and sand-stones, 'the charge of detritus and sand is so great that, despite a flood discharge of about 200,000 cusecs, the river has no permanent deep channel, but . . . tears through the flat country in numerous capricious channels'. Its general move-ment, of course with regressions, is to the west (i.e. cutting into the right bank, like other Northern hemisphere rivers), and two centuries ago it flowed by Purnea town; between 1934 and 1936 its lower course shifted 12 miles (35 km.) to the west. A wide tract is scarred with its abandoned channels – the numerous Burhi (old) or Mara (dead) Kosis. The Kosi has been responsible for enormous devastation by flood or by spreads of micaceous sand: 'How quickly and deeply it can overlay the country is apparent from the fate of indigo factories which have been abandoned owing to its encroachments. In comparatively few years all that can be seen of them is the chimneys, for the buildings are buried deep in sand.'[37] It is no wonder that the taming of the Kosi has caught the imagination of India, though it may well seem to the local people 'like taming a mad elephant'. (See also p. 472 above and p. 569 below.)

Devastating also, but to a less extent, have been the other great rivers, Ghaghra, Great Gandak, Burhi Gandak, Kamla. Their khadar floodplains are wider than in the Upper Gangetic Plains, and even on the doabs there are many *jhils*, more or less permanent lakes, and *chaurs* – 'long semi-circular marshes which develop into a vast and intricate chain of temporary lakes during the rainy season'; one such chain, an old course of the Great Gandak, covers 140 sq. miles (363 km²) when full. The landscape is thus rather more diversified and of distinctly more humid aspect than that of western Uttar Pradesh. Associated with this is the fact that northern Bihar has India's biggest output of freshwater fish, half the catch being sent to Calcutta, and her migratory fishermen travel as far afield as Assam.

South of the Ganga the alluvial filling is shallow, a mere veneer; the Peninsular edge is very ragged, and many groups of small craggy hills (up to 1,600 ft., 488 m.) form islands of bare rock or scrub. This alluvial strip is some 85 miles (137 km.) wide in the west, where the Son makes a great deltaic re-entrant into the older rocks; but in the east the Rajmahal Hills, the extreme northeast of the Peninsula, abut almost directly on to the Ganga. Most of this fringing plain is bhangar, and the inundated areas are fewer than north of the Ganga in Tirhut. But they are not unimportant. The Ganga bank itself lies high, except in Shaha-bad District, and at high water the tributaries are ponded back; the Punpun valley, parallel to the Son on the east, is thus annually flooded. Both north and south of Ganga the construction of railways athwart the drainage causes local, but sometimes disastrous, waterlogging and flooding. Some of these temporary inundations, however, are agriculturally useful; rabi crops are grown on them when they dry out, or they are bunded for dry-weather rice.

[37] L. S. S. O'Malley, *Bengal, Bihar and Orissa, Sikkim* (1917), 49. Cf. E. Ahmad, 'The rural population of Bihar', *GR* 51 (1961), 253–76 (at 265–6) for the human effects.

The khadar consists largely of light sandy loams; most of the area more than 20 miles (32 km.) north and east of Great Gandak and Ganga is *matiyar* clay with some loams; in places lime-rich clays and loams are associated with a high incidence of goitre, unusual in the plains. The *diaras* or alluvial islands in the great rivers are mostly sandy, as is the wide tract wasted by the Kosi. South of Ganga heavier loams and clays prevail.

Very little natural vegetation is left. In the north the terai carries sal forest and tall reedy grasses; but most of the unreclaimed terai lies beyond the Nepal border, leaving Bihar only a very thin strip east of the Kosi. Floodplains and *diaras* have a riverain jungle of sissoo, tamarisk and reeds.

Agriculture

The region is perhaps rather less diversified agriculturally than is the Upper Gangetic Plain, although most of the drier crops of its western margin continue into Bihar, and in the east a new one, jute, appears; since Partition it has been extended along the terai into western Uttar Pradesh.

Between 55 and 60% of the plains is under cultivation, giving something over 20,000,000 ac. (8,090,000 ha.) as the NSA; with the increasingly humid conditions and the large area of easily inundable khadar, double-cropping brings the TSA to nearly half as much again. Rice easily leads, with around half the NSA, followed by barley, wheat, gram; oilseeds and sugar-cane are also important. Cotton fades out in the west, but in the east jute is increasingly important and no longer confined to Purnea. Potatoes are important in Patna.

The broad change from west to east can perhaps be best illustrated by comparing the six Divisions wholly or mainly within the region: Varanasi, Fyzabad and Gorakhpur in Uttar Pradesh, Tirhut, Patna and Bhagalpur in Bihar. Rice is easily the dominant in all six; in Fyzabad wheat acreage is still half or more that of rice, but falls to under an eighth in the east. Except in Varanasi and Fyzabad, jowar and bajra are negligible; conversely, oilseeds are unimportant in these two Divisions. Sugar, with its considerable demand for moisture, breaks across this west–east zoning and is strongest in the north.

In Bihar north of Ganga, only about 5% of the NSA is irrigated, and that mostly west of Muzaffarpur, and in the westernmost districts of Gangetic Bihar (Champaran and Saran) this rises to 12%.[38] The plains south of the river have over 52% irrigated, more than this near the Ganga, and account for over 80% of Bihar's irrigation. Larger-scale canal irrigation is almost confined to the lower Son valley, especially in Shahabad District in the Son-Ganga angle; here climatic conditions are normally secure but the topography is exceptionally favourable, with a slope of 2–3 ft. per mile and no drainage lines to cross. The rest of these southern plains is mostly irrigated by *pynes* or *pains*, small private canals, for the most part mere inundation cuts, though they may reach 20 miles (32 km.) long. The larger and more elaborate may suffer from the changing and conflicting

[38] *Techno-Economic Survey of Bihar* (Asia, Bombay, 1959), Table 12.

interests of the many landholders concerned, and some pass out of repair; they also suffer from the vagaries of rainfall, which led to an actual decline in irrigated area of a million acres (403,000 ha.) between 1943 and 1956, despite the extension of canal irrigation.[39] These southern Districts (Bhagalpur, Patna, Gaya, Shahapur) contain, especially on the low plateau-margins, a good deal of irrigation from tanks or *ahars*. These are usually formed by bunding small streams ;again they are more or less temporary, and like the *pynes* they suffer from neglect due to lack of co-operation. Wells are less important except in Saran, the angle between Ghaghra, Great Gandak, and Ganga; unlike *pynes* and *ahars*, which mainly inundate paddy-fields, the wells are chiefly used for the rabi.

The appearance of a three-harvest year marks a further stage in the transition to the humid delta: the kharif of the west is replaced by a *bhadai* (autumn) and *aghani* (winter) harvest. The gradual shift is well described by Dayal:[40]

'On account of an earlier monsoon and pre-monsoon showers in May, the agricultural season starts here earlier than in the United Provinces with the result that in place of two well-marked seasonal crops "kharif" and "rabi" as in the latter, we have three seasonal crops in Bihar. But the early rainfall in Bihar is neither so early nor so heavy as in Bengal. Consequently not only is the "bhadai" harvest much less important in Bihar than in Bengal, but the crops grown are different. Moreover, while it is possible for an East Bengal cultivator to harvest his "bhadai" crop so early as to transplant the "aghani" rice crop on the same land, this sort of double-cropping is generally impossible in Bihar . . . the cultivator must choose between a "bhadai" and an "aghani" crop just as is to be found to a certain extent in Western Bengal. Further, while the area under "rabi" crops is very small in the Ganges Delta, they occupy in in Bihar an even larger acreage than the "aghani" crops. . . . But there is a difference between the "rabi" crops grown in Bihar and those grown in the United Provinces especially west of Allahabad. In the latter they are valuable crops like wheat, barley, oilseeds, but in Bihar a considerable amount of the "rabi" harvest consists of inferior catch-crops such as "khesari" [chickling-vetch] and gram, grown on the "aghani" rice lands.'

The bhadai crops – quick-growing rice, maize, millets, jute – are sown May–July and harvested August–September; they are most important in the north-east, approximating to Bengal conditions. In the west the rabi acreage exceeds kharif, bhadai and aghani combined, but in central Tirhut aghani predominates; some 90% of it is rice sown at the beginning of the rains and harvested November–December. The rabi crops are much more varied than those of the rains-sown harvests, but contribute comparatively little to local food supply, being largely cheap catch crops such as pulses or cash crops such as oilseeds, tobacco and wheat. 'Good bhadai and good rabi go hand in hand,' but aghani rice stays too long on the ground to leave time for the better rabi crops; the

[39] *Ibid.* 24.
[40] P. Dayal, *The Agricultural Geography of Bihar* (London Ph.D. thesis, 1947), 262–3 Dayal's analysis of the correlations of soil, climate, topography and harvests is extremely interesting, but unfortunately too detailed to summarize.

bhadai-rabi combination also offers better security against the mischances of the seasons.

The detailed crop distribution, implicit above, calls for little comment, or else for much more than can be attempted here. We may, however, note: (i) the remarkable concentration of maize on the wedge of light loams between Ganga and Burhi Gandak and on the sandy Kosi soils, and its corresponding absence on the heavy *matiyar* with its tendency to waterlogging; (ii) the rather similar distribution of barley in eastern Uttar Pradesh and western Bihar, but more restricted towards the east than is maize owing to the increasing rainfall and the increasing dominance of rice, barley being essentially a 'rabi after bhadai' crop; (iii) the strong localization of sugar in Tirhut, which has a high proportion of the cane area and refineries. Indigo and opium, once important cash crops, have disappeared. There is some Ganga-side market gardening for the Calcutta market.

Population and industry

Density is very high; Enayat Ahmed distinguishes the floodplain proper (600–700 to the square mile), the irrigated plain south of the Ganga with 700–1,000, the northern plains with 1,000–1,500 except on the great Kosi cones with only 300–400. There is a remarkable gap in the distribution of large towns (Fig. 18.8); Bihar has under 10% of its population in its 127 'towns', only Assam and Orissa falling below this figure. The mass of the people live in compact villages, on the whole smaller than those in Uttar Pradesh, probably because there are more water-points. Even so, urbanization is increasing, if only as a result of rural poverty; the small temple town of Ballia, for example, a local service centre, has more than doubled in size since 1931.[41]

With decreasing grain production and increasing population (an annual deficit of 3,000,000 tons is quoted), and with a per capita income 25% below the national average, this is a crisis area.[42] Basti District, north of the Ghaghra in the west, has been minutely studied as a particularly depressed area; the suggested palliatives are flood control, crop rotation, industry and migration.[43] There is however little industrial potential, except for the agriculturally based industries which are practically all developed to a considerable extent already.

These include sugar-refining (in part a successor to indigo) in the north, but this is declining through inefficiency, though there is some hope in the development of molasses and alcohol plants. Rice mills, also mainly in the north, draw much of their supplies from the Nepal terai. Varanasi of course has its luxury and tourist crafts, Bhagalpur its famous silk-weaving, Monghyr the largest cigarette factory in India; jute milling has made a hesitant start at Purnea. At Dalmianagar, really on the Peninsular foreland, there are cement, soap and

[41] R. L. Singh, 'The trend of urbanization in the Umland of Benares', *NGJI* 2/2 (1956), 75–83; cf. the works of Singh and Ahmad cited in fns. 23 and 24 above.

[42] *Techno-Economic Survey*, 30 sqq.

[43] Natl Ccil of Applied Economic Research, *Rehabilitation and Development of Basti District* (Asia, Bombay, 1959).

asbestos factories. The trend, however, is for decreasing industries in Bihar's northern plains and increasing industrialization in its southern extension, Chota Nagpur, into the Peninsula (below, p. 633).

Power extension is tied up with the difficult Kosi scheme; the plans for controlling this destructive river (Ahmed calls it the Hwangho of India) have been progressively whittled down by fears of earthquake damage and of gross soil erosion and landslides in the catchment area, which have so far defied control. However, large flood-control embankments have been built on the cone, and a small barrage has begun to bring canal irrigation to the area. There are also some power possibilities on the Gandak.

Transport also remains a major difficulty; north of the Ganga most lines are metre, south of it broad gauge (with the through lines largely double-tracked); northern Bihar is almost a backwater, though this may be relieved by the new bridge, replacing a ferry, at Mokameh Ghat, half-way between Patna and Bhagalpur. Water traffic is declining, what there is being mainly carried by country boats on the Ganga and the Son-Ganga Canals.

Of the three important towns, Varanasi has already been described. Patna (364,594), the capital of Bihar, is an ancient city; as Pataliputra it was described by Megasthenes and it was of great importance in Mauryan and Guptan days; remains of Asokan palace have been excavated. Primarily an administrative centre, it has some, but not very significant, industry, and has given its name to the finest-quality rice. Gaya (151,105) lies on the very margin of the plains and is most famous for its Buddhist associations: the Enlightenment took place at Buddh Gaya a few miles to the south. Modern Gaya has a few mills (rice, cotton, oil) and rail shops, and craft industries are still carried on, largely the manufacture of small images for the tourist trade. Gorakhpur (180,255) is of interest as displaying the still-active role of the railway as a catalyst in Indian urban growth.

Sarnath, hard by Varanasi, and Gaya are the places most associated with the life and work of Gautama Buddha, greatest of all teachers who have walked Indian roads; and for a few centuries around the beginning of the Christian era this region, Magadha, was the focus of the most flourishing civilization of India. But in modern times the Middle Gangetic Plains seem to lack individuality, unless indeed the individuality of backwardness. They have indeed great interest for the geographer, but as illustrating the transition from the drier plains of the west into the Bengal Delta, rather than from any distinctive regional quality of their own.

BIBLIOGRAPHICAL NOTE

There is still value in two older works:

R. K. Mukerjee, *The Regional Balance of Man* (Madras, 1938) – a very full study of 'human Ecology'.

B. Ganguli, *Trends of Agriculture and Population in the Ganges Valley* (London, 1938) – a thorough and detailed study of the agricultural economics of the whole valley from Delhi to Dacca.

These must be supplemented by M. Shafi, *Land Utilization in Eastern Uttar Pradesh* (Muslim University, Aligarh, ?1962). The treatment of Bihar owes much to two London Ph.D. theses, *The Agricultural Geography of Bihar* by P. Dayal (1947) and *The Industrial Geography of Bihar* by S. A. Majid (1949). Of great importance is the National Council of Applied Economic Research, *Techno-Economic Survey of Bihar* (Asia, Bombay, 1959).

Under the guidance of Professor R. L. Singh of the Hindu University, Varanasi, geographers in the region have given great attention to settlement, and particularly urban, geography; the papers, published mainly in the *National Geographical Journal of India* (Varanasi), are too numerous to be cited in detail, but we may mention Singh's studies of Gorakhpur (1/1, 1955) and Ballia (2/1, 1956), as well as his Mirzapur (*Geogl Outlook* (Ranchi), 1/1, 1956). An important paper not hitherto cited is by U. Singh, ' "Kaval" Towns: ... functional aspects of urban centres in Uttar Pradesh', *NGJI* 8/3–4 (1962), 238–49.

CHAPTER 19

The Bengal Delta
(Region XII)

The Region and its sub-divisions

Almost the entire area of the old Province of Bengal – now included in East Pakistan and the Indian State of West Bengal – is, in a popular sense, deltaic – it has been succinctly described as 'new mud, old mud, and marsh' – and if we take in all the areas of generally deltaic aspect, including the Surma Valley, it is probably the largest delta in the world. But in a strict sense the Ganga, Ganga–Brahmaputra, or Bengal Delta is much smaller, and by no means easy to define. The whole of Bengal[1] (apart from the highland fringes in the extreme north, southwest and southeast) has, however, a common structural history and a very similar way of life based on rice; it had for some centuries possessed an historic entity, and, except for the brief interlude of Curzon's partition (1905–11), it was until 1947 a linguistic and cultural unit focused on Calcutta. Even now that it has been partitioned, it is difficult to divide it into more than one region, on the scale on which that term has to be used in a book treating of a sub-continent; but, following a general review (especially of the physical aspects) the increasing differentiation between Pakistani and Indian sub-regions is taken into account.

Nevertheless there is a good deal of physiographic variety within the general pattern of alluvial and detrital plains, and sub-division is necessary. The general limits may be taken as roughly those of the old Province, less the Himalayan fringe in Darjeeling District and the definitely non-alluvial margins of the Peninsular block and the Assam–Burma Ranges. The regional boundary is then that between the alluvium and the older rock of the surrounding hills; in the northeast and northwest, where the alluvium is of course continuous into the Brahmaputra and Ganga plains, the political boundaries of Assam and Bihar respectively are taken for convenience. The area thus defined is approximately 80,000 sq. miles (207,000 km²) supporting upwards of 72,000,000 people.

The main bulk of the region is taken up by the true Delta and the great mass of alluvial fans – Strickland's paradelta – to the north. There have been many attempts at defining the Delta, most of which appear decidedly odd to a geographer. No purpose would be served by reviewing them here; this has been

[1] Bengal used without qualification refers to the Province as existing before the 1947 Partition. Sylhet, formerly a District of Assam but now of East Pakistan, is tacitly included.

571

done by Bagchi, and on the whole his delimitation and sub-division appear valid, and in fair conformity with Strickland's distinction between 'the area of transcendent deposition', the delta, and 'that of corrasion', the paradelta.[2]

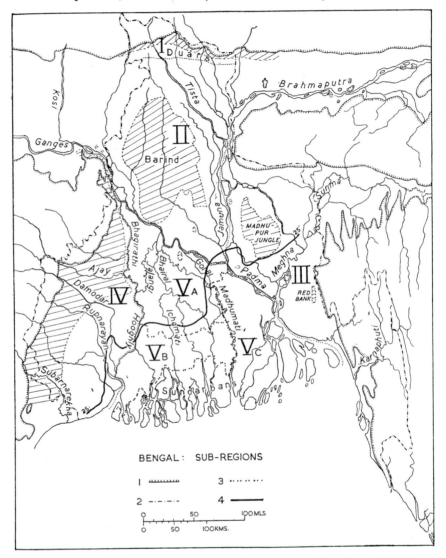

FIG 19.1 BENGAL PHYSICAL FEATURES AND SUB-REGIONS. 1, boundary of alluvium; 2, of undivided Bengal; 3, of sub-regions; 4, 25 ft. contour. Shaded areas older (largely lateritic) alluvium.

[2] K. Bagchi, *The Ganges Delta* (Calcutta, 1944), Chapters I–III; C. Strickland, *Deltaic Formation with Special Reference to the Hydrographic Processes of the Ganges and the Brahmaputra* (Calcutta, 1940), 8.

We have then (Fig. 19.1):

I. The sub-montane terai, here known as the Duars.

II. The northern paradelta, or the Ganga–Brahmaputra Doab and the Barind.

III. The eastern margins: the Surma valley, the plains along the Meghna and along the Chittagong coast.

IV. The western margins: (i) the largely lateritic piedmont plain between the Hooghly and the Peninsular Block; (ii) the Contai coastal plain.

V. The Ganga Delta proper (hereafter 'the Delta') between Hooghly–Bhagirathi, Padma-Meghna and the sea; further subdivided into (A) moribund, (B) mature and (C) active sections.

Of these, all of III, all of II except Jalpaiguri and Cooch Behar in the north and the Malda area in the west, and all of V except the western margins of V(A) and V(B), are in East Pakistan. For convenience, the non-deltaic country of the Chittagong Hill Tracts is treated in the Pakistani portion.

Before considering the sub-regions individually it will be appropriate to discuss generalities: hydrography, climate, agriculture.

The rivers

It will be evident already that 'the deltaic plain of Bengal has a double, or even a multiple, origin: one should not say the delta, but rather the deltas'.[3] The literature of hydrographic change in Bengal is vast and confused as the subject itself; only brief reference can be attempted here, and it will not be necessary to go back to the days of the Indobrahm nor even to those of the more legendary King Bhagirathi who is said to have excavated the Bhagirathi distributary about 2000 BC.

The cardinal factor in the later history of the Delta has been the eastwards shift of the Ganga waters from a main outlet along the western margins – the Bhagirathi–Hooghly – to the present main course, the Padma–Meghna, with such streams as the Ichamati, Jalangi, Matabhanga, Gorai, representing intermediate (not necessarily successive) positions of the most important channel. Whether this is mainly due to alluviation at the heads of successive main spillways, to tectonic change,[4] to shifts in the balance of the Delta due to changes of course elsewhere (e.g. the great shift of the Tista), or to secular swing to the east, are questions which admit of large and inconclusive debate. The exact sequence

[3] A. Geddes, *Au Pays de Tagore: La Civilisation rurale de Bengale occidentale et ses facteurs géographiques* (Paris, Colin, n.d. (?1928)), 45.

[4] J. P. Morgan and W. G. McIntire, 'Quaternary geology of the Bengal Basin . . . ', *Bull. Geological Soc. of America*, 70 (1959), suggest deep faulting or structural subsidence along a trough running northnorthwest from Barisal into the Ganga–Brahmaputra doab; this is based on the apparent structural trends of river and faulting along the western edge of the Madhupur Jungle. The 'islands' of Older Alluvium are presumably still subject to some uplift. The suggestion, though here sophisticated, is not entirely new; cf. A. I. H. Rizvi, 'Pleistocene terraces of the Ganges Valley', *Oriental Geogr* (Dacca) 1/1 (1957), 1–18 *ad fin*.

of events also remains an open question, the evidence depending largely on the interpretation of obscure literary texts; it seems possible, for example, that although Sanskrit tradition ascribes an early and special significance to the Bhagirathi, in Ptolemy's day the main outlet was in the east: we might then envisage a swing to-and-fro analogous, on a vaster scale, to the lateral wanderings of an individual stream meandering across its floodplain.

It is at least clear that the Bhagirathi, or one of its several branches (Hooghly, Sarasvati, Adi Ganga or 'Tolly's Nullah') was the most important distributary in the 17th century, but has been silting at least since 1770, when the Damodar, which helped to keep it clear, shifted its mouth 80 miles (129 km.) to the south. The lower reaches of this line, the Hooghly proper, retain their vitality, being fed by streams from the Peninsula such as the Damodar and the Rupnarayan. More recently the most striking event has been the diversion of the Tista into the Brahmaputra, about 1787. This led to a relative decline in the old Brahmaputra course east of Dacca, already ponded back by the waters brought from the Surma valley by the Meghna. The main Tista–Brahmaputra outlet was by the Jamuna, and the immense volume of water and silt brought down to the Padma near Goalundo backed up the Ganga waters and opened up the Gorai, in 1764 a mere creek, in 1863 the main steamer route from Calcutta into the upper Ganga.[5]

From all this follows the well-known contrast between the decayed west, scarred with silted or stagnant *bhils*, the *disjecta membra* of dead rivers, and the active east; with all the secondary consequences, of which the prevalence (until recently) of malaria and the absence of fertilizing silt in the west are the most important. The mechanism of deltaic deposition is discussed in stimulating detail (and obstetric terminology) by Strickland. Perhaps his most interesting point is the explanation of the more or less continuous line of large bhils eastwards from the Salt Lakes of Calcutta, with the associated slightly higher 'ledge' towards the sea face. This ledge corresponds to a zone in which the tidal masses rise about 18 ft. (2·4 m.) throughout the year, leading to rapid silting of the interior basins of the saucer- or horseshoe-shaped banks which are the beginning of land-building; the result is the formation of this belt of more continuously firm ground. Behind the ledge deposition is less sustained since flooding varies with the vagaries of rainfall.

The transverse channels between distributaries are largely kept open by tidal flushing, and are thus best developed (as in the Irrawaddy delta) towards the sea face, or at least the ledge: 'The tidal influence is the most important factor in their preservation, for they do not appear in lake deltas or in deltas in tideless seas, and as the delta is elevated out of tidal influence the cross-channels disappear.'[6] The varying hydrographic conditions of the Delta give to some of these channels a considerable tidal gradient; thus while the tidal range at Chandpur

[5] Strickland, *op. cit.* 103.
[6] *Ibid.* 14.

on the Meghna during the spring equinox of 1935 was only 3 ft., on the Hooghly the mean ranges of ordinary springs are nearly five times as large.[7]

Climate and vegetation

Juxtaposition to the Bay of Bengal, and the lie of the surrounding highlands, are the proximate determinants of the climate. On the one hand temperature ranges are moderate: cold weather means are around 64° F., hot weather only 80–85° (18 and 27–29° C.). The Calcutta figures are typical:

J.	F.	M.	A.	M.	J.	J.	A.	S.	O.	N.	D.	Ra.
65·3	70·3	79·3	85·0	85·7	84·5	83·0	82·4	82·6	80·0	72·4	65·3	20·4 (11·3° C.)

This moderation in the hot-weather temperature, however, is paid for by excessive humidity from mid-March through October.

In general rainfall is at least adequate, although on the western margins, with about 55 in. (1,397 mm.), there is enough variability to make an extension of irrigation desirable. West Bengal (excluding its wetter northern protrusion) gets between 50 and 60 in.; most of East Bengal between 60 and 95 in. (1,270, 1,524, 2,413 mm.). The highest falls are naturally in sub-montane Jalpaiguri, around the Meghna mouth (100–120, 2,540–3,048 mm.), and in the Sylhet funnel between the Shillong Plateau and the Tripura–Lushai Hills (*c.* 150 in., 3,810 mm.).

The usual Indian régime is, however, modified by violent cyclonic disturbances – the 'Nor-westers' – in March and April, often accompanied by heavy rain, sometimes by hail. These months generally receive 2–3 in. (51–76 mm.) each, but in Dacca and Chittagong April has 6–7. These storms are of considerable value to the *aus* paddy and the jute crops, but several times a century they are catastrophic, especially when they coincide with high spring tides in the funnel-shaped Meghna estuary: on the night of May 25th, 1941, between 5,000 and 10,000 people lost their lives around Barisal and Noakhali, and there was heavy loss of life in 1962 and again in 1964. The turn of the monsoon is also a period of intense cyclonic activity; the Calcutta hurricane of October 1864, which destroyed much of the shipping in the port, drowned 48,000 people, while in October 1876 large areas around the Meghna estuary were flooded: in Bakarganj District 74,000 people were drowned and 50,000 fell victims to cholera, while the total loss of life, direct and indirect, has been put as high as 400,000. In the paradelta the Tista floods of 1787 cost the lives, by drowning, disease or famine, of one-sixth of the population of Rangpur District. The indirect suffering and the economic dislocation of such catastrophes can hardly be estimated or exaggerated.

Except in the sal forests of the terai, little natural vegetation remains on dry land, though the lateritic areas of the Barind, the Madhupur Jungle, and the western shelf carry some degraded forest or scrub jungle, and what Geddes calls 'the arid tropical steppe succeeding to the destroyed forests', stretches of all but useless grass and bush. But the countryside is in general far from treeless: villages, semi-dispersed hamlets, or separate homesteads carry their clumps of

[7] *Ibid.* 111; and cf. Bagchi, *op. cit.* 62 fn.

bamboo, the toddy-palm and the Indian date, banyans, *pipal*, tamarinds and mangoes. The aquatic flora is richer: *bhils* are often choked with reeds and sedges, while on the sea face (with protrusions along the streams) are the great tidal jungles of the Sundarbans. These take their name from the *sundri* (*Heritiera*

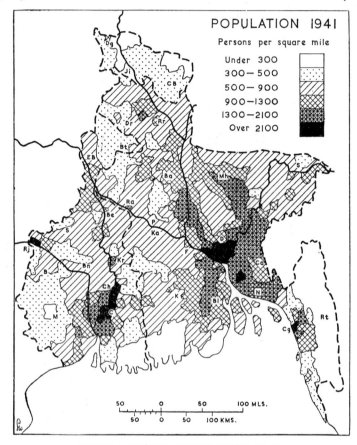

FIG 19.2 BENGAL: POPULATION, 1941.

fomes), a pneumatophore reaching 80–100 ft. (24–30 m.) and supplying useful constructional timber; mangroves provide fuel, the huge fronds of the nipa palm thatching, and gewa (*Excolaria agallochia*) is the basis of a newsprint factory at Khulna. In the past two or three decades the water hyacinth has spread with its usual disastrous proliferation, blocking many waterways to navigation and drainage.

The agrarian life of Bengal

The agriculture of Bengal is dominated by paddy and jute; in East Pakistan, rice actually exceeds the NSA of about 20,000,000 ac. (809,000 ha.) which is 57% of the entire area – but multiple cropping brings the TSA to 86%. Jute comes second, but a long way after, with under 8% of the rice area.

Of other crops tea is marginal to the region, though grown in the Duars and Sylhet; tobacco and sugar, rape and mustard are significant. In general greater

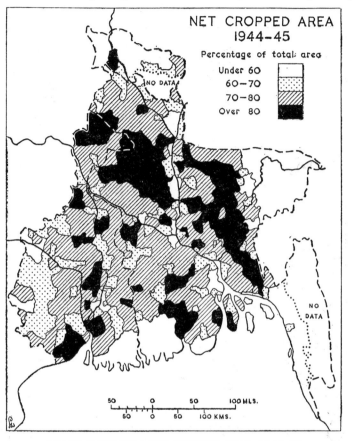

FIG 19.3 BENGAL: NET CROPPED AREA, 1944-45.

diversity would be an advantage, especially in the practically monocultural western margins: in Birbhum and Midnapore the acreage under crops other than paddy may be as low as 4%. Cotton, once a great crop here, has virtually disappeared before the competition of more favoured areas; but sugar, tobacco and oilseeds could be extended, at least if the pressure of the population for rice permitted; but this is a large question. Figs. 19.2–5, though formally out of date, illustrate some basic elements in the situation.

There are two main paddy crops. *Aman* is transplanted in May and June, harvested in November–January, thus corresponding to the kharif; *aus* or *bhadoi* is a quicker crop, sown with the pre-monsoon rains of April, harvested in

577

July–September. In some areas advantage can be taken of the drying margins of the marsh to secure a hot-weather harvest (*boro*); but *aman* is about 75% of the total, and rabi crops of oilseeds and pulses are significant west of the Ganga-Padma and in the Meghna depression.[8] Rice yields are low; the demand for seed paddy alone accounts for a considerable acreage.

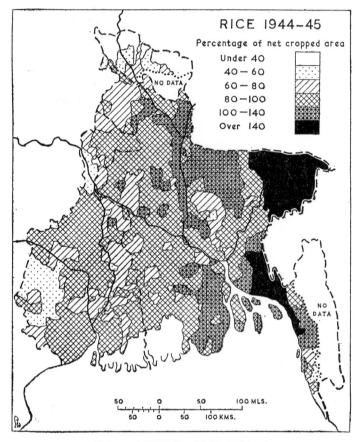

FIG 19.4 BENGAL: RICE, 1944–45.

Jute is in competition with rice for the soil of the Delta proper, and raises special problems. An exhausting crop, it is at its best in the east with its constant alluviation: the yield is also susceptible to variations in the monthly and the total incidence of rainfall, while world demand is notoriously elastic. Jute acreage and yield thus fluctuate widely, though these fluctuations are by no means comparable to the price movements. Jute production is therefore a double gamble –

[8] B. L. C. Johnson, 'Dry season agriculture in East Pakistan', *Geogl Studies*, 5/1 (1958), 61–71, a first-class detailed study with pointers for possible development; also his 'Note on cropping systems . . . in East Pakistan', FAO Memo 57/9/5835.

on the weather and on the world market – and may be expected to meet increasing competition from substitutes, bulk loading, and possibly from new producing areas. Yet it is almost the only cash crop of the Bengali peasant, although owing to the proliferation of middlemen far too small a proportion of the price comes

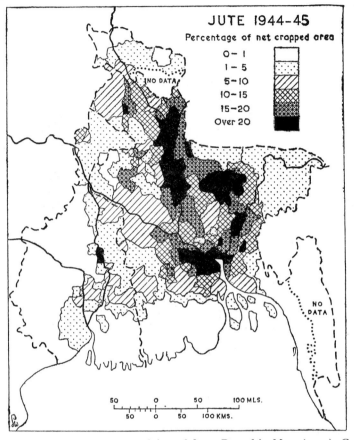

FIG 19.5 BENGAL: JUTE, 1944–45. Adapted from *Bengal in Maps* (1949). *Courtesy of S. P. Chatterjee and Orient Longmans*. Though based on old statistics, these maps indicate some continuing basic areal differentiations; Figs 19.3–5 refine on the maps by Districts in Ch. VIII. On Fig 19·4, areas with over 100% give an indication of double-cropped areas, except for two tracts: along the Meghna and in the triangle English Bazaar–Pabna–Berhampore.

back to the cultivator. It is not too much to say that the solvency of East Pakistan is bound up with this one highly speculative crop.[9]

The usual wearisome catalogue of agrarian miseries holds – small holdings (4·7 ac. in West Bengal, 3·5 in East Pakistan – 1·9 and 1·4 ha.) fragmentation,

[9] S. A. Chaudhuri and M. A. Ali, *Report on Survey of Cost of Production of Jute* (Govt of Pakistan, Dacca, 1962); they give 5·71 ac. (2·3 ha.) as the average jute holding.

debt, collectively excessive and individually inadequate cattle, and the rest. But in addition Bengal has suffered the crushing burden of the Permanent Settlement

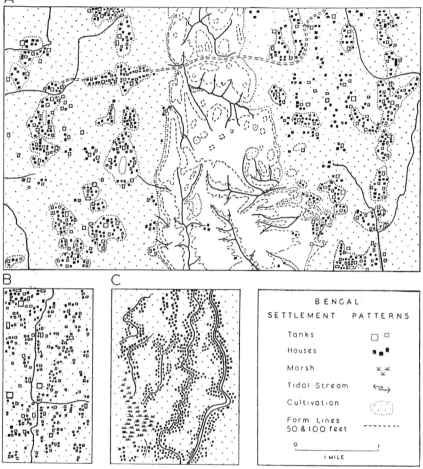

FIG 19.6 BENGAL: SETTLEMENT PATTERNS. A, 2–12 miles southwest of Comilla; settlements dispersed or in amorphous clusters, many tanks; in east some linear, probably on higher ground of old creek-bank. Upland part of 'Red Bank of Comilla', an island of older lateritic alluvium. *SOP* 79 M/3. *Courtesy* SOP.

B, 9 miles northeast of Noakhali; close stipple of homesteads with tanks. *SOP* 79 N/1. *Courtesy* SOP.

C, inside Damodar bend; linear along banks of past or existing creeks. From B. Mukerjee, *The Hooghly and its Region* (thesis), Fig 40b.

of 1793. The intention was good: to create from the *zamindars*, the semi-feudal class responsible for collecting Mogul land revenue, enlightened and improving landlords after the model of the English Agrarian Revolution. The results were disastrous in the extreme. *Vis-à-vis* the *zamindars* the EIC voluntarily limited itself to a revenue laid down for all time as a fixed demand, not variable with output or land values. The Company specifically reserved the right of intervention on behalf of the *rayats* or peasantry, but although, after the middle of the 19th century, this right did not remain altogether a dead-letter, it was exercised with stultifying timidity. The *zamindars*, who after all in Mogul days were essentially removable officials (though with the usual feudal tendency to keep the job in the family), became hereditary absentee, and often all but absolute, sovereigns of the soil. In 1793 there was more land than labour available; but with settled conditions and the consequent increase of population this situation was soon reversed and the lord of the land had the whip-hand, and used it. While the *zamindar's* contribution to the state changed not at all – in fact really decreased with the fall in the value of money – rents increased four- or five-fold, or even more. Sub-infeudation created in some cases as many as six or seven layers between the government which claimed and the peasant who ultimately paid the revenue; and each extorted his share – legal, extra-legal, often sheerly illegal.

Nor were the absentee landlords themselves exempt from the effects of this vicious social system; in many cases they became parasitic hangers-on of the Anglicized culture of Calcutta. There have of course been shining exceptions, the Tagore family for one, or Ram Mohan Roy, the first modern thinker of India (*fl.* 1815–40). The Permanent Settlement did not long survive British rule, but its lesions have penetrated deep into the very tissue of Bengali life and it will be many years, perhaps decades, before its effects cease to be felt.

The population of East Pakistan in 1961 was 50,840,000 and of West Bengal 34,926,000; the projected total of both together for 2001 AD is 134,000,000. At a liberal estimate, *and allowing for multiple cropping*, the total cultivated area is half an acre (0·2 ha.) per head. The prospect is indeed alarming; but unpublished quasi-official reports suggest that at least a fourfold increase in output is possible by a major reformation of the traditional farming pattern to permit perennial irrigation (and hence an extension of multiple cropping in all three seasons, as against double-cropping), crop rotations to include fodder, and flood control in the bordering hills. It is suggested that 35,000,000 ac. (14,160,000 ha.) could in time be perennially irrigated. Fisheries, especially inland fisheries (where an encouraging start has been made with *Tilapia*) could be greatly expanded.

These are long-term visions; immediately, there is scope for extending agriculture in the northern paradelta by irrigation from the Tista barrage; elsewhere in diversification and intensification, including dry-season cropping, whether from major schemes such as the Ganges–Kobadak (above, p. 372) or the spread of irrigation using small diesel pumps.[10]

The 1943 famine was, it is true, due to an altogether exceptional combination of factors: the impounding of country boats to deny them to the Japanese (which

---

[10] See *inter alia* B. L. C. Johnson, 'Technology and the economic development of Pakistan', *Oriental Geogr* 6/1 (1962), 71–78.

naturally dislocated paddy movements); crop failure; hoarding and revolting mal-practices on the part of some trading groups; the deprivation of the small but qualitatively important 'pump-priming' rice import from Burma. But this dis-aster, in which certainly one and perhaps two millions perished, is all too clear an indication of the razor-edge on which is balanced not the prosperity but the mere existence of many of these 80,000,000 human beings.

The Duars

In Bengal the terai, which is found mainly in Jalpaiguri District, is known as the Western Duars, the 'doors' of Bhután. The Duars have the usual feature of terai country, and about a quarter of the 2,000 sq. miles (5,180 km²) is still under forest, mainly sal; but much of the grass and reed jungle has been cleared for rice, jute and tobacco. Soils are naturally much coarser than farther south, often sandy or even gravelly. The Siwaliks are absent in north Bengal, great Himalayan thrust-masses abutting directly on the plain, and the fierce erosion (rainfall is 120–150 in., 3,048–3,810 mm.) may also contribute to this breach of continuity. In the north wooded plateaus at 1,200–1,500 ft. (366–457 m.) form a transition to the mountains; some have been cleared for tea plantations, but most of these lie farther north.

The Ganga–Brahmaputra Doab: the Barind

The country between the Ganga and the Brahmaputra–Jamuna is essentially Strickland's 'paradelta': a vast plain falling from about 300 to 100 ft., scarred by innumerable old river-courses, and liable to disastrous floods, especially along the Tista which, like the Kosi, is an exceptionally violent stream, its largely ice- and snow-fed Himalayan catchment debouching on to the plain through narrow gorges. In the heart of the doab lies the Barind, the large 'island' or terrace of older quasi-lateritic alluvium. The Barind still carries much scrub and degraded remnant forest, and forms a marked negative tract on the population map.

Soils are varied: old alluvium, clayey silts, sandy clays and loams; naturally they become finer and more fertile towards the Ganga. Most of the area gets 60–80 in. (1,524–2,032 mm.). On the whole the agriculture is rather more diversified than in the rest of Bengal, except in the overwhelmingly jute/paddy tract around the Tista–Brahmaputra confluence. Most of the barley and a large proportion of the sugar, pulses and oilseeds of Bengal are grown here, while tobacco as a money crop is largely confined to Rangpur District; the Tista barrage allows winter irrigation of some 30,000 ac. (12,000 ha.) in Pakistan. Most of the sub-region lies in East Pakistan; parts of Dinajpur and Malda Districts, and the former state of Cooch Behar, are Indian. The most important line of communication (apart from the Jamuna navigation) is the (broad-gauge) East Bengal Railway running north to Jalpaiguri and Siliguri, whence a 2 ft. 6 in. mountain line runs to Darjeeling; Jalpaiguri town is on the Tista, with a ferry to Barnes Ghat on the east bank, railhead for the old metre line into Assam. Communications in this area have, however, been badly cut up by quite irrational boundary delimitation; but the new railway into Assam bridges the Tista. Apart from the District headquarters, there are no towns of more than local importance except Siliguri (above, p. 476); and industry is lacking except for sugar-milling at Mahiniganj and Rangpur and the paper mill at Kishorganj.

The eastern margins

The area east of the Jamuna–Padma–Meghna line forms a great embayment of lowland – the Meghna–Surma Valley – between the Shillong Plateau and the parallel ranges which extend from just east of Comilla to beyond the Burma border. All of it, except a small strip of Sylhet District (which before Partition was in Assam) and the plains section of Cachar (which still is), is in East Pakistan, the boundary of which approximates very closely to the limit of the plains, except in the southeast where the Chittagong Hill Tracts are included.

The country along the Padma and the lower Meghna is of course very similar to the active Delta across the estuary. But it is backed by the Madhupur Jungle, a much-dissected older alluvial terrace rising some 40 ft. (12 m.) above the general level. This interruption of the slope down to the sea, the ponding back of the local water by the main Ganges Brahmaputra current, and the high rainfall (75–95 in., 1,905–2,413 mm.), combine to make the Meghna–Surma embayment perhaps the most amphibious part of Bengal during the rains. The lower tracts are flooded to a depth of 8–15 ft. (2·4–4·6 m.) and the homesteads are built on earth platforms 15–20 ft. high (Fig. 19.7 (C and E)).

> 'The water is green with jute. . . . In the height of the inundation no land is to be seen, and all travelling has to be done by boat. To say that travelling has to be done by boat gives, however, but an inadequate idea. . . . Half a dozen huts are clustered together on a hillock a few yards square, and the inhabitants cannot proceed beyond that hillock, whether to visit their neighbours or their fields, to go to market or to school, without wading, swimming, or travelling in or on something that can float [including] circular earthenware pipkins, more difficult of navigation than a coracle.'[11]

Apart, then, from the grass and scrub of the Madhupur Jungle, the area is a sea of paddy and jute, except in Sylhet where some marsh and jungle still await reclamation, and where there are tea plantations. Sylhet indeed is now the only outlet for population-saturated East Bengal, and it is limited – only 4,655 sq. miles, which had already in 1941 a density of 587. In the other Districts 90% or more of the land 'available' is already cultivated. Jute normally accounts for perhaps a quarter of the cultivated area in Mymensingh and along the silt-bringing Brahmaputra. Average holdings are under 5 ac., but this is to some extent compensated by the constant accretion of fertile silt and by the profits of

[11] Quoted in L. S. S. O'Malley, *Bengal, Bihar and Orissa, Sikkim* (1917), 8–9.

jute, which can sometimes be grown as a second crop in paddy-fields. The discovery of natural gas in Sylhet gives new hope for East Pakistan's industrialization; it provides power and raw material for a fertilizer plant at Fenchuganj

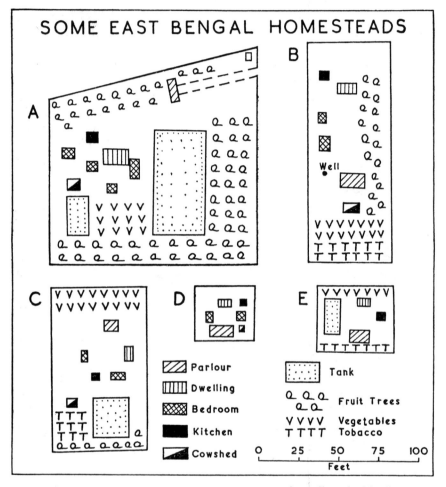

FIG 19.7 SOME EAST BENGAL HOMESTEAD TYPES. A, well-to-do Muslim non-cultivator in drier north; B, Muslim, and C, Hindu, cultivators 'in comfort'; D, poor Muslim, and E, poor Hindu, cultivators. C and E are on platforms above marsh. Adapted from J. C. Jacks, *The Economic Life of a Bengal District* (Faridpur) (1916). *Courtesy Oxford University Press.*

and power for cement making at Chattack, which still uses limestone from Assam.

Southwards, along the Bay shores, Chittagong District and the east of Noakhali are only partly deltaic: Bagchi speaks of the area as being made up of coalesced alluvial cones; it is in fact a narrowing coastal plain, backed by low Tertiary ranges, built up by independent streams of which the most important is the Karnaphuli, at the mouth of which stands the port of Chittagong. With rainfall over 100 in. (2,540 mm.), the plain is almost monocultural to rice, and the paddy fields penetrate far into the longitudinal valleys, where villages of *jhumi* (shifting) cultivators cling to the ridges.[12]

Communications, other than the net of waterways, are at a discount in this land of great rivers, universal inundation for much of the year, and no road-metal: the straight-line distance from Dacca to Calcutta is about 150 miles; by rail it is 380 miles (241 and 612 km.), with a break of gauge as well as a long ferry across the Jamuna; and there is no through road. Such railways and roads as there are tend to hug the piedmont (e.g. the line from Chittagong to Comilla, Sylhet and Assam) or to follow the rather higher ground along the old Brahmaputra course (Jamalpur–Mymensingh–Dacca or Bhairab Bazar). But there are about 2,200 miles (3,540 km.) of all-year steam navigation, and up to 4,000 miles (6,437 km.) in the rains: an immense volume of jute and paddy traffic is carried by country craft, poled, rowed or sailed, as well as by steamers, and there are several small ports – Cox's Bazar, Noakhali, Chandpur, Narayanganj (the port for Dacca) and Chalna. The final site for a western port to supplement Chittagong has not yet been decided, but meantime a considerable export, mainly jute, is handled at Mangla anchorage, some 30 miles (48 km.) downstream from Chalna.

More important than these is of course Chittagong (1961: 364,205), the Porto Grande of the Arab–Portuguese Mugh pirates of the 17th century. Before Partition it was not really much of a port: some river moorings and only four jetties; now it has fourteen and eight more are planned. Jute and tea are the main exports, but imports are five times greater, including cotton, grain and oilseeds from West Pakistan, development and consumer goods. Constriction and congestion remain serious problems, especially as industry is expanding with Karnaphuli power: tea blending, jute, tobacco and cotton factories, while a steel mill is being built with Japanese and an oil refinery with French help. The Karnaphuli project itself has pulp and paper plants. Even with increased steamer navigation into the Delta, however, the long and tenuous metre rail link to the north is a bottle-neck.

Dacca (556,712), the capital of East Pakistan, is by far the largest town. In the 17th century the seat of the Mogul governors of Bengal, it was famous for the almost incredible fineness of its muslins, 'woven wind',[13] a trade ruined by machine competition in the 19th century. The urban morphology is interesting: the administrative fringe of 1906 (when Dacca became the capital of Curzon's short-lived Province of East Bengal and Assam) is now surrounded by a similar but more grandiose development, very modern and imposing, a typical bureau-

[12] Interesting changes in this area are well analysed in D. E. Sopher, 'Population dislocation in the Chittagong Hills', *GR* 53 (1963), 337–62, and 'The Swidden/Wet Rice transition zone in the Chittagong Hills', *Annals Ass. Amer. Geogrs* 54 (1964), 107–26.

[13] Seven thicknesses were said to be necessary for decency.

cratic boom town; and now there are great industrial suburbs, on the western (leeward) side devoted to leather and to the northeast and south producing consumer goods, cotton and jute. Ten or twelve miles away Narayanganj (162,054) is the nerve-centre of the jute industry, one large mill alone employing 25,000 people, with other industry (cotton, matches, vegetable oils) spreading along the river banks. The thermal power station will be supplemented by Karnaphuli.

The industrial prospect of East Pakistan, gloomy indeed at Partition, has been brightened by Sylhet gas and Karnaphuli power; it is still far from dazzling. Apart from textiles and minor consumption goods, the only important plants are the fertilizers and cement associated with Sylhet gas and the paper with Karnaphuli. There are extensive peat deposits in Faridpur, but exploitation will be difficult in the wet Delta; and there are recent reports of deep coal at Bogra in the west. Otherwise, except for jute (and this is vulnerable to bulk loading and new packaging methods), the resource basis is slight, although it is fair to say that a good deal has been made of it in the Dacca–Narayanganj industrial complex.

Urbanization is slight, a fact which throws into higher relief the appalling population pressure in East Pakistan. Despite the inclusion of the poor and thinly peopled Madhupur Jungle, the 11,715 sq. miles (30,342 km^2) of Dacca Division carried in 1961 15,294,000 people – a density of over 1,305 (504 per km^2); yet only Dacca and Narayanganj, totalling 719,000, had over 100,000 people; and in the whole of East Pakistan, with its 51,000,000 inhabitants, only 1,211,000 lived in the four towns of this size. The *total* urban population was only 5·2%, and the average *rural* density for a country of over 55,000 sq. miles was 874 (over 377 per km^2), and it is twice this figure for extensive areas. Clearly this raises problems which will tax East Pakistan's exiguous resources to the utmost.

The western margins

This sub-region may be defined as the area between the Bhagirathi–Hooghly and the surface outcrop of the solid rocks of the Peninsula; like the eastern margins, it falls into a northern and a littoral section; but there the resemblance ends. The west is a shelf of lateritic old alluvium (the Rarh), flanked by the coalesced fans of rivers draining the Peninsular plateaus – Ajai, Damodar, Rupnarayan, Kasai – which in turn fall to a 'dead delta' zone below the higher land along the Hooghly banks. In the south, lowland Midnapore is only partly deltaic, with a prograding coastal plain marked by lines of old beach-ridges, which give rise to linear settlement patterns around Contai.

The lateritic areas (*khoai*) are very poor, with a decidedly xerophytic aspect. The firm shelf has been from early times an avenue of settlement, between the dense jungle of the plateau and the marsh of the delta; the forest destruction has brought the usual nemesis of erosion. On the lateritic interfluves poor short grass, thorny bushes, scattered wild dates and the rust-red laterite in roadside cuttings combine to present a landscape of drought and desolation, relieved only by the countersunk paddy-floored valleys.[14] Farther east the area within the great bend of the Damodar is especially liable to floods, breaching levees and embankments, and between the Damodar elbow and the Hooghly is a most typical dead delta zone. Here the small streams, some formerly spill channels of the Damodar, have lost their headwaters by silting or shifts of that river, while the Hooghly has probably been pushed to the east by the detritus of the plateau streams. This is thus a region of silted and stagnant *bhils*: 'the villagers laconically remark that their land is infested by blind, dying and choked rivers.'[15] Incompetent embanking and river-training, the numerous culverts on roads and railways (which generally run athwart the drainage), and the spread of water-hyacinth have added the dislocation of drainage. Add to this the great floods of the Damodar which has a wide catchment area on impervious rock, funnelled down through a narrow valley succeeded by a right-angled bend, and it is not surprising that the Damodar is a problem river second only to the Kosi, nor that the sub-region, with its poor rainfall, is in general perhaps the most wretched and poverty-stricken part of Bengal, with malaria hyperendemic until the last ten years. The reformation of the Damodar by a TVA-type scheme is discussed elsewhere (below, p. 636).

If not flood, drought: the rainfall of between 50 and 60 in. (1,270–1,524 mm.) is irregular enough for crop failures to be not infrequent. This is the more serious in that the area is again almost monocultural: there is practically no jute, and although dry crops (wheat and barley) are of some slight importance on the uplands, secondary crops of all kinds (including those just mentioned) cover only 4–9% of the cultivated area in this tier of districts. The growth of the Hooghly-side conurbation, however, has led to an extension of market gardening irrigated from the *kanas*, the blind rivers of the Damodar–Hooghly belt. Irrigation in the sub-region has a history of bad planning, and its remodelling and extension form a much-needed part of the Damodar project.[16]

The sub-region is largely a transit zone: along or across it radiate the main railways from Howrah to the Ganga Plains, to the Damodar coalfields, through the Jamshedpur gap to Bombay, and south along the coast to Madras. The towns, such as Midnapore and Burdwan, are mainly administrative and commercial, except the largest, Kharagpur (147,253), originally merely the railway suburb of Midnapore, now an important junction with workshops and much larger than its parent; it has an important Institute of Technology. The sub-region is one of increasing urban and declining rural population.[17] The Hooghly-side towns are of course in a different category.

[14] A small area around Tagore's *ashram* at Santineketan is the field of what is probably the best geographical (and historical) analysis, in real detail, of any area in India: Arthur Geddes, *Au Pays de Tagore* (Paris, n.d., ?1927). Unfortunately space prevents me from rifling this fascinating study as liberally as I should like. It may be supplemented by C. Mukerjee, 'Changing landscape of a rural area', *Khadi Gramodyog* (Khadi Industries Comn, Bombay), February and March 1963, 318–38 and 413–20.

[15] S. C. Bose, *The Damodar Valley Project* (Phoenix, Calcutta, 1948), 31.

[16] *Ibid.* 34–41, 61–62.

[17] D. Mookerjee, 'West Bengal: its urban pattern', *GRI* 19/4 (1957), 67–72.

The Ganga Delta proper

The contrast in health and prosperity between the west and the east of the Delta is well known – the former a region of decadent rivers, stagnant *bhils* and malaria; the latter continually revivified by the silts of a very active river-system, which enables it to support, if perhaps precariously, a denser population. But of course the tidal influence along the sea face introduces a third aspect, and Bagchi's three-fold sub-division of the Delta seems on the whole most in accord with the general development.[18]

(i) *The moribund Delta.* This lies mainly in Nadia, Jessore, and Murshidabad Districts, the northeastern quadrilateral bounded by Bhagirathi, Padma and Madhumati, and on the south by a line roughly along the northern boundaries of 24-Parganas and Khulna. Here the off-takes of the old distributaries in the north have been silted up, and the rivers themselves flow on old levees. Even in flood the country in general is not inundated; on the other hand the interfluves are ill-drained and locally saline owing to their saucer section, and their decayed and neglected *bhils* were the epicentres, as it were, of malaria. There are some interesting recent developments in irrigating the higher lands, using tube-wells and diluted industrial waste water from the tissue factory at Tribeni.[19] Densities are up to 1,130.

(ii) *The mature Delta.* Between the moribund Delta and the Sundarbans is a belt, roughly the northern half of 24-Parganas and Khulna, where the rivers are more 'live' and some silting occurs along the larger ones. They still carry a good deal of water from the local rain, but in general they are deteriorating, and are becoming more and more brackish or saline in the dry weather. Along the western and eastern confines – Hooghly and Madhumati – the land is still being built up to some extent. The demographic conditions are thus variable. Densities in Khulna and 24-Parganas are 510 and 1,223 respectively, but the former is reduced by the large empty area in the Sundarbans, the latter inflated by the Hooghlyside towns.

(iii) *The active Delta.* The southern boundary between the mature and the active Delta is approximately the line of large *bhils* running eastwards from Calcutta (cf. above, pp. 573–4); the active Delta consists of the Sundarbans (on southern Khulna and 24-Parganas) and of the country between Madhumati and Meghna (Faridpur and Bakarganj). The great tidal forests stretch along the seaface for about 170 miles (274 km.), and reach 60–80 miles inland; they are, however, subject to recession along the northern border as land is reclaimed for paddy. The Sundarbans themselves are almost devoid of habitation; Faridpur and Barisal on the other hand, the deltaic districts *par excellence*, have densities of 1,127.

[18] Bagchi analyses the population thana by thana (Chapters 11–14); cf. also the elaborate discussion and maps in A. Geddes, 'The population of Bengal, its distribution and changes,' *GJ* 89 (1937), 344–68.

[19] S. P. Chatterjee, Presidential Address to Geogl Soc. of India, *GRI* 25/1 (1963), 5.

There is some debate as to whether the Delta is still advancing seawards, or whether it is losing by marine erosion more than it gains. Local erosion doubtless exists, but on the whole it would seem that accretion predominates. It is true that there seems little difference between the general lie of the coast shown on Rennell's map of 1770 and by modern surveys; but the presence of old beach-ridges in the Sundarbans certainly points to accretion, and in the east, where Padma, Meghna and above all Brahmaputra bring down vast quantities of silt, all stages in the process of land-building are very clearly seen from the air.

The soils of the Delta naturally show a good deal of variation. The moribund Delta is mainly sandy loam, with some areas of stiff clays; the Sundarbans (and a strip to the north, now reclaimed) are clays, with fresh sands along the sea-face, and of course strongly saline. Between these, in the mature Delta and along the Madhumati, are clayey loams, becoming more sandy towards the Meghna mouth, while farther up along the Padma are pure silt-loams. In detail, of course, there are numerous complications; for example, in the west 'on all the higher parts of the levees the soil is mainly sands and sandy loams which grade into pure loam on the lower slopes, which in its turn merges into the depressed clayey bhil areas. . . . Corresponding to this is a gradation of crops, e.g. vegetables, pulses, and *aus* paddy on the higher levees, jute and oilseeds on the lower slopes, and winter rice on the lower marshy areas.'[20]

The three sub-divisions, and the soil zones which by and large correspond with them, have differing agricultural emphases; jute, for instance, is associated with lighter, loamier, but not too sandy soils, and agriculture is rather less monocultural than in the eastern margins. The Ganges–Kobadak scheme, of which the first stage is complete, allows irrigation of part of the moribund Delta in East Pakistan, but Johnson considers that physical development has outstripped the peasant's psychological preparedness for water he is asked to pay for; the less ambitious promotion of small diesel pumps, involving only local co-operation, is more acceptable.[21]

Densities, as we have seen, run high; the moribund Delta is almost certainly over-populated on any view, while Khulna's low figure masks the congestion on the cultivated area by including the Sundarbans wastes. The very high figures for Faridpur and Barisal are attained with practically no towns of any size – only one, Barisal (69,936), exceeds 50,000. Barisal is an important rice and jute collecting centre, and a great market for betel.[22] Urbanism indeed is slight, apart from Hooghlyside, and that is obviously to a large extent grafted on to rather than growing out of Bengal. The basis of its industry is of course jute, but the impetus was originally and in some measure still is that of alien commerce and capital, and the bulk of its industrial labour is immigrant. Land com-

[20] Binapani Mukerjee, *The Hooghly and its Region* (London Ph.D. thesis, 1949), 80; cf. Map 6 in S. P. Chatterjee, *Bengal in Maps* (Orient Longmans, Calcutta, 1949).

[21] B. L. C. Johnson, *op. cit.* in note 10 above.

[22] For betel, see N. Ahmad and F. K. Khan, 'Betel vine cultivation in East Pakistan', *Oriental Geogr* (Dacca) 2/1 (1958, 1–10.

munications, except along the Hooghly banks, are very poor, waterways excellent, the jute mills still fed to some extent by thousands of small country craft. The towns, then, are administrative and market centres, and only Khulna (127,970) of much more than local significance; as a river port and railhead for the Chalna–Mangla anchorage, it has attracted industry – oil, jute, matches, a steel re-rolling mill, ship-repairing and a big paper factory using gewa towed in barges from the Sundarbans.

Politically most of the Delta has gone to East Pakistan, West Bengal's share being a strip adjoining Bhagirathi–Hooghly. The economic dislocation is obvious, and in detail the division is sometimes inexplicable.

The countryside

The settlement-pattern of much of Bengal (especially the east) is distinctive in lowland India in that the homestead, and not the compact village, is the unit. There are of course exceptions, especially in the poorer west where the terrain of lateritic interfluves and paddy valley-floors favours some concentration. But for the rest there are few nucleations, and such clusters and hamlets as exist (Fig. 19.6) are not tight packed in the Punjab or Uttar Pradesh manner. Yet where densities are so high it would be an abuse of language to speak of the population as dispersed; this may be the case in the newer reclamations of the Duars and the Sundarbans fringes, but in general there is a close stipple of homesteads – often very close indeed, and yet never more than two or three together. Over large areas there is no real 'pattern' at all, so homogeneous is the environment; elsewhere river levées or the margins of an upland or, as in Contai, old beach-ridges, impose linear layouts.[23]

No less striking is the aspect of the homesteads themselves. Huts are universally gabled, usually high-pitched to shed the rain, with thatching of palmyra or nipa leaves, or with corrugated iron where this is readily available and within the means of the householder. Corrugated iron has the great merit of being fire-proof, but otherwise is obviously far less suited to the climate than is good thatching, whether in the hot weather, the cold weather, or the rains. Walls are of split bamboo, reed, or jute-stalk matting (the last none too weatherproof), or of mud, more rarely of wood and very rarely indeed (except in towns) of brick. Floors are of mud, often scrupulously clean. Altogether the matting/thatch combination gives an airiness very desirable in the humid heat.

'The homestead is neither a cottage nor a house as Europe knows them. . . . It never consists of a single hut – even the poorest families always have a separate kitchen. . . . A prosperous family builds larger huts and more of them',[24] up to

[23] For some sub-regional differentiations, see N. Ahmad, 'Pattern of rural settlement in East Pakistan', *GR* 46 (1956), 388–98.

[24] J. C. Jacks, *The Economic Life of a Bengal District* (Oxford, 1916), 21. Chapter I of this book gives a very detailed (if rather idyllic) account of the Bengali home as seen in Faridpur; conditions on the other side of the Hooghly are described in Geddes, *op. cit.*, *passim*, but especially Chapter III (Les Villages).

half a dozen or so, grouped round a little court with a tank for bathing and domestic water supply. Sleeping, living and cooking quarters, and reception rooms, are under separate roofs, although any room may be used casually as a store or a sleeping-place, and much of the life of the family is carried on in the open air or on verandahs. A great variety of mats and baskets, large storage jars, a few chests, form the most of the furniture, and, in areas where the streams are tidal or flood in the rains, nets and other fishing gear are prominent.

The individual buildings are universally on mud plinths, and in the active Delta and the Meghna–Surma valley the annual inundation forces the homestead, or the hamlet where such rough groupings exist, to be itself on a platform up to 15–20 ft. (4·6–6 m.) above the general level, the necessary earth being obtained from the excavated tanks. The countryside in the east is thus dotted with scores of thousands of tiny islets. The tanks would form in aggregate a very substantial reduction of the area available to support the dense population, but they are not unimportant agriculturally (or rather horticulturally), their banks carrying vegetables, tobacco, mango and other fruit trees, as well as the indispensable bamboo and (south of a line roughly Howrah–Jessore–Khulna–Comilla) coconut palms. This varied bush and tree culture and the many small bodies of water give an extremely agreeable diversity to the landscape, and indeed nothing can well be more beautiful than the east Bengal countryside seen from the air after the mango-showers and just before the rains – a vivid carpet of various green, inset with countless tanks, the homesteads nestling in groves of feathery bamboo, coconut or the darker masses of mango trees, all with the precise delicacy of a Japanese colour-print. The reality of life on the ground is doubtless earthier, but there is a culture of great stability and individuality.

In this environment the great mass of Bengalis lives: under 10% of the population is urban, and of the urban population over half is in the great Hooghlyside conurbation. This indeed completely overshadows town development in West Bengal; in East Pakistan only Dacca and Chittagong have anything much in the way of independent status. The sparsity of sizeable towns is most noticeable; but the eight major towns of Hooghlyside contained in 1961 over 4,400,000 people, of whom over two-thirds were in Calcutta and Howrah.

CALCUTTA AND HOOGHLYSIDE

Despite its eccentric situation, in the littoral which after 1869 was the farthest from Europe, Calcutta remained the British capital of India from 1773 until 1912. This peculiar site for the seat of government was hardly improved by the costly annual migration of most departments to Simla (1,100 miles away) for the hot weather; although of course the energetic (largely Scots) commercial oligarchs who really made Calcutta were less migratory. As Reclus remarked, Calcutta is not the natural centre for 'the concentration of local energies' even for Bengal alone; such a centre would be near the Delta-head, and here in fact

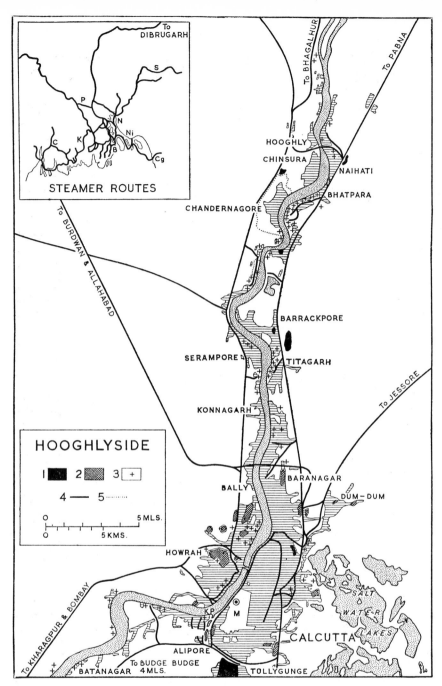

FIG 19.8 HOOGHLYSIDE. 1, rice-milling areas; 2, jute mills; 3, main concentrations of engineering works; 4, railways; 5, old Franco-Indian boundary; KP, Kidderpore (docks); M, Maidan and Fort William (circle). Based in part on map in B. Mukerjee, *op. cit.* for Fig 19.6. The riverside built-up area is now practically continuous.

Inset: B, Barisal; C, Calcutta; Cg, Chittagong; K, Khulna; N, Narayanganj; Ni, Noakhali; P. Pabna; S, Sylhet. Note much greater development in E. Based on *Bengal in Maps*, Fig 99. *Courtesy S. P. Chatterjee.*

were the indigenous capitals of Bengal, now mostly jungle-smothered ruins: Gaur, Tanda, Pandua, Rajmahal. Although individual sites were at the mercy of shifting streams, this node retained its importance in the early European phase, when Murshidabad, Cossimbazaar and Malda (English Bazar) were still the leading trade counters; the selection in 1608 of Dacca as the Mogul provincial capital exemplifies the duality of the Delta. Dutch and English shipping developed bolder courses across the Indian Ocean than did the Portuguese, who had come well up the African coast before striking across for India: hence the eastern littoral came to be of more immediate access than the western, and of course penetration upcountry by the great rivers was easier than on the west coast, shut in (except around the Gulf of Cambay) by the steep wall of the Ghats. Once off Bengal these energetic European traders, anxious to tap the wealth of the Gangetic Plain, with its flourishing Mogul cities supplying (it is ironic to recall) fine textiles for European markets, fixed on the westernmost and shortest entry as the all-important one. This is attested by the list of early factories, which includes Hooghly town (Portuguese, earliest of all), Chinsura (Dutch till 1825), Serampore (Danish till 1845) and Chandernagore, which remained French until 1949. Even the feeble Austrian Ostend Company tried its hand at Cossimbazaar.

Calcutta, destined to dwarf all these, was originally the least significant: when Job Charnock located the English factory in 1692–94, the site was occupied by three petty villages, its only positional advantages being the deep water on the outer side of the meander and (a little later) the intervention of the Hooghly between it and possible Maratha raids – which did not exclude the desirability of a defence (the Maratha Ditch) on the eastern side. The approach, some 120 miles (193 km.) from Sandbanks up a trickily shoaling estuary, was difficult, not to say dangerous, in sailing days, and today is feasible thanks only to costly and unremitting pilotage, conservation and dredging services. In fact, 'its situation is so bad by nature that there is little more that man could do to make it worse, but that little has been faithfully and assiduously done'.[25]

On this unpromising site, pent narrowly between the river and the Salt Water Lakes (of some use as a vast cesspool), there rose a 'city of palaces' – and a far larger city of hovels. The nucleus is Fort William (rebuilt in 1758–73 – after Plassey – and a notable museum-piece of 18th-century fortification) and the Maidan, a vast open space littered with statues of generals and philanthropists. North from the Maidan lie Dalhousie Square, on the site of the great tank which was the 18th-century water supply, Government House, and the commercial and banking core around Clive Street – now, by one of time's revenges, Netaji Bose Street, after the leader of the Japanese-sponsored National Army. Flanking the Maidan on the east is Chowringhee, the main shopping and entertainment thoroughfare. Central Calcutta has at least some space and dignity, even though

---

[25] A writer of the 1880s, quoted by Sir Torick Ameer Ali in *Journal of the Royal Central Asian Society*, Vol. XXXII (1945), 177.

the neo-Grecian palaces (except the really fine Government House) seem now overwrought and faded, and Curzon's white marble Victoria Memorial has little to recommend it but its impressive (or oppressive) size.[26]

Around this nucleus the mass of the city presents the standard features of Indian urbanism: flat-topped buildings, the taller blocks of offices and flats crazy with balconies, teeming bazaars, trams and bullock carts and bulls, the cinema and the shrine; villas hidden in great gardens in the better suburbs; and, despite decades of piecemeal improvement, vast areas of *bustees*, the hovels of the submerged proletariat, areas which rank with similar zones in such cities as Osaka and Johannesburg as the most revolting expressions of our industrialism.

Calcutta proper had 2,927,839 inhabitants in 1961. Across the river lies the great industrial town of Howrah (512,598), hardly to be regarded as a suburb, with the terminals of the railways to the west and south; since 1943 the famous bridge of boats has been replaced by a great structure of steel. The Hooghly wharves and moorings in Calcutta itself are mostly used by smaller shipping; the main port activity is now centred round the docks at Kidderpore. Farther downriver are specialized installations such as the oil depot at Budge Budge. The conurbation extends as far up river as Hooghly town, 25 miles (40 km.) from Calcutta itself (Fig. 19.8).

In the orientation imposed on the economic geography of 19th-century India by its gearing to British needs, the advantages of the Calcutta neighbourhood were many: the sea-entry to the areas of greatest population and (at least until the rise of Punjab and Deccan cotton) of highest agricultural productivity – including that of the great early staple exports, opium, tea, indigo; a monopoly of world jute supply at its doors; the only well-developed network of internal navigation in India; the region where British territorial power on any large scale was oldest; the seat of government and above all of a forceful, not to say ruthless, dominant minority of British business men. Calcutta soon outstripped Madras and was not seriously challenged by Bombay until the cotton boom of the American Civil War and the opening of the Suez Canal. By then the mineral wealth of the Bihar–Orissa border, so accessible to Hooghlyside, was realized, and its exploitation provided the incentive to a more diversified and increasingly Indian-owned industrial development in this century, so that by 1921 a third of the factory population of India was concentrated in the narrow strip from Hooghly town to Budge Budge; with the spread of industrial development generally this had fallen to about a quarter by 1941. With all this the fact that even in the truncated province of West Bengal industrial workers are only about 10·5% of the occupied population is a reminder that, in relation to area and population, India is still backward industrially. Calcutta proper is more commercial and administrative than industrial, being outstripped in this regard by

[26] Reclus and Sion both note the parallel with St Petersburg, with a slight shift of emphasis significant in view of Reclus' political views; see E. Reclus, *L'Inde* (Nouvelle Géographie Universelle, T. VIII (1883), 375; J. Sion, *Asie des Moussons* (1929), 306. The later version is inferior.

Howrah, while such towns as Titagarh and Bhatpara are solidly industrial, factory workers and their dependants forming 65–85% of the total population.

Jute mills are strung out along the river from below Budge Budge to Naihati, with notable concentrations north of Howrah and above all in and around Bhatpara. The industry has a long history, the first mill dating from 1854, though power was not introduced until 1859: the Crimean War had blocked hemp supplies to Dundee, and the Scots connection then established is unbroken, though weakening: although most of the capital is now Indian, the firms of Managing Agents who actually run the industry are still largely Scots in spirit and personnel.[27] By 1910 Dundee itself was outstripped, and manufactured jute is now India's leading export, its value being about five times that of raw jute.

The Partition, however, left some 80% of jute acreage and output in East Pakistan, which has made considerable strides in its efforts to industrialize and so retain the profits of manufacture. At times the politics of jute, so vital to both Bengals, have led to serious Indo-Pakistani friction, and although the two countries together have a very commanding position in world output of jute and allied fibres (in 1961, 2,710,000 metric tons out of a world total of 3,530,000) this quasi-monopoly may be vulnerable. Bulk-loading and substitutes[28] have already made inroads on the demand, other tropical countries (e.g. Brazil) may well turn seriously to production of raw jute, and finally the cheapness of labour, a prime factor in the success of the industry, is becoming less significant in view of the general rise in Indian costs and money wages.

Other textile industries include hosiery and silk, but apart from cotton they are of little account. Of much greater importance are the very diversified engineering and metallurgical industries, developed in close association with Asansol–Raniganj coal and Jamshedpur iron and steel. There are hundreds of engineering works of all sizes and types; all but a few are in Calcutta or its immediate suburbs and Howrah. Machine parts for the jute mills and a wide variety of light machinery are manufactured; a recent development of interest is the rolling of aluminium sheets and bars from ingots at Belur. Railway workshops, ship repairing, motor assembly, and allied industries are important; a motor-vehicle plant is projected at Konnagar.

With so large a market there is naturally a great variety of consumption goods; this of course is typically metropolitan, but Greater Calcutta is distinctive in having the bulk of one of the major industries of the country, namely jute. Perhaps the most important miscellaneous lines are rubber, chemicals (Calcutta is perhaps the leading Indian centre), rice-milling (especially in the southern suburbs of Calcutta, close to the market and with access by country boat from

[27] For a description of the system, and discussion of its advantages and drawbacks (the latter are now perhaps the greater), see D. H. Buchanan, *The Development of Capitalistic Enterprise in India* (1934), Chapter VIII *passim*; also Natl Ccil of Applied Economic Research (Calcutta), *The Managing Agency System* (1959).

[28] Cement, for example, is now almost entirely bagged in paper.

the Delta), and paper. The last is of exceptional importance, the mills at Tita-garh and Naihati producing a large proportion of the Indian output; this is doubtless connected with the importance of Calcutta as a publishing and educational centre. Finally we may note the large boot and shoe factory at Batanagar, a name which explains itself.[29] The Czech firm was able to employ workers of many castes, even though leather-working is traditionally a low caste occupation; this is an extreme case of the effect of industrialization on caste.

This concentration of industry has not been gained without the exaction of a heavy price in human suffering. The conurbation as a whole has a population of about 6,000,000. The population of Calcutta itself grew between 1931 and 1941 from 1,164,000 to 2,109,000; Howrah from 225,000 to 379,000; seven of the minor towns of the conurbation increased by 500% in fifty years. Central Calcutta, it is true, shows the normal metropolitan trend to a stationary or declining population, but the city as a whole showed an increase of 81% in 1931–41, and four of its immediate suburbs increases of 138–158%. These are extraordinary figures, and even though current rates of increase in the older parts of the conurbation are slackening (Calcutta 15% in 1951–61, Howrah 17%), they must be seen against the fact that for decades deathrates have exceeded birthrates in most sections; in 1941, the Calcutta city birthrate was 25·7 per mille, the deathrate 31·7. Few wards show any natural increase, and the increases are supported mainly by continual immigration of new victims for the smoky altars of industry. In Titagarh and Bhatpara, two of the most purely industrial units, in 1931 the percentages of the population born *outside Bengal* were 86 and 72 respectively; even in 1951 in old-established Howrah 39% of the people were immigrants – and of these only 36% were females.[30] Truly these cities are eaters of men.

The reason is not far to seek: it lies in the remark of a very well-travelled journalist that, of all the cities he knew, Calcutta cared most for money and least for men. Much of the population still lives in *bustees*, huddles of grossly over-crowded single-room huts some 10 ft. square, huddled together by the hundred in lanes a yard wide; as Binapani Mukerjee remarks, the internal structure of a *bustee* area can only be photographed when half of it has been burnt in a com-munal riot. Open drains lead to stagnant pools full of decaying garbage; men and children defecate on scraps of fetid waste ground; standpipes are so few and distant that the pools too often serve as the local water supply, at least for washing. The 'lines' of the organized factories, both Indian and European owned, are usually much better, sometimes with really good *pucca* (brick-built) quarters, and some riverside jute mills have even a certain aesthetic appeal. But

[29] Details drawn largely from Binapani Mukerjee, *The Hooghly and its Region* (London Ph.D. thesis, 1949), and S. P. Chatterjee, *Bengal in Maps* (Calcutta, 1949), 88–93. Cf. also Chapter XI, Sections II and III above. See also N. R. Kar, 'Economic character of Metropolitan sphere of influence of Calcutta', *GRI* 25/2 (1962), 103–38.

[30] A. B. Chatterjee, 'Demographic features of Howrah City', *ibid.* 20 (1958), 146–69.

others are nearly as bad as the *bustees*.[31] The appalling figures quoted above represent some – not, fortunately, all – of the reality behind the commercial and industrial progress of what used to boast itself the second city of the British Empire. And yet the efforts of the women to maintain cleanliness, spreading their saris to dry on dusty and dirty roadside verges, are as heroic as they are pathetic.

The future of Calcutta is hardly likely to be as brilliant as its past; the transfer of the bulk of the jute area and much of its food area to a different political entity cannot fail to affect it adversely. Still, the trade of the Ganga valley will remain and probably expand; Calcutta had generally some 35% of the seaborne trade of India before the war, running neck and neck with Bombay. Moreover, the immense vested interest of Hooghlyside, the accumulation of capital, financial skill, enterprise and the technique and installations of trade, represent a solid asset. The limited hydro-electric development in the Damodar Valley and the much larger thermal contributions to the grid may further the industrial development of the Hooghly region as a whole, while permitting a desirable decentralization. Yet in the long run it seems that the division of Bengal and the spread of modern industry in India generally will probably spell some lessening of Calcutta's relative position among the foci of economic activity. By and large Calcutta seems destined to be outstripped by Bombay both in population and dynamism.

The Partition and its problems

The Radcliffe Award of 1947 left West Bengal as a rump of about 34,000 sq. miles (88,000 km²); with the major portion of Sylhet District from Assam, East Pakistan has a little over 55,000 sq. miles (142,000 km²). The very arbitrary boundary of some 1,700 miles (2,736 km.) paid no attention whatsoever to communications, necessitating the building of a 140-mile (225-km.) railway to link Assam with the rest of India. The 4,000 sq. miles (10,360 km²) of Tripura, a wedge between Sylhet and the Chittagong Hill Tracts, is perhaps significantly a Union Territory controlled directly from New Delhi; it has about 1,142,000 people.

It is ironical that Bengal was perhaps the only province in India with a real linguistic unity, except possibly Sind: in 1931 some 86% of Bengali speakers were within its borders, and they in turn formed 92% of the provincial population, the rest being tribesmen in the extreme north and east, and the immigrants (Biharis very largely) to Hooghlyside.

Neither of the Bengals is a strong unit. West Bengal, with its enormous urban concentration on Hooghlyside, now swollen by refugees, is a food-deficit area, its agriculture being qualitatively as well as quantitatively inferior to that of East Pakistan. Economically there seems very little justification for its continued

---

[31] In one case cited by Mukerjee 373 workers were provided with 8 seat-latrines, 18 urinals, and 2 taps for drinking and bathing. These revolting details are, after all, part of the 'cultural' landscape. For many recent sources see Learmonth 1965 *op. cit.* in Chap. 4.

existence: the Asansol coalfield is only a fragment of the much more important Bihar fields, and the Damodar Valley project cuts across the provincial boundary and would probably be simpler to administer were that boundary not there.

But less tangible factors are far stronger than these material considerations. Calcutta was the heart of Hindu Bengali culture, a culture which, with all its faults of excitability and emotionalism verging on hysteria, had played a great part in the development of Hindu nationalism, of pride in the cultural heritage of Mother India, and in the literary renaissance of this century; nor does it lack self-consciousness and sensibility. The tradition is too strong for a merger to be practical politics. But for some time it has seemed that the vitality of Bengal lay in the east rather than in the over-sophisticated society of Calcutta. Certainly the Bengali Hindu, with all his good points (alertness of mind and a fine ironic humour are notable), is regarded in India as the very type of the *babu*, a talker inveterate even by Indian standards; and the political scene, in the war years and since, has been far from inspiring. And, in any case, the teeming life of Hooghly-side is kept alive only by a continuous blood transfusion, largely of Biharis.

East Pakistan is in some ways more promising, or rather would be so were it not so isolated from the rest of Pakistan – and in that other body of Pakistan resides most of the drive which made the new state. With the seat of government in the West, East Pakistan, conscious of its larger population, has felt itself a poor relation, despite political and economic devices to redress the balance; nor did its politics yield anything to West Bengal in factionalism and corruption. It is arguable that, like West Pakistan, the East depended on the export beyond her own limits of primary products, jute and some tea, and that therefore the high protectionism characteristic of industrial India would not be in accordance with the interests of East Bengalis. But that is not the end of economic argument. At the time of Partition East Pakistan had not a single jute mill, and hardly any other industry; apart from raw jute, some tobacco and tea, there were hardly any industrial resources. This position has changed with the harnessing of Karnaphuli power and Sylhet gas, and a fair start has been made; but there are many difficulties in the way, not least the shortage of capital and technicians.

Yet, without industrialization on a scale which, for some considerable time to come would seem dubiously 'economic', East Pakistan may well appear an overcrowded rural slum. It is very marginally self-sufficient in food; imports are often necessary, and natural disasters can still tip the balance towards famine. The economic stand-by is jute, a crop very fluctuant both naturally and in response to world prices, which on the whole show a downward trend. There is a dilemma of rice or jute, food or cash; and the *lebensraum* of Assam, into which there used to be a big migration of Bengali Muslim peasants, is now cut off. Great efforts have been made, and there is doubtless a psychological relief in freedom from the hegemony of Calcutta; yet to a geographer, it must seem that the root of much of the malaise in both West Bengal and East Pakistan is simply that where there had been one State, there are now two.

BIBLIOGRAPHICAL NOTE

Older sources – Strickland, Bagchi, Jacks, Geddes, Chatterjee's *Bengal in Maps* – have been indicated in the notes. The region is fortunate in possessing a full-scale modern treatment in Nafis Ahmad, *An Economic Geography of East Pakistan* (OUP, 1958), even though it is already beginning to date. On the Indian side, P. Sen Gupta, *The Indian Jute Belt* (Orient Longmans, New Delhi, 1959) is an authoritative survey.

On Calcutta, apart from the reports of various metropolitan planning bodies, there is a long and thoughtful article by N. K. Bose, 'Social and cultural life of Calcutta', *GRI* 20 (1958), 1–46; this may be supplemented for Pakistan by A. F. A. Husain, *Human and Social Impact of Technological Change in Pakistan* (OUP, Dacca, 1956). See also R. Murphy, 'The city in the swamp', *GJ* 130 (1964), 241–55.

There are many detailed studies, especially of towns and land-use, in *The Geographical Review of India* (Calcutta) and *The Oriental Geographer* (Dacca); in the latter see for example Ahmad on the urban pattern of East Pakistan (1/1, 1957), Johnson on Chittagong (1/2, 1957), Ahmad and Rahman on Dacca industries (4/2, 1960), Ahmad and Khan on Narayanganj (6/1, 1962). Important papers, with valuable maps, are B. L. C. Johnson, 'Rural population densities in East Pakistan', *Pacific Viewpoint* (Wellington, NZ), 3 (1962), 51–62; and 'Crop-association regions in East Pakistan', *Geography* 53 (1958), 86–103.

CHAPTER 20

The Eastern Borderlands: Assam and NEFA
(Regions VII. 3, VIII, XIV, and XIX)

The individuality of Northeast India

As in the west, the eastern marches of India present a difficult problem of description: hills sharply marked off from the plain physically and culturally, yet so linked locationally that to some extent they must be treated together. The State of Assam possesses a very marked individuality. It is in a sense transitional towards High Asia and Indo-China (in the broad sense), and even to China itself; the word 'Assamese' as applied to the people conceals a multitude of ethnic groups with strong Mongoloid elements, and it is significant that to mediaeval India Assam was *mlechha* – foreign. Nor were even the Moguls able to reduce the Ahoms, a branch of the Shan peoples of the Sino-Burmese marchlands.

Geomorphologically, Assam itself consists of three entirely distinct regions, belonging to all three of the structural macro-divisions: the ranges of the Assam/ Burma border belong to the extra-Peninsular mountains; the Assam or Brahmaputra Valley is an extension of the Indo-Gangetic trough; while the Shillong Plateau is essentially an outlier of the Peninsula, separated from it by the relatively shallow Rajmahal sill stretching across the head of the Bengal Delta (Fig. 1.1). Further, it is convenient to treat here the easternmost section of the Himalayas themselves, now known as the North East Frontier Agency (or Tract; NEFA), a fringe little known and little regarded until the Chinese encroachment brought it forcibly into prominence; it too is in every sense a borderland.

Finally, from the economic point of view Assam includes the phenomenon, unique in India, of an underdeveloped or even underpopulated monsoon lowland, the last natural farming pioneer fringe. Nowhere in India does the term 'culturable waste' approach nearer to reality, and there is still room for the expansion of agriculture as well (if the hydro-electric resources can be developed) as industry.

The regions will be treated separately but, with some violence to their macro-affinities, in juxtaposition, followed by a discussion of some general matters affecting the whole. The fragment of Sylhet left to Assam, and the Cachar lowland, are simply extensions of the Surma plains already treated under the Bengal Delta, and here left out of the reckoning. Politically, Tripura and Nagaland, on the Burmese border, have been Union Territories like NEFA, but the latter is being constituted a separate State.

THE ASSAM VALLEY

Physical considerations

The great ramp-valley, from Dhubri to its blind end beyond Sadiya, extends for over 400 miles (644 km.), with a remarkably even breadth of about 60 miles (97 km.), except where the Mikir and Rengma Hills narrow it slightly. Most of this

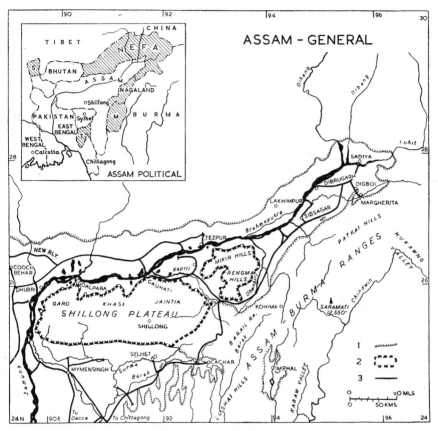

FIG 20.1 ASSAM: GENERAL. 1, boundary of alluvium; 2, outlier of Peninsular Block (small relics black); 3, railways.

Inset: shaded areas: S, Sikkim (Indian protectorate); NEFA, North-East Frontier Agency; M, Manipur; T, Tripura – all Union Territories controlled directly from New Delhi; Nagaland was formerly a Territory, now being raised to statehood.

great area is formed of the alluvial terraces of the Brahmaputra and its numerous tributaries. On the northern flanks the outer ramparts of the Himalayas tower up abruptly; the southern margin is less precise, the alluvium giving way to the Tertiary foothills of the Naga and Patkoi Ranges, with some outlying fragments of the older Shillong rocks along the river between Gauhati and Dhubri. On either side of the Mikir Hills the Kapili and Dhansiri Rivers form re-entrants of alluvium in a complicated area which may once have been occupied by the main Brahmaputra cutting across the Barail Range to the Barak (Surma) valley.

The master-stream is undoubtedly one of the most astonishing rivers in the world, whether we consider its immense hairpin-shaped bend (some 1,800 miles, 2,900 km., from the Tsangpo sources to the Meghna confluence), the wild Dihang gorges cut some 18,000 ft. (5,485 m.) below Namcha Barwa (25,445 ft., 7,757 m.) and linking the Tibetan Tsangpo with the Indian Brahmaputra, or the width and power of the main stream. Already at the Dihang–Dibong–Lohit confluence, 900 miles from the sea, the stream even in the dry season is broader than Rhine or Rhone in their lower courses. At high stage, after snow-melt and in the rains, it is an immense corridor of waters five miles and more wide, with a discharge at Goalpara of half a million cusecs. 'During the second half of the monsoon period . . . the main river rises by about ten to fifteen feet, near Gauhati. Such a rise in level may not appear great, if one forgets the general dimensions of the river, viz. a general width of fifteen hundred yards [1,372 m.].'[1] The channel is of course braided and shifting on a scale proportionate, a factor which hampers steam navigation and compels settlements as a rule to lie well back, with in some cases dry-weather extensions to the shore. The great floods are a main factor in inhibiting the clearing of the waste.

The climate shows some modification of the classic monsoonal type, the hot season being shorter than usual and with the low average temperature of 85°F. (29·4°C.). This is due to the relatively large rainfall (up to 20% of the total) received from the 'Nor'-westers'; the actual amounts are 10–20 in. (254–508 mm.) or more, and are of great importance to the tea crop. Rainfall is high enough to obviate the need for irrigation, but there is something of a rain-shadow effect along the southern flanks of the valley, Shillong getting 159 and Gauhati only 67 in. (404 and 172 mm.), the latter being about the minimum, while Cherrapunji on the southern brow of the Plateau is generally stated as receiving 428 in. – 10·7 *metres*! Farther up the valley, however, perhaps owing to the access provided by the Barail saddle, 80 in. (2,032 mm.) and more are received. Precipitation is naturally higher on the Himalayan slopes and generally the mountain tributaries have pushed the Brahmaputra over to the south; but in the extreme east the blind end of the valley is another pocket of very high rainfall.

Large areas are covered with sal forest and tall reed jungle in the swamps and *jhils* of the immense floodplain. In these swamps the one-horned white rhinoceros, elsewhere extinct, survives.

Indigenous agriculture and settlement

Before the Partition, rice and jute were by far the most important peasant crops, and although a disproportionate share of both was held by the single District of

[1] V. S. Gananathan, 'Physical environment and human responses in Assam', *IGJ* 25/3 (1950), 1–9.

Sylhet, most of which went to Pakistan, remain the chief non-plantation crops. Other cereals are not very important; rice is followed by rape and mustard, and then by an increasing acreage of jute in areas settled by East Bengali immigrants, who have also brought tobacco to the valley. Cultivating holdings are or were small, averaging 5 ac. (2 ha.) but with more than a third under 2 ac., and frag-mentation was intense: paradoxical in a 'new' area, but perhaps accounted for by the pre-existence of big estates in this previously rather empty area; Goalpara District, for example, was mainly comprised in eighteen estates. Three big *zamindari* holdings are now in process of abolition.

Settlements are for the most part in large hamlets rather than villages, sur-rounded by fruit trees (plantain, pawpaw or papaya, mango, jackfruit) and bamboo groves. Assamese villages, mainly on the terraces, are somewhat apart from those of the immigrant Bengalis on land won from the floodplain; here land use and its techniques are reminiscent of the deltaic conditions whence the people came.[2] Until recently the whole State below 5,000 ft. (1,525 m.) was intensely malarial, except for the upper end of the valley where the active nature of the streams was probably responsible for freedom from the disease.

The tea industry

The most individual feature of Assamese agriculture is the great extension of tea estates: there are about 800, generally on the higher terraces of the plains/hill margins, covering over 400,000 ac. (162,000 ha.) or something under half the Indian area, but producing over half the Indian output of more than 300,000 tons and employing in one way or another over 1,500,000 people.

Indigenous tea plants had been discovered in the northeast corner of Assam in 1823, and after it lost the monopoly of the Chinese trade in 1833 the EIC became interested in an alternative source of supply. The first consignment, twelve chests from a Company farm, reached London in 1838, and by 1871 the total Indian output was over 2,740 tons. The early days of the industry were marked by frantic speculation, non-existent estates in the midst of unmapped jungle being sold over and over again, and the acute shortage of local labour being met by beguiling Biharis and Madrassis with glowing promises, convoying them under guard, and keeping them in what were virtually concentration camps. In eighteen months over 18,000 out of 50,000 coolies died or vanished into the jungle.[3]

All this is now a thing of the past. Legislation, humanity and perhaps an en-lightened self-respect, have combined to produce housing and health conditions much better than those of the average Indian labourer. Since Independence the industry has had reasonably stable conditions, though the heavy annual demand for labour (largely female) for picking, as compared with the small force of

[2] T. F. Rasmussen, 'Population and land utilization in the Assam Valley,' *Jnl Tropical Geography* (Kuala Lumpur), 14 (1960), 51–76.
[3] See D. H. Buchanan, *The Development of Capitalist Enterprise in India* (NY, 1934), Chapter IV, for the early development.

skilled labour needed all the year round, poses formidable problems; and there have been complaints that the strongly organized labour force is making costs too high to be competitive. While there has been some Indianization, the largest and most efficient estates are still European, and managed by about half a dozen agencies in Calcutta. With 12% to 15% of Assam's population dependent on tea, as well as its demand on the plywood, coal, and fertilizer industries, the continued prosperity of the estates is basic to the State's economy.[4]

Other resources

Coal is still exploited at Margherita, mainly for the railways but on a limited scale, being costly to work and inferior in quality to Bihar's; but oil has a different story. The old Digboi fields are declining, but further discoveries nearby contribute increasingly to Digboi's refinery, and new ones have gone up at Gauhati and at Barauni in Bihar. In time Assam may even supply half of India's requirements. There are reserves of natural gas, which may allow of chemical industries; and in the future coal reserves around the Shillong Plateau, at present difficult of access, may be exploited.

Assam has more forest than any other state, and with careful management there is obviously a considerable potential here.[5] Sal extraction lost ground with the loss of the Pakistan market for railway sleepers, but there are other valuable construction timbers, as well as 'minor forest products' – resins, tan- and dye-stuffs, lace, some tung oil. The new railway through the north of West Bengal has restored connections with the rest of India, and a tramway brings the timbers of the bhabar forest to Goalpara, where veneer and plywood factories and tea-chests are made; Dhubri has a large match factory.

The alliance of terrain and climate all along the flanks of the valley produces an enormous power potential. Actual development is so far limited to the Umtu project near Gauhati and the Barpani Dam to serve the Khasi Hills, as well as a much older small plant supplying Shillong. The trouble is the lack of effective demand in one of the least urbanized of Indian States. There might be a fairly wide development of fertilizers, bamboo paper, cement and fertilizers, using natural gas and the limestone of the hills; as it is, at a long interval after the tea factories come the wells and mines of Digboi–Margherita and apart from these there are only the usual petty saw, rice and oil mills, a little printing, and so on. 'The industries are so scattered and so seasonal that any power scheme loaded with high capital and maintenance costs could not hope to be a paying concern for many years, and then only, perhaps, if the cheap power supply enabled considerable industrial development to take place.'[6] The circularity of the argument faithfully reflects the facts. Advances in long-distance transmission would theoretically enable export; but the great Hooghlyside market is more cheaply

[4] S. S. Sharma, 'Tea cultivation in Assam', *NGJI* 5/2 (1959), 91–108.

[5] P. D. Stracey, 'Development of forestry in Assam', *Indian Forester* (Dehra Dun) 82/12 (1956), 619–23.

[6] G. Kuriyan, *Hydro-Electric Power in India* (Indian Geogl Soc., Madras, 1945), 54.

supplied by Damodar and thermal sources, and East Pakistan, a conceivable market, is solving her own power problem from Karnaphuli water and Sylhet gas.

The former dependence on handloom and home-made clothing is yielding, except in the more remote areas, to factory products; but in 1956 Assam, with about 2·8% of India's population, had a seventh of her handlooms. The emphasis is now on special fabrics, but trade is slight, and there is perhaps more point in fostering cottage silk industry.

Towns and communications

Urbanization is the second lowest in India, with only 7·6% of the 1961 population (against Orissa's 6·3%) living in the so-called towns; Assam used to be lowest of all. Digboi (23,691) is important as the centre for the oil and coal fields; Greater Gauhati (66,626) has outstripped Shillong (58,512); both towns are growing rapidly. The great length of the valley in relation to its breadth hardly favours any particular centre, and its floodplain offers few good sites: Dhubri, Gauhati and Tezpur are all on tiny outliers of the Shillong Plateau rocks. Other towns are either railheads or river ports on the widely variable banks of the Brahmaputra.

Waterways have always been of great importance: the Brahmaputra is navigable right up to Sadiya in the head of the valley, and coped with the tea traffic for many years until the advent of the railways. These were at first stimulated, but then grossly worn out, by wartime demands; and they were then dislocated by Partition, necessitating a new link with West Bengal, and by the 1950 earthquake. The line through Pakistan is technically available, but its use is inhibited by political considerations. All the railways are single-track metre gauge.

Roads are difficult to construct and maintain; they were extended and improved during the war, but although a metalled road now runs practically the length of the valley, the system is still somewhat disjointed.

THE SHILLONG PLATEAU

The Shillong or Assam Plateau is also known as Meghalaya – 'Abode of Clouds' – a finely appropriate Sanskrit name which we owe to Professor S. P. Chatterjee; it is divided into the Garo, Khasi and Jaintia Hills, but these are merely administrative or tribal divisions of one unit. Here, for the first time since leaving Potwar and the Salt Range, we meet (not without relief) some solid geology: the Plateau is in fact a detached block of the Peninsula, some 150 by 60 miles (241 by 97 km.), with summit levels at 4,500–6,000 ft. (1,370–1,830 m.).[7] To the north the Mikir and Rengma Hills are further fragmented outliers. The bulk of the Plateau is formed by Archaean (Dharwarian) quartzites, shales and schists, with granite intrusions and some basic sills; but in the south these are overlain by horizontal

[7] The Plateau has been studied in detail in S. P. Chatterjee, *Le Plateau de Meghalaya* (Paris, 1936).

Cretaceous and Eocene sandstones, which on the outer flank dip steeply south-wards. This steep edge overlooking the Surma valley is extremely straight and precipitous, rising over 5,000 ft. in 10 or 12 miles (1,525 m. in 16–19 km.); scoured by the highest rainfall in the world, it is naturally wildly dissected and covered with dense jungle. To the east the Plateau is linked to the Barail and so to the Assam–Burma Ranges by a saddle, geologically extremely complex, which sinks below 3,000 ft. (915 m.). The recent discovery of coal on the Plateau is of some significance to the Assam tea industry.

Much of the Plateau is under heavy forest – with pines on the higher ridges – but elsewhere centuries of shifting cultivation have produced a mixture of wood-land and secondary bush, in which rhododendrons and orchids are prominent, with some more or less open downland.

The tribes – Garo, Khasi, Jaintia – have Mon-Khmer or Tibeto-Burman affinities; they are generally matrilineal and in some of them the initiative in the affairs of life, including marriage, rests with the women as of right, instead of being merely usurped, as is more usual. They live by shifting subsistence agri-culture; the villages often shift with the fields (*jhum*). Potatoes and oranges are the chief cash crops; vegetables, rice and maize are planted in the ashes of slowly-burned lantana scrub – a trick now proving useful to foresters in the eradication of this pest.

Shillong (58,612) a hill station about 45 miles (72 km.) from the nearest rail-way, is still the capital of Assam, although it has no obvious advantages except possibly a cool climate conducive to bureaucratic efficiency.

THE ASSAM-BURMA RANGES

The Shillong Plateau and its outliers play in the northeast the same role as the concealed extension of the Peninsular Block in the northwest: around it are wrapped Tertiary ranges of the mountain rim. The great Arakan arc consists of tightly-packed parallel ridges and valleys, in a belt up to 150 miles (241 km.) broad, formed of Cretaceous and Tertiary sandstones, limestones and shales. The drainage shows an extraordinarily regular trellis-pattern of Jura rather than Appalachian type, since the folding is open and regular and relief is usually not yet inverted. The ridges rarely exceed 7,000 ft. (2,135 m.), though Saramati (Mt Victoria) on the actual Indo-Burmese boundary reaches over 12,500 ft. (3,810 m.) and sometimes carries snow in the midst of the jungle.[8]

With a normally-distributed monsoon rainfall of up to 80–100 in. (2,032–2,540 mm.), the hills have a heavy forest cover, ranging from tropical evergreen with giant dipterocarps in the wetter and lower south, through monsoon deciduous forest, to some pine and even grass on the highest ridges. But it has been much affected by *jhum* cultivation (the Burmese term *taungya*, 'mountain

[8] This sudden phenomenon on air-photos once gave a great deal of puzzlement to the topographers of South East Asia Command.

field', is perhaps better known and more expressive), and this has resulted in very dense secondary scrub-jungle and, on the Arakan border, vast stretches of *kayinwa* bamboo (a potential resource for paper making), 'like a hayfield 40 feet high'. This is reputed to be about the most impenetrable type of jungle there is.[9]

The hill peoples are a mosaic of tribes, mainly Mongoloid, of whom the various Naga clans are perhaps the most prominent. Villages are on the whole more stable than on the Shillong Plateau, the houses occupying commanding heights, partly to avoid the malarial valleys and partly for defence: many are still stockaded and head-hunting was practised till quite recently. Around the village the fields, in use or abandoned, spread out along the spurs, the only areas of more or less level ground; tracks keep to the ridgeways as much as possible. From the air the whole arrangement looks like a giant amoeba, the village as the nucleus and the fields as the pseudopodia. In the southwest, however, the Tripura wedge is deeply penetrated by parallel valleys running up from Sylhet, and these are occupied by permanent cultivation, mainly terraced paddy.

The peoples are attractive for the most part, with high standards of courtesy and decency (the latter perhaps more moral than physical). But normally they contribute little or nothing to the economic life of Assam – as indeed why should they? Millet, maize, dry hill rice, buckwheat, tobacco; buffaloes, goats and poultry; and the innumerable products of the jungle, from bamboo to honey, wax, and lac (an important cash 'crop'), provide them with the essentials of an existence not without culture.

Routes across the hills, until the war, were mostly mere trails: the Taungup Pass road, farther south in Burmese territory, was adventurously motorable; the main route in Assam ran from Kohima to Imphal and on to Tamu, the border town in the Kabaw valley. The administrative centre of Nagaland is Kohima, a hilltop village with a few official bungalows: the District Commissioner's tennis court, one of the few level patches, was the prize of some of the fiercest fighting in the Japanese war.

In 1937 a British traveller expressed the pious hope that the hill people 'might long be spared from the terrible consequences of Western Civilization';[10] in 1942–45 civilization descended on them in strange and terrible forms. The old isolation or innocence was gone for ever; but the Nagas have been understandably reluctant to come to terms with the new age. For years there was serious unrest, involving 'punitive action', in the hills; in an effort to exorcize it a separate political unit, directly under New Delhi, but destined to become a State, was created in 1961: Nagaland, with an area of 6,366 sq. miles (16,487 km²) and 369,000 people. It is receiving considerable amounts of federal aid for development, but unrest, and even demands for independence, continue.[11]

South of Nagaland is a distinctive area, the old princely state of Manipur, now

[9] But cf. General Wingate's order to the Chindits: 'No jungle is to be reported impenetrable until it has been penetrated.'

[10] E. T. D. Lambert, 'From the Brahmaputra to the Chindwin', *GJ* 89 (1937), 32–33.

[11] G. N. Patterson, 'The Naga problem', *Jnl Royal Commonwealth Soc.* 50 (1963), 30–40.

like Nagaland a Union territory of 8,628 sq. miles (22,336 km²) with 780,000 people. Here an intermont basin, floored with paddy, occupies about 150 sq. miles (388 km²) around the reedy Loktak Lake, and provided the base for a political unit more advanced and stable than that of the hill tribes, yet too small to stand on its own. Manipur is indeed the only parallel to the larger Shan States, with similar basin-bases, on the other side of Burma: it was bound to fall into either the Burmese or the Indian orbit, and the war of 1824–26 brought the Indian boundary to the foot of the western wall of the Kabaw valley, only a few miles from the purely Burmese Chindwin. On rather older and firmer ground north of the silting lake is the capital, Imphal, a strange agglomeration in these scantily-peopled hills: although rather a collection of villages round the ruler's seat than a real town, with a 1961 population of 67,717 it was the largest settlement in the sub-continent east of Chittagong.

THE ASSAM HIMALAYA: NEFA

The final sweep of the Himalayas is still relatively little-known and its physical – and recently its political – affinities are the subject of dispute. It is administered centrally as the North-East Frontier Agency or Tract, with five sub-divisions, and is eventually to be integrated with Assam.

Beyond Namcha Barwa and the wild Dihang gorges through which the Tsangpo breaches the Himalaya to become the Brahmaputra, lie the north–south furrows of Salween, Mekong, and Yangtse; it remains doubtful whether the Himalayas bend round into the great virgation between the Shillong and Yunnan blocks, or whether an originally latitudinal range has been segmented by these great rivers. At all events, the Lohit branch of the Brahmaputra seems to have captured some originally Irrawaddy drainage. At this blind end of the great valley, some rain is forced into the mountains through such deep gashes as those of the Lohit and the Dihang gorges; and here the Tibetans reach their lowest altitude – about 3,500 ft., 1,070 m. – at Rima.

The area of NEFA is 31,438 sq. miles (81,424 km²) and the 1961 population, entirely rural, is given as 336,558. The people are mainly tribal and animistic, but there are wide differences in their way of life. In the west are the Buddhist Monpas, with intricate terraced cultivation and substantial houses; farther east the once-notorious Abors of Siang, now at their own request called Adis (hill-men) to indicate their advance to a 'progressive and co-operative community'; in the northern marches live such groups as the wild Tagins, 'where the climate is abominable, the people under-nourished and tormented by diseases of the skin ... with little of the song and dance of other tribal areas'.

NEFA policy for the tribal people seeks to be enlightened and to avoid for its protegés the tragic fate so often experienced by such peoples suddenly exposed to 'civilization'. The *laissez faire* of the British period is unthinkable in the current political climate with the Chinese on, or over, the border, and it is hoped to find a middle way between this and rapid and complete detribalization by a planned development. The improvement of communications, in any case imposed by military needs, is the first step: one major road has been built into 'the hidden land' and airstrips are being constructed; at times local famines have been relieved by air-drop from military aircraft. *Jhum* agriculture, recognized as an essential of the people's way of life, is to be improved rather than abolished. Efforts are made to improve the health of the people who, while sturdy and self-reliant, have more than their fair share of disease.

Assam as a whole

In the first quarter of the 19th century large areas of the valley, especially in the east around the Ahom capital Sibsagar, were virtually depopulated by incessant Burmese invasions, and Assam is still the pioneer province of India. As a result of the Burmese War, Assam came definitely under British rule in 1824–26, although the hills were long quasi-independent, and some were hardly administered even by 1947. In 1892 the total population was only 5,364,000; by 1941 it had risen to 10,204,733 (including Sylhet) – an increase of 90% against 39% for India as a whole. Excluding Pakistani Sylhet, it rose by 20% in 1941–51 and by 31% in 1951–61, and in the last of these years it was 11,872,772, excluding the Union territories.

Most of these increases were due to immigration to the tea plantations and (in this century until 1947) of Muslim family squatters from overcrowded eastern Bengal, especially Mymensingh. This movement affected particularly Sylhet and Cachar (which in 1941 had 37% of the people on 17% of the area), but also affected the valley Districts, with decreasing intensity eastwards; by 1921 the outposts had reached North Lakhimpur, over against Sibsagar. This was a true pioneer drift, 'without fuss, without tumult, without undue trouble to the district revenue staffs', somewhere between half a million and a million farmers just moved in. These intrusive Mymensinghias cultivated much more intensively than the Assamese, but they gave rise to fears that they would entirely subvert Assamese culture, more surely even than the Burmese incursions.[12]

Recognition of the value of this *lebensraum* was reflected in exaggerated claims for all or part of Assam to be included in East Pakistan. While the excision of Sylhet has eased Assam's problem of assimilation, it leaves East Pakistan with a more desperate problem of adjustment of excessive numbers to land – so desperate, in fact, that according to Indian sources some Muslim immigration persisted even after Partition.

This population is very unevenly distributed: the valley Districts had a 1961 density of 422·5, the hill Districts (including Cachar) only 106, Manipur 90, Tripura 283, Nagaland 58. Urbanism, as we have seen, is very slight. There is also the problem of the assimilation of the tribes, who in the hills are extremely fragmented, speaking scores of languages (many, of course, closely related

[12] Census of India 1931, Vol. I, Part 1, 65.

'splinters'), but who yet form a larger proportion of the total population than in any other large unit of India. As the experience of the Nagas has shown – not to look to the more distant precedents of the Gonds and the Santals – their assimilation into a wider society, without exploitation and cultural impoverishment, will be a delicate and difficult task.

Assam until 1948 did not possess a University, symbol of respectability and maturity in Indian States. Yet it has a strong individuality, very unusual possibilities of agricultural expansion, a wealth of hydro-electric potential were there industries to use it. The war stimulated economic activity and left a heritage of improved communications and a wider diffusion of technical knowledge. Yet urbanization is extraordinarily low and the dependence on agriculture – especially tea – excessive, while the profits from tea and oil go largely beyond the state borders. Such development as there is has been almost entirely due to outsiders, British or Indian; the Assamese themselves seem to have their share of the pleasant but unpractical Indo-Chinese insouciance.

Materially, therefore, the possibilities are good. Assam is now India's last frontier of settlement of much significance; yet the irruption of alien enterprises, the unleashing of an expansionist capitalist economy, cannot fail to have disintegrating effects on what seems to have been a reasonably well-adjusted society, in both valley and hills; and the current emphasis of development is in the industrial rather than the agricultural field. Is the alternative to 'an undeveloped monsoon country' with too few men to be a developed one with too many? Precedents, unfortunately, suggest that the answer is too likely to be yes.

BIBLIOGRAPHICAL NOTE

The revision has relied heavily on P. C. Goswami, *The Economic Development of Assam* (Asia, Bombay, 1963); for NEFA the main source is Verrier Elwin, *A Philosophy for NEFA* (Shillong, 1960). R. C. Muirhead-Thompson, *Assam Valley: Beliefs and Customs of the Assamese Hindus* (Luzac, London, 1948), though of little geographical interest has two chapters on Village and Town Life. There is of course a large ethnographical literature, notably by J. H. Hutton (on the Nagas) and C. von Furer-Haimendorf. The war produced many books which give an idea of the Assam–Burma borders: perhaps George Rodgers, *Red Moon Rising* (NY, 1943), is especially notable for its fine photographs.

CHAPTER 21

The Aravallis and Central India

(Regions XIV–XVIII)

The heart of India

This heart of India – roughly the triangle between Delhi, the Gulf of Cambay, and Bengal – is an area of great physical complexity, including as it does the very ancient Aravalli Ranges and a great series of scarped plateaus and troughs which represent the buckling of the northern foreland of the Peninsular Block under the stress of the Himalayan mountain-building. Other elements are the pene-plains of Chota Nagpur, the complex topography of the Maikal block, the highly dissected gneissic terrain of Bundelkhand, and the great northern salient of Deccan Lava in Malwa. From a human point of view the area is transitional between the Indo-Gangetic Plains and the Deccan, lying between the two great structure-lines of Indian historical geography, that from the middle Yamuna axis to Cambay, and that along the Narmada–Chota Nagpur line; and it includes the Malwa passageway from Hindustan into the Deccan. In social organization it exhibited a widespread archaism with few (but important) sectors of modern development, notably those associated with the most productive coalfields of India; but until recently the general cast of society was largely represented by the tribes of the junglier hills and the ancient feudality of Rajputana, though the Malwa states (Gwalior, Indore, Bhopal) were economically more active. This is changing rapidly, and political simplification is a large element in the change.

This indeed was a great shatter-zone, stretching from Kathiawad to Orissa and containing the great majority of the nearly 600 Indian states, none of them very large in either area or population.[1] Except for Kathiawad and one or two adjacent states (now in Gujarat), all these are now in Rajasthan or in the enlarged Madhya Pradesh. The area also includes the major part of the Chota Nagpur Division of Bihar, Dhulia and Jalgaon in Maharashtra, the bulk of Madhya Pradesh (successor-state to the British Central Provinces), and the long, ragged projection of Uttar Pradesh in Jhansi District – presumably a strategic bridge of British territory to meet the old Central Provinces. Even today, its political geography still carries, in its twisting boundaries, a reflection of its past as the marchland between the powers of the Indo-Gangetic Plains and of the Deccan,

---

[1] Exception might be made for Marwar (Jodhpur) with its 36,120 sq. miles (93,550 km²); the largest population was that of Gwalior, 4,006,159.

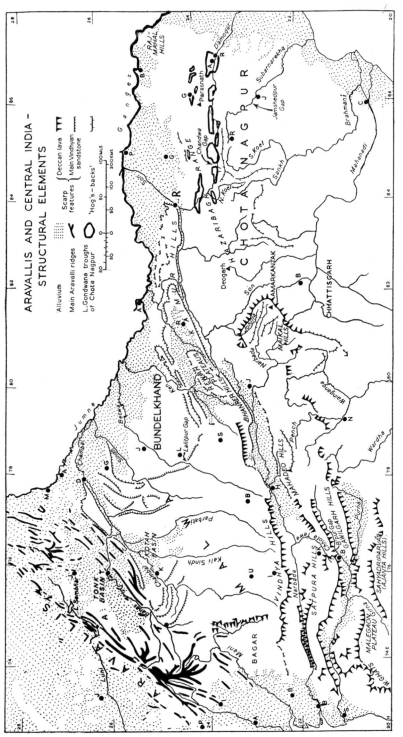

FIG 21.1 ARAVALLIS AND CENTRAL INDIA: STRUCTURAL ELEMENTS. Cf. Fig 21.2; for key to towns, Fig 21.5.

for example in the position of Jhansi: paradoxically, this stems from local reluctance to join up with adjacent Princely states (even one so progressive as Gwalior), and Jhansi owed its ninety years of direct British Raj to the fact that its ruler, though a woman, was the only patriot of the lot in 1857!

It seems best to begin with a general description of the whole area in its physical aspects, since the various definite regions which it contains are much interlinked; details will be reserved for separate sections on the main regions into which it may reasonably be divided.[2]

Physique. The structural setting has already been discussed (Chapter 1, pp. 16–23). The area as a whole is often termed the Peninsular Foreland ('North Indian' by Wadia; much is included in Stamp's 'Rajput Foreland'); but it seems desirable to emphasize the separateness of the Aravallis, and for the rest the neutral 'Central India' avoids illegitimate extensions and implications such as might be raised by the attractive term 'Vindhyan India', which expresses the general latitudinal grain of much of the area and the wide exposure of Vindhyan rocks.

The dominant factors in the geomorphological evolution of the area – apart from the general opposition of Gondwana block and Himalayan folding – are probably the gnarled Aravallis in the northwest, the gneissic block of Bundel-khand in the north, the massive Archaean peneplains of Chota Nagpur in the northeast; and over against these the great Deccan table. These rigid masses have probably controlled the layout of the plateaus and troughs squeezed between them. Working north from the Deccan and excluding the Thar we have:

(*a*) the faulted Tapti trough[3];

(*b*) the Satpura block, linked eastwards by the Mahadeo Hills to the Maikal 'culmination';

(*c*) the Chota Nagpur peneplains, continuing the Satpura–Maikal trends still farther east[4] and carrying the higher Hazaribagh Range and the faulted Damodar trough;

(*d*) the great Narmada–Son furrow, bounded sharply on the north by

(*e*) the *Vindhyan Hills* (Deccan Lava) and

(*f*) the Bhanrer–Kaimur Hills (Vindhyan *rocks*);

(*g*) the long slope of Deccan Lavas in the Chambal basin north of the *Vindhyan Hills*, masking the southerly continuation of

[2] The regional division is exceptionally difficult, and, although that adopted here is the result of a good deal of permutation and combination of various possible layouts, and seems a refinement on earlier schemes, we would emphasize that it makes no claim to be more than convenient and provisional.

[3] From a human point of view this area might well go with the Deccan, to which it is transitional; but the Narmada–Tapti parallelism justifies its treatment here: the Ajanta Hills on its southern border are the last major east/west line.

[4] 'Continuing' obviously implies no genetic relationship, merely a continuation in plan; the links between (*b*) and (*c*) are exceedingly obscure.

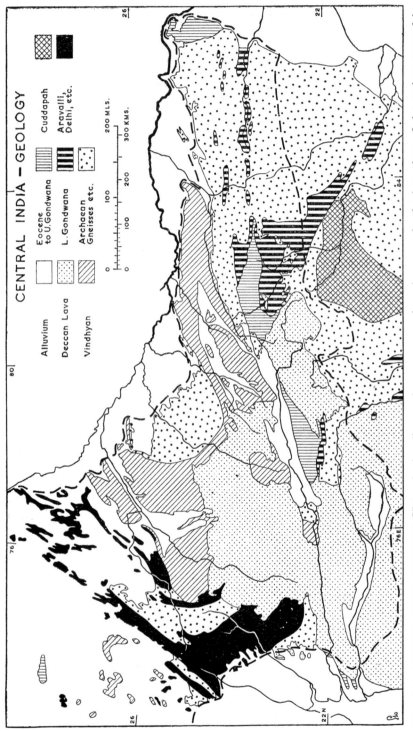

FIG 21.2 CENTRAL INDIA: GEOLOGY. Heavy broken line marks, very approximately as a rule, the boundary of the regions treated in this chapter; in the Thar/Rajasthan marchland no boundary is possible.

CENTRAL INDIA — GEOLOGY

Alluvium

Deccan Lava

Vindhyan

Eocene
to U. Gondwana

L. Gondwana

Archaean
Gneisses etc.

Cuddapah

Aravalli,
Delhi, etc.

0   100   200   300 KMS.

0   100   200 MLS.

(*h*) the triple outward-facing Vindhyan *rock* scarps of northern Malwa, with a great boundary fault marking them off from

(*i*) the Aravallis;

(*j*) east of Malwa is gneissic Bundelkhand, and between it and the Narmada–Son furrow are

(*k*) the scarped plateaus of Vindhyan sandstone in Rewah.

It will be noted that the latitudinal belts tend to break up into eastern and western sections, shown very clearly by the difference between the Narmada and the Son valleys. It seems likely that some deep-hidden structural feature lies transverse to the generally latitudinal lines, perhaps indicated by (i) the Gondwana Godavari trough; (ii) the Jabalpur gap; (iii) the Narmada/Son contrast, with the change in rock-type (Deccan Lava/exposed Vindhyan) and in direction (west/east to westsouthwest/eastnortheast) on the northern flanks of the furrow between Hoshangabad and Jabalpur; (iv) the great east-facing scarp of Vindhyans overlooking Bundelkhand; (v) the northern side of the Jodhpur–Jaipur saddle. Far away in the same direction[5] are the Kirana–Sangla Hills in the Punjab, which, as we have seen, attest a concealed extension of the Peninsular Block. The coincidences seem too many to be fortuitous, and we have here yet another addition to the immense agenda of Indian geomorphological problems.

Grouping together some of the physical components set forth above, we may divide the whole area apart from the Thar into the following regions, some of which might, however, rank strictly as sub-regions:

1. THE ARAVALLIS	5. NARMADA–SON FURROW
2. MALWA AND THE VINDHYAN HILLS	6. SATPURA/MAHADEO/MAIKAL HILLS
3. BUNDELKHAND	7. CHOTA NAGPUR
4. THE REWAH PLATEAUS	8. THE TAPTI VALLEY

Some sub-division will, of course, be necessary in the detailed treatment.

Climatically the area ranges from the very arid Thar (5–10 in., 127–254 mm.) to reasonably humid conditions in Chota Nagpur (45–55 in., 1,143–1,397 mm.); the 200-in. isohyet runs roughly along a line Gwalior town–Cambay, while the south and east of a line Rohtas–Lalitpur–Bhopal has over 40 in. (1,016 mm.) Temperatures vary to some extent with altitude and aspect: January means are around 60–65° F., May 90–95° (15·6–18·3, 32·2–35·0° C.). Daily ranges are high, as much as 20–30° F. (11·1–16·7° C.) in both of these months.

All except the more arid margins was originally forested; and even the semi-desert often carries a very open acacia scrub. Considerable areas of forest remain, especially in Chota Nagpur, and on all the higher country thence to the Satpuras (cf. Fig. 3.1). Thorn forest prevails in the west, closed monsoon deciduous forest (largely sal) in Chota Nagpur, more or less open and degenerated dry deciduous in the intervening areas; in the Thar, of course, a practically semi-desert open thorn scrub.

[5] Hardly, as Wadia has it, 'on a prolongation of the Aravalli strike'.

THE THAR

Between the irrigated lands of the Indus and Sutlej riverain and the eastern edge of the Aravallis stretch the desert and semi-desert wastes of the Thar, covering approximately 100,000 sq. miles (259,000 km²). Most of the Thar lies in the former large Rajasthan states of Bikaner, Jodhpur and Jaisalmer, but it also includes large portions of Bahawalpur, Khairpur and Thar Parkar in West Pakistan. The desert is not total, but bad enough; Jaisalmer has a density of under 10.

Most of the Thar is presumably a sanded-over pediplain. The strike of the great sand-ridges is generally transverse to the southwest winds, but in the south, where the winds are stronger, they are longitudinal to the wind-flow and up to 500 ft. (152 m.) high. Through the sand project Vindhyan, Jurassic and Tertiary inliers, themselves largely sandstones, and the Lower Gondwana Talchir Boulder Bed is also represented. In Jodhpur are bare rocky hills of granite and rhyolites, extrusions on to the old Aravalli surface. Of the recent deposits, the calcareous conglomerates found along the larger wadis, such as the Luni, suggest earlier more humid conditions. In the *pat* desert, adjoining Khairpur, impervious clays beneath the sand hold up groundwater, *dhands* (saline lakes) are numerous, and there is a relatively thick grass cover in the valleys.

Except in the extreme south rainfall is under, generally well under, 10 in. (254 mm.). Mean monthly temperatures range from 60° F. (January) to 95° (May; 16–35° C.), but diurnal ranges are naturally high – 20–30° F. (11–16·7° C.) at all seasons. Vegetation is extremely stunted and thorny open scrub, largely acacia: 'the term "tree" is rather a courteous acknowledgement of descent than an indication of size.'[6] In the south conditions are rather better, and in good monsoons there is good grass; the limestone ridge country on the Jaisalmer/ Jodhpur border north of the Luni is to some extent sheltered from the sand-drift and is rather less waste than the 'great desert' to the west or the 'little desert' to the east. But the desert seems to be gaining on the sown as the sand-laden winds break out on a wide front, especially in the Sirohi gap. Afforestation seems the obvious answer, but the problem of 'stopping the desert' has given rise to controversy about the best land use. Trees as shelter-belts and to fix the sandy soil and reclaim waste-lands in a wood-starved economy would seem incontrovertible; yet roadside plantings of *Prosopis julliflora* in Jodhpur are getting out of hand, and Kaul wonders whether trees do not create problems as well as solving them.[7]

Along the old Ghaggar bed canal irrigation, mainly for wheat, has more than trebled the population of Bikaner in forty years (660,000 in 1921, 2,141,000 in 1961). Elsewhere a primitive and precarious dry cultivation is carried on in the damper lows where the finer soil-particles accumulate between the sandhills;

[6] *Rajputana Gaz.* (Calcutta, 1908), 9.

[7] C. M. Mathur, 'Forest types of Rajasthan', *Indian Forester* (Dehra Dun), 86/12 (1958), 734–9; R. N. Kaul, 'Roadside plantings . . . in Rajasthan', *ibid.* 83/2 (1955), 457–70. Cf. P. Legris, *La Végétation de l'Inde* (Inst. Français de Pondichéry, 1963), 258–84.

bajra is the most important crop. The Rajasthan Canal Project is beginning to bring water over 400 miles (644 km.) from the Sutlej at Harike, in a lined channel to prevent soakage loss; there will eventually be almost 4,000 miles of canal, the main one running parallel to the Pakistan border and about 25 miles away from it. The aim is to irrigate about 10,500 sq. miles (27,200 km²) of the Great Desert, where a 1951 population of 81,000 is expected to grow to 2,000,000. Underground reserves lie deep and are too brackish for irrigation. Wheat and rice, as well as bajra, could be grown with new irrigation.[8] Pastoralism is still important, however, although harmful to the vegetation cover; the camel is still one of the chief means of transport.

An economic activity of more than local significance is the exploitation of the brine pits of the Pachbhadra lake, or rather marsh; this and other salt-pans are apparently concentrations of salt particles wind-borne from the great tidal flats of the Rann of Kutch. The pits are served by a railway.

In this as yet thinly peopled tract there are two large towns, Bikaner (150,634) and Jodhpur (224,760). These were essentially nodal centres on caravan routes, and their isolation has enabled indigenous trading families and methods to survive and flourish; craft industries, largely based on sheep and goat wool and hair, are important. In the north the Ghaggar irrigation is served by railways in Bikaner and Bahawalpur, producing a marked 'strategic' pattern on the map.

THE ARAVALLIS

The Aravallis are one of the oldest mountain systems, still retaining some relief, in the world; their tight-packed synclinoria in quartzites, schists, etc., of Delhi–Dharwar age (Algonkian–Huronian) were probably first uplifted in pre-Vindhyan (pre-Torridonian) times.

From Gujarat to Delhi (430 miles, 692 km.) the main southwest/northeast strike is remarkably regular, though the steep front to the aeolian plains of the Thar is formed of discontinuous and sometimes echelonned ridges: the highest point, the great granitic mass of Mt Abu (5,646 ft., 1,721 m.) lies off the main axis in the extreme southwest.[9] Around Udaipur the Aravallis reach their culmination (3,500–4,000 ft., 1,070–1,220 m.) in a great node of spurs and curving ridges; thence another series of ridges strike off eastnortheast along the Great Boundary Fault, enclosing the alluvial basin of Tonk and finally linking up with the western axis in the extremely tangled country of small quartzite hills half-smothered in the Gangetic alluvium, which lies north of the important saddle (c. 1,200 ft.) between Jaipur and Jodhpur.

[8] There are many sources on the project and its development; of special interest is C. S. Chandrasekhara and K. V. Sundaram, 'A note on anticipated land use changes in the Rajasthan Canal Area', *Bombay Geogl Mag.* 10/1 (1962), 61–69.
[9] See Pigott, *Some Ancient Cities of India* (1945), 65–70, for a vivid description: the exfoliated boulders round the Jain sanctuary 'look like nothing so much as the Creator playing at being Mr Henry Moore'.

The whole area suffered planation in the later Mesozoic and was afterwards warped, so that in Udaipur summits are around 4,000 ft., south of Delhi around 1,000. A probable second peneplain (on rather softer schists and gneisses) is found on the plains east of the western axis and in the strike valleys; much of it is covered by a thin veneer of older alluvium, which, according to Heron,[10] has

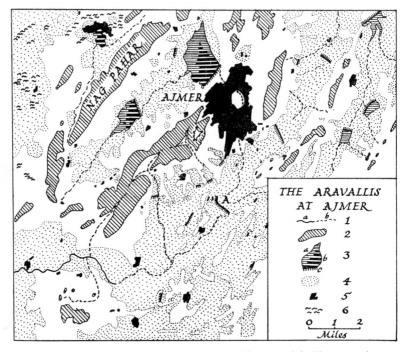

FIG 21.3 THE ARAVALLIS AT AJMER. 1, streams (a) perennial, (b) seasonal; 2, over 2,000 ft.; 3, (a) seasonal and (b) perennial tanks, (c) bunds; 4, cultivation; 5, settlement; 6, sand-dunes creeping in from Thar. Some of the larger ridges carry rather open forest; the *daman* around them (area left white) is mostly open scrub and waste, dissected by many dry stream beds, and west of Nag Pahar ('Snake Hill') very badly ravined. Cultivation mainly by bunding valleys; note how tanks have been silted out of existence, e.g. at A. *SOI* 45 J/11. *Courtesy* SOI.

itself been recently peneplaned. These Tertiary and Pleistocene pene- or pediplains meet at about 1,400 ft. (427 m.) in central Rajasthan; west of the main axis the alluvium is at about 1,000 ft. and smothered by the blown sand from the Thar. All the hills are dissected by generally dry but at times torrent-filled nullahs, and surrounded by pediment-fans.

There is obviously much room for human diversity in so large and physically complex an area. In the west, in Jodhpur or Marwar ('region of death') and

[10] A. M. Heron, 'The physiography of Rajputana', *Proc. 25th Indian Science Congress* (Calcutta, 1938), Part II, 119–32. The physical account above is based on this excellent presidential address to the Geography section of the Congress.

Bikaner it merges into the Thar. Here 'the people are semi-nomadic in habit, and on the advent of a period of scarcity they drive off their animals to other parts of the State, going as far as Kathiawar, central India and the Punjab in search of grazing for their cattle and work for themselves; at such times their villages are left in the charge of a few of the older men and women . . . villages are small and consist for the most part of quite unsubstantial huts of beehive form roofed with thatch'.[11] The water-table may be as much as 400 ft. down, and life is harsh in the extreme.

It is easier, but not much, in the Godwar, the long *daman* skirting the main ridges and dissected by numerous nullahs (of which a few are perennial) flowing to the Luni, which itself reaches the Rann of Kutch – sometimes. Here, with about 20 in. (508 mm.) of rain and despite encroachment by blown sand (and in the Jaipur–Jodhpur saddle dunes come right across the main axis; cf. Fig. 21.3), irrigation is possible by wells and small tanks; possible, but difficult, since the average depth of wells in Jodhpur is estimated by Fergusson at 150 ft. (46 m.), and except when wells are unusually full it takes a long time to bring up the often saline water by the 30–40-gallon sacks hauled by a pair of bullocks or a camel. Hence these wells are used mainly for stock, but nearer the hills and along stream-beds Persian wheels can be used. As for the tanks, they are shallow – merely bunding across nullahs – and with an annual rate of evaporation of 7·5 ft. only a few hold water for more than three or four months in the year. Their improvement by deepening and providing better drainage into them has had good results and the effect of famine, formerly very severe, have been mitigated by the construction of metre-gauge railways. It has been suggested that the hot summer *loo* winds might be harnessed to pump water from deeper levels; other possibilities are diesel pumps and – in time – grid electricity.[12] But irrigation is as yet very limited, though in good years there is a fair rabi production, mainly of wheat. The rainfed kharif (millets and gram) is obviously an essential part of the economy of Rajasthan west of the main Aravalli Range, and it will be equally obvious that the kharif is at best precarious.

Around the Jaipur–Jodhpur saddle are several small basins of interior drainage of which the most important is that of Lake Sambhar, the major source of salt in northern India. Sambhar covers 90 sq. miles (233 km²) when flooded, but is really a playa, almost dry in the hot weather. The salt is possibly brought by wind from the Rann of Kutch; output and reserves are considerable.

East of the main axis the topography is more varied. In the north the tough Delhi Quartzites form a series of flat-topped ridges, gaunt bony fingers half buried in the alluvium. Around the Banas river lies Mewar, a dissected plain of Archaean gneiss; the Banas is superimposed in a most striking manner, turning at right angles to cut through a strong Delhi Quartzite at Rajmahal; its course

[11] F. F. Fergusson, 'Famine and water supply in Western Rajputana', *GJ* 93 (1939), 39–53. This and the succeeding paragraph are based on Fergusson's work.
[12] Letter by S. S. Sarwal, *Indian Forester*, 82/6 (1956), 265.

appears to antedate the Mesozoic warping. These gneissic plains have poor, thin soils, but the numerous pegmatite (sometimes micaceous) and quartzite dykes facilitate the construction of small tanks. From Sambhar to Udaipur the Aravallis form the Gangetic/Cambay watershed; the tributaries of the Mahi, with only about one-tenth as far to go to base-level as the Banas headstreams, have dissected southern Udaipur into a very confused terrain of innumerable valleys. This area, the Bagar, is extremely isolated, inhabited largely by Bhil tribes practising shifting agriculture. Just south of Udaipur town Mukerji has described an interesting contrast between the large fields of rabi and kharif plots of the Rajput farmers, and the smaller rather poorly farmed fields of Bhils, practising fixed agriculture but ignoring so far the possibilities of market gardening for the city, and really more interested in labouring opportunities in Udaipur itself.[13]

A gnarled, dry land on the whole: rainfall varies from 11 to 25 in. (279–635 mm.; up to 50 on Mt Abu) and is highly variable; droughts and dearths are frequent, and, on occasions such as the cloudburst of 1943, floods may burst the tanks and devastate the little cultivated valleys below. There is a good deal of forest on the hills, but of an open xerophytic type, degraded by human and animal depredation, with much thorny acacia: and where it is naturally denser, in the slightly more humid southwest, it has been much depleted in many places by Bhil shifting cultivators. There has, however, been some successful rehabilitation of degraded teak forests here and in the Vindhyas. Yet Rajasthan is not without its favoured areas: essentially a land of refuge, last stronghold of the chivalric Rajput tradition, but with the bases for fairly extensive and solid states like Jaipur, Jodhpur and Udaipur (Mewar), whose former princely capitals are now more than usually elaborate District headquarters and increasingly important tourist centres and university towns.

The possibilities of irrigation have been seen; without it, agriculture is poor and precarious. This is *par excellence* the millet area of India, with jowar and bajra the dominant foodgrains, together over two-thirds of the NSA. Wheat, gram and pulses come next, with some sesamum, cotton and sugar. Camels are important west of the main Aravalli axis, goats everywhere, with deleterious effects on what vegetation cover there is.

Mineral resources are greater than was once estimated. Most important is mica, second only to Bihar in output, and often with associated beryl, which is also mined separately in Ajmer and stockpiled by the government for the use in future nuclear reactors. The Lake Sambhar salt is important, and the gypsum of playas in Jodhpur and Bikaner supplies all the needs of the Sindri fertilizer plant. India's only sources of lead/zinc and wolfram are at Zawar and Degana respectively. But the only fuel is in the poor Tertiary lignites of Bikaner, and iron deposits are uneconomic at present. Ball clays, steatite and bentonite (used in oil refining) are now exploited. A fair proportion of the mineral output is still in

---

[13] A. B. Mukerji, 'Land use pattern in a Newar village in Rajasthan', *GRI* 25/1 (1963), 11–34.

building stones: the Aravallian rocks produce fine marbles of many colours, including the dazzling white marble of Makrana, beloved by the later Moguls and used for the grandiose Queen Victoria Memorial in Calcutta; but for this it was transported free on the railways, and freight rates as well as changes in taste have reduced demand in an India enamoured of ferro-concrete.

The 1961 population of Rajasthan (including the Thar) was 20,156,000 on 132,152 sq. miles (342,275 km²), a density of 152. Urbanism is somewhat lower than in India as a whole, but Rajasthan has six cities of over 100,000: Jaipur (402,444), Ajmer (231,240), Jodhpur (224,760), Bikaner (150,634), Kota (120,345) and Udaipur (111,139). Of these Bikaner belongs essentially to the Thar, Kota to Malwa; the others are Aravallian. Ajmer grew as the capital of a British strategic enclave in the heart of the Rajput country, Jodhpur and Bikaner were in their origins caravan towns with craft industries dependent on their princely courts. Jaipur, the capital of Rajasthan, is perhaps the most interesting of the towns; in an excellent position on the more favoured side of the saddle, it was the centre of the finest flowering of Rajput culture under the remarkable astronomer-prince Jai Singh (*fl.* 1699–1743); like Udaipur in the south, it attracts some tourist traffic to Amber or Old Jaipur, a romantically beautiful fortress and palace town on the hills above. Modern industry is only beginning in Rajasthan, except for the railway workshops, but the old Court-fostered crafts – fine textiles and metal work – retain some importance.

The princely houses were Rajputs, the flower of the Kshatriya or warrior caste, claiming descent from the Sun, the Moon or more modestly from the heroes of the *Mahabharata* epic: at all events, their genealogy is of respectable antiquity in a country where (contrary to popular belief) most of the princely states represented simply the more successful bandits of the moment when British hegemony froze the 18th-century chaos. The Rajputs were forced into their hills by Muslim invasions into Hindustan proper; Rajput princelings are also in the Himalayan foothills. Of the peoples of Rajasthan, the great majority are Hindus; but aboriginals (mostly in the south) number over 1,500,000, and Jains over 325,000 – a quarter of the Indian total. The devotional life of the Jains centres on the temples of Mount Abu, fantastically sculptured and fretted in white marble; their more mundane interests have taken them as far afield as Calcutta, Rangoon, Nairobi and Durban, where 'Marwari' traders and moneylenders are a power in the land, and, if common repute be true, by no means always a beneficent power. The exaggerated sanctity attached even to insect life apparently does not extend to the livelihood of less adroit men.

MALWA

Malwa forms a great triangle, based on the *Vindhyan Hills*[14] and bounded on the northwest by the Great Boundary Fault of the Aravallis, on the east by the

[14] In this chapter *Vindhyan Hills* is italicized to avoid confusion with the large areas of Vindhyan rocks.

sharply-defined scarp overlooking Bundelkhand. Most of it is drained by the Chambal and its right-bank tributaries; but it includes in the southeast the upper courses of the Ken and Betwa, in the southwest a very irregular and dissected Deccan Lava brow overlooking the wild Bagar.

Physically it falls into two very different divisions, which might indeed form separate regions but for the practical difficulties of treatment on a reasonable scale. These are the Vindhyan scarplands of the north, the great Deccan Lava plateau in the south (Figs. 21.1, 21.2).

The major Vindhyan scarps (1,500–1,900 ft., 455–580 m.), formed in massive sandstones and separated by shales, are three, facing outwards – to the south-southeast between Banas and Chambal, to the east over Bundelkhand; the general effect is that of a syncline pitching south. In the northwest there is a strong scarp-feature flanking the left bank of the Chambal, and beyond this a scarped block occupying the former states of Dholpur and Karauli. Here the usually almost horizontal Vindhyans are folded and faulted, presumably by the rigid Aravallis which are overthrust on to them along the Boundary Fault. This contact may have been responsible for the warping of the Mesozoic surface in the Aravallis; warping and the displacement of the Boundary Fault are of the same order, 4,000–5,000 ft. (1,220–1,525 m.) decreasing northeast and southwest.[15]

The river system is interesting. The Chambal, Ken and Betwa rise within 20 miles (32 km.) of the Narmada and appear as consequents on the Mesozoic surface, superimposed on the scarps: the Chambal in particular cuts straight across them, with subsequent tributaries on the softer shales. In the east the Kuna and Kunwari appear subsequents, but the former cuts through the innermost scarp at Nayagaon; it may have developed as a consequent on an older surface and reached its present position by lateral shifting down the dip. The Chambal and its tributaries Kali Sindh and Parbati have formed a triangular alluvial basin at about 700–900 ft. (215–275 m.) in Kota, above the narrow trough of the lower Chambal. Severe gullying, possibly initiated by rejuvenation but aggravated by misuse of the land, make this perhaps the worst area of erosion in India, particularly towards the edge of the foreland. Some 1,400,000 ac. (567,000 ha.) are deeply-gashed badlands, a hideout for the local dacoits but now the scene of trial rehabilitation schemes by bulldozing terraces and planting quick-growing grasses and trees.[16]

The Deccan Lavas of the south abut on the outer scarp, and their eroded edge suggests that the main lineaments of the underlying Vindhyans are similar to those exposed on the north. They form a great table-land, rising gently from about 1,400 ft. to 2,500 (430–760 m.) in the great brow overlooking the Narmada. This 'scarp' is known as the *Vindhyan Hills* but it hardly deserves that name: big, bold and impressive from the trough below, from above the existence of the

---

[15] Heron, *loc. cit.* 123, 129.
[16] R. N. Kaul, 'Management of Chambal ravines in Rajasthan', *Indian Forester*, 88 (1962), 725–30.

scarp is hardly suspected until one is almost on the edge: at Mhow, only 12 miles to the north, there is nothing to suggest that the gently undulating plateau does not extend indefinitely onwards. South of Bhopal the scarp is formed in a window of Vindhyan rocks; here the main Bombay–Agra railway climbs it by a narrow transverse valley. In places there are sheer precipices of 400–600 ft. (120–180 m.); but even here the box-like Vindhyan Sandstone mesas soon give way to the gentler outlines of the lavas.

Such are the general features of relief: in aspect, of course, there is a great contrast between the Vindhyan and the Deccan Lava landscapes. The former is harsher, bonier, more rugged and more arid in appearance: an alternation of large or small basins with large or small plateaus, often with sheer walls of 200–400 ft. Large parts of it have only a few inches of soil, or even bare rock-surfaces in places: poor grassland and open acacia scrub interspersed with rather poor agriculture. The lava country as far south as Indore is practically a plain; beyond this it rises into gentle swells, with few of the mesas so typical of Maharashtra (below, 692). Cultivation appears much more widespread and flourishing; it might almost be an East Anglian landscape minus its hedges, but a little too big and coarse in scale. Along the *Vindhyan Hills* the country becomes wilder; woodland (with teak) predominates, but is very open in many places, with almost more glades than trees, and the rounded hills give a Hercynian effect.

In the north, except in the larger alluvial plains, villages show marked topographical preferences, nestling at the foot of scarps, at gaps, grouped around forts on little isolated hills. On the more homogeneous lavas topographical influence is naturally less marked; settlement is so confined to rises, and rises to settlement, as to suggest that the hillocks on which the villages stand are simply the accumulated rubbish of generations. Houses are of stone (especially in the Vindhyan country) or mud, roofs of thatch or stone slabs or, in the south, semi-cylindrical tiles reminiscent of the Deccan. Fields in the Vindhyan country are sometimes bounded by mud or dry-stone walls capped with thorns. The *Vindhyan Hills* themselves are very empty, and in places wood-cutting for fuel or charcoal appears a main activity.

With rainfalls of 25–35 in. (635–889 mm.) and fairly high variability, millets – mainly jowar – are of course dominant, with cotton a strong second on the moisture-retaining black soils (regur) of the lavas. The contrast suggested in the preceding paragraphs is strikingly brought home (Fig. 21.4) by the land-use figures for two Districts of the former Gwalior state, now in Madhya Pradesh. Sheopur – now included in Morena – is entirely Vindhyan, lying along the right bank of the Chambal northwest of Kota; Shajapur entirely Deccan Lava. Although the area of Morena is much greater than that of the old Sheopur, extending right down to the plains, its density is still less than that of Shajapur (174 to 220), and the latter had about thrice the density of the old Sheopur. Old as the figures are (1938–39) they yet point out a basic and permanent contrast.

Only a small fraction, under 5%, of the cultivated area is now irrigated, even with the 500,000 ac. (202,000 ha.) added by the Chambal scheme; tanks have fallen into disuse, but wells are very important. Reclamation of the badlands and 'culturable waste' – that elusive classification – may add considerably to the cropped area; a good deal of mechanized reclamation has been undertaken.

Historically Malwa displays a curious duality: the Deccan Lavas provide the only really extensive agricultural base in central India, and so it has retained its individuality; yet, as a land of passage, it has constantly changed hands, 'the invariable appanage to the domains of every monarch, native or barbarian, who became the master of the Gangetic plain'.[17] This is too strong; but Fig. 6.1

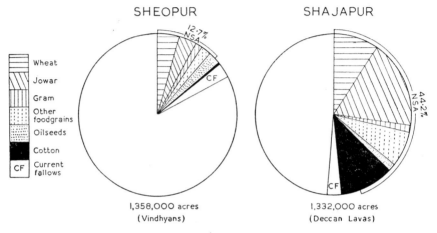

FIG 21.4 THE LAVA/VINDHYAN CONTRAST.

indicates that the frontiers are least persistent in the north. This is, in part at least, inherent in the geography of Malwa compared to that of its neighbouring regions. On the one hand lie the burning wastes of the Thar and the natural and artificial strongholds of the Aravallis; on the other the mass of excessively broken and jungly terrain around the Maikal Hills, and farther east the broad forested plateaus of Chota Nagpur. The Son, pent in between Vindhyan cliffs and Gond jungles, has never been an important entry; in any case it leads backwards, as it were, in relation to the drive of invaders down the Ganga. The centre of power in the north – continuously since the Muslim conquests, and often before them – was in the Delhi–Agra region: the way into the South Country, Dakshina or Deccan, was over the more open Deccan Lavas. The *Vindhyan Hills* and the Narmada once crossed, the Burhanpur gap and the broad embayment of Chalisgaon led on to Nasik. The more difficult part of the Malwa passageway is in the Vindhyan north: it is significant that the railways avoid the funnel of the lower Chambal. One line crosses the Karauli Plateau into the Tonk basin, reaching the Chambal well up, almost on the Deccan Lavas, by

[17] 1931 Census, Vol. XX, Pt. I. 3.

the gap at Indorgarh (which incidentally looks as if the Aravalli/Vindhyan boundary ranges have been breached by superimposition or river capture); the other goes through Bundelkhand and reaches the lava plateau by a well-marked gap south of Lalitpur, where the Vindhyan outcrop is reduced to a single narrow scarp.

In peace, as in war, the Malwa route was one of the most significant in India; alike in Ptolemy's day and in that of the Discoveries, it led from the Cambay sea-entry at Barygaza (Broach) or Surat to Ujjain and so by Bhilsa, with its great Buddhist monuments, to Pataliputra (Patna), later to Agra and Delhi. With the coming of the railway and the concentration of so much of India's trade on Bombay the actual lines of movement shifted, but they remain within this broad zone.

The old princely states were either Rajput or foundations by chiefs of the great but loose Maratha confederacy; the most important were Gwalior and Indore; Bhopal, by exception, was Muslim-ruled. These three were among the most progressive in India, but all have been merged into the great Hindi-speaking State of Madhya Pradesh. The bulk of the population of Malwa is Hindu, but with sizeable tribal minorities.

Indore is the largest town (394,941), outranking Gwalior (300,587), but the latter has more general importance; Bhopal (222,948) was formerly less significant, but as capital of Madhya Pradesh it is growing more rapidly than the other two and has a Central Government plant making heavy electrical equipment.[18] Indore reflects the generally higher standards of the cotton-growing Lavas; it has a number of cotton mills and other light industries. At Gwalior, Lashkar ('the Camp') is the new (18th-century) town below the old fortress on the astonishing Rock of Gwalior, a cliffed plateau nearly 2 miles long rising sheer 300 ft. (91 m.) from the plain, walled all round the periphery, and carrying in the cliff rock-cut Jain statues nearly 60 ft. high. This stranded Gibraltar is one of the most impressive holds in a country liberally provided with *tours de force* of fortification.[19] The town proper is a flourishing industrial centre – textile mills and handlooms, textile engineering, leather, pottery, biscuit and cigarette making. The only other town of much note is ancient Ujjain, the traditional capital of Malwa. It also is growing fairly rapidly (144,161) and has cotton mills, but is more famous for its brilliant past, whether commercial as an important stage on the Yamuna–Cambay trade route, or cultural as the half-legendary seat of King Vikramaditya, the traditional patron of Kalidasa who immortalized the city in the most splendid of Sanskrit lyrics, the *Meghaduta* or *Cloud-Messenger*. Through Ujjain, regarded as the centre of the world, ran the prime meridian of Sanskrit geographers, and it is almost on the Tropic; Jai Singh of Jaipur could

[18] For a recent account of these towns see S. N. Methrotha, 'Urbanisation in Madhya Pradesh' *GRI* 23/4 (1961), 29–46.

[19] The landscape of central India, with every tactical strongpoint crowned by a keep, hardly bears out the view of a mythical Golden Age when such wars as there were passed harmlessly over the peasant in his fields. Robber barons were probably much the same on the Chambal or on the Rhine.

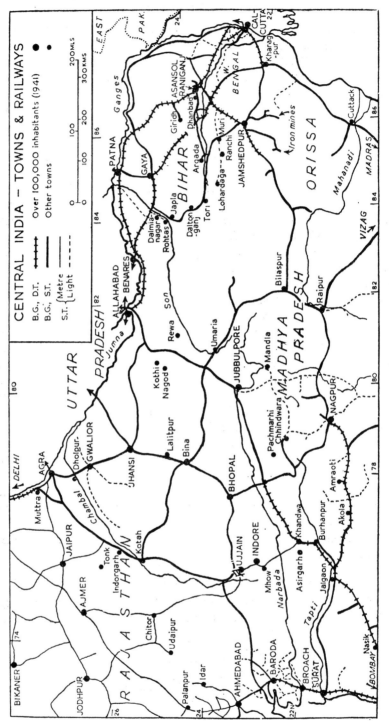

FIG 21.5 ARAVALLIS AND CENTRAL INDIA: TOWNS AND RAILWAYS.

hardly overlook so fitting a site for an observatory, and his reckoning of its latitude, 21° 10', was only one minute out.

BUNDELKHAND

Bundelkhand need not detain us long: physically it is a homogeneous dissected upland, politically – except for the tongue of Uttar Pradesh in Jhansi – it was occupied by obscure and backward petty states, now amalgamated in Madhya Pradesh. The country is recognizable at once, without a geological map: a mass of rounded hummocky hills, with almost a *roches moutonnées* effect, typical tropical exfoliation-weathering in the reddish Bundelkhand Gneiss, cut across by innumerable white quartzite dykes, in all sizes from veins of a few inches to massive walls. The frequent constriction of drainage by the dykes favours a multiplicity of small half-natural half-artificial tanks and so enables agriculture to be carried on with some security in a region of variable rainfall, around 45 in. (1,143 mm.). The vegetation is largely open scrub and bush.

Agriculture is extensive, and pulses and gram bulk large. 'Proper soil preparation has to give place to hurried tillage, and single crops to mixtures like gram and wheat, or gram and linseed, or even gram, linseed, and wheat in the rabi, and sesamum and arhar, or jowar and arhar, in the kharif. In the hope of striking a lucky combination of a large sown area and a favourable season more land is farmed than can be properly controlled with the man and bullock power available.'[20] Hence the spread of *kans*, a weed of creeping habit, which is controlled – again extensively – by grazing it for fifteen years or so, or flooding it for a couple of monsoons. There is much rough grazing, and the number of cattle owned is often evidence of status.

Villages are small, stoutly built, often of stone; outer walls are blind and doorways massive and low – relics of the old insecurity visibly attested also by the hilltop holds which are easily the most striking features of the cultural landscape.

The only centre of any importance is the railway town of Jhansi (169,712). The last Rani of Jhansi is a romantic figure in the gallery of Indian national heroes: described by her opponent Sir Hugh Rose as the best and bravest of Mutiny leaders, she was killed in action at the age of 20, riding as a trooper; she is not alone as a reminder that generalizations about Oriental subjection of women are generalizations after all, and that human realities will break through the forms of social convention.

THE REWAH PLATEAUS

The country between Bundelkhand and the Son is occupied by a great series of wall-sided plateaus, a belt 300–400 miles long and 50 wide (480–645 and 80 km.)

[20] W.Burns (ed.). *Sons of the Soil* (N.D., 1941) 46. Arhar is a highly nitrogenous pulse (*Cajanus indicus*).

terminating very abruptly in the south in the Kaimur scarp dominating the Son; less abruptly, but still sharply enough, in the north. The Vindhyans are mainly massive sandstones, with some limestones and shales. The Kaimur crest lies at 1,500–2,000 ft., rising 1,000 ft. (305 m.) above the Son; except for a very narrow strip along the Son, discussed in the next section, most of the drainage is to the Ganga via the Ken or the Tons: these rivers cross the northern scarp in a series of falls and cascades. Above the scarp they are mature, and much of the region is a high alluvial plain at about 1,000 ft.

Rainfall is 40–50 in. (1,016–1,270 mm.); there are many tanks, but probably more ground is cultivated by bunding valleys and sowing in the moist soil after the rains: this gives relatively high yields. Much of the alluvium is a fertile black loamy soil well adapted to wheat. The margins and much of the higher ground within the plateau are forested, but locally soil erosion is severe.

The whole area is extremely isolated and backward. Despite the fair rainfall and soil conditions, probably not more than 20–25% of the area is cultivated. The principal crop is probably *kodon*, the smallest of the millets, which is adapted to poor soils with fairly good rainfall; in bad years, consumption of a poor vetch is responsible for outbreaks of lathyrism, a paralysis affecting mainly young adult males.[21] Rice, wheat and maize account for the bulk of the remaining cultivation. Other economic development is negligible, and the only town of any size is Rewah (43,065). Former 'princely' capitals such as Kothi and Nagod are mere villages of 6,000–8,000 people.

THE NARMADA–SON FURROW

This 'region' falls into very distinct sections: the alluviated fault-trough of the Narmada, and the much narrower but more complex immediate valley of the Son. The two are curiously interdigitated north of Jabalpur. To the north the Vindhya–Kaimur scarps flank the trough for 600 miles (965 km.) or more.

(*a*) The *Narmada* rises on Amarkantak, most prominent of the Maikal Hills, and has a complex course as far as the Marble Rocks gorge, below Jabalpur. Below this it enters the great trough; the rift character is illustrated by a boring, only four miles within the alluvium, which found no solid rock at 491 ft. (150 m.). The geomorphological problems presented by the Narmada and Tapti have been discussed in Chapter 1 (pp. 20–21 and Fig. 1.3); we need note here only that the steepness and straightness of the lower Narmada gorges suggest a recent origin, and that it seems likely that the Narmada originally flowed out on the Tapti line via the Burhanpur gap.

The human interest of the Narmada is considerable. Its sanctity is rivalled only by the Ganga; indeed local patriotism avers that mere contemplation of

[21] T. L. McCombie Young, 'Lathyrism in Rewa', *Indian Jnl Medical Research*, 15 (1927), 453–80 – an old reference, but occasional outbreaks are still reported from various parts of India. See Learmonth, 1965, *op. cit.*, in Chapter 4.

the Narmada is as efficacious as bathing in the Ganga, which, in the form of a black cow, must be washed white of her annual accumulation of sins in the Narmada. High merit may be obtained by the *pradakshina*, a pilgrimage up one bank from Broach to Amarkantak and down the other; the round trip is about 1,600 miles. The river historically was considered as the boundary between

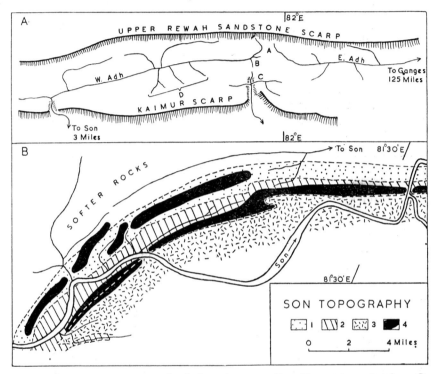

FIG 21.6 SON TOPOGRAPHY. A: A, broad open valley; B, recent steepening; C, gorge with boulders too large for transport by misfit stream (originally flowing to N); D, main valley cut down, side valleys rejuvenated owing to capture by W Adh.

B: 1, volcanic ash (porcellanite); 2, shales with hard quartzite capping; 3, crystalline gneisses, etc.; 4, high ridges.

Based on R. D. Oldham, *Mem. GSI* XXXI (1901). *Courtesy GSI.*

Madhyadesa and Dakshinapatha, the Middle and the South Land; to the Marathas all to the north was foreign – and indeed, as we have seen, the river forms part of the most persistent internal frontier in India.[22]

The *Vindhyan Hills* rise steeply to heights of 1,000 ft. above the valley floor. To the south the Satpura and Mahadeo scarps are less well-marked and less continuous, yet bold enough. The valley floor is some 20–40 miles wide and within it the river is sunk between banks 20–40 ft. (6–12 m.) high. This has

[22] *Central India Gaz.* (1908), 104–5.

hampered irrigation, which would be useful in an area with 30 in. (762 mm.) of rain. There is no scope for dams on the tributaries from the hills on either side, and the valley floor is badly gullied by the Satpura torrents. However, minor remedial projects are now possible. Wheat, cotton, jowar and sesamum are the chief crops. Lumbering and charcoal-burning are important on the bordering hills, particularly perhaps on the Mahadeo slopes. The lower gorges run through almost empty forest country, inhabited mainly by Bhils.

The southern side of the trough is followed by an important railway between Jabalpur and Khandwa, whence it crosses to the Tapti. Two lines cross the Narmada: a metre line Khandwa–Indore (and so to the north by Kota), and the broad gauge Itarsi–Bhopal, part of the main Bombay–Agra–Delhi line.

Khandwa and Hoshangabad are local centres: the site-values of the former, at the debouchment of the Burhanpur gap and the bifurcation of the two railways, are obvious; the latter is on the actual main-line crossing of the Narmada. Both are outshadowed by Jabalpur (367,014); occupying a commanding position at the head of the Narmada trough, with relatively easy routes north around the end of the Bhanrer Hills to Allahabad, south between the Mahadeo and Maikal Hills to the Wainganga valley and the Deccan: Narmada and Wainganga headwaters approach to within 2 or 3 miles of each other, in a col not much over 1,500 ft. (455 m.) above sea-level. The Bombay–Allahabad line was the first through rail route in India (1870), linking Bombay with both Calcutta and Delhi; not till 1888 and 1889 respectively were more direct lines opened. These have to some extent weakened Jabalpur's relative position, but its advantages of centrality and nodality have led to some canvassing of its suitability as a capital. The tradition of Delhi is too strong, however; meanwhile Jabalpur remains as the only large town in a very wide area, with railway shops, ordnance factories, pottery and glass works, furniture and other timber trades. Other centres of growing importance are Burhanpur, a cotton and grain market with textiles and craft industries, Chandni with a newsprint mills, and the railway junction town of Katni-Murwara with limestone quarries and cement works. Bauxite from Amarkantak may be capable of development, using power from Rihand on the Son.[23]

(b) The Son, in sharp contrast to the Narmada, is not followed by a railway, nor even a continuous road; the physical interest of its valley far outweighs the human, and it has a very different history from that of the Narmada.[24]

For some 300 miles (483 km.) the river runs close under the Kaimur scarps rising 500–1,000 ft. above the narrow valley floor. Mainly resistant sandstones interbedded with porcellanite (volcanic ash), the Kaimurs are practically the watershed, only a few very short obsequents cutting back and developing

[23] B. K. Mahendra, 'A plan for establishing aluminium industry in Central India', *Bull. Geol. Mining and Metallurgical Soc. India*, 16 (1956), 1–32.

[24] R. D. Oldham analysed the evolution of the Son landscape in detail in 'Notes on the geology of the Son Valley' (*Mem. GSI* 31 (1901), 1–178). This excellent paper, with some by Vredenburg and others, is evidence of an early interest in geomorphology among the Survey geologists.

subsequents along the shales between the more massive sandstone members; here and there Ganga drainage has been captured (Fig. 21.6(A)). Nor are there any deeply-cut windgaps to suggest an originally northward consequent drainage dismembered by the growth of the Son as a strike stream. This lack of windgaps is an anomaly in so long a scarp, and the asymmetry of the valley is also very striking: although the northern watershed is so close to the river, there are several right-bank tributaries rising 100 miles away. In places the Son is definitely superimposed (Fig. 21.6(B)). Oldham envisaged a peneplain with very open relief of the order of 300 ft., with the Kaimur scarp already outlined but much lower: general uplift and a lowering of the valley floor later etched it out.

There is little alluvium along the Son; in Mirzapur (Uttar Pradesh) the river is sunk in a low terrace, which disappears westwards in Rewah. Farther up there are, of course, alluvial patches, and in some places fine unstratified loams which seem aeolian. There is evidence of slight recent rejuvenation, but Oldham thinks that it is at least as likely that the change is due to the extensive clearing of forests as to a general movement of elevation.[25]

The Son valley is in general an empty land of great sal forests, with isolated patches of subsistence cultivation. Only where it begins to open out into the Gangetic Plain is there much development. Here, near Rohtas, an outcrop of 'fat' (80% calcium carbonate) limestone in the Kaimur scarp has been exploited for cement works at Japla (connected with the quarries by a 5-mile ropeway across the Son), Dalmianagar, and Kalyanpur. Clay is available locally, coal from the little Daltonganj field some 40 miles away; only gypsum has to be brought from the Punjab or Rajasthan. Dalmianagar (38,092) founded by the self-made magnate Seth Dalmia, is a model industrial town just north of the older and now growing town of Dehri at the head of the Son. It has a well-integrated industrial set-up, with paper from bamboo (rafted down the Son, or by rail from the North Koel valleys), alkalis and sulphuric acid, vegetable ghee, saw-milling and so on.[26]

THE SATPURA–MAIKAL RANGES

The Narmada is flanked to the south by a series of scarped plateaus, generally at 2,000–3,000 ft. (610–915 m.). In the west the Satpuras ('Seven Folds') proper are simply a steep-sided Deccan Lava block, sinking between Burhanpur and Khandwa to 1,200 ft. (365 m.) in the gap followed by the main Bombay–Agra railway and guarded by the great hill-fort of Asirgarh. As we have seen, the Narmada may have flowed through this gap; the Chhota Tawa valley suggests the actual course. In the angle between the upper Tapti and its tributary the

[25] *Loc. cit.* 51. This remark has probably a wider application.

[26] For an unusually vigorous commentary on the urban landuse maps, see K. N. Singh, 'Morphology ... of Dehri-Dalmianagar', *NGJI* 3/3–4 (1957), 169–79; and for another aspect of the area, A. N. Bhattacharya and L. N. Verma, 'Rural settlement forms in the Son Valley', *Indian Geogr* 2/2 (1957), 294/304.

Purna the Gawilgarh Hills are another Deccan Lava horst: the displacement along the fault which bounds them to the south is between 1,800 and 4,000 ft. (365–1,220 m.). Farther east, in the Mahadeo Hills (sometimes included in the Satpura Range), is a great window of Archaeans and Middle Gondwanas, thick masses of red sandstones forming small plateaus with precipitous scarps. East again, beyond the Jabalpur gap, the great bastion of the Maikal Range is crowned by Amarkantak (3,493 ft., 1,065 m.), the sacred mountain in which the Narmada rises. Most of this dissected plateau drains by deep-cut valleys into the Narmada; but in the extreme east the Johilla tributary of the Son has a curious course separated from the broader parallel valley of the upper Son by a narrow ridge of Deccan Lava. The plateau is tilted to the northwest, falling from 3,000–3,500 ft. in the abrupt scarp overlooking Chhattisgarh to about 2,000 ft. around Mandla where the Narmada headstreams converge.[27]

Economically this is on the whole a poor area. Some manganese is worked on the southern Mahadeo flanks, and there is a small coalfield near Chhindwara in the Pench valley. In the Mahadeos the upper Wainganga and Pench valleys widen out into small plains where wheat, jowar, kodon and a little cotton and sugar are grown; elsewhere agriculture is patchy, except in the Burhanpur gap, while on the higher hills to the east shifting cultivation is carried on by the various Gond tribes who have given their name not only to all the area between the Son and Chhattisgarh but (through the Gondwana rocks) to the great ancient landmass which bulks so large in geological history. There is some good grazing, and lumbering is important: the hills still carry much forest, though on their lower skirts this is very open and scrubby, and in many places shifting cultivation has had serious effect. Sal is important in the east, except on the lavas; there is some teak in the west, and bamboos are widespread. The most striking features of the cultural landscape in the tiny towns strung out along the Khandwa–Itarsi railway are timber yards and charcoal kilns. Many Gonds have been trained as forest workers and live with their families (educated by the Forest Department) in about a hundred forest villages, where they grow millets on specially allocated land.

Pachchmarhi is a local hill station; Chhindwara a minor administrative centre. Otherwise there is no urban development worth mentioning, except Khandwa and Burhanpur, and these are really in the Narmada and Tapti Valleys respectively. The whole region is in fact a barrier broken by the two gaps, at Asirgarh and south of Jabalpur.

CHOTA NAGPUR AND THE DAMODAR

(a) *The Plateaus*

East of the ridge separating the Johilla and the Son is a mass of extremely confused hill country around Deogarh (3,365 ft., 1,025 m.) on the very irregular

[27] There is a useful survey in I. Banerjee, 'A preliminary study of the Maikal Plateau' *GRI* 22/4 (1960), 37–50.

Son-Mahanadi watershed. It is formed mainly of Gondwana rocks with patches of Archaeans and Deccan Lavas – the last outposts of these; at Umaria is an extraordinary occurrence of marine Permians, and a tiny coalfield. There is no doubt that geomorphologically this country would be extremely interesting if it were known; but geographically speaking it is *terra incognita*, rocky, jungly, isolated, backward and almost empty.

Beyond the Behar tributary of the Son, however, we have firmer lines: a great rectangle of some 40,000 sq. miles (103,600 km²), mainly Archaean gneisses forming rolling plains, bisected longitudinally by the fault-trough of the Damodar with its Lower Gondwana coal. Most of this area lies in the Chota Nagpur Division of Bihar, which extends beyond it into the Jamshedpur Gap.

The Hazaribagh surface north of Damodar lies at about 1,300 ft. (395 m.). Across it, and slightly diagonal to its east/west extension, runs the Hazaribagh 'Range', really a higher plateau (*c.* 2,000 ft.) with some monadnocks rising to 2,800 ft. (6,100 and 8,535 m.). The plateau on the whole is rather open, and there is a fair amount of cultivation. On the north it falls abruptly, but with many spurs and outliers covered with open jungle, into the Gangetic Plain; to the southeast descent is more gradual and the upper Ajai and Damodar–Jamunia valleys provide routes giving Calcutta access across the plateaus into the Middle Gangetic Plain. In the northeast the Rajmahal Hills, highly dissected basalts of Gondwana age, rise steeply from the alluvium in the Ganga bend. Considering the terrain they are well cultivated and densely peopled; the Santals occupy the broader valleys, keeping large herds of buffaloes in the smaller side-valleys, while farther up the Paharias ('Hillmen') cultivate remarkably steep slopes.

The Damodar basin will be treated separately. South of it lie the Ranchi plateaus, occupied in the west by the *pats*: little mesas, largely basalt, with intricately fretted and extremely steep sides, the relics of a high surface. Some of their flat tops are cultivated, but soils are lateritic and many are practically inaccessible. The main plateaus are at about 2,500, 2,000 and 1,000 ft. (762, 610, 305 m.); the middle one is most extensive, the lowest borders the Subarnarekha. They form open, broadly rolling country, with mature valleys (Sankh, South Koel) bordered by low gullied terraces, which may be due to some rejuvenation or to greater run-off as the forest is cleared. The plateaus are broken by monadnocks, fantastic cones and domes of gneiss 'looking as if they had been exuded from the earth as gigantic bubbles that had become solid instead of bursting'.[28] East of the Subarnarekha the plateau sinks gradually into the deltaic alluvium, and is generally veneered with laterite.

Much of Chota Nagpur, especially perhaps the centre and west, is under forest, which covers about a third of the whole Division. A good deal of it is poor scrub jungle, but almost all has now been taken under government control. Fuel

[28] G. C. Deprée (1868), quoted in P. Dayal, *The Agricultural Geography of Bihar* (London Ph.D. thesis, 1947), 31. There are many geomorphological papers, of very unequal merit, scattered through the Indian journals; see particularly P. Verma, 'Diastrophic forces . . . in the Ranchi Plateau', *IGJ* 36/4 (1961), 123–31.

wood and hard timbers lead in value, but minor forest products, notably lac and tusser (*tasar*) silk, are important, and a little industrial alcohol is distilled from the flowers of the mahua tree. Chota Nagpur produces about half India's lac, but overseas competition, especially from Thailand, and the use of substitutes have led to a decline in the industry. Bamboo and *sabai* grass for paper, pit-props for the coalfields, are also important. But agriculture is far from negligible.

Soils, indeed, are for the most part thin and poor – sandy or clayey red soils on the gneisses, badly leached and deficient in organic material (except in forest clearings), nitrogen and lime. In enclosed fields around the villages, however, even these upland soils, highly if erratically manured, can give two crops a year – often maize followed by rabi mustard. On the slopes, terracing for paddy catches the soil-wash, checking erosion and retaining subsoil water. Rainfall would seem adequate, but the long dry season is a limiting factor. Only the northern fringe of the Hazaribagh plateau and the lowest part of the Damodar basin receive less than 50 in. (1,270 mm.) and the higher plateaus south and west of Ranchi have over 60 in. (1,524 mm.); 85–90% falls in the monsoon months, but in the southeast 5 in. or so falls during March through May, a continuation of the Bengal régime. Less than a third of the area is cropped, and of this only about 15% is irrigated, more on the plateau fringe than on the plateau itself. There, much of the rice itself is not irrigable, and there is a certain precariousness. Rice, however, is spreading, and only in the westernmost District, Palamau, does it fall below 60% of the NSA; but only in the extreme east is rice over 80% of NSA, and only here is NSA more than 40% of the total area. Maize, gram and oilseeds are the next most important crops, and all are obviously stronger in the west.

As in the adjacent lowlands of Bengal, the west at least has a three crop year, *bhadai*, *aghani* and rabi, of which the first is far the most important, except in Santal Parganas and Purulia (formerly Manbhum and now in West Bengal). Rabi is relatively unimportant as it needs deep moisture-retaining soils, while in the Ranchi and Hazaribagh plateaus perhaps two-thirds of the cultivated area is *tanr* or dry upland. Owing to the small proportion of cropped area, pressure on the land is almost as severe as on the plains: Saran, in the Ganga–Ghaghra angle, has a density of 1,343, Hazaribagh only 340 ; but the density per square miles of TSA is much the same – in the 1200s – for each. In the more forested areas density is below 300, on the denuded plateaus, where villages are mainly at valley-heads or on the divides, it is between 300 and 400, rising to 400 or 600 on the plateau margins towards the Ganga. Forest occupations afford some relief to population pressure, and so does mining, but the dry weather remains a time of agricultural idleness.[29] Many cultivators find work in Damodar mines or Hooghlyside factories, but this male emigration raises new social problems.

Chota Nagpur Division has by far the most important mineral concentrations

[29] Studies of the rhythm of life in Chota Nagpur will be found in A. Geddes, *Comptes Rendus du Congrès Internationale de Géographie*, Amsterdam (1948), Sec. III, *c.*, 365–80.

of India. Apart, however, from the Hazaribagh mica and Damodar coal, most of the mining localities lie south of the Jamshedpur saddle and will be there treated (below, pp. 637-8).[30] Recently, however, the great reserves of bauxite in the laterites of the *pat* country have been exploited; the metre gauge railway from Lohardaga takes the bauxite to the smelter at Muri, south of the Damodar. There are also large limestone deposits in Palamau.

By far the most important mineral (reserving Damodar coal for separate treatment) is the mica. The deposits occur in the dissected northern fringe of the Hazaribagh plateau, in pegmatite veins in a discontinuous belt of Dharwarian rocks. Much of the production is from primitive digging following the better veins into the hillside, and often 'picking the eyes out'. Transport is poor, the mica belt being barely skirted at one end by the railway to Gaya and having little internal communication except unmetalled tracks. In the smaller mines, working conditions are extremely poor, the miners' temporary camps being mere barracks in the jungle; owing to waterlogging, bad roads and the return of the workers to their fields, work practically ceases in the rains. The labour situation is difficult, workers being often lorried from a considerable distance. Improved methods are being introduced, however, and perhaps a third of the output now comes from about a dozen relatively large mines.

India is the world's leading mica producer, and Bihar accounts for 40–50% of her output; production is increasing, and there may be scope for the making of mica bricks for the new steel works. The number of miners is now under 20,000, processing workers at least thrice as many; the 'factories' are usually tiny workshops. Here the large supply of female and child labour is an asset on the splitting and dressing side: wages are lower than for almost any other occupation, except perhaps *bidi* making, but the work is not strenuous and can be done at any time. No machine yet devised equals the skill of the women and children of Hazaribagh, who are said to split sheets to 1/1000th of an inch. On their fingers the electrical industries of the world largely depend, even if decreasingly as substitutes develop.[31]

Away from the coalfield there are no large towns in Chota Nagpur except Ranchi (140,253), the educational and administrative centre of the Division, with some tourist trade, a lac research station, workshops producing lacquered toys and trinkets, and now a large Central Government plant for heavy industrial equipment. An electric porcelain factory is to be established.[32]

[30] At this point the path of the regional geographer is exceptionally hard. There is much to be said for detaching the Jamshedpur area from its somewhat anomalous 'Mahanadi annex' region and taking it in with Chota Nagpur; or conversely, for treating Chota Nagpur in the chapter devoted to the Peninsular interior. The major physiographic trends point one way, the developing economic integration another, and both paths are made thorny by the political divisions. The solution adopted may be unsatisfactory, but it seems likely that any alternative would be no less bothersome.

[31] Details from S. A. Majid, *The Industrial Geography of Bihar* (London Ph.D. thesis, 1949), Chapter VI, and P. P. Karan, 'The Bihar mica belt', *NGJI* 4/1 (1958), 16–34.

[32] See R. L. Singh and B. Mukherjee, 'Functional zones of Ranchi', *ibid.* 3/3-4 (1957), 117-24.

(b) *The Damodar Valley* (Fig. 21.7)

The Damodar basin occupies only a small area, some 7,500 sq. miles (19,425 km²), but its human significance is immense. In the past this has been expressed positively by its use as a railway corridor and the production from its down-faulted basins of the great bulk of India's coal; negatively by the devastation brought to West Bengal by its frequent floods. These are the natural consequence of the convergence of drainage from the impervious crystallines of the plateaus into the narrow bottleneck at Asansol, and of the right-angled bend where the lower Damodar emerges on to the plains near Burdwan; but they have been much aggravated by deforestation and soil erosion. The Damodar Valley Authority has set out to transform this negative into a positive by an integrated approach to the problem – afforestation, dams, power and irrigation developments.

The Gondwana rocks of the basin form generally low undulating terrain. The main stream runs west–east, providing a col at a little over 1,500 ft. (455 m.) into the North Koel valley; the railway through this Chandwa gap, however, is of small significance except to the little industrial concentration in the Son valley (above, p. 631). But the larger tributaries, all on the left bank, provide routes cutting across the great arc formed by the Ganga. The watershed between the parallel Ajai and Damodar is a mere height of land, and this interfluve is fol-lowed by a railway with a branch to the small coalfield at Giridih in the valley of the Barakar. This, the largest Damodar feeder, is followed by a road only; but east of the isolated peak of Parasnath (4,480 ft., 1,365 m.; a Jain sanctuary) the Jamunia opens a direct line, across the upper Barakar, from Calcutta to Gaya and Patna: this is used by the 'Grand Chord' railway line and the old Grand Trunk Road. Southeast again the Bokaro enables the east–west railway to avoid a jungly stretch along the Damodar and to open up the Bokaro field; and to the south, the recession of the Ranchi plateau scarps gives easy access to the Subarnarekha and Jamshedpur. The west of the Damodar basin, around Tori and the Karanpura coalfields, is as yet undeveloped jungle country.

The Coalfields.[33] The coal is preserved, thanks to displacements which are of the order of 5,000–9,000 ft. (1,525–2,745 m.) along the southern flank of the basin. The measures are little folded or faulted, though in the east they have been adversely affected by ultra-basic dykes and sills; seams are up to 30 ft. thick and working is generally too easy, facilitating very wasteful early exploitation; sand stowage to replace most of the coal removed is now necessary to prevent roof col-lapse and excessive ground subsidence over the thicker seams. The coal is sub-bituminous to bituminous, but often with rather high ash content and friable. The best coking coals are in the Barakar seams on the Jharia field; although reserves as a whole are good, some anxiety is felt as to future coke supplies (above, pp. 283–6).

After an abortive beginning as early as 1774–75, production in Raniganj, the

[33] Again following Majid, Chapter 5.

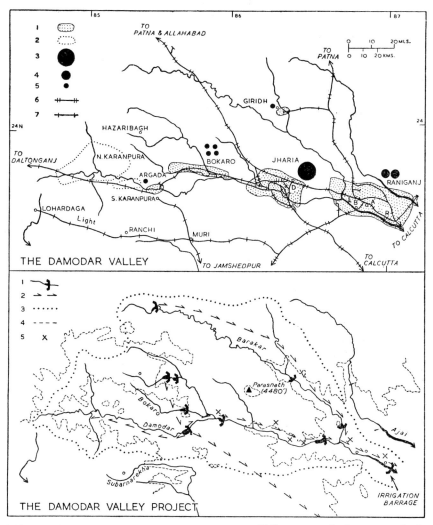

FIG 21.7 THE DAMODAR VALLEY AND PROJECT. Valley: 1, worked, 2, unworked, coalfields; 3–5, approx. order of magnitude and of annual output of coalfields; 6, BGDT; 7, BGST (except light Lohardaga line). D, Dhanbad; B, Barakar; A, Asansol; R, Raniganj.

Project: 1, dams and reservoirs; 2, power transmission lines; 3, Damodar watershed; 4, contours at 200 and 500 metres; 5, thermal electric stations (installations under 1, 2 and 5 all projected or building).

Based on maps and text in S. A. Majid, *The Industrial Geography of Bihar* (thesis, 1949), and S. C. Bose, *The Damodar Valley Project* (Calcutta, 1948).

first field to be opened, has been continuous since 1815. But it was negligible until the railway development after the Mutiny, and it was not until the real beginning of modern industry in the 1890s that production reached considerable figures: in 1900 Indian production, over 90% from the Damodar, was 6,000,000 tons. The two wars and the establishment of Tata's iron and steel works provided further stimuli: Jamshedpur alone now takes over 1,000,000 tons. On the Raniganj and Jharia fields, almost alone in India away from the greater cities, there is a real industrial landscape: collieries with their attendant spoil heaps and many subsidence flashes, the irregular and squalid settlements of the miners, a dense rail and road net, ropeways bringing sand from the Damodar for stowage and for sealing-off fires by surface spreading.

The most important problem facing the industry is probably labour. The labour force fluctuates widely from year to year and also – more significantly – with the seasons: most of the colliers are still cultivators as well. Normally seed-time and harvest spell absenteeism: coal raisings in slack agricultural months exceed those in the planting season (June–July) by 30–50%; and it is only in years of deficient rainfall that labour is abundant for the mines. The human price for economic advance has been shamefully high. Most of the miners were tribesmen (Bauro or Santals) who were said, probably with truth, to be reluctant to leave their wives at the surface, and in some cases to have two: a butty in the pit and a housewife at home, which is presumably a long way off. Casual absenteeism and sickness take a great toll; the average miner is a miner for only about 190 days in the year. But if the indiscipline of the tribal workers inhibits reasonable working of the mines, it also militates against any organization of their own, and working and housing conditions (a few very recent model pits and villages apart) remain appalling. Output per worker is naturally very low, about half that in Britain; mechanization is hampered by lack of capital, the general backwardness of many mines (especially perhaps on the conveyance side), and the fact that labour is after all cheap on a short view.

The general technical level is not high; wastage, bad stowage, avoidable fires, robber exploitation of the best seams, poor grading, are prominent features, though they are decreasing. Concessions were farmed out by *zamindars* to small and under-capitalized operators, and as in agriculture, uneconomic fragmentation was rife. Units remain very scattered, although there is an increasing dominance by the Public Sector, the National Coal Development Corporation assuming direct responsibility for new or smaller mines.

Until recently industrial development, other than that strictly connected with coal exploitation, was limited to an iron and steel plant at Burnpur, the manufacture of firebricks, mainly at Mugma on the Jharia field, and glass, located here because of accessible fuel and refractories, and proximity to Calcutta for sales and for the import of soda ash. But the war and Independence have brought expansion of far more than local significance: the first developments were aluminium at Muri, fertilizers at Sindri, locomotive works at Chittaranjan, and now India's fourth integrated steel plant is going up at Bokara, west of Jharia. Muri draws its bauxite from the Lohardaga *pat* country 75 miles (121 km.) to the east, and the alumina produced goes to Alwaye in Kerala and Hirakud in Orissa, where ample hydro-electricity is available to produce the high temperatures needed for smelting. Expansion of the aluminium industry is limited by the water supply, but a new smelter-refiner is under construction at Purulia, quite near to Muri. Sindri draws its gypsum mainly from Khewra in Rajasthan; the industry is expanding to produce superphosphate as well as ammonium sulphate, to help in meeting a national demand approaching 2,000,000 tons a year.[34] Some of the phosphatic component is supplied by local apatite mining in Singhbum District, but the bulk is imported. The firebrick industry at Jharia has greatly expanded, and Dhanbad has a small lead/zinc refinery as well as hand tool and radio assembly plants.

The towns, once mainly colliery and communications centres, are becoming increasingly diversified industrially. The Dhanbad–Jharia–Sindri town group had 200,618 people in 1961, and Asansol, in West Bengal, had doubled itself since 1951, to reach 168,689.

The Damodar Corporation.[35] This project was one of the first undertaken by independent India, but has to some extent been overshadowed by other great works such as Bhakra and Hirakud. The objective was threefold: flood control, irrigation, power. The first was intimately linked with reafforestation and small-scale 'gully-plugging' dams, as well as controlling access and burning in the existing forests. A large area on the lower reaches of the Damodar, on the margins of the Bengal Delta, is being irrigated from a weir between Raniganj and Burdwan, and there is a complex system of hydro- and thermal-electric stations in the upper basin, including a big thermal station at Bokaro. The scheme, however, has met with difficulties, not the least being friction between Bihar and West Bengal on the allocation of costs, responsibilities and benefits, and the states have now taken over responsibility for most functions except electricity generation and transmission.

THE TAPTI VALLEY

The valley[36] is essentially a transitional zone between central India and the Deccan: Khandesh was not infrequently a debatable land between Malwa and Maharashtra. Physically the region falls into two parts: the main Tapti trough continued in that of the Purna, and the upper Tapti valley in its northeast-southwest course through the Burhanpur gap. But the east/west climatic division is of more significance.

[34] See O. H. K. Spate, 'Konarak and Sindri: fertility ancient and modern', *Let Me Enjoy* (Australian National Univ., Canberra, 1965), 15–32.

[35] S. C. Bose, *The Damodar Valley Project* (Phoenix, Calcutta, 1948); W. Kirk, 'The Damodar Valley – "Valles Opima"', *GR* 40 (1950), 415–43; R. M. Gorrie, 'The DVC's forestry task', *Empire Forestry Rev.* 33 (1954), 228–33; H. C. Hart, *New India's Rivers* (Orient Longmans, Bombay, 1956), Chapters 4 and 5 – an optimistic view.

[36] See C. D. Deshpande, *Western India* (Dharwar, 1948), 148–54.

The main valley floor lies at 600–900 ft. (185–275 m.), with the river itself entrenched as much as 50–60 ft. (15–18 m.) below. To the north the steep face of the Satpuras and (in the Purna valley) the Gawilgarh Hills mark it off sharply, except at the Burhanpur gap; to the south the Sahyadriparvat or Ajanta Hills are set farther back, but no less boldly formed, except in the southwest where there is a gentle rise, in the Girna valley, to the little gap-town of Manmad; but here, on the Malegaon plateau, we are on the threshold of the open plains of Nasik in the upper Godavari basin.

The entire area, except for the alluvial filling of the trough, is Deccan Lava country. Rainfall is 40 in. (1,016 mm.) on the western margin, but falls below 25 in. (635 mm.) in East Khandesh (now Jalgaon District), where variability is over 25% and agriculture not too secure, despite the presence of moisture-retaining regur. Jowar is the main crop, with bajra, pulses and oilseeds, including groundnuts; cotton, no longer dominant, is still significant. Rice is negligible. There is a distinct difference between the moister, but hillier and more forested, east and the more open plains of the west, where cotton becomes more prominent until in Amraoti District – perhaps really regionally, as well as politically, Maharashtrian – it exceeds 40% of NSA.

The margins of the area are poorer; in the Burhanpur gap villages are few and far between and there is rather broken country with light woodland; the Malegaon plateau in the southwest is dryish, with much grass, thorny scrub and big masses of euphorbia; here cultivation is confined to valley-bottoms below the marked break of slope at the foot of the lava mesas, and is aided by well irrigation.

But on the whole the heart of the region is flourishing enough. This is perhaps in part due to the emphasis on cash crops, cotton and oilseeds amounting to a third or more of the cropped area. This emphasis was fostered by the good rail connection with Bombay, and has led to the growth of a cotton industry. Settlement avoids the entrenched banks of the lower Tapti, but on the broad valley-floor is a remarkable concentration of small towns and large compact villages, often walled and looking like little forts, a reminder of the marchland role of Khandesh which is most strikingly displayed in the enormous fortress at Asirgarh on its spur overlooking the railway through the Burhanpur gap. Railway towns like Akola (1961: 115,760), Amraoti (137,875), Dhulia (98,893), and Jalgaon (80,351) in Maharashtra and Burhanpur (82,090) in Madhya Pradesh have developed into minor commercial centres with some textile industry. The lower Tapti itself, though followed by a railway, is now of little importance, the trade which once went down it to Surat having long ago been drawn to Bombay. Even the Lower Tapti irrigation and power project is to benefit mainly the coastal tracts. But the importance of the area as the vestibule into the Deccan from Malwa, lying athwart the routes from Bombay into its northern hinterland, remains a significant feature of its life.

BIBLIOGRAPHICAL NOTE

The main sources have been indicated in the text. There may be added: for Rajasthan, B. Ghose and A. K. Sen, 'Some preliminary observations on the geomorphology of the Lower Luni Basin', *GRI* 23/4 (1961), 47–54; for Malwa, A. C. Mayer, *Caste and Kinship in Central India* (Univ. of California, Berkeley, 1960); for Madhya Pradesh, the *Techno-Economic Survey of Madhya Pradesh* (Asia, Bombay, 1960) contains a wealth of detail; for Chota Nagpur, E. Ahmad, 'The rural population of Bihar', *GR* 51 (1961), 253–76, is important. Ahmad's *Bihar: A Physical, Economic, and Regional Geography* (Ranchi University, 1965), despite some bibliographical omissions, sets a new standard in State geographies.

CHAPTER 22

The Western Littoral
(Regions XX–XXIV)

The west coast of India has been historically the most active, partly for reasons inherent in its own nature – a coast with numerous havens, creek or roadstead, a narrow immediate hinterland with a few well-defined routes into the interior – and partly by virtue of its location facing the intercontinental nodes of southwest Asia. Maritime activity goes back to the beginnings of history, and this was the first part of India to receive the attention of Renaissance Europe; indeed some fragments of the Portuguese empire here survived the British. But, in contrast to the east coast, geographical and political factors impeded territorial expansion, and the development by Dutch and British of more southerly routes from the Cape of Good Hope led to a relative decline as against the Bengal entry. Later the cotton boom of the American Civil War (1861–65) brought a few years of very rapid development, and the ensuing slump was followed closely by the opening of the Suez Canal (1869), which revived the older locational values.

The whole area falls into five major regions: Kutch and Kathiawad; Gujarat; the Konkan; Goa and Kanara; Kerala. Of these Goa and Kanara form a distinctive transitional zone between the Konkan and Kerala; Kerala itself is more or less coterminous with the Malabar coast, and as the region coincides with the new state of Kerala, it seems preferable to use the local name which is standard among Indian geographers. The Western Ghats are treated in the next chapter, but as their seaward scarps are intimately connected with the lowland beneath them, some reference to them is essential here.

The coast in general

As we have seen (Chapter 1), subsidence on a macro-regional scale and at a late date seem necessary to account for the hydrography of the Ghats, with an almost total absence of large-scale river capture in conditions apparently exceedingly favourable to it. Except just south of Goa the great fault-line scarp of the Ghats is continued as a remarkably sharp feature on the Archaeans, and although the watershed recedes in places from the coast, so also do the Ghats: watershed and crest are never very far apart except in the break south of Goa. The old theory, still in some vogue in India, that the Ghats are old sea-cliffs can hardly survive examination of large-scale maps; nevertheless the coast has some difficult complexities. South of the Goa–Kanara transitional zone there is not much difficulty: the land is obviously in ascendant. But the Konkan coast appears to suggest a plane of marine erosion, with bevelled surfaces in Deccan Lava surmounted by isolated hills which look very much like old offshore islands. On the other hand the submerged forest at Bombay and the ria-like appearance of the Deccan Lava coast strongly suggest recent depression; though there is also the low platform of littoral concrete seen on the western side of Bombay Island, at Bandra Head, and other places, and there has been sufficient stability to allow great mangrove-flats to grow up behind the bayhead bars.

Summing up the scattered pieces of evidence we seem to have: some sub-mergence in the north (Cambay submerged forest) but a seawards advance of the land (Rann mudflats, linking of Kathiawad with mainland, miliolite belt on south coast); continuing earth movements in five earthquakes between 1819 and 1876; prograding shores of the Gulf of Cambay; in the Konkan macro-regional subsidence of Arabian Sea, emergence of plane of marine erosion, with some sinking followed by a still-stand as the latest phases (not excluding minor oscillations); a 'hinge' around Goa; possible uplift assisted by prograding on a low shoreline of emergence in the south.

That movements of these types in the various regions have taken place is obvious from the map, but in the absence of any precise data as to levels and sequences it is impossible to attempt to trace their origins and history, whether mainly isostatic or eustatic. The sagging which would appear natural as a result of the weighty outpourings of Deccan Lavas would seem too early (Eocene);[1] the macro-faulting *might* be associated with the Miocene Himalayan orogeny, but the problem of the Ghats watershed suggests a very late date; in the south the uplift might be connected with the punching-up of the Nilgiri, Anamalai-Palani, and Ceylon horsts, if that be indeed their origin.

KUTCH AND KATHIAWAD

The quadrilateral of some 46,000 sq. miles (119,000 km²) between the Rann of Kutch and the Gulf of Cambay is a world apart; and this is, of course, especially true of Kutch.[2] The Rann is a vast expanse of naked tidal mudflats, a black desolation flecked with saline efflorescences, or the sudden flights of great flocks of flamingos; here and there the banks of dead creeks are picked out in a white skeletal outline of salt or scum. To the north the desert of mud and the desert of sand in the Thar merge almost imperceptibly. The normal dendritic pattern of the creeks has been interrupted by earthquakes, notably that of 1819 which interrupted the old Indus distributaries into the Rann by the formation of a

---

[1] But Sahni, on the evidence of the flora of some intra-lava beds, would place much of the extrusion in the Miocene.

[2] The arrangement of this section is my own, but the facts are mainly from C. D. Deshpande, *Western India* (Dharwar, 1948), 208–22.

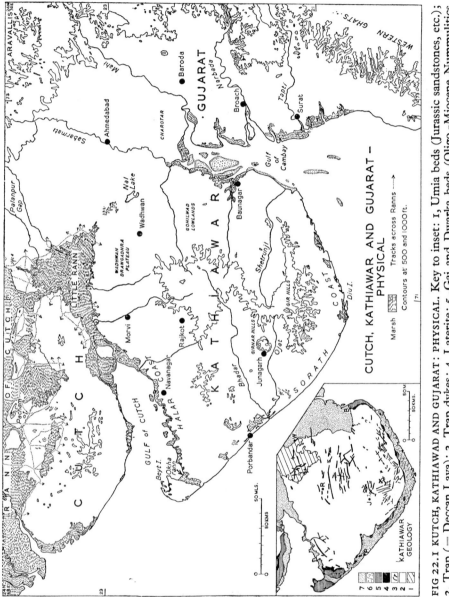

FIG 22.1 KUTCH, KATHIAWAD AND GUJARAT: PHYSICAL. Key to inset: 1, Umia beds (Jurassic sandstones, etc.); 2, Trap (= Deccan Lava); 3, Trap dykes; 4, Laterite; 5, Gaj and Dwarka beds (Oligo.-Miocene Nummulitics and clays); 6, Miliolite; 7, Alluvium.

fault-scarp 10–18 ft. high and some 50 miles long, the Allah Bund ('God's Dyke'). Yet isolation is not complete nor the waste entirely trackless.[3]

To the east there is no such barrier: gas seepages and oil exploration on the Cambay shores suggest that the Gulf was part of the Sind depositional area in the late Tertiary, and Kathiawad may have been semi-insular as late as the 17th century.[4] But prolonged silting by the mainland rivers[5] and tectonic uplift have attached it to the mainland, despite very high tidal ranges in the Gulf. The old channel (doubtless tidal or seasonal) joining the Little Rann (southeast of Kutch) and the Gulf of Cambay is marked by the lakes and marshes of the Nal depression. Entry was easiest in the north, by the low plateau between Drangadhra and Wadhwan, the latter anciently a fortified strategic centre and still of trading importance owing to its rail nodality.

Physique, climate, vegetation

Within this framework of sea and marsh the broad outlines of relief and geology are simple enough, but the detail complex. Kutch has a discontinuous backbone (up to 900–1,100 ft., 275–335 m.) of Jurassic–Miocene rocks, mainly sandstones with intrusive and interbedded basalts, flanked by alluvial and aeolian deposits; the highest point (1,525 ft., 465 m.) lies away to the north on Pachham Island in the Rann. Physically it is an alternation of little flat-topped steep-edged plateaus, much dissected round the margins, and tiny alluvial basins. The Rann itself appears to be a broken anticline.[6]

The great mass of Kathiawad is formed of sheets of Deccan Lava intersected by swarms of trap dykes (Fig. 22.1, inset); in the north the Drangadhra–Wadhwan Plateau is mostly sandstone of Jurassic age. Except in the north the basalt platform is flanked by younger rocks – Tertiary clays and sandy limestones in the extreme west (Dwarka) and east (Bhavnagar), and between these a belt 20–30 miles (32–48 km.) wide, of alluvium and miliolite. This latter is a wind-blown sand, largely formed of foraminiferal casts, in a calcareous matrix; at Junagadh, 30 miles inland, it is 200 ft. (61 m.) thick. It is an attractive building-stone, creamy-white and easily worked, and is exported as 'Porbandar stone'. The actual edge of the lavas is marked by a discontinuous strip of laterite, and there is of course a good deal of alluvium. Most of Kathiawad lies below 600 ft. (185 m.), but there are two hill-masses, east of Rajkot in the north (1,100 ft., 335 m.) and the higher and bolder Gir Range (up to 2,100 ft., 640 m.) in the south. These two dissected plateaus have a perfect radial drainage pattern; they

[3] See the splendid description in E. Reclus, *L'Inde* (Nouvelle Géographie Universelle, Tome VIII, 1883), 226–9.

[4] D. N. Wadia, *Geology of India* (Macmillan, London, 3rd ed. revised, 1961), 308; *Bombay Gaz.* (1909), II. 346.

[5] '... currents setting into the Gulf of Cambay prevent the free movements of Narbada and Tapti silt out of the gulf.' A. N. Harris, 'Factors controlling port-sites [in] Western India', *Geography*, 18 (1933), 118–25.

[6] R. K. Shah *et al.*, 'Possibilities of the reclamation of the alkaline soils of the Little Rann', *Jnl Soil and Water Cons. India*, 6/3 (1958), 132–7.

are linked by a narrow and sinuous neck over 600 ft., separating the two major rivers of Kathiawad, the Bhadar flowing west and the Shetrunji east. A few miles west of this watershed rises the remarkable circular group of the Girnar Hills culminating in Goraknath, the highest point of Kathiawad (3,666 ft., 1,117 m.). This igneous complex (gabbros, diorites, and syenites) seems to be intruded through the Deccan Lavas, but from the same magmatic reservoir.

Despite the areal preponderance of the lavas, the numerous dykes and the fairly wide range of younger rocks, with aeolian and alluvial deposits, introduce considerable local diversity of terrain, soils and hydrology. The environment is generally arid enough, but the region lies between the dry shores of Sind and the fluctuating flank of the Arabian Sea branch of the monsoon, and there is some climatic variation. Kutch averages 12–15 in. (305–381 mm.) and as little as 1·4 have been recorded; from the air the arid aspect of its erosional features is striking. The Kathiawad coastlands, except in the southwest, receive 15–20 in., but the highland centre and the Cambay coast have over 25 and Junagadh, lying close under the western side of the Girnar Hills, about 40 (381–505, 635, 1,016 mm.). The rainfall is precarious, variability being everywhere over 50%. Mean temperatures run high, 80–85° F. in January and 90–95° in May (27–29 and 32–35° C.) when mean maxima are around 110°, 43·3° C. The natural cover of most of the region is dry thorn forest, very open and stunted, with small patches of dry deciduous on the Gir and Girnar Hills; on the north coast of Kathiawad and in Kutch the scrub breaks down into poor grass and bush, almost desert in places. Mangroves are exploited for fuel along the coast. The Kutch Desert Immobilization Scheme was begun in 1956 to halt the expansion of the desert through overgrazing and salt infiltration, by means of wasteland and roadside afforestation with *Prosopis juliflora* and *Acaciaa catechu*, and rotational grazing in demonstration areas.[7] In the Gir forest the lion, extinct in the rest of India, survives, thanks to state protection.

Agriculture

Over most of the region agriculture is naturally dominant, but in Kutch it shades off into a semi-pastoral economy. Water is of course the primary determinant of agriculture, but the influence of terrain in the narrower sense is often striking: much of the land is waste not only on the hills but also, at least in the north of Kathiawad, along the streams, the banks of which are often badly gullied on the plateau and marshy, often saline, farther down. The larger blocks of cultivation are thus often located at the foot of the ridges or low plateaus, or on the broader interfluves. Altogether about 50–60% of Kathiawad is cropped, no small proportion given the low and unreliable rainfall, and obviously possible only by careful exploitation of all available sources of water. There are no large irrigation

[7] N. J. Joshi, 'The Cutch Desert Immobilization Scheme', *Indian Forester* (Dehra Dun), 85/1 (1959), 43–50.

works in this area which, until very recently, was split up among scores of statelets; but tanks, valley-bunds and especially wells are used. Wells are often aligned along the dykes in the Deccan Lavas; in some cases the intrusive traps

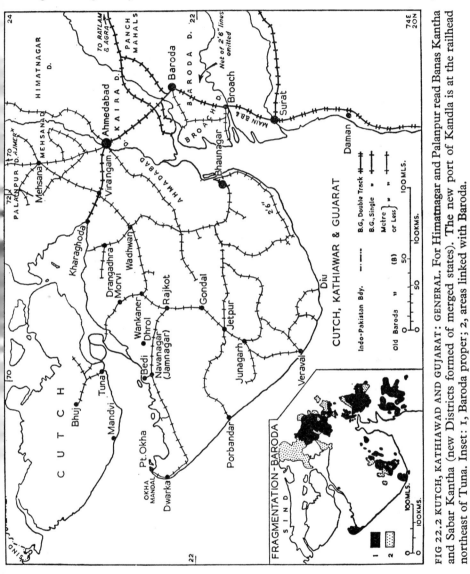

FIG 22.2 KUTCH, KATHIAWAR AND GUJARAT: GENERAL. For Himatnagar and Palanpur read Banas Kantha and Sabar Kantha (new Districts formed of merged states). The new port of Kandla is at the railhead northeast of Tuna. Inset: 1, Baroda proper; 2, areas linked with Baroda.

are themselves aquifers, but more often perhaps they hold up the movement of water in the country rock, producing local rises in the water-table.

In the east the alluvial Gohilwad lowland along the Nal depression is one of the more favoured areas; the relatively high rainfall (20–25 in., 508–635 mm.)

indeed sometimes causes flooding in this tract where the drainage-lines are obviously impeded by the greater amounts of silt brought down by the mainland rivers. Cotton is the main crop here, followed by millets. Along the Cambay coast ground-water is brackish or saline and soils sandy; but inland large areas are devoted to bajra, wheat, cotton and jowar. On the Drangadhra–Wadhwan plateau cotton covers nearly half the cultivated area and jowar a quarter; here over 60% of the area is cultivated. The southern coast (Sorath) is very unequal in agricultural potentialities; rich where alluvial, it is poor on the laterites and miliolites. Casuarinas (for fuel) and coconuts are important here. Around the lower courses of the Bhadar and Ojat are large areas of salt marsh, but above them the *gher* or 'sweet water' lands raise rich crops of jowar and bajra, cotton and oilseeds. The Bhadar basin is perhaps the richest agricultural area of Kathiawad, owing largely to the regur soils and the numerous dykes: cotton, oilseeds, jowar are the chief crops.

Dwarka and the Halar coast in the north represent a transition to definitely marginal agriculture. Dwarka, almost cut off by the Okha Rann, is formed largely of clays and marls with higher limestone areas; soils are light, rainfall poor, and under a third of the land is cultivated, mainly to bajra and the rest jowar. The Halar is mainly marshy creeklands or dry thin-soiled interfluves; millets and oilseeds are grown, but pastoral activities tend to be more important than tillage. In Kutch these tendencies are accentuated; there are belts of irrigated alluvium (wheat and cotton), but livestock are more important, especially in the arid Banni country in the north; Kutch is, or at least was, noted for its breeds of horses and camels. Holdings in the light sandy soils are large, but in any one year about half lie fallow, and the land actually cropped is less than a fifth of the total area. There is a constant search for new water supplies, so far largely unsuccessful, partly on account of costs. Drinking water comes from wells 30–40 ft. (9–12 m.) deep; artesian water is too saline, streams only seasonal, shallow wells short-lived.[8]

Villages over much of Kathiawad are strongly nucleated and tend to be large, sited on rises, bluffs along the valleys, hill-foot fans, or river crossings. In Halar and Kutch, however, they are often mere hamlets, and great stock corrals are prominent features of the cultural landscape.

General development: towns

Kutch is now a District of Gujarat. Density is only 41, and the only places of any importance are Mandvi port (26,609 – a fall of 7% since 1951) and the capital, Bhuj (40,180), which has a light railway to the tiny port of Tuna. The most interesting thing about Kutch culturally is the eclectic attitude of its Rajput tribe, which has evolved a curiously distorted mixture of Hinduism and Islam.

Kathiawad is very different. Until the formation in 1948 of the Union of

[8] R. K. Shah *et al., loc. cit.*

Saurashtra it was politically the most fragmented portion of India,[9] with 86 distinct territorial units (including en- and ex-claves) on 21,451 sq. miles (55,555 km²); on the south coast Portugal held three villages and the little island of Diu, useless but treasured for the memory of the defence against the Sultan of Gujarat. All are now part of Gujarat State. Lying off the main routes of war and trade in India, Kathiawad has been a land of refuge, but its peninsular situation has invited overseas contacts – Arabs, Portuguese, even Africans.

The almost incredible *morcellement* of Kathiawad obviously impeded any really well-found development, administrative or economic; Junagadh, the largest state by both area and population, had only 3,337 sq. miles (8,643 km²) and 670,719 people in 1941. On the other hand, the administrative demands of the half-dozen or so larger states, and their desire to cut some small figure in the world, led to an urbanization nearly double that of all-India (33·8% against 17·3% in 1951), some local industry, some port activity, and a fairly close net of metre railways. Following the merging of the states, many of the former petty capitals are now in decline.[10] Industries include quarrying of Porbandar stone, cotton textiles (especially at Bhavnagar), leather, matches, potteries, cement and chemicals, the last two particularly at Dwarka, with accessible salt and limestone; here Tatas manufacture soda ash, bleaching powder and hydrochloric acid.

Minor ports, as is natural in a peninsula of such dimensions, have been of great importance; but they are now overshadowed by the growth of Port Okha and Bhavnagar at the extremities of the peninsula. Bhavnagar (176,473) is situated where firm ground abuts on its creek, and is not so liable to silting as ports farther up or across the Cambay Gulf, but the main anchorage is 8 miles away; small coasting steamers can lie on the mud in the creek itself. Local cotton and oilseeds provide the staple exports and some industry. Okha, when a far-flung exclave of Baroda, was developed by that state. It is completely modern in equipment, if on a modest scale, and is a useful entrepôt. The war years saw a sharp decline, but the unification of most of its hinterland augurs well for its future as the outlet for most of Kathiawad, although for wider relations it suffers from isolation. Cement exports account for about half the total volume of trade; cotton, oilseeds and salt are also exported; imports are mainly oil, sugar, china clay, textiles, construction and transport material. The only other port which calls for mention is Bedi, a few miles from Jamnagar town, and little more than a tidal basin with warehouses and a railway. Bedi and other 'ports' of the Halar coast are handicapped by the low marshy shores and shallow waters of the Rann of Kutch, and also by the development of the Wadhwan–Rajkot–Okha railway which takes traffic out east and west. They are in fact mere break-of-bulk points for goods lightered to shipping in the roadsteads; all commercial functions are carried out at the inland centres. But a

[9] Cf. Fig. 15 (p. 154) in W. G. East and O. H. K. Spate (eds.), *The Changing Map of Asia* (Methuen, London, 4th ed. 1961).
[10] Personal information from Dr C. D. Deshpande.

new port has been developed at Kandla (Kutch) to relieve Bombay of the added burden of East Punjab trade diverted from Karachi.[11]

Of the inland marts the largest and most important is Jamnagar (148,572), capital of the old Navanagar state. Of its older crafts dyeing has survived, and some new light industries have been added; but it is more important as a commercial centre. Morvi (50,192) is the centre of an important cotton tract on the Drangadhra–Wadhwan Plateau, Wadhwan (27,104) the main point of entry on the Gujarat side. Rajkot (194,145), though commercially limited by the competition of Jamnagar and Gondal on either hand, remains an important administrative centre. On the south coast the little ports – Porbandar (75,081, noted for its excellent building stone), Veraval (60,857), Mahuva (32,732), are somewhat overshadowed by Okha and Bhavnagar, except perhaps for Mahuva, but there are a number of flourishing inland centres, generally on defensible sites of past strategic significance; the most important is Junagadh town (74,298), the centre of the Bhadar basin.

THE GUJARAT PLAINS

Gujarat might almost be described as an intrusion of Indo-Gangetic conditions into the Peninsula: a great tract of alluvium formed by the Sabarmati, Mahi and minor parallel streams, actively prograding into the Gulf of Cambay. Historically it was for long periods a flourishing independent kingdom, controlling the seaward terminals of the great Cambay-Agra route and marked off from Malwa by the dissected jungly country where the Aravallis and the Deccan Lavas break down into the plain: this zone has been a minor shatter-belt, as shown by the very numerous 'states' and statelets (down to a population of 96 and areas of a square mile!) which existed before 1948; all are now part of Gujarat State, except the former Portuguese Damão and its enclaves, now the Union territory of Daman, Dadra and Nagar Haveli. Northwards the limits of the region lie in the Palanpur gap between the Aravallis and the Ranns; southwards the impingement of the Deccan Lavas on the coast is taken as the boundary with the Konkan.

Climate and agriculture

Physically there is little for comment. The region falls into three north/south belts: the alluvial piedmont (above 200 ft., 61 m.) between the highland and the plain; the coastal marshes; and between them the great shelf of firm alluvium, some 250 miles long and up to 60 wide (400 by 95 km.). This is of course the main agricultural area; the great estuaries are surrounded by unreclaimed tidal marshes, the east is still largely under dry deciduous jungle, much degraded by the shifting cultivation of tribes such as the Bhils.

Climate is more difficult to evaluate: the region lies in a critical position on the flank of the Arabian Sea branch of the monsoon. Rainfall thus decreases rapidly

[11] S. L. Kayastha, 'Kandla: a study in port development', *NGJI* 9/1 (1963), 12–24.

from 60–70 in. in the extreme south to 41 at Surat and 29 at Ahmedabad (1,524–1,778, 1,041, and 737 mm.); the higher east, of course, receives rather more, but this is offset by the broken terrain and poor soils. Reliability also decreases, and northwest of a line from a little north of the Narmada mouth past Ahmedabad variability is over 30%. Rainfall is often very local and patchy, both at any one time and over a run of years. The village of Atgam, near Bulsar in the south of the region, has about 75 in., but annual falls have varied from 40 to 116 (1,905, 1,016 and 2,946 mm.). Here even 48 in. can give good crops if well distributed seasonally; but the right distribution is extremely delicate, as the following table shows:[12]

Period	Desirable Rainfall		Agricultural Work
	in.	mm.	
June 13–20	8	203	Preparing for sowing
26–30	2	51	Broadcasting paddy
July 1–7	7	178	Growth of seedling paddy
7–15	10	254	Preparing beds for transplanting paddy
15–31	3	76	Transplanting paddy
Aug. 1–31	10	254	Crop growth
Sept. 1–30	10	254	Crop growth, and rabi planting
Oct. 1–31	2	51	Rabi crops

This is of course a minimum demand; but the point is that even with a normal total for the year, maldistribution in the growing months may be disastrous; and in fact at Atgam good, fair and bad years are equally common. North of the head of the Gulf lies an area traditionally liable to famines; that of 1630–32 was perhaps the worst in all India's long history of such calamities. Flooding is also a risk. Irrigation was mainly in the north, from tanks and wells, but there is a scheme for large-scale irrigation in Kaira, east of Ahmedabad, from the Mahi; and the Kakrapara Canal project on the lower Tapti should irrigate over 500,000 ac. (202,000 ha.) when completed.

In most of the Gujarat plains the NSA covers 60–80% of the area. This is one of the most famous of India's cotton tracts, but the crop is not so dominant as this reputation would suggest: only in Broach and Baroda Districts is it the first ranking crop, with 30–40% of the NSA. Rice is fairly widely grown in the humid south, and in Kaira, where it depends on large tanks, but except in this District it does not reach 20% of the NSA. Bajra and jowar are the most important cereals, with maize towards the north, where in Sabar Kantha (north of Ahmedabad) groundnut is the ranking crop (of many). But the recent development of tubewells is further diversifying the crop pattern, and giving more stability; wheat is replacing bajra near the wells, and tobacco has been introduced. Deshpande

[12] G. C. Mukhtyar, *Life and Labour in a South Gujarat Village* (Bombay, 1930), 26–30.

points out the need for more careful evaluation of groundwater resources if stability is to be maintained.[13] But it will be evident that there are no clear lines, rather a mosaic of differing crop associations dependent on local water-supply, soils and markets, with variable proportion of food and cash crops and of the cereals. The proximity of the Bombay and Ahmedabad markets has also given rise to some dairying, especially in Charotar, probably the richest tract of Gujarat, an area of very fertile and well-watered alluvium between the lower Sabarmati and the Mahi Rivers.

Villages are especially large in Kaira, where their average population in 1931 was 1,027: elsewhere it was 600–700 except in Panch Mahals (in the backward east) where it was under 500. The siting in estuarine areas is typically on low sandy rises, at once dry- and water-points as fresh water is held in the sand above the denser saline ground-water of the marsh. Social factors provide interesting variations: the overwhelmingly Hindu population is much caste-ridden, but the castes fall into two great divisions – Kaliparaj, the 'black races', embracing most of the lower strata, and the socially superior Upaliparaj. The Kaliparaj live in little hamlets (*falias*) of 8–10 houses, lying within three or four miles of the village nucleus, which is very small and inhabited mainly by Upaliparaj. At Atgam 'The vernacular school, patel's office, and the Post Office are located here. In this space are found two grocers' shops and an open space in front of the village where, under a tamarind tree, some villager occasionally sets up a temporary shop selling chillies, onions, garlic and a few vegetables. Here also are seen a temple of Rama and a mosque. On its outskirts to the east dwell the untouchables.' This hamletted occupance is not without advantages in an area where holdings are small and much fragmented, as the average distance from house to field is much shorter than in a nucleated village with the same field and holding pattern. Poorer houses are generally of mud and grass, with thatched roofs; tiles are an indication of individual economic advance.[14]

The industrial towns of Gujarat

Four great towns dominate Gujarat: Ahmedabad, Baroda, Broach, Surat. The last two, in their day the most flourishing ports of India, have long ceased to have any significance as such, but have taken a new lease as minor industrial centres; Baroda owes its importance largely to its former function as a princely capital; the architectural glories of Ahmedabad are now overshadowed by the mills of the largest inland factory city of India.

Ahmedabad (1,206,001, the seventh city of India) was originally a strategic centre, commanding the first easy crossing of the Sabarmati above the Cambay marshes. Under Gujarati Sultans and Mogul viceroys it was one of the most brilliant Indian cities; its magnificent mosques and tombs represent a remarkably

[13] C. D. Deshpande, 'North Gujarat Tubewell Scheme', *Bombay Geog. Mag.* 5/1 (1957), 5–13.
[14] Mukhtyar, *op. cit.* 24–25, 61, 150–2.

successful fusion of Islamic, Jain and Hindu traditions, and are especially notable for the fine stone tracery of windows and screens. These monuments of the past consort strangely with the grim cultural landscape of the new industry; but this industry has transformed the post-Mogul decline and stagnation into rapid growth: in seventy years the city grew by 830% from a total of 144,451 in 1891. The first mills were opened about 1859–61; there are now more than in Bombay city itself, though Bombay units are larger. Large-scale development started later than in Bombay, and the Ahmedabad millowners had the benefits of cheaper labour, raw cotton on the spot. A larger proportion of Ahmedabad's production is in the finer counts than is that of Bombay. A peculiar feature of the city is the building plan in *pols*, self-contained blocks of houses which may contain up to 10,000 people, often inhabited by members of one caste only and forming virtually self-governing neighbourhood units. The larger ones indeed are almost little towns, traversed by a street with gates at either end and with separate courts on each side of the thoroughfare.

Baroda (298,398), lying on the Mahi/Narmada doab, was central to its fragmented state; this, and a local eminence, led to its development as the capital of the Maratha Gaekwars. The surrounding country includes some of the richest land of Gujarat; the town itself is well laid out, with the amenities of a progressive educational and cultural centre; there is some industry, mainly textiles, chemicals and pottery. The merging of Baroda state in Gujarat has reduced the city's relative importance to some extent, but it remains the administrative and commercial focus of this central portion of Gujarat, and has a notable University.

Broach (73,369) and Surat (288,026) occupy strategic points at the lowest crossings of the Narmada and Tapti respectively. Surat, seat of the first English factory in India (1608–13), was the most active port of India in the first half of the 17th century, centre of a bitter triangular conflict between Portuguese, Dutch and English; its outport Swally Roads was the scene of hard fighting. After the great sack by Sivaji in 1664, when the Dutch and English factories alone held out, 'a Maratha raid was almost an annual certainty'. Already Broach was declining before Surat; Cambay silting, the increased size of ships, the shift of trade routes and European interests to the Bay of Bengal coasts, local warfare, and the rise of Bombay brought both towns to a state of all but complete decadence.[15] But as late as 1695 Surat could be described, doubtless with exaggeration, as 'the prime mart of India . . . no ship trading in the Indian Ocean but what puts into Surat'.[16] It recovered before Broach, mainly as the centre of railway-building in Gujarat in the 1860s when the American Civil War cotton boom brought prosperity and wild-cat speculation to all this part of India. The old gold- and silver-thread crafts and silk-weaving are still carried on; there are many handlooms and some modern cotton and other textile mills, but Broach has more factory industry.

---

[15] Populations: Broach in 1777, *c.* 50,000; 1812, *c.* 38,000; Surat in 1811, *c.* 250,000 (?); 1816, 124,000; 1847, 80,000; 1881 and 1891, 109,000.

[16] *Bombay Gaz.* (1909), I. 331.

The core of Surat is the once fortified area on the high southern bank of the Tapti; eastwards lies an industrial zone along the railway, to the southwest well-to-do suburbs extend along the estuary. As a port Surat is dead, and despite the Tapti valley railway the trade of Khandesh is never likely to be diverted from Bombay to its old channels down the river. But lying as it does at the gateway from the Konkan into Gujarat, where the plain widens out, Surat remains an important centre of internal trade.

THE KONKAN

The Konkan[17] is the coastal lowland as far south as Goa: lowland, not plain, though it has some of the features of a plane of marine erosion. The lowland, 330 miles long and 30–50 broad (530 by 48–80 km.), is much broken by hills, some of considerable extent and elevation. In the north indeed there is a flat alluvial belt along the coast, but this is only 4–8 miles wide, and behind it lies a series of parallel ridges reaching 1,500–2,000 ft. (455–610 m.) in which rivers like the Vaitarni, Ulhas and Amba have lower courses more or less parallel to the coast before reaching it transversely. The Ulhas and its tributaries form a great amphitheatre between the Ghats and the Matheran outlier. South of Bombay the pattern changes: streams are shorter and directly transverse, though some, like the Vasishti and Savitri, have also formed amphitheatres under the Ghats. Active headward erosion in the massive horizontal lava flows is obviously taking place, and it is clear, for example, that the upper Koyna cannot long survive, geologically speaking (Fig. 22.3). South again, in southern Ratnagiri, the great feature is the series of extensive laterite-capped residual plateaus. And throughout its length the Konkan is dominated by the tremendous scarps of the Ghats, rising sheer a matter of 3,000 ft. in a mile or two, fretted into wild canyons at the valley-heads.

Rural Konkan

With a rainfall of 75–100 in. (1,905–2,540 mm.) practically everywhere, rice is the dominant crop. A good way after come ragi, pulses and fodder crops; coconuts are increasingly important as we go south; and the Bombay bazaars call for some market gardening. But the valley-bottoms are given over mainly to paddy, with some ragi on the upper margins and pulses intercropped. Jute and mesta have been introduced since 1947. In the estuaries mangroves are important for fuel. The once forested laterites are very barren, in places merely a surface of iron-stained pebbles and slabs, at best supporting poor millets. The hills and the tangled country below the Ghats, like the Ghats themselves, are covered with tropical semi-evergreen forest.

The whole region is dominated by Bombay, now practically linked by dormitory and industrial suburbs to its satellites Thana and Kalyan. There is a string of tiny ports, mostly decayed; some once Portuguese (Chaul, Bassein), others once

[17] Thana, Kolaba and Ratnagiri Districts, with Bombay.

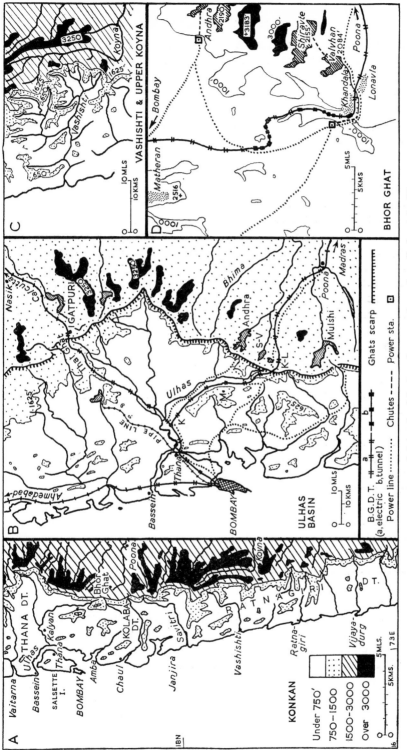

FIG 22.3 THE KONKAN. A large hydel plant has now been installed on the Koyna.

strongholds of Mogul or Maratha piratical chiefs, such as Vijayadrug, which dominated 150 miles of coast and was reduced only by a full-scale naval attack in 1757. Bassein had a good strategic position guarding the approaches to Salsette Island; the typical market town (28,238), with its wooden houses and carved balconies, lies in a countryside still dotted with wayside crosses, but Bassein Fort was inhabited in 1943 by two Franciscan fathers and a score or so orphans, two or three families of peasants, and a Hindu hermit, living in the midst of ruined baroque churches and surrounded by the complete 16th-century walls of what was once a town of 35,000 people.

In the south the string of ports is paralleled by a string of towns at the head of river navigation, once trading stations on the pack-routes through the fortress-crowned spurs of the Ghats. Ratnagiri (33,000) is the only place of much importance – for fishing, the coastal trade and the emigrant traffic to Bombay. This migration is an index of the poverty of the District: most of the migrants go to the cotton mills, the police and domestic service, and most are young men. Remittances probably form a substantial part of the local income. Industry based on Koyna power, and the development of mangoes and cashews, which will grow on the impoverished and eroded *varka* soils of the lateritic interfluves, seem to offer the best chances for improvement.

BOMBAY

The setting of Bombay forms as complete a contrast as can be imagined to that of Calcutta, its only rival as a commercial and industrial metropolis: an island site, dominated by the blue wall of the Ghats and the nearer hills across the broad harbour, as against the flats of Hooghlyside. The large-scale locational advantages of Bombay are obvious: centrality on the active littoral facing the southwest Asia portages revivified, after long eclipse by the Cape route, in 1869. The link between these continental/oceanic values and the more local positional factors is the Ulhas basin (Fig. 22.3), the watersheds of which lead up to the Thal and Bhor Ghats (1,900 and 1,800 ft., 580 and 550 m.) used by the railways to Nasik and Poona respectively. As for the site itself, the island is now rather cramped, but the harbour, with an effective area of about 75 sq. miles (194 km²) of sheltered deep water, is unrivalled in India.

The rise of Bombay

The seven Deccan Lava islets which are now joined to form Bombay Island were held by the Portuguese, who made little use of them, though the local officials were aware of their value and put every obstacle in the way of their cession as part of Catharine of Braganza's dowry in 1661. Bombay soon supplanted Surat as the chief English base on the west coast, but although commercial progress was steady no territorial expansion took place until the seizure of Salsette in 1774, and no considerable expansion until the collapse of Maratha power in 1818.

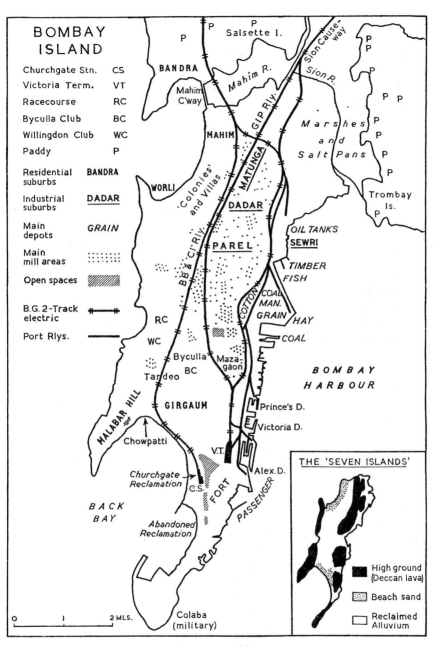

FIG 22.4 BOMBAY ISLAND. Man. = manganese.

In the second quarter of the 19th century the population rose from under 250,000 to over 500,000: the opening of the improved Bhor Ghat road to Poona (1830) and the steamer service via Suez for home mails were the chief events of this period; by 1843 Bombay was within 30 days of London. In 1853 the first 20 miles of railway in India, Bombay to Thana, were opened, and by 1864 the rail had reached Ahmedabad and Poona. At the same time the blockade of the South in the American Civil War led to a spectacular boom in cotton prices, and the population in 1864 was over 816,000 – a figure not reached again until 1881. The collapse in 1865 was catastrophic; but the opening of the Suez Canal to some extent mitigated the disaster, and meanwhile the bases of a modern textile industry had been laid: one mill in 1854, seven by 1860; by 1885 there were nearly fifty with over 30,000 workers. Apart from Hooghlyside and (in cotton alone) Ahmedabad the primacy of Bombay as an industrial centre is unchallenged, and the initiative and drive have been indigenous to a much greater extent than in Calcutta. The place originally held by the Scots in Bengal belongs in Bombay to the Parsees, who built up the 18th-century shipbuilding industry. It is sufficient to mention the great house of Tata, which has some share in nearly all the major modern activities of India, from soap to steel, and for long held a quasi-monopoly of some of the most important. Apart from some minor state schemes in Mysore and Kashmir, Tatas led the way in the development of hydro-electricity in India, their first plant dating from 1915; and this is still a most significant feature of the city's industrial development.

The port

Bombay has been by far the leading west coast port for two and a half centuries, and only recently have rivals appeared in Cochin, Kandla and Marmagão, but these are unlikely seriously to challenge Bombay's hegemony. From the bulk oil storage at Sewri to Alexandra Dock, a straight-line distance of 5 miles, the eastern side of the island is given over to port installations; the Port Trust estates cover nearly 1,900 ac. (770 ha.), about one-eighth of the whole island. The three main docks – Prince's (1880), Victoria (1888), and Alexandra (1914) – contain over 100 ac. of water with depths of 28–37 ft. and 31,000 ft. (9,450 m.) of quayage, to which the bunds or wharves add another 30,000. These are served by about 120 miles (193 km.) of Port Trust railway. The layout is shown on Fig. 22.4; the Cotton Depot, descendant of the famous 'Cotton Green' of early days, alone covers 127 ac. (51 ha.) and its godowns have a capacity of a million bales.

The trade of the port has changed greatly since Reclus' day, when raw cotton, wheat and opium were the chief exports, and Bombay had lost its place as an exporter of cotton goods – a line regained with the rise of factory industry. Cotton still has its place in the export list, but is outranked by cotton goods; other main lines are oilseeds and manganese. Imports, which normally exceed exports, consist mainly of constructional and consumption goods and mineral oil from abroad, grain and raw materials by the coasting trade.

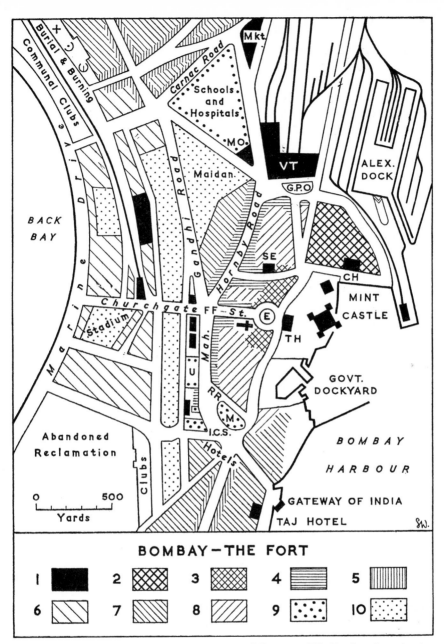

FIG 22.5 BOMBAY: 'THE FORT'. I, public buildings; 2, 'Big Business'; 3, banks
and offices; 4, main shops; 5, minor retailing; 6, modern residential (Churchgate
flats); 7, middle-class residential, largely Anglicized; 8, poorer residential; 9,
educational, etc.; 10, open spaces.

MO, Municipal Offices; VT, Victoria Terminus (GIP Rly); CH, Custom
House; SE, Stock Exchange; TH, Town Hall; E, Elphinstone (now Horniman)
Circle; FF, Flora Fountain; U, University; ICS, Indian College of Science;
M, Museum; RR, Rampart Row.

The hinterland of Bombay extends roughly as far as Delhi, Jabalpur, Nagpur and Hyderabad; for exports as far as the oilseeds areas of southern Andhra. No small proportion of its considerable entrepot trade is carried on by hundreds of sailing country boats; nor is this merely coastal, though of course the bulk of it is with the minor ports from Dwarka to Cape Comorin: the *baghla*, a high-pooped lateen-rigged craft of up to 400 tons, sails as far as the Persian Gulf, Aden and Zanzibar. These vessels are the little-changed descendants of the 'Arab' boats which handled the traffic of the Indian seas before the dawn of history.

Industry[18]

As we have seen, Ahmedabad leads Bombay in number, but not in size, of cotton mills; but this is far outweighed by the 'metropolitan' diversification of industry in the greater city, and Bombay still leads in total spindles and looms.

Textiles, indeed, are dominant, with hundreds of factories of all types and perhaps a quarter of a million workers: the heart of the industry is in Parel, where land was cheap in the earlier decades. Bombay yarn is mainly coarse, and piecegoods (apart from the home demand) are exported mainly to low purchasing-power markets, especially southwest Asia and East Africa. The industry's adjustments to meet new competitors have been to some extent handicapped by the Managing Agency system, and there are definite signs of at least relative decline, attributable to high overheads in this intensively developed area and to competition in the immediate market by imports landed on the spot. Since 1915, however, economies have been effected by the change to hydro-electric power.[19]

Next comes engineering, largely located in Mazagaon, close to the port and railway installations. The *raison d'être* of the machine trades is obviously the general demand of a great conurbation and the special needs of the textile mills. Other important lines are printing (largely in the commercial Fort area), food, drugs and chemicals, motor assembly and manufacture, and of course a host of consumption industries, large and small, catering for the metropolitan market. The film studios in the northern suburbs are the most important in India, and India turns out perhaps the largest footage of any country.

Hydro-electrification has been most significant in recent years (Fig. 22.3). There are three power stations, fed by great storage reservoirs on the reverse slope of the Ghats – Andhra, Shiravte–Valvhan and Mulshi Lakes. The water is led through the Ghat crest by tunnels – that from Mulshi is nearly 3 miles long – and the head at three stations ranges from 1,660 to 1,740 ft. (502–530 m.). These were built by Tatas and had a total capacity around 200,000 kW. They power most of the industry of Greater Bombay, as well as the Bombay trams and the electrified sections of the railways to Virar beyond Bassein and up the Ghats

---

[18] Deshpande, *op. cit.* 174–5, 250–2; cf. T. R. Sharma, *Location of Industries in India* (Hind Kitabs, Bombay, 2nd ed., 1949), Chapters II–III.

[19] Originally the power came from Durban coal.

to Igatpuri and Poona; the latter, opened in 1929, was the first main electric line in India. The domestic supplies in Bombay and Poona, originally thermal, now take their electricity in bulk from these projects. The Koyna project in Ratnagiri should ultimately add 540,000 kW.

The city

Bombay Island covers about 25 sq. miles (65 km²) and Greater Bombay about 186 (482 km²) with 4,152,056 people in 1961; if the conurbation ranks second to Hooghlyside, the city itself outranks Calcutta. In 1931 one area of the city had 375,000 to the sq. mile. The ordinary phenomenon of central depopulation exists, though distorted by the fact that the commercial 'centre' – the Fort and surrounding Esplanade area, roughly that shown on Fig. 22.5 – is geographically excentric. Large open spaces and blocks of offices bring the density of much of this zone below 30 per acre. Sion in the northeast, still largely marsh, had before the war a similar figure; the densest belt (400–700 per acre) lay in the geographical heart of the city, between Girgaum and Mazagaon.

The Island is really formed of two lines of Deccan Lava hills; the intervening valley, originally tidal marsh, has been reclaimed, but the location of the most close-built areas in this central plain implies serious drainage and sewerage problems. The Island is separated from Salsette by the Mahim River, a broad tidal stream, and the largely silted Thana creek. These are crossed by road and rail from Mahim to Bandra, leading to Santa Cruz airport, and by the Sion Causeway carrying the main Poona road and the railway up the Ghats. The population of some 4,000,000 is thus restricted to two links with the mainland, apart from coastal shipping. Rail, bus and tram routes converge on the Fort – the commuting core, despite its peripheral location – and the narrowness of the Island behind Back Bay and the harbour adds to the resultant congestion.

Setting aside the docks and related areas in the east, the city falls into three or four main sections:

(i) the Fort and lower Bombay;
(ii) the densely populated area between Malabar Hill and Mazagaon;
(iii) the northern suburbs: (a) residential in the west, (b) industrial in the centre and east.

(i) *The Fort.*[20] This, as the name implies, is the original European settlement around the Portuguese Castle, a part of which still remains intact. The line of the 18th-century enceinte (demolished 1862) is marked by Hornby Road and Rampart Row (RR); within it is the old town, an area of small businesses and shops, with a marked concentration of banking and insurance around Elphinstone Circle (E),[21] the first Cotton Green. Northeast of this core is the 'Big Business'

[20] Letters in parentheses refer to Fig. 22.5.
[21] Now Horniman Circle, after a local English editor who threw in his lot with Indian nationalism.

of the Ballard Reclamation, housing the greater banks and international firms. South of the old town is the old cantonment of Colaba; north is the Victoria Terminus (VT), a building of stupendous size and astonishing ornament; but indeed the more grandiose architecture of the Fort as a whole is an Arabian Nightmarish medley of styles, all bad, and several groups would certainly be on the short list for the most hideous architecture in the world.[22] Beyond the main European-style shopping streets (Hornby Road and lower Mahatma Gandhi Road) are public buildings – Courts, Secretariat, the Italo-Gothic University clocktower and library – and a belt of open spaces. Beyond these again lies the Churchgate Reclamation, begun to give space for the terminus of the railway from the north and added to in a long history of wild-cat speculation. As in so many double-fronted coastal towns, there is a complete contrast between the harbour and the Back Bay waterfronts: the latter is occupied by vast blocks of 'modernist' flats along the great promenade of Marine Drive; from Malabar Hill the sweep of Back Bay looks like nothing so much as a vast toothy grin of too-regular dentures. This is an upper-middle class and rather cosmopolitan residential area with clubs, hotel and restaurants; but the main hotel area for foreigners is south of the Fort, by the old Gateway of India, a large and not unimpressive but pointlessly-sited triumphal arch.

(ii) *The main city mass.* Immediately north of this excentric core lies the vast amorphous mass of Indian Bombay; the cultural divide at Carnac Road is extremely sharp. At the head of Back Bay, north of the recreational area devoted to Gymkhana Clubs catering for the various communities, is the little bayhead beach of Chowpatti, Bombay's Marble Arch, venue for political and religious meetings and for general recreation on high days and holidays. Back Bay is closed on the northwest by the heights of Malabar Hill, covered with the houses of the wealthy, generally hideous Indo-Baroque palaces but with a few older and pleasantly rambling bungalows and the inevitable piles of luxury flats.

Eastwards across to Mazagaon is the densely-peopled zone of petty commerce, artisan crafts, bazaars and so on. Byculla is a fossil 19th-century outer suburb, left behind by the industrial expansion: a middle-class area with clubs and other recreational facilities. Amorphous as this main mass of the city appears, however, it is internally well segregated, not so much on class or economic lines (though these play their part) as by religion and language.

(iii) *The northern suburbs.* Northwards the development becomes looser, with islands of densely-built industrial housing as in Parel and Dadar: the skyline is broken by mill chimneys and the vast blocks of workers' tenements (*chawls*),

[22] Holdich's reference (*India* (1904), 309) to 'a city adorned with architecture worthy of the Government of an Indian Empire', if not so obviously sincere might well count as one of the bitterest gibes ever levelled at the British Raj. But exception must be made for the pleasantly Doric Town Hall, built – significantly – in 1833, before the booms. Much better is the remark (p. 308) that 'a dirty picturesqueness (which is almost Italian) pervades most of the back premises of Bombay'.

often unspeakably congested and insanitary.[23] Such development is mainly east of the railways; to the west, in Mahim, is the usual untidy villa and garden-and-shack zone found on the outskirts of a great city. These outer suburbs also contain planned suburban estates or 'colonies' sponsored by communal building societies. Mahim, like Bandra across the bay, has a considerable Portuguese Christian element, largely descended from refugees from the fall of Bassein. The northeast of the Island has still much tidal marsh, with important saltpans along Sion Creek; and across this marshy stream, on Trombay Island, are India's first two nuclear reactors.

Greater Bombay

The relationship between Salsette Island and Bombay is complex. In the west, along the electrified railway is a string of dormitory suburbs such as Bandra (a third of its people are Christian; it is dominated by its three big Portuguese churches), Santa Cruz, Ville Parle, Andheri, Juhu, the last with the Bombay airport and fine bathing beaches. Even Bassein on the mainland is within commuting distance. These west Salsette towns have developed between the coastal marshes and the hills eastwards, right to Thana and the Mahim River, and even beyond it towards Kalyan, there is now almost continuous industrial development. A Greater Bombay Plan was published in 1948, but a decade elapsed before it was given legal teeth, by which time speculative and uncontrolled development had largely by-passed its provisions. Metal industries predominate, with pharmaceuticals and chemicals. The Plan envisages the gradual removal of factories from the heart of Bombay as leases expire, and major industrial development along the Agra road, minor along the Western railway.[24] At Kurla are the slaughter-houses and leather industries; interspersed with the raw new industry, dairying, market gardening, and paddy growing linger.

Thana commands the most important crossing to the mainland; Kalyan, the natural route-focus of the Ulhas basin, was one of the leading ports of western India at the beginning of our era. Both are now mere satellites of Bombay, but since hydro-electricity became available there has been a considerable development of light industry, which:

> 'tries to avoid the high land values and overhead costs so characteristic of Bombay proper, and yet tries to retain the benefit of high finance and management of the "city", and the advantages derived from bulk handling in the premier port of India. The Kurla Match Factory and the Ambernath Chemical

[23] In 1931 no fewer than 256,379 people lived in rooms housing 6–9 persons each; 80,133 in rooms with 10–19 inhabitants; 15,490 in rooms actually tenanted by 20 or more persons – a total of over 30% of the population in the three classes. Overcrowding is not of course confined to the industrial zones; there are slum enclaves in the Fort itself. 'Improvements' have probably been swamped by the increase of street-dwellers; see K. A. Abbas, *One Thousand Nights on a Bed of Stones* (Jaico, Bombay, 1957).

[24] K. R. Dixit, 'Some problems of land use planning in Greater Bombay', *Bombay Geog. Mag.* 6–7/1 (1959), 65–79.

Works are two leading examples of this kind. Even the port of Bombay at times finds a serious rival in these Salsette ports where the cargo of the ocean-going vessels is unloaded and "broken" in transport by means of country craft to avoid the dock charges.'[25]

Other local industries include brick and tile works at Kalyan and, across Bombay Harbour, at Mora; these again use country boats as cheap transport for their bulky products. The whole of Salsette is thus directly subsidiary to Bombay either as a commuting or as a supply zone; as Deshpande remarks, the difference between the dormitory and the producing sides of the island represents an extrusion of the similarly differentiated northwest and northeast of Bombay Island itself.

The immediate influence of Bombay extends as far as Matheran: a hill station in complete miniature on its little plateau (2,500 ft., 760 m.) reached by a tiny 2 ft. 6 in. 'mountain' railway. Not until the resorts and sanatoria of Khandala and Lonavla, at the top of the Bhor Ghat, is there another urban pull, that of Poona; and even this tract, with its great hydro-electric plants powering the metropolis, is clearly more directly tributary to Bombay.

An Indian microcosm

In many ways Bombay was a microcosm of Indo-British society, or rather societies, though east and west were more integrated here than elsewhere owing to the invaluable social lubricant provided by the Parsees, occupying a key inter-mediate position; and it still sums up many aspects of the New India.

The street-plan and street-names of the Fort still reflect the layout of the 17th-century trading station; here are the official monuments of John Company in an area remarkably tidy and compact and with a tendency to the grandiose which for the most part achieves only the grotesque. Here, too, there are the international contacts of the great trading houses on Ballard Estate and the slick modernity of Churchgate, yet near at hand the tight-packed streets of the old town with its sailors' taverns: Cosmopolis and the sea.

Malabar Hill represents the picturesque half-splendid and half-shabby India of Government House and Civil Lines, Cantonments and the Princes, an always-afternoon land with a touch of weirdness in the Towers of Silence where the Parsees exposed their dead to the scavenger fowls of the air. North of this the densely-packed mass of Indian Bombay, still tightly organized but leading its own life, bound up with the world market and yet aloof: bazaars, temples, mosques, communalism. There is little European about it, but not a little Eurasian in islands of Victorian provincialism.

Beyond the close building the cultural landscape of the alien bureaucracy can still be recognized in the framework of roads and railways and public works; but in the interspaces, chaotically untidy, hives the real life of India. Mostly (and this is less typical) it is the new industrialism, spawned from the West but growing

[25] Deshpande, *op. cit.* 170.

up outside the British environment, if within the steel frame of British imperialism: the mills and the chawls, the Hindu masses. Here and there are the relic villages to remind us that India is a land of villages; and in the harbour, on Elephanta Island, there is another India in the cave temple where the three colossal faces of Siva Trimurthi, Creator, Preserver and Destroyer, brood eternally in darkling majesty.

GOA AND KANARA

The Ghats breaches

Between 16° and 12°N, Goa and the Mysore Districts of North and South Kanara are in most respects transitional between the Konkan and Kerala. The coastal topography cannot be evaluated without more detailed studies than are available. Around the island of Goa conditions are more deltaic than anywhere else on the Western Littoral, but both north and south the high ground comes down to the sea and the estuaries have a definitely ria aspect. But a few miles south of Karwar at the Tadri mouth, we get the first hint of the spit-and-lagoon shoreline characteristic of Kerala. Inland the lateritic topography of Ratnagiri continues, and there are signs, in river terraces and possible planes of marine erosion, of negative shoreline movements. All this tends to confirm the suggestion of a 'hinge' of the whole coast about Goa.[26]

The Ghats themselves are exceptionally interesting in this section. Near the northern boundary of Goa the Deccan Lava gives way to the Archaeans and the change is marked by a series of breaches in the mountain wall: the Kalinadi, Gangavati-Bedti, Tadri, and Sharavati have all definitely encroached on the Krishna–Tungabhadra drainage, setting the watershed some 80 miles back from the coast instead of the usual 25–35 miles (129 and 40–56 km.); more significantly, this also marks a major recession of the watershed not only from the sea but also from the Ghats crest (Figs. 1.1, 22.6), while in other embayments the watershed and the scarp swing back together. Possibly this has developed on an older surface not buried by the Lavas; but the continuation of the very strong Ghats scarp on the Archaeans well to the south of the Sharavati is a major difficulty on this view. At all events the 2,750–3,000-ft. (840–930-m.) crest of the Lava Ghats breaks down here for about 200 miles, before rising again to 6,215 ft. (1,895 m.) in Kudremukh (South Kanara District) and more in the Nilgiris; and indeed between the Bedti and Varada Rivers the col is only *c.* 1,600 ft. (490 m.).

This lower altitude, however, does not make access to the interior much easier, since the valleys are deep gorges two or three miles (or less) across and 1,000 ft. (or more) deep. Moreover it is precisely in this section that the coastal lowland

[26] It might be hazarded that the deltaic conditions around Goa are associated with this relative stability, and possibly also with the position at the centre of the broad front on which the monsoon drift of the Arabian Sea impinges on the coast. It seems significant that, on the whole, coastal depositional forms at river mouths tend to run south–north in the Konkan and north–south in Kerala.

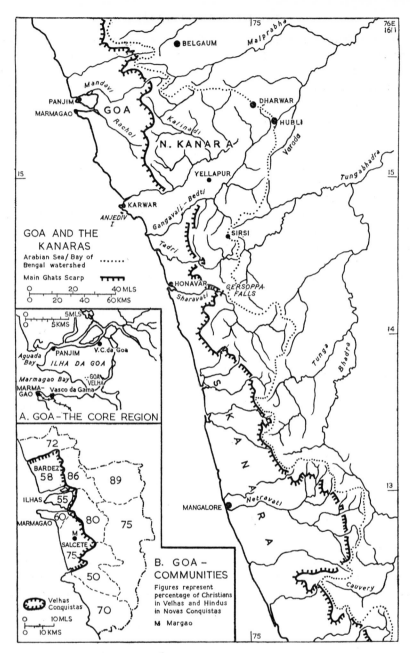

FIG 22.6 GOA AND THE KANARAS

is narrowest and most broken, affording but a small base for commercial activity other than piracy; 30–45 miles (48–72 km.) wide behind Goa, it narrows to 3 or 4 miles at 14°N, where the Ghats crest is only 8 miles from the sea. Tracks, and even some good roads, do cross the Ghats in this sector, and contributed to the old importance of Karwar and Honavar; but only the Bedti valley is used to any extent by these routes, and it is more significant that the chief towns in the Ghats (Yellapur, Sirsi and Siddapur) are all on strongly-marked ridgeways. The most important economic value in this area, apart from forestry, is likely to be the Mahatma Gandhi power station at the Gersoppa or Jog Falls, where the Sharavati has the most spectacular waterfalls in India, one of the four having a straight leap of 829 ft. (271 m.).

From the human point of view also this is a transitional zone. The solid Marathi of the north is succeeded by its regional version Konkani, which in Goa has a strong infusion of Portuguese loan-words; in the Kanaras, Dravidian speech is dominant, Kanarese in north with some Tulu in south Kanara; beyond, in Kerala, is another solid block, of Malayalam. Keralan conditions are also foreshadowed by the increasing importance of the coconut.

Climatically the entire area is hot and humid. Once more the transition is clearly shown, this time by the increasing length of the rainy season to the south:

Rainfall in inches		Total	May	%	June–Sept.	%	Oct.–Nov.	%	
Ratnagiri	16° 59′ N	100·0*	1·4	1·4	93·6	93·6	4·6	4·6	Konkan
Marmagao	15 25	94·9	2·6	2·7	86·1	90·7	5·1	5·4	Goa
Karwar	14 49	120·1	3·2	2·7	108·5	90·3	7·5	6·3	N Kanara
Mangalore	12 52	125·7	6·2	5·0	106·8	85·0	10·6	8·5	S Kanara
Calicut	11 15	118·6	9·5	8·0	88·5	80·5	15·2	13·0	Kerala
Cochin	9 58	114·7	11·4	10·0	74·8	64·5	19·6	17·1	Kerala

* 100 in. = 2,540 mm.

The human geography of each of the three components of this region is highly distinctive, and physically also they are sufficiently distinct to rank as sub-regions; it seems best to abandon the standard regional layout and give each a general treatment.

GOA

Goa, with 1,268 sq. miles (3,282 km²) and over 600,000 people, was the only considerable component of the Portuguese 'State of India'.[27] Small as this territory is, however, it had a tangible as well as sentimental value. Marmagão is the best (and best-equipped) port between Bombay and Cochin, and there were resources of manganese and iron ore. It was annexed by India in 1961.

At the beginning of the 16th century Goa was part of the Bijapur kingdom. The Portuguese had already factories and forts farther south – notably at Cochin and Cannanore – in which, however, they probably felt themselves straitened.

[27] Deshpande, 186–91; D. E. Sopher gives a very fine and detailed account of Goa in his *Annual Summary Report 1959* (Geography of Indian Coasts), US Office of Naval Research NR 388–041; a shorter but more accessible version is in his 'Cultural landscapes of Portuguese India' *Yearbook Asstn Pacific Coast Geogrs* 22 (1960), 34–39.

The geopolitical eye of Afonso de Albuquerque at once grasped the advantages of the island site: large enough to give a secure food-producing base, but with the defensible moat of the Mandavi and Rachol estuaries; central to the active littoral and well-placed with respect to the important northwestern sector of the Arabian Sea. He took the city by assault in 1510; in 1543 the rest of the Velhas Conquistas (Bardez and Salcete) were added. By this time Goa Dourada, 'Golden Goa', was at once fortress and mart, a Renaissance city transplanted to the east. The Portuguese decline is part of general history; so far as Goa was concerned the subjugation of Portugal by Spain (1580) laid it open to the attacks of the Dutch.[28] By the mid-18th century the old city, Velha Goa,[29] was so decayed that it was gradually succeeded as the capital by Panjim or Nova Goa. The melancholy beauty of Old Goa has often been described, a city of baroque churches half-hidden by jungle, dead except for the great pilgrimage to the tomb of St Francis Xavier in the magnificent cathedral of Bom Jesus. Incessant warfare with the Dutch and the country powers, Muslim or Maratha, silting of the river and increase in malaria, reduced the population, said to have reached 200,000 in its prime, to a handful of clergy.[30]

The deltaic area – Ilhas, 'the Isles' – between Aguada and Marmagao Bays has the dense populations associated with rice/coconut culture; so also have the coastal tracts of Bardez to the north and Salcete to the south. The inland Novas Conquistas (acquired in an intermittent warfare with the Marathas in the 18th century) have large areas of laterite and rise through jungle-clad foothills and scarps to the crest of the Ghats; they are thinly populated, mainly by Hindus (Fig. 22.6 inset), and economically backward. The Marmagão peninsula has an interesting urban development, tiny as the towns are. Marmagão and Vasco da Gama, two miles apart, are practically one town in two distinct functional parts. Marmagão consists of little but harbour buildings with an airport on the low (200-ft., 61-m.) laterite plateau behind. The harbour is well protected by breakwaters; ships of 22–30 ft. draught can come alongside the quay, which has good cranage and warehousing and the wharfside railway (metre, connecting with the Indian railways between Belgaum and Dharwar). Vasco da Gama is larger and more residential, but has large oil installations. Towards the root of the peninsula Margão is the nodal and market centre of Salcete. The economic activity of Goa, apart from agriculture, is largely concentrated in this little peninsula, and is not inconsiderable. Manganese is mined near Marmagão, iron ore is increasingly important; coconuts and copra, fresh and dried fish, cashew nuts and salt are

[28] So strict was the Dutch blockade that the ship bearing news of the regaining of independence (1640) had to send in its message by a small boat at night.

[29] Strictly Velha Cidade da Goa, the Portuguese keeping 'Velha Goa' for the ruined pre-Muslim city in the south of the island.

[30] There is a good description in Reclus, Nouvelle Géographie Universelle, Tome VIII (1883), 476–8); but it should be remembered that Reclus was a Communard, and the clerical dominance often alleged as a main cause in the Portuguese decline was more probably a collateral.

exported, and now that there are no longer political barriers the transit trade with the Deccan should revive and expand.

The social geography of Goa is indeed fascinating. Dense population and high taxation lead to much emigration, some as far afield as Mozambique, though some two-thirds of the emigrants go to Bombay City. Educational standards are reasonably high, and Goanese are prominent in clerical occupations, teaching, medicine and in the Indian marine, as well as in entertainment and domestic service; a large proportion of the emigrants are females, and the hotel staffs of western India are largely Goanese. Their earnings play a large part in Goanese economy, and in Bardez the cultural landscape is somewhat anglicized, with the modern bungalows of returned emigrants and a fair prevalence of English speech. Emigration is of course mainly from the crowded, and Christian, coastal areas.

Here four and a half centuries have produced a high degree of cultural fusion, extending even to the peculiar Goanese language. Christians form about 40% of the total population (Fig. 22.6 inset), and there was probably a certain metropolitan sentiment among the *Catholic* Goanese. It is ironic that the Portuguese empire in India should have survived, however briefly, the British Raj; still more ironic that the most serious resistance to the Indian forces was made by the sloop *Afonso de Albuquerque*. Culturally, however, the impress of Portugal will long outlive the Estado da India; nor can a certain immortality be denied to a city which knew St Francis Xavier, the Apostle of the Indies, and Camões, the greatest poet of his time in any country and of his country in any time. The grandeur and the decadence of Goa meet in his work; she is at once 'Senhora de todo o Oriente' and the Babylon of those bitter sonnets which are perhaps the most poignant utterances of genius exiled in an alien land.

NORTH KANARA: COASTLANDS AND GHATS

(a) *The coast*. Alone of the Western Littoral sub-regions, North Kanara is more essentially highland than lowland.[31] The lowland is indeed almost restricted to pockets along the lower courses of the rivers which breach the Ghats and, *per contra*, thus warrant an extension of the 'Western Littoral' well inland. The alluvial lower section of each valley is a unit focusing in the small port at or near its mouth; places of great historical interest but of little significance today.

The coastal taluks have densities of 300–400, but only about half (or in the south a third) of the land is cultivated, and densities in relation to arable land are high – about 1,200. Rice is dominant, with over 60% of NSA, with coconut on the sandier coastal soils and ragi millet on the poorer laterites inland. The low-level laterite (200–400 ft., 61–122 m.) is indeed largely given over to scrub and poor grass; south of Sharavati it dominates the lowland. The Ghats forests reach down to the sea in several places, and for the whole District NSA is under 20% of the total area.

Karwar (23,906) on the Kalinadi is the most important of the little ports, with

[31] Here we rely more heavily than ever on Deshpande.

a fairly well-sheltered harbour in Baitkul Cove. But the building of the Marmagão railway hampered Karwar's development, the immediate hinterland is poor and rugged, and such activity as exists, mainly timber-rafting, is not at the Cove but on the Kalinadi estuary itself, two miles north. The Sharavati is navigable by small craft to Gersoppa, and the estuarine plain is very fertile; but again the lack of a wider hinterland limits possibilities at Honavar (10,543), though road transport is now important and there is a brisk export of manganese ore. For all these little ports the wider hinterland of Karnataka (formerly in Bombay, now Mysore), once tapped by bullock-cart tacks, has been drained off to Bombay by the railways. The extension of Mysore to the sea has certainly led to a revival of interest in this coast, but improvements in the coastal highways, including the replacement of estuarine ferries by bridges, is tending to concentrate traffic, and hence facilities, on Mangalore, and perhaps in the future on Marmagão.

(b) *The Ghats.* Differential erosion, river capture, faulting, lithological variety, combine to make this an extremely dissected area; the high rainfall favours a dense forest growth. The lower spurs and terraces are largely lateritic, with poorish teak and bamboo; above them is the evergreen zone; the drier eastern slopes carry stunted or pole forests and grass. In the south sandalwood is important. Much of this forest has been badly damaged by shifting cultivation (*kumri*), now officially discouraged.

In this jungly and till recently malarial terrain densities are naturally low and cultivation sparse. Rice is the main food crop, and spices (areca nut, pepper, cardamom) are cultivated, with some skill, along permanent water-courses, attracting seasonal labour from the coastal plain.[32] The spice-villages have a distinctive settlement pattern, generally linear along the break of slope above the valley-bottom, with holdings running across the valley to secure equitable allotment of soils and water; houses are widely spaced.

Of more importance is the forest, on which indeed the spice-gardens are dependent for their heavy demands in leaf-manure, while dwellings, household utensils, and decorative crafts are mainly wood or bamboo. The best teak is in the north around Yellapur; to the east, light timber is obtained from the pole forests. Some of the timber goes out to the east by rail, but most down the convenient rivers to Karwar and Honavar.

The area had until recently a declining population and is essentially negative, a barrier to movement. Roads and tracks follow the lower reaches of the rivers, then climb the terraces and tend to keep to high ground; eastwards, on the open Deccan, movement was and is mainly on north–south lines. Such towns as exist are points of convergence for the plateau roads before they pitch steeply down the Ghats: such are Yellapur (21,240) and Sirsi, both centres of the spice trade which, owing to its high value for bulk, is relatively well adapted to the poor transport facilities.

[32] L. S. Bhat, 'Geography of the spice gardens', *Bombay Geog. Mag.* 5/1 (1957), 21–29, gives up to 87% of the cultivated area of some tracts as under spices.

SOUTH KANARA

South Kanara,[33] like the Ulhas basin and Goa, is an embayment of lowland, widest (c. 45 miles, 72 km.) in the Netravati valley behind Mangalore. The setting back of the Ghats permits a greater development of alluvium than in North Kanara, broad wedges rather than narrow strips. These are backed by a low (150–400 ft., 45–120 m.) plateau of laterite, covering perhaps half the area, and essentially sterile despite the heavy rain. Towards the lower margin of this platform the laterite appears redeposited rather than formed *in situ*, but nearer the Ghats this detrital form overlies that weathered directly from the gneissic or granitic country rock. The laterite in general appears to correspond in age to the late Tertiary Warkalai beds of Kerala; in the extreme south it has lignite beds similar to those of the Warkalais. The laterite platform, like the Warkalai surface, is held by local observers to be a plane of marine erosion and two terraces in the major valleys also point to a general negative movement.[34]

The laterites, and in places the alluvium also, are broken by ridges and isolated hills of Archaean gneisses and granites, some of which appear to have been offshore islands. In the north the Ghat scarp (here formed of Dharwars) is very sharply defined; but although it is higher in the south (rising to 6,000–6,500 ft., 1,830–1,980 m.) the headwaters of the Netravati and other rivers have etched it into a series of deep coulisses; the drainage-pattern along the watershed, especially across the border in Coorg, is of a beautiful complexity. In the extreme south, as in the north, Ghat spurs reach nearly to the coast.

Rainfall is everywhere over 125 in., and on the Ghats over 200 (3,375 and 5,080 mm.). The extensive laterite and the Ghat foothills, however, limit agriculture, and only about a quarter of the District is cultivated. Of the rest most is forested, but only a third of the forest is Reserved. The relations of forest and cultivation show interesting peculiarities. The jungle was largely occupied by tribal remnants practising shifting *kumri* cultivation, now almost extinct: they have wandered over the land to such an extent that only some 10% of the forest is untouched, mainly on the wildly dissected and inaccessible main Ghats scarp. The remainder is badly degraded secondary jungle. Before 1860, however, the forest was protected by the settled cultivators of the valleys, who used it mainly as a source of leaf-manure. The forest land up to the ridgetops bounding the valleys was known as *kumki* (= 'aid' to cultivation) and in it the cultivator had considerable rights. But in 1860 this privilege was restricted to a distance of 100 yd. from the fields; all beyond this became unoccupied government land, and before the creation of the Forest Department in 1882 was exploited without control: what the shifting cultivator spared the timber speculator gutted. The

[33] There are ten papers in *JMGA* 13/3 (1938); more recent details in A. T. A. Learmonth, *Mysore State: I. Atlas of Resources II. Regional Synthesis* (Asia, Bombay, 1964) and E. Weigt, 'Süd-Kanara und seine Wirtschaft', *Petermanns Geog. Mitt.* 102 (1958), 90–100; Weigt includes the Malayalam-speaking Kasaragod taluk, now part of Kerala.
[34] V. D. Krishnaswamy, *JMGA* 13/3 (1938), 253–5.

results of this spoliation are still visible, and the indigenous tradition of con-servation has been so undermined by the influence of a money economy that – as elsewhere in India – there is agitation not only against an expansion of the Reserves, but actually for their diminution.[35]

Forestry, however, remains a chief source of wealth. Teak is increasingly becoming a plantation rather than a natural crop; and, besides other timber trees, minor products such as sandalwood, bamboos, canes, cutch, honey and wax are important. The cashew nut, introduced by the Portuguese in the 16th century, now grows wild all over the District and is being planted: the fleshy fruit can be distilled for power alcohol, the dried kernels (some are imported from Africa for processing) supply the world's cocktail parties, and also yield an oil used in plastics, paints and varnishes, and locally in boat caulking and wood preservation.[36]

Agriculture displays the usual features of the humid littoral: concentration on rice in the loamy alluvium, with coastal coconuts, and ragi and pulses on the laterites, where these are not given over to coarse grass and bush or secondary scrub-jungle. The valley ribbons support densities of about 800, the low laterite plateaus 150–150, the true coastal plain as much as 1,100–2,000; this is made possible by a good deal of double-cropping.[37]

There are no towns of any importance except Mangalore (170,253). The 'port' is a mere roadstead two or three miles offshore, useless in the monsoon; small country craft can harbour in the creek. Owing to its proximity to the Mysore plantations, however, it handles about three-quarters of the coffee trade of India; other exports are pepper, tea and cashew nuts. It has an interesting local industry: Mangalore tiles are famous throughout southern India, and the industry has some geographical localizing factors: demand for roofing on this rainswept coast, good local clay, and transport on the rivers between which Mangalore lies. But the change from petty artisan to factory production seems to have been a mere historical accident, a result of the initiative of the Basel Mission which established the first factory in 1865 and still runs two of the three largest. There are altogether thirty or forty factories with an output of 500,000,000–600,000,000 tiles a year; local sailing coasters supply markets from Karachi to Colombo, and there is some export via Bombay to East Africa, Persia and Malaya. But competition from Malabar and, much more serious, from cement and asbestos roofing is adversely affecting the industry, which is declining.[38] Other industries are of little importance: iron-founding (ancillary to the tile factories), and soap, based on local and imported copra; Mangalore is the main port for the

[35] E. V. P. Pillai, 'The Forests of S Kanara', *JMGA* 13/3 (1938), 269–78.

[36] Pillai, *loc. cit.* 275; A. K. Menon, *ibid.* 280; Records of 9th Silvicultural Conference, *Indian Forester* (Dehra Dun), 83 (1956), 194.

[37] A. T. A. Learmonth, *op. cit.* II. 4–9; table in Weigt, 91.

[38] Weigt (*loc. cit.* 99) gives figures for the port in the open season September 1953–May 1954: of a total trade of 240,000 tons, exports were two-thirds and tiles accounted for 125,000 tons; 82% of the trade was by coastal *sailing* craft.

Laccadive islanders. A feature of some interest is the prominence of Portuguese names among the larger concerns, both in coffee-curing and in tile-making.

KERALA

Both physically and culturally Kerala is one of the most distinctive regions of India. Historically it has been somewhat isolated from the rest of the Peninsula, but accessible to maritime influences. Homogeneous in speech, it is probably more caste-divided than any other area, and it is here that 'untouchability' developed the more fantastic extremes of 'unapproachability' and even 'unseeability', while the Nairs who form the bulk of the minor gentry preserve a matrilinear organization in which both polygamy and polyandry play a part.[39] Perhaps by reaction against caste, the region has the highest percentage of Christians in all India – 25–35% according to locality. This element long antedates the vigorous Portuguese missions, which succeeded in bringing into the Roman fold most of the 'Syrian' (i.e. Nestorian) Christians, whose traditions go back to St Thomas the Apostle; there were Christian communities 1,500 years ago. The 'White Jews' of Cochin are another ancient fossil kith. Extreme population pressure, and perhaps the rival traditions of utmost Hindu orthodoxy and of dissent, have given the new State an unusually extremist political cast: here alone Communism presents a serious governmental challenge to Congress.

The physical setting

Tokens of uplift are numerous and decisive, including the existence of coral reefs below the alluvium some miles from the present coast.[40] Literary and place-name evidence points to continuing growth of the land within proto-historic or even historic times. It seems likely that there were at least two phases of relative upward movement, represented by erosion surfaces in the laterite at around 250 and 600 ft. (76–183 m.), while the last stage – that reflected in legend and literature – added the eight miles or so between the existing shore and a line of villages in whose names 'sea' or 'island' is a component; some places mentioned by Ptolemy as sea-ports now lie at a similar distance inland. But all these are near the great Cochin backwater, which suggests – as do the large-scale maps – that normal prograding on a low shoreline of emergence is responsible for this accretion, rather than an actual change of levels. Probably associated with this are the Malabar mudbanks, which lie off all the river mouths. They are up to eight miles long, and their extremely finely comminuted lateritic mud forms as

[39] The best easily accessible account for geographers is in C. D. Forde, *Habitat, Economy and Society* (London, 1934 and later eds.), Chapter XIII. See also G. Slater, *Southern India* (London, 1936), Chapters XVI–XVII.
[40] Legend ascribes the formation of Kerala to the impatience of a local saint ('during the thousandth year after the [biblical] flood') with the unspecified improprieties of his aged mother. He threw an axe from Gokarna (near Goa) over the sea; it flew to Cape Comorin and the sea retreated beneath its flight. This does correspond with the actual area of emergence.

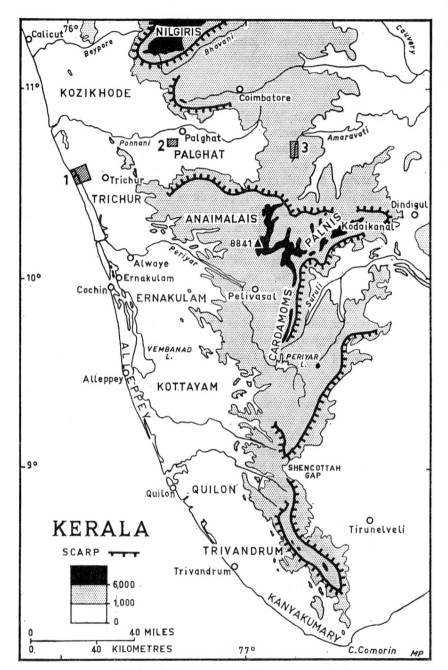

FIG 22.7 KERALA. Heights in feet. 1, area of Fig 22.8; 2, of Fig 22.9; 3, of Fig 25.6.

it were an emollient which deadens the ocean swell; in their lee are safe road-steads for the small ports of the coast.

The general tripartite longitudinal division is found: alluvial coastland, low lateritic plateaus and foothills, gneissic highlands. The division is indeed rather more clear cut than in the more complex northern lowlands, but each zone has certain peculiarities. In the alluvium is the great development of lagoons and backwaters, saline or fresh, which, with some artificial cuts, form splendid waterways for some 150 miles (341 km.) from the Ponnani mouth to Trivandrum. The largest of these, behind Cochin, widens out southwards into Vembanad Lake. The laterites (including the ?Pliocene Warkalais) form plateaus at 200–600 ft., with much grass and scrub; into them project spurs of the Anaimalai-Cardamom Hills which, south of Palghat, have a very strong southeast/northwest trend, shown by the Periyar valley. The hills themselves, rainswept and forested, will be treated in the next chapter, but it may be noted here that the plantation agriculture of Kerala is confined to them, and the development of hydro-electricity from Pallivasal is of great importance to the agriculture and industry of the lowland.

The Ponnani, the headwaters of which rise on the northern slopes of the Anaimalais, leads up to the Palghat Gap, nearly 20 miles wide and not much over 1,100 ft. (335 m.) on its broad sill, which lies beyond the regional limits. Farther south the higher (nearly 1,500 ft., 455 m.) and much narrower Shencottah gap gives access to the extreme south of Madras. It is noteworthy that in both these gaps there were exclaves of Cochin and Travancore territory, extending well east of the watershed in the latter; these, with the ancient walls across the Kanya Kumari lowland, emphasize the importance of these sole easy points of contact between Kerala and Tamilnad.

Climate and agriculture

The climate represents the nearest approach in India to equatorial conditions. Maximum temperatures rarely exceed 90° F. (32° C.), minima rarely fall below 70° F. (21° C.), the annual range at Cochin is only 6° and the diurnal is about 10° F. (3·3 and 5·6° C.). Apart from the very high falls in the hills, rainfall decreases from around 120 in. (3,008 mm.) in the north to half that at Trivandrum, a third in Kanniyakumari, where major irrigation is needed. But this decrease is balanced by a better distribution: of Trivandrum's 64 in. (1,626 mm.), 39% falls in June–August, 33% in September–November, and 28% in December–May, an almost completely dry season in most of the sub-continent.

Kerala, including the hills, has an area of 15,000 sq. miles (38,850 km²) and a 1961 population of 16,904,000 – an overall density of 1,127. About a fifth is under forest; of the rest, most of what can be cultivated is already taken in. Rice dominates, although in the south it falls below 40% of NSA, in part because of the acreages of tea, rubber and pepper in the hills. Paddy is grown not only on the alluvium but, after burning, on the lateritic hills, especially in the wetter northern areas. The analysis of local variations given by Kuriyan is worth summarizing.[41]

(i) In the extreme south rice is grown by canal – and in Shencottah taluk (east of the hills and really outside the region) by tank-irrigation. With intensive watering and careful transplanting crops can be obtained both in September–October and in February–March. In Chittur taluk – the Cochin outlier in Palghat – there is also a little irrigation by *anicuts* or weirs feeding canals, and here cotton and groundnuts are grown. These three areas are strongly influenced by Tamil methods.

(ii) Along the backwaters (*punja* and *cole* areas) the problem is not to get water on the land but to get it off. These areas are divided into blocks of up to 50 (exceptionally 100) ac., 20–40 ha., bounded by double dykes enclosing a channel. From July to September–October the ground is submerged, sometimes to a depth of several feet; after the rains the water is lifted into the bounding channels by Persian wheels; latterly oil-driven and still more recently electric pumps powered from Pallivasal have been introduced. The land lies three or four feet below the water-level in the channels, and sluices regulate various inundations during the growing season. Should the bunds be burst the half-drowned crop may be reaped from boats by cutting off the heads.

(iii) Along the backwaters on the Cochin–Malabar boundary the soil on areas liable to salt-water inundation is heaped up into mounds about one foot high and five feet round, on which the paddy is sown just before the rains. When the monsoon bursts the surrounding water is freshened and transplanting takes place. This is a rather precarious method, illustrating the devices enforced by severe population pressure.

(iv) In the wet lowlands above the backwaters more normal methods prevail, but the early onset of the rains enables planting to take place in April–May and harvest in September; the continuance of the rains then often permits a poor second crop (not necessarily paddy) harvested in January; very occasionally a third is possible.

After rice, coconut is the chief crop, typically, of course, in the sandy coastal strip but also on alluvial loams and (with more careful preparation) on laterites. In Travancore the coconut acreage is nearly equal to that of rice; in Quilon taluk, indeed, it covers most of cropped area. Next to rice as the essential food, the coconut palm is the basis of life in Kerala:

'Apart from the several uses of the chief products, viz., coir, copra, coconut oil, oil-cake, the hollowed trunk serves as a canoe, the nut forms a staple article of diet, the leaves may be used for many of the purposes of paper, are frequently employed as thatch and for the manufacture of brooms, baskets, umbrellas, tattis [screens kept soaked to cool rooms], and fans, and utilised as

[41] G. Kuriyan, 'Some aspects of the regional geography of Kerala', *IGJ* 17/1 (1941), 1–41. This section on Kerala has in general also profited by mapping, and personal communications to A. T. A. Learmonth, by R. Ramachandran.

crude torches in a dried form, or burnt as fuel, as it is [*sic*] or in the form of charcoal. In addition, the fresh or fermented juice of the stem is consumed as a beverage, by evaporation it is made into jaggery and by subsequent treatment even sugar is obtainable. When distilled, the toddy becomes arrack and finally vinegar.'[42]

Of the 'industrial' workers of Kerala – most of them, of course, cottage workers – about one-third are in various processes connected with coconut products, and of these two-thirds are women. The coir 'yarn' is almost entirely cottage-produced, its working-up into mats and so on largely a small factory industry.

The most important other crops (apart from plantation rubber and tea in the hills), are cassava (tapioca) and pepper, mainly in the foothills. The former is grown as a food crop on poorer lateritic soils and up into the foothills; pepper is perhaps the chief peasant-produced cash crop after coconut. Cereals other than paddy are negligible, as are oilseeds except for a little sesamum (gingelly), often as a third crop on the higher wet-rice lands. Nearly every homestead has its plantains and other fruit trees, and ginger and the betel vine, with its associated areca palm, are also grown widely but in tiny patches.

Tapioca deserves special mention. Introduced about 1920, it is grown on the lateritic soils (picturesquely described as 'about as attractive for agriculture as railway ballast') in tiny holdings by the poorest of the poor. As Gourou points out, there is a sort of social inversion: the better-off rice farmers in the valley bottoms, and a hundred feet or so above them a very wretched (largely Christian) peasantry.

Other occupations

Fishing, both sea and freshwater, plays a big part in the life of Kerala but, as usual in India, is still to a large extent primitive in technique and organization, though improvements, including some motorization of boats, better storage and marketing, are under way in a joint Indo-Norwegian project. There are some interesting features: Portuguese influence in the so-called 'China nets' and the crossbow used for shooting fish from river-banks, and the many varieties of basket-work fishtraps.[43] The catch of 'sardines' is largely used for manuring coconut; prawns are taken in the flooded paddy-fields, the skins used as manure and the pulped flesh exported. Normally Burma was a good customer: the time of transport raised no difficulty as high putrescence was regarded with favour.

There are hydro-electric plants at Pallivasal on the Mudrapuzha River and elsewhere; the great reservoir impounding the Periyar headquarters (below, p. 775) was built to supply irrigation water, by tunnel, to the Madras side, but also provides power for Kerala. Pallivasal also powers the industries of Cochin town with the near-by aluminium works at Alwaye, formerly dependent on imported

[42] Quoted in Kuriyan, *JMGA* 11/4 (1937) 286. Cf. P. K. Paniker, 'The coconut – its cultivation on the Malabar Coast', *IGJ* 18/2 (1943), 78–88.
[43] A. K. Menon, 'Fisheries of Cochin', *IGJ* 14/3 (1939), 229–36; C. D. Forde, *op. cit.* 269.

alumina but now increasingly supplied from Muri in Bihar; a recent development is the use of electric pumps for 'dewatering' the *cole* lands.

Except for local clays and laterite, and some unexploited lignite, the only minerals are the ilmenite, monazite and zircon sands of the beaches from Quilon to Kanya Kumari. These contain 8–10% thorium oxide and were exploited for the manufacture of gas mantles; the spread of electric lighting ruined this demand, but recent technological changes have led to a remarkable recovery. Titanium from the ilmenite and cerium from the monazite are essential in some highly specialized electrical and chemical industries – electrodes, tracer bullets, and as a catalyst in benzine synthesis, among others; and these deposits are now of great strategic significance in relation to atomic power. Production in 1925 fell to one hundredweight (51 kg.); in 1961 ilmenite alone accounted for 174,000 metric tons.

Although there is as yet little modern industry, small-scale industry based mainly on agricultural products is important: coir, soap and cosmetics from coconut; the cashew industry now imports nuts from Africa; there is tile-making from local clay.

Population and settlement

The demographic situation of Kerala is very serious. The overall density of 1,127 rises in Trivandrum and Alleppey Districts to 2,060 and 2,595 respectively, and even deducting these two towns, they are 1,703 and 2,400 – these in a purely rural environment. In 1941, Elankunnapuzha village had 18,173 people on its 3·8 sq. miles – a density of 4,782 or 1,855 per km². The 1951–61 increase, though lower than that of several other states, at 23·3% was slightly higher than the average for India as a whole. Taking a liberal view of the possibilities of 'culturable waste', Kuriyan calculated that only 2,000,000 people additional to the 1931 total could be supported; the increase has been over three and a half times as much – 7,396,000. Holdings are extremely small, and cultivation intensive, though there is a slack season from May to August in both farming and fishing. Diversification and expansion are perhaps more possible in the foothills. Webb seems to feel that large-scale modern industrialization might do more harm than good, since there is already a high proportion of small-scale and home handicraft workers, and modern industry might give rise to more displacement of these people than new employment to the surplus rural population; and such industries as coir and cashews are vulnerable to world trends either in demand or competition. Power development along Ghats, for a wide dispersal of small industries, may help; in this connection Webb stresses the value of the high rate of literacy – nearly half the population of all ages, with the lowest disparities between rural and urban and male and female population.[44]

As for settlement patterns, the extreme density of population and the ample water supplies produce (as in Bengal) a close stipple of habitations; rather than solidly compact villages, a mere thickening and running together of homesteads

[44] G. S. Gosal, 'Literacy in India', *Rural Sociology*, 29 (1964), 261–77.

except in the transitional areas – Kanniyakumari, Shencottah, Palghat, parts of Malabar. The importance of food-producing trees (coconut, areca, plantain, jackfruit) fits in with this: they are grown in the house compounds, so that the actual dwelling-space subtracts hardly anything from the cultivation-space, while at the same time the compounds ensure that the 'village' is loosely built, and may indeed spill all over the village lands (Fig. 22.8). At the same time, densities are

FIG 22.8 KERALA: COASTAL SETTLEMENT. 40 miles north of Cochin town. Dots, habitations; shaded, paddy. Note contrast between linear settlement on beach-ridges (under coconut) in west and ring settlement around lateritic rises in east. *SOI* 58 B/2. *Courtesy* SOI.

so great that the modern road traveller has a marked impression of quasi-urban life.[45]

Along the coast there is a marked linear tendency, houses and coconuts on the sandy ridges with their fresh ground-water, paddy in the lows. Inland the lateritic

[45] The 14th and the 20th centuries tell the same tale. 'Mulaybar, which is the pepper country, extends for two months' journey along the coast . . . there is not a foot of ground but what is cultivated. Every man has his own orchard, with his house in the middle and a wooden palisade all round it.' (Ibn Battuta, *Travels in Asia and Africa, 1325–1354*, trans. H. A. R. Gibb (1929), 231–2). Along the 40 miles from Quilon to Trivandrum one is never out of sight of habitations or foot-travellers; G. Slater, *op. cit.* 172.

topography exercises a marked effect, settlement being strung out along valley-flanks or interfluves or forming a complete ring around the rises (Fig. 22.9).

Towns

The towns of Kerala are for the most part either ports or crossing-points on the backwaters. There is virtually no indigenous maritime tradition, but from the very early times spices attracted traders from East and West: Arabs, Graeco-Romans, Chinese.[46] With the Discoveries the Malabar coast became the scene of

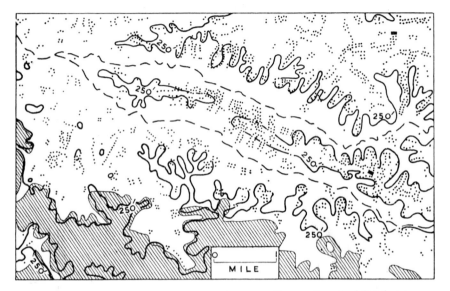

FIG 22.9 KERALA: INLAND SETTLEMENT. 5–10 miles southeast of Palghat town; lateritic foothills in approach to Palghat Gap. Dots, habitations surrounded by groves; shaded, forest; blank, cultivation; broken lines, seasonal streams. *SOI* 58 B/10. *Courtesy* SOI.

a fierce struggle between the Portuguese and their Muslim and European rivals. Relics of the era of European conflict were the tiny French settlement of Mahé (26 sq. miles, 75 km²), population (1941, 14,092) and the exclaves of former British territory at Cochin itself and in Travancore at Anjengo and Quilon (Tangasseri), which last had an area of 99 acres!

In Cannanore District Tellicheri (44,763) exports much of the Coorg coffee and some pepper and copra; Khozikode (Calicut; 248,548) has a similar trade but is more important administratively. Both ports are mere roadsteads, ships lying 2 or 3 miles offshore and lighters working from one or two piers, but at Tellicheri the shelter of offshore reefs enables some traffic to be carried on during the monsoon.

[46] On the Chinese shipping, see Ibn Battuta, *ed. cit.* 235–6.

Cochin is far more important: it really consists of several adjacent settlements: Cochin proper, at the passage through the sand-spit, essentially a European foundation with distinctive Portuguese and Dutch architecture; Mattancheri, the traditional Indian port; Ernakulam across the backwater; and with these the Census groups Alwaye to give a total population of 313,050. Cochin is in fact the oldest European settlement in India; on Christmas Day 1500 Cabral arrived, and from then until the Dutch supplanted them in 1663 the Portuguese were in alliance with the rulers of Cochin against the Muslim Zamorin of Calicut. The port has considerable locational advantages: it is central on the backwaters, the Palghat Gap lies about 125 miles (by rail) to the northeast, and it is about 300 miles (483 km.) nearer Aden and Durban than is Bombay. It may even rival Colombo as a transit port, as a call at Cochin adds only 40 miles to the Aden–Fremantle run.[47] The development of the modern port was for long impeded by its curious political situation; it lies on a breach in the long spit separating the greater backwater from the sea, but while the major installations and the approaches lie in what was British territory, the inner harbour – in which much of the trade is carried on – was in Cochin state, and much of the backwater was Travancorean. Real development – including the cutting of a channel through the bar across the natural breach, and much reclamation – began only in 1920–23; later a 3-mile approach channel was dredged to a width of 450 and a depth of 37 ft. (137 and 11 m.), so that the inner harbour is now accessible to any ship which can pass Suez. Rail and road bridges cross the backwater, and a large airport has been built on reclaimed land; the old metre line through the Palghat has been changed to broad gauge. The volume of trade increased from 450,000 tons in 1920 to 7,270,000 in 1961–62. The exports are the usual Kerala ones: coconut products, especially coir and copra, tea, rubber, cashew nuts. Soap factories in Ernakulam and rice-milling as at Mattancheri are also important. Trichur (73,038, only 4,000 more than in 1951), has cotton spinning and weaving mills and tile factories; it shares with Palghat command of the gap.

The south, formerly Travancore state, is less urbanized than the north, but Trivandrum (302,214), once a pleasant princely seat, is the new State capital. Alleppey (138,834) and Quilon are ports of ancient fame now decayed; mere roadsteads, they still carry on a considerable backwater traffic and have some industry, notably cashew processing. Alleppey, protected by a mudbank, is slightly the better port, but Quilon has the advantage of its situation on the metre line from Trivandrum through the Shencottah gap.

THE MALDIVE AND LACCADIVE ISLANDS

These groups of coral atolls extend from the Equator to about 15°N, 180–300 miles (290–483 km.) from the Malabar coast. The Laccadives and Minicoy are

[47] *Handbook of Commercial Information for India* (Delhi, 1937), 79; personal information from Sir Robert Bristow, who had a great part in building up the port.

attached to India, the Maldives are under their own Sultan and internally independent, but defence and external affairs are a British responsibility and an air base is being developed to replace those in Ceylon, to which the islands were formerly attached. These affiliations represent historical accident merely. The submarine swells on which they are based show opposing gravity anomalies, positive in the Laccadives, negative in the Maldives. Glennie concludes that the former occupy an upthrust, possibly on a continuation of the Aravalli strike; the Maldive ridge is possibly the result of volcanic extrusions on a crustal downwarp.[48]

The Laccadives (*Laksha divi*, 'hundred thousand isles') have in fact nine inhabited islets, plus Minicoy which is really the most northerly of the Maldives; the total population was 24,108 in 1961. Minicoy is about the largest: $1\frac{3}{4}$ sq. miles (4·5 km²) and is over one-tenth of the total land area. They are of course formed of coral detritus, but (except on Minicoy) the humus from the coconut palms is used for garden cultivation of millet, yams, jackfruit and plantains; there is no rice. The people are Malayalam-speaking but Muslims; fine seamen, they obtain rice and other necessities by taking coir, turtles, sea-slugs and other marine products to the Kerala ports. The people of Minicoy have a different language, are akin to the Sinhalese, and use a duodecimal numeration instead of the formerly universal binary counting of India. Though Muslims they are monogamous, and 'the women take the lead in everything but navigation'. The 220 inhabited Maldives (out of over 2,000) cover 115 sq. miles (298 km²) with about 90,000 people; again the population is Muslim, and the economy is similar to that of the Laccadives.

BIBLIOGRAPHICAL NOTE

On the northern sections, Deshpande's *Western India* remains a basic text, supplemented by numerous articles in the *Bombay Geographical Magazine*. Farther south, there is a more ample modern documentation: besides A. T. A. Learmonth on the Kanaras in the Mysore Regional Survey, and Sopher's work on Goa, both already cited, there are a series of articles, old but still valuable, by G. Kuriyan in the *Journal of the Madras Geographical Society–Indian Geographical Journal*: 11 (1937), 283–90; 12 (1937), 1–8; 13 (1938), 125–46; 16 (1941), 340–54; 17 (1942), 1–41. Three highly perceptive papers, which would deserve fuller incorporation did space permit, are: P. Gourou, 'Quelques observations de géographie tropicale dans l'Inde', *Revue de l'Univ. de Bruxelles* (1950–51); J. Dupuis, 'Kerala', *Cahiers d'Outre Mer* (Bordeaux), 2 (1958), 213–31; M. J. Webb, 'The coast plains of Kerala', *IGJ* 36/1 (1961), 1–27. There are some fascinating comments on old Goa in G. E. Hutchinson, *The Clear Mirror* (Cambridge, 1936).

[48] The standard reference is J. S. Gardiner (ed.), *The Fauna and Geography of the Maldive and Laccadive Archipelagoes* (Cambridge, 1903). See also H. St. C. Smallwood, 'A Visit to the Maldive Islands', *Jnl Royal Central [sic] Asian Soc.* 48 (1961), 83–89,

CHAPTER 23

The Deccan

(Regions XXV–XXXI)

———————→ ⊂———————

Generalities

The vast mass of the Peninsula is difficult to divide into satisfactory units of study; this would be difficult in any case, but the political divisions pose an added problem. If Kerala forms a unit where the physical and the political are in remarkably close accord, and if it seems legitimate enough to treat the narrow coastal strips of Maharashtra State and Mysore in the Western Littoral, Andhra Pradesh stretches back so far on to the plateau as to cause acute discomfort; Orissa is not quite so bad, since its hill country is not very significant in itself, and the much-reduced Madras State does not overlap too grossly on to the higher plateaus. Andhra remains recalcitrant, and it may be suspected that the physical dichotomy may come to be reflected in its politics: the deltas are very poorly integrated with the vast plains of upland Telengana. We have fallen back on a subjective impression of what is 'Deccani'; and this is reflected in the substitution of 'The Deccan' for 'The Peninsular Interior' in the title of this chapter.

The Deccan Lavas have indeed a characteristic physical aspect and a high degree of cultural individuality as the Maratha homeland; but for the rest plateau merges with plateau, river-basin with river-basin, and the border ranges are discontinuous in the east, a mere fillet in the west. Any division must thus give more weight than usual to factors of location and even mere convenience of handling. As the criteria are so empirical, the *raison d'être* of the division can best appear in the treatment of individual regions; it is some comfort to note that the broad outlines are similar to those of Stamp, Richards, Baker and others. The regions adopted are then:

1. The Western Ghats, including Coorg
2. The Southern Blocks (Nilgiris, Anamalai, Cardamom Hills)
3. The Deccan Lava (essentially inland Maharashtra State)
4. Karnataka (essentially inland Mysore)
5. The Upper Mahanadi and adjacent basins: (*a*) Wainganga valley; (*b*) Chhattisgarh; (*c*) Upper Brahmani and Jamshedpur gap
6. Telangana (the bulk of inland Andhra Pradesh)
7. The Anantapur–Chittoor Basins (also Andhra)
8. The Eastern Hills: (*a*) Orissa and Bastar Hills; (*b*) Cuddapah Ranges and valleys (Andhra).

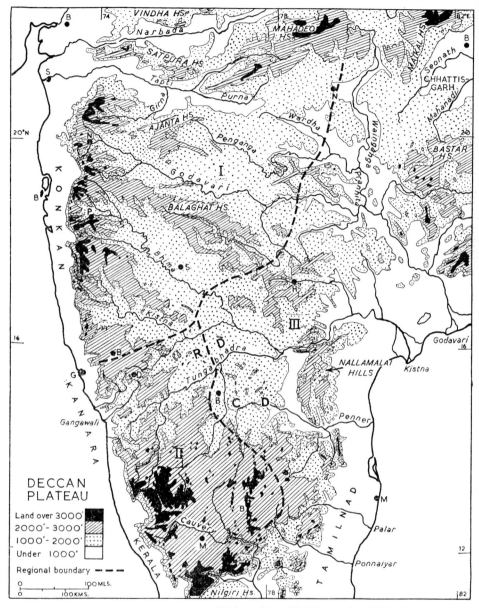

FIG 23.1 THE DECCAN PLATEAU. I, Maharashtra; II, Karnataka; III, Telangana; RD, Raichur Doab; CD, Ceded Districts.

Most of these are clear and legitimate enough, but it must be admitted that the 'Upper Mahanadi' is something of a monster. It has a distinctly recognizable core in the irrigated Chhattisgarh Plain, but the area described extends from the

Wainganga to the Subarnarekha, and these extensions east and west are linked with Chhattisgarh simply because on our scale of work they can hardly stand as regions by themselves, and cannot well be linked with anything else; as we have seen (above, p. 635), there is a case for shifting Chota Nagpur into the Deccan (and yet it has not a Deccani air about it), or for taking Jamshedpur with the Damodar to which it is economically linked. However, this Upper Mahanadi region as a whole has a certain unity of function in that it forms a corridor lying between the Chota Nagpur plateaus and the jungly Orissa highlands, linking Bengal and Maharashtra. But this is largely a development of the railway age; historically the great movements of war and trade have been north–south, or between the interior and the nearest accessible coast, not across the root of the Peninsula.

Structure has been described in Chapter 1. We may note briefly the extraordinary maturity of the Peninsular rivers, graded almost to their heads in the Western Ghats, but cutting through the Eastern Hills or descending precipitously from the high Mysorean plateaus in gorges. The major relief features are usually no more than the flanks of plateaus or of fault-troughs, or residual crests on the heights of land between the main river-basins; but there is a good deal of local diversity, the mesas and buttes of the Deccan Lavas, the fantastic tors and gnarled ridges of the Archaeans and the Dharwar Schists.

Climatically the entire area, except for the Eastern Hills, the Western Ghats and the rain-shadow of the latter, could be described as tropical savannah with monsoonal modification; but such a description conceals considerable variations. There is a broad distinction between the northeast, with 40 in. plus and considerable humidity, and the drier (20–40 in., 508–1,016 mm.) and more variable west and south, which in the lee of the Ghats receive less than 20 in. in places. The boundary between these is a line running roughly along the lower Godavari and produced northwestwards. Temperatures practically everywhere range from means of 65–75°F. in January to 85–95° in May (18–24 and 29–35°C.); except, of course, where modified by high altitude.

THE WESTERN GHATS AND COORG

The astonishing contrast between the scarp and the plateau faces of the Ghats is brought out by Fig. 23.2: on the one side deep ravines and canyons, on the other flat-topped spurs intersected by mature valleys. The spurs lose height to the eastwards fairly rapidly, becoming mere flat-topped relic ridges on the watersheds, with outlying mesas and buttes; the actual dissected belt, the Ghats proper, is only a few miles wide as a rule; generally 2,500–3,000 ft. (760–915 m.) high, it reaches 4,500 (1,370 m.) or more in the culminations whence spring the transverse spurs, such as the Tryambak massif at the root of the Balaghat Hills. It is a negative area: in some places, as the Peint forests and the Dangs (south of the Tapti) and behind Ratnagiri and Goa, a tangle of dense jungle, including teak on terraces and valley floors; elsewhere it carries more open forest with not a little bare rock on the flanks of the more massive lava flows. On spurs east and west are the great hill forts, bases whence the 'mountain rat' Sivaji gradually extended his power over the Konkan and the more open Maharashtra country. Except in the Kanara sub-region already discussed (pp. 669–73), there is little economic activity apart from jungle agriculture, forestry and the increasingly

GHATS SECTION

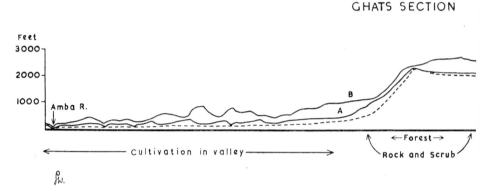

FIG 23.2 SECTION ACROSS THE GHATS. The scarp is here 32 miles WNW of Poona. flanks; B, along interfluve 1 mile north of A; C, crest of spur between Pauna R. (Mula confluence) only 1,820 ft. Drawn from *SOI* 47F/6; vertical exaggeration

important hydro-electric development at the Jog falls. The only places of much importance are the little gap towns and sanatoria behind Bombay (Igatpuri, Lonavla, Khandala) and Mahabaleshwar (6,029), a hill-station at 4,000–5,000 ft., used by middle-class Bombay citizens. Its excessive rainfall (260 in., 6,604 mm.) gives it a short season; Panchgani, only 12 miles east, receives no more than 60 in. (1,524 mm.) and has a less fluctuating population, receiving not only some of the hot-weather exodus from the plains, but a rains exodus from Mahabaleshwar itself.

Farther south the dissected belt is higher and wider in the coulisses of Coorg, around the Cauvery headwaters; some points in the girdle of ranges on all sides but the east reach over 5,500 ft. (1,675 m.). Most of Coorg was originally evergreen forest and bamboo jungle, with some parkland to the east. The average annual temperature is only 60° F. (15·6°C.), humidity high, rainfall at the capital, Mercara, 133 in. (3,378 mm.). Of the million acres of Coorg a third are forested and nearly a third cultivated, though of that about half is generally fallow. Rice accounts for over half and coffee (mainly plantation, but some peasant-grown) for about a third of the cropped area; oranges are another useful tree-crop. Coorg was formerly a state on its own, but is now a District of Mysore, with 322,829 people on its 1,600 sq. miles (4,145 km²). It is inhabited by a remarkably sturdy peasantry, with their own language (Kodalu): isolated, perhaps fortunately, from the main currents of Indian life, they half-cultivate half-gather cardamoms, collect wax and honey, and hunt, to supplement the product of their paddy-fields: it is typical that even the backbreaking labour of transplanting paddy seedlings ends in a race.[1] The Wynaad Plateau links Coorg with the great boss of the Nilgiris; the tea and coffee plantations of the plateaus extend down the slopes into Kerala, where Mangalore and Khozikode are the main outlets.

WEST OF POONA

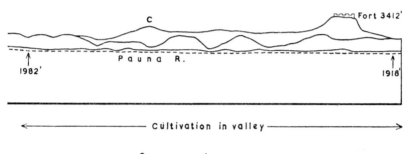

Horizontal Scale

8 miles south of Bhor Ghat. Broken lines, thalwegs; A, general line along valley and Lonavla. Note that Pauna is graded almost to its head; base level at Poona 2·1.

THE SOUTHERN BLOCKS

On either side the Palghat Gap is dominated by the highest mountains of the Peninsula, Nilgiris to the north and the Anaimalai–Palani–Cardamoms group to the south. According to Wadia these are great horsts, corresponding to similar structures in Ceylon: 'one cannot but ascribe such extraordinarily abrupt inequality of the ground in ancient Archaean terrain to mechanical dislocation and recent block uplift.'[2] But there are difficulties in accepting this view.

These are the great plantation areas of the Peninsula, and the power from their rejuvenated streams is a main factor in the modern industrial development of Tamilnad and Kerala.

(a) *The Nilgiris*

The Nilgiris ('Blue Mountains'; Fig. 23.3) form a compact plateau of about 1,000 sq. miles (2,590 km.) with a summit level of 6,000–8,000 ft. (1,830–2,440 m.), rising with extreme abruptness on all sides: on the eastern slopes there is a fall of 6,000 ft. in 1½–2 miles, the face to the Coimbatore Plateau is hardly less steep, and on the north the Nilgiris are cut off from the 3,000–4,000-ft. Mysore plateaus by the deep straight gash of the Moyar (the 'Mysore

[1] For a full and interesting, if disjointed, account of Coorg, see L. A. Krishna Iyer, 'Coorg ethnology' (*IGJ* 22 (1947), 157–225).
[2] D. N. Wadia, 'The making of India' (Presidential Address, 29th Indian Science Congress; Calcutta, 1942), 17.

ditch'), the narrow floor of which lies at 1,000–2,000 ft. The massif is as it were islanded between the Moyar and the Bhavani to the south; the headwaters of these rivers have obviously been captured by the shorter west-flowing streams.

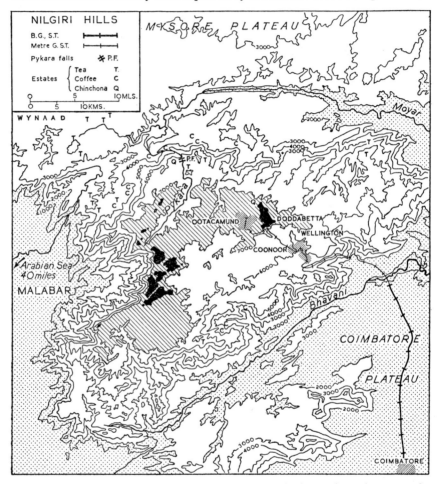

FIG 23.3 THE NILGIRI HILLS. Contours at 1,000 ft. interval; under 2,000 ft. stippled, 7,000–8,000 ft. shaded, over 8,000 ft. black. *SOI* 1/253,440 58 A. *Courtesy* SOI.

With a rainfall of 60–160 in. (1,524–4,064 mm.), according to aspect, and temperatures of 38–68°F. in the cold weather, 55–75° in the hot (3·3–20 and 13–24°C.), the Nilgiris form a little botanic realm of their own, with affinities to the Assam flora. Half the area is under forests; but much consists of open, boldly rolling downland interspersed with gallery forests (*sholas*). Quick-growing eucalypts and wattles have been introduced from Australia to supply fuel to the hill-stations, and there are Government cinchona plantations; but the substitution of synthetics and the use of DDT in mosquito elimination is leading to experiments with other medicinal and aromatic plants. 'In the *sholas* grow rhododendron, ilex, ferns of many varieties, bracken, tree-orchids with delicate blossoms, the hill gooseberry, blackberries, the sweet-scented Nilgiri lily, the alpine wild strawberry. . . . Hedges are often made of heliotrope, fuchsia, and geraniums.'[3] With the added attraction of shootin' and fishin' it is no wonder that the Nilgiris are the leading holiday resort of southern India.

The economy of the Nilgiris is atypical: plantation crops, tea and coffee, dominate the agriculture; potatoes have increased – and so has erosion; rice is less important than other food grains; the tribal Todas still graze their buffaloes on the downlands. Much of the local activity still revolves around the hill-station of Ootacamund, lying under the highest point of the plateau, Dodabetta (8,760 ft., 2,670 m.). 'Ooty' and its satellites Wellington and Coonor have the usual hills layout of straggling bungalows; they are reached by a metre-gauge rack-railway with gradients of 1 in 12½. There is a little local industry of the kind associated with resort functions, sodawater factories and so on; but some electrified light industry is being added, such as photographic films and processing; tea and eucalyptus oil are processed, and at Wellington the Government cordite factory had one of the earliest hydro-electric installations in India. Of much greater importance are the power station at Pykara Falls; the utilization of the Pykara tail-water over a 1,200-ft. (365-m.) drop in the Moyar valley is linked with the Mettur scheme in Madras and the new Canadian-Indian Kundah project.

(b) *The Anaimalais, Palanis and Cardamoms*

This remarkable group of hills (Figs. 22.7, 25.10) is more complex than the Nilgiris, and in Anaimudi itself they have the highest peak of the Peninsula, 8,841 ft., 2,694 m. The front to the Palghat Gap is remarkably steep and in the east remarkably straight; the southeastern flanks of the Palanis, overlooking the upper Vaigai re-entrant, are also remarkably abrupt, as are the Cardamoms and their protrusions (Varushanad Hills) south of the Vaigai. But to the northwest the hills fray out into long southeast–northwest ridges; and indeed over much of the area this trend is most marked, the rivers (e.g. the Periyar) having longitudinal stretches of such straightness as to suggest control by faults, with transverse gorges producing a perfect trellis-pattern. Between 10° N and the Shencottah Gap the active streams of the exposed Arabian Sea front have pushed the watershed back to within 4 or 5 miles of the eastern edge of the hills: here the change from jungle-clad mountains to the tank-pitted Tamilnad plain is very sudden (Fig. 25.10).

Again, apart from the shifting cultivation of tribes some of whom (e.g. Cochin Kadars) are hardly more than hunters and gatherers, the economy is atypical: forests, plantations, hydro-electricity. The most exploited forests, served by special light railways, are in the northwest, on the western slopes of the

[3] *Madras Gaz.* II (1908), 296–7.

Anaimalais. As for plantations, these are not confined to the western flanks but are more numerous there, where there is a broader plateau development than on the east. A little coffee and tea is grown in Cochin and in Madurai District (Madras), but the major share of the plantations is in the Travancorean part of Kerala, which is also by far the most important rubber-producing area of India, with the bulk of India's 264,000 ac. (107,000 ha.). It is grown on the lower slopes, generally below 1,000 and never above 2,000 ft. (610 m.), with 80–120 in. (2,032–3,048 mm.) rain. Above the rubber, tea extends to nearly 6,000 ft., and indeed more than half of it is grown above 4,000 ft.; rainfall is usually 100–150 in. It is noteworthy that over half the rubber is produced on Indian-owned estates.

As for hydro-electricity, the hills are dotted with falls and rainfall on the western flanks is everywhere high and reliable. So far the most important large development is at Pallivasal in Travancore, which powers the aluminium smelters at Alwaye and also works pumps draining the flooded paddy-fields of Kerala. A project of great interest is that for utilizing the great Periyar Reservoir (Fig. 25.10) for power; the Periyar headwaters have been impounded and are taken through the watershed by tunnel to irrigate the Suruli-Vaigai valley in Madurai.

The western flanks of the hills are too rainswept to have much settlement except on plantations, forest camps and power installations. In the east Kodaikanal, lying at 7,000 ft. (2,135 m.) on the Palanis, is a minor hill-station, noted for its mission schools and an old-established physical observatory.

THE MAHARASHTRA PLATEAUS

Maharashtra, the Maratha country *par excellence*, may be taken as roughly coterminous with the main mass of the Deccan Lavas above the Ghats. To the north the Tapti valley, flanked by typical lava plateaus but floored by alluvium, forms a transition to the central Indian scarplands; in the south, along the Malaprabha, there is another belt where Archaeans and lavas interdigitate and where cultural allegiance is divided between the Marathi and Kannada (Kanarese) languages. But to the east the boundary between Marathi and Telugu, Maharashtra State and Andhra, was reflected in the division of the old Hyderabad state into Marathwara and Telangana, and shows a striking accord with the edge of the Lavas (Fig. 23.4).

The terrain

It is a region of extraordinary physical homogeneity, in the gross at least, although detailed study reveals significant differences in erosional features, soils, vegetation and farming practice depending on the varying petrology of the lavas; for example, the reduction of essential *level* cultivated land by detritus from steeper slopes, following deforestation, and gullying from the valley bottoms.[4] The

[4] See the fine study by C. D. Deshpande, L. S. Bhat and M. S. Mavinkurve, 'Chandenapuru valley – a study in land use . . . in the Deccan Lavas region', *Bombay Geog. Mag.* 6–7/1 (1959), 5–15; and more generally V. S. Gananathan, 'Western districts of upland Maharashtra', *IGJ* 37/4 (1962), 121–32.

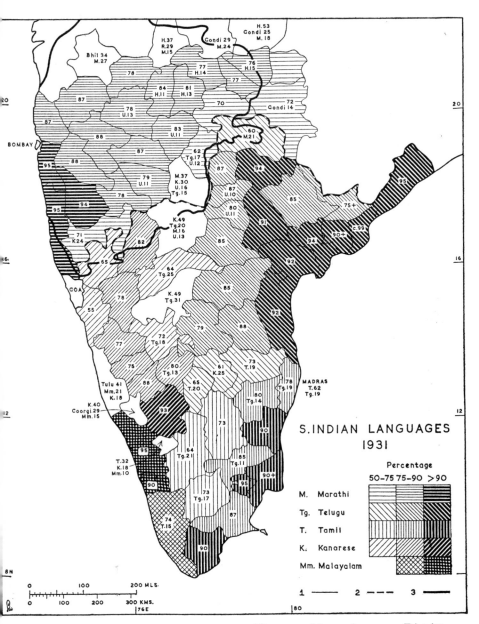

FIG 23.4 SOUTH INDIAN LANGUAGES. Figure = % speakers. 1, District boundaries; 2, boundary between Aryan- and Dravidian-speaking majorities; 3, boundary of Deccan Lavas. H, Hindi; U, Urdu; R, Rajasthani.

general slope to the east and southeast is gentle: Poona lies at 1,800 ft., and it is over 100 miles down the Bhima to the 1,500-ft. contour – only 91 m. in 161 km. From the Ghat culminations long tongues of higher ground (over 2,000 ft.) run east and divide the plateau into compartments which (except on the upper Krishna) are mature or even senile in aspect: the plains of Berar and Nagpur, the great basin of the upper Godavari, the Bhima from Poona to behind Sholapur. But these 'ranges', prominent as they appear on small-scale maps, are quite unlike the sierras which compartmentalize the Meseta: they are really only flat-topped tablelands with more or less steep flanks. The most prominent uplands are the Sahyadriparvat or Ajanta Hills, but their eminence is owed mainly to the faulting-down of the Tapti trough below. South of these is the Balaghat 'Range'; one can drive from Poona on to its 'summit' at Ahmadnagar without noticing more than a bolder modelling of the relief, which looks like an impossibly idealized textbook block diagram. Poona itself has been variously described as a 'hill-girt city' and as lying in a landscape so flat as to make one believe in the flat-earth theory; either statement is true according as one looks south or north. Everywhere the Deccan Lavas carry their sign-manual: mesas and buttes, the tops remarkably accordant, often as if sliced off with a knife: slightly incised streams, with some definite valley bottoms bounded by the bevelled edges of the little plateaus (Figs. 23.2, 23.7). The flanks of the hills are often stepped by the great horizontal lava flows and/or constructional benches, and the whole country then looks ridiculously like a relief model so badly constructed that the cardboard layers show through the modelling. The valleys are graded to local base-levels at the confluences with the main rivers; the general effect of the flat floors and relatively steep sides where they impinge on the plateaus strongly suggests lateral corrosion. The upper Krishna and its tributaries (especially the Koyna), however, have steeper profiles and show more signs of vertical erosion, and on the Andhra Pradesh border the Krishna descends in rapids of 400 ft. in 3 miles, 1 in 40.

Despite this general homogeneity, the uplands are less mature, more dissected, with greater available relief than the basins; and these factors introduce important variations in value. The steep slopes, and in places the summits, of the plateaus may be stony and barren, and elsewhere carry but poor vegetation, often short grass; cultivation is mainly millets. Soils in the valleys are deeper, more mature, and more fertile than the thin washed-out soils of the plateaus; the valleys also have more trees, though even there these are rather scattered.

Climate and cultivation

The region as a whole lies in the rain-shadow of the Ghats, though the north-eastern fringe (Purna and Wainganga valleys) is reached by Bay of Bengal influences and receives over 40 in. Good rainfall spills over the Ghats as far as Poona and Belgaum; beyond this a roughly north–south belt 50–60 miles wide is the most marked rain-shadow area (20–30 in., 508–762 mm.) and is also the area of maximum variability. Belgaum, in this Malvad (Maval) or Ghat foothill strip, has 50 in. (1,270 mm.; probably the lowering of the Ghats by the Kanara breaches has some effect); Poona, on the inner edge of the better-watered belt, 27 in. (686 mm.). Bijapur and Ahmadnagar, with 20 and 22 in., represent the rain-shadow area, Akola, with 30 in., the transition towards Nagpur. The retreating Bay of Bengal monsoon showers are important for rabi crops as far inland as eastern Maharashtra.

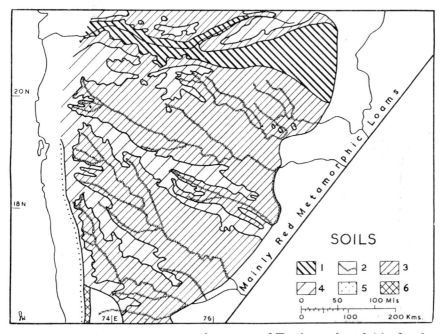

FIG 23.5 MAHARASHTRA: SOILS. 1, deep regur of Tapti trough and (2) of main valleys (agriculturally first class); 3, medium regur (good); 4, thin black or red soils (poor); 5, laterite (very poor); 6, forest loams (first class). Adapted from Fig 2 in E. Simkins, *Agric. Geog. of the Deccan Plateau. Courtesy of the author and the Geographical Association.*

Soils are of great importance. The more mature black earth of the alluvial Tapti trough extends across the Amraoti height of land (Purna/Wardha watershed), with some change in appearance but little in agronomic value, on to the lavas and to the eastern limits of the region around Nagpur; but elsewhere it is found mainly in the larger valley bottoms (Fig. 23.5). Most of the soil is 'medium regur', and the higher ground carries immature regur or even red soils; these are notably poorer. As we have seen (Chapter 3), the black soil is by no means confined to the Deccan Lavas; but here the limits of Lava and regur do coincide fairly closely. The characteristics of the regur are well described by Simkins; we may recall the high moisture content, and the aeration and

693

'working-over' of the soil layers by deep cracking in the hot weather. (See also Chapter 3.)

The agriculture presents some highly individual features. For so large an area of mainly non-alluvial land, not very humid, a very high proportion is cultivated: except in one or two eastern Districts, NSA is 60–80% of total area; but there is hardly any double-cropping. There is also a high proportion of fallow, and on the areas of poorer and drier soils one might almost speak of an approach to the long-fallow *chitamene* type of shifting cultivation. Yet the area of stable cultivation is very large, accounted for by terrain and soil – the wide flattish expanses of good regur – together. There is relatively little difference between NSA and TSA, irrigation being as yet little developed and mainly by wells, except in some of the Maval valleys. The most important existing works are the Mutha and Nira Canals in Poona District; but they are for protection rather than intensive culture. Elsewhere there is some irrigation in Ahmadnagar and Sholapur, but it is really significant mainly on the margins – in the Malvad, and the marches with Telangana and Karnataka where Archaeans and Lavas interdigitate locally. Yet the unreliability of the rainfall warrants the extensions now proposed. Of these the most important is on the Ghataprabha, in the south, which will ultimately command 300,000 ac. (121,400 ha.) on the Mysore border. The big Kakrapara project on the Tapti will benefit mostly Surat District, outside the region. Unfortunately the scope for irrigation is most limited where it is most needed, away from the Malvad; and the hydroscopic virtues of well-developed regur themselves render it not very suitable for irrigation, since it becomes very heavy and sticky to work when wet.

Probably no region of the sub-continent, comparable in size, has so little rice, only about $2\frac{1}{2}\%$ of the cropped area, nearly all in the irrigated pockets under the Ghats. With local exceptions wheat is the great irrigation crop; in Wardha the irrigated rice area was returned as one acre! But increasingly sugar is grown by irrigation, in some cases 'factory cane' grown by the refining firms on land leased from the cultivators.

This is pre-eminently the realm of jowar and cotton (Fig. 23.6): the former covers about a third of TSA in most districts, and 40–70% in the Poona–Sholapur area; in most it is the ranking crop also, replaced by cotton in Parbhani, Akola and Buldana. Cotton has in general declined somewhat, but still covers 30–50% of NSA in these Districts. Bajra, oilseeds and wheat are also important. These five crops account for over three-quarters of the arable, the rest being mainly gram, other pulses and fodder crops, all mainly on the poorer uplands. Jowar is clearly the staple food-grain, and its large stalks and the leaves are very useful fodder; indeed it is sometimes grown for stalk and leaf rather than grain.

Although cotton nowhere exceeds 50% of TSA, as it did before the war in its main concentration on the deep regur of the north, its proportion of the area remains very high for an Indian cash crop, and provides an index of the extent to which the economy is tied to outside markets. The cottons here are mainly the short-stapled (⅜ to ⅝ in.) 'Oomras'. Beyond the Ajantas is a second zone in the upper Godavari valley, but neither intensity nor yield is as high as in the northern zone. A third area in the south (Belgaum and Bijapur, now in Mysore) has a much smaller acreage, but its 'kumpta' strains have a longer staple, up to ⅞ in. Cotton stays long on the ground, being planted in July–August and not harvested until February or March.

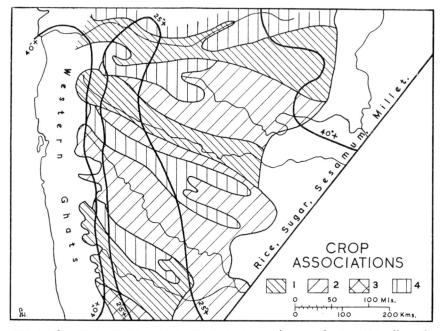

FIG 23.6 MAHARASHTRA: CROP ASSOCIATIONS. I, jowar, wheat, cotton, linseed, pulses: 2, jowar, cotton, bajra, pulses; 3, rice, sugar, cotton, millets; 4, bajra, pulses; 5, approx. isohyets. Cf. Fig 23.5. Adapted from Fig 26 in Simkins, *op. cit.* as for Fig 23.5, Despite changes, the map still indicates general cropping relations.

Bajra is especially strong in the west (it is the leading crop in Nasik), and tends to replace jowar on the higher ground and thinner soils. The distribution of wheat (rabi) follows that of cotton fairly closely; the other great rabi crop is one or other of the oilseeds, but especially groundnut, which towards the south-east is locally the second ranking crop. A new crop of interest is *mesta*, a wild plant some 10 or 12 ft. high with a fairly good fibre which can be mixed up to 20% with jute; it is now being grown on a small but increasing scale as a jute substitute.

Agriculturally, then, the region is outstanding in India by the insignificance or irrigation and rice, by the very great importance of cash crops, and in some areas (such as the Krishna/Panchganga doab) by increasing specialization backed by industry, e.g. for sugar. The wide expanse of good land in the open regur plains, their easy communications, and the metropolitan stimulus of Bombay, have fostered this commercial bias. The total food-grains proportion of TSA is remarkably low. Fortunately the main cotton tract is the most secure of the region; most risky are Ahmadnagar, Sholapur and Bijapur Districts, where one year in five is likely to be too dry; Bijapur especially is liable to severe dearths.

Prosperous as Maharashtra is, it is not immune from the usual risks and ills of Indian agriculture, and the emphasis on cash crops may itself be a source of weakness. Efforts are being made to increase the food proportion (though demands for more cotton acreage are not lacking), and the rolling terrain provides some opportunities for expansion: much of the mechanized preliminary preparation now being sponsored by government is taking place on the old fallows of this region. The existing garden cultivation in the Malvad, for Bombay and Poona markets, favours an extension of fruits and roots such as plantains and sweet potatoes which diversify the diet and some of which add vitamins.

Population and settlement

District densities generally lie between 125 and 500, and are naturally highest in the Malvad close under the Ghats, and in the deeper regur. Villages are usually large and compact, but more widely spaced than in the Ganga valley or the eastern littoral plains. Houses are often stone or brick, the latter with attractive detail in doorways and recesses, and have low-pitched roofs of semi-cylindrical tiles, or flat mud roofs. Many villages are grouped round a little fort or retain the old gates. Water-points are favoured sites; tanks, other than village ponds, are few, but the Lavas include some aquifers and wells in the valleys are usually reliable. The discontinuous lines of trees in the valley bottoms give some variety to the wide and open landscape. Fig. 23.7 illustrates some of these points.

As a general rule the larger towns of Maharashtra were strategic in origin and took on administrative and commercial functions in consequence; they are generally grouped round a massive citadel. Such are Ahmadnagar (119,020), the old Bahmani capital, and Aurangabad (97,701) in the north, Kolhapur (193,186), a former state capital, in the south. In the northwest Nasik (215,576), an old religious centre, owes its continued importance to its situation on the upper reaches of the Godavari, midway between the little gap towns – mere railway colonies – of Manmad, controlling the entrance from the Tapti, and Igatpuri at the top of the Thal Ghat. Under the new prohibitionist régime Nasik's distillery has been converted to power alcohol (there will doubtless be some leakage); its leading industry is probably the great government press for security printing, but it may add to its stature as irrigation and small power schemes are developed on the Godavari headwaters. Deolali, a few miles away, was probably the largest military transit camp in India – the first high and open (hence healthy) ground on the railway from Bombay into central India.

Other towns are primarily collecting centres and administrative headquarters, with a little industry, owing their rise to cotton and the railway: Akola (115,760),

Amraoti (Amravati, 187,442), and Wardha (49,113) in Madhya Pradesh; the last was famous as the site of Gandhi's *ashram* and partly for this reason is now the centre of an experiment in comprehensive regional development. Similar is Belgaum in the south, the junction for the transit trade to Marmagão, and really a contact town on the Karnatak border, as shown by its inclusion in Mysore; it too has hopes from power development on the Kalinadi.

There are only three really large towns: Nagpur (690,302), Poona (737,426), and Sholapur (377,583). The last is of least general importance, an isolated phenomenon, a predominantly industrial town with no *raison d'être* save its position in a cotton tract. Originally a strategic centre commanding the Bhima route into or out of Maharashtra, it is now one of the few predominantly industrial towns of India, and perhaps the most homogeneous, since its life revolves around its cotton mills. Otherwise there is relatively little industrialization in Maharashtra, away from Poona, and not very much scope for development: except for bauxite and the excellent building stone there are no noteworthy minerals. The bauxite is mostly in Kolhapur, and reserves are large; but their exploitation must wait on power development. This will come from the 300-ft. high multi-purpose dam across the narrow Koyna valley.

Nagpur, meeting-place of the Central and South Eastern Railways, is the focus for the Purna and Wainganga valleys: essentially a contact town. Originally the capital of the Maratha Bhonslas, it remained the administrative centre of the Central Provinces (now Madhya Pradesh) when the Bhonsla territory lapsed to the EIC in 1853. Apart from centrality in the sub-continent and its position on the edge of the Lavas, there is little of note about its site; nor can it claim much antiquity. Its importance was mainly administrative and commercial, with some cotton mills and minor industries, which find some support in the coal from very local fields in the Wainganga valley. Until the jet age its central position made it the stopping-place for night planes between Bombay, Calcutta, Delhi, Madras, and the small hours saw a mingled liveliness and sleepiness of acquaintances from the four corners of India around its wide-ranging airport bookstall.

Poona is of great and growing significance as the cultural and educational focus of the very considerable regional consciousness of Maharashtra; this, of course, is an inheritance from its past as the seat of such central authority as the Maratha confederacy possessed. Marathi literature has an exceptionally strong historical wing, and this is based largely on the archives of the Peshwas at Poona. It was also a centre of British–Indian society, connected with its wide-spreading military establishments, which form a fascinating contrast (analysed in Chapter 7) with the old Maratha town; and it is more and more becoming an industrial centre; already in 1951 a quarter of its working population was in industry. The older city is now ringed with industrial estates; there are textile, rubber and paper mills, and a great variety of light metal trades.[5]

[5] G. S. Kulkarni, 'Industrial landscape of Greater Poona', *Bombay Geog. Mag.* 8–9 (1961), 3–12.

The individuality of Maharashtra

The whole region bears the imprint of the Marathas: a tough, cheerful, hard-working peasantry, ably served by an adroit Brahmin élite which maintained

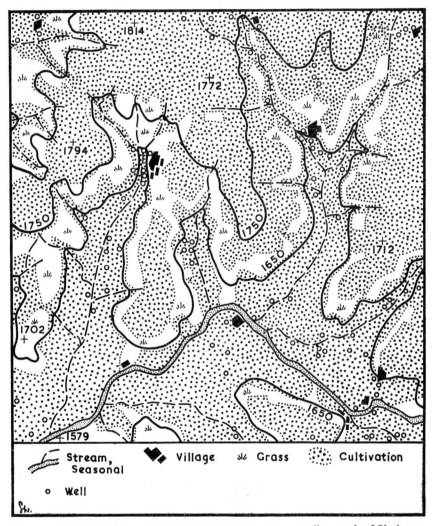

FIG 23.7 MAHARASHTRA: SETTLEMENT ON THE LAVAS. 30 miles north of Sholapur. Flat plateaus and graded valleys cultivated (cotton, millets); grass on steeper slopes. Wells and few trees mainly in valley bottoms. Villages compact, evenly spaced, but much farther apart than in Gangetic Plains. *SOI* 47 N/16. *Courtesy* SOI. Scale as on Fig 23.8.

close touch with the people. The Marathas first defied Muslim and Mogul power from the great holds and petty forts which command the spurs and river-crossing of the Ghats and the Malvad, and later overran most of India on horses light-built and wiry to match the men; and here, too, aggressive Indian nationalism was launched in the 1890s by Tilak. All is distinctive: the terrain of

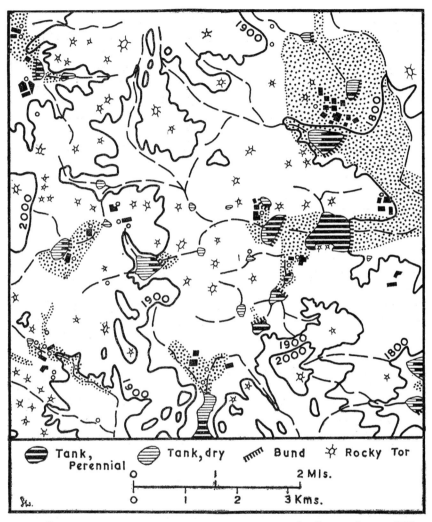

FIG 23.8 TELANGANA: SETTLEMENT ON THE GNEISSES. 8 miles northwest of Hyderabad city. Rocky terrain (original map shows 437 'tors'); cultivation (ragi, rice) in small tank-fed basins. Blank area rocky ground, with very open scrub and bush, largely acacias and euphorbias. Other symbols as on Fig 23.7. Note that on this map and Fig 23.7 all streams are dry half the year. *SOI* 56 K/7. *Courtesy* SOI.

wide rolling swells and abrupt mesas, the simple but extremely pleasing village and small-town architecture, even the women's dress, with saris tucked up between the thighs to make business-like breeches when real work must be done.[6]

The correlation of Marathi speech with the Lavas is not simply a matter of political power based on the splendid light cavalry country; much of the Deccan is just as suitable for their mobile guerilla warfare, and Maratha chiefs founded principalities in Gujarat, Malwa and Tanjore. Nevertheless it does seem to be a matter of terrain. The Marathas were essentially a millet-eating people, jowar and bajra; beyond the Lavas, with a rainfall of over 40 in. to the northeast, and better terrain for tanks on the Archaeans to the southeast, rice becomes much more important, even though the masses may be limited to ragi.[7] And with this goes a complex of cultural as well as agricultural aptitudes. The contrast is shown in Figs. 23.7 and 23.8.

With a strong historic personality, a distinctive agriculture, the power resources in the Ghats, and a rural society which (despite its integration with cotton prices) seems on the whole healthier and better balanced than the average, Maharashtra yet posed a serious problem in the linguistic reorganization of the states, primarily because of the rivalry between the Marathi hinterland and the dominantly Gujarati capitalism of Bombay City and Ahmedabad; and in 1960 Bombay State was divided into Gujarat and Maharashtra.

KARNATAKA OR MYSORE

This is the real 'Carnatic', which name came to be entirely misapplied to the Madras littoral.[8] The region extends from the Deccan Lavas on the north to the Moyar in the south; the western limit is of course the Ghats crest, and to the southeast the border hills and scarps of the Mysore plateaus provide a fairly sharp boundary between the Moyar and the Palar. But in the northeast the high plateaus break down into the isolated basins south of the Penner and the Cuddapah Ranges, and in the north the Raichur Doab, between Krishna and Tunga-bhadra, was the marchland between the Muslim Deccani Sultanates and Hindu Vijayanagar, which city occupied a forward position on the Tungabhadra, near Hampi village. The Doab is still a marchland between Karnataka, Andhra, and to a less extent Maharashtra. In general the region corresponds with the area in which Kannada (Kanarese) speech is dominant; but the lower levels of the Raichur Doab and Anantapur District go more naturally with Telangana. There is of course a belt of 'cultural conflict' with Maharashtra in the north, and the breaches of the Ghats south of Goa make for some overlap with the Western Littoral. There is thus some vagueness in the north and northeast. The new Mysore State covers 74,210 sq. miles (192,204 km²) and is nearly two and a half

[6] But it could be wished that they would favour some colours other than the muddiest purples and dingiest browns. Not far off a police inspector has recorded 'the ugliest women in the world, but fought over more than any women anywhere'; both high claims.
[7] We may recall the contrast between the Maratha and Kanarese rats, cited above, p. 236.
[8] See *Madras Gaz.* I (1908), 182–4.

times as large as the old princely state, incorporating Coorg; South Kanara and Bellary from Madras; North Kanara, Belgaum, Bijapur and Dharwar Districts from old Bombay; Raichur, Gulbarga and Bidar from Hyderabad – to the no small confusion of statistical geographers.

Within this area there is some diversity, e.g. between Malnad and Maidan (see below), and there are a number of plateaus at altitudes from about 2,000 to about 4,000 ft.; but on the scale of this book it seems not unreasonable to treat the region as essentially one, with perhaps a sub-division into the northern (formerly Bombay) Karnatak, the Malnad and the Maidan.

Physique

The entire area, apart from a fringe of Cuddapah (Algonkian–Torridonian) rocks along the Deccan Lava boundary, consists of a basement of Archaean gneisses and granites, intersected by great belts of much metamorphosed Dharwarian (Huronian) sediments, mostly phyllites, schists and slates, occupying the bottoms of tight-packed synclinoria (Fig. 25.1). The precise relationship of the Dharwars and the gneisses is difficult to unravel; although the former are in general erosion products of an Archaean land-mass, they are sometimes interbedded with the gneisses. 'The complex foldings of the crust in which these rocks have been involved have obliterated nearly all traces of their sedimentary nature, and have given to them a thoroughly crystalline and schistose structure, hardly to be distinguished from the underlying gneisses and schists. They are besides extensively intruded by granite bosses and veins and sheets, and by an extensive system of dolerite dykes.'[9] They are naturally well mineralized, iron, manganese and gold being especially important.

The plateaus rise from about 1,500–2,500 ft. in the north to about 3,000–4,000 ft. (455–760, 915–1,220 m.) in the south. The northern border is more complex; here the great scarps of the Kaladgi (Cuddapah) sandstones and limestones, cut across by the superimposed Ghataprabha and Malaprabha, form a belt of poor scrub-clad hills, a barrier zone marked by a great proliferation of ancient forts and local capitals on sites 'more defensible than the open plain, less cramped than the jungle'.[10] South of these hills is a plain of good black soils (on gneisses), the Dharwar cotton tract.

In Mysore there is a fundamental division – again recognized in both traditional and official nomenclature – between the forested Malnad in the west and the more open 'champaign' country of the Maidan (here='parkland') in the east: the transition is in places remarkably abrupt. In the extreme west, the Malnad really overlaps into the Ghats, here reaching 5,000–6,000 ft. (1,525–1,830 m.). It is highly dissected by the headwaters of the Tunga and Bhadra, and of the Cauvery, all of which rise on the very crest of the Ghats, only 30 miles (48 km.) or so from the Arabian Sea. The drainage system would repay study:

[9] D. N. Wadia, *Geology of India* (Macmillan, London, 3rd edition revised, 1961), 94.
[10] Deshpande, *Western India* (1948), 115. This is Deshpande's home ground.

the rivers (e.g. upper Tungabhadra, Hagari, upper Penner and Chitravati) flow in long south–north stretches, apparently structurally controlled, to the middle Tungabhadra or to the Penner. Some of the Penner tributaries have a southwest–northeast trend – parallel to the presumed faulting of the trough between the Mysore plateau-scarp and the Javadi–Shevaroy axis (below, 750), but this is cut across by the northwest–southeast trend of the upper Palar and Ponnaiyar. In the south the Cauvery breaks right across the plateau in a more or less west–east direction, but between the great Cauvery Falls at Sivasamudram and the Bhavani confluence it has reaches in both the northwest–southeast and northeast–south-west directions. The highest plateaus – 4,000 ft. plus – lie south of the Cauvery, separated from the Nilgiris by the Moyar trench. Here, where the great scarp is most strongly marked, is another important power node, developed at Sivasa-mudram and Mettur.

A strip about 6–14 miles wide in the extreme west carries tall evergreen forest, but most of the Malnad (roughly Shimoga, Kadur and Hassan Districts) has a mixed deciduous cover, with teak, sissoo and the most important sandalwood areas of India. The most interesting of the many complex small ranges of the Malnad is the Babu Bhudan group. These hills reach 6,317 ft. (1,925 m.) – the highest point in the region – and were the first home of coffee in India, the seeds being brought from Mocha by a 17th-century Muslim saint who gave his name to the hills: the first European plantation dates only from 1840. The Babu Bhudan Hills are now more important as the source of ore for the iron works at Bhadravati; the original charcoal smelting is now supplemented by coke and electricity to produce a limited quantity of high-grade steel, metal alloys and iron pipes, strips, etc. Other industries include paper, cement and wood distillates (see Chapter 11).

The Maidan consists in general of rolling plateaus rising in the east (between Tumkur and Kolar) into disjointed granitic hills of fantastically irregular plan and elevation. But there is a great deal of local diversity. 'The level plains, of blackish soil, in the north, are covered with plantations of sugar-cane and fields of rice; those irrigated by tanks have groves of coconut and areca palm; the high-lying tracts of red soil, in the east, yield ragi and other 'dry' crops; the stony and widespreading pasture grounds, in the central part of the country, are stretches of coarse grass, relieved by shady groves of trees',[11] among which acacia and wild dates are prominent.

The north is rather precarious climatically, with a rainfall of around 25 in. (635 mm.). The Mysore plateaus have 30–35 in. (762–889 mm.), but an important feature is that while most of the rain falls in the standard five months (June–October), there is a peak of c. 5 in. (127 mm.) in May followed by a drop until the major peak is reached in September or October; and there is appreciable fall in November. In the west (e.g. Shimoga) there is also a double peak, but the régime is nearer the normal west-coast pattern, with most rain in July. This

[11] *Mysore Gaz.* (1908), 2.

extension of the rainy season is of the greatest agricultural value, the May 'mango showers' being essential to the flowering of coffee and in places to an early (*kar*) crop of gower or ragi. Figures for Bangalore illustrate these points.

J.	F.	M.	A.	M.	J.	J.	A.	S.	O.	N.	D.	Total
0·2	0·3	0·6	1·2	4·5	3·0	4·1	5·8	7·4	6·2	2·4	0·4	36·0 in. (J.–O. 26·5)
												(914 mm.) (673 mm.)

The retreating monsoon has thus some influence in the east. Temperatures range from a mean of 69°F. in December to 81° in May (20·6–27·2°C.). Night frosts are not unknown on the higher levels.

Agriculture

The work of Deshpande, and more recently of Learmonth and his colleagues, brings out a degree of sub-regional diversity to which justice cannot be done here. There are such interesting variations as the importance of specialized crops such as vegetables and green fodder in the Krishna floodplain. Much of the area is unsuited to irrigation, except by tanks, for both physiographical and pedological reasons; but on some of the Kaladgi rocks and the high-level laterites of Belgaum irrigation is possible, and on crystalline rocks in the Varada valley both tanks and wells are used.[12] Indeed in a 'belt about 20 miles [32 km.] wide running almost parallel to the Poona–Bangalore railway . . . practically everything is transitional. Valleys open out to form the undulating surface features of the plateau. A rapid decline in the rainfall favours the growth of transitional vegetation type of medium sized trees and open grasslands. Tank irrigation is possible since narrow streams can be easily bunded. A variety of agricultural products, from rice the representative of subsistence agriculture to commercial crops of tobacco and cotton, is grown.'[13]

Tank irrigation is at a peak in the Mysore Maidan; there are thousands of tanks, most of them very small and subject to deterioration, and wells are locally important in alluvial tracts with a high water-table. Canals water an important sugar and rice tract below the Krishnaraja Reservoir, while Tungabhadra water is increasingly used. Uncultivated land accounts for a high proportion of the total area, especially in the south; some is classed as forest, but much of this is little more than ridgetop scrub, and there are areas of bare rocky plateau. In such areas the general poverty is shown by the high percentage of ragi and gram, the poor man's crops. But coconut and areca are grown in favoured valleys, where a surprisingly lush stretch of spice gardens may be hidden from the casual observer, who might well dismiss the area as a red and desolate land.

In the northern Districts the proportion of NSA is 60–80% – in Bijapur, of which about half is Deccan Lava, it rises to 80%; but in the southern Malnad it is under 40%. Over most of the north jowar is the ranking crop (40–60% NSA), yielding to rice in the southern Malnad, to ragi in the southern Districts of old Mysore. Cotton is important (20% or more of NSA) in a belt from Dharwar into the Raichur Doab; groundnuts in the southeast (Tumkur and Kolar) as well as in

---

[12] Not to be confused with the larger Varada in old Mysore.
[13] Deshpande, *op. cit.* 105.

the Raichur Doab and farther north in Gulbarga; coffee and tea in Chikmalagur and Coorg, where the Malnad descends to the Wynaad Plateau, threshold to Kerala.

A feature of interest is the importance attached to cattle-breeding. This stems from the days of Haidar Ali, who developed a breed of tough fast-trotting bullocks for use in his very mobile warfare. Pastoralism is particularly important in the forests of the southeastern scarps, spilling over into Salem District (Madras), where the bulls at least are half-wild. The Mysore breed is a very valuable strain and there is a large export to the plains.

The settlement geography is complicated.[14] In the north, larger villages and main roads tend on the whole to avoid the immediate river banks, on account of flooding on the Krishna and intense gully erosion on the smaller streams. But waterpoints are the fundamental siting factors, and houses are 'arid' in aspect, with mud walls and flat roofs. Villages, however, are large and on the whole prosperous except in the drier parts and on the higher infertile ridges. In the Mysore Malnad there is a strong tendency, except in the larger valleys, to semi-dispersal, tiny hamlets or even scattered homesteads. In the Maidan, with its dependence on tanks, there is more nucleation, but even here dependent hamlets are common. Houses are generally mud-walled or stone, usually low-built around a courtyard which may be surrounded by carved and painted verandahs. As so often, thatch is the rule and tile, though common, indicates individual prosperity, but in the drier east flat roofs are not unusual.

Towns and industry

Northern Karnataka is in many aspects a transitional zone between Maharashtra and Mysore, and between the Western Littoral and the Deccan. Its towns are thus for the most part contact settlements: Belgaum and Bijapur are virtually on the very edge of the Lavas, Dharwar and Hubli actually on the Arabian Sea/Bay of Bengal watershed. The local sites of all but Bijapur are at the margin of hill and plain; and they are all essentially depots for the transport of cotton and oil-seeds to Bombay or Marmagão. Belgaum (146,790) is the junction for the transit trade to Marmagão, a 'brink town' where routes from the plateau converge before the steep Ghats pitch, as well as a contact town with rising cotton industries. Bijapur (75,854) is an extraordinary misfit: the capital of the Adil Shahi kingdom (15th–17th centuries), its immense domes look out over a poor and precarious countryside, the administrative offices occupy part of the citadel, and the rest of the modern town is lumped in a corner of the vast enceinte, with straggling village-suburbs in the ruins.[15] Dharwar and Hubli are interesting as twin and rival cities, only 10 or 12 miles apart on the junction of a Dharwarian

[14] It is superfluous to remark that A. T. A. Learmonth's *Sample Villages in Mysore State* (Dept of Geography, Univ. of Liverpool, 1962) contains a wealth of illustrative detail. [O.H.K.S.]

[15] Deshpande, *op. cit.* 111–12. I owe the useful term 'brink town' to my student, Dr K. B. Ryan.

syncline with the gneissic black soils. Hubli (171,326) is growing more rapidly than Dharwar (77,163); the latter's role is mainly administrative, while the larger town has added to its old commercial importance modern industries: cotton ginning, pressing and weaving, railway shops employing 6,000 hands. Farther east Gadag–Bettegiri is so typical of the collecting centres of the Deccan as to merit an extended quotation:[16]

> 'Gadag dominates the southern cotton tract and cotton dominates the town and its annual rhythm of activity. Its cotton market is the focus of urban life. By the beginning of the picking season the town bursts into activity; commercial agents flock in; there is a flow in cart caravans bringing cotton into the market; the market bustles with activity and the rest of the town follows the pace; ginning mills and cotton presses lying idle for a long time are now set to work; cotton finds its way out in a compact and well-graded form to the metropolitan city of Bombay for export, or to cities like Sholapur for industrial consumption. By the middle of June this activity is at its zenith. The town accomplishes its major ambition and settles down to a quiet life during the next eight months. . . . '

Gokak (21,854), also on the Lava edge, is more industrial, its old handicrafts, textiles and toys, being supplemented by cotton mills powered from the Ghataprabha. Bellary (85,673) in the east is an important railway town and has small sugar and vanaspati (vegetable ghee) mills.

In old Mysore, minerals and hydro-electricity gave rise to considerable industrial development, mainly of light consumption goods, but with the important iron of Bhadravati and assembly plants (telecommunications equipment, motor-vehicles, aircraft electronics) of Bangalore. Nearly all India's gold comes from fields around Kolar (146,760 oz., a decrease of over 12,000 since 1951); the ore is in quartz reefs in the Dharwars, and mining has been carried down 7,400 ft. (2,255 m.). The Baba Bhudan field yields considerable amounts of iron ore, and Shimoga District the bulk of India's output of chromite. Manganese output fluctuates but is at times considerable; small amounts of magnesite and silver and even smaller of copper, graphite and mica (from Wynaad) are mixed. Other minerals include kaolin, corundum, garnets and ochre.

The famous Cauvery Falls (320 ft., 98 m., in all) around the little island of Sivasamudram were the first in India to be exploited on any large scale (1902). But development is limited, by agreement with Madras, in order to prevent undue abstraction of water. Since 1927 Sivasamudram has been linked with the great barrage at Krishnarajasagar; this is partly for irrigation but also helps to maintain the flow at Sivasamudram, where the natural *monsoon* discharge has varied between 18,000 and 200,000 cusecs. These installations, linked with Shimsha and Mettur, supply Kolar, Mysore and Bangalore cities; the 93 miles (150 km.) to Kolar was one of the longest transmissions in the world when opened. In the west the great Jog–Sharavati scheme, in the south Shimsha–Sivasamudram, are

[16] *Ibid.* 118.

largely for Mysore though inter-state links between grids are now in being; there are also schemes on the Bhadra and Tungabhadra.

The old Mysore government was one of the most progressive in India; it had 750 miles of metre railway and had developed an unusually good road net for south India, as well as fostering industrial development. Cotton and silk, leather and soap, ceramics and chemicals are main lines; and electric power may revivify some of the craft industries.

Bangalore (1,206,961), which has displaced Ahmedabad as India's sixth city, is the capital: a close-packed old town, with over-planned gridiron suburbs north and south, and a vast sprawling cantonment area to the east. It has large-scale assembly plants, an aircraft factory, many textile mills, and important institutes of scientific research. Climate and urban amenities have attracted retired people from much of southern India, but the large proportion of Tamil speakers reflects in part rural depopulation in drought-stricken areas to the east. The city has no physical barriers to expansion, but has a major water problem, until it is linked with the Cauvery, 90 miles away and 700–800 ft. lower.[17] Mysore city (243,865), a former capital and princely seat, is much more 'Indian' and more humanely planned, but relatively stagnant.

Karnataka as a whole

With the Telugus of Andhra Desa, the Kannada people have been in the fore-front of the movement for a linguistic division of India: convenient enough when it was a question of attacking the British Raj for its arbitrary mutilation of living cultural entities in the interests of mere administration, the issue became em-barrassing to realistic statesmen. Yet the great reorganization of 1956–60 was politically inescapable, and despite strains and stresses (more acute in the north-east of the Peninsula) has worked reasonably well.

The core of Karnataka is obviously old Mysore; but it should be observed that Fig. 23.4 conceals the fact that there are considerable groups of Tamil and Telugu speakers: retired folk in Bangalore, professional and official groups in the towns, a slum-dwelling proletariat, largely Harijans. Still, the great bulk of Mysoreans are Kannada speakers. But the Bombay Karnatak is in large part a debatable land, the theatre of very interesting inter-ramifications of geographical and historical factors. The destruction of Vijayanagar by the Muslim Deccani kingdoms, and their short-lived supersession by the Moguls, followed by Maratha dominance and the rise of Hyderabad, fatally weakened the unity of Karnataka. The towns in the northern frontier zone, Maratha adminis-trative centres and border-fortresses, are mainly Marathi-speaking, and Marathi has also spread along the hill country of the Ghats. Moreover, a century of ad-ministration from Bombay and – even more important – commercial ties with that metropolis have forged very strong links. 'It would be difficult to claim that

[17] See N. P. Gist, 'The ecological study of an Asian city', *Population Rev.* 2 (1958), 17–25.

without the aid of Bombay Port and the market of Western India, Northern Karnatak would be able to maintain its economic progress. The very geographical position and political position of Northern Karnatak have placed it in a peculiar position: it owes a cultural allegiance to the south and an economic allegiance to the north.'[18] Economic flows tend to follow the old channels, and the new state had to amalgamate with old Mysore and Coorg portions of three other states (Bombay, Madras, Hyderabad), all with differing administrative patterns. The difficulties of the linguistic reorganization are plain to see; its viability has been on the whole encouraging.

THE UPPER MAHANADI BASIN AND ITS ANNEXES

The plains and basins which extend east of the Deccan Lavas and lie between the Maikal Range and Chota Nagpur to the north, and the Orissa Hills to the south, have really no regional cohesion – rather they are what is left over when the well-defined regions mentioned have been delimited. In the west the Wainganga valley is separated by low discontinuous hills (running south from the Maikal Range) from the upper Mahanadi basin, the heart of which is Chhattisgarh. Beyond lies the much smaller basin of the Brahmani, east of which again the Orissa Hills and Chota Nagpur approach each other on either side of the Jamshedpur gap; the lower Subarnarekha is transitional to the lateritic shelf of West Bengal.

THE WAINGANGA VALLEY

Immediately east of Nagpur the Deccan Lavas give place to generally Archaean terrain, irregularly undulating country at about 900–1,100 ft. (275–335 m.), broken by small disconnected hills up to 500 ft. high and rocky or covered by scraggy open forest. Rainfall is 44–55 in. (1,118–1,397 mm.) with a strict monsoonal distribution; Bhandara receives just 90% of its total 54 in. in June through September. Variability is greater towards the end of the rains and irrigation is at least desirable for security, and is mainly from thousands of small tanks formed by bunding the irregular little valleys; a handful of the larger ones are really small lakes of 5–10 sq. miles (13–26 km^2).

A considerable proportion of the Wainganga valley itself, as well as the hills to the north and east, is heavily forested. This is the great domain of sal; minor products – bamboo, charcoal, myrobalans, lac, the leaves used for covering *bidis* (cheap 'cigarettes'), fodder – are extremely important elements in the economy of the whole of this region, except Chhattisgarh itself. Rice dominates the cultivated area, which is itself severely limited in parts by forested hill country; after rice, wheat and oilseeds, especially linseed, are the leading crops. The Wainganga marks the transition from the agriculture of Maharashtra, with its uncertain rain but moisture-retentive *regur*, its wide plains and commercial bias,

[18] Deshpande, *op. cit.* 121–2; cf. *ibid.* 267–76.

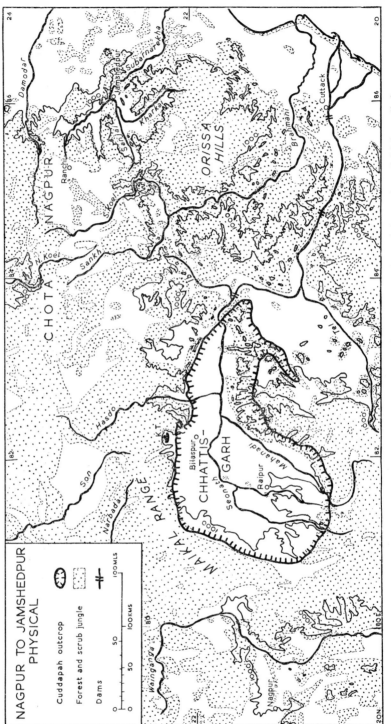

FIG 23.9 NAGPUR TO JAMSHEDPUR: PHYSICAL. KT, Kurug Tank. Note sites of the projected Mahanadi dams.

to the realm of paddy in the better-watered but more broken northeast Peninsula.

The most important mineral exploited as yet is manganese; Madhya Pradesh production is around 60% of the Indian total. The great Gondwana trough, which continues the line of the lower Godavari valley, has a number of small coalfields, extending from the Pench and Son valleys in the north to Singareni and Tandur in Adilabad District, on the Penganga–Godavari doab; Warora and Bellarpur in Chanda (Madhya Pradesh) are the main producers. In the south there are great reserves of good haematite (60–70% Fe), as yet little exploited. The haematite forms monadnocks such as the Dholi and Rajhara Hills in Durg (on the Chhattisgarh border) and Lohara in Chanda: the Rajhara Hills alone contain some 7,500,000 tons of ore, while Lohara, in area 700 by 200 yd. (640 by 180 m.), is practically a solid mass of haematite. The focus of economic life is Nagpur.

THE UPPER MAHANADI: CHHATTISGARH

Between the Maikal and Orissa Hills lies the great plain, 80–100 miles (130–160 km.) wide, of the upper Mahanadi. Most of the plain lies west and north of the Mahanadi and is drained by the Seonath; on the northwest it is sharply limited by the Maikal scarps, on the south it rises into the jungly hills of Bastar, but west and east the watersheds with the Wainganga and Sankh-Brahmani are mere residual crests, bold but broken hills. For a good deal of its west–east course the Mahanadi hugs the Orissa Hills before plunging into them below Raigarh, which lies in a corridor, 20–25 miles wide, between the river and the tangled Chota Nagpur foothills.

The heart of the plain is occupied by a great basin of Cuddapah rocks (Fig. 23.9) (grits, quartzites, sandstones, shales), resting on the Archaeans which form the irregular margins, and bevelled off in perfect peneplains at about 900–1,000 ft. (275–305 m.). The rivers are extraordinarily mature as a whole; but here and there the master-streams are incised, not very deeply, in gullied banks. This suggestion of rejuvenation may be due to renewed erosive power consequent on forest destruction, or perhaps to rains in tributary catchments when the base-level is lowered a few feet by the dry-weather shrinkage of the main streams.

This plain of Chhattisgarh ('36 Forts') is girdled by more or less broken forest country, and until the coming of the Marathas was historically an isolated Gond kingdom; it stands out vividly on forest and population maps. 'The surface is an expanse of small embanked ricefields, sometimes 50 to an acre . . . over large areas there are few trees other than the mango groves adjoining the more important of the frequent clusters of mud-roofed huts which form a Chhattisgarh village.'[19]

With a rainfall of about 55 in. (1,397 mm.) irrigation is desirable. Canal irrigation is important but recent; it is practically confined to the Seonath/Mahanadi doab, the margins being dependent on tanks, many of which are of

[19] *Central Provinces Gaz.* (1908), 3.

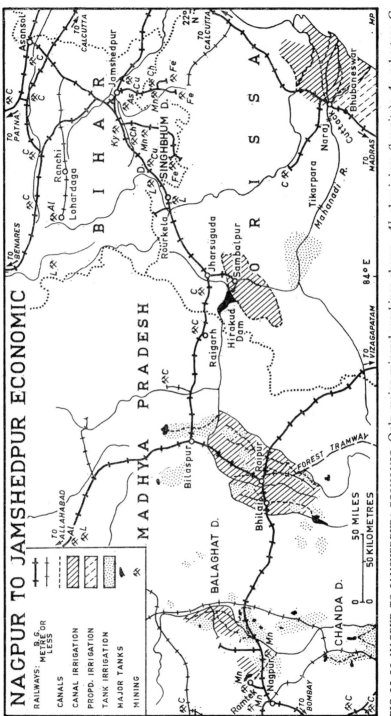

FIG 23.10 NAGPUR TO JAMSHEDPUR: ECONOMIC. Only major mineral workings shown. *Al*, aluminium (bauxite); *As*, asbestos; *C*, coal; *Ch*, chromite; *Cu*, copper. *Fe*, iron; *Ky*, kyanite; *L*, limestone; *Mn*, manganese.

large size, such as the 8-mile-long Kurug Tank north of Bilaspur. On the fertile black silts of the central plain paddy is dominant; in Raipur District as a whole it accounts for over 60% of the NSA, with rabi linseed as the second crop, followed by wheat; much the same holds for adjacent Durg and Bilaspur. Double-cropping is of great importance, especially in Raipur. A feature of farming practice is the extensive use of silt from the tanks as fertilizer; cultivators are also adept in the siting of ditches sub-parallel to the contours to bring water to the fields. Well irrigation with pole-and-bucket lift is used for specialized crops such as betel vines, and the sandy river-beds are used for dry weather garden cultivation.

Villages are definitely at waterpoints, close-packed, mud-built with mud or tiled roofs; they have a pueblo aspect enhanced by mud walls joining up farm-stead buildings and separating the fields; in places dry-stone walls, and slabs of rock 'mortared' with mud, are used.

The most important mineral is coal, mainly on the northeast flank of the basin where a long Gondwana trough lies between the Mahanadi and the Brahmani. Some seams are of great thickness (100 ft. or more) but much of this is made up of carbonaceous shale. The whole of this belt, down to Talchir on the lower Brahmani, contains probably about 200,000,000 tons of coal; exploitation is increasing both near Raigarh and at recently opened mines at Korba to feed new thermal power stations and the new steel town of Bhilai. There is some limestone and dolomite quarrying around the margins of the basin, particularly towards the Jamshedpur side.

Densities are fairly low (125–250) and this has been one of the least urbanized areas of India, but there are signs of change, consequent on irrigation and railway development and perhaps the general economic changes influenced by the proximity of Jamshedpur. The main Calcutta–Bombay railway skirts the northern margin of the plain to Bilaspur, whence a line strikes northwest to the Son valley. Bilaspur (86,706) has been greatly stimulated by the Bhilai development, as have other small mining and timber centres. Beyond Bilaspur the main line runs along the Seonath/Mahanadi doab to the grain centre, Raipur (139,792) which, since the construction in 1932 of the line to Visakhapatnam, has developed rapidly as the regional centre of Chhattisgarh. Most of the railway towns have now a little industry; at Jharsuguda in the extreme east is one of the largest paper mills in India.

THE UPPER BRAHMANI AND JAMSHEDPUR

East of the Mahanadi–Brahmani watershed the hills to north and south converge, leaving a corridor of hilly lowland, drained by the Sankh and the South Koel (which unite to form the Brahmani) and the Sanjai and Kharkai, tributaries of the Subarnarekha. Except for Singhbhum District (Bihar), the area was parcelled out among various petty states, which have now been merged into Madhya Pradesh and Orissa, except Seraikela and Kharsawan, which have gone to Bihar.

These two had an area of only 600 sq. miles (1,555 km²), but their mineral wealth is not an unimportant addition to that of Singhbhum.

The confused topography is developed mostly on Dharwarian rocks. In the

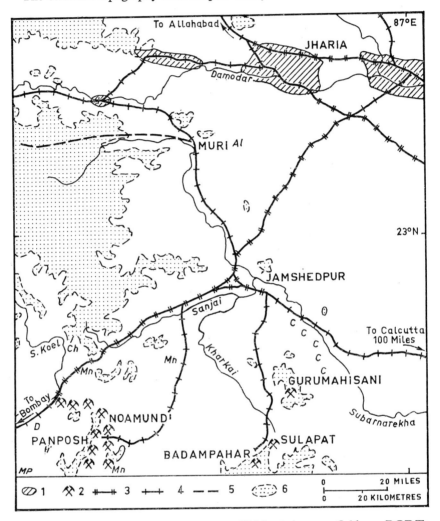

FIG 23.11 JAMSHEDPUR: RESOURCES. I, coalfields; 2, iron ore fields; 3, BGDT; 4, BGST; 5, metre ST to Lohardaga; 6, over 600 *metres*. Minerals: *Al*, alumina; C, copper; *Ch*, chromite; *D*, dolomite; *Mn*, manganese. Originally based on map by S. A. Majid.

north, on the Chota Nagpur flanks, the main ridges reach nearly 3,000 ft. (915 m.) with a rough east–west trend cut across by the north–south valleys which lie at about 1,500–2,000 ft. On the southern flank the main trend of the Orissa Hills is southwest/northeast, but the spurs are extremely irregular. A very large proportion of the sub-region is under forest, much of it sal and much of it open. Population density is thus generally low and the people largely tribal. Agriculture is for the most part primitive and backward.

JAMSHEDPUR

From every point of view the Jamshedpur area is by far the most important part of the sub-region. Here the convergence of Sanjai, Kharkai and Subarnarekha forms a fair-sized (though broken) lowland, with a good deal of tank-fed, or at least tank-secured, paddy in the trellis-patterned valleys. The passage-function of the sub-region is also very clearly shown here: railways from West Bengal meet near Jamshedpur, coming from Asansol in the Damodar coalfields and direct from Calcutta by Kharagpur, and the main line to Bombay uses the Sanjai to cross over to the Brahmani valley by a col at no more than 1,100–1,200 ft. (335–365 m.). But above all this tract is significant as the seat of the largest individual industrial undertaking in India, and one of the largest in the British Commonwealth, the Jamshedpur (Tatanagar) iron and steel works: an island of heavy industry in a sea of jungle and subsistence cultivation, an output of capitalism in a human environment otherwise mainly tribal. In 1911 Jamshedpur had a population of 5,672; by 1961 it had grown to 328,044 – over 5,500% in fifty years.

The locational advantages are striking and are sufficiently displayed in Fig. 23.11, which shows the position of Jamshedpur in relation to the important Hooghlyside market and to local fuel and raw material supplies, all of which except the flux lie within 70 miles (113 km.), though for some it is now necessary to go farther afield. The 'Iron Ore Belt' in Singhbhum and adjacent Districts has reserves estimated at not less than 2,700,000,000 tons of haematite (Fe content 60%). Of alloy metals, local manganese is costly and inferior to that imported from Madhya Pradesh, and Orissa chromite competes successfully with that from the thin and expensively worked seams of Singhbhum. Kyanite, increasingly needed as a refractory, is mined locally, and there is also apatite; fireclay from Jharia, silica from Manbhum, add to the list of locally accessible ancillary materials. Magnesite so far comes from southern India. Copper is a deficit mineral in India, and so far the main production is from the Bihar Copper Belt along the Subarnarekha, only 35 miles (56 km.) away; it is smelted at Ghatsila and rolled at Manbhander.[20] To the north is the aluminium plant at Muri and the new refinery at Purulia; to the south, the bauxite deposits of Orissa, smelted at the Hirakud hydro-electric station. The main source of coking coal is in the Damodar basin. Altogether, there can be few heavy metallurgical centres so well situated as regards access to materials.

Unskilled labour is drawn from local tribes, mainly Santals; more skilled workers from all parts of India, but especially Bengal and Bihar, and the British

[20] S. A. Majid, 'The copper industry of Bihar', *Geogl Outlook* (Ranchi), 1/1 (1956), 9–15.

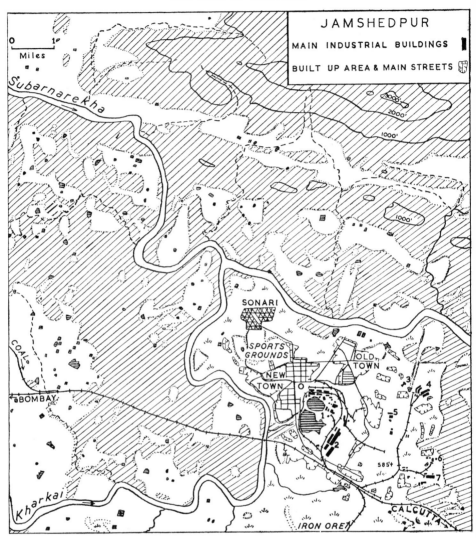

FIG 23.12 JAMSHEDPUR: THE SITE. O, Tata offices; 1–2, Tata Iron and Steel works – 1, furnaces and cooling tanks, 2, rolling mills, etc.; 3, agricultural implements; 4, tinplate; 5, cables; 6, steel wire; 7, loco works. The built-up area is now only the core of the expanded town. Jungle shaded. *Courtesy* SOI.

and American technologists of the early days are now almost entirely replaced by Indians; but while labour efficiency has increased remarkably in the last three decades, it is still below western standards and this offsets low money wages.[21]

[21] A lively account of the growth of the industry is given in J. L. Keenan, *A Steel Man in India* (Gollancz, London, 1935): not much direct geography, but one of the less stereotyped 'climates' of Indian life given with much verve.

The various Tata enterprises connected with Jamshedpur are the major employers in the town, and an enlightened welfare policy has led to a considerable degree of labour stability – in some cases even a labour aristocracy of families whose sons naturally join the firm – but there is still doubt as to the real acceptance of modern ways by Santal labour. Jamshedpur–Tatanagar really consists of a number of separately planned, but integrated, settlements around the great steel works and the associated plants; standards of housing, health and amenity are far higher than in most Indian industrial centres, and architecturally the town for long had a 'new look'. It is, however, outgrowing its planned confines, *bustee* areas are appearing in the interstices, and the older industrial suburbs now look almost as dated as a Saltaire or a New Lanark.

There had been many false starts before Jamshedji Tata launched his carefully thought out project in 1908, and expert opinion then held that in the economic climate of India visions of a great heavy metals industry were visions and no more. The preliminary reconnaissances were thorough; operations started in 1911, and in 1914 some 160,000 tons of pig-iron were produced. The First World War almost cut off iron and steel imports and gave Tatas a flying start, and with the aid of protection the depression of the 1930s was surmounted. Railway, bridge and construction materials have always been prominent, the main lines in this group being bars, light constructional steel, rails and fishplates. The Second World War saw a great expansion in quality and range, including the production of light armoured vehicles. Associated industries include heavy motor vehicles, railway rolling stock, tinplate, cables, wire and wire nails, agricultural implements, enamelled and galvanized sheets, all types of castings. Most of the undertakings responsible for these products, as well as the mines and quarries on which they are based, are part of the multifunctional 'Tata group'. The metallurgical and engineering side has thus elements of both vertical and horizontal monopoly; until the rise of the new plants in the Public Sector, Tatas had never produced less than 50% of the Indian pig-iron output, and had reached 80% in some years. Under the Plans the works have doubled in size, still as a private undertaking; but they must now compete with the nationalized plants at Bhilai, Rourkela and Durgapur. Tata remains an industrial empire: in Bombay are its general staff and its service corps; here, set down in the incongruous jungle, is its arsenal.

TELANGANA

The remainder of the Peninsular interior, within the bordering Eastern Hills, forms the Deccani component of Andhra Pradesh, the Telegu-speaking state. When first formed in 1953, the state consisted only of the indisputably Telugu Districts of Madras, to which were added in 1956 the similar Districts of old Hyderabad Telangana. The state is nearly as much of a composite as new Mysore: a tier of coastal Districts, all formerly in Madras, from Srikakulam on the Orissa border to Nellore which reaches nearly to Madras city; the plateaus of Hyderabad Telangana; and four inland Districts of Madras – Kurnool. Anantapur, Cuddapah, Chittoor, the old 'Ceded Districts'. These Anantapur–Chittoor Basins are a region on their own, if something of a 'left-over' one, alongside the more distinctive Cuddapah Ranges region. 'Telangana' – the term and the area seem well accepted by local geographers – may then be said to consist of Andhra Pradesh north of the Tungabhadra–Krishna and west of the Eastern Hills, where lay the old boundary between Madras and Hyderabad, now the boundary between Telangana and coastal Andhra. As we have seen the state boundary with Maharashtra corresponds reasonably well with that between Deccan Lavas and Archaean gneisses.

In the past this was a poor and neglected area and a centre of acute agrarian troubles, culminating in the Communist-led *jacquerie* which began in 1946, was a significant factor in the Indian occupation of Hyderabad in 1948, and ended only in 1951. It contains one great city, Hyderabad itself, now the capital of Andhra Pradesh; but its area of about 44,400 sq. miles (115,000 km²) supported in 1961 only 12,712,000 people, a density of 286; this includes the 1,251,119 people of Hyderabad city, without whom the density would be only 258. The old Ceded Districts are even poorer: 6,175,000 people on 28,900 sq. miles (74,850 km²), only 214 to the square mile. In contrast, the coastal Districts, which include the Godavari and Krishna deltas, had 16,339,000 people on 33,500 sq. miles (86,765 km²), a density of 488. This very marked contrast seems to indicate a possible source of weakness in the new state.

The physical aspect

The bulk of the region consists of plateaus developed on the Archaean gneisses. In the north, however, faulting has preserved a belt of Gondwanas (with some coal) along the lower Godavari trough: much of this is under 500 ft. (150 m.), but with its dry dissected terrain it has remained very largely under forest of a dryish deciduous type.

The most general levels lie between 1,600 and 2,000 ft.; in the southwest, below the rather ragged break of slope down from the Mysore plateau, the Krishna and Tungabhadra valleys lie, at 1,000–1,500 ft. (305–455 m.) and to the northwest the watershed between the Bhima and the Godavari is a great swelling upland reaching 2,400 ft. (630 m.) in places. But the general aspect nearly everywhere is that of practically senile pene- or pedi-plains, intersected by broad, open, almost completely graded valleys, and littered with monadnocks which range from considerable hill-groups to innumerable fantastic tors which look like dumps of gigantic road-metal. Around Hyderabad city these form 'a chaos of granitic boulders . . . piled up in bizarre heaps, as if giants had amused themselves with childish games'; in places these rocky belts form a wilderness wide enough to act as a marchland.[22] With the poor sandy red soils of the gneisses and

[22] E. Reclus, *L'Inde* (1883), 506; cf. *Hyderabad Gaz.* (1909), 2.

granites, a variable rainfall of 25–40 in. (635–1,016 mm.), and May mean temperatures in the 90s (around 35°C.) life is hard except in favoured basins, where soilwash and tank irrigation give some prosperity. Bare hills, reddish-khaki plains with scattered thorny scrub, rivers merely ribbons of sand for half the year or more, tanks bunded into the little valleys, all combine to produce a landscape with a desolate and brooding charm. The contrast between the Marathwara and Telangana parts of the old Hyderabad state (Figs. 23.7 and 23.8) is extremely striking.

Conditions worsen to the south.[23] In Marathwara there is hardly any surface water in the hot weather, except in the bigger streams; in southern Telangana (and still more so across the Krishna in the Kurnool District) even this exception hardly holds. The railway bridges are stoutly built to withstand the immense volume of monsoon water in rivers which are then half a mile or more wide; in the hot weather they traverse great flats with a yard or so of water in the middle, and the herds of cattle or goats crossing the bed are recognizable from afar by their great clouds of dust.

Except for the jungles of the north, the region presents a decided savannah aspect, poor savannah with widely spaced acacias. Most of the tors are absolutely naked, and their skirts (with much of the more or less level ground) carry only a thorny scrub, in which euphorbias are prominent, while in damper depressions there are scattered palms, toddy or the wild Indian date. The scrub is secondary, on ground long subject to the depredations of sheep and especially goats, or once cultivated.

Agriculture

Since the region lies farther from the lee of the Ghats and more open to Bay of Bengal influences, rainfall is a little higher and more reliable than in eastern Maharashtra, but differences in terrain and soil are decisive. The NSA is 20–40% of total area in the northeast, the Districts along the Godavari, 40–60% in the southeast; much lower than in most of Maharashtra. Irrigation is more important than in Maharashtra, but it is mainly from tanks: tank irrigation is found in 71 of 72 talukas and is of some significance in 44 and considerable significance in 21 of them; the corresponding figures for canals are 53, 12 and 4. Wells are locally important.[24] Jowar is usually the first ranking crop, with 40–60% of NSA oilseeds – mainly castor and groundnut – the main cash crop, and often the second ranking crop. Bajra and gram are widespread, and maize is locally important. Although Anantapur is strictly outside our Telangana area, the Lava/Archaean contrast is well brought out by Fig. 23.13, which although based on old figures still states the fundamentals.

[23] For some vivid remarks, see J. C. Molony, *A Book of South India* (London, 1926), 166.
[24] B. N. Chaturvedi and K. S. Reddy, 'Irrigation in Telangana – sources and problems', *Deccan Geogr* (Hyderabad) 2/2 (1964), 154–70.

There is much internal variation. Rice is more important than in Maharashtra; dependent on the tanks, it is the food of the better-off agricultural classes. Cotton, though much less important generally as a cash crop than oilseeds, is grown on the black soils along the greater rivers, extrusions from Maharashtra. 'Groundnut is the most valuable kharif crop on light soils, where the soil is not heavy enough for jowar and rainfall not high enough for rice.'[25] In the southeast, a high proportion of the rain comes late in the wet season – at Anantapur 57% of the total

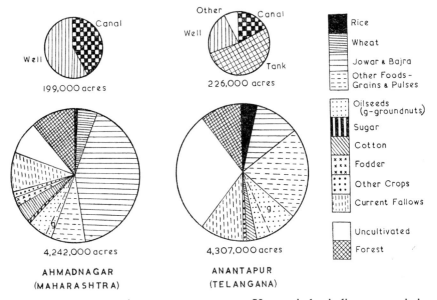

FIG 23.13 THE LAVA/ARCHAEAN CONTRAST. Upper circles indicate areas irrigated.

27·4 in. (696 mm.) falls in June through September, half of it in the latter month; and in such conditions the rabi crop tends to be more important than the kharif, especially on heavier soils which, with the intense May heat and late start of considerable rains, may not be workable till August. While groundnut is the kharif crop, cotton is entirely rabi. Jowar is grown for fodder as well as grain; ragi and other millets as well as rice are often wet crops; and millets are sown mixed with pulses, which take longer to mature and are a safeguard against the failure of the cereals.

Differences of expert opinion in Mysore and Madras impeded work on the great dam, $1\frac{1}{2}$ miles long and 160 ft. high, now built across the Tungabhadra and beginning to revivify the villages under its command and to introduce new cash crops and increase local processing, for instance of sugar. Nevertheless the poor

[25] S. Velayudham, 'Groundnut in Madras', *IGJ* 21/3–4 (1946), 100–12 and 153–73; reference at p. 157.

Archaean terrain and the vagaries of the monsoon impose severe limitations on Telangana, which for the most part remains a region of some difficulty.

Other resources: settlement and towns

The mineral resources of Telangana are scattered and little exploited. The most important production is probably that of Gondwana coal, mined chiefly at Singareni; in the northeast are some outliers of the great iron zone of the Orissa Hills. There are small deposits of lead (Nalgonda) and graphite (Warangal), while the southern trans-Krishna Districts have non-ferrous metals (manganese, antimony), corundum and barytes; but most of the minerals here are associated with the bordering ranges to the east, and in any case are almost untouched. Golconda diamonds belong to history – and legend – rather than to modern economy. The forest resources around the Godavari are not very accessible, though it would seem that more use might be made of the river itself as an outlet, and preliminary surveys have been made of the power potential of the rapids where the river breaks through the Eastern Hills.

Population densities are not high, generally 250–500. Villages are essentially tied to waterpoints, often in association with tanks, and generally built of mud or stone set in mud, with thatched roofs. Apart from Hyderabad city, towns are few and small. Warangal (156,106) is the largest, and of merely local importance. Except for cotton ginning and so on, industrial development is slight.

Hyderabad (1,151,119) was founded in 1589 by the Muslim king of Golconda and became the capital of the Mogul Viceroyalty of the Deccan and of the independent state which arose on the Mogul ruins; old Golconda, an impressive hill-fortress, lies 5 miles to the west. The significance of Hyderabad is essentially administrative and cultural, as is evidenced by the high proportions of Urdu and Tamil speakers; the former represent the semi-feudal class dominant in the state until 1948, the latter the clerkly bureaucracy. The city is close-packed, mostly unplanned, with palaces perhaps more remarkable for size than beauty, around large tanks. Most notable of modern buildings is perhaps the fine Osmania University. Six miles to the north is the enormous cantonment of Secunderabad, designed under the British Raj to afford protection to Our Faithful Ally the Nizam, and perhaps not less to ensure his continued faithfulness – a precaution not unwarranted in the stirring and in all senses intriguing days when the rising British power was at grips with the Marathas and the Mysore of Haidar Ali and Tipu, and when French influence was not altogether dead in the Deccan. The varied craft industries which served the Nizam's Court are giving way to light engineering and metal trades, food processing, and so on. As the capital of Andhra Pradesh, the city retains and is indeed adding to its administrative importance. As an example of the enormous planning problems faced by the city, the schools had to be multiplied many times almost overnight after the police action; as a result nearly all schools, except a few old mission schools, etc., are in poor, unsuitable, often rented accommodation. So schools have to be built for nearly all the children of a million city.

Telangana : aspect and prospect

The former princely state of Hyderabad, with its 82,000 sq. miles (212,000 km^2) and 1951 population of 18,655,108, its own internal posts (with yellow pillar-boxes), its integration of road services with the Nizam's State Railway, and with a reasonably good administration, was a state of weight not inferior to that of many a sovereign member of UNO. But large parts of it were still under practic-ally feudal *jagirs* and the tension between a Muslim aristocracy and bureaucracy, and the Maratha/Telugu peasantry, was a fundamental weakness. As the only notable survivor of the Muslim Mogul succession-states, it was an Islamic cultural and political outlier fatally isolated from the Islamic bases in the north-west and Bengal. These things were obvious to the casual traveller: as one passes from the lava mesas of Maharashtra the cultural landscape changes as much as the physical. At Gulbarga, on the lava edge, the tombs of the Muslim Bahmani Sultans dominate the gently rolling country, their domes rising like giant bubbles over the flat skyline; on the station platforms the local petty bourgeoisie and bureaucracy, gathered to meet the train and always easily recognizable, no longer wore the dhoti or completely anglicized office clothes, but were clad in the long tight-fitting Muslim *sherwani* coat. But the Muslim hold was thin, and they were a minority of 12·8%. Geographically one weakness of the state was of course its separation from the sea – doubtless not accidental on the EIC's part.

Today, however, all the Telugu country has at last been united into an Andhra state, despite the great gap in economic development, and perhaps in economic interests, between the harsh and arid plateau and the paddy-plain of the Andhra littoral. In any case, the development of the essentially poor land of Telangana will call for great capital expenditure without, perhaps, much prospect of cash returns. The future depends largely on the progress of the great Tungabhadra scheme; but the history of large-scale irrigation here is discouraging, though of course much experience has been gained since the Kurnool failure. With the development of hydro-electricity there may come decentralized industrial development on the Mysore model; but Mysore had a more solid backing in at least some industry, sericulture and Bhadravati iron for instance, to give a base. Telangana is not without resources such as oilseeds and fibres (including sheep and goat wool), and one or two small coalfields, and in view of India's shortages in non-ferrous metals development of the poor communication net might lead to at least some exploitation of the scattered minerals. Up till now, however, manu-facturing industry is confined to a handful of towns and cities with over 20% of their people dependent on industrial income, and the one large centre of Hydera-bad–Secunderabad.[26] Handicraft industry is still fairly active in places, but

[26] See S. A. Hameed, 'Industrial Patterns of Telangana', *IGJ* 37/2 (1962), 45–56, for interesting details.

probably with a good deal of under-employment. All told, Telangana still gives the impression of a relatively backward and poor country.

THE ANANTAPUR-CHITTOOR BASINS

Between the bold scarp of the Palkonda Range and the higher Mysore levels are a series of basins around the middle courses of the Penner tributaries – Chitravati. Papagni, Punchu/Cheyyeru, the last two with a remarkable confluence-gorge in the Palkondas. To the southeast the sub-region breaks down to the Nellore/ Coromandel plains through the little intermont basins of the Nagari Hills (up to 2,800 ft., 855 m.) and through the broader Swarnamukhi valley, which may occupy a fault-trough under the Palkondas. The whole area is crossed by north/ south or northeast/southwest trap dykes, which may also have some influence on the remarkable drainage-pattern.

The area is isolated and poor, except in the extreme southeast – the Nagari valleys, culturally transitional to Tamilnad. Densities are fairly high considering the general poverty in resources – 327 in Chittoor and 226 in Anantapur; jowar and bajra are the main food crops, but are actually outranked by groundnuts, which of course can also be used directly as a food crop.

There is no urban or industrial development worth mentioning. The Nagari basins are better cultivated than those of the plateau, but even they are not very impressive agriculturally: their flattish floors are broken by patches of sandy soil, almost bare but for a thin grass/acacia cover, and by naked rock exfoliation sur-faces, looking like *roches moutonnées* and often used as threshing floors.[27] Around the plain a lateritic piedmont slope fringes the craggy hills, with boulders as big as a small house on the talus slopes. Below the lateritic apron is a better-watered and more fertile piedmont strip, which is in places a solid belt of paddy, the zone of bush and trees along the laterite margin being a favoured settlement-line. It is a strange landscape: fantastic hills, stacked and pinnacled, long ridges capped by massive quartzites, reflected in the still waters of the big tanks with their borders of toddy palms; an eerily attractive picture under iron-blue or grey skies.

THE EASTERN HILLS

The term 'Eastern Ghats' is honoured by time but by nothing else; its use gives a misleading impression of comparability with the Western Ghats, and suggests an entirely non-existent homogeneity. The hills which border the Peninsular interior on the east have in fact no continuity, structural or topographic. In the north they are elevated highly-dissected plateaus (largely Charnockite) cut across by the Gondwana Mahanadi/Brahmani trough; but south of the similar lower Godavari trough there is an absolutely different element in the Cuddapah Ranges. South again are the Javadis, Shevaroys, etc., cut off from the Mysore

[27] For a type village, see C. Nirmala, 'Vittalam village', *IGJ* 35/3-4 (1960), 53-56.

plateaus by the middle Palar/Ponnaiyar trough; these are better considered as a separate group in Tamilnad. The word 'ghat' was applied here by historic accident; it must be remembered that one significance of 'ghat' is a pass or way through, and it was down the ghats in this sense that the armies of Haidar Ali and Tipu descended to the 'Carnatic' – another misnomer. By extension all the hill-masses were lumped together as 'Eastern Ghats'; but it seems best to confine the term to the Mysore scarp overlooking the Palar/Ponnaiyar trough which is indeed analogous to the Western Ghats, and to use the non-committal term 'Eastern Hills' for the groups discussed here.

ORISSA AND BASTAR

Between the Jamshedpur Gap and the Godavari breach lies a great tract of wild hilly country, mainly on Archaeans with an extensive development of Charnock-ites in the higher portions. It falls into three main masses. (i) The northernmost (old Keonjhar and Mayurbhanj states) is largely Dharwarian and reaches 3,824 ft. (1,165 m.) in Meghusani in the northeast; but much of it is an extensive dis-sected plateau at 1,800–2,000 ft. (550–610 m.; once continuous with Chota Nagpur?) lying west of the Kharkai. In the irregular monadnocks along its northern edge are the main iron supplies of Jamshedpur, notably at Gurumahi-sani (Fig. 23.11). This mass is separated from the others by a remarkable transverse trough, partly floored by Gondwanas (including the famous Permo-Carboniferous glacial boulder-bed at Talchir) and flanked by the gorges of the Mahanadi and Brahmani, which are paralleled to the north by the smaller Baitarni Valley; the drainage-pattern here would repay careful study.

South of the Mahanadi the mountain mass widens to *c.* 125 miles (200 km.) divided into (ii) a definitely northeast/southwest-trending section in the east and (iii) the lower and less defined plateaus of Bastar in the west. The eastern section is largely formed of Khondalites (gneisses and schists, perhaps the oldest rocks of India) and Charnockites; most of it lies at over 3,000 ft. with a few summits at nearly 5,000 (915 and 1,525 m.). The northeast/southwest trend is well shown by the line of the Tel-upper Indravati–Sabari and Sileru Rivers, marking it off from Bastar (2,000–3,000 ft., a few points 4,000). Bastar is a highly dissected and almost entirely forested plateau, most of which drains to the Godavari via the Indravati; it contains a few Cuddapah inliers, but is for the most part a mass of undifferentiated gneiss, covered by a mass of jungle.

Nearly all this area was divided among a multiplicity of very backward states which, except for Bastar and Kanker (which have gone to Madhya Pradesh) are now merged with Orissa, increasing its area by 85% but its population by only 58%. A large proportion of the region is covered by dense or open deciduous forest, with some sal; in Bastar, indeed, open ground amounts to only a small fraction of its 15,000 sq. miles (38,850 km²). The largest, indeed the only ex-tensive, non-forested area is the Tel valley, where Bolangir is the only District of the whole area to have over 40% NSA; Koraput is more typical, with three-

722

quarters of its area under forest or scrub. Dry hill-rice, with some terraced paddy in the valleys, is the most important food crop, followed by rabi and gram; the limited cash-cropping is mostly of rape and sesamum. Shifting agriculture, supplemented by the collection of forest products, is prevalent; mahua flowers are distilled. Some efforts are being made to settle tribes such as the Bhuiyas on agricultural colonies,[28] and there is the ambitious Dandakaranya scheme (named from a mythical battle of good against evil) to resettle refugees from East Pakistan in agricultural enclaves in the forests; but inter-State difficulties, tribal reluctance to accept newcomers, and the Bengali reluctance, amounting to intransigence, to change their way of life, have combined to create some problems. This is also the area where Vinobha's Gramdan movement (above, p. 272) has achieved most success.

Yet this region, formerly perhaps the most jungly of all India, is now, in places at any rate, the scene of an industrial revolution, notably in connection with the Rourkela steelworks built on the upper Brahmani with German help; Rourkela itself had 90,287 people in 1961. These are situated between the iron and manganese of Bonai and Keonjhar, and Jharia coal; there is power from the great Hirakud dam on the Mahanadi near Sambalpur, and potentially from the Koel. Several of the small towns have electrically powered cotton mills, there is a 10,000-ton paper mill at Bhadrajnagar, and sugar mills are planned; at Hirakud aluminium is smelted from local bauxite, and cement is made at Rajganpur.[29] In addition, hundreds of small-scale workshops produce attractive handloom cottons, using individually dyed threads, especially around Sambalpur and Bargarh; and the making of *bidis* from the leaves of *Diospyrus melanoxylon* gives more employment than any other cottage industry.

THE CUDDAPAH RANGES AND BASINS

Another Gondwana trough lies along the lower Godavari, and for about 100 miles the rampart of hills is completely breached, the plateau breaking down through dissected and forested country to the Godavari/Krishna deltas. Beyond the Krishna (which is in fact superimposed across their tip) lie the most interesting of the Eastern Hills, which from their rocks and position may be collectively styled the Cuddapah Ranges and Basins (Figs. 23.14, 23.15).

The region forms a great crescent, the heart of it being the wide Nandyal valley (c. 700–800 ft., 215–245 m.), drained by the Kunderu, formed on Kurnool (Lower Vindhyan) limestones and shales and extending from the Krishna/Tungabhadra confluence to Cuddapah. To the west this trough is marked off from the Deccan plateaus by the out-facing scarps of the Erramalais/Seschalam Hills/Palkondas, formed of massive quartzites interbedded with slates and lavas; in the south especially the Palkondas, here reaching 3,000 ft. (915 m.) form a

---

[28] N. Patnaik, 'Daleisera revisited', *GRI* 19/2 (1957), 6–16.
[29] B. N. Sinha, 'Heavy industries: their problems and possibilities in Orissa', *ibid.* 21/1 (1959), 17–29.

very fine scarp overlooking the Anantapur–Chittoor basins (Fig. 23.14). The
eastern limb of the central Kunderu basin is formed by the parallel Nallamalais

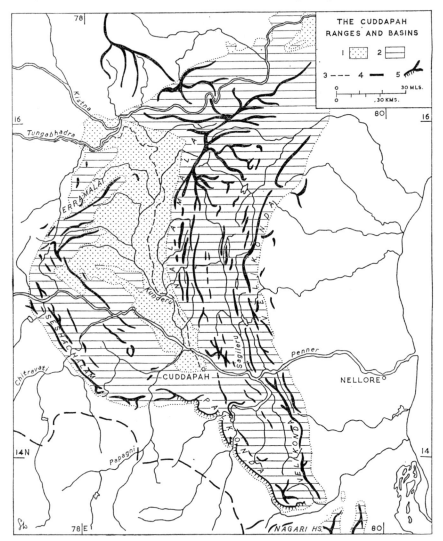

FIG 23.14 THE CUDDAPAH RANGES AND BASINS. 1, Vindhyan; 2, Cuddapah, outcrop; 3, Kurnool–Cuddapah Canal; 4, approx. edge of Mysore plateau; 5, main
ridges and scarps.

and Velikondas ('outside hills'), 2,500–3,000 ft. high and separated by a beautifully regular development of longitudinal valleys. The evolution of this remarkable drainage-pattern, with its elements of superimposition and of strike
subsequents, would make a fascinating geomorphological study; especially

notable are the gorges of the Krishna, Penner and Cheyyuru. In the east, especially in the Velikondas, the Cuddapah rocks have been subject to great overthrusting and inversion to the west; the lithology here indicates deposition in shallow but not sheltered waters, and the general lie of the east coast may thus be of great antiquity. The change in strike between the Orissa Hills and the Cuddapahs is very closely followed by the coast.

The hills are wooded and the pattern of relief stands out clearly on forest and population maps (Fig. 3.1); but the forest is thin, partly because of biotic control; rainfall is only about 40 in. (1,016 mm.) and the rocks are porous or fissured. The few inhabitants are mostly Chenchus, an aboriginal tribe living a semi-pastoral existence eked out by the collection of honey, bamboos, fuel for the railways and other minor forest produce.

The valleys, however, though on the whole poor enough, have a fair amount of cultivation, mostly jowar, other millets, groundnut, with some irrigated paddy. The topography in the longitudinal valleys favours the construction of large tanks by bunding a transverse tributary gorge. The main Madras–Bombay railway strikes diagonally across the south of the region, and is one of the most interesting traverses in India. The hill country is first entered in the Nagaris, which are the last Cuddapah outliers; here Renigunta and the pilgrim centre of Tirupati are little towns controlling at once the route up the Swarnamukhi, the crossings of the river, and the col to the north between Palkondas and Velikondas. Beyond, in the Razampeta corridor, the contrast between cultivated floor and barren hills is exceedingly sharp. The generally arid aspect is mitigated by groves of mangoes around the tanks; houses are stone- or mud-walled, and round beehive huts, striped vertically in white and rusty red, attest the Telugu country. After crossing the wide bed of the Cheyyeru, the line emerges at Cuddapah from grey and arid hills into a greyer plain, a vast ash-coloured expanse largely given over to dry cultivation. The region lies on the margin of the October–December rainfall area of the Madras littoral, and the rivers rise in the dry Mysore Maidan, not in the Western Ghats as do Krishna and Tungabhadra; hence, even in August, the great streams – Penner itself, Cheyyeru, Papagni, Chitravati – may be spreads of quartzite boulders, shingle or sand, several hundred yards wide with a line of water a yard across, or even not a drop on the surface, though the channels for spring-channel irrigation may strike water a mile or two upstream from the fields to be watered; while only 90 miles (145 km.) to the north the Ghats-fed rivers are full, great ribbons of muddy water half a mile or more wide.

Through the Kunderu valley runs the ill-starred Kurnool Canal, constructed in 1860–76 by a private company which apparently failed to notice the difference in the régimes of Peninsular and extra-Peninsular rivers; the complete, but inefficient, canal had eventually to be taken over by the government in 1882 after two decades of mismanagement. The topographical layout is obviously encouraging, and it is now proposed to recast the whole project, with reservoirs on the Krishna and at Someswaram in the lowest of the Penner watergaps; the project,

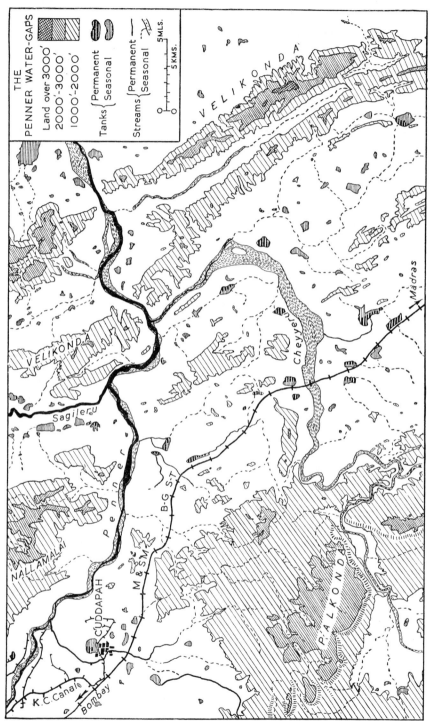

FIG 23.15 THE PENNER WATER-GAPS. *All* permanent water on original map is shown. *SOI* 1/253.440 57 J and N. *Courtesy SOI.*

if carried out in full, would irrigate no less than 3,000,000 ac. (1,210,000 ha.) mostly, however, in the coastal plain of Nellore.

The mineral wealth of the region is probably considerable in the aggregate, but scattered and not very accessible. It includes unworked copper and antimony; in asbestos and barytes the region produces practically all India's output, but the amounts are small. Cuddapah has a little industry; Kurnool (100,815), was the capital of Andhra Desa, the state formed from the Telugu-speaking Districts of Madras, from 1950 to 1956; with the choice of Hyderabad as the capital of the enlarged Andhra Pradesh, it has relapsed into being a rather sleepy District headquarters, but may revive as the canal project matures.

BIBLIOGRAPHICAL NOTE

There are two good papers on the neglected Western Ghats by Y. Satnayaran in the *Proceedings* of the symposia on Humid Tropics Vegetation (Tijawi, Indonesia, 1958) and on the Impact of Man on Humid Tropics Vegetation (Goroka, New Guinea, 1960): these are 'Ecological studies of the evergreen vegetation of the Western Ghats' (Tijawi proceedings (1960), 196–214) and 'The effects of shifting cultivation in Western Ghats' (Goroka proceedings (1962), 216–31); both are published by the UNESCO Science Co-operation Office for South East Asia.

For the Deccan in Maharashtra and Mysore, the older work of Ethel Simkins, *The Agricultural Geography of the Deccan Plateau* ([British] Geographical Asstn, 1926), retains some value as an introduction, and C. D. Deshpande, *Western India* (Students' Own Book Depot, Dharwar, 1948) is still invaluable. For enlarged Mysore, A. T. A. Learmonth and others, *Mysore State: I. An Atlas of Resources; II. A Regional Synthesis* (Indian Statistical Inst., Calcutta, 1960, 1962) is basic. A valuable detailed study of changes in a 'wet' and a 'dry' village in Mysore is T. S. Epstein, *Economic Development and Social Change in South India* (Manchester Univ. Press, 1962). Asia Publishing House has *Techno-Economic Surveys* of Madhya Pradesh and Andhra Pradesh.

Papers are scattered through most of the Indian journals; special mention may be made of *The Bombay Geographical Magazine* and *The Deccan Geographer*. A significant paper not cited in the text is W. H. Wake, 'The causal role of transportation improvements . . . in Madhya Pradesh, 1854–1954', *IGJ* 37/4 (1962), 133–52.

CHAPTER 24

The Eastern Littoral: Orissa and Andhra Desa
(Regions XXXII and XXXIII)

Generalities: the littoral as a whole

The Eastern Littoral forms a strong contrast to the Western: instead of the narrow platforms of the west, there is in general a much wider coastal plain, formed in part of the great deltas of the Mahanadi, Godavari, Krishna and Cauvery; elsewhere are in-facing cuestas developed on Cretaceous and Tertiary marine sediments. In the south the coastal lowlands are some 80 miles (129 km.) wide and are backed not by a steep and practically continuous wall, but by the broken hills of Tamilnad and the low plateaus around the middle Cauvery; the Velikondas present a sharp front to the plains, but then come the great breaches of the Krishna and Godavari, paralleled again by those of the Mahanadi and Brahmani. The contrasts between the interior plateaus, or even many of the really hilly areas, and the coastal lowlands are thus as a rule much softer than on the Western Littoral.

The climatic variation on this 1,200 miles (1,930 km.) of coast is highly significant. The north lies full in the track of the Bay of Bengal branch of the summer monsoon and receives *c.* 60 in. (1,524 mm.); but southern Orissa lies on the fluctuant flank of this great current and receives a lower (*c.* 50 in., 1,270 mm.) and less reliable fall. As we move south we enter the largest area of anomalous rainfall régime in the sub-continent, the dry southeast which has its rainy season in the months of the retreating monsoon, October through December. Southwards from the great bend of the coast at the Krishna delta this régime is dominant, and the lie of the coast – sub-parallel to the track of the rain-bearing depressions – contributes to the generally low figures. The extreme south, Ramanathapuram and Tirunelveli, is sheltered from the Arabian Sea branch by the high Anaimalai/Cardamom block, while to the north the great projection of the Cauvery delta, low-lying as it is, yet milks off some of the rain from the retreating monsoon. (And there is a change in general trend of coast and hills.) Here we have remarkably low figures (25–30 in., 635–762 mm.) for a coastal area in almost equatorial latitudes.

The agricultural contrasts which would be expected to result from these differences are to some extent masked by irrigation in the great deltas, but even so are striking: Fig. 24.1, though drawn from data some twenty years old, brings out the basic variations. Orissa is as typical a paddy-land as Bengal – indeed the

THE EASTERN LITTORAL

RAINFALL RÉGIMES

UTICORIN (TINNEVELLY)
21·9"

MADRAS (CHINGLEPUT)
49·6"

GOPALPUR (GANJAM)
43·3"

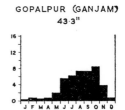

IRRIGATION, RICE AND MILLETS

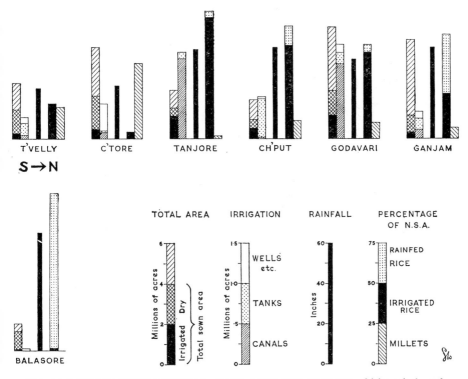

FIG 24.1 THE EASTERN LITTORAL: RAIN, RICE AND MILLETS. Although based on old figures, the diagram brings out the salient features, but for the recent importance of jute in the north.

northernmost District, Balasore, is practically monocultural, with over 95% of the TSA in *unirrigated* paddy (*c.* 1950). Millets are absent here, but begin to have significance in the northernmost District of Andhra Pradesh, Srikakulam; in Nellore, the southernmost Andhra District, jowar is the ranking crop. In all other Districts rice is the leading crop, but from Srikakulam southwards it depends on irrigation, and tank-irrigation is dominant everywhere away from the deltas.

The primary division, then, is that between the areas of standard and anomalous season of rain; but this is cut across by the deltas and, especially in the south, there is considerable regional diversity. Culturally there is the great distinction between Oriya-speaking Orissa and the Dravidian south, itself divided between the Telugu speakers of Andhra Desa and the Tamils of Madras: this latter state indeed corresponds almost exactly to Tamilnad, home of the most intensively Dravidian culture. The great quadrant of Tamilnad, between the Mysore plateaus, the Southern Blocks, and the sea, is indeed very complex, and it seems best to separate its treatment from the rest of the Eastern Littoral.

With all this in mind the northern portion can be divided as follows:

1. Deltaic Orissa.
2. Andhra Desa:
    (*a*) Visakhapatnam/Srikakulam coastal plain;
    (*b*) Godavari/Krishna deltas;
    (*c*) Nellore coastal plain (transitional to Tamilnad).

DELTAIC ORISSA

Three rivers, Baitarni, Brahmani and Mahanadi, combine to form a great alluvial salient, 125 miles (169 km.) across the base from Balasore to Lake Chilka and generally over 50 miles wide. The Mahanadi indeed is one of the most active depositing streams in the sub-continent, and its discharge is extremely irregular – the maximum recorded near its mouth is as large as that of the Ganga, nearly 2,000,000 cusecs, while it has dwindled to 1,125. Flood has been the greatest hazard to Orissan agriculture, but Hirakud and the other great dams will presumably change this.

There is the so frequent three-fold division: the lateritic shelves on the irregular upland margin; a zone some 40 miles (64 km.) wide of firm alluvium; marsh and dunes on the prograding seaface. Towards the west are many outliers of the gneissic hills, which in the Nilgiris of Balasore, and again north of Chilka, reach nearly to the sea. Lake Chilka itself varies in size from 350 to 450 sq. miles (906–1,165 km²) and is salty and fresh alternately. Only a few feet deep, it is bounded on the seaward side by a long and complex spit, and is important as a fishing ground and a source of reeds for thatch. Casuarinas are planted to fix the coastal dunes and to supply fuel. In the south, Ganjam District is not really deltaic; its core is the Rushikulya valley, with fertile black loams and clays and red hill-foot soils; but it is cut up by outliers of the gneissic hills, and much of the District is hill country pure and simple.

Rainfall is around 60 in. (1,524 mm.), and the fairly extensive canal irrigation is of value essentially as a guarantee against occasional drought. The main head-works are at the head of the Mahanadi delta proper, above Cuttack; the canals were originally designed for navigation as well as irrigation, in order to break down the notorious isolation of the province, which until 1912 was a part of Bengal and thence till 1936 grouped with Bihar, an unnatural administration grouping which contributed to the justified feeling of neglect among the Oriyas. But the railway destroyed the *raison d'être* of the coastal canal, and the high level one skirting the landward margin of the plain is of most use as providing an outlet for upland flood water; as Reclus pointed out, control at the debouchment of the valleys is the real essential here.[1] Rice is naturally the dominant crop, occupying 80–90% of NSA; other crops are almost negligible, except for jute, which has expanded rapidly since Partition and is the second crop in all Districts except Puri and Ganjam, where gram and ragi come in; the latter District especially contains large hilly areas. Sugar and oilseeds are of local significance.

The region is the heart of Orissa State; its area of 9,000 sq. miles (23,300 km.) was under a third of the area of the old province (before state mergers) but contained over half its population. Densities are high: Cuttack, 720, Balasore 566, Puri 466. Orissa is linguistically one of the most homogeneous Indian States, the great majority speaking Oriya, and it is solidly Hindu except for tribal remnants in the hills; in the past it was a centre of a rich civilization to which the great and very beautiful temples of Bhubaneswar, Puri, and above all Konarak still bear witness.[2] But it has always been isolated, as was shown dramatically by the great famine of 1867, which followed a year of drought and one of flood and took the authorities so completely by surprise that it is said that one Commissioner knew nothing of it until he found a starving woman eating his soap. The only road to Calcutta was unmetalled and unbridged, the monsoon practically inhibited import through the few open roadsteads, and mortality was between a quarter and a third, in Puri at least 36%. The state is not so isolated now, but it ranks with Assam as one of the least urbanized Indian States, with only 6·3% of its 1961 population living in towns.

All this is changing: industry, slow in starting, is of increasing importance, especially in and around Cuttack. Here are foundries, steel rolling mills, rail shops, and fair-sized glass and paper works; not far away a new port is being developed at Paradip for iron ore export. Rice milling is carried on in some large and many small units; sugar mills in the coastal market towns are on quite a large scale and more are likely to be set up as the tempo of development increases. There is a long list of small-scale and cottage industries, including jewellery and

[1] E. Reclus, *L'Inde* (1883), 20.
[2] See O. H. K. Spate, 'Konarak and Sindri: fertility ancient and modern' in *Let Me Enjoy* (Australian National Univ., Canberra, 1965; Methuen, London, 1966), 15–32.

toys as well as pleasing horn carvings and steatite images for the pilgrim trade. The southern area is likely to benefit from Machkund power, but in the interior poor communications are still a severe handicap.[3]

Towns of any size are very few. Cuttack (146,308) is at the very head of the Mahanadi delta – an admirable site, as Reclus remarked, were the rivers of any use. It is the main industrial centre, although so far this does not amount to very much, and the seat of the University. In 1951–61 it grew by nearly 50% despite the shift of the capital of Orissa to an entirely new town (on an ancient site) at Bhubaneswar a few miles to the south. Here, in a landscape dotted with magnificent old temples, is to be found a rarity – architecture which is distinctively modern and yet shows a happy blending of local and traditional character with the new style. The edges of Bhubaneswar are raw and ragged, however, and its progress has been rather fitful, depending on the interest of the state government of the day. Apart from these, the only place of more than local note is Puri, where the Jagannath ('Juggernaut') temple is still one of the most famous shrines of India and gave to the English language one of its longest-lived journalistic metaphors, now happily dead from overwork; the alleged suicides beneath the great temple car were mostly involuntary, caused by the pressure of the crowds.[4] A few miles away, close to the seashore at Konarak, stands the finest jewel of medieval Orissan culture, a temple in the form of the massy chariot of the Sun-God, Surya.

A brighter future seems in store for Orissa. The merger of the hill states increased the area by 85%, to 60,000 sq. miles (155,400 km²), though of course the population gain was smaller. The ending of the fantastic political fragmentation of the back-country has facilitated co-ordinated development of the great power and flood-control projects at Hirakud and other dams on the Mahanadi. As we have seen (pp. 722–3), the northwest of the state, between Sambalpur and Rourkela, is becoming industrialized, and Rourkela with over 90,000 people is now the second largest town in the state. As in Andhra Pradesh, there is an interior/littoral dualism, shown by the growth of industry around Cuttack and around the Rourkela steel works; but the Mahanadi itself may become a link.

ANDHRA DESA

Andhra Pradesh falls clearly into three units: Telangana; the inland Districts south of Krishna (formerly the 'Ceded Districts' of Madras); and the coastal Districts from Srikakulam to Nellore. The last two units formed the original

[3] B. Sinha, 'Heavy industries in Orissa: their problems and possibilities', *GRI* 21/1 (1959), 17–29, and 'Large-scale medium and cottage industries . . . in Orissa', *ibid.* 22/1 (1960), 34–47.
[4] They were hardly favoured by the priests since they obligated complicated purificatory ceremonies. The cult includes very ancient, possibly pre-Hindu, features; Reclus (*op. cit.* 430) gives a vivid but fairly balanced description: 'Religion is in fact the great, almost the only, industry of Puri, whose 20,000 inhabitants live directly or indirectly on the exploitation of the Faithful.' There is now also a parody of a European seaside resort.

Andhra State of 1953, enlarged into Andhra Pradesh by the addition of Telengana in 1956. Andhra Desa, 'the Andhra country', seems an appropriate name for this littoral region. The Aryan Oriya speech of Ganjam yields suddenly to Telugu where the bold peak of Mahendragiri (4,923 ft., 1,500 m.) narrows the coastal plain to a few miles, and Telugu holds sway as far as the Nagari Hills on the southern borders of Nellore.

The region, including Ganjam but less Nellore, formed the Northern Circars, brought under Muslim rule by the Golconda kings about 1575, ceded to the French in 1753; twelve years later the EIC obtained a grant of the whole from the Mogul Emperor, though of course his nominal subordinate the Nizam of Hyderabad had exercised what government existed, apart from that of petty warring rajahs; this was the Company's first considerable territorial acquisition outside Bengal. Despite the Telugu culture and the modern historical identity, the region seems to lack unity. The proliferation of small ports and trading stations in the early European phases is perhaps a reflection of this; the Dutch factories at Bimlipatnam and Kakinada (Cocanada) were not ceded to the EIC until 1825, and they had forced the early English settlement at Pulicat to move in 1625 to Armagon, the parent of Madras. In Masulipatnam the factory at French-pettah was not handed over to India until 1947, while in the same town English-palam and Volanda [Hollander]-palam mark the settlement of those nations.[5] Nizampatnam was the first English station on the east coast (1611), and Yanaon survived until 1947 as a last relic of the 18th century French holdings – a relic of 5 sq. miles (2 km²) and about 6,000 people.

Climatically the region is a transition zone. In the north we have the normal monsoonal distribution of rainfall, but southwards the October–December proportion increases steadily, with a decrease in total amount (except on the seaward margin of the deltas) and in rainy days. Already around the Krishna delta a third of the rain falls in the last quarter of the year, but these rains are less certain than those of the more usual monsoon months.

The total area, including considerable hill fringes north and south of the deltas, is 33,416 sq. miles (86,547 km²) with about 16,339,000 people in 1961, an overall density of 488. The deltaic Districts however have over 600 – up to 664 in West Godavari – and Nellore, a very large District with more Archaean terrain than the central Districts, and less (and less reliable and well distributed) rain than the northern, has only 255.

THE NORTH: SRIKAKULAM AND VISAKHAPATNAM

Essentially this is the area with over 40 in. (1,016 mm.) of rain; the three southern taluks of Visakhapatnam fall a little short of this. The lowland narrows to 12 miles (19 km.) under Mahendragiri, but on either side of this gate are the embayments of the Rushikulya (in Ganjam) and the Languliya and Vansadhara valleys;

[5] See S. M. Alam, 'Masulipatam – a metropolitan port in the 17th century', *IGJ* 34/3-4 (1959), 33-42.

the black-soiled valley floors grade upwards into poorer red soils, and there are numerous irregular outcrops of older, generally gneissic, rock. Visakhapatnam itself lies between the 1,600-ft. (490 m.) Kailana ridge to north and the 1,100-ft. (335 m.) Yaroda to the south, the latter running out to sea in the bold cliffs of

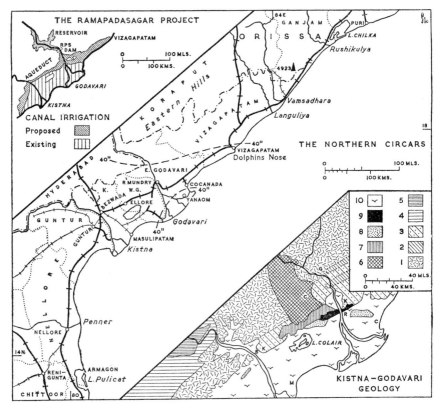

FIG 24.2 ANDHRA DESA: THE NORTHERN CIRCARS. On main map, dotted line District boundaries – K, Krishna, WG, West Godavari Districts; all railways ST, BG (thick line) or metre. Geology: 1, Archaean gneisses; 2, Charnockites; 3, Khondalites; 4, Cuddapah; 5, Vindhyan; 6, Lower, 7, Upper, Gondwana; 8, Tertiary; 9, Deccan Lava outlier; 10, alluvium. G, graphite; K, kaolin; C, coal (doubtful value); other initials towns, as on main map.

Dolphin's Nose, which shelters the port; in the northern suburbs are the peculiar Waltair Highlands, c. 150 ft. (46 m.) high and formed largely by the accumulation, since the Pleistocene, of red loams partly fluviatile and perhaps partly aeolian.[6]

Rice takes up about a third of the cultivated area, followed by ragi; groundnuts and gingelly are the leading oilseeds, and there are some millets and pulses.

[6] See the very original paper by C. Mahadevan and N. Sathapati, 'The origin of the Waltair Highlands', IGJ 24 (1949), 26–51.

Irrigation is on the whole unimportant, much of it being dependent on temporary mud-and-brushwood dams across the short rivers.

Mineral resources are few – graphite, manganese, kaolin, mica – and hardly developed; a potential resource of some interest in this atomic age, though limited in comparison with the wealth of Kerala, is the ilmenite and monazite in the beaches around Visakhapatnam.[7] With the very important exception of the shipyards at Visakhnapatnam, industrial development is very slight – only a few jute and sugar mills in little coastal towns. Hydro-electric developments in the hills, such as the Machkund scheme, may alter this.

There is only one real town, Visakhapatnam (formerly Vizagapatam) itself, with 182,004 people. 'Vizag' has developed considerably since the opening of the railway up the Languliya valley to Raipur and the subsequent dredging of a deep-water harbour in the tidal marshes; accommodation at quayside is limited, but it is more up-to-date than at most east coast ports. The selection of Vizag as the main shipbuilding centre of India was presumably on account of its situation as the nearest *ocean* port to Jamshedpur, but it was still a long way round. Now, however, Rourkela is only 300 miles (483 km.) away by rail, and the new plant has been designed to produce suitable steel. Ships of up to 8,000 tons have been launched, and there is a delightful Indian variant of traditional techniques: for religious reasons, instead of tallow the slipways are 'greased' with squashed bananas, and in deference to Prohibition a coconut is cracked instead of champagne. The port's hinterland extends to Nagpur; so far the trade has been chiefly in Madhya Pradesh manganese, in oilseeds and oils, and some jute and tobacco; but more varied development may be expected as the Raipur–Rourkela area develops. A steel plant for Vizag is being seriously considered.

This area, with neighbouring and even poorer Orissa, was a great exporter of 'coolie' labour to Burma and Malaya, and with the cessation of this emigration small ports such as Bimlipatnam and Gopalpur declined; the former has some jute and oilseed exports and the latter some activity as a seaside resort.

THE DELTAS

These, like North Kanara on the west coast, form an 'overlap' region, the breaching of the Eastern Hills by the Godavari and the Krishna leaving the limits in the hinterland indeterminate where the hills virtually disappear for about 100 miles. There is, it is true, a marked break of grade where the rivers cross the line of the hills – the Krishna is actually superimposed across the northern end of the Cuddapah Ranges (Fig. 23.14), and here the gradient is $3\frac{1}{2}$ ft. or more to the mile ($1/1,600$), five or six times the gradient near the sea. Their discharge is irregular (cf. above, p. 43); it has been estimated that in high flood the Krishna carries enough silt 'to cover daily an area of 5 sq. miles to a depth of one foot'.[8]

The worn-down margin of the Archaean hinterland is poor country: undulating plains broken by little hills, with much waste and stony ground; soils are

[7] *Ibid.* at p. 29.   [8] *Madras Gaz.* I (1908), 167.

mainly red clays with some loams. The coast for several miles inland is largely fringed with mangrove swamp (valuable as a fuel reserve) or sand-dunes rising to 30 or 50 ft. Between the relatively negative upland and the almost completely negative coast lie the rather limited areas of true delta. At Vijayawada (formerly Bezwada), 45 miles (72 km.) inland, the Krishna cuts across a gneissic ridge in a gap 1,300 yd. (1,188 m.) wide; this is utilized for the headworks of canals irrigating some 900,000 ac., 364,000 ha. The Godavari delta begins about the same distance inland at Dowleshwaram, where a dam 2 miles (3·6 km.) long feeds canals for another 1,000,000 ac. The deltas are vulnerable to flood, at times disastrous, and cyclones are also a danger: that of 1864 took 30,000 lives and ruined the prosperity of Masulipatnam port. In the Godavari delta below Dowleshwaram 'the country is a vast expanse of ricefields dotted with gardens and villages. During the rains the greater part of this tract becomes one sheet of water, only village sites, canal banks, roads and field boundaries appearing above it. Later in the year, as the rice grows higher, the dividing boundaries are hidden; and the whole country looks like a single ricefield, the groves around the villages, the road avenues and the white sails of the boats gliding along the main canals breaking the uniform sea of waving green crop.'[9] There is still a certain amount of local traffic, chiefly paddy, on the canals.

Between the deltas Colair Lake occupies a depression cut off from the sea by the river deposits and not yet silted up, though constantly diminishing by natural and artificial encroachment; covering about 100 sq. miles (259 km²) in the rains, it has at times dried out. Its numerous islands are intensively cultivated and there is a good deal of fishing.

Rainfall exceeds 35 in. (889 mm.) only in the seaward half of the Godavari Delta, while the tendency to October maxima is unfavourable to the groundnut and early paddy harvests, and cotton sowings must be late. Irrigation, if not essential, is at least highly useful; its importance is reflected in the high densities, up to 1,100–1,200 or more, of some delta taluks. In the strictly delta Districts of West Godavari and Krishna, NSA is over half the total area and double-cropping adds 20 to 40% to this. In West Godavari rice is over 80% of NSA, and it is everywhere the dominant crop by far. The second ranking crop is usually jowar or sesamum, and groundnuts are strong in East Godavari and Krishna. Tobacco covers at least 200,000 ac. (80,900 ha.), the best being grown on temporary sand-islands in the larger streams. Some sugar is grown, but this tall and long-standing crop must be protected from cyclones by expensive fencing with bamboos.

Again mineral potentialities are slight and development slighter. There are two small coalfields in the Gondwanas of the Godavari trough; graphite and kaolin are worked in a small way, mainly for Rajahmundry paper mills, which use paddy straw as well as bamboo from the hills, and for the small crucible industry at the same town. Salt evaporation at Kakinada might lead to a chemical industry. As well as the Rajahmundry works, and the rice and tobacco trades to

[9] *Ibid.* 268–9.

be expected, there are cement, fruit-canning and vegetable ghee works; most of these are congregated along the Krishna below Vijayawada and between Rajahmundry and Kakinada. Varied as it is, the total is not impressive, most of the units being quite petty: the most industrialized District, East Godavari, has only about 6% of its population returned as in industry, and about a third of these workers are employed on a household scale. Such as it is, however, this industrial development has in a few tracts already led to an ominous, if incipient, competition for land between paddy and tobacco.[10] Fortunately the region as a whole has as yet a substantial food surplus.[11] The industrial, and to some extent the agricultural, future of the region might well depend on the ultimate execution of the great, but long-deferred, Ramapadasagar multi-purpose project on the Godavari partly opened in 1965.

This is much the most urbanized part of Andhra Pradesh: excluding Hyderabad, the state had ten towns with a population of over 100,000 in 1961; eight of these were in Andhra Desa, and of these only Visakhapatnam and Nellore lie outside this central deltaic region. The site-significances of Vijayawada (Bezwada; 230,397) and Rajahmundry (130,002), at the delta-heads, are plain; Guntur (197,122) and Eluru (Ellore; 108,321) are trading and administrative centres with a little industry. The old ports of Kakinada (Cocanada; 122,865) and Masulipatnam (101,417) are now of little use. At Masulipatnam large ships must lie 5 miles offshore (weather permitting!) and the half-dozen wharves are 3 miles up a winding creek; yet in early European days it was a place of great importance, famous for carpets and chintzes. The opening of the longitudinal coastal railway completed the ruin begun by the cyclone of 1864; yet it is still often known as Bandar – 'the port'. Kakinada is rather better, with more wharves and jetties; yet again the anchorage is five or six miles offshore. The ports might – at large expense – be developed to serve Telangana as that backward region develops; but obviously the actively prograding deltas impose severe difficulties on any reconstruction; at Kakinada constant dredging is needed to keep a depth of 4–6 ft. (LWOST) in the bar. In the great days of the coolie traffic, before the depression and the Indo-Burmese race-riots of the 1930s, Kakinada had an enormous migrant turnover.

NELLORE

The traditional southern border of the Telugu country lies along the Tirupatti escarpment, overlooking the Renigunta basin; beyond is Tamilnad, a country, almost a nation, on its own. The transition is reflected in the increasing importance of tank-irrigation, though this will be changed if ever the Penner is fully utilized.

[10] Based mainly on: V. L. S. P. Rao, 'Industrial problems . . . [in] the Lower Godavari Region', IGJ 23 (1948), 1–15; V. V. Ramanadhan and V. L. S. P. Rao, Economic Atlas of Andhra Desa (Calcutta, 1949).

[11] See B. N. Chaturvedi, 'Andhra Pradesh: a surplus state in a deficit country', Deccan Geogr (Hyderabad), 1/1 (1962), 54–67; some of the general comments seem much too optimistic, but the details are interesting.

Physically also the transition is marked by patches of marine Jurassics and the coastal belt of sub-recent Cuddalore sandstones; both become more important in the Madras coastal plain (Fig. 25.1).

Most of Nellore is poor country: low peneplains of Archaean gneisses and schists, stony or lateritic and largely covered with scrub. Even allowing for the margin of the District in the Velikondas, agriculture is severely limited: NSA is well under 40%. Jowar is the main crop, followed by rice; cotton and groundnuts are grown, but not on an important scale. The Penner and its associated tanks are already important for irrigation, and will be more so if the old scheme for an anicut at the Someswaram watergap through the Velikondas is carried out.

The coast is fringed by a belt of alluvium up to 14 miles (22·5 km.) wide, between low-level laterites and the blown sand of the shore. The most interesting coastal feature is the great salt-water lagoon of Pulicat; the islands in the lagoon are used for burning lime from the great shell-banks (this is a main source of chunam plaster for Madras building) and salt smuggling is or was important.

Away from the Cuddapah Ranges, the only mineral wealth consists of laterite, building-stones, the coastal salt and shell-lime and mica from the Archaean schists; but its output is far below that of Bihar. Nellore town (106,776) is mainly administrative and commercial; it has a little pottery, but other industrial development is practically absent. The District, though lying athwart the main Madras–Calcutta railway, seems curiously isolated: the main links between Telangana and the Anantapur–Kurnool area and Andhra Desa converge on Guntur and Vijayawada, and – as the connections of Pulicat show – in Nellore the influence of Madras is already felt.

BIBLIOGRAPHICAL NOTE

On Orissa, there is an interesting series of articles by Bichitrananda Sinha: in the *Geographical Review of India* on its natural regions (19/2, 1957), heavy industries (21/1, 1959), smaller industries (22/1, 1960); in the *Deccan Geographer*, on population growth and economy (1/1, 1962) and fragmentation of holdings (1/2, 1963). On Andhra Desa, see V. V. Ramanadham, *The Economy of Andhra Pradesh* (Asia, Bombay, 1959). A well worked-out study on a neglected aspect of agricultural geography is J. Banerji, 'Pastures of Guntur', *Indian Forester*, 84/7 (1958), 390–6 – a transect from delta to hill-edge.

CHAPTER 25

The Eastern Littoral: Tamilnad
(Region XXXIV)

━━━━━━▶◀━━━━━━

Regional sub-divisions

The Tamil country, now equivalent to the State of Madras, consists of the great quadrant, a little over 50,000 sq. miles (129,500 km²), lying between the sea and the Deccan plateaus, which are here well recessed from the coast. This is the 'Carnatic' of the 18th-century Franco-British wars; a misnomer which will not be used here.[1] The coastal plain proper extends from Krishna to Kanya Kumari; but as we have seen, Nellore is transitional, and the Cauvery delta makes a great breach in the continuity of the *emergent* lowland, while the area south of the delta has distinct differences from that north of it. Inland we have the discontinuous Tamilnad Hills, sufficiently distant and distinct from the Mysore plateaus to receive separate treatment; and behind them there is the trough which extends from the Cauvery across the Ponnaiyar (or South Penner) to the Palar. Across the middle Cauvery lies the Kongunad plateau leading up to Palghat.

There is thus a good deal of regional diversity, and Tamilnad may best be described under six sub-regions:

1. The Coromandel coastal plain (Madras hinterland);
2. The Tamilnad Hills;
3. The Ponnaiyar/Palar trough (Baramahal);
4. Kongunad (Coimbatore Plateau and Palghat);
5. The Cauvery Delta;
6. The Dry Southeast:
   (*a*) Upper Vaigai basin;
   (*b*) Madurai–Ramanathapuram tank country;
   (*c*) Tirunelveli Black Soil plain;
   (*d*) Tamprabarni basin.

The most distinctive characteristics of the region are its homogeneously Tamil culture and its rainfall régime with most of the rain falling in October through December. With these is associated, in most areas, a great development of tank irrigation.

[1] The Muslims who overran most of southern India after the fall of Vijayanagar extended the term Karnataka from its true seat on the Mysore plateaus to include all the south, except Kerala or Malabar; and from them Europeans took over the name, applying it to the land 'below the Ghats'. See *Madras Gaz.* I (1908), 182–4.

Physically the structure is very complex. Jacques Dupuis, whose admirable survey (1959) supersedes older work, regards the higher areas as essentially horsts of Cretaceous age, separated by contemporaneous grabens; and such a general structural explanation is certainly called for by the marked parallelism

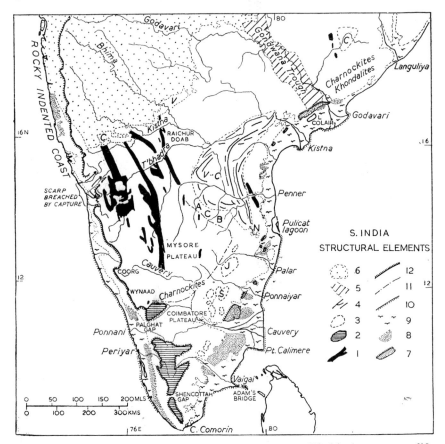

FIG 25.1 SOUTH INDIA: STRUCTURAL ELEMENTS. All blank areas undifferentiated Archaean gneisses, etc. 1, Dharwarian synclinoria; 2, Southern Blocks; 3, outliers of higher plateaus; 4, Cuddapah ranges; 5, Gondwana trough; 6, Deccan Lavas; 7, marine Jurassic and Cretaceous, cuestiform on coastal plain; 8, late Tertiary Cuddalore (in east) and Warkallai (in west), shelves or low cuestas with some laterite; 9, alluvium; 10, definitely prograding or emergent shorelines; 11, approx. boundary of Mysore plateau; 12, main Ghats scarp. C, Cuddapah, V, Vindhyan, outcrops. ACB, Anantapur-Chittoor basins; N, Nagari, J, Javadi, S, Shevaroy Hills.

between the Tamilnad Hills and the Palani/Varushanad trends, together with the strong drainage lines, southwest/northeast turning northwest/southeast, in both areas. While the higher plateaus, especially in Mysore, are regarded as peneplains, the low plain (down to 500 ft., 150 m.) fringing the Tamilnad Hills and the Southern Blocks, is essentially formed of great pediments produced in semi-arid to arid conditions. Below this, but continuous without any marked break of slopes, is a plane of marine abrasion formed by a Miocene transgression well to the west of the Cretaceous shoreline. There was emergence in the Pliocene and finally a Neolithic emergence of the order of 6 to 7 ft. (2 m.) – originally rather more, but partly masked by a small recent submergence.

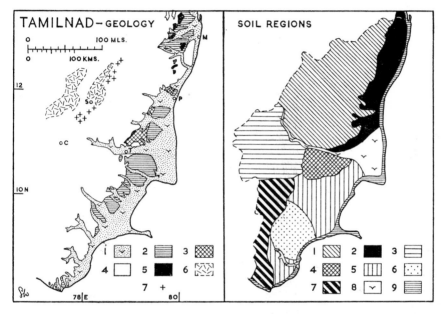

FIG 25.2 TAMILNAD: GEOLOGY AND SOIL REGIONS.

Geology: 1, recent; 2, Cuddalores and laterites; 3, Cretaceous; 4, unclassified gneisses, etc.; 5, U. Gondwana; 6, Charnockites; 7, granites. Initials for Madras, Salem, Coimbatore, Pondicherry and Tiruchchirappalli.

Soils: 1, red, sandy, leached and lateritized, some black soil in depressions; 2, loamy, black in south to red in north; 3, thin Archaean soils; 4, poor red soils, alkaline in south; 5, red soils, saline in places; 6, black cotton soils; 7, colluvial red loams; 8, alluvium; 9, grey littoral sands.

Adapted from maps by K. Ramamurthy, *IGJ* 23 (1948). *Courtesy G. Kuriyan.*

THE COROMANDEL COASTAL PLAIN

This name, from Cholamandalam, the country of the Cholas, seems a reasonable one for the portion of the coastal plain centred on Madras: Chingleput and South Arcot Districts, with adjacent parts of North Arcot and Tiruchchirappalli (the former Trichinopoly). The lowland below 500 ft. is 50–60 miles (80–95 km.) wide and falls into five belts:

(i) the Miocene surface below the Tamilnad Hills;

(ii) remnants of marine deposits (Cretaceous and Jurassic);

(iii) the Cuddalore Sandstone/laterite shelf;

(iv) a young alluvial plain, with embayments behind Madras (Korteliyar, Cooum, Palar valleys) and Pondicherry (Ponnaiyar), with the Vellar basin as a transition to the Cauvery delta;

(v) a very recent alluvial strandplain, still prograding in places.

Of these (ii) and (iii) are discontinuous; the older rocks come close to the sea south of Madras, indeed right to the shore where the famous Seven Pagodas of Mahaballipuram are built, or rather carved, of local granite. Here the landscape is broken by numerous *inselbergen*, generally 250–500 ft. (75–150 m.) high but reaching 700–800 (215–245 m.) and often aligned northeast–southwest, 'the stocks of very ancient folded chains'. Dupuis traces their detailed variation and distribution, in part affected by climatic processes.[2] The marine deposits consist of calcareous or argillaceous sandstones, and often carry scrub jungle. The older view that the Cuddalores are uplifted marine sediments has been discredited by Dupuis, who sees in them the relics of great Mio-Pliocene detrital cones.[3] In South Arcot they form distinct, if very subdued, cuestas reaching over 250 ft.; they are much lateritized and carry a generally xerophytic scrub of euphorbia and bamboo, with palmyra and coconut palms.

The coast follows the main strike of the Deccan Charnockites, with the great change in trend at 16° N. The coarse nature of the outer Velikonda deposits suggests that the general line was early established, with regressions of which the Miocene was the most important. There is, as usual, evidence for both emergence and submergence in the later phases: on the one hand, stranded cliffs north of Pondicherry and uplift in the Palar and Korteliyar deltas, on other, archaeological and literary evidence for recent submergence in the San Thomé-Mahaballipuram area. Krishnaswami has established a sequence of four terraces, from over 100 to 8 ft. (30–2·4 m.) on the Korteliyar, and these range from Acheulian into the Upper Palaeolithic. There is dispute as to the full interpretation of these findings, but it seems that the main formation of laterite (at 100–125 ft., 30–38 m.) was the result of an intense pluvial period, and in part at least antedates human settlement in what may have been heavily forested country.[4]

The 'strandplain' is narrow, and still being added to by marine and aeolian deposition: the beaches and dunes of Madras, for instance, have grown up as the result of the interruption of longshore drift by the harbour walls. Behind is a lagoon and backwater belt which, except at Pulicat, has been largely filled in and is very restricted compared with that of Kerala. Inland again the alluvial embayments widen out between the little uplands, their black loams contrasting vividly with the more or less lateritized soils around them.

[2] Dupuis 1959, 127–34; for full reference, see Bibliographical Note. [3] *Ibid.* 77–84.
[4] V. D. Krishnaswami, 'Environmental and cultural changes of prehistoric man near Madras', *JMGA* 13/1 (1938), 58–90; discussed in Dupuis 1959, 90–2.

Before the 11th century the Palar appears to have taken a line well to the north of its present course, debouching north of Ennore. The Korteliyar, Cooum and Adyar, misfits in relation to their wide alluvial belts, probably represent old channels of the Palar; the diversion would seem to be the conjoint result of exceptional floods and human interference. There are many other examples of river diversion on the wide glacis where there are hardly any defined thalwegs.[5]

Agriculture

The gneissic fringe has generally red sandy soils, leached and lateritized, with black clays and loams in wetter depressions where oxidization is inhibited (Fig. 25.2). The remainder of the sub-region has generally black loams, best in the 'inner' alluvium, e.g. of the Vellar, behind the line of higher Cuddalore terrain in the Capper Hills behind Cuddalore and the Red Hills at Pondicherry. But north of Madras the red soils predominate, and of course the calcareous or sandy uplands of marine deposits and the lateritized Cuddalores are very poor. The immediate coastal strip is almost pure sand, often saline.

The rainfall is less effective than its amount (40–45 in., 1,016–1,143 mm.) would suggest, as about two-thirds of it is concentrated into three or four months. With taluk densities of 500–700 (over 900 in parts of South Arcot) irrigation is clearly essential to extend the growing season. The rivers contain hardly any water for nine months of the year, and recourse is therefore had to tanks and 'spring channels'; the tanks are fed by the cold-weather rain and by leats taken off from springs and waterholes in the river beds, and these spring-channels are independently used for specialized high value crops such as garden produce. Rice is dominant, over 60% of NSA in Chingleput, with ragi or bajra as the second crop. North Arcot has one of the strongest groundnut concentrations of India, and this spills over into South Arcot behind Pondicherry. Forests are negligible, covering about one-eighth of Chingleput with the scrubbiest scrub, mainly used for grazing and even so very poor.

Agricultural rhythms differ notably from those of more monsoonal rainfall régime. In the hot weather (March–May) the country is completely parched and purely agricultural work is at a standstill, except for garden crops, irrigated by wells, jaggery-making, and so on. This is the season for fuel-cutting, building, thatching, work on tanks, wells and weirs, pilgrimages, religious plays, and the great games of match-making and marriage. With June's two or three inches of rain the village as it were clears for action: new tenancies are taken out, cattle bought, ploughs repaired.[6] 'The half-built house, the half-raised wall, are all left off suddenly to be taken up for completion at the next slack season. The Indian

---

[5] P. G. Dowie, 'The physical aspects and geology of the neighbourhood of Madras', *JMGA* 14/4 (1939), 320–401, at 379; Dupuis 1959, 124–6.

[6] The village carpenter, a person of importance in Adi (June–July) becomes unpopular when he has to be paid in kind at harvest in Thai (January–February); as the local proverb has it, 'The master-carpenter of Adi becomes the carpenter-boy of Thai.'

peasant knows instinctively the immense importance of taking time by the fore-lock so far as cultivation is concerned. . . .'[7] The *kar* paddy crop, and such dry crops as ragi, sesamum, groundnuts and pulses are now sown, to be harvested in September–October when the real rain begins. Then the main (*samba*) paddy crop is transplanted; harvest is about mid-January – again a marriage season. There remains a short and relatively cool (70–75° F., 21–24° C.) season in which another crop may be grown – the third on really good wet land, but more usually the second; this crop of course depends on tanks since the total rain from January through May is not more than 3–4 in. (84–86 mm.).

Other activities; towns

The narrow coastal strip has its own life: tree cultures, fishing, salt-making. Coconuts and toddy (palmyra) palms thrive on the sandy soils; the casuarina is grown as the main source of fuel. Remarkably quick-maturing, the tree can yield annually about 5 tons of good fuel-wood per acre; the little plantations have now spread to the sandier soils and laterites inland. The casuarina checks the inland movement of dunes and, where not gleaned by the village women for kitchen kindling, the fallen leaves (like pine-needles) give much needed humus; the root nodules also add nitrogen. This improvement of the soil may enable an extension of pasture or even dry crops. The men from the tiny fishing-hamlets are adept in the use of their exceedingly primitive log catamarans; most of the catch is dried and salted. At Ennore, just north of Madras, and at several smaller places there are salt-pans; the Pulicat lime-burning has already been noted.

Casuarina fuel, Pulicat *chunam*, salt, dried fish, make up almost all the traffic on the Buckingham Canal, which was constructed piecemeal (1806–82) along the backwaters and reaches 200 miles (322 km.) north of Madras and 60 south. Despite expensive reconstructions after 1880, the Canal is a poor piece of work, unfit for craft drawing over 3 ft., and cost of maintenance has always exceeded receipts. Such as it is, however, it is the main avenue by which these cheap but bulky commodities come to Madras. Mineral resources, apart from laterite, are negligible, if we except the lignite area in South Arcot, estimated to contain 2,000,000,000 tons, now being exploited with Russian assistance and already with important contributions of power to the electric grid.

Kanchipuram (82,714) has already been described (Chapter 7); Cuddalore (79,168) is the usual creek-and-roadstead port, with an important trade in groundnuts and some associated industry (oil-pressing, etc.). Away from the coast Vellore (122,761) has nodal advantage, where the Palar route around the north of the Tamil Hills is crossed by a north–south piedmont route; its main importance is as a grain mart. The coast is dotted with decayed relics of early European activity – Armagon, Pulicat, Fort St David, Porto Novo; of these Pondicherry alone retains some importance simply by historic accident: it is

[7] N. Subrahmanyam, 'Seasonal control . . . in the Conjeeveram Region', *IGJ* 17/2 (1942), 100–9.

doubtful whether it would have been developed had it been under the same political jurisdiction as Madras.

Pondicherry, largest of the French possessions, had an area of 185 sq. miles (479 km^2) divided into about sixteen fragments; there was even a village held jointly by British and French India; with such a frontier, it is probable that smuggling contributed largely to the flourishing trade. The chief cash crop of the territory and its hinterland is groundnuts, exported to Marseilles; the town 'also exploits its political connections. Its most important manufacturing enterprise . . . exported yarn to the hand-loom weavers of French Indo-China, and coloured cloths to Madagascar, in each case getting the benefit of free entry into a protected market.'[8] There are also small foundries and rolling-mills using scrap. There is a 300-yd.-long (274 m.) pier, and ships can anchor within 200–300 yd. of it.

About a quarter of the 369,000 inhabitants of the territory live in the town itself, which contrasts remarkably with the standard Euro-Indian urban type. Most of the Indian workers live in the outlying villages; Pondicherry town, closely but regularly built, is largely French or at least Gallicized, an enclave of Mediterranean culture. Although it has now been ceded to India, this cultural tradition is recognized by assuring it a special municipal status, temporarily at least; it is not yet 'dry'.

MADRAS

Madras (Fig. 25.3) is India's fourth city, with 1,729,141 people, having been ousted from third place by Delhi. Strictly speaking its site has no advantages whatever, except that its position midway between Penner and Ponnaiyar probably counts for something. But in the general setting of early English activity along this coast some commercial and administrative centre was bound to develop, and any site once developed was bound to maintain its position since, if it had no special values itself, no possible rival had any either, and a going concern had a certain pre-emption. But it is obviously and solely a matter of history that Madras is today more important than Pondicherry.[9]

There were, it is true, two very local factors which may have influenced Francis Day in his choice in 1639: the Cooum creek, capable of taking ships up to 50 tons burden, and the defensive values of a shallow lagoon paralleling the coast about a mile inland. But later in the 17th century East Indiamen already ran up to 1,500 tons or more, and half a dozen places offered similar site values, though some, such as Porto Novo, were already taken up by Portuguese or Dutch. The really decisive factor seems to have been nothing more or less than the cheapness of local cloth.[10]

[8] G. Slater, *Southern India* (1936), 162–4.

[9] The point is developed in O. H. K. Spate, 'How determined is Possibilism?', *Geogl Studies*, IV/1 (1957), 3–12. The description in the *Madras Gaz.* (I. 497–521) is very good and not entirely out of date, and there are some brilliant chapters on Madras in Dupuis, 1960.

[10] C. S. Srinivasachariar, *JMGA* 14/2 (1939), 134–5.

The city owed its earlier importance to the opportunities of the Franco-British conflict in the Peninsula; even so, while it was far from being an isolated laggard like Bombay, it is significant that Calcutta – the gateway to really profitable aggrandisement – supplanted Madras as the nerve-centre of British

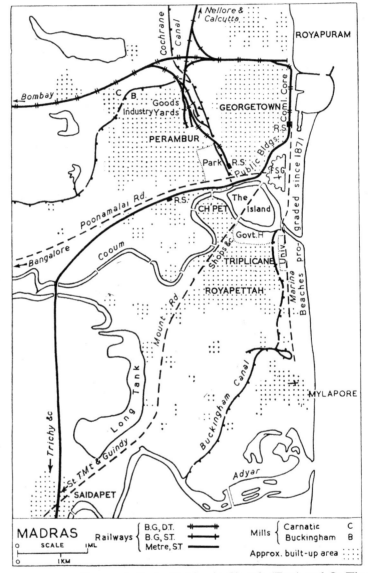

FIG 25.3 MADRAS. Crosses indicate St Mary's Church (Fort) and St Thomas's Cathedral (Portuguese, Mylapore). Ch'pet = Chintadripet; St T. Mt = St Thomas's Mount; F.S.G., Fort St George. Practically the entire area is now more or less built up.

power as early as 1773, only fifteen years after Plassey and the first serious territorial acquisitions. Nevertheless, at the first Census in 1872 Madras was returned as the fifth city of the British Empire.[11] It is astonishing that this position was attained by a port of which the 'facilities' were a jetty and a roadstead, from which most passengers and goods were landed by not too safe surf-boats. Nor was industry of much real weight until quite recently.

The morphology of Madras, if such it can be called, is as bizarre as its development. The city area was unchanged from 1798 until 1923, when a small extension was made. Within its 30 sq. miles the 1941 density was only about 40 per acre, very unequally distributed: ward densities in 1931 were from 175 per acre down to 11; since at least 1921 increment has been most rapid on the periphery, but the centre remains congested. Such a distribution implies gaps in the building pattern, and in fact Madras is rather a congeries of more or less contiguous suburbs and even rural villages than a city; Georgetown apart it might almost be called, in Robert Graves' phrase, the suburbs of itself. It is not only an absence of planning, but almost an absence of structure.

There is a nucleus: Fort St George and Georgetown. The Fort is typical 18th-century work and contains the Secretariat, barracks and so on, as well as the oldest Anglican church in India (St Mary's, 1678–80). On the landward side is an irregular maidan, with courts, colleges and hospitals skirting it. Georgetown was previously Blacktown, renamed in 1906 in honour of the visit of the then Prince of Wales: close-built, with some modest but not unattractive buildings, mostly chunam; and here, in the commercial core facing directly on to the harbour, are some tall office buildings comparable with the standard CBD of a great modern city. Georgetown and the Fort are marked off from the rest by the Cochrane Canal (the first section of what became the Buckingham Canal) and the meandering Cooum, which except in November–December is a foul green backwater. Beyond lies the sprawl. To the west is the suburb of Egmore, cultural and residential, the ribbon-development along the Poonamalai Road, and industrial Perambur, with the famous Buckingham and Carnatic cotton mills. The Cooum Island is open development – parade-grounds and clubs – and to the south are the Government House grounds.

South of the Cooum, for the three or four miles to the Adyar, is an extraordinarily mixed area: Chintadripet is an unbelievably squalid slum, and yet more village than town; Triplicane simply a normal Indian provincial town; Royapettah an agglomeration of pleasant old-fashioned small-town bungalows. Mount Road, the main axis, runs from Government House to St Thomas's Mount, through the anarchically developed suburb of Saidapet (headquarters of Chingleput District) and Guindy, with the race-course, another Government House, and various clubs. In the central part of Mount Road is the main shopping, hotel and cinema area. The Gazetteer's description of 1908 remained

[11] In thousands: London 3,254, Calcutta 795, Bombay 644, Liverpool 493, Madras 398, Manchester 351, Birmingham 344.

largely valid 50 years later: ' . . . anything but typically urban in appearance. Most of the roads of this part run through avenues, and are flanked by frequent groves of palms and other trees; the shops in the wide Mount Road, though many of them are imposing structures, often stand back from the street with gardens in front of them; the better residences are built in compounds which have almost the dignity of parks; the rice-fields frequently wind in and out between these in almost rural fashion.' This extraordinarily open development, as compared with Calcutta and Bombay, is probably a function of unimpeded terrain and cheap land; but now the skyline is being changed by the erection of large blocks of offices and flats.

The southern suburbs are historically interesting. St Thomas's Mount is the reputed site of the martyrdom of the Apostle, and here a Christian (Nestorian) inscription has been found, written in Pahlavi, probably of the 8th century. The existing church on the summit of the Mount is Portuguese (1547), as is the great church of Mylapore (Ptolemy's Meliapuram) where the reputed tomb of the Apostle may be seen; Mylapore has still some Lusian connections.

Although Madras was more nearly dependent on trade alone than most cities of its rank, nothing was done to provide it with a harbour until 1871, when the great breakwaters were begun, replacing the old iron jetty. Originally the harbour entrance faced east, straight out into the Bay, and in 1910 – only twenty years from completion – it was found necessary to shift it to the northeast, mainly to avoid shoaling. As late as 1904 conditions were almost fantastically primitive.[12] The present facilities are inadequate for a great port, but berthing space has been increased and bulk handling facilities are planned. The import trade is very miscellaneous, Madras being the great entrepôt for south India; exports include groundnuts, hides, raw and manufactured cotton. Cochin and Visakhapatnam are already strong rivals, and Madras is far behind Bombay and Calcutta.

Industrially also Madras is outstripped not only by Bombay and Calcutta, but by several towns within the State, such as Madurai and Coimbatore. Yet the Madras government was far in advance of the Centre and of other Provinces in its encouragement of indigenous manufacturing, starting an aluminium utensils industry, for instance, as early as 1906.[13] Private enterprise also made an early start; the Buckingham and the Carnatic Mills date from 1874–83 and have been among the most progressive in India. These two are the only cotton mills in Madras (there were four in 1911) and employ about 11,000 workers – the largest single organized industry. A feature of their policy is that recruitment is mainly from the children of employees, and this stable labour force is probably a factor in the high reputation of the product.

The simple fact is of course that Madras was not well placed as regards either raw materials or power until the electric grid changed the perspective. Assembly

[12] For a vivid description, see G. C. Armstrong, 'The Port of Madras', *JMGA*, 14/2 (1939), 146–54.
[13] The deliberate suppression of this initiative in the interests of *laissez-faire* is described in Slater, 33–39.

and small consumption factories are spreading, in the city itself or in satellites within 20 miles or so: bicycles, cars, tractors, lorries, rolling stock, paint, matches, chemicals, glass, pencils and so on. Leather is important, though tanning is not allowed within the city itself: the large factory at Chromepet owes its existence to the initiative of the provincial Department of Industry in experimenting with chrome tanning, and there are perhaps 200 more indigenous tanneries. Among the crafts handloom weaving (especially *lungyis* for overseas Bay of Bengal markets) and *bidi*-making are notable. *Bidis* are accurately described by Lokanathan as 'tobacco dust rolled into a cigarette-like thing', and as the poverty of the of the Indian masses compels production at the cheapest possible rate, it is not surprising that *bidi*-making is one of the most sweated occupations in the world. 'No adult worker can hope to earn a living wage even by working 12 hours a day,' and the manufacture is carried on almost entirely by boys in a multitude of tiny sweat-shops. There are, of course, the usual metropolitan trades: foundries and workshops (the largest are the railshops at Perambur), minor metal crafts and printing. But the sum total of Madras industry, except perhaps for tanning, is not impressive.

This account has perhaps over-stressed the negative aspects of the city's life: there are others. Electrification of the local railways has led to some good suburban development, especially to the southwest whence come most of the commuters. The inner western suburbs are for the most part depressing, and the most degrading poverty is terribly apparent in places like Chintadripet, divided from cultured Egmore merely by the Cooum. Yet there is space as well as scope for rehabilitation; 'congestion is not due to scarcity of land but to failure in providing for an ordered city growth,' and here are at least signs of change. Above all Madras is the conscious centre of modern Dravidian culture, especially of course Tamilian; about two-thirds of the people speak Tamil, one-fifth Telugu, and English is widespread. There are no keener or more cultured intellects in the world than those of many Madrassi Brahmins and educationally Madras is a centre of the first rank; the city which has produced a statesman like Rajagopalichariar, a mathematician like Ramanujan, is no mean city, whatever it may look like. The Indo-British architecture (as usual when the Public Works Department goes gay) indulges in a profusion of comic cornices and futile volutes, but the colleges of the University along the Marina (the old seafront now faced by wide prograding beaches) are not unworthy of their setting. With all its muddle and (as compared with Bombay, Calcutta or Delhi) its air of provincialism, Madras is perhaps a more likeable and more liveable-in city than any of the three; its charm is odd and irritating, but charm none the less.

THE TAMILNAD HILLS

Between Palar and Cauvery the coastal plain is backed by a discontinuous line of highland, made up of small but bold hill-masses of which the chief are the

Javadis, Shevaroys, Kalrayans and Pachaimalais (Fig. 25.4). There seems to be no collective name for them, and 'Tamilnad Hills' seems reasonable.[14] North of the Palar smaller and even more broken hills link up with the tail of the Cudda-

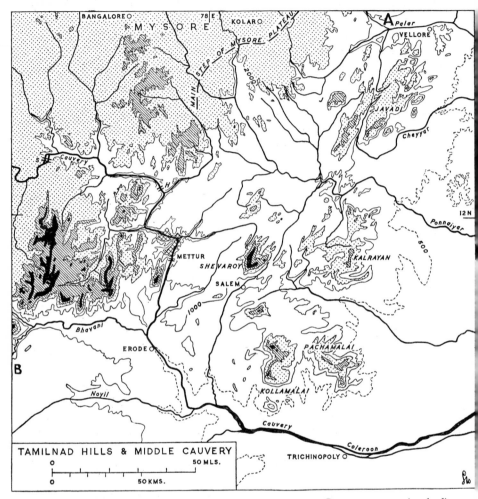

FIG 25.4 THE TAMILNAD HILLS AND MIDDLE CAUVERY. Contours at 500 (pecked), 1,000, 2,000, 3,000, 4,000 ft. (2,000–3,000 stippled, 3,000–4,000 shaded, over 4,000 black). Mettur Lake cross-hatched. J, Jalarpet gap; S, Sivasamudram; H, Hagenakal Falls. *SOI* 1/1M 57, 58. *Courtesy* SOI.

[14] This section is in general confirmed by Dupuis, 1959. He suggests (p. 18) that the term Ghat should be retained for these hills, on the grounds that its omission masks the evident relationship between the massifs of the west and the east. This is true on the local scale, but its retention would lead to the more serious confusion of equating the whole line of highlands, from Orissa southwards, with the Western Ghats, which Dupuis himself admits would be unjustifiable.

pahs in the Nagari Hills; across the Cauvery further detached massifs north of Madurai lead on to the long Varushanad–Andipatti Range and so to the Cardamoms. Behind this disjointed wall lie the inner plateaus of Tamilnad, in the Palar/Ponnaiyar trough, the mid-Cauvery valley, and the upper Vaigai embayment. This layout is itself suggestive, and it will be convenient to take up here some of the structural relations hinted at in the opening of this chapter (Fig. 25.1).

The more prominent ridges in the hills are usually Charnockites, 'intruded as sills along the foliation planes of the older gneisses'; the general strike is northnortheast/southsouthwest, as shown e.g. in the remarkably straight and wall-sided Cheyyur/Agaram through-valley which bisects the Javadis and appears to mark the line of weakness of the Charnockites/gneiss contact. These northnortheast/southsouthwest trends are cut across perpendicularly by other structure-lines, seen in the parallel courses of the Palar and Ponnaiyar and many of their tributaries down the Mysore Ghat. Similar alignments are seen on the Vaigai/Periyar watershed, far to the south (Fig. 25.10), while the Cauvery between Sivasamudram and Erode swings from one trend to the other in great right-angles. It is probably significant that the middle Palar, the section of the Cauvery below Hagenakal Falls, with the tributaries entering at each end of this section, and the upper Bhavani all lie in the same straight line (A–B on Fig. 25.4). The whole pattern, on both the Mysore Ghat and the Cardamom flanks, strongly suggests control by reticulate faults – macro-jointing, as it were, and this accords with the general nature of these hills as horsts, an interpretation suggested by Wadia and accepted by Dupuis.

West of the middle Palar the Mysore Ghat descends in a series of steps, from a general level of 3,000 ft. plus through a broad shelf at *c.* 2,250 ft. (915 and 685 m.). Both the Ghat scarps and the line of the Javadis have in general straight trends conformable with their origin as horsts, and there is much evidence of faulting. The valleys above and below the Mysore Ghat are at least late mature, but the scarp is dissected by many gorges, often with spectacular falls. Although Dupuis holds that the Mysore uplift was in general Jurassic and that of the Tamilnad Hills was Cretaceous, he suggests some rejuvenation of the Mysore Ghat in the latter period; Kalyanasundaram argues for an even later date. In either case, it may well be linked with the Arabian Sea subsidence and the formation of the Western Ghats.[15]

The Tamilnad summits are generally rather higher than the opposite heights of the Mysore Plateau: 3,600–3,800 ft. in the Javadis, 5,000–5,400 in the Shevaroys (1,095–1,160 and 1,525–1,645 m.). The Charnockites were formed at greater depths than the main mass of Archaean gneisses, but all along the east of the Peninsula the charnockite zone is relatively higher. This again may point to relative vertical movement and greater isostatic mobility in the lighter Charnockites.

[15] V. Kalyanasundaram, 'Some aspects of the physical geography of North Arcot', *IGJ* 18/4 (1943), 204–12; Dupuis 1959, 20, 34–48, 121.

The steep flanks of the hills are usually forested, but within this girdle of jungle the plateaus carry a surprisingly large agricultural population: in the Shevaroys[16] Yercaud taluk (practically equivalent to the main plateau) had a density of 289 on its 60 sq. miles, and only 2,000–3,000 of the 17,000 people were in the tiny hill-station of Yercaud itself. The Malayalees (='hillpeople'; not to be confused with the Malayalams of Kerala) are mainly agriculturalists, growing ragi, cholam, gram, oilseeds and fruit; there is some terraced rice. Cattle-keeping is secondary, and there are the usual minor forest products, including some sandalwood and lac. The mild climate (range c 60–87°F., 15·6–27°C.) with its good rain (128 in., 3,251 mm. at Yercaud) has led to a certain amount of coffee-growing. There is some unexploited bauxite.

THE PONNAIYAR/PALAR TROUGH AND SALEM[17]

The general limits of the trough between the Mysore Ghat and the Tamilnad Hills are well defined, but in the south the area around Salem raises difficulties. It might well be better to link the plateau around Salem with that of Coimbatore (Kongunad) and the Palghat across the Cauvery; but on the whole the river seems to make a marked divide from an economic if not from a physical point of view, and the links of Salem are mainly to the north and east.

The general aspect of this region, known as the Baramahal, is that of a pedi-plain at about 1,300 ft., sinking in the south to 1,000 ft. (395–305 m.); here it is separated, as we have admitted rather arbitrarily, from the Kongunad plateau by the Cauvery. The Ponnaiyar breaks across it in long rectilineal stretches, obviously tectonically controlled, entering and leaving by narrow gorges; but to the north its valley is separated from that of the Palar by a mere col at Jalarpet, and the Palar may indeed have flowed into the Ponnaiyar by this gap. In the northeast the Palar valley widens out and falls below 1,000 ft., and Vellore, as a typical contact town, may be taken as the limit here.

Climate and agriculture

Shut in as the region is, the rainfall of 30–33 in. (762–838 mm.) is at least as much as can be expected. Where it opens out to the south Salem town gets 39 in. (991 mm.) with a puzzling distribution:

J.	F.	M.	A.	M.	J.	J.	A.	S.	O.	N.	D.
0·3	0·3	0·5	1·8	4·7	3·0	3·8	6·8	6·6	6·7	3·7	1·0

This is clearly an interior rather than a southeast littoral régime; the area is not particularly open to Arabian Sea influences since, as we shall see, the effect of the Palghat Gap is much more narrowly restricted than might be expected. Mean temperatures at Salem range from 76 (December–January) to 98°F. (April; 24·4–36·7°C.). Soils are generally red and sandy but on the whole not infertile: soil wash from the Ghat slopes is probably responsible for this.

[16] V. Natarajan, 'The Shevaroys Region', *JMGA* 11/2 (1936), 162–73.
[17] Based mainly on eleven papers in *JMGA*. 11/2 (1936).

Rainfall is not too reliable, but only about a sixth of the cultivated area of Salem District is irrigated, 80% of the irrigation being equally divided between small tanks and wells. The ingenious device known as the *kabalai* is widely used here and elsewhere in the Tamil country. This consists of a large leather bucket ending in an open tube; when the bucket is drawn up the tube discharges directly into the irrigation channel. The advantage of this is that both filling and emptying are automatic, and only one man is needed, to drive the bullock, against two with the *mhote* of northern India, one of whom has to control the bucket.[18] This is essentially a dry crops area: the three main millets are the staple food crops, rice being really important only towards the margins of the region – where the Palar opens out and on the southern flanks of the Javadis, and here it is the second crop, ragi being second in Salem. In both North Arcot and Salem, groundnuts are the first ranking crop.[19] An interesting feature is the intrusion of the Telugu-speaking Reddis along the Ghats margin; these are skilled tank cultivators, perhaps especially for ragi, and appear to have worked along the piedmont even across the Cauvery into Madurai.

On the shelf below the main Mysore Ghat much land is still under forest, mostly rather open and used mainly for grazing. This is geographically, and perhaps historically, an offshoot of the famous cattle-breeding of Mysore; the Dharmapuri/Krishnagiri cattle markets are the main source of heavy draught animals for an area stretching from Malabar to Chittoor, while the best animals used to be sold as far afield as Madurai and Tinnevely as coach bullocks.

'The breeding herds live on the forests for the greater part of the year, where they are kept in pens at night time. They are brought back to the village at harvest, when the harvested fields provide grazing for some time, and the cattle supply the necessary manure for the succeeding ragi-crop. . . . The breeders . . . cannot be considered as ryots. They . . . certainly grow crops for their own requirements, but by profession they are breeders of cattle, dependent on the sale of their calves for their livelihood. . . . A good number of the breeding bulls . . . live in a semi-wild state.'[20]

Minerals

Gold, mica, corundum and copper occur here and there on the flanks of the Mysore Plateau, but the most important mineral deposits are around Salem town. Large quantities of magnetite iron ore are found in the Killamalais and Talamalais (southern outliers of the Pachamalais); nearer Salem in the isolated Kanjamalai and Godumalai; and in the conical Tirthamalai (3,500 ft., 1,065 m.) rising sharply from the outer (Coromandel) plain just south of the Ponnaiyar

[18] For a fuller description see Slater, *Southern India*, 76–77; and cf. Fig. 89 in C. D. Forde, *Habitat, Economy and Society* (1931 edition, p. 269).

[19] For a type village, see R. Ramachandran, 'Mahammadapuram', *IGJ* 35/3–4 (1960), 76–86.

[20] R. W. Littlewood, 'Alambady cattle', *JMGA* 11/2 (1936), 126–9.

gap. In all these little mountains the massive magnetite beds stand out from the gneissic country rock; the Fe content is poor – 36% compared with Orissa's 60%; limestone is available. These deposits are interesting as providing the basis of one of the EIC's few displays of economic initiative. Talus from the slopes had been immemorially worked in primitive furnaces, and in 1826 Josiah Heath set up extensive works, powered by bullocks and fuelled by charcoal; the foundries were at Porto Novo. The Madras jetty was built of Salem iron; but irrigation obstructions on the Cauvery (used for transport) and the exhaustion of the more accessible forest made success impossible, and a long history of failure ended in 1867: though projects for revival were under consideration as late as 1925.[21] The development of coking quality briquettes on the Neiveli lignite field in South Arcot will remove a major obstacle to utilization within the state.

Corundum is still worked to some extent, and steatite (used locally for pots and exported as a refractory) is obtained from some of the hills. Far more important is magnesite; the 'Chalk Hills' between Salem and the Shevaroys contain large quantities (82,000,000 tons) of this ore, 95% $MgCO_3$ and easily worked open-cast. The demand for magnesia in paper, glass, pharmacological, alloy, refractory and plastic industries is increasing, and the Salem deposits are India's major source, although the export prospects are limited by cheaper methods of recovering magnesium from seawater.[22]

Communications and towns

Despite its girdle of hills, the region has been far from isolated historically. The Baramahal ('twelve forts' or palaces, and by extension administrative areas) represents the farthest Muslim advance after the destruction of Vijayanagar: and in the 18th century this was a debatable land between the rising British power and the new and very virile dominion of Haidar Ali and Tipu Sultan in Mysore: sweeping down the Ghat and through the gaps in the Tamilnad Hills, especially the remarkable break by which most of the drainage of the region leaves it via the Ponnaiyar, Haidar exploited to the full his advantages of mobility and local knowledge. To the British the northern entry, by the Palar, was the most important as nearest to the Madras base; hence the significance of Clive's defence of Arcot and that of Vellore in 1780–82.

Salem (249,145) increased by 287% in 1921–51; it is rapidly developing as a textile centre, powered by Mettur and Pykara. The Attur gap (1,250 ft., 380 m.) between the Kalryans and the Pachamalais gives easy access to the coast.

[21] The Madras pier was sold for scrap to the Pondicherry rolling-mills, and this suggested the last scheme, which involved electrical concentrating on the Cauvery and the co-operation of Schneiders. For details see *ibid.* 9/2 (1934), 104–7, and Slater, *op. cit.* 81–84.

[22] *Techno-Economic Survey of Madras* (Natl Ccil of Applied Econ. Research/Govt of Madras, 1961), 157.

THE CAUVERY VALLEY

The Cauvery (Fig. 25.4) is physically, perhaps, the most remarkable river of the Peninsula; its delta presents some extremely distinctive physical and human features; its power is a main factor in the remarkable recent growth of the Tamilnad towns. It is thus intimately associated with the life of all its border regions, and we may break off the regional description to look at its basin as a whole, and to gather up the scattered notices of hydro-electric development in southern India, on the whole the part of the sub-continent most advanced in this use of water.

The Cauvery is not a large river by Indian standards, only about 475 miles (765 km.) long and draining about 28,000 sq. miles (72,500 km²). Above the great Krishnarajasagar reservoir, 12 miles from Mysore city, it is simply a rocky mountain stream; below it becomes increasingly important as an aid to cultivation. Just above the confluence of the Shimsha, the main left-bank tributary, the Cauvery crosses the 2,000-ft. (610-m.) contour at Sivasamudram Island, on either side of which is a succession of falls and rapids with a total drop of 320 ft. (98 m.); the wider fall 'in the rainy season pours over the hillside in an unbroken sheet a quarter of a mile wide'.[23] At Sivasamudram the first fair-sized hydro-electric plant in India was installed as early as 1902. Below the island the river plunges through a succession of wild gorges, with right-angle bends conforming to the northwest/southeast and southwest/northeast stresses of the plateau-edge; the Hagenakal Falls may be taken as the end of its plateau course. There is, however, another narrow straight gorge, west of Salem, and this provides the emplacement for the Mettur Dam. Mettur was the first combined power and irrigation project in India (1925–34) and its dam is one of the world's largest: the river here was 1,100 ft. wide, the dam itself is 5,300 ft. long and 176 ft. high, impounding a 60 sq. mile lake of 93,500,000,000 cu. ft. capacity.[24]

The Cauvery now enters its plains course, the 500-ft. (150-m.) contour being crossed between the Bhavani confluence and Erode: the Bhavani and its tributary the Moyar drain the Nilgiris, and on their northern flank is the Pykara power station, shortly to be extended by an installation on the Moyar with Mettur and the new Kundah project; these are main links in the expanding South Indian grid.

A few miles above Tiruchchirappalli the river bifurcates around another sacred island, Srirangam, the northern (Coleroon) branch being the larger. From here on is deltaic country, mainly in Thanjavur (old Tanjore) District, which has been irrigated since at latest the 11th century, when the Chola kings constructed the Grand Anicut – a mass of masonry 1,080 ft. long and 40–60 broad. The Mettur Dam was projected primarily to add to the delta irrigation, but it has not perhaps been entirely satisfactory from this point of view (below, p. 766), and its power function is equally important (Fig. 25.5).

[23] *Madras Gaz.* I. (1908), 175.
[24] Metric equivalents: 335 m., 1,615 m., 54 m., 155 km², 2,600,000,000 m³.

The Cauvery basin indeed accounts for about two-thirds of the hydro-electricity generated in South India, Mettur, Shimsa-Sivasamudram and Pykara each producing some 50,000 kW. Neiveli lignite will add a quarter of a

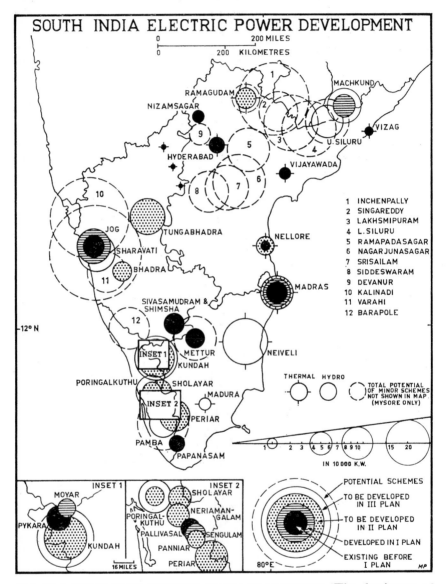

FIG 25.5 SOUTH INDIA ELECTRIC POWER DEVELOPMENT. The dominance of hydel is noteworthy, despite increased thermal capacity especially on the Neiveli lignite field, now coming into production. *Source:* R. Ramachandran in A. T. A. Learmonth and L. S. Bhat (eds), *Mysore State I. An Atlas of Resources* (1961).

million, and with the schemes on the Southern Blocks the power situation in Madras should be at least adequate for the increasing demand. Sivasamudram was developed in the first place to power the Kolar Gold Fields, 93 miles (150 km.) away – an immense transmission distance for 1902 – and to light Bangalore. Of the total Mysore power, nearly 90% is devoted to industry – with a strong sector in decentralized light industry and an increasing agricultural demand; yet Madras uses a higher proportion in rural areas, and this shows a marked increase in the irrigation season. Pykara (1932) led to an immediate development of textiles and cement at Coimbatore, with some as far as Madurai; this station also serves the Nilgiri tea factories, and irrigation pumps in Coimbatore District. At Erode Pykara and Mettur are linked; a light industrial estate has grown up at Mettur itself, which also supplies Tiruchchirappalli (textiles, cement, rail-shops), Salem and small towns in Salem District (textiles), and Nagapattinam (rolling-mills); lighter lines go as far as Vellore. Wide fluctuations in the Cauvery discharge to some extent limit the regular supply from Mettur, but this has been remedied by the integration with Pykara and ultimately of the resources of the hills south of Palghat, which include Pallivasal in Kerala and Papanasam in Tirunelveli District.

The results have been especially notable in the growth of the four great Tamilnad towns, Coimbatore, Salem, Madurai, Tiruchchirappalli. Of perhaps even greater importance in the long run are the possibilities of rural electrification for wells, sugar-crushing and (in Kerala) drainage. Again, in view of the absence of coal in southern India, and the obvious dangers of burning up the forests as loco fuel, the possibility of railway electrification is receiving attention.[25] The Neiveli lignite will at least cut down coal imports and, briquetted, may even be used in steel making.

KONGUNAD: THE COIMBATORE PLATEAU AND PALGHAT[26]

Between the Cauvery and Palghat lies an extensive low plateau, rising gradually from 400–600 ft. along the river to 1,200–1,500 in the west (120–180 and 365–455 m.), and broken here and there near the hills by granitic or gneissic monadnocks and a bony limestone ridge. The individuality of the region is attested by the survival of its ancient name Kongunad – roughly Coimbatore District and southwestern Salem; but it was never an historic entity. Some at least of the reasons for this are perhaps inherent in its location between centres of power based on intensively-cultivated paddy-plains and themselves less open; it is

[25] The difficulties of both water- and fuel-supply are illustrated by an incident – clearly a routine one – at Sidhout in the Cuddapahs in May 1945, when the writer saw 20–30 women collecting water in brass pots from an engine tender, and paying for it at the rate of one billet of wood per pot. The wood was quite likely taken from railway piles anyway, but not all got their water, and it was a pathetic business to watch.

[26] This section is based mainly on fourteen papers in *JMGA* 5/2–3 (1930).

significant that near the Amaravati–Cauvery confluence three of the greatest and most stable Dravidian kingdoms marched together: those of the Cholas and Cheras who gave their names to Coromandel and Kerala, and the Pandya kingdom of Madurai. Significant also is the fact that the place-name ending *-palayam*, meaning an encampment, occurs no fewer than 94 times in Erode taluk, the gateway both from Mysore via the Ponnaiyar, and from the Cauvery Delta. This area was again a storm-centre in the Anglo-Mysorean wars.

Relief and climate

The topography is simple enough. In the west the broad Palghat sill is eaten into by the Ponnani headwaters, and from the watershed three rivers, each about 100 miles long, drain very mature valleys into the Cauvery. Of these the Bhavani and the Amaravati,[27] drawing from the rainy heights of the Nilgiris and the Anaimalais, are fairly perennial, though the Amaravati gets very low towards the main river. Between these two, however, the Noyil (or Noyyal) is dry for most of the year, with practically no water in its lower course and little in its middle: it rises in a horseshoe of hills west of Coimbatore and is effectively cut off from much precipitation. What water it had was very carefully conserved – it had more *anicuts* than the other two put together – but it has now been almost completely ruined by deforestation around its sources, so that its spring channels have decayed.

The climatic effects of the wide and low Palghat Gap are much less than might have been expected. The rainfall in general is 27–30 in. (686–762 mm.), but although Pollachi taluk, actually athwart the gap, gets 36 (914 mm.), its plains portion is not much better off than its neighbours. Significant, however, is the seasonal distribution:

	June–Sept. %	Oct.–Dec. %
Pollachi taluk	48	32
Central plains	19	54
Bhavani and Cauvery valleys	30	43
Kollegal taluk (Mysore Plateau)	43·5	26

All stations have a double maximum, in May and October, the latter everywhere the wettest month: this may represent, as it were, a convergence of Southwest and 'Northeast' monsoons. The central plains are on the arid side: Dharapuram has only six months (April–May, September–December) with over 1 inch. The taluks on or bordering the Mysore Plateau have more rain in May than in June and July put together. Air masses at various levels are obviously involved,

[27] The *Western* Amaravati; as often there is another river of the same name rising in the same watershed, but flowing in the opposite direction.

and there is a subject for intensive research here. Meantime, however, we may note that the interior of the southern Peninsula has rains at times of shifting climatic belts and indeterminate conditions but is in rain shadow at the time of the rain monsoons and the drought.

The influence of Palghat is better seen in other factors than rainfall. The temperature range is remarkably slight for an inland (if low) plateau – the December–January mean is $73 \cdot 7° F.$, April $83 \cdot 3$ ($23 \cdot 2$ and $28 \cdot 5° C.$); the heat is tempered by the breezes and light showers of the Southwest monsoon.

Agricultural individuality

Agriculturally the region has some very individual features: the negligible position of rice, the importance of wells, millets and pastoralism. Of the millets jowar is by far the most important; groundnuts (the second ranking crop) and cotton are the main cash crops. Almost all the rice, but only a small proportion of the millets and very little of the cotton, are irrigated. While wells account for most of the irrigation, canal irrigation from the Bhavani is increasing.

This broad quantitative statement conceals very interesting adjustments. Soils are varied: the east and a good deal of the west are occupied by the usual thin red sandy Archaean soils, but on the Palghat sill there is a good deal of medium *regur*, and valley bottoms often contain good black loams which amply reply the careful culture they receive. The Anaimalais are often fringed with lateritic shelves, but there is also some 'colluvial' – rain-wash – soil of much higher value.

Paddy is practically confined to *ayacuts* (areas supplied from *anicuts* or weirs) in the major valley bottoms. Coimbatore has the largest cumbu acreage of any Madras District, followed closely by Salem with Tiruchchirappalli a fair third; for ragi only Salem outranks it. In cotton, the two leading Madras Districts, Coimbatore and Turunelveli, have about the same area. The local *Karunganni* cotton is intermediate in staple between the usual Indian varieties and the long-stapled Cambodia, which is grown only on irrigated red soils. A large area is covered by the drought-resistant strain CO_2 evolved from Cambodia by the Coimbatore Agricultural College; this is exceptionally well adapted to Tamilnad conditions and has spread widely in the last two decades. *Karunganni*, a dry crop on black soils, is still areally dominant, however.

Perhaps the most notable success of the Agricultural College (one of the most important in India) has been with sugar, but this has benefited the north rather than Madras, although the harvesting might be spread over ten months instead of the four of the Gangetic Plain. As we saw (above, p. 245) the existence of a plantation/factory tradition for indigo played an important part in the evolution of the sugar industry in Bihar and Uttar Pradesh. However, sugar factories are spreading in southern India, usually in conjunction with canal irrigation. There is a competing production of jaggery from the palmyra, particularly in Tirunelveli.

In irrigated garden cultivation the region is pre-eminent. The Coimbatore

759

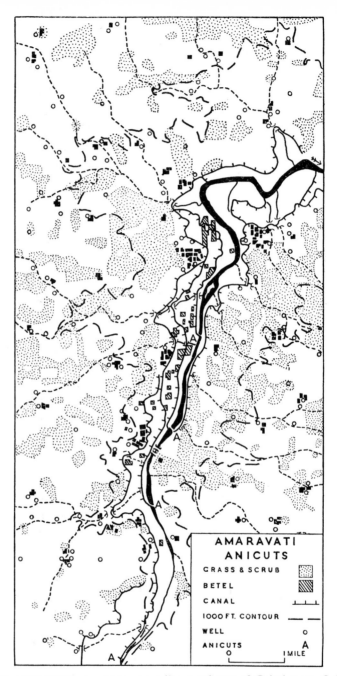

FIG 25.6 AMARAVATI, ANICUTS. 40 miles southeast of Coimbatore. Solid lines perennial, broken seasonal, streams. Note (i) absence of tanks; (ii) moderate relief (only two tiny residual hills on whole sheet, c. 275 sq. miles). Canals follow contours, large settlements at edge of floodplain. *SOI* 58F/6. *Courtesy* SOI.

ryot is an exceedingly assiduous gardener, fencing his compact holdings and temporarily at least living in field-huts on them – a factor of significance for this type of culture. Cereals, cotton, sugar are grown in rotation with sweet potatoes, onions, turmeric, chillies and a variety of other intensive cultures; betel-vines are especially noteworthy. All this is dependent on anicuts with spring-channels or leats and on wells; Fig. 25.6 shows something of the irrigation and settlement pattern in the Amaravati valley-bottom. The Kongunad farmers are adept well-sinkers, some of their shafts going down 100 ft. into solid rock.

There is a corollary to this emphasis on wells. Unless oil-engines or the increasingly numerous electric pumps are available, the deeper wells need exceptionally stout beasts to work them, and in the almost arid centre of the region animal husbandry is a specialized occupation. Kangayam, on the Noyil/ Amaravati watershed, is the main breeding centre: it lies in a tract of light rain-fall, with few streams or trees, and a light red loam with some kanker. The specific Kangayam stock is reared only by a handful of well-to-do peasants for whom breeding is their main business; but the general Kongu breed is also an excellent animal when well cared for. 'Kangayam looks down on communal and mixed grazing, and cattle have been provided private and enclosed grazing grounds on which the famous grass' Kolaikattai pul (Pennisetum cenchroides) is grown. Cholam is grown by well-irrigation for fodder in February–March – just before the most trying season for cattle – and cumbu-, paddy- and ragi-straws are also used for feed; the black soil tracts and the garden grounds are dotted with cholam stacks at this time of year. The Kangayam bullock is in great demand in the garden lands and in the black cotton soils of the southeast, as far as the Tampra-barni.[28]

Coimbatore town

Erode (73,762), an important rail crossing of the Cauvery, has some textile industry, developed rapidly with expansion at Mettur. But Coimbatore (286,305) is the only town of real importance; its population has more than quadrupled since 1921, mainly owing to industrial growth based on Pykara power and local cotton. This is strikingly shown by some comparative figures for 1932 and 1937,[29] between which years the Bombay Presidency cotton industry actually declined slightly:

	Mills			*Spindles*			*Hands*		
	1932	1937	Incr. %	1932	1937	Incr. %	1932	1937	Incr. %
Coimbatore	8	20	150	177,408	352,040	97·0	6,703	14,228	109·0
Madras Prov. . . .	26	47	81	820,870	1,150,866	40·0	34,753	49,110	42·0
All India	340	370	9	9,506,083	9,730,798	2·3	403,226	417,276	3·5

[28] For details of the garden culture and the cattle rearing of Kongunad, see K. C. Ramakrishnan, 'Agricultural geography of Coimbatore District', *JMGA* 5/2–3 (1930), 95–107, and A. S. Ayyar, 'Cattle of Kongunad', *ibid.* 108–11.

[29] C. M. R. Chettiar, 'Growth of modern Coimbatore', *JMGA* 14/2 (1939), 101–16; reference at 113.

The industry at Coimbatore actually started in 1888 with two mills; local raw materials, labour, markets and capital[30] were there; only cheap power was lacking. In 1938 there were 26 mills with over 21,000 workers. This initial spurt has died down, but there are a number of other industries – coffee mills, tanneries, oil-presses, and near at hand a large cement works fed by local limestone.

The town itself has little of interest but is not unimpressive even to an impatient traveller delayed at the airport. It has a fairly healthy situation at 1,300–1,400 ft. (395–425 m.) on the Noyil, but the Palghat Gap, only a few miles away, hardly affects the rainfall, and water is brought in a tunnel from a small catchment on the windward side of the surrounding horseshoe of hills. The original core, as often in Tamilnad, was the intersection of the four large streets for temple cars; recent growth has been disorderly, with slums and congestion but also attempts to plan better things. A minor point of urban morphology is interesting: the original cotton mills, dependent on export, clung to the railway, in the heart of the town; ginneries and presses, with their bulky import, clustered in the eastern outskirts, towards the source of supply. Now, however, expansion includes outlying mills in surrounding villages, with their own industrial housing for at least some of the workers.

THE CAUVERY DELTA[31]

This region (Figs. 25.7, 25.8) covers some 4,000 sq. miles (10,350 km²); most of it lies in Thanjavur District which in turn is almost entirely deltaic and covers 3,740 sq. miles with a 1961 population of nearly 3,250,000, a density of 868. The build of the delta is remarkable: from the Coleroon (or Kollidan) the seaface runs straight southwards for about 80 miles (129 km.) to Point Calimere, where it makes a right-angled bend and runs west for 30 miles until it abouts on older ground at the mouth of the Agniar. The tendency in Coromandel for a northwards deflection of river mouths, influenced by the dominant of the Southwest monsoon, is here inhibited by the bulge of the delta itself, like a vast groyne across the limited fetch of Palk Strait (limited by the Adam's Bridge structure), and shutting off the normal longshore currents. Hence the eastern face, especially in the north, is exposed to the northeast and is suffering some erosion; the rivers are normal to the coast, debouching directly into the sea with little or no deflection. But south of Nagapattinam the belt of dunes, backed by a long marshy low, strongly suggests prograding, and west of Point Calimere material brought by the longshore drift from the southwest piles up, so that the shoreline is backed by a mass of fetid mudflats, the Vedanniyam salt swamp, some 5–6 miles (8–10 km.) wide. In conformity to this view of the coast is the lie of the 5-fathom line:

[30] It is true in strange hands – Multanis to exploit raw millowners, 'Kabulis' (Pathan moneylenders) to exploit their workers (*ibid.* 110–12).

[31] This section relies largely for its basic outlines on: fifteen papers on Trichinopoly District, *JMGA* 8/3 (1933); seven papers on Tanjore District, *ibid.* 12/2 (1937). These are the Tiruchchirappalli and Thanjavur Districts of today.

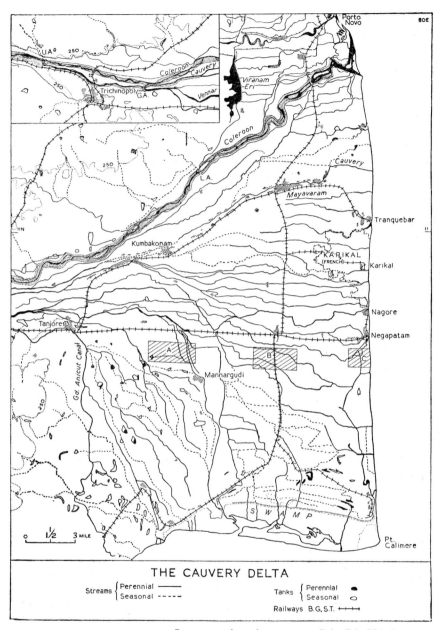

THE CAUVERY DELTA

| Streams | { Perennial ——— | Tanks | { Perennial ● |
| | { Seasonal - - - - | | { Seasonal ○ |

Railways B.G,S.T. ┼┼┼┼

FIG 25.7 THE CAUVERY DELTA. Inset: continuation to west. LA, GA, UA, Lower, Grand, Upper Anicuts; all permanent water on original shown. A–C, area of Fig 25.8. *SOI* 1/2253,440 58N. *Courtesy* SOI.

only a mile or less offshore from the Coleroon to Karikal, it is 2½ miles at Naga-pattinam, and 8–13 miles (13–21 km.) off the southern face. Point Calimere itself is a blunt cuspate foreland formed of a complex of beach-ridges built up by the alternating dominance of the monsoons.

The drainage pattern is also interesting, with its bundle of streams packed into 8–10 miles between Tiruchchirappalli and Thanjavur, but fanning out into a quadrant 75 miles (121 km.) across; it must be remembered that the whole area has been intensively worked over by man for more than a millennium; the Grand Anicut was constructed in the 11th century. The slope is steep for a delta: Tiruchchirappalli, at the delta-head, is on the 250 ft. (75 m.) contour, but it is only 30 miles (48 km.), from the sea; and heights of 25–30 ft. (not dunes, but possibly old beach-ridges) are found within three or four miles of the shore.

The alluvium extends far to the west of Tiruchchirappalli in a highly fertile belt about a mile wide; to the east it varies in quality. The Coleroon/Cauvery interfluve as far down as Kumbakonam is the richest part of the delta, but south of the Vennar (which runs by Thanjavur) underlying calcareous deposits reduce fertility, and towards the coast soils are markedly sandy. Within the deltaic area a patch of laterite and/or Cuddalores forms the low (180 ft., 55 m.) 'Vallam Tableland' in the southwest, and around the delta on the west and south is the usual fringe of red gneissic terrain with thin red soils tending to red loams in the more favoured portions. Soils in general are open, porous and permeable, on the whole very 'thirsty'. Westwards there is a transition to the Coimbatore/Salem plateaus.

A thin sliver of country along the coast receives 55 in. of rain; inland this diminishes regularly: Nagapattinam 55, Kumbakonam 47, Thanjavur 37, Tiruchchirappalli 35 (from 1,397 to 889 mm.). It has a very typical southeast littoral distribution, these stations having respectively 72, 54, 50 and 45% of their fall in October through December. All of them have a small secondary peak (1·5–3 in., 38–76 mm., increasing inland) in May, 'mango showers' associated with thundery cyclonic disturbances. An interesting concomitant of the rainfall distribution is the dry evergreen forest which survives in small patches, as at Point Calimere.

Irrigation and agriculture

Although rice is strikingly dominant, with over 80% of NSA in Thanjavur District, the agricultural economy of the delta and its margins is complex. Paddy falls off rapidly in the delta margins, but even in Thanjavur we have the rather odd feature, for a fairly humid delta, of a significant acreage of groundnuts, admittedly largely on the higher inland margins but also on sandy soils near the coast. The greater millets are scarcely represented. It seems simplest to write off the marginal areas briefly and to concentrate on the old and new irrigation of the delta proper.

On the margins, then, the deltaic area north of the Coleroon and between that river, the Vellar (debouching at Porto Novo), and the Viranam Tank is mainly under paddy, and paddy extends as the major crop well up the Vellar. Upstream from this great tank, however, the paddy belt along the Coleroon is narrow, and the high and dry Coleroon/Vellar interfluve is mainly dry crops – cumbu, ground-nut, some sugar. Up the main Cauvery from Tiruchchirappalli the agriculture rapidly becomes poorer towards Karur (cholam and ragi as food, castor as a cash crop) and in Karur taluk, on the Coimbatore plateau/Cauvery delta border, gram is perhaps the leading crop. In all these areas, of course, rice is grown where irrigation facilities permit, as also cotton, chillies and tobacco. The delta has also an unusually strong concentration of coconuts.

The older irrigation of the delta was a combination of inundation canals and in the higher west, tanks fed from them; tanks of any *agricultural* significance are not found east of a line Kumbakonam/Mannargudi. This highly integrated system was dependent on the great *anicuts* at either end of Srirangam Island. The Coleroon has a straighter course and a lower level than the Cauvery, and by the 19th century the Cauvery offtake was silting and its branches deteriorating. The Upper Anicut (1836–38, remodelled 1899–1904) was designed to offset this, and is supplemented by regulating dams across all main offtakes.[32]

The dominant irrigated crop was of course paddy, but there was an interesting specialization of plantains 'rotated with paddy on wet lands with an unfailing supply of water from irrigation channels, the rainfall alone being insufficient and ill-distributed for the very high water requirements of the quickly growing and bulky plantain'. In contrast to the usual view of the banana as conducive to laziness, the cultivation here is exceedingly intensive: 'the labour that is demanded is indeed prodigious compared with that involved in the case of paddy or of any other intensively cultivated crop except sugar-cane. . . . The village itself is rarely able to supply all the labour needed',[33] and there is some seasonal im-migration from the surrounding uplands. Other intensively cultivated crops are betel and sugar-cane.

The Mettur scheme was intended to protect the delta irrigation against floods, to regulate supplies in the older-irrigated region (where previously the period of available water shortened to the east), and to add to the irrigated area a further 300,000 ac. (121,000 ha.) west of Mannargudi. The essential principle is to substitute for direct flow, dependent on the irregular natural levels of the river, storage enabling supply to be regulated to the differing needs of the delta; the semi-saline soils near the coast, for instance, require frequent flushing to wash away the salts, and this cannot be attained satisfactorily by inundation methods. But the results attained illustrate the complex problems involved in new-modelling an already highly developed system, problems far more difficult than

[32] A description of the main channels is given by K. Ramamurthy, *IGJ* 24/2 (1949), 30–33.
[33] K. C. Ramakrishnan, 'A model of intensive cultivation in the Cauvery Valley', *JMGA* 8/3 (1933), 179–87.

those of breaking in new ground, as in the Punjab.[34] Although the paper on which the following description is based is an old one, and there have doubtless been changes for the better as experience has grown, similar difficulties have been met in more recent irrigation projects elsewhere in India, and the analysis is still of value.

The main feature of the scheme was the construction of the Grand Anicut Canal, turning south at Thanjavur town and running along the contours down the higher flank of the delta; its length is 66 miles (106 km.), that of its distributaries nearly 700 miles; full discharge at offtake 5,000 cusecs, at tail 300. Perhaps the chief difficulty is that due to interference with the watertable. 'With the Canal flowing for more than six months of the year, and the monsoon rains, the proper drainage of the area has become an acute problem,' despite siphons where the canal cuts across drainage-lines, as a contour canal must. The distributaries naturally follow the higher levels, to command wider *ayacuts*, and this seems to have overcharged the natural drainage below them. The problem is further complicated, though to a less extent than in West Bengal and Bihar, by the construction of railways and roads transverse to the natural slope. There was an initial increase in malaria, but this is now under control.

The newly irrigated area was previously mostly rainfed, with some tanks, growing coarser paddy, groundnuts, gingelly (sesamum), millets and pulses. Soils are varied and difficult to manage. In the circumstances the risks of over-irrigation, with consequent waterlogging and alkali panning, are very real. The rise in the watertable is reported to have adversely affected the important jack-fruit and casuarina groves of the area. There is also a conflict of interest between the activities of inland fishermen (building bunds, scoops, etc.) and the needs of canal maintenance.

A further difficulty lies in the disturbance of a well-established agricultural rhythm:

'. . . the cultivators in the deltaic tracts complain of the shrinkage in the volume of water supplied to them and the present system of irrigation interferes with their normal agricultural operations. During the natural flood season under the direct flow system, operations commence almost simultaneously both at the head and tail of the delta area. Thus with the first freshes in the river there is bound to be an all-round and sympathetic activity throughout the entire villages. There is, however, much truth in the complaint that the control system makes the tail-end cultivator wait indefinitely long . . . so there is considerable uncertainty regarding the method of cultivation to be adopted and the crops to be raised. . . . Errors in calculation of the "duty" have also been responsible for the failure of the control system to meet the requirements of agriculture especially in critical times in 1935 "the low level sluices could not

[34] The remainder of this section is based on the remarkable analysis by T. Krishnaswami, 'Recent irrigation changes in the Cauvery', *JMGA* 14/3 (1939), 237–71. The caution should be added that, as Krishnaswami admits, the period of five years between the opening of Mettur and his paper is too short for a final evaluation.

meet the demand at a critical period during the transplantation season, even though they were fully open". Added to this, the popular misconception that the greater the irrigation the greater the produce has to be removed if the "duty" is to approximate to the actual needs. The difficulty of the tail-end cultivators is more pronounced in the case of double-crop areas under paddy.'[35]

In the long run, of course, such initial difficulties are likely to be more than offset by greater regularity than can be attained by relying on natural flood, taking one year with another.

This last conclusion, however, may not apply to the very serious matter of loss of silt. It has been argued that most of the silt is actually supplied by the Amaravati and the Bhavani. But the Bhavani has now been dammed,[36] and against this view is the provision for adding to the height of the Mettur Dam to allow for an estimated accumulation of 10 ft. of silt in fifty years; as Krishnaswami says, this certainly suggests that the complaints of cultivators have some substance. On the other hand, 'with the limitation and regulation of water in the Coleroon, . . . larger quantities of sand are now brought down the Cauvery, or deposited by its distributaries in the lower reaches', a long-standing difficulty, which has led to increased flooding in the delta. It seems that too little attention has been paid to the problems of aggrading river-beds.

Much dissatisfaction is doubtless the reaction of rural conservatism to a sudden change in conditions, and one feels at times that Krishnaswami is a devil's advocate. But on the whole it is difficult to resist his cautious conclusion that 'it is not possible to definitely assert that the Canal irrigation is under all circumstances an unmixed blessing'.

Settlement and towns

The delta is densely populated: the deltaic portions of Thanjavur District, *excluding* towns of over 20,000 people, have an average density of over 700, rising in parts to over 1,200.

The settlement patterns are extremely interesting (Fig. 25.8 A–C). In the west (Thanjavur to Mannargudi, A) there is a tendency to fairly strong nucleation associated with large semi-perennial tanks; there is a fair amount of waste, casuarina groves are common, and the pattern is rather coarse. This area will be affected by the new irrigation. Beyond the Kumbakonam/Mannargudi line the pattern of the channels is much closer and more rectilinear (cf. eastern portion of Fig. 25.8A), settlements on the whole are smaller and more scattered, but although there is thus some 'loosening' there is nothing like the close stipple of homesteads in Bengal. Casuarinas are very few in this tract, but coconut palms begin to join the ubiquitous toddy; tanks are small, merely for domestic supply, and practically all perennial. There is the usual deltaic tendency to settlement

[35] Krishnaswami, 263–4.

[36] There is also agitation for construction of major works on the Amaravati, but it seems likely that with the harnessing of the Bhavani the Cauvery basin would be utilized to the fullest extent possible. This is confirmed by the *Techno-Economic Survey*.

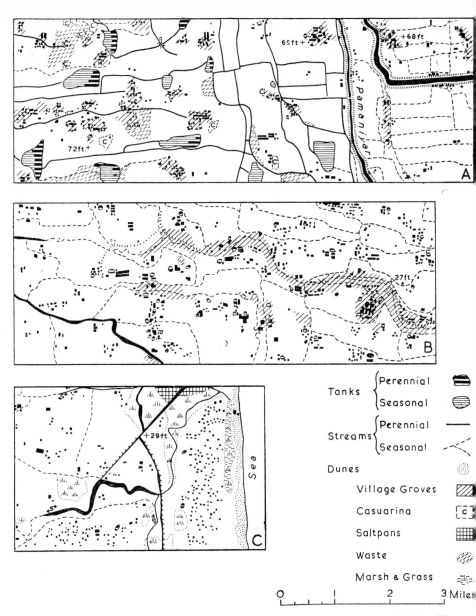

Tanks	Perennial
	Seasonal
Streams	Perennial
	Seasonal
Dunes	
Village Groves	
Casuarina	
Saltpans	
Waste	
Marsh & Grass	

0   1   2   3 Miles

FIG 25.8 THE CAUVERY DELTA: SETTLEMENT. All 3 maps on 10° 45′ N (see Fig 25.7). A: old delta, large tanks, nucleated villages; east of Pamaniyar older canal irrigation, in west new irrigation from Grand Anicut Canal; few palms west of Pamaniyar, toddy palms in fields to east; linear settlement along levees beginning in east.

B: mainly linear. Size and position of tanks (nearly all perennial) very different from those of A. Most palms toddy but coconut coming in to east; no casuarina.

C: dunes coast; semi-linear (approach to Kerala type, cf. Fig 22.8) on sandy belt (paddy/coconut/casuarina) between marsh and dunes. Dunes about 30 ft. high; better marked, with linear settlement on old beach-ridges, to south of area. *SOI* 58N/6, 10, 14. *Courtesy* SOI.

along levees, but also some linear *across* the drainage lines (B), and towards the southeast of the delta at least a strong suggestion of old beach-ridge settlement. Finally (C) there is the negative area of the old lagoons along the line of the Vedaranyam Canal, succeeded by an approximation to the Kerala settlement type in the sandy littoral strip, with its paddy/coconut/toddy/areca economy.

The delta is reasonably well served by communications, but from Erode to the sea the Cauvery/Coleroon has only three rail crossings (Erode, Tiruchchirappalli. and near the coast) and two complete road bridges, at Trichy and the Lower Anicut. The Grand and Upper Anicuts have roadways, but these cross only the Cauvery and the Coleroon respectively, and so give access merely to Srirangam Island. The numerous ferries used coracles at least until recently.

The towns of the region fall into three groups: interior markets, ports, and in a class by itself Tiruchchirappalli. Those of the first group are not of much importance, except for Kumbakonam (96,643) and historic Thanjavur (Tanjore; 111,099). Many of the coast towns are most interesting as survivals of the European intrusion: thus Tranquebar has still some buildings of the Danish occupation (until 1845); the seat of the first Protestant mission to India, it retains a Lutheran bishopric. The French enclave of Karikal (53 sq. miles, population in 1941, 60,000) was not fragmented like Pondicherry, but its licit trade in groundnuts was supplemented by high-value low-bulk smuggling; on the southern border Karikal merchants established 'a town entirely of shops and nothing else', and S. R. Pandyan formally, and doubtless correctly, included smuggling among the indigenous industries of adjacent Nagapattinam.

Nagapattinam (Negapatam; 61,305; Fig. 25.9) has suffered from the removal of its railway workshops to Tiruchchirappalli, but this has to some extent been offset by the establishment (with Pykara power) of steel rolling-mills, which share the old railshops with a cinema. The town has still many traces of Portu‑guese and Dutch occupation; as usual, the latter left a few buildings and the former a more intimate cultural and ethnic influence, including a whole village of Roman Catholic fishermen. The port is a mere roadstead, with a couple of cranes on a creek-side wharf, but it flourishes as the outlet of the delta. Trade is mainly with Ceylon, Burma and coastwise, much of it by country craft, in which con‑nection the large number of Muslims is significant: in 1941 they were over 22% of the population, against 7·9% in all Madras. Most of them are merchants and seamen. Nagapattinam is mainly an exporting port and used to be the main groundnut port of the state, outstripping Cuddalore which is nearer the main groundnuts area but even worse as a port. Its export list is strangely varied: jaggery, vegetables, tiles, rice husk meal [*sic*], bidis, coriander seeds; 'betel' (areca) nuts from Ceylon, and timber, are the only listed imports. Cottons from Madurai are dyed and printed; this trade was in Muslim hands.[37]

[37] S. R. Pandyan's very interesting and well-mapped paper (*JMGA* 11/4 (1937), 291–318) is the warrant for this extended note, presented as a type-specimen of the minor Indian ports; trade details from *Techno-Economic Survey*, 180.

Tiruchchirappalli (249,862) used to be Trichinopoly or, even more conveniently, just 'Trichy'; the change is, if one may say so, appalling. It commands the most important crossing of the Cauvery, and has besides the attraction of the great shrine of Srirangam (41,949), a town mostly built four-square within the

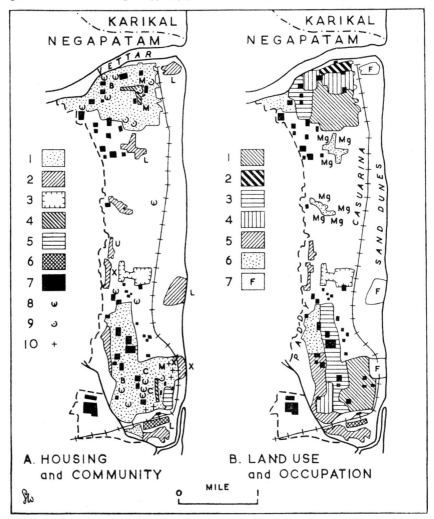

FIG 25.9 NEGAPATAM (NAGAPATTINAM). A: 1, tiled houses; 2, thatched huts; 3, European-style bungalows (local officials, etc.); 4, shops; 5, godowns; 6, old SIR works (now steel rolling-mills and cinema); 7, tanks; 8, temples; 9, mosques; 10, churches. B, Brahmins; C, Chettiars and traders; X, Christians; M, Muslims; L, Lower castes (coolies, fishermen); U, Untouchables.

B: 1, traders; 2, smugglers; 3, clerical and professional; 4, priestly class; 5, poor working class; 6, cultivators; 7, fishermen. Mg, market gardens.

Adapted from maps in S. R. Pandyan, 'Negapatam', *JMGA* XI (1937), 291–318.

vast temple enceinte. The city itself is dominated by the famous Fort on an isolated rock towering 270 ft. above the town. Modern industry started late and lags behind that of other Tamilnad cities; there are some textiles, cement works at Dalmianagar, and the loco and carriage shops in the well-planned railway colony of Garden Rock.

THE DRY SOUTHEAST

This is a complex area, and but for considerations of scale its sub-regions might well be promoted to full regional rank. The dominant factor is low rainfall; sheltered by the Cardamoms from the Arabian Sea monsoon, off the main track of the advancing Bay of Bengal branch, and to some extent at least losing the full effect of the cyclones of the retreating monsoon by reason of its position in relation to the Cauvery delta bulge and Ceylon.

This is the main cotton region of Tamilnad, the three Districts (Madurai, Ramanathapuram and Tirunelveli) accounting for well over half the cotton acreage in Madras State. Tank-irrigation reaches its peak in Madurai and Ramanathapuram, while Tirunelveli has the most important black soil tracts outside the Deccan. Historically the region has the distinction of having never been subject to a central power before that of the British Raj.

Physique

Physically we have the standard pattern: low gneissic pediplain beneath the hills; alluvial and marine/aeolian deposits along the coast, up the major valleys; and between these the discontinuous Cuddalore/laterite shelves. The northwest of the region, however, is complicated by the layout of the hills: the Suruli/upper Vaigai valley is set within the arms of the Palanis (west-southwest/east-northeast to south-southwest/north-northeast) to the north, the Varushanad and Andipatti Hills to the southeast. These ranges almost converge around the great curve of the Vaigai, and are continued to the northeast by fairly large outliers (up to 3,000–4,000 ft., 915–1,220 m.) on the Cauvery watershed – the Surumalais, Karandamalais, Nattam and Alyar Hills. The parallelism of the trough between the Mysore Ghat and the Javadis, and of the upper courses of the Bhavani, Noyil, Amaravati and Suruli/Vaigai, is very striking, as is the sharp southeast front of the Palanis: can this upper Vaigai embayment be structurally analogous to, or even connected with, the Palar/Ponnaiyar trough?

East of these bordering hills stretches the broad pediment, and here we find tank country *in excelsis*.

'The morphological interpretation of this area demands the imaginative reconstruction of conditions of erosion which man has almost everywhere caused to disappear. In effect the development of irrigation has for centuries, in some cases for millenia, suppressed all natural flow. To seek out the course of a stream in this country means to recognize the irrigation ditches which link the artificial ponds. Thus all flowing water is captured from the start, held in the thousands of tanks scattered over the countryside, then methodically distributed.'[38]

The Vaigai itself thrusts great wedges of alluvium up between the hills and down to form the Ramanathapuram Peninsula. The great bulge of alluvium south of the Tamprabarni may mark a more southerly embouchure of that river, which has ancient bunds on the right bank, while black soils, probably formed in a marshy valley-bottom, occur in a strip between the present and the possible old course – the only occurrence south of the river. Here, from the Vaippar southwards, the Cuddalores and laterites disappear, only small patches occurring in the extreme south, around Kanya Kumari.

The determinants of regional differentiation here are largely soil factors, but allowance must be made for position and physiography. The area can be subdivided as follows:

1. Upper Vaigai valley.
2. Madurai-Ramanathapuram tank country.
3. Black Soil tract.
4. Tirunelveli: (a) piedmont; (b) Tamprabarni basin; (c) red soil and *teri*.

Before discussing these we may deal with the coast in general.

The coast and the Teri tracts[39]

The coast as a whole shows evidence both of prograding and uplift. Apart from patches of doubtful Cuddalores in Tirunelveli (and their marine origin is now discredited), there are extensive outcrops of undoubted marine calcarous sandstones, in places pure limestone, false-bedded and dipping gently seawards; their fossils are recent and there are records of interbedded pottery, though this may have been washed down from still more recent beach-rock. South of the Tamprabarni these are overlain by the remarkable red *teri* (='sandy waste').

The teri deposits are definitely aeolian, though capillary oxidization has consolidated them, so that in general only a thin surface layer is now being re-worked by wind. The *teris* form little rolling plateaus, up to 20 sq. miles (52 km²) in area, at 100–220 ft. (30–65 m.). They carry a thin vegetation of palmyra (toddy) palms and thorny scrub, and in some places are still active, advancing to the east-southeast at 5 to 15 yd. a year and ponding up (but eventually filling) small lakes around their margins, and sometimes overwhelming tanks. Naturally there is hardly any surface water, but their ground-water emerges in springs along the flanks; these springs are sometimes led off into irrigation channels, while in depressions, which are sometimes loamy, well-irrigation is possible. Some of the *teris* appear to be a thin veneer over the marine sandstones at 200 ft. (60 m.) plus;

[38] Dupuis 1959, 4.
[39] P. G. Dowie, 'Geology of the Tinnevelly District', *JMGA* 15/4 (1940), 303–29; V. Kalyanasundaram, 'Changes of level in the S.E. Coast of Madras', *IGJ* 18/1 (1943), 30–36.

this indicates an uplift to this extent since the Pleistocene. In the *teris* chert cores and flakes and sherds of pottery have been found.

The coastal dunes speak to prograding; they reach 178 ft. (54 m.), the highest parts being consolidated by solution and redeposition of comminuted shells. Old islands off Tuticorin are now attached to the mainland, and there is also direct and incontrovertible literary evidence of advance of the land. Korkai, identified with Ptolemy's port of Kolkhoi, is now 4½ miles inland; Kayal (= 'backwater' or 'lagoon'), Marco Polo's Coel, 2¾ miles. Here the settlement level is two or three feet below the alluvial surface, and in it fragments of Arabian and Chinese pottery have been found.

In 1881 Bishop Caldwell estimated an emergence of 45 ft. (13·7 m.) as fossils of species of pectens and oysters now living about the 5-fathom line are found 17 ft. above sea-level near Tuticorin. This is exactly confirmed by similar evidence from Pamban (Rameswaram) Island. On the north of the island are a fringing and a raised reef, the latter forming a scarp 3–5 ft. high, continued on the mainland across Pamban Strait. These straits themselves are nearly bridged by a reef, so regularly jointed as to give the appearance of an artificial mole, and indeed it is to all intents used as such by the railway.[40] Adam's Bridge itself is basically a coral reef killed by uplift and consolidated into coral rock.

For all that, one can hardly avoid preferring the account in the *Ramayana*: the bridges were built by the admirable monkey-king Hanuman and his followers to aid Rama in the expedition to regain his wife Sita, abducted by the ten-headed Ravana, the demon king of Lanka or Ceylon. On his return Rama built the vast Rameswaram temple, its quadrangle of 650 by 1,000 ft. flanked by pillared corridors exceeding in length St Peter's nave. Unfortunately stylistic experts coldly assign a 17th-century date– AD 1550 at earliest – to this magnificent work.

THE UPPER VAIGAI

The headwaters of the Vaigai rise in the broad but rugged Varushanad valley, as it were the aisle to the nave formed by the main embayment, which it joins transversely. This main valley, about 50 miles by 15 (80 by 24 km.) is flat-floored at about 1,000 ft. (305 m.), and from its relations to the surrounding hills would seem structural in origin. The upper (Kambam) valley is in fact drained by the Suruli, one of the headstreams of which actually rises to the west of the straight Cardamom scarp (X on Fig. 25.10). The fall is indeed very much steeper on the Tamilnad side, but given the rainfall it would seem that this is a relic of an old drainage to the east, now mostly captured by Periyar headwaters. The drainage-pattern on either side of the scarp presents some very remarkable adjustments to structure, and this is an equally remarkable discordance.

To the northeast the axis of the trough is continued by the col (under 1,000 ft.)

[40] Kalyanasundaram, *loc. cit.*; personal observation; the railway may fall into disuse following great damage and loss of a passenger train without survivors during a typhoon and storm surge in 1963.

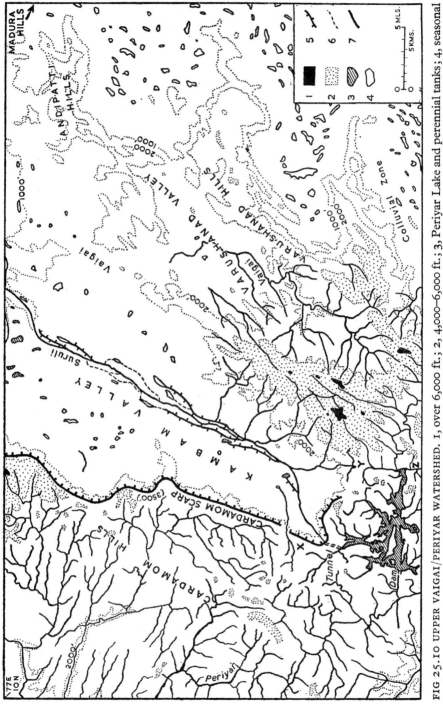

FIG 25.10 UPPER VAIGAI/PERIYAR WATERSHED. 1, over 6,000 ft.; 2, 4,000–6,000 ft.; 3, Periyar Lake and perennial tanks; 4, seasonal tanks; 5, permanent, 6, seasonal canals; 7, perennial streams (all shown; seasonal streams, numerous in east, omitted). X, fragment of old E-flowing drainage above scarp; Y–Z, probable old course of U. Suruli, now captured by Periyar headwaters. Source of Periyar is about 16 miles south of Z. SOI 1/253440 58 G. *Courtesy SOI.*

leading between the Palanis and the Karandamalais to Dindigul: but the Vaigai itself breaks through to the southeast in a great sweeping curve. The trends of the Palar/Ponnaiyar region are thus duplicated here. It may be noted finally that the Vaigai is perennial only in the high Varushanad valley, in contrast to its tributary the Suruli, which has feeders direct from the Cardamoms, as well as an artificial supply of Periyar water.

The Kambam valley is floored by the red loams – 'colluvial' soil-wash, deep and with an underlying layer of rock fragments. These are thus well watered, drained, and aerated; 'into these soils the water draining the mountain slopes penetrates very easily, and the soil climate is comparatively humid even in adverse seasons'.[41] There is some tank-irrigation, wells are much used, and the Kambam valley is also served by the Periyar reservoir across the mountains. Such a scheme was first mooted at the beginning of the 19th century, and carried out at its close; hydro-electric development has now taken place. The masonry dam, 173 ft. (53 m.) high, impounds a lake of 8,000 ac. (3,250 ha.), and the water is taken through the crest in a mile-long tunnel, but most of the water-body lies below the tunnel-level and simply lifts the rest up.[42] There is some irrigation in the Suruli/Vaigai valley, but most use is not in this fairly secure tract but outside the Andipatti Hills in the great Vaigai bend; the water has the negative quality of being entirely silt-free.

Rice and millets are the staples, with a considerable cotton area. In the north, on the Cauvery watershed, the tobacco area around Dindigul is limited in extent, but the most famous in India. Betel is also grown. The proximity of the hill forests enables the irrigated area to be well fertilized with leaf-mould.

An isolated area, much of it was given over to large *zamindari* estates, one of which occupied the entire Varushanad valley. But good soil, fair rain and Periyar water combine to produce densities of at least 450–650. The little market towns are collecting centres for the forest products of the hillmen – bamboos, honey, wax, dye- and tan-stuffs, cardamoms. Dindigul (92,947) lies across the watershed, in the Amaravati drainage, but its links are to the south with Madurai; it is famous for its cheroots, poor compared with those of Burma but the best which India has to offer. Unlike the Tamilnad *bidi* manufacture, this is a factory industry.

THE MADURAI–RAMANATHAPURAM TANK COUNTRY

The topography of this area is shown in Fig. 25.12, which covers an entire quarter-inch sheet (one degree square, 4,625 sq. miles or 11,980 km²) between the Varshalei and the Vaippar. On the ground the landscape is not striking: coconut and palmyra, paddy and millet, not a little bare ground or short ragged grass and low bush, lateritic surfaces gravelly or actual 'pan', carrying low but locally dense thorny scrub. On the Ramanathapuram–Tiruchchirappalli railway one does not see a hill for the first 80 miles (129 km.), and then it is a hummock

[41] K. Ramamurthy, 'Some aspects of the regional geography of Tamilnad', *IGJ* 23/4 (1948), 24–34.
[42] Details in Ramamurthy, *IGJ* 24/3 (1949), 33–35.

50 ft. (15 m.), high at most; not until Pudukottai – continuation of the 'Vallam Tableland' – is reached can the ground be called even undulating. On this flat, gently-sloping shelf (the 250-ft. contour is 30–40 miles from the sea) the only

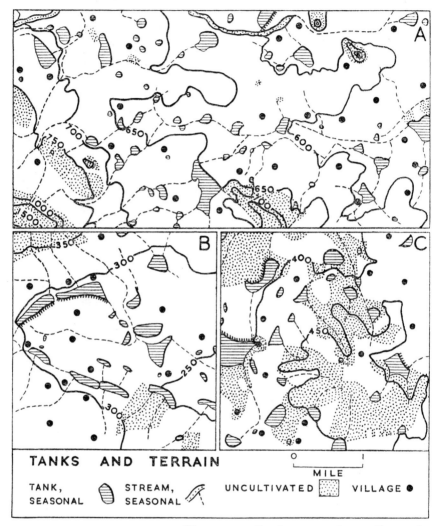

TANKS AND TERRAIN

TANK, SEASONAL STREAM, SEASONAL UNCULTIVATED VILLAGE

FIG 25.11 TANKS AND TERRAIN. Three types of tank pattern: A, 30 miles south-west of Trichy: tanks along streams near hills, villages on valley sides. *SOI* 58J/6.

B, 8 miles west of Pudukottai: tanks on flanks and around head of valley. *SOI* 58J/10.

C, 18 miles south of Trichy: tanks and villages radial around lateritic rise. *SOI* 58J/10. *All courtesy* SOI.

All tanks and streams seasonal, generally holding water July–December in A, September–February in B and C.

776

noticeable elevations are the tank-bunds, and in the dry weather at least only the biggest of these are very noticeable. In fact such swells and hollows as exist are as it were flattened out by the surpassing skill with which even the shallowest

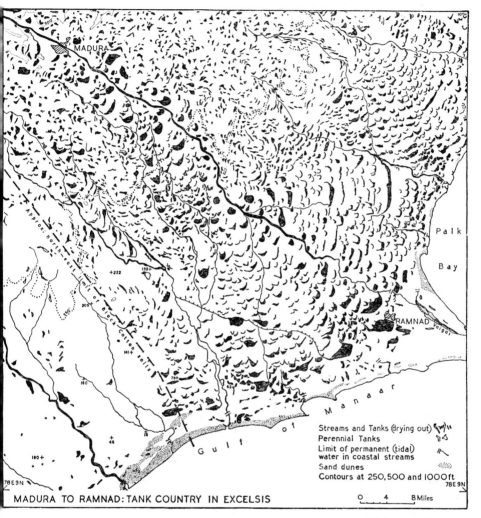

FIG 25.12 THE MADURAI–RAMANATHAPURAM TANK COUNTRY. All 'water' features on original map shown; they 'usually contain water after heavy rain'. Note relative absence of tanks on black soils in southwest. *SOI* 1/253,440 58K (whole sheet). *Courtesy* SOI.

depressions are bunded, producing a skyline of flat planes imperceptibly merging into one another.

From the air, however, this is certainly one of the strangest landscapes in the

world. Fig. 25.11 shows some of the possible arrangements of tanks in relation to
relief; Fig. 25.12 the remarkable over-all pattern. Among the more notable
features are the way in which a large tank inhibits the formation of smaller competitors within its domain; the string of large gibbous tanks, often paired, on either
side of the main rivers, which obviously have levee characteristics; the alignment
along contours, which could almost be interpolated from the pattern; the
suggestion of an old deltaic fan on the lower Vaigai; the crescent or fish-tail
shapes of the majority of tanks. This last is due to the obvious economy of
bunding below a confluence, so that the resulting tank has two arms wrapping
around the blunt end of the interfluves; the paired crescents usually lie on either
side of a larger stream. Except after heavy rain, usually in November–December,
practically all tanks and streams are dry; and from above the landscape is a
medley of all shades of khaki, ochreous yellow and rusty red, with a few bottle-
green blobs below the less-silted tanks: the whole looks like a surface of vast
overlapping fish-scales. For most of the year the impression is arid and desolate
in the extreme; the dune-fringed coast is relieved to some extent by patches of
dry thorny scrub or, more pleasantly, by coconut and palmyra groves. But even
so the contrast between the wall of green standing almost straight out of the
water at Talaimanaar on the Ceylon side, and the almost Red Sea coast at
Dhanushkodi, is more striking than enlivening.

Apart from this astonishing terrain, little need be noted. With a rainfall of only
34 in. (864 mm.) and poor lateritic or gneissic soils, this would indeed be a poor
country were it not for its intensive refashioning by the hand of man; and this
refashioning has been so intense that no streamlet, however miserable, escapes
unchecked to the sea without yielding up its toll of water. Even as it is, the region
is hardly prosperous; most of the tanks are more or less silted up and there is
scarcely room for new ones, while loss by evaporation from these water-bodies of
small volume in relation to surface is very high. Something under 40% of the
two Districts is cultivated: rice is the main crop in both, followed by jowar in
Madurai and cotton in Ramanathapuram; cumbu is fairly generally grown, and
small amounts of other millets and pulses. After cotton, oilseeds are the main cash
crops, especially groundnuts in Madurai. Although there is a high proportion
of irrigation, very little land is double cropped, and it is fairly safe to assume that
even this small fraction was in the 'colluvial' zone of the far west where the whole
piedmont is commanded by tanks of which many are perennial (Fig. 25.10).

Settlements are fairly compact, usually under the tanks; a notable feature is
the large number of tiny market towns; Ramanathapuram District has half a dozen
larger centres with 25,000–50,000 inhabitants. Most of the area was *zamindari*
and rather backward. The only places of more than local importance are on
Pamban Island: Rameswaram as a place of pilgrimage, Dhanushkodi as the ferry
port for Ceylon. But Rameswaram is only a large village (*c.* 6,000), and Dhanushkodi scarcely that.

Closer to the hills conditions are rather better, and in the Madurai taluks within the Vaigai bend there is a fair amount of Periyar irrigation. Madurai itself (424,810), the second city of Tamilnad, dominates the entire southeast, which was the domain of the Pandya dynasty from the 3rd century BC till the 10th AD, when it fell under Chola sway. Madurai was sacked by Ala-ud-din's general Malik Kafur in 1310, but Pandynad and adjacent Kerala formed the only part of the Peninsula not subject to Asoka, Muhammed bin Tughluk, or Aurengzeb. The city's most brilliant period was under the Naik dynasty (16th–18th centuries), when the great temple with its nine towering *gopurams* was built, and also the 1,200-ft. square Teppakulam Tank, walled and revetted of granite. But with almost pre-eminent sanctity in South India goes a strong indigenous craft tradition and modern industry. The Naiks introduced silk-weavers from Gujarat (a Gujarati dialect was still spoken in the first decades of this century), and the handloom and dyeing tradition of the city may have played a part in the rise of factory methods in the 1890s. Especially since the advent of Pykara power, Madurai has rivalled Coimbatore as the leading textile centre of Tamilnad; in marked contrast to its neighbour Tiruchchirappalli, it nearly trebled its population between 1921 and 1951, and is still growing more rapidly.

TIRUNELVELI: THE BLACK SOIL TRACT

Some 10 or 12 miles east of the Vaippar the tanks end almost abruptly (Fig. 25.12); this is associated with the occurrence of an extensive regur tract, mainly in the north of Tirunelveli (formerly Tinnevelly) District.[43] It is true that tanks reappear in the 'colluvial' belt, into which the black soil tract grades; but they are much fewer, and a fair proportion are perennial.

This is well brought out by the following figures for 15-minute squares (each *c.* 296 sq. miles, 767 km²) on the 1/253,440 sheets, 58G and 58K; the squares analysed form an east/west strip about 120 by 16 miles (310 by 41 km.) from the Varushanad Hills to the sea. Sheet 58K is represented on Fig. 25.12, which shows about 2,600 tanks, of which only 30 or so are perennial, and these include some coastal ones which are probably partly lagoons.

¼-in. sheet	Square	All tanks	Perennial	Remarks
(West) 58G	B/3	46	21	Half hills, half colluvial.
	C/3	111	nil	Tanks concentrated in colluvial west.
	D/3	41	nil	Largely black soil.
58K	A/3	52	17	Largely black soil; most tanks very small.
	B/3	149	3	Only parts of 3 perennial; most very small; adjacent square to north has 315 tanks, none perennial.
	C/3	168	nil	Some up to 4½ sq. miles.
(East)	D/3	83	9	This square includes Ramanathapuram and is largely sea; the 4 completely perennial perhaps rather lagoons; dry tanks up to 6 sq. miles.

[43] The following sections are based mainly on ten papers in *JMGA* 15/2 (1940) and S. M. Das, 'The Tamprabarni Basin', *ibid.* 13/2 (1938), 161–8.

This area has almost the lowest rainfall of Tamilnad; Tirunelveli District as a whole has an average of 29 in., but in the *regur* tract it is only 25–27 in., at Tuticorin as low as 22 in. (737, 635–686, and 559 mm.). The *regur* developed on the gneiss has not the transitional *murum* found between rock and soil on the Deccan Lavas; it is less moisture-retentive than the Maharashtra deep *regur*, but more easily worked. It cracks deeply, and the soil layers are well aerated and mixed. The best black soil, locally known as *karisal*, is about 3–6 ft. deep, and on the whole is rather deficient in organic and nitrogenous compounds.

The major crops are cumbu, cholam, and cotton, grown in rotation. Cumbu is more intensively cultivated and manured than is cholam, so that the following crop is better, and hence the rotation is usually cumbu-cotton-cholam. The varieties grown are much the same as in Coimbatore; Cambodia has a yield $2\frac{1}{2}$ times that of *karunganni*, but it thrives only with irrigation, and is thus largely limited to the piedmont colluvial belt: here in Sankaranayinkovil, Tenkasi, and Koilpatti taluks, under the hills, are most of the District's 36,000 wells and a third of the tank-fed area. CO2 has a wider range than pure Cambodia, while the poorer *vepal* soils of the east, with lower and later rain, concentrate on the relatively inferior 'Tinnies'. Well-irrigation may be extended when Papanasam power becomes available to tap underground sources. Farming practices are good: much use is made of tank silt and cowdung (the fuel situation is obviously easier than on the Gangetic plains), ploughing is early, the rotation gives little slack time. Cattle – largely the Kangayam breed from Coimbatore – are well cared for, fed on cotton seed, gram and cumbu and cholam straw. Pulses are often intercropped with the millets. With all this yields are relatively good, and with the emphasis on millets in mind, it is interesting to note the presence of a fair proportion of Telugu Reddis in the District.

Such industrial activity as exists in the small towns is associated almost entirely with cotton: ginneries, a few small mills. The most important centre is the port of Tuticorin (127,356). The town received its main impetus with the American Civil War cotton boom; its surroundings are unattractive in the extreme, marsh and sand, and the development has been very haphazard. As so often on the east coast, the roadstead is 5 miles offshore and goods have to be lightered to the three jetties; two-thirds of trade and shipping is purely coastal. There is some industrial development, mainly cotton; the Madurai Cotton Mills employ about 5,000 hands, while some 2,000 are engaged in salt-pans and stevedore work.

The port facilities of Tuticorin are antiquated and Cochin has made inroads on its trade, which has several interesting features. Raw cotton, yarn and piece-goods are the chief exports, raw to Europe and manufactured to Ceylon and Malaya. Sheep and goats, tiles, senna, salt and cement are also exported; imports include grain, manures, machinery and fuel-wood. Highly specialized local products include senna leaves, palmyra fibre and chank (conch) shells for the Calcutta bracelet trade. Pearling on the Indian side of the Gulf of Mannar was never very important and is now dead. Fishing and shell-diving are practically a monopoly of the Roman Catholic Paravans (tribe, caste or sect?), who form a quarter of the population in Tuticorin and a considerable element along the coast.

TIRUNELVELI: RED SOIL AND TERI

Little need be said of the red soil area proper; much of it is simply waste, poor acacia scrub; paddy is grown under the many rain-fed tanks, but more often only poor crops of the poorer millets, gram and gingelly are possible. The only specialized crop is senna. Here and there well-irrigation, with tank-silt and farmyard manure, enables better crops to be grown; oil-pumps have been introduced, and there are hopes of hydro-electric power from Papanasam.

More interesting is the palmyra economy of the *teri*. The palmyra or toddy palm (*Borassus flabellifer*) is widespread throughout Tamilnad, more important on the Tinnevelly red soils, and of prime importance in the *teri* which as a rule produces nothing else whatever. There are probably some 10,000,000 palms in Tirunelveli, providing full- or part-time employment to a large fraction of the population. The palmyra here is probably only less useful than the coconut in Kerala. The broad fan-shaped leaves are used for thatching and even fencing, as fans and sun-shades, for basketry and mats, or, when dyed, to make toys; the fibres of the stem for brushes, ropes, and webbing. But the juice of the stem is the most valuable element: it is the main source of toddy or 'country spirit'[44] and large quantities are used to make jaggery; the District has several sugar factories based on palmyra. The curious light railway in the extreme southeast was laid down in 1905 by the East India Distilleries Co. to convey palmyra juice and jaggery from the *teri* to its sugar refinery at Kulasekharapatnam.[45] This went out of production in 1927, and the line was taken over by the local authorities for passengers and goods. With the advent of freedom and Prohibition distilling has fallen under a cloud, and the depressed caste of toddy-tappers, the Shanars, are probably now still more depressed: but the presence of 10,000,000 palmyra trees suggests that enforcement may well prove inordinately expensive, not to say oppressive.

TIRUNELVELI: THE TAMPRABARNI VALLEY AND KANNIYAKUMARI

'A splash of green to the naturally dull brown of vegetation map of Tinnevelly', the Tamprabarni Valley, with that of its tributary the Chittar, accounts for three-quarters of the District's canal irrigation; but this is less than the area commanded by wells and less than a third of the tank area. The river is exceptionally favoured: rising at 6,000 ft. (1,830 m.), its sources receive rain from both the main and the retreating southwest monsoons, and its bed is never dry; and the valley moreover coincides almost exactly with a narrow east–west belt which receives 30–35 in. (762–889 mm.) of rain.

[44] Which smells like ammonia, but when fresh has a cinnamon flavour and might pass as an aperitif; not fresh it is probably deadly.
[45] The company also used a pipeline, but the chemical reactions were disastrous.

There are 8 *anicuts* on the main river, 18 on the Chittar, 12 on other tributaries; nearly all are ancient works. With the regular régime, the cultivating season lasts for ten months and 94% of the irrigated area is double-cropped, generally with two rice crops. Other wet crops are plantains, betel, turmeric and sugar-cane; chillies and gingelly are occasionally irrigated. Ragi and cholam are rain-fed, or irrigated from wells in the off-season on the lower reaches of the Chittar, which has really plentiful water only from October to January.

Apart from agriculture, there is little of note in the present human geography of the area: a little oil-pressing, and an interesting local craft (entirely in Muslim hands), the weaving of grass mats which before the war were exported as far as Burma and Malaya. The only large towns are Tirunelveli and the District capital Palayankottai (Palamcottah, 51,002) across the river from each other and indeed so practically contiguous that the towns are virtually one, and the total population of the Census group of four towns is over 190,000.

The real interest of the Tamprabarni, its irrigation apart, lies in the future. The Tamprabarni is probably unique among Indian rivers in that it was harnessed to provide direct hydraulic power for cotton spinning: the first of two turbine-driven mills was set up in 1885. At Papanasam there is a 300-ft. (91-m.) fall now developed for hydro-electricity, despite doubts as to the need of conserving water for irrigation; but the possibilities of cheap electricity in this area are manifold: foremost perhaps an increase of well-irrigation in the half-dead edaphically arid tracts, and industrially the revivification of the palmyra sugar industry, the extension of cotton in all its branches. Oilseeds could certainly be more widely cultivated in the red soil area, possibly leading to soap and allied industries, and the hills contain vast reserves of bamboo for paper-making.

Around the corner of India, the Tamil-speaking area in the extreme south of Kerala has now been added to Madras as the little District of Kanniyakumari. There is canal irrigation in the Kodayar valley, and most of the cultivated area is devoted to rice and coconuts. The headquarters is Nagercoil (106,207).

THE ANDAMAN AND NICOBAR ISLANDS

These two groups, administered directly under Delhi, continue the trend of the Arakan Yomas, linking them to the Sumatran ranges. They differ between themselves to a marked extent, both physically and culturally.

THE ANDAMANS

These number over 200, extending north-northeast/south-southwest between 10° and 14° N; the total area is 2,500 sq. miles (6,475 km²) of which the great bulk is in the three major islands of North, Middle and South Andaman. These three, indeed, are separated only by narrow mangrove-fringed inlets, so that they are often referred to as virtually one island, Great Andaman. The islands are formed of sandstones, limestones, clays, probably mainly Tertiary, and some

serpentines and are highly dissected, rising to 2,400 ft. (730 m.). With a temperature never far from 85°F., rainfall over 100 in. (29°C., 2,540 mm.), and a
monsoonal distribution with no really rainless season, they are naturally jungle-
covered: mangrove along coasts and inlets, tropical evergreen along valleys and
on steeper wetter slopes, elsewhere moist deciduous.

The total population recorded in 1941 was 21,316, but this included a strange
medley: aborigines, convicts and ex-convicts with their 'local-born' children,
officials. A century ago the aborigines probably numbered about 5,000; in 1931
they were estimated at about 460, in 1941 at 62; many tribes have died right out.
At once shy and savage, they had a reputation for ferocity, and early settlement
was avowedly to protect shipwrecked mariners from massacre. Despite efforts
at conciliation there was violence on both sides; the Jarawa still ferociously resist
all approaches. Attempts were made indeed to settle some of the more friendly
groups in an 'Andamans Home' as fishers of trepang (sea-slug) and collectors of
edible bird-nests, both for the Chinese market. But the only result was to
civilize them out of existence, largely by venereal disease.[46] The Andamanese are
– perhaps one should say were – Negritos, and as they represented perhaps the
nearest approach to a 'pure primitive' society both ethnically and culturally,
these hunters and gatherers have attracted anthropological attention out of
proportion to their numbers.[47]

Transportation of convicts to the Andamans began after the Mutiny. Latterly
there was a change of emphasis, hopeless criminals being retransported to India
and the settlement becoming in effect an open prison for young men condemned
to life sentences for more or less excusable homicide. After a few months in jail
convicts were allowed to become wage-earning employees of government, to
wear ordinary dress, and to marry or bring out their wives. These changes were
reflected in the sex composition of the population: 15,158 males to 2,980 females
in 1901, 14,872 to 6,444 in 1941. The cultural landscape also changed: 'Everywhere the ephemeral huts of former times are giving way to well-constructed
two-storeyed houses of sawn timber and iron roofs,' and a good deal of reclamation of malarial swamp took place around Port Blair. The communal composition
of the population was an odd reflection of social conditions: in 1941 Muslims
were about a third, largely Moplahs from Madras deported after their 1921
rebellion; Sikhs were 3·5% against an All-India total of 1·5%, Buddhists – i.e.
Burmese – over 13%. This corresponds to the prevalence of dacoity in Burma
and to the Sikh *penchant* for 'liquor, love, and fights'.

During the war, under Japanese occupation, the population fell markedly; but
after re-occupation the penal settlement was formally abandoned and the population is now around 50,000. Some 600 East Bengali families have been resettled

[46] 1931 Census, Vol. II (Andamans and Nicobars), 11–23.
[47] The classic treatments are those of Sir Richard Temple in the 1901 Census and of
A. R. Brown in *The Andaman Islanders* (1922). There is unfortunately little geography in
the latter book; what there is is largely summed up in L. Garrard's 'sociograph' in *Studies
in Regional Consciousness and Environment* (ed. I. C. Peate, 1930), 82.

on cleared forest in Middle Andaman; the Burmese have mostly been repatriated, there are still a thousand Moplahs, but recent papers[48] make no mention of Sikhs. Economic development is mainly around Port Blair, a town of some 15,000 on South Andaman; it has one of the largest saw-mills in Asia. Rice and coconuts share equally the small cultivated area, and the teak plantations have been revived using immigrant labour from Ranchi. Plywoods, hardwoods and matchwoods are exported.

THE NICOBARS

This group extends from about 6 to 10° N, Car Nicobar lying 75 miles (121 km.) from Little Andaman, Great Nicobar 91 miles (146 km.) from Sumatra. Of the nineteen islands totalling 635 sq. miles (1,645 km²) twelve are inhabited. The population in 1961 was about 14,500, of whom a few hundred were Shompens, a jungly inland tribe ('pre-Dravidian' ?) on the otherwise scarcely inhabited Great Nicobar, and a few hundred traders and officials on Car Nicobar, the most important of the group. The rest are Nicobarese proper, whose affinities seem to be with the Mon-Khmer peoples of the Indo-Chinese Peninsula.

The northern group, which includes Car Nicobar, have a basis of Tertiary serpentine, in places weathered to a light clay; the southern group, with Great Nicobar, of lower Tertiary sandstones and quartzites. Heights increase north and south, indicating a sinking of the former Burma–Sumatra arc at its apex. Extensive slightly raised coral flats girdle some islands and here are most of the coconuts and the people.[49] Great and Little Nicobar are very much dissected and forested; the others are mainly covered with tall *lalang* grass or coconuts, and abandoned coconut groves around Great Nicobar tell of a former larger population; conflict with the Shompen is apparently responsible for this abandonment.

With a temperature range of 65–98° F. (18–37° C.) and a rainfall of 90–170 in. (more on Great Nicobar) conditions are ideal for coconut, and with fish and imported rice it forms the stable diet. 'In a rich man's household often as many as 300 coconuts are consumed in one day. Some 200 of these are used in feeding the family's pigs in the jungle.'[50] The Shompen practice a primitive agriculture with fire-sharpened digging sticks, though they also obtain iron *dahs* (Burmese choppers or knives) by raid or trade from the coastal villages.[51]

Dutch pirates and French Jesuits had contacts with the islands before the Danish East India Company took on the task of 'civilization' in 1756. The British occupied the islands during the Napoleonic wars, but spasmodic and rather inept

[48] These include: P. K. Sen, 'A study of population in the Andamans', *Indian Geogr* 4/1 (1959), 115–36; 'Agriculture in the Andamans', *GRI* 19/4 (1957), 48–58; 'Some aspects of recent colonisation in the Andamans', *ibid.* 16/1 (1954); H. I. S. Kanwai, 'The Andaman Islands: India's ocean frontier', *Indian Geogr* 4/1 (1959), 142–9.

[49] K. Mylius, 'The Nicobars and a bibliography of the Islands', *Oriental Geogr* (Dacca), 6/1 (1962), 82–96.

[50] 1931 Census, Vol. III, 74.

[51] *Ibid.* 87–88.

Danish efforts at colonization and evangelization continued until they admitted defeat in 1848: the chief relic of their interest is the herd of half-wild buffaloes on Kamorta. In 1867 and 1876 Prussians and Austrians made gestures towards developing the islands, which in the intervals were used by Malay pirates (led by a deserter from the Royal Navy) who concealed their activities by only attacking ships actually calling at the islands and by leaving no survivors: they seem to have been responsible for the ill-deserved Nicobarese reputation for ferocity. Finally in 1869 the British accepted responsibility for the protection of mariners. After the failure of a penal settlement and of an attempt at importing Chinese colonists, administration was practically confined to keeping out 'fire-arms and firewater' and to licensing traders. These are mainly Penang Chinese, but country craft come from Burma, the Maldives and even Kutch. During the war the Japanese built a base on Car Nicobar, and recently some official attempts have been made to introduce coffee and rubber.

Coconuts are by far the most important export and are in effect the currency. Other exports, in which a Chinese bias is evident, include trepang, edible nests, trochus shells, areca nuts and rattans; imports rice, tobacco (which is also grown on some islands), *dahs* and cloth, much of the last item being destroyed in funerary ceremonies.

BIBLIOGRAPHICAL NOTE

G. Slater's *Southern India* (1926) (cited simply as 'Slater') does for Tamilnad something of what Darling does for the Punjab; slighter, but with many good points, is J. C. Molony's, *A Book of South India* (1926). Slater's *The Dravidian Element in Indian Culture* (1928) is suggestive, and his *Some South Indian Villages* (1918) initiated village surveys; see also P. J. Thomas and K. C. Ramakrishnan (eds.) *Some South Indian Villages: A Resurvey* (Madras, 1940). As will have been seen, there are many useful papers in the *Journal of the Madras Geographical Association*, later the *Indian Geographical Journal*.

However, special mention must be made of two books by Jacques Dupuis: *Les Ghat Orientaux et la Plaine du Coromandel* (Inst. Français de Pondichéry, Travaux de la Sect. Scientifique, Tome II, 1959), and above all *Madras et le nord du Coromandel: étude des conditions de la vie indienne dans un cadre géographique* (Adrien-Maisonneuve, Paris, 1960). This monograph, *un ouvrage vraiment magistral*, is an extremely skilful blending of sociological and geographical approaches, a work so rich in detail and interpretation that it is difficult to summarize from it. The Institut Français is a continuing source of excellent material.

CHAPTER 26

Ceylon

By B. H. FARMER

*(Fellow of St John's College, University Lecturer in Geography and
Director of the Centre of South Asian Studies, University of Cambridge)*

Although Ceylon is separated from India by a strait only some 20 miles wide, it has a very marked individuality. This is not primarily a matter of physical geography, for Ceylon is essentially a detached portion of the Deccan, with land forms, climatic regions, natural vegetation and soils which can be broadly matched in south India; but it is, in the main, a cultural phenomenon, a matter of differences between the society and economy of Ceylon and those of adjacent areas of India.

It is not that the insularity of Ceylon has kept it apart from India, for throughout history almost every phase of Peninsular Indian civilization has found its way to Ceylon, from early Buddhism and ancient architecture to the modern renaissance of art and music. There have also been actual movements of peoples across Palk Strait; Tamil immigration in medieval, and perhaps in ancient, times has made its mark on the traditions and language of the Sinhalese,[1] and founded a distinctive community of 'Ceylon Tamils' in the Jaffna Peninsula,[2] while more recently Tamil labourers have come to work on plantations.

The island nature of Ceylon has, however, reduced the intensity of cultural change and allowed local differentiation. (Here an analogy may be drawn with the relations of Britain and continental Europe.) Thus the Sinhalese have retained their Buddhism and in so doing have had considerable influence on other Buddhist lands; and, in spite of continual coming and going between Jaffna and South India, the Ceylon Tamils have themselves grown different from their Indian cousins. Again, the presence of the sea undoubtedly reduced the pressure of settlers from India, so helping in recent centuries to produce the relative emptiness of the Dry Zone between the Jaffna Peninsula and the Sinhalese areas of the centre and southwest.

Much of the individuality of Ceylon may be attributed to the fact that it is not only an island but an island in a prominent position in the Indian Ocean. It

---

[1] Sinhalese (Singalese, Cingalese)=member of, language of, the majority community in Ceylon; Ceylonese=any native of Ceylon.

[2] For place-names see Fig. 26.2 and 26.8.

lay on early shipping routes between the two coasts of India, and between the
Graeco-Roman world, and later the Arab world, and China; later still, it lay in

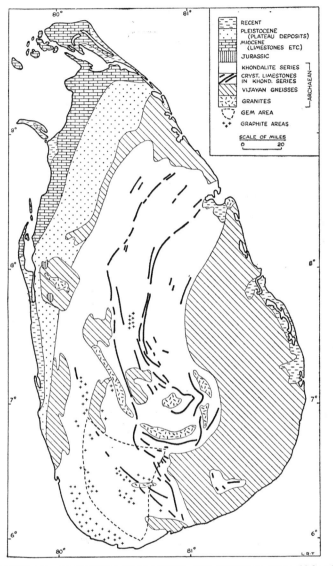

FIG 26.1 CEYLON: SIMPLIFIED GEOLOGICAL AND MINERAL MAP. (After L. J. D.
Fernando, *op. cit.*)

the track of Europeans sailing round the Cape, while in modern times it is, of
course, on the Suez route to Australia and the Far East. Maritime influences are
therefore strong. It is fairly certain, in fact, that the original Sinhalese themselves

came by sea from north India and not across Palk Strait, for they speak a tongue which is recognizably Aryan. The great differences between Sinhalese and the

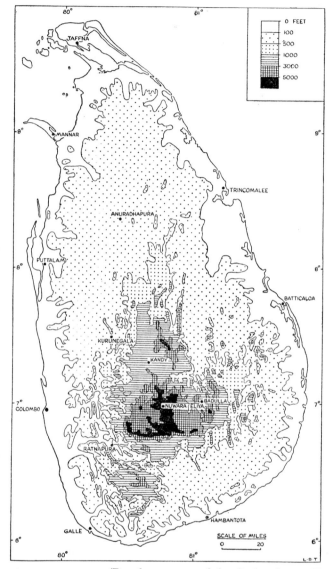

FIG 26.2 CEYLON: RELIEF. (Based on a map of the Ceylon Survey Department, by kind permission of the Surveyor-General, Ceylon.)

Dravidian languages of south India have helped to maintain Sinhalese culture. The island was later visited by Arab traders, whose descendants, the so-called Moors, are prominent in the coastal population to this day, and later still by the

Portuguese and the Dutch. All of them were attracted by intrinsic wealth as well as by positional advantage. The two European powers in turn controlled the maritime regions, where they left a strong mark on society (e.g. the Roman Catholic religion and Roman-Dutch law); but they failed to conquer the high-lands. The British took over from the Dutch in 1795–96, mainly in order to control Trincomalee, and at first attempted to govern the island under an arrangement with the EIC. But by 1802 it was apparent that Madras-trained officials were, apart from other disabilities, quite unable to understand the language and customs of the Sinhalese, and Ceylon became a Crown Colony. The British, having thus recognized the distinctiveness of Ceylon, made it even more distinctive, especially when, after 1815, they came to control the whole island. British influence varied in intensity with local conditions, but, by and large, was greater than in any but the most exceptional parts of India. To mention only a few of its effects, a plantation economy was superimposed on the older peasant economy, the English language became well established, and English systems of education were adopted by the new urban middle class; and in many other ways British rule modified the cultural and economic pattern of Ceylon, continuing a process begun by the Portuguese and further differentiating Ceylon from near-by India. Since February 4th, 1948, the distinctiveness of Ceylon has found a new political expression, and the country has become an independent entity within the Commonwealth of Nations.

I. THE PHYSICAL SETTING

Structure and relief

Although systematic geological mapping in Ceylon is by no means complete, enough has been done to establish the main lines of the geology and structure of the island and to demonstrate its kinship with south India.[3] The whole of Ceylon, with the exception of the Jaffna Peninsula and northwest coast, and of small, mainly coastal strips elsewhere, consists of crystalline pre-Cambrian rocks, which have undergone varying degrees of metamorphism, granitization and deformation. The 'Khondalite Series', similar to the series of the same name in Madras and Orissa, is now believed to occupy a broad belt in the interior of the island (see Fig. 26.1). It is made up of metamorphosed sediments, largely quartz-ites, schists and crystalline limestones, which have a considerable influence on relief, hydrology and human geography; and, in the southwest especially, contain the island's principal mineral, graphite or plumbago. (The Khondalites also contain gem-bearing veins, but most of Ceylon's precious stones are obtained from secondary sources, i.e. alluvium.) The Vijayan Series consists mainly of biotite-gneisses and schists; its discontinuous outcrop fringes that of the Khondalite

[3] See especially L. J. D. Fernando, 'The geology and mineral resources of Ceylon', *Bulletin of the Imperial Institute*, 46 (1948), 303–25; and the Ceylon *Geological Survey Memoirs*.

Series, but the relation between the two Series is by no means clear. There are also certain ancient intrusive rocks, and charnockites similar to those of India.

Solid sedimentary rocks are virtually confined to the Jaffna Peninsula, where almost horizontal Miocene limestones have a dominant effect on water-supply and human activity, and to the northwest coast, where there are areno-argillaceous beds as well as limestones; Gondwana deposits are limited to one or two tiny outcrops of sandstones.

The solid geology is masked in certain areas by superficial deposits which are frequently of importance because, in a country of generally impermeable crystalline rocks, they provide limited supplies of underground water. Thus in the northwest many of the interfluves are capped with 'plateau deposits', comprising quartz pebble gravels, red earths and ferruginous concretions; these are thought to be remnants of Pleistocene fluvial deposition.

In the pre-Cambrian terrains of Ceylon some observers have seen three more or less eroded peneplain-like surfaces,[4] rising from the sea like the treads of three steps, and separated from each other by mural scarps. In their view, there is a 'lowest surface' developed mainly in the 'Vijayan Series', maturely dissected, and recognizable in hilltops up to 400 ft. (120 m.) high in the coastal plain (which is narrow in the west and south, but wider in the east and covers most of the north of the island); a second surface developed in both the 'Khondalite' and 'Vijayan Series', with a less mature relief and an altitude of about 1700–1900 ft. (520–580 m.); and a third with juvenile relief, entirely in the 'Khondalite Series' or in intrusions in it, at about 4,000–6,000 ft. (1,220–1,830 m.) but with an appreciable slope northward, so that the scarp bounding it disappears in the same direction. Adams[5] considers that the surfaces are subaerial peneplains and represent successive stages in the uplift of the island, the lowest being the youngest. Wadia,[6] on the other hand, considers that they are the result of block uplift of an ancient erosion surface in two stages, the earlier lifting the second 'peneplain' above the first, and the later stage lifting the third above the second. If this is so, the mural scarps are fault or fault-line scarps. More recent work suggests that the denudation chronology may in fact be complex.

The stepped nature of the relief of Ceylon cannot, however, be gainsaid, and has important corollaries. Thus the mural scarps and deeply eroded valleys form obstacles to communications, while there are many waterfalls of great beauty along the scarps.

In detail, the pattern of dissection is very clearly influenced by the strike of the underlying rocks and by faults and joints. The strike is especially evident in the outcrop of the 'Khondalite Series', where quartzite ridges stand high above

---

[4] See D. N. Wadia, 'The three superposed peneplains of Ceylon', *Records of the Department of Mineralogy, Ceylon*, Professional Paper No. 1 (1943), 25–32; see also F. D. Adams, 'Geology of Ceylon', *Canadian Journal of Research*, I (1929), 425–511, and K. Kularatnam, 'The Face of Ceylon', *Proceedings of the Ninth Annual Session of the Ceylon Association for the Advancement of Science* (1953).

[5] Adams, *op. cit.*   [6] Wadia, *op. cit.*

deep vales cut in less resistant materials. Particularly fine ridge-and-valley topography of this kind may be studied in the Ratnapura District,[7] while a series of quartzite ridges stretches northnortheast from the Matale area to the sea at Trincomalee; Trincomalee harbour consists, in fact, of a series of ria-like embayments between low quartzite headlands. Grain is less evident, but still present in country formed of Vijayan gneisses; this is well demonstrated in the broken relief of Bintenne in the hinterland of Batticaloa. North of about the latitude of Vavuniya there is virtually no relief at all. The Jaffna limestone region also has very slight relief, and nowhere rises more than 50 ft. (15 m.) above sea-level; hence shallow wells reach the water-table, and the region does not suffer the fate of high-pitched tropical limestone areas such as those of Java.

Finally, a word may be said about coastal forms. In most parts of the shoreline, except the very exposed southwest, the coast of Ceylon is characterized by a series of offshore bars, spits and tombolos, often covered with blown sand and enclosing lagoons. The Kalpitiya spit, enclosing Puttalam Lagoon, and the long bar south of Batticaloa, are good examples. The silting of lagoons often gives wide alluvial stretches, as does also the deltaic discharge of the Mahaweli Ganga, Ceylon's biggest river, into Koddiyar Bay, south of Trincomalee. There are also alluvium-filled drowned valleys, especially in the southwest.

Climate[8]

As might be expected, mean monthly temperatures in lowland Ceylon are high, and show little variation from month to month or from station to station. Thus the mean monthly temperature at Colombo (altitude 24 ft.) varies only from 77·5° F. in December to 82·1° F. in May, and at Trincomalee (altitude also 24 ft.) from 77·8° F. in January to 85·4° F. in June (25·3–27·8 and 25·4–29·7° C.). These examples illustrate the fact that mean temperatures in the hottest month are higher in the north and east than in the southwest. Reliable uniform temperatures, with the intake of solar radiation which they betoken, are among lowland Ceylon's greatest assets, and approach the optimum for the growth of rice. In the hills, lower temperatures are of course experienced; thus at Nuwara Eliya (altitude 6,170 ft., 1,881 m.) the mean daily temperature hovers around 60° F. (15·6° C.) but the temperature when the sun is shining is much higher.

Broadly speaking, Ceylon is from late May until August or September under the sway of the Southwest monsoon, and from November until January under that of what passes locally as the 'Northeast monsoon' (more correctly it is the retreating Southwest monsoon). Between the monsoons local convectional circulations tend to spring into action. The Southwest monsoon wind is on the whole stronger than that of the Northeast monsoon, and, descending from the hills with something of a föhn effect, is partly responsible for temperatures on the northeast coast which may reach 100° F. (37·8° C.) in the daytime.

[7] See the excellent ¼-inch and 1-inch maps published by the Ceylon Survey Department.
[8] For climatic data for Ceylon see the *Reports* of the Colombo Observatory.

Relative humidity at Colombo and other southwestern stations remains high at all seasons (70–80% by day, 85–95% by night); the same is broadly true of northwestern stations. In the north and east, however, relative humidity falls to a monthly mean of 60% or less during the Southwest monsoon; this helps to

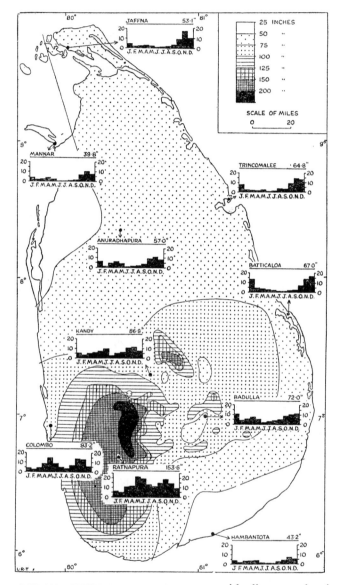

FIG 26.3 CEYLON: MEAN ANNUAL RAINFALL: with diagrams showing Mean Monthly Rainfall. (*Isohyets by kind permission of the Director of Meteorology, Ceylon.*)

lower the sensible temperature, but increases the loss of water by evaporation. Relative humidity, as measured by monthly means, shows little change with altitude. The physiological effects of high humidity are in many places mitigated by wind.

Fig. 26.3 shows that southwest Ceylon, the region usually known as the 'Wet Zone', has a much higher average rainfall than other sectors of the country, with totals exceeding 200 in. (5,080 mm.) in parts of the hills. On the other hand, in much of the north and east (i.e. the 'Dry Zone') the mean annual rainfall is below 75 in. (1,905 mm.). For the geographer, however, the mean annual figure has much less significance than the seasonal distribution, variability and effectiveness of the rainfall. Of these, the first is illustrated by the diagrams which accompany Fig. 26.3. It will be clear that the Wet Zone tends to have some rain at all seasons; Colombo has two maxima, one in each inter-monsoon period, and is typical of lowland Wet Zone stations; the higher-up country stations have a single maximum during the Southwest monsoon, while certain intermediate stations have a triple maximum, one for each inter-monsoon period and one for the South-west monsoon; all, however, tend to receive some rain during the Northeast monsoon, although they are on the lee side of the island, since rainfall then is frontal as well as orographic. In the Dry Zone, on the other hand, conditions are very different. The Southwest monsoon brings very little rain, and the months June, July and August, constitute the dry season. The September–November inter-monsoon period registers fair amounts in the mean monthly rainfall graph; these are due to convection and to the passage of depressions. In all Dry Zone stations a large proportion of the mean annual rainfall comes in the Northeast monsoon months (60% of the annual total at Jaffna and 54% at Trincomalee). Finally, a secondary maximum, due to convectional and cyclonic rains, occurs in some areas in April and May; these rains are prominent at Anuradhapura, but a very minor feature at Jaffna.

The rainfall of Ceylon is subject to considerable variability. Even in the Wet Zone, there are apt to be occasional disastrous droughts, but the problem is far more serious in the Dry Zone.[9] There the dry season nearly always has a very low rainfall, and, moreover, the mean expectancy is a great deal lower than the arithmetic mean. But spells of drought are apt to occur at other seasons too, and the annual total of days of absolute drought[10] is apt to be a high one (e.g. a mean of 118 days annually at Anuradhapura in the years 1931–44). The rainfall of the inter-monsoon period is particularly unreliable at many stations. Months of little or no rainfall are not unknown during the Northeast monsoon, while at other times exceptionally heavy Northeast monsoon rains may bring disastrous floods, as in 1957–58.

[9] See E. K. Cook, 'A note on irrigation in Ceylon', *Geography*, 35 (1950), 75–85, and G. G. R. Thambyahpillay, 'Rainfall fluctuations in Ceylon', *Ceylon Geographer*, 12 (1958), 51–74.

[10] As defined in *British Rainfall*, viz., 'any period of at least 15 consecutive days to none of which is credited 0·01 inches of rain or more'.

However, mere variability of rainfall tends to be a statistical abstraction, and what matters to the cultivator is the reliability of effective rainfall, i.e. rainfall

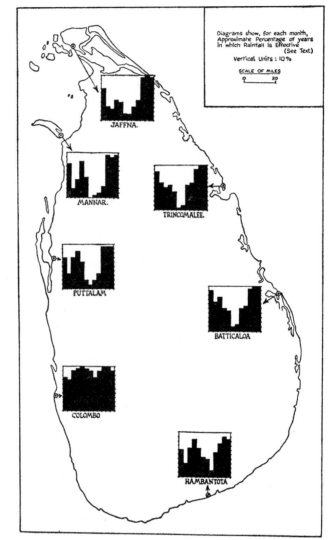

FIG 26.4 CEYLON: APPROXIMATE RELIABILITY OF EFFECTIVE RAINFALL.

which is sufficient to counteract evaporation and to maintain soil moisture above wilting point.[11] This is especially true in the Dry Zone of Ceylon, where because

[11] See B. H. Farmer, 'Rainfall and water supply in the Dry Zone of Ceylon', in R. W. Steel and C. A. Fisher (eds.), *Geographical Essays on British Tropical Lands* (1956); also P. G. Cooray, 'Effective rainfall and moisture zones in Ceylon', *Bull. Ceylon Geog. Soc.* 3 (1948), 39–42.

of high temperatures and, locally and seasonally, of low relative humidity and high wind velocities, evaporation is high. Rainfall in a given month may show a low statistical variability, but be in many years ineffective. Fig. 26.4 is an attempt to indicate the percentage of years in which effective rainfall may be expected in seven Ceylon stations; it is necessarily tentative but serves to emphasize certain important points. Thus rainfall is rarely ineffective in the Wet Zone, but often so in the Dry Zone. In the latter, the Northeast monsoon appears usually, though not invariably to bring effective rainfall, although rather less often in January; while the Southwest monsoon rainfall is apparently almost always ineffective at most stations. Both of the inter-monsoon periods seem to present roughly a fifty-fifty chance of effective rainfall, a singularly tantalizing state of affairs for the cultivator. There is also a chance of very long spells of ineffective rainfall, say from February to November.

It will be clear that climatic factors, and particularly rainfall, play a major part in the regional differentiation of Ceylon. The contrast between the Wet Zone and the Dry Zone is especially marked, and, as in so many tropical islands, the transition between the two is relatively abrupt. This is true in both highland and lowland Ceylon. It will also be clear that, in a general way, the Wet Zone climate is analogous to that of Kerala, except that in Ceylon the seasonal contrast in the rainfall régime is less marked; the Dry Zone has climatic affinities with Tamilnad, although the climate of the two regions is not identical.

It may here be noted that the distribution of endemic malaria in Ceylon was controlled by climate.[12] Malaria has until recently been endemic in most parts of the lowland Dry Zone (although it was perhaps not so of old). It was carried by a mosquito, *Anopheles culicifacies*, which breeds in shallow and relatively stagnant water, and thus found ideal conditions in the reduced streams of the lowland Dry Zone in the dry season. In the Wet Zone, on the other hand, stream-beds are normally kept flushed and clear of larvae, except in times of drought; malaria used therefore to be epidemic in such times.

Hydrology

The rivers of Ceylon are for the most part short and radial, rising at high or intermediate elevations and tumbling by stages to the plains (see Fig. 26.5). The only really large river is the Mahaweli Ganga, which rises in the Wet Zone hill country about 30 miles (48 km.) south of Kandy and flows through Kandy to the sea just south of Trincomalee. Although the radial pattern is the dominant element in the drainage system, many streams show local adjustments to the strike of the pre-Cambrian rocks, especially in the 'Khondalite Series'. The ridge-and-valley country of Ratnapura has already been remarked upon; the long north–south trench of the middle Mahaweli Ganga may be aligned along the strike or along a zone of faults.

Navigation on the rivers of Ceylon is unimportant and the chief problem posed

[12] See C. L. Dunn, *Malaria in Ceylon* (1936).

by their hydrology is that of controlling and using their waters in the interests of cultivation. In the lowland Wet Zone rice is the traditional crop of the peasantry,

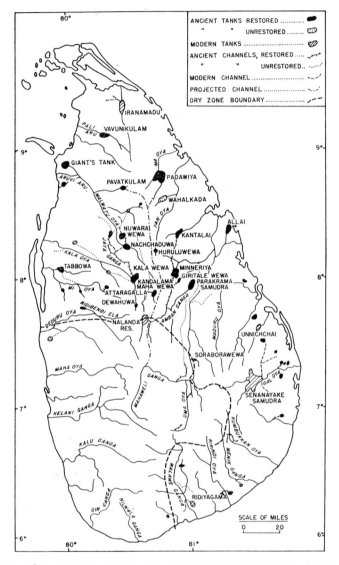

FIG 26.5 CEYLON: RIVERS AND MAIN IRRIGATION WORKS (1965).

and although it could in many places and in many years be grown using only the rain actually falling on the paddy fields, it is in practice often irrigated. Irrigation, however, here presents few difficulties: the small village works take water from the local streams, most of which are perennial. There is, in fact, usually an excess of water, and much runs to waste in the sea. Since but few rivers rise in the Wet Zone and flow into the Dry Zone, and since relief in general inhibits the artificial connection of Wet Zone and Dry Zone catchments, little can be done to use this waste water where it is sorely needed. A scheme is, however, under discussion to tap the Mahaweli Ganga near Kandy and to divert part of its flow through a tunnel to the north-central Dry Zone. The greatest local problem of Wet Zone hydrology is that of flood control.[13] Flooding is almost inevitable in a country where rainfall is torrential, slopes steep, and run-off from an impermeable terrain rapid, but it was undoubtedly accelerated by the deforestation of the highlands and the early planting of coffee, followed by tea. Much has been done to protect low-lying coastal areas from floods, but the problem remains serious.

In the Dry Zone, it is seasonal shortage of water which is the main problem. The cultivation of rice using rainwater only is possible during most Northeast monsoons, but irrigation is usually desirable; while it is essential at other seasons. Direct tapping of streams, as in the Wet Zone, is usually impossible in the dry season, when most rivers are reduced to a mere string of sandy pools. Underground water is meagre in quantity; the crystalline rocks are mainly impermeable, although the limestones and quartzites of the 'Khondalite Series' nourish springs which are locally valuable. The porous mantle of 'plateau' and residual deposits and coastal sands is an aquifer, but dry season ground-water in them is limited to narrow belts near perennial tanks or rivers. Outside the Jaffna Peninsula (where conditions are clearly very different) the Dry Zone therefore has to fall back mainly on river water, stored in tanks as in Tamilnad, and subject to a high rate of loss by evaporation. From very ancient times streams in the Dry Zone were dammed, and as technical knowledge improved the Sinhalese constructed large tanks, many of them interlinked by channels, so that those which lay on small rivers prone to dry up could be supplied from more reliable sources.[14] The conservation of surface water also helped to raise the water-table. Many ancient tanks and channels have now been restored, and a few new works constructed; a large multi-purpose reservoir has been built on the Gal Oya. It must be realized, however, that the supply of water for irrigation is strictly limited, and much is lost by evaporation.

Very little that has been said about the problems of water-supply applies to the Jaffna Peninsula. Here the need for water is, in view of the liability to long spells of ineffective rainfall, even greater than in many other parts of the Dry Zone, but, fortunately, there are abundant, though not unlimited, supplies of underground water, kept relatively free from evaporation in cavities in the limestone. The water-table may be reached by shallow wells some 15–30 ft. deep, and well-irrigation is the mainstay of agriculture. There seem also to have been some wells in ancient times in the Miocene strata of the northwest coast.

[13] See Cook, *loc. cit.* 76–77.
[14] See Fig. 26.5.

Natural vegetation[15]

The natural vegetation of the Wet Zone has largely disappeared. Enough patches and forest reserves remain, however, to make it clear that the original covering of the lowlands was a wet evergreen forest (the local equivalent of tropical rain forest), passing towards the Dry Zone boundary into a drier facies, and up the slopes of the central highlands into wet evergreen montane forest. Much of the Dry Zone is still covered with a dry mixed evergreen forest containing species adapted to seasonal drought; this passes into a moister facies in Bintenne, but towards the coasts (particularly in the northwest and southeast) into low thorny scrub. Much of the Dry Zone jungle is thought to be secondary, the product of centuries of shifting cultivation. Human intervention in the form of periodic firing also seems to be responsible for the *damanas*, savana-like grasslands to be found particularly in the eastern part of the lowland Dry Zone, and for the *patanas*, grasslands which cover a large part of the eastern hill country, between Nuwara Eliya and Badulla and which also exist in a wetter form in the western hills. None of these 'natural' grasslands are of much use for grazing in unimproved form; somewhat better pastures are however to be found along the middle Mahaweli Ganga.

Ceylon had in 1959 nearly 2,500,000 ac. (1,012,500 ha.) of State forests, mostly in the form of reserves intended for the production of timber. Most of these are in the Dry Zone (producing timbers which include ebony and satin-wood).

Soils

The soils of Ceylon have recently been classified by F. R. Moormann and C. R. Panabokke.[16] In accordance with a modern tendency to recognize soil-forming processes in the humid tropics as essentially podzolic,[17] the soils of most parts of the Wet Zone and of the hills are classed as 'red-yellow podzolic'. These soils are developed on a wide range of parent materials and in many differing topographical situations, and a number of sub-groups may be recognized. In the Wet Zone lowlands the B horizon commonly contains soft laterite (*cabook* in Sinhalese) capable of being cut out and dried for use as bricks. The red-yellow podzolic soils are not particularly fertile, but grow tree-crops (especially rubber and tea) and give a good response to fertilizers; anti-erosion measures are necessary on steep slopes. In the Kandy and Kegalla Districts they give way to immature brown loams and to what are described as 'reddish-brown lateritic soils': these are

[15] See C. H. Holmes, 'The broad pattern of climate and vegetational distribution in Ceylon' in *Studies of Tropical Vegetation: Proceedings of the Kandy Symposium, 1956* (Paris, UNESCO, 1958); and 'The grass, fern and savannah lands of Ceylon', *Imp. Forestry Inst. Paper* No. 28 (1951). Compare H. Gaussen, P. Legris, M. Viart and L. Labroue, *Carte Internationale du Tapis Vegetal, Notice de la Feuille* CEYLON, Inst. Français de Pondichéry, Travaun de la Sect. Scientifique, Hors Série No. 5 (1965).

[16] See F. R. Moormann and C. R. Panabokke, 'Soils of Ceylon', *Tropical Agriculturist*, 117 (1961), 3–69. The author is grateful to Dr Panabokke for details of soil geography which have emerged since the publication of this paper.

[17] Cf. G. F. Carter and R. L. Pendleton, 'The humid soil: process and time', *GR* 46 (1956), 488–507.

young soils derived largely from slope colluvium in areas of rejuvenated relief and grow good garden and plantation crops. (The term 'lateritic' is not very satisfactory: certainly there is no laterite horizon.)

Over most of the northern and southern Dry Zone, and much of the east, there occur soils classed as 'reddish-brown earths'. Some of these soils are more fertile than is usual in tropical soils but need careful handling; but they also include extents of poor soils on quartzite outcrops and on rough topography. In parts of the eastern Dry Zone, notably north of the Gal Oya, 'non-calcic brown soils' are developed on acid parent materials; these possess a very restricted agricultural potential. The same applies to the saline soils of the mainland southeast of Mannar, of some of the Jaffna islands, and of the strips south of the Jaffna lagoons and of other Dry Zone coasts. In the north-western coastal strip are another group of infertile Dry Zone soils, the 'red-yellow latosols', which have a striking uniformity of profile to a considerable depth and appear to be old soils, probably lower Pleistocene, formed from coastal alluvium under climatic conditions that no longer obtain. They retain water very poorly, have rarely been used in traditional agriculture, and will be difficult to develop. In the Jaffna Peninsula, however, a calcic version of the latosols, derived in the same way but influenced by the underlying limestone, is intensively cultivated.

Ceylon has sizeable stretches of alluvial soils, notably in the Mahaweli Ganga delta and in the infilled east and west coast lagoons. Narrower bands follow the principal river valleys.

In the case of many of Ceylon's soils groups, notably the reddish-brown earths of the Dry Zone, a soil catena is evident: well-drained soils on watersheds and upper slopes pass into poorly drained gley or 'paddy' soils in valley bottoms.

Minor soils in Ceylon include rendzinas on crystalline limestones; and 'grumusols' akin to black cotton soils in certain northwestern Dry Zone localities.

II. HUMAN RESPONSES

The general distribution of settlement: ancient and modern

There is a great deal of evidence to show that, during the many centuries when ancient Sinhalese civilization flourished, settlement was very largely concentrated in the Dry Zone, especially in the southeast and in the central region round Anuradhapura.[18] This settlement, based as it was on the growing of irrigated rice, was almost entirely rural apart from the capital city, which was first Anuradhapura and later Polonnaruwa. It may be significant that it was largely concentrated on the better of the 'reddish-brown earths', avoiding the more infertile Dry Zone soils. It tended to avoid the hills and the Wet Zone alike. Probably the early Sinhalese were deterred by the scarcity of paddyland in the former and by the difficulty of penetrating and clearing the rain-forest of the

[18] Much work on the historical geography of Ceylon remains to be done; for ancient history see Mendis and Codrington (cited in Book List, below), also R. L. Brohier, *Ancient Irrigation Works in Ceylon* (3 vols., Colombo, 1934–35).

latter. Malaria, the scourge of the Dry Zone in modern times, may then have been absent or less virulent.

The glory of ancient Ceylon came to an end during a confused period from about AD 1235 onwards; thereafter Sinhalese kings ruled over an attenuated kingdom from the hills or from the southeast, and Tamil kings over Jaffna and the north. It is customary to ascribe the collapse of the old order to internal dissension and the Tamil invasions, and the consequent breakdown of the irrigation systems, but it is possible that the arrival or increased virulence of malaria may have played a part. Certainly the effects on settlement were revolutionary. The densest areas of Sinhalese settlement came by stages to be in the Wet Zone and in the lower hills, especially round Kandy. Apart from relatively dense settlements of Tamils in the Jaffna Peninsula, along the Batticaloa coast, and in a few places on the northwest coast, the Dry Zone became for the most part a region of sparse settlement, inhabited by a few miserable remnants of the Sinhalese population living precariously around small tanks; they were too few and too enfeebled by malaria and malnutrition to repair the breaches in the ancient irrigation systems, which almost everywhere remained derelict. Early European travellers, Portuguese, Dutch and British alike, paint a depressing picture of the decay which had afflicted the Dry Zone, making it that rare thing in the Indian sub-continent, a relatively large region capable of supporting a greater population.

The Portuguese and Dutch,[19] important as their cultural influence was, did little to modify the settlement pattern of Ceylon, although their trading stations at such places as Colombo, Mannar, Jaffna, and Batticaloa introduced a new urban element which was especially alien when it was set amid the wastes of the Dry Zone. The British, however, came to rule the mountain fastnesses of the Sinhalese, and soon began to introduce plantation agriculture. Today the up-country regions of tea and rubber estates rival the Wet Zone and the Jaffna Peninsula in density of population (see Fig. 26.6). During the last century or so there has also been a movement of people northward into the hinterlands of Negombo and Chilaw, a response to the spread of commercial coconut cultivation. The British period has also seen a growing urbanization, especially in Colombo and adjacent townships; other towns grew too, as did villages along the new roads, but some of the smaller ports suffered an absolute or relative decline after the introduction of big ships and after the export element in Ceylon's trade began to triumph over the entrepôt trade so important in the days of the Portuguese and Dutch. In the Dry Zone, the Jaffna Peninsula and Batticaloa coast continued to have fairly dense settlement, the prosperity and population of the latter increasing especially after the coming of coconut plantations to the coastal sands and the restoration of some of the ancient tanks by the government. The policy of restoring ancient irrigation works also attracted population to the southeast coast and the Anurad-

---

[19] For the modern history of Ceylon see Codrington, *op. cit.*, and G. C. Mendis, *Ceylon under the British* (Colombo, 1944).

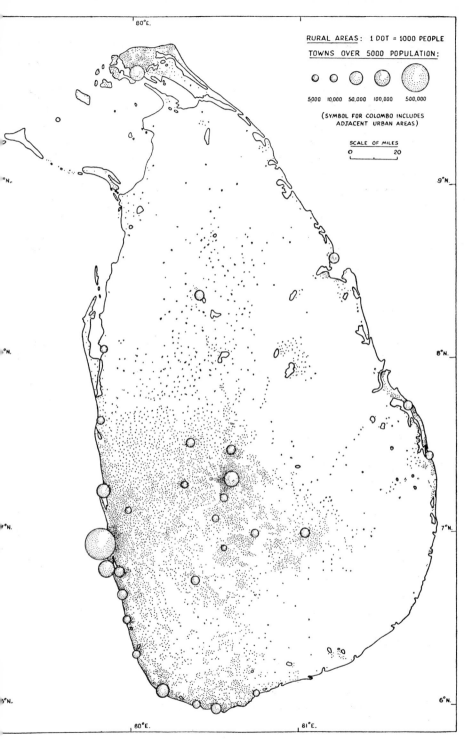

RURAL AREAS: 1 DOT = 1000 PEOPLE

TOWNS OVER 5000 POPULATION:

5,000 10,000 50,000 100,000 500,000

(SYMBOL FOR COLOMBO INCLUDES
ADJACENT URBAN AREAS)

SCALE OF MILES
0   20

FIG 26.6 CEYLON POPULATION, 1953.
(*Courtesy Royal Institute of International Affairs and Oxford University Press*).

hapura area, but elsewhere, until 1931 at any rate, it had but little effect on settlement. Most of the Dry Zone remained sparsely peopled, and malaria brooded everywhere.

In 1931, Ceylon received a measure of self-government which in effect gave to Ceylonese the control of internal administration, and newly roused patriotism gave a fillip to attempts to re-people the Dry Zone; a little later, the economic depression of the 1930s and the war of 1939–45 provided a further stimulus by focusing attention on the need for more home-grown food. A new policy towards colonization in the Dry Zone was evolved: conditions of tenure were changed, and, after 1942, it became the policy to provide the colonist with a ready-cleared and ploughed farm, not merely with a patch of jungle as previously.[20] Great strides have also been made in the control of malaria, by DDT spraying, so that the old fear of the Dry Zone has gone and settlement, both spontaneous and state-aided, is proceeding apace. But, as Fig. 26.6 shows, the main concentrations of settlement in Ceylon remain in the well-peopled Wet Zone, in the hill country, in the northern peninsula, and in a narrow east-coast strip.

The indigenous economy and society
Ceylon is often said to have, like Malaya, a dual economy and plural society; more widely than in much of India, indigenous systems are overlain by systems due to the impact of the West, and although the former are today much influenced by the latter, it is convenient first to consider some important autochthonous elements in contemporary Ceylonese economy and society, always remembering that in modern Ceylon it is in many areas impossible to discuss the social and economic pattern without reference to Western influence.

The indigenous economy of Ceylon was, and to a large extent still is, centred on the cultivation of rice on irrigated land; rice is the basic foodstuff, but is supplemented by various fruits and vegetables grown on unirrigable or 'high' land, and locally by grains grown by *chena* or shifting cultivation. In 1954–55, about 1,032,000 ac. (420,000 ha.) of Ceylon consisted of paddy-land (see Fig. 26.7), largely in the valley bottoms of the Wet Zone but also in cleverly terraced fields in the hills, and in the Dry Zone. There are two main seasons for paddy cultivation, the *maha* or great season during the Northeast monsoon, and the *yala* or little season during the Southwest monsoon. In any one year, some fields are cultivated for one season only, some for both, some not at all. On the whole, land use is more intensive in the Wet Zone than in the Dry Zone. The peasants of the region west of Kandy and the Jaffna Tamils are known for their skilful cultivation, but elsewhere standards are generally lower than in, say, Japan. Not enough manure is used; cultivation is poor (partly owing to the shortage and low quality of draught animals); seeds are inferior and often sown broadcast instead of in nursery beds. Much effort is being directed to the technical instruction of the peasant; the process is a difficult one, but improvements are becoming

[20] See B. H. Farmer, 'Agriculture in Ceylon', *GR* 40 (1950), 42–67, and *Pioneer Peasant Colonization in Ceylon* (1957).

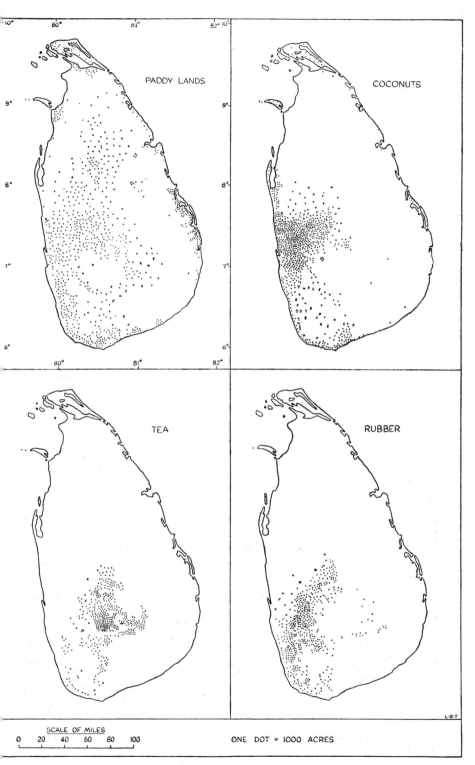

FIG 26.7 CEYLON: DISTRIBUTION OF FOUR PRINCIPAL CROPS, 1946. (Based on *Census of Ceylon, 1946;* more recent data are not available in sufficient detail to enable these maps to be revised. Note that paddy *lands* are indicated: not all of these were under a crop in 1946.)

accepted at an accelerating rate. Paddy yields have increased from about 30 bushels per acre in 1951 to 38 bushels per acre in *maha* 1963–64.[21]

Among 'high' land crops the coconut is especially valuable as a universal provider of food, drink and shelter; and, with the coming of a money economy, its products may also be sold for cash; there are also many small holdings of tea and rubber. Another valuable palm, the palmyra (*Borassus flabellifer*), is very prominent in the Jaffna landscape. Almost everywhere in Ceylon the huts of the peasantry are surrounded by mixed gardens of palms, fruit trees and vegetables, whose products help to lend variety to the otherwise monotonous rice diet.

In some parts of Ceylon, particularly in the Dry Zone and the hill fringes, *chena* or shifting cultivation raises special problems. Such cultivation is, of course, widespread in the remoter parts of monsoon Asia, but in Ceylon it is practised by people who are well aware of sedentary methods of cultivation and who possess draught animals. *Chenas* probably existed in ancient Ceylon, and are certainly common today. The crops grown include millets, maize, dry paddy and cash crops, and the *chenas* are abandoned after a year or two, generally when weeds, rather than decreasing fertility, make cultivation too arduous. Crops are grown during the Northeast monsoon, and, when and where possible, during the 'little monsoon'. The system has the advantages and disadvantages of shifting cultivation everywhere. But *chena* cultivation is certainly one way of using un-irrigable Dry Zone land, although it is clearly desirable to try to replace it with something more permanent, and experiments have been made, not without success, to advise a system of ensuring continuing cultivation and a continuing economic yield on Dry Zone 'high' land.[22]

Of non-agricultural occupations in the indigenous economy, fishing is important but long neglected; more is now being done to exploit the rich fisheries of the sea, the lagoons, and the tanks. Craft industries still exist, though, as in India, they are hard hit by imported wares; the Sinhalese have long had a reputation for metalwork, especially in gold and silver. The government is now striving to encourage cottage and other small-scale industries.

The production of minerals is a relatively unimportant part of the indigenous economy, but salt is obtained by the evaporation of seawater at such places as Hambantota and Puttalam and an increased production is envisaged. Graphite is mined from the Khondalites; gems are extracted from alluvium around Ratnapura; and lime is burnt from crystalline and other limestones.

This essentially agricultural economy was originally one in which exchange played a small though not insignificant part; it is clear that one of the effects of Western influence has been the increasing penetration of this economy by trade and commerce. The peasant today tends to exchange a greater part of his produce for cash or for goods, especially in the Wet Zone, but also in colonization schemes and accessible villages in the Dry Zone. Marketing methods have long left much

[21] 1 bushel per acre = 0.9 hectolitres per hectare.

[22] See E. R. L. Abeyaratne, 'Dry land farming in Ceylon', *Tropical Agriculturist*, 112 (1956), 191–220.

to be desired, however, and it has been an object of government policy to encourage co-operative methods, with variable success.

It must be stressed that the social pattern associated with the indigenous economy was, and is, very complex, as might be expected in an island which has received many influences from both Peninsular India and the sea. But four aspects may be selected as being of particular significance to the geographer.

In the first place, the social unit is a closely-knit village society, which traditionally regulated irrigation and cultivation and had the authority to make every man do his share of repairs to village works.[23] The nature of this social unit is important in many matters, from the study of settlement types[24] to the practical politics of Dry Zone colonization, although in the towns and overgrown villages the old social bonds have largely been destroyed, and in many places a new leadership has challenged the old village aristocracy.

In the second place, the village society is very closely attached to its land. Land tenure in Ceylon is a very complicated matter; many systems are in force, some of them deriving from ancient service tenures. But some 60% of the paddy holdings are owned by the cultivators[25] and handed down from generation to generation, so that the attachment of the peasant to his land is understandable. It is also understandable that, in the absence of alternative employment, subdivision of holdings is considerable; in the Kandy District the average holding is only three-tenths of an acre; holdings are largest (average 6·9 ac., 2·8 ha.) on the Batticaloa alluvium. Landlordism is also common, however: *ande* tenure, by which the landlord receives a share of the crop, is frequent in the Kandy, Matale, Ratnapura and Matara Districts. Legislation for the control of tenancy now exists but it remains to be seen what its effects will be.

In the third place, society in Ceylon is stratified in terms of caste.[26] The stratification is most evident in the predominantly Hindu Tamil areas, though at Jaffna it is less marked than in India; but it has also affected the theoretically casteless Buddhist society of the Sinhalese. The results are not so stultifying as in India, but among them a tendency to immobility of labour is important; thus fishing, a low-caste occupation, is not taken up by cultivators at times when there is little to be done in their fields, and a potential addition to their meagre food-supply is neglected. Labour is more mobile today than it used to be, but in other ways modern changes have been less beneficial. The descendants of the ancient leaders of rural society have tended to acquire Western book-learning and to move to the towns, attracted especially by government service, so that an educational difference and a white-collar complex have been superimposed on caste; and English-educated Ceylonese have tended to be badly out of touch

[23] For a recent study of a Dry Zone village, see E. R. Leach, *Pul Eliya* (1961).

[24] For a geographical study of village patterns, see E. K. Cook, *Ceylon* (2nd ed.) revised by K. Kularatnam (Madras, 1951), 279–314.

[25] See G. Ranasinha, *Census of Ceylon* (1946), Vol. 1 pt. 1, Colombo (1950), p. 258. The figure of 60% for the cultivator-owned paddy-fields is an average; conditions vary greatly from area to area. See also *A Report on Paddy Statistics* (Colombo, 1956).

[26] See B. Ryan, *Caste in Modern Ceylon* (New Brunswick, N. J., 1953).

with the countryside. The villages have fallen under the influence of a new, vernacular-speaking leadership who have proved a potent force in politics.[27]

Finally there are the related problems of literacy and of attitudes to economic and social change. According to the 1953 Census, 60% of the 'educable' population (i.e. those of 5 years of age and upwards) were literate in the sense that they could read and write a language, a considerable improvement on the figure of 40% for 1921. There was, however, a contrast between the literacy of males (75%) and of females (53%). Literacy is highest in the towns and lowest in the Dry Zone and in the hills (especially among estate labourers). Apart from the wider issues, the importance of literacy as the first stage in the technical and political education of the peasant is self-evident.

The impact of the West: dual economy, plural society

It will be clear from what has been said that Western influence has greatly modified the indigenous economy and society, but to differing extents in different regions; in fact, the differences between the Low Country and the Kandyan Sinhalese are attributable to the former group's longer and stronger European contacts. But there is also the entirely new economy and society which have been imposed on Ceylon by the Europeans, and especially by the British.

The plantation, or estate, is the chief geographical expression of this new economy; it is essentially monocultural, growing tea, rubber, or coconuts (or more rarely other crops) for export, and is worked by hired labour. (Coffee-growing, once widespread, has now almost died out.) The ownership and management were originally European. Today about 55% of the acreage under tea estates, about 85% of the acreage under rubber estates, and almost all of the coconuts, are owned by Ceylonese. Tamil labour from South India was brought in to work on coffee, tea, and rubber estates, since the Kandyans were then unwilling to work regularly for hire; the 'Indian Tamil' labourers must not be confused with the 'Ceylon Tamils' of Jaffna. Indian Tamils supplied most of the 984,327 'Indians' resident in Ceylon, but not citizens of Ceylon, at the time of the 1953 Census. The problem of their status has been the cause of considerable friction between the governments of Ceylon and India.[28]

[27] B. H. Farmer, 'Politics in Ceylon' in Saul Rose (ed.), *Politics in Southern Asia* (1963).
[28] The numerical strength of the major communities at the 1953 Census was as follows:

Low Country Sinhalese	3,464,126
Kandyan Sinhalese	2,157,206
Ceylon Tamils	908,705
Indians	984,327
Ceylon Moors	468,146
Burghers	43,916
Europeans	5,886
Others	66,325
	8,098,637

(When possible 1963 Census figures are quoted in this chapter; unfortunately they are not yet available for all purposes, nor in such a form as to make possible a revision of Fig. 26.6.)

The hill country was the area most affected by the new agricultural system, though to varying extents in its various regions. Thus only about 25% of the cultivated area immediately around Kandy is under estates, but the proportion rises to about 75% in the Badulla area and even higher at Nuwara Eliya. The low country in the triangle Colombo–Kurunegala was also greatly changed by the spread of coconut estates (mainly because of Ceylonese enterprise), although here the small holding was more characteristic. And around the turn of the century rubber estates and small holdings began to occupy much of the 'high' land right down to the coast in the southwest (see Fig. 26.7). The tea, rubber and coconut estates and smallholdings together form most of what is today recognized as Ceylon's 'export sector', as distinct from the 'peasant sector' presumed (not with complete justification) to be working mainly for the home market.

If the hills received the main impact of the new economy, and the lowland Wet Zone shows a less marked effect, the changes wrought by it in the Dry Zone were almost negligible. Coconut plantations were established on the coastal sands between Negombo and Puttalam, on Mannar Island, in the Jaffna Peninsula and south of Batticaloa; and there are a few rubber estates on high ground in Bintenne. But elsewhere the private capital which was attracted to the Wet Zone and the hills was repelled from the Dry Zone by its unsavoury reputation for drought and disease, and by its evident unsuitability for the staple plantation crops. And occasional optimistic forecasts that commercial cultivation would develop beneath restored irrigation tanks were entirely falsified in the event.[29]

The communication pattern in Ceylon has also been greatly influenced by the coming of the newer element in the country's dual economy. It is true that early road makers (e.g. Sir Edward Barnes, 1824–31) were mainly concerned with the construction of a network which would make government possible, and that, in a later phase, the construction of such enterprises as the light railways to Trincomalee and Batticaloa were, at least in part due to a desire to help the depressed Dry Zone;[30] but the railway from Colombo to the estate-clad hills is still the main line of the Ceylon Government Railways, and the closest road network, apart from the coastal belt of the Wet Zone, is in the estate areas. In fact, much road and rail construction has resulted from the need to move estate produce to Colombo, which has become the major port and the undisputed focus of the island's communications system (see Fig. 26.8).

Nearly all of the tea and rubber grown in Ceylon, and probably about half of the coconut products, are exported, mainly through Colombo; and together account for some 90% of the country's visible exports in most years. As the table shows, however, the value of these products fluctuates considerably from year to year with the vagaries of world prices and, more recently, as a result of

[29] E.g. schemes at Minneriya Tank; see R. L. Brohier, *The Tamankaduwa District and the Elahera-Minneriya Canal* (Colombo, 1941), 26–28.

[30] See G. S. S. Gordon, 'Extension of the Ceylon Government Railway', *GJ* 66 (1925), 471–2; for a more general account of the development of the railway system see G. F. Perera, *The Ceylon Railway* (Colombo, 1925).

British and American buying policy. Over half of Ceylon's exports (by value) usually go to Commonwealth countries: the United Kingdom is Ceylon's best

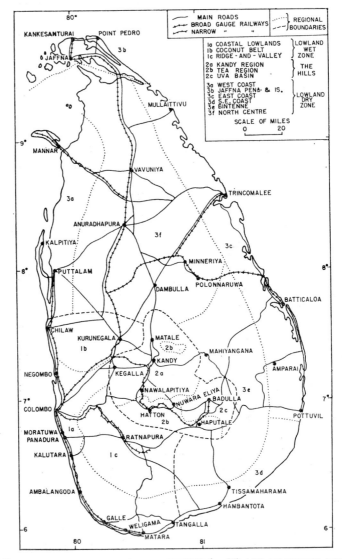

FIG 26.8 CEYLON: TOWNS, COMMUNICATIONS (1966) AND REGIONAL DIVISIONS. (Based on maps of the Ceylon Survey Department, *by kind permission of the Surveyor-General, Ceylon.*)

customer, followed (though not always in the same order) by Australia, the United States and China (trade with which hinges largely on the exchange of rubber for rice).

As will be seen from the table, Ceylon imports considerable quantities of rice and other foodstuffs; but, as a result of efforts to increase home production, only about 35% of the rice consumed in 1963 was imported. Ceylon imports most of her needs of manufactured goods.

In recent times, especially since Independence, Ceylon has tried to lessen her reliance on such a narrow range of export crops and to diversify her economy. Since 1959 a Ten-Year Plan for economic development has been in operation.[31] The planners took full cognizance of Ceylon's present explosive rate of population growth, and estimated that the population would double in the next twenty years. The broad strategy of the plan is to achieve progressive industrialization, not by building up heavy industry (for which Ceylon can provide neither adequate resources nor a large enough market) but by importing the equipment needed for lighter industry. The necessary foreign exchange is to come from increases in exports (especially of tea, rubber and coconuts) and by reductions in imports of food and consumer goods brought about by increased home production of these things. Home-grown rice supplies, in particular, are to come from the improvement of yields on existing ricelands and from the development of new rice-lands.

In the few years since 1959 strides have in fact been made in a number of the directions required by the Plan. Notably, tea production and tea exports have risen, as have yields of home-grown rice. The planners inherited nascent industries (notably a cotton mill near Colombo and a cement works at Kankesanturai in the Jaffna Peninsula) and a number of new factories have been built since 1959. It is clear, however, that development is not proceeding as fast as is required by the Plan.

VALUE OF CEYLON'S EXTERNAL TRADE, 1959–63
(In thousands of Rupees)

	1959	1960	1961	1962	1963
Exports					
Tea	1,045,013	1,095,679	1,113,967	1,147,924	1,139,720
Rubber	297,820	378,373	260,032	290,235	256,848
Coconut products	283,986	205,178	221,961	267,382	243,666
Other exports	65,321	95,559	84,573	60,522	64,253
Total	1,692,140	1,774,789	1,680,533	1,766,063	1,704,487
Imports					
Rice	282,966	242,295	217,327	195,025	192,385
Other foodstuffs and tobacco	528,688	522,232	467,409	444,590	449,789
Raw materials, fuels	186,755	183,209	173,318	177,666	167,026
Manufactures and miscellaneous	1,006,515	1,011,887	845,286	842,293	690,794
Total	2,004,924	1,959,623	1,703,340	1,659,574	1,499,994

Source: *Statistical Abstract of Ceylon*

[31] *The Ten-Year Plan* (Colombo, 1959). See also B. H. Farmer, 'The Ceylon Ten-Year Plan, 1959–68', *Pacific Viewpoint*, 2 (1961), 123–36.

III. THE REGIONS OF CEYLON

Ceylon is capable of four-fold division, there being 'low-country' and 'up-country' in both Wet and Dry Zones. For convenience, however, the two 'up-country' zones may be grouped together, and one may adopt a three-fold division: the Lowland Wet Zone, the Hills, the Lowland Dry Zone. These three divisions may further be sub-divided on the following scheme (see also Fig. 26.8):

1. The Lowland Wet Zone	(a) The coastal lowlands
	(b) The Negombo–Kurunegala–Chilaw coconut belt
	(c) The ridge-and-valley country of Sabaragamuwa and adjacent areas.
2. The Hills	(a) The Kandy region
	(b) The regions of the monoculture of tea
	(c) The Uva Basin.
3. The Lowland Dry Zone	(a) The west coast
	(b) The Jaffna peninsula and islands
	(c) The east coast lowlands
	(d) The southeast coast lowlands
	(e) Bintenne
	(f) The north centre.

THE LOWLAND WET ZONE

The belt of transition between the Wet Zone and the Dry Zone is, both on the northwest and southeast of the former, a narrow one, although in some years Dry Zone conditions may occur a little way into the Wet Zone, and vice versa. The line drawn to delimit the Wet Zone in Fig. 26.8 agrees well with such indices as changes in vegetation and density of settlement. A line between the Wet Zone and the Hills is less easy to draw, in spite of the presence of great mural scarps. The line chosen represents a generalized 1,000-ft. (305-m.) contour, except that it is so drawn as to include in the Wet Zone the detached mass of the Sabaragamuwa hill country.

THE COASTAL LOWLANDS

The coastal lowlands of the Wet Zone form a narrow belt roughly parallel to the coast from Negombo to Tangalla; they also send a tongue from Colombo towards Kandy. Into this slim belt are crowded most of the towns of the island together with a very dense rural population, a fact which is clear from Fig. 26.6. To the north, population thins out fairly suddenly beyond roughly the latitude of Negombo.

The coastline is formed in the main of a series of sandy spits and tombolos, springing from or linking rocky headlands such as those on which Colombo and Galle are based. Inland is a discontinuous belt of lagoons which have often become choked up with alluvium and turned into swamps. Still more often they have become wide alluvial spreads which are usually cultivated as paddy-fields. These spreads send curving tongues of paddy-land up the valleys of the numerous rivers. Between the tongues, and also, island-like, in the old lagoon flats and the coastal sands, rise low, very maturely dissected hills, whose summits rarely exceed a few hundred feet. Outcrops of solid rock are rare. The soils in general show the same three-fold division as the relief, with sandy soils along the coast, paddy soils on the alluvium, and 'red-yellow podzolic' soils (containing laterite) on the low hills. The three divisions may perhaps be regarded as 'stows' on Unstead's scheme.[32]

Everywhere the climate is uniformly hot and humid, often depressingly so. The rainfall varies down the coast from 70 to 100 in. (1,778–2,540 mm.) and is normally well distributed throughout the year, with maxima in the two inter-monsoon seasons. Although in most years the rainfall is effective, droughts are not unknown, and used to be followed by epidemic malaria. The natural vegetation must once have been wet evergreen forest or its littoral equivalent, but has been largely destroyed except on some of the higher hills. The rivers are perennial, and provide readily available water for rice fields. The trouble is, however, *un embarras des richesses*, for this is the worst region of Ceylon for floods; the Nilwala Ganga is a notorious offender. Undoubtedly the floods have been made worse by deforestation and by the planting of estate crops on steep slopes in the upper reaches of the rivers.

The majority of the people are Low Country Sinhalese. Here European influence has been most intense and continuous, to say nothing of Arab influence even earlier. Besides Colombo, towns like Galle, Matara and Kalutara were greatly used by the Portuguese and Dutch. Not surprisingly there are many of the insignia of European contact: Portuguese surnames,[33] Roman Catholicism, burghers of mixed Dutch and Sinhalese ancestry, often a high degree of literacy in English. There is evidence that settlement in the coastal lowlands was dense in pre-European days, but the modern intense economic development has certainly increased the density. There are now houses almost all the way from Negombo to Tangalla, and only in such areas as those well to the north of Galle and Matara or inland from Kalutara is there fresh land for cultivation and that not of high quality.

In spite of the concentration of places which are classed as towns, agriculture is still, outside the fishing villages, the most important single occupation in the coastal lowlands. There is the characteristic twofold division of land between paddy and 'high' land; on the latter mixed gardens of coconut, jak, breadfruit and other trees predominate, but there are many small-holdings and a few estates

[32] See J. F. Unstead, 'A system of regional geography', *Geography*, 18 (1933), 175–87. Cf. also the threefold division in Kerala and coastal Tamilnad (above Chapters 22 and 25).
[33] Not all Portuguese surnames date, however, from Portuguese days; some are change-names adopted by Sinhalese in order to conceal caste.

growing coconut, tea, rubber and (in the south) cinnamon and citronella. The swollen villages are strung along the 'high' land, especially on the coastal sands. The impact of a money economy has been strong. The problem of improving agriculture is complicated by flooding, poor methods of cultivation, bad marketing, and indebtedness. In fact, despite the great density of population, land use is imperfect, and to improve it is the foremost problem of the rural coastal lands.

Of the towns, Colombo is *sui generis*, and is almost entirely a result of the impact of the West, although in its early days it owed a great deal to the Moors. For several centuries it was less important than Galle, but it pulled ahead in the 19th century with the consolidation of British rule over the Kandyan country, the establishment of estates, and the consequent northward shift of the centre of gravity of the island's commerce. Moreover, it commanded two relatively easy routes into the Kandyan country, one by the Maha Oya and the Kadugannawa Pass, the other by the Kelani Ganga and the Ginigathena Pass; and, with the increase in the size of shipping, it out-distanced ports like Puttalam although its own harbour is artificial. The British made it the centre of their road and rail networks, and their capital. It also, of course, became an important port of call. Today it stands a Triton among the minnows, the one big town in the island, with 510,947 people within its municipal boundaries in 1963, and 767,836 in the whole conurbation.[34] Limited by swamps and paddy-fields to the east, it has expanded southwards, and many of the smaller towns along the coast are in part its dormitories.

The string of towns between Colombo and Tangalla is equally a product of Western influence. Not, of course, that they are ports of consequence (with the bare exception of Galle), but that they are market towns and bazaars, foreign to the indigenous economy. Many of them have a strong Moor element, and some have small-scale industries. In fact, the light industries which seem likely to result from recent government and private activity will mainly, and for obvious reasons, be concentrated in these southwestern lowlands.

THE NEGOMBO–KURUNEGALA–CHILAW COCONUT BELT

This region, though wider, has the same three relief elements as the last, viz. coastal sands, alluvium, and interfluvial hills. But the sands recur on the inland side of some of the lagoons, interspersed with latosols; and the low hills tend to cover a greater proportion of the total area. Towards the east these hills also change in character; they are higher, more abrupt and rockier; and in them were formerly many primitive graphite mines, few of which now remain. The climate and hydrology are also similar to those of the previous region, although towards the north Dry Zone conditions begin to creep in and there is a greater liability to drought.

[34] The Colombo conurbation is here (and in Fig. 26.6) taken to include the City of Colombo together with the Urban Districts of Dehiwala–Mount Lavinia, Ja-ela, Kolonnawa, Kotte, Wattale–Mabole and Peliyagoda.

But it is fundamentally its human geography which distinguishes this region from the last. There are, it is true, paddy-fields much like those of the southwest coast, cultivated in much the same manner and attended by much the same social and economic problems; but everywhere it is the coconut which dominates both the landscape and economy. The climate and soils are generally said to suit it, though it is noticeable that well inland the palm is more stunted, and drought, too, causes trouble in some areas. Coconut is largely cultivated by small holders, who often own very few trees indeed and tend them in an indifferent manner. After the depression which set in in 1927 there was much debt, poverty and even emigration. Where the palm is grown on estates (these are mainly Ceylonese-owned) conditions are rather better, although mortgaging and decreasing yields, due to the age of the trees, present problems. Although there are rubber estates in the east, and although fishing is carried on along the coast, the region as a whole suffers from an undiversified economy. It is far too closely tied to the variable fortunes of coconut, and virtually the only industries are those concerned with the processing of coconut products.

This is a region of many small villages and fewer large ones, characteristically located on the lower slopes of the interfluvial hills; the people are mainly Sinhalese. The density of population is high, though not as high as in the south-western coastal ribbon; much of the settlement is recent, for in the years around the turn of the century there was a great growth of population, associated with the coconut boom and due partly to immigration and partly to natural increase. The largest towns are Negombo, Kurunegala and Chilaw with respective populations in 1963 of 47,026, 21,293 and 14,070. Both the latter are marketing centres for the coconut industry, while Negombo is a small port.

THE RIDGE-AND-VALLEY COUNTRY

The rocks of this region are almost entirely of the 'Khondalite' Series whose denudation has given rise to three types of landforms. There are first a very prominent series of parallel ridges, often very steep-sided, following the arcuate strike of the Series; across the ridges are cut transverse gorges, while between the ridges there run long 'subsequent' valleys. There lies here a fascinating field for geomorphological research. The ridges become higher and wilder in the south, where they reach over 3,000 ft. (915 m.); between them and the mural scarp of the central highlands there is a corridor uniting the Kelani Ganga and Walawe Ganga Basins. In this ridge-and-valley country lies most of the little mineral wealth which Ceylon possesses, particularly graphite and gems. There are also said to be some 5,000,000 tons of iron ore, soon to be worked in connection with a steel project near Colombo.

The climate here is a wetter version of that of the coastal lowlands; the mean annual rainfall exceeds 200 in. (5,080 mm.) in some places. The region still has considerable remnants of the rain-forest which once covered it. Reafforestation is in progress, and is vital as a measure of flood control. Soils are mainly 'red-yellow podzolic', though there is bare rock and skeletal soil on steep slopes.

The northern part of this region is the main rubber-growing area of Ceylon. Until the rubber boom of the years after 1904 it was fundamentally a region of valleyside villages growing paddy and cultivating *chenas*. But rubber estates spread rapidly into the hinterland of Kalutara and into the country southwest of Kegalle, and later into the Ratnapura area. The climate was suitable, and there appeared to be plenty of free land, though in practice the *chena*-making propensities of the peasant were locally rudely checked. There was much immigration of Low Country Sinhalese and of Indian Tamils into this traditionally Kandyan area, and the old order was destroyed. There are still many paddy-fields, but today the region depends mainly on its rubber. It lies at the mercy of the fickle market for that commodity, but has in the last few years benefited greatly from replanting with budded rubber. Ratnapura (21,582 in 1963) is the only fair-sized town here.

The southern area of more rugged relief and difficult communications is one of a thinly-scattered peasant population living mainly by paddy and *chena* cultivation. There is a little rubber in small holdings, and recently a wave of new colonization from the overcrowded coast has been moving into the region. But the only considerable settlement is in the corridor north of these hills, where Balangoda is the centre of a tea-growing area.

THE HILLS

The relief of the central highland massif of Ceylon, developed as it is from the Khondalite Series and from igneous intrusions, is very complex in detail, and it is not yet possible to discuss it in genetic terms; consequently any attempt to sub-divide the region on the basis of its detailed physiography is bound to be wearisome and merely descriptive. It seems better to adopt a simple threefold division, recognizing each of the two main nuclei of Kandyan civilization (the Kandy region and the Uva Basin), and the areas dominated by the monoculture of tea. There is, of course, a broad physiographic basis for this scheme, since it was areas above 2,500 ft. (760 m.) which were not settled by the Kandyans, and hence were available for planters.

THE KANDY REGION

This very beautiful region consists broadly of a basin developed at above 1,000-2,000 ft. and drained by the Mahaweli Ganga in its course from Nawalapitiya to Kandy and thence eastward into the valley known as Dumbara. Other streams fret the mural scarp of the 'peneplain' and provide gates into the Kandyan fortress; the two from the west (Kadugannawa and Ginigathena) have already been mentioned, and there remains the Matale Valley, to the north of Kandy, by which the Sinhalese entered the Kandy Basin during their retreat from the Dry

Zone. Above the general level of the Kandy Basin rise steep ridges of higher ground.

In the Kandy Basin temperature is moderated by altitude, but rainfall is in general as high as in the lowlands to the west, and in some places higher (75 to 100 in., 1,905–2,540 mm.). The rain is in most places well distributed, with a tendency, as has been mentioned to three maxima. To the north and east of Kandy, Dry Zone conditions begin to appear, and drought in the southwest monsoon makes itself felt. Very little of the natural vegetation is left; uncultivated hills are mainly covered with secondary scrub or wiry grass, but forests remain in Dumbara. Soils vary, and many, in their immaturity, reflect the strong relief.

The Kandyans remained unconquered and relatively out of touch with Europeans until their city fell to the British in 1815. Although affected by nearly a century of contact, they still retain many characteristics which distinguish them from the Low Country Sinhalese: greater independence, greater attachment to their hereditary lands, a better-preserved though not invulnerable aristocracy, a lower standard of literacy but a distinctive culture; their ceremonial dancing is famous. The traditional economic basis of their life is the familiar method of cultivating both paddy and 'high' land; but here much of the paddy-land has been laboriously built *from* 'high' land on terraces which in places rival those of Java, and whose construction must seem impossible to the valley-bound Low Country Sinhalese. Associated with this laborious husbandry there is, especially in the metropolitan Districts immediately west of Kandy, a higher standard of cultivation than is usual in Ceylon. The Kandyans were quick to begin to cultivate cash crops even in the early days of coffee, and still have much tea, rubber and cacao in small holdings. One of their main problems is the pressure of population (the Districts just mentioned have over 1,000 people per very hilly square mile); and perhaps in the future they will, like other highland folk, prefer to descend to the plains and live less laborious lives.

Some 25% of the cultivated land in the Kandy District is under estates, mainly on higher ground where, it is claimed, the land was unused by Sinhalese. (The latter, however, are apt to tell a different story.) Tea is the main crop, with some rubber and cocoa. The problems raised by hill estates can be postponed until the next section.

Kandy is the nerve-knot of its basin, and had a population of 67,768 in 1963 (with Low Country Sinhalese in the majority!). Besides its commercial function it is, of course, a cultural and religious centre of renown, and near it have risen the new buildings for the residential University of Ceylon to complement those at Colombo. Matale (22,197 in 1963) is also a sizeable town.

THE TEA REGIONS

The main region dominated by the virtual monoculture of tea lies at over 3,000 ft. (915 m.). The mural scarp is very marked to the south, whence the magnificent views from Haputale; but on the west, overlooking the Kandy Basin, it is fretted by tributaries of the Kelani Ganga which tumble off the plateau in splendid waterfalls. The Laksapana Falls now form the site of Ceylon's major hydro-electric scheme, and there is undoubtedly room for further development near by. In detail, the relief is complex, for the strike of the Khondalite Series is very variable and much broken by intrusions, so that the clear linear patterns of the ridge-and-valley country are absent or obscured. There are, however, areas of recognizable plateau surface, as around Hatton. Above the plateau remnants rise the highest hills of the island, such as Pidurutalagala (8,281 ft.), the spectacular Adam's Peak (7,360 ft.) and the detached Knuckles (6,113 ft.) north of Dumbara (2,524, 2,243, 1,865 m.).

The mean annual rainfall is heavy, in most places over 100 in. (2,540 mm.), and with régimes as in the previous region, except that there is a tendency to a single Southwest monsoon maximum in the highest hills. The natural vegetation, montane forest with the probably secondary patanas, has been largely cleared, but areas of both forest and grassland remain. There has also been considerable reforestation. Soils are in general 'red-yellow podzolic', but vary; there are also areas of bare rock.

These upland regions were never apparently settled by the Sinhalese, and lay empty when the British arrived. In the decades after 1830 they were transformed by the wholesale clearing of natural vegetation and the planting of coffee, until disease swept away the plantations in the 1880s.[35] There followed the even more widespread planting of tea, for which the region's climate and altitude are ideal. Road and rail construction kept pace with the spread of estates, often with considerable engineering difficulty. Today tea gardens spread almost continuously over the area within about 8–10 miles' radius of Hatton, and, after a gap, there is another large concentration to the east round Haputale; in all of these regions there are many immigrant Indian Tamils, although today the community is in an absolute majority only in the Nuwara Eliya District. The population map (Fig. 26.6) shows that in all of these formerly empty areas there is now a considerable density of population. The two main urban centres are Nuwara Eliya and Hatton-Dikoya (populations respectively 19,988 and 12,302 in 1963); the former is a famous health resort.

A number of problems face the tea region. Soil erosion is a function of the steepness of the slopes and of the heavy rainfall; many remedial measures are however being taken. There is then the problem of labour; costs are rising, and fresh immigrants from India are discouraged; the number of Sinhalese labourers is growing. Any great increases in tea acreages are unlikely in the near future, for little suitable land remains. The paramount need is for an increase in yield on areas already planted, and much is being done to this end.

THE UVA BASIN

This interesting, healthy, and distinctive region consists of the upper parts of

[35] See E. C. Large, *The Advance of the Fungi* (London, 1940).

the basins of a series of streams which drain to the Dumbara reach of the Mahaweli Ganga. (The lower parts of these catchment basins are very different, and will be considered with Bintenne.) The Uva Basin lies mainly at 1,000 ft. to 4,000 ft. (305–1,220 m.); how it fits into a scheme of 'peneplains' is far from clear. The ridge which bounds it to the east drops to Bintenne by a spectacular scarp.

The mean annual rainfall is, in the Basin proper, less than 75 in. (1,905 mm.), and, more significant, there is a maximum during the Northeast monsoon, with a secondary maximum to correspond with the 'little monsoon'. The Southwest monsoon period is one of drought, and the variability of rainfall shows Dry Zone features. It is true that temperatures and therefore evaporation rates are lower than in the Dry Zone, but high winds partially offset this effect. Dry *patana* clothes the unplanted hills of Uva, and gives them, rounded as they are, something of the aspect of chalk downland, with browns replacing greens. In many parts of the Basin trees are now confined to river banks. Soils are mainly 'red-yellow podzolic'.

It may be that it was in Uva that the Sinhalese, approaching by the north–south Mahaweli Ganga trench, adapted their irrigation techniques to a region of strong relief, and terraced the hillsides. Certainly many irrigation works here are of some antiquity; they even include tunnels through hills.[36] Some of these works have been restored recently. The villages of Uva have something of the aspect of the Kandy countryside, though in a different physical setting; settlement is also much less dense and there is nothing to correspond to the metropolitan district of Kandy. Uva was also somewhat less affected by the coffee and tea booms, although there are many tea gardens here in spite of the dry climate, and over one-third of the population work on estates. The Uva estates have the same problems as those to the west, with the added dangers of drought. Some Uva peasants have taken up the growing of tea or English style vegetables on small holdings, and many have swallowed their pride and found work on the estates.

The area with most estates, i.e. that south of Badulla, has the densest population. Outside the estate areas, further restoration of irrigation works would help to attract settlement to what at present is an area of generally sparse population; and there is also the problem of utilizing the remaining *patanas*. The regional centre, Badulla (27,088 in 1963) is an ancient city and the modern railhead.

THE LOWLAND DRY ZONE

The criteria by which the Dry Zone may be separated from the Lowland Wet Zone and the Hills have already been discussed. The Dry Zone itself is full of contrasts, but for the purpose of the present brief study will be divided into six sub-regions whose boundaries pass through uninhabited or sparsely-peopled territory.

[36] See R. L. Brohier, *Ancient Irrigation Works in Ceylon*, Pt. III (Colombo, 1935).

THE WEST COAST

This is a region of very subdued relief, largely dominated by blown sand and salt-accreting soils along the coast and by 'red-yellow latosols' inland; some diversity is provided by belts of riverine alluvium. The mean annual rainfall is comparatively low (40–50 in., 1,016–1,270 mm.) with a November maximum and a marked dry season. The 'little monsoon' and occasional trespasses of the Wet Zone régime are felt in the south, but their effect diminishes northwards. Variability is considerable, while a tendency to long spells of ineffective rainfall increases to the north. It is not surprising that the present vegetation is largely scrub, although this may not be the true climax.

It is also not surprising that rural settlement is sparse and has apparently always been so, though some alluvial areas are not without signs and legends of past prosperity. Malaria has until recently been hyperendemic. Because of the coastal position of the region, the population is mixed, with Moors dominant in the south and Ceylon Tamils farther north. But there are not many rural settlements outside two areas: the northern prolongation of the coconut belt, and the lands beneath Giant's Tank in the Aruvi Aru alluvium. There are also coastal fishing settlements, but the pearl-fisheries have declined. Puttalam (13,250 in 1963) profits by its dry climate to make salt from sea water and is to have a cement works; while Mannar is a decayed ancient port.

THE JAFFNA PENINSULA AND ISLANDS

This is a unique region with a strong personality in which traits due to its physique, its people, and its position may all be discerned. The climate is harsh in the extreme; heavy, almost excessive rains in November and December are followed by a variable tail-end of the monsoon, an inter-monsoon period in which rainfall is slight or absent, and a very dry Southwest monsoon. There is thus a strong tendency to spells of ineffective rainfall or of absolute drought. But fortunately the limestones of Jaffna store underground water, and the well is an essential part of the Jaffna landscape. However, the calcic latosols are thin, and in many places bare rock pokes through, giving tracts in which cultivation is impossible except where soil is laboriously carted and spread. There are also large areas of blown sand or of old dunes, equally useless except, perhaps, for coconuts; this is especially true of the eastern part of the peninsula and the islands,[37] while some of the latter have saline soils. The population is, in fact, concentrated into a few areas (Fig. 26.6).

Because of its position, the Jaffna region was one of the first to receive Tamil settlers from India. The Ceylon Tamils have, with their industry and resourcefulness, made a strong mark on their rocky little homeland, and are locally packed as tightly as in the southwest coastlands. They grow paddy, together with

[37] See T. H. D. Abeygunawardena, 'The islands to the west of the Jaffna Peninsula', *Bull. Ceylon Geog. Soc.* 4 (1949), 62–71.

palmyra and coconut palms, tobacco, and a host of other laboriously irrigated crops, and they do it with skill. The Jaffna region is one of the few in the Dry Zone to show a continual natural increase throughout the period of census-taking, and there was much emigration. In particular, educated Jaffna men left for government service or for other posts both in Ceylon and overseas, in India and Malaya.

Jaffna itself is today the second largest town in Ceylon, with a population of 94,248 in 1963. Although it has lost the pre-eminence as a port and administrative centre which it had in Dutch days, it still retains some trade in small ships and is, effectively, the railhead. It has small-scale tobacco and textile industries.

THE EAST COAST LOWLANDS

This region borders two stretches of coast made up of sandbars protecting lagoons or alluvium, separated by the belt of quartzite ridges which comes out to the sea at Trincomalee. The northern stretch, with a few exceptions, receives relatively short rivers liable to dry out, whereas the southern stretch, the 'Batticaloa Coast', receives longer and more reliable streams such as the Gal Oya; and the great Mahaweli Ganga reaches the sea just south of Trincomalee.

Most of the east coast receives a higher mean annual rainfall than most of other parts of the Dry Zone (60–70 in., 1,524–1,778 mm.), but there are the familiar wet and dry seasons separated by a 'little monsoon' with slight rains. Batticaloa's rainfall is less variable than elsewhere in the Dry Zone. All along the coast the wet season's rains are usually effective, the dry season's ineffective, and the little monsoon's effective for about half the years in a given period. The region is mainly covered with reasonably fertile reddish-brown earths, but has few restored irrigation works apart from Padawiya Tank.

The northern stretch of coast is inhabited mainly by Tamils and Moors, but there are relatively few of them. In the immediate vicinity of Trincomalee are larger clusters of population near the coast, based on the growing of paddy, coconuts and tobacco. The inhabitants have the benefit of water from irrigation works fed from the Mahaweli Ganga. Just inland Kantalai tank supports a colonization scheme and a sugar project.

Trincomalee town stands apart from its region. Although something of a port in Kandyan days, its fortunes in modern times have fluctuated not with trade but with the degree of use made of it by the British Navy. Thus the war of 1939–45 caused its population to increase from 10,160 in 1931 to 28,334 in 1946 (1953, 28,236; 1963, 34,872). Its use as a naval base and its commercial future are alike problematical, though congestion and labour trouble in Colombo have recently enforced its use for the export trade.

The Batticaloa coast has long had a reputation as a successful paddy-growing area. The alluvium behind its lagoon carries some of the largest continuous stretches of paddy in Ceylon. Here, on solid islands in the alluvium, are settlements of cultivators, usually tenants of absentee Moor landlords. But the densest settlement is on the sandbars, where there are coconut groves (Figs. 26.6, 26.7). The Batticaloa region was one of the first to profit from the government policy of restoring irrigation works and providing communications, and the results were more satisfactory here than in remoter regions. The population has grown steadily, though not without setbacks due to disease and drought. Batticaloa town, the local centre, had a population of 22,957 in 1963, and has profited from its position as railhead for the Gal Oya scheme.

This scheme has involved the damming of the Gal Oya (to produce the largest tank in Ceylon, Senanayake Samudra) and of a number of minor streams and the opening up of over 100,000 ac. (40,500 ha.) for the cultivation of paddy, sugar-cane and other crops. Soils are extremely variable (reddish-brown earths being unfortunately subordinate to infertile non-calcic brown soils and to very sandy alluvium) and were not properly surveyed before the scheme was inaugurated.

THE SOUTHEAST COAST

This is a region of low plains, fringed by lagoons, swamps and sandbars, crossed by a series of radial streams and covered largely with variable reddish-brown earths, though saline soils also occur. Like the Puttalam–Mannar coast, it is a region of low mean annual rainfall, in most places less than 50 in. (1,270 mm.), but here there are certain mitigating circumstances; the seasonal contrast of excessive rain and parching drought is less marked, variability is on the whole lower, and there is not such a tendency to long spells of ineffective rainfall; but drought is nevertheless very much to be reckoned with.[38] As in the north-west, the vegetation is mainly scrub, though some at least of this may be due to shifting cultivation. Malaria has until recently been hyperendemic.

The southeast coast was the nucleus of Ruhuna, an important part of the ancient Sinhalese realm, and had many ancient irrigation works, and, presumably, a considerable population. But when it was visited by British travellers in the middle of the 19th century the belt east of Hambantota was a desolate wilderness. A great deal was done to restore irrigation works, and the population of the irrigated areas rose steadily from 1871 onwards, partly by natural increase but also by the immigration of Sinhalese from the crowded Galle and Matara Districts. But the revenue from these irrigation works did not meet current expenses, to say nothing of capital cost, and the population appears to have remained poverty-stricken. There are now several modern colonies in the region. Great new works on the Walawe Ganga have also been started. Hambantota, the small urban centre and minor port of the region, has a salt industry like that of Puttalam.

East of Tissamaharama is a great empty belt with no irrigation works and no coast road. Here are a national park and game and forest reserves. Irrigation may come to parts of this belt, but water is scarce and soils poor.

[38] See the novel by Leonard Woolf, *The Village in the Jungle* (1931).

CEYLON

BINTENNE

Bintenne is a region of higher and more confused relief than has hitherto been met in the Dry Zone, and is floored mainly by the ancient 'Vijayan gneisses' which give rise to much bare rock and to generally poor 'non-calcic brown' and other soils.

Bintenne is essentially a region of difficulty. True, it has a greater mean annual rainfall than the areas just surveyed (over 75 in., 1,905 mm., for the most part). But away from one or two of the southeastwards-flowing rivers there are few large ancient irrigation works or modern restorations, largely it seems on account of relief and soil. (The Gal Oya reservoir is in Bintenne, but benefits mainly the east coast.) Moreover, the region has been extremely malarial and excessively isolated, at least away from the Badulla–Batticaloa road. It was aptly described as the 'terai of Ceylon'.

Its population is in general sparse, except where a few tea and rubber estates have overspilled from the Uva Basin; and contains such few Vedda as remain.[39] There is very little settled cultivation, the peasants depending largely on *chena*; this practice may be responsible for the *damanas* (grasslands) which cover so much of the country. The people have suffered much from sickness and poverty, and until recently deaths have exceeded births. Bintenne has so far profited less than other Dry Zone regions from recent colonization and development; but in 1965–66 schemes were announced for the large-scale commercial cultivation of subsidiary food-crops on the right bank of the Mahaweli Ganga.

THE NORTH CENTRE

This large region is essentially a plain, rarely rising above 500 ft. (150 m.), but containing many isolated hills and strike ridges which complicate irrigation but help to form soil catenas within the 'reddish-brown earths' and hence to concentrate plant nutriment in irrigable areas. There is a tendency to higher temperatures in the hot season than in the other parts of the Dry Zone; and the mean annual rainfall is everywhere 50–70 in. (1,270–1,778 mm.), with a typical Dry Zone régime. There is, locally at any rate, a tendency to high variability in some months.

The whole region abounds in ancient irrigation works, including most of the complex interlinked schemes. It must all have carried a considerable density of population in ancient times; today there is a noticeable concentration around Anuradhapura (Fig. 26.6). Early British travellers[40] found here numerous isolated Sinhalese villages, grouped round small tanks and hence at the mercy of severe drought, and cultivating paddy and *chena* crops on a subsistence basis. Many such villages remain, though they are now affected by a money economy, but in addition there has since 1870 been a fairly strong wave of immigration, following

[39] The number of Vedda is decreasing not so much because of their gradual extinction but because of their absorption into Sinhalese or Tamil communities.
[40] E.g. Sir J. Emerson Tennent, *Ceylon*, II (1859), 602–25. The whole work is well worthy of study by the geographer.

the restoration of irrigation works and the building of roads and railways. Until recently, however, health conditions were bad, and immigration concealed an excess of deaths over births. Today there is an air of great activity hereabouts, with a number of new colonies and experimental farms; the population of the North-Central Province increased from 97,365 in 1931 to 229,174 in 1953.

Anuradhapura has changed greatly since Tennent found there a few huts only, and wrote, 'the air is heavy and unwholesome, vegetation is rank, and malaria broods over the waters as they escape from the broken tanks'.[41] The town had 29,397 inhabitants in 1963, and was over twice as big as it had been in 1946.

Southeast of the series of quartzite ridges which links the Hills with Trincomalee lies Tamankaduwa with its great irrigation works of antiquity, Minneriya and Parakrama Samudra. Until very recently this region lay almost empty, and was notorious for fever. Irrigation restoration came relatively late, but alone was not enough to attract people to this remote and unhealthy area, and the provision of communications helped but little. But recent intensive efforts at colonization have begun to have their effect. Over 50,000 people moved into Tamankaduwa between 1931 and 1953. The total population increased by 634% in the same period, and by 96·7% between 1953 and 1963. Polonnaruwa is now a considerable urban settlement (population 5,921 in 1963).

There remains the Wanni, north of Vavuniya, another problem area. Here climate tends towards the rigours of Jaffna, and there are few large rivers to fill major tanks. The Wanni, further, was very badly devastated by conflicts between the inhabitants and the Dutch and British. Restored irrigation works and communications came late, and the region had a most unsatisfactory bill of health. A number of tanks have now been restored (Fig. 26.5), pioneer settlement has taken root, and Vavuniya town has grown in population from 2,878 in 1953 to 7,176 in 1963.

IV. CEYLON SINCE INDEPENDENCE

Ceylon gained her independence within the Commonwealth on February 4th, 1948. Until 1957 Britain was pledged to aid in the defence of Ceylon, in return for continued rights at Trincomalee and in certain airfields; but since the abrogation of the defence agreement (at Ceylon's request) and the assumption by Ceylon of a position of neutralism in foreign policy, the country has depended on its own resources for its defence. Almost imperceptibly (and certainly almost without comment in Ceylon) this brought Ceylon closer to, if not into, the India defence system. For India would clearly not tolerate the establishment of a hostile power in Ceylon; as K. M. Panikkar has said, Ceylon 'is for all defence purposes an integral part of India. . . . Ceylon can neither feed herself nor defend herself, nor in respect of any other important matter, stand on her own feet.'[42] So far, however, peace has prevailed in Ceylon's relations with the outside world.

[41] See Tennent, op. cit. 603.
[42] K. M. Panikkar, The Strategic Problems of the Indian Ocean (New Delhi, 1944), pp. 5, 18.

Unfortunately, the same cannot be said of Ceylon's internal situation. True, all seemed at peace in the first eight years or so of independence: law and order prevailed, communal tensions which had been in evidence during the negotiations leading up to independence seemed to have eased, and Ceylon was often held up as a model of a country with a plural society which had yet achieved, without disturbance or fission, the transition from colonial status to independence under democratic and parliamentary forms of government. Then, in April 1956, came the elections which brought to power the government of Mr S. W. R. D. Bandaranaike: before long, bitter feelings between Sinhalese and Ceylon Tamils mounted to levels without precedent in modern times, and culminated in riots in 1956 in Colombo and in the Gal Oya colonization scheme, and in the even more disgraceful communal disturbances of 1958. Since then communal tensions appear to have relaxed (though the position of the Indian Tamils remains most unsatisfactory, and the Ceylon Tamils are not completely happy about their status and treatment in a Sinhalese-dominated state). But political instability has taken other forms: the assassination of Mr Bandaranaike in 1960, abortive military coups in 1962 and 1966, frequently-recurring strikes and other evidence of labour unrest.

This is no place in which to initiate a full enquiry into the reasons for the sudden change from stability to instability.[43] It is sufficient to say that communal disharmony has always been latent in the Ceylon situation, and that it has been brought to the surface by social, economic and political forces. The social forces were associated with the rise of the new Sinhalese village leaders (already mentioned) who were convinced that the Buddhist religion and their place in society depended on the recognition of Sinhalese as the sole national language (and it was largely the language issue that inflamed Tamil feeling). The economic forces were a consequence of such associated phenomena as the explosive growth of population, the filling of nearly all vacant land in the Wet Zone, and exacerbated problems of employment and under-employment; the Sinhalese-educated were increasingly concerned about employment and about the alleged unfair advantages possessed by the Tamils and by the English-educated in the search for jobs, especially in government service. In terms of politics, the feelings and frustrations of the Sinhalese village leaders were used to electoral advantage, and in turn exaggerated and embittered (wittingly or unwittingly) by Mr Bandaranaike and other politicians.

What must be said here is, however, that recent political events have reacted adversely on economic affairs. True, it was under the Bandaranaike régime that the Ten-Year Plan was formulated, and a number of valuable developments in irrigation, in agriculture, in industrialization, and in other directions have taken place since 1956. But, to a Western observer at any rate, the problems created by

[43] See in this connection W. Howard Wriggins, *Ceylon: the Dilemmas of a New Nation* (Princeton, 1960); and B. H. Farmer, 'Politics in Ceylon', *op. cit.*, and *Ceylon: a Divided Nation* (1963).

extremely rapid population increase[44] in a context of poverty, unemployment and under-employment are the most pressing problems facing Ceylon today, while it has been the effect of recent political events to create a different set of priorities: the language issue and a variety of communal, sectional and personal squabbles have agitated the public mind, to the partial exclusion of economic affairs; and there has been insufficient realization of the economic predicament of the nation. Ceylon's particular brand of political instability has, moreover, discouraged the investment of indigenous and foreign capital, and lowered the morale of the public service at a time when there is a pressing need for sound administration.

During these years of trouble the existence and character of the export sector have given Ceylon's economy resilience, and the availability of unused land in the Dry Zone has given it a reserve to fall back on; both of these would in similar political circumstances be denied to India and in a large measure to Pakistan. Such is Ceylon's good fortune. But time grows short, and there is a pressing need for more vigorous, sustained, realistic and undistracted economic development and for measures to stabilize the population below the danger level.

SELECT BOOK LIST

E. K. Cook, *Ceylon* (2nd edition, revised by K. Kularatnam, Madras, Bombay, etc., 1951).

S. F. de Silva, *The New Geography of Ceylon* (Revised edition, Colombo, 1954).

A. D. Baptist, *A Geography of Ceylon for Schools* (Madras, etc., 1956).

H. A. J. Hulugalle, *Ceylon* (*OPIA* No. 6, 1944).

L. J. D. Fernando, 'The geology and mineral resources of Ceylon', *Bulletin of the Imperial Institute*, 46 (1948), 303–24 (with maps).

H. W. Codrington, *Short History of Ceylon* (Revised edition, 1938).

G. C. Mendis, *The Early History of Ceylon* (Calcutta, 1938).

——, *Ceylon under the British* (Colombo, 1944).

A. Sievers, *Ceylon* (Franz Steiner, Wiesbachen, 1964).

E. F. C. Ludowyk, *The Story of Ceylon* (Faber, London, 1962).

The Ceylon Geographer (formerly *The Bulletin of the Ceylon Geographical Society*).

The Economic Development of Ceylon (Report of an International Bank Mission), 2 vols. (Colombo, 1952) and 1 vol. (Baltimore, 1953).

B. H. Farmer, *Pioneer Peasant Colonization in Ceylon* (OUP, 1957).

The Ten-Year Plan (Colombo, 1959).

W. Howard Wriggins, *Ceylon: The Dilemmas of a New Nation* (Princeton, 1960).

B. H. Farmer, *Ceylon: a Divided Nation* (OUP, 1963).

[44] 31·5% between 1953 and 1963.

A Summing-up

This book has sought to set forth the geographical facts necessary to an understanding of the life of the peoples of India and Pakistan. Inevitably this has involved a consideration of many social facts and trends, some directly related to the geographical setting, others with but tenuous links with the environment, or even with none discernible, yet essential to form a picture which, if it cannot hope to be a true picture of reality, is at least free from conscious distortion, and it is hoped from hasty judgments. The length of the discussion may well have been wearisome to the reader, yet is certainly not commensurate with the vastness and complexity of the problems involved. Alike in its physical environment, in its economy, and in its societies, the great sub-continent is as it were a world apart; and the regional chapters have shown, or should have shown, the huge internal diversities of its regional structures and of the local societies and economies living in or based upon them. This is true even of the seemingly monotonous plains where the nuances of regional differentiation can as yet be analysed but incompletely, though they are increasingly being unravelled by the work of Indian and Pakistani geographers, agronomists and sociologists; to whom must now be added a very distinctive contingent of American students. At every turn both in the general and the regional chapters, we noted items – a selected few only – of the immense agenda which faces Indian and Pakistani geographers. Many monographs have fed into these chapters, and almost any chapter might be the starting-point of a dozen more; and this is no virtue of the writers, but inherent in the theme. The abiding impression is of an intricacy fascinating by its very difficulty, challenging to the utmost the determination to penetrate to the causes of things: *felix qui potuit rerum indicarum cognoscere causas*.

At this stage no more is possible than a few bold strokes towards a synthesis. The social history of the few decades which preceded the first edition of this book is largely summed up in two distinct but not unrelated trends: the increasing population pressure, the increasing integration into world economy, from which indeed India has never been entirely detached (at least since the Discoveries) but an integration now no longer confined to ports and factories, but taking to itself new modes and reaching into the remotest corners of the country. This integration, by its substitution of cash and contract for custom and status, has meant among other things a progressive decay of that once-adjusted rural society which lies at the basis of the future of India and Pakistan, no less than their past.

In itself the breakdown of outmoded traditions, of customs which were an affront to the dignity of men and women, of the isolation of the village, carries capabilities for good; and at all events, in a world increasingly compacted by revolutions in transport, it cannot possibly be reversed, even by a Mahatma, unless by a catastrophe – unfortunately not inconceivable – which might reduce the world we know to a scatter of petty poverty-stricken localisms. Yet the impact of modern technique and economy on a society singularly ill-fitted to take the shock has had effects little short of disastrous. Paradoxically, it is not only the weakness of rural society which is responsible for this, but also its strength – the strength of numbers. Its mere mass and extension ruled out an easy surrender to the new forces; nothing is more striking than the unconscionable time its doomed trades and traditions take a-dying. Mass and extension again make it difficult to move on new ways; but the example of China, whether regarded as good or evil, at least discourages overmuch reliance on commonplaces about immemorial tradition, inertia, rural conservatism and the like.

To the two great trends of social history already noted a third must be added, which – more especially in India – has been dominant in the years since this book first appeared: the immense and conscious effort to break out of the old circles of poverty and backwardness by large-scale planning, to counterbalance the increase of population by a more efficient use of the resources of the sub-continent.

These are in total considerable: water for irrigation and power, ores, oils, fibres, forest products, incalculable wealth in iron and manganese. Many of these are perhaps not abundant in relation to the size of the population – they are certainly not so in Pakistan, and especially East Pakistan – but they are at least capable of a much greater degree of development than now exists, even after a decade and a half of planning. Despite all that has been done, the tempo of development is still in urgent need of quickening. This quickening obviously depends on many essentially political factors, both internal and external; and here must be noted with regret not only the interruption, both to national confidence and to actual programmes, caused by the Chinese encroachments in the north, but the continuing tension between India and Pakistan, countries which have so much to offer each other and yet seem so reluctant to come to reasonable terms. The purely fiscal problems of development are themselves extremely complex. In the last resort it seems unlikely that any really stable advance will be possible without a more resolute and widespread limitation of births; and, although definite beginnings have been made, in the social context of both India and Pakistan that is still a gigantic question-mark. Yet without heroic measures it seems too probable that economic advances may be whirled away in the unceasing flow of new mouths to feed.

It is still true that the prime needs of India and Pakistan are more fertility in their fields and less in their homes. Certainly, there is more productivity now than when these words were first written; but it would be very bold to say that a real break-through is yet in sight, that the index of food production as yet does more than run neck-and-neck with that of population, now rising above it by a precarious margin, now slipping below. Only when it clearly shakes itself free from that other line of population for a good run of years will success be really in sight. Should this come about, the resources for further advance are there, and the increase in human energy, the liquidation of disease and malnutrition, would open prospects of a new and happy culture, prospects which are now little more than a dream. There has been considerable advance in some sectors; in few or none much real retrogression; and yet, for all the activity displayed, there is an impression not perhaps of stagnation, but of running hard to stay in the same place. And if in the next five or ten years the break-through is not made, whether by striking advances in productivity or by a striking fall in birth-rates, or by both, it is difficult to avoid the feeling that real social catastrophe might result.

To avert this danger, to arrest the decadence of the countryside, to build the better life which should be possible with the aid of modern techniques, are tasks which call for revolutionary zeal and energy; and also perhaps for a tact which does not always go with these qualities, the tact to preserve some at least of the values of the old tradition. Energy there is in plenty, but it seems not always wisely directed, and it is too often only the surface energy of brave words and paper plans. Bhoodan, Panchayati Raj, even the memory of the Mahatma, are too often expedient evocations, or invocations, which disguise a lack of solid common-sense work. And yet it would be a shade too facile and too cynical, despite much temptation, to murmur *plus ça change, plus c'est la meme chose*. It is still true to say that as yet no man can truly tell how far the depths beneath have been stirred; whether, when, in what direction the tremendous latent energy of their collective mass will be released. One may, one must, discount a great deal of official optimism and woolly rhetoric; yet there can be little doubt that at least the idea that change not only can but should be accepted is penetrating deeper into rural masses both in India and Pakistan. This may not seem much, but it is the essential first step from which all else must follow, and without which Community Development, Panchayati Raj, Basic Democracy, are but so many words, and Five Year Plans but aggregations of statistics signifying nothing very much.

The world today is divided no less deeply than it was ten or fifteen years ago; and with the rise of Communist China and the independence of Africa it is now divided in a much more complex way; there are alignments even within non-alignment. The fate of 550,000,000 human beings is a matter of very large concern to the whole balance of the world; however the shifting balance of world forces may resolve itself, we may be sure that one vital factor will be success or failure in the titanic task of rehabilitating the life of the millions who toil in the fields, and now the factories, of India and Pakistan.

Changes in Indian Place-Names

Since Independence, there has been a not unnatural trend towards abandoning Anglicized renderings of many place-names, in favour of forms more linguistically correct; it is unfortunate that the latter are usually also longer. In this book, the new (or resurrected) forms are normally employed, though doubtless the attentive reader will find some anomalies. For towns, the older style is usually given in parentheses at the main reference, and cross-references from the older forms are given in the index. Following is a list of altered forms as used in this book; for details, reference may be made to M. P. Thakore, 'Changes in place-names in India', *Indian Geogr* 1/1 (1956), 51–54, and S. D. Gupta, 'The changing map of India', *GRI* 22/3 and 22/4 (1960), 23–33 and 13–32.

New form	*Older form, and remarks*
Amravati	Amraoti, Maharashtra
Avadh	Oudh; as the name is used here mainly in contexts referring to the British period, it seems reasonable to retain the Anglicized form.
Banaras, *see* Varanasi	
Banaskantha	New District, Gujarat
Chickmagalur	Kadur District, Mysore
Deoria	New District, part of old Gorakhpur District, Uttar Pradesh
Dhanbad	New District, part of Manbhum District, Bihar
Durg	Drug, Madhya Pradesh
Eluru	Ellore, Andhra Pradesh
Faizabad	Fyzabad, Uttar Pradesh
Ganadki	Apparently used for the Gandak in Nepal, but Gandak is standard in current literature and is retained here.
Ganga	Ganges; but note that Pakistani usage retains Ganges, and is employed here where appropriate.

New form	Older form, and remarks
Ghaghra, *also* Ghaghara ...	Gogra
Gomati	Gumti, Gumtee
Himachal Pradesh	Punjab Hill States
Jabalpur	Jubbulpore, Madhya Pradesh
Kakinada	Cocanada, Andhra Pradesh
Kanchipuram, *also* Kanchee-puram	Conjeeveram, Madras
Kanpur	Cawnpore, Uttar Pradesh
Kanya Kumari [Cape], Kannyyakumari [District] ...	Cape Comorin
Kathiawad	Kathiawar
Kaveri, *also* Koveri	Cauvery; although these forms seem more correct, they are not yet in general use, and Cauvery has been retained.
Kozhikode	Calicut, Kerala
Krishna	Kistna
Kutch	Cutch
Lakhnau	Lucknow, Uttar Pradesh; the older form is still in common use, and retained here.
Madurai	Madura, Madras
Masulipatnam	Masulipatam, Andhra Pradesh
Mathura	Muttra, Uttar Pradesh
Nagapattinam	Negapatam, Madras
Narmada	Narbada
Palayankottai	Palamcottah, Madras
Palani	Palni Hills
Panjab	Punjab; Panjab is the more correct transliteration, and was often used (as was Panjaub) by older British writers, as well as in the title of the Panjab University, Lahore; but it does not seem to have caught on in either India or Pakistan, and Punjab is retained here.
Pratapgarh	Partabgarh District, Uttar Pradesh
Ramanathapuram	Ramnad, Madras
Sabarkantha	New District, Gujarat
Sagar	Saugor, Madhya Pradesh
Saharsa	New District, part of old Bhagalpur District, Bihar
Srikakulam	Chicacole, Andhra Pradesh
Surendranagar	Wadhwan, Gujarat

New form	Older form, and remarks
Thanjavur, *also* Thanjvur, Tanchavur, Tanjavur ...	Tanjore, Madras; Thanjavur appears to be the official form and is used here.
Tiruchchirappalli, *also* Tiruchirapalli	Trichinopoly, Madras; the longer form is on official political maps, but the shorter is apparently used for postal purposes, and (understandably) even Trichy will still find it.
Tirunelveli	Tinnevelly, Madras
Varanasi, *also* Banaras ...	Benares, Uttar Pradesh
Vijayawada	Bezwada, Andhra Pradesh
Visakhapatnam	Vizagapatam, Andhra Pradesh
Yamuna	Jumna
Zalwad...	New District, Gujarat

Index

There is a separate Index of Authors and Works cited. There is, of course, some selectivity in the General Index; the judicious reader will not expect to find every passing mention of say *rice* or *Ganga* listed, and merely 'marker' references such as that to Delhi on p. 14 are omitted. Attention is drawn to the following major heads, under which relevant entries are gathered: COAL, COTTON, DEVELOPMENT PROJECTS, ELECTRICITY, GEOLOGICAL FORMATIONS AND PERIODS, IRRIGATION, LAKES, MOUNTAIN AND HILL RANGES AND PLATEAUS, MOUNTAIN PEAKS AND HILLS, PASSES, RICE, RIVERS, SOIL TYPES, TRIBES AND CASTES, VEGETATION and WARS.

Major references are shown in bold-face; *pm = passim*

851

Index of Authors and Works cited

Political personalities who are also writers, such as Gandhi and Nehru, are entered in either the General or the Author Index according to context: thus Gandhi appears in the former for p. 196, the latter for p. 561.

Joint articles in periodicals are entered once only, with names in the order given in the original.

Abbas, K. A., 663
Abeyaratne, E. R. L., 804
Abeygunawardena, T. H. D., 818
Abu Bakr, M., 483
Acharya, B. C., 103
Adams, F. D., 790
Afforestation Scheme . . . for West Bengal, 111
Agarwala, A. N., 305
Agricultural Atlas, Indian, 233
Agriculture in India, Royal Commission on (RCAI), 10, 117, 225, 227, 230, 254, 266–7, 388
Ahmad, E., xi, 45, 132, 204, 207, 222, 549, 556, 565, 568, 641
Ahmad, F., 18, 19, 45
Ahmad, K., 372, 380
Ahmad, K. S., xii, 9, 75, 130–1, 300, 302, 375, 389, 410, 526, 529, 532–3
Ahmad, N., xi, 301, 306, 383, 389, 533, 590, 599
Ahmad, N., and Khan, F. K., 590, 599
Ahsan, S. R., 337
Ahuja, P. R., 112
Ali, A., 12, 222
Ali, N. A., 112
Ali, S. M., 264, 538
Ali, T. A., 593
Anand, M., 544
Anand, M. R., 12
Andhra Pradesh, Techno-Economic Survey of, 727
Andrus, J. R., and Mohammed, A. F., 275, 278–9, 389
Ansari, T. A., 508
Armstrong, G. C., 748
Arndt, H., 335
Atmanathan, S., 58
Aubert, G., 101
Auden, J. B., 33, 34, 37, 45, 458, 478
Aurobindo, Sri, 13
Ayyar, A. S., 761

Badaruddin, M., 525
Bagchi, K., 572, 575, 588, 599
Bailey, E. B., 498
Bailey, S. D., 824
Baker, J. N. L., xii, 407, 409, 545, 683
Baksi, R. D., *et al.,* 105
Balasubramanian, C., and Bakthavathsalu, C. M., 50
Banerjee, B., 475
Banerjee, I., 632
Banerji, J., 738
Banks, A. L., 41
Baptist, A. D., 824
Basham, A. L., 12
Basti District, Rehabilitation of, 568
Battuta, Ibn, 679–80
Bauer, P. T., 388
Beri, S. G., *see* Jathar, G. B.
Beringer, C., 369
Bernier, F., 197
Bettelheim, C., 388
Bhabha, H. J., 345
Bhadran, C. A. R., 113
Bhagavad Gita, 175
Bharadwaj, O. P., xii
Bhargava, M. P., 329
Bhat, L. S. (*see also* Learmonth, A. T. A.), xii, 129, 220, 670
Bhatia, S. S., xii, 72, 234
Bhatt, V. V., 336
Bhattaacharjee, J. P., 272–3
Bhattacharya, A. N., and Verma, L. N., 631
Bhattacharya, A. P., 112
Bhattacharya, S., 111
Bhunan, S. J., Zacharia, M., and Rahman, F., 111
Bihar, Techno-Economic Survey of, 566, 568, 570
Binder, L., 172
Bjerkness, H., 59
Blanford, H. F., 46, 55
Blanford, W. T., 24
Bondurant, J. V., 157